The original theatre of the City of New York
from the mid-sixties to the mid-seventies.
Book 4.

Peter Schumann's
Bread and Puppet Theatre

VOLUME 2

Schumann's Bread and Puppet Theatre is the next in the series, *The Original Theatre of the City of New York*, on the culturally revolutionary florescence of the American Theatre, circa 1963-1973, considered as a facet of that decade's libertarian spirit, and as part of The New American Art (c.1947-1973). The first two books were *Queer Theatre* and *The Theatre of Visions: Robert Wilson*. The author of the series is a German-born doctor of philosophy and writer of poetry, and lives in New York City.

The original theatre of the City of New York from the mid-sixties to the mid-seventies.

Stefan Brecht
The original theatre of the
City of New York from the
mid-sixties to the mid-seventies.
Book 4.

Peter Schumann's
Bread and Puppet Theatre

Volume 2

Methuen Drama

To my sister Barbara, affectionately,
with gratitude, with admiration.

First published in two volumes
as a Methuen Paperback original in 1988
by Methuen Drama
Reissued 1994
by Methuen Drama
an imprint of Reed Consumer Books Ltd
Michelin House, 81 Fulham Road, London SW3 6RB
and Auckland, Melbourne, Singapore and Toronto

Typeset by Kelmscott Press Limited
Printed and bound in Great Britain
by Cox & Wyman Limited, Reading, Berkshire.

ISBN Volume 1 0 413 59890 X
       Volume 2 0 413 60150 8

Contents

Part V.

1970-1974. The Goddard period.

Withdrawal from direct moral address and from address to the big-city crowd. Rejection of the 'spirit of the '60s.' Cryptic portrayal of the human condition: defined by a dialectic of individual and crowd. Theme of suffering. Message: drop out. Performance as presentation of a representation. The gesture of presentation carried by 'pseudo-narrational' performance elements: a non-narrative frame that designates the performance as theatre and that is itself performance element. Paradigm: fair booth and barker. Schumann's productive focus on indoors theatre. Pseudo-communal form of production. Actually he is putting up a smoke-screen while he is working up his act.

Contents: Part V.

1. Nature of his work during the Cate Farm/Goddard period, '70-'74. Presentation of a representation of human suffering in a world offering the exclusive alternative of integration into the crowd and murderous individuality. Cryptic theatre.

He reverted from the form of direct address to the crowd — on the street, indoors — to a more traditionally theatrical use of elevated stage, framing proscenium and even curtain, restored the distance to the audience, and a presentational form that he (interview, '79) refers to as 'pseudo-narrational': elements of performance (not of the structure in which it is presented) indicating it, and signifying that it is theatre and that it is a representation, and to this extent like narration, but pseudo-narration in not indicating any author or theatre-maker (teller of the tale). Presentation replaces address, representation (moral) exhortation. This formal shift parallels the thematic shift from guilt (of complicity in the imposition of suffering) to suffering: both are shifts from action to event.

During this second period, what Schumann was interested in doing in theatre was presenting an idea of the human condition, *his* idea, that is, his feelings about it and his judgment: not particularly or not at all anxious to get it across, but trusting its veracity and his art to make it understood, seeing how that condition was in fact that of his audience. His theatre suddenly became obscure.

The human condition as he saw it was the condition of suffering. In the broad sense of undergoing determination, and in the specific sense of this being painful, both intrinsically and because of how it was done. This was matter for a statement, but in addition Schumann had — or over the period worked out — an explanation. The explanation was society. In society, individuals have to compete to affirm themselves as individuals, they fight and hurt one another, or else, or even so, become swallowed up by the crowd: form crowds to escape the danger they represent for one another, escape into crowds from the challenge of individuation and its danger, are molded into crowds by self-affirming individuals (leaders), as crowd force others to integrate or suffer the consequences of not belonging, and suffer equally from the crowd to which they do not belong and from their ingurgitation by the crowd — and not less than from their abrasions in their competitive struggles with one another. The human condition is defined by the crowd's pressure for conformity on the individual and by the individual's correlative need for security within the crowd, need for being a part of it, but also by the individual's need for individuation contingent on separation from the crowd, whether by antagonistic competition with other individuals, or by creative transcendence of the

5

crowd's standards, and finally, crucially, by the inter-dependence of these conflicting needs: the crowd's integration is an indispensable palliative of the competitive struggle, the individual's self-affirmation needs the crowd as matrix, foil and audience, e.g. as material to be used and molded by the artist or the leader, and the crowd's self affirmation feeds on individual recalcitrance and deviation and consists in his (or her) reduction, or in submission to him or her.

The relative clarity of these formulations is deceptive, however. For in this condition, vision is obscure. The individual trying to realise him/herself does not know what he/she is, is all in his/her future, and the reglemented, crowd-contained individual shares but can only sense the sense of the crowd, and the crowd's vision must be murky for the sharing of it by its members; and both the competitive struggle between individuals and participation in crowd life precludes the calm, the focus and the distance of clear vision. If such is the condition of man, man cannot have a clear view of this condition. The crowd, for the member of it, does not appear as a crowd; the individual struggling competitively for self-realisation does not appear to him or herself. Analogous arguments for the ineluctability of obscurity apply to the core-vision, that of suffering as man's essential state. To be true to the vision, Schumann had to be obscure. It just did not have the clarity of the moral challenges of his previous period, nor the simplicity of his offerings of hope of the following — not because guilt and hope are intrinsically simpler or clearer than suffering or its individual-crowd dialectic, but because whereas the abstractive, volitionally muscled stances in proclamation of them — indictments/exhortations, sharings/offerings — are by their nature adequately expressed in a simple, strong, clear manner (all apology and doubt cast aside), a mode of existence — suffering as a social state — is falsified by reduction: must be represented with its ambiguities and conflicts. The basic shift was not in his perception of human existence, but in his stance; in what he was going to use theatre for: not an exhortation, but a representation. If during the '60s he had chosen to deal with violence, good, evil, guilt, as dimensions of human existence, representationally, his '60s theatre would have been equally murky. If during the early '70s he had chosen to recommend individuation and/or communalisation — be an individual! join a community! get back into society! (up with family life! down with free love!) — his '70s theatre would have been as clear as his '60s. But he wasn't up to it. He opted for the neutrality of representation.

True, Schumann also intimated something like a solution to the dilemma of the individual torn between him/herself and society: family life around the core of the lovingly giving woman, wife and mother. Domesticity during this period in his theatre emerges as positive alternative to negative (and interdependent) alternatives of murderous individuation and violent and repressive crowd socialization.

6

But this part of his vision did not allow him a clear statement either: the family is a mini-crowd and there is competitive conflict within it, and love, the social force that as sustained organizing principle would reconcile individual and family and make them transcend intra-familial competition and conflict unfortunately is not intra-familially confined, and so in fact disrupts the family as much as it sustains it. The man will fuck around. Erotic love during this period is glimpsed in this theatre as escape and as, all in all, negative principle, destroying the family and allied to the cruelties of individuation. Here again the vision is intrinsically obscure: an outlook on a mess. And his personal and professional circumstances did not allow the brazen cutting of Gordian knots. This was a time in his life of the sowing of wild oats and of confused and conflict-laden relations to his co-workers, the puppeteers, and to the (college) 'community.'

His crowd/individual ideology had been activated, I would say, not so much by his perception that the movement of liberation of the '60s where it was not rapidly degenerating into the comfort-seeking consumerism of the sheep returning to the fold had degenerated into the resentful outlashings of groupuscules functioning, animal-like, as mini-crowds, as rather, more directly (personally), on the one hand by his more acute feeling himself The Individual because of his fame — the European fame he won by his tours of '68 and '69 — and by his strong awareness that the political ideas his followers would hold him to, and that by his work of the '60s he had come to stand for, had been merely the tip of the iceberg, that his personal ideas had all along been more complex, those political stances the mere outcroppings of a highly idiosyncratic inner turbulence; and on the other hand by his experiences with his own traveling group's crowd psychology, their bland comfort in being together and as one, and their blind desire to amplify this colonial cohesion, a communality he could use, but which when it exercised pressure on him became rigorously unacceptable to him as well as, contrariwise, by his having had to deal with the fervid hunger for individuation (as artists and as persons) of at least certain of his performers, a nuisance to him, but at the same time a desire he could not help but respect, if only because that drive was his own also. His street theatre of the '60s had been address to the crowd, and his indoors theatre had assumed the same form. From '67 onward, as we have seen, he had become critical of this audience, of 'the people', and his criticism may be put: the people, out of fear and hungers goes into the other-emulative, collectively moving or non-moving and leader-following crowd-form — recalcitrant to his message as it was to that of Jesus. The Resistance Movement graphically had assumed such crowd form. The evil leaders are prominent in his work of the '60s: they now drop out of it. This is odd because they are the crowd's correlate. But Schumann himself was a leader — leading his group — and in the context of the crowd-individual conceptualization, the evils of leadership probably seemed epiphenomenal to him.

7

But some of the obscurity of his treatment of the theme during the God-dard period probably is also due to an unwillingness of his to focus on this role of his, with which he was uneasy.

Furthermore — we recall his fantasies of Genghis Khan — this ideology of his, as he may have with some discomfort somewhat realized, had a certain resemblance to fascist ideology, was rooted in his German back-ground, and so was in need of his working it out to differentiate it from that fatuous cynicism. He needed to express his ideas in the area of this ideology (if only to work them out), but could do so only in cryptic form, both because of their suspect nature, and because though he was certain they were different, their difference was not clear to him. This applied not only to the crowd/individual but also to the man/woman dichotomy and dynamism.

My chief point, however, is not that Schumann at this point was bent on doing a cryptic theatre in which communication between him and his audience would be imperfect, but one in which it was cut off, no matter how much of his ideas the audience in fact got, it being not a theatre of communication, but one in which the audience would encounter a certain situation pertinent to it. It would be the presentation of such a situation rather than a communication, let alone an exhortation to action. He accomplished this by a set of technical and a formal device: an approach toward marionettry or to a 'mechanical theatre', uses of strings and modes of staging suggesting to perception that the show or theatre was self-contained, did not particularly come from anybody (author or performers) — its approach to a mechanism at the same time conveying some of Schumann's particular ideas concerning the human situation, viz. mass man's lack of self-determination; and non-narrative narration, i.e. a framing of the show by the traditional means of frame and curtain and by performers really a part of it but so segregated from it visually and by their action as to indicate — the point here is delicate — a show/subject-matter-of-show relation, i.e.: that it was not (and was not being presented as) a self-contained reality, but was about something or referred to something. Narrational form normally stresses the subjective factor, the existence of an author, the teller of the tale, but in this case stressed denotation. It was non-narrative narration in that Schumann in fact let the shows tell their own story: with less verbal aid or comment, even, than during his preced-ing period: their form did not get him into the picture, but on the contrary kept him out of it.

The form — presentation of a representation — and content — suffering — characteristic of this period emerge in his 'theatre' or indoors pieces (on which during this period, his intentions to the contrary, his creative ener-gies were focused): *Difficult Life*: Humanity as busy Crowd vs. the blind and destructive Individual; *Lamentation/Mississippi*: destruction of the Individual by the Crowd: *Grey Lady Cantata II*: the Individual as suffer-

8

ing being; *Emilia*: the Family as state of sequestration; *Birdcatcher*: the Venal Moloch, or the Individual saved by murder; *Whitewashing*: Individuality squashed; *Stations*: destruction of the Individual by Humanity qua Crowd; *McLeod*: self-destruction of the Individual reacting against the Crowd; *Simple Light*: the Family as escape from the cruelties of individuation and Crowd-socialization.

There is one apparent but only apparent exception from presentation of representations: the '70/'71 circuses in terms of their ending: the audience is invited to join in a procession in the Ark for All, to the singing of *The Storm is Here*; one near or possible exception, the street-playlet *Hallelujah*, which textually seems a warning against pollution and such; one probable exception, the *Cry*-derived disciple parades and/or Last Supper/ Crucifixion shows run by Schumann himself, '70/'71 – I suspect they differed in the manner indicated from their like predecessors of the '60s, but I don't have enough information to say whether or how they did; one sure exception, I would say, the *Cry*-derived *Building of Jesus* parade or parades run by Dalrymple and/or Konnoff in '70 – exhortations to resistance, surely.

The circuses' endings did not make them the statement 'since things are this bad and apt to get this much worse, save yourselves!' for the simple reason that their concluding invitation merely invited the audience to join in the play, in the making of whatever statement the circus made, which itself was unaffected by this invitation, and thus remained rather 'under the circumstances prevailing there is only one thing left to do, get the hell out': an attitude exhibited. The audience was not invited to drop out.

Hallelujah was done as good-natured fun (which none of Schumann's '60s street agitation had been done as): the spoilation of nature was not – as it was by Schumann during the later '70s – presented as sacrilege. There was no moral issue raised that would have carried implicit exhortative address.

The theatrical form of the following period – offering – and its content – hope – are broached during this period in Schumann's circus pageants by the Ark for All, and in his *Hallelujah*: but, I would say, only in a marginal and irresolute manner.

Schumann's own (as distinct from his lieutenants') *Cry*-derived Jesus-mongering probably had the effective form of an exhibition of sorrow-fulness rather than of moral condemnation.

There were some other parades that seemed in a straightforward way to continue the exhortative mode of Schumann's street agitation of the '60s: his Administration of Justice parade of early '70, his (and Konnoff's) Be-hold Yourself parades in which a mirror-carrier was supposed to pose to the public the question of where they stood as regarded what the simul-taneous main parade was about – of the spring of '70. But the former, so far as I can see, merely pointed out what pass things had come to in this

9

land of ours, and in the latter the mirror-presentation functioned as 'pseudo-narrational' frame of the main parade, and effectively for its moral issue substituted the indication that a moral issue was being posed and a presentation to the audience of itself: there you are: and aren't you a sorry bunch!

During his Cate Farm Goddard period, the clear quadri-partite structure of his work output during the preceding period disappears, though there are — of course — faint analogies. His agitational street work (re-oriented toward college students and neighborhood) and his Christian demonstrations continue, but in a petering-out though occasionally explosively vehement manner, and we can perhaps regard certain intimate Cate Farm efforts — small stuff around the home — as equivalent of his somewhat painful efforts to provide entertainment for children during the '60s. But while during the '60s a certain unity accrues to work that for that period by his effort by it to institute, to make clear to himself and to master the medium he has invented (is inventing, creating) stands out as something like 'theatre proper', by '69 he is in possession of his art and instead of any block of work relevantly characterizable as theatre proper or by a search for form, we find three large, fairly well-defined projects applying his now fully established art: two directed toward popular theatre, one toward art theatre: his Coney Island or Black project and his Travelling Circus project, respectively directed toward the Afroamerican sub-proletariat, the inner city demos, the living heart of his chosen country, and toward the white American nation, neither middle nor lower class in his mind or theirs, but People or even — his feelings about the Blacks being ambivalent — The People, and to his mind country (including Small Town people); and his Grey Lady project, a painful effort to rectify his artificial, ideological image of woman, to express his feelings about his mother, to image his at this time essential category of life, that of the suffering of the individual, to publicize without revealing (which is the essence of artistic activity) his intimate feelings. In this third more expressive, more audience-directed line of effort he focuses on The Individual, who here, for the first time, appears in his work — initially as suffering mother, then as a suffering woman, progressively more active. In addition to work executing one or another of these three large projects, we find two or three Big Position-Resuming plays (*Difficult Life* and *Simple Light*, with the '71 *Birdcatcher* possibly a third).

Those three projects all failed. He was rejected by the Blacks at Coney Island. His travelling circus proved impossible and to the extent it was realized reached only college audiences. His Grey Lady series produced another false image of woman, and when at the end of the period with the '74 fourth *Grey Lady Cantata* (and later on with the '75 sixth one) he tried to make a 'real individual' out of her, activize and terrestrialize her it turned into surrealist slapstick.

10

His work during this period has no backbone the way his political street activity during the '60s was its backbone, nor does it have the steady rhythm (appropriation by Self of Time) then given it by his Christian observances. It recovers both during the following period or periods — his circuses then again give it backbone and rhythm.

2. Eviction from Manhattan, extraction from the crowd, withdrawal from the city. Copping out? Plans and hopes. The Coney Island project. The Cate Farm Project.

As I have previously told, having lost the Old Courthouse, Schumann moved his operations (though not his residence) across the East River, finding refuge first (January 4-March 2) in the Bank — I remember the stove in the middle of the workspace, its flame, a clear yellow, flared above it — and then (mid-March to mid-June) in the Old Boston Theatre in Coney Island: way out on the subway, though Schumann mostly drove the theatre bus out there, the girls flashing their cunts into his rearview mirror. There was no way to perform at the Bank, but he got his next piece, *Difficult Life*, ready there. On Coney Island he could both create and perform his pieces. In the meantime, however, on the initiative and thanks to the machinations of friends on the faculty — Michael Appleby, Jules Rabin — he was obtaining resident artist status at Goddard College, near the village of Plainfield in northern Vermont, a mid-April visit there with 'Uncle Fatso and a new version of the Easter pageant involving as many students as possible' (Schumann, *Bread and Rosebuds*, April 25, '70) clinching the deal, and this is where he went, giving up his apartment on East 6th Street, in mid-June.

When Schumann left New York, there were a certain number of raised eyebrows in the Movement, not so much his friends, probably — older people who had families themselves and lest they be judged not given to judging others — but among the younger and more radical people, in his group and around: he was perceived as copping out.[1] Up front, he would

---

1. 'Well, you know, I almost don't want to say, because it would sound as if I'm somehow antagonistic to the position of the theatre, and I don't mean to say that. People do what they have to do. You know, I did my thing, and I'm sure that Elka and Peter would have a hard time understanding my present styles and endeavors. But nevertheless, that's what I did. So I'm certainly not condemning theirs. I think you can either stay in a situation where something is built and expand it. Leaving the Lower East Side, to me, was not good. Going to a residential college was not good — for me . . . Going to Cate Farm was not so good. And I couldn't tell if it was me being possessive. You know, stay small, stay on a base. Or — being realistic in terms of how I wanted things to go for my life — so I had a disagreement, in that sense . . . I feel that he had the idea. Subjectively he had the idea that a community could be built. There was also trouble on the Lower East Side. His wife was attacked at one point. Held up at knifepoint with the payroll for people. The children were not so safe on the streets. We were all experiencing this. A tremendous number of drugs at that time came into the Lower East Side. It was a low rent area, a mixed area. A good place to go if you don't have money and you're on drugs. And we started to have trouble that we didn't expect . . . And Peter somewhat reacted to that. Reasonably so. He

give the fuck-off reasons of urban insalubrity, his family, the same as any second-generation American moving from the nicer borough his parents had moved to to the suburbs, and perhaps his disenchantment with the protest Movement — he was going to keep up protest (cf. infra), but not as part of the Movement, not so his theatre would be identified as protest theatre.[2] And though in '70 there was no Cate Farm commune, the idea of

---

had several children. Had the idea always of a community together. Had always that idea. From the beginning. And felt it would be better to do that in the country. What better place to go than where you can farm and do your theatre and tour? Objectively, it put it in a stance with larger companies and in a circle that wasn't good for me. I didn't see myself in that. Nor did I see Peter particularly fitting in that. But that was my idea . . . I was off the scene and I don't know what happened subsequently to that. But I felt that mold was not good. And — that was my subjective feeling about it. Although I never blamed Peter for what he did. I also felt that Peter required a tremendous amount of personal power in order to be able to direct. He needed people to believe in him completely. And that's not unusual, I would imagine, although I'm not a theatrical person with directors who need to have a kind of charge built up among the players. And I could not give that because I felt that I would have to lend myself to this theatre, you know, when he needed me, and essentially would be abandoned, you see, when the theatre moved on. Now, what was my only grievance was that in order to create, we needed a tremendous amount of mutual charge together, but then there was no life, you see. No way of continuing that support. I think it's a problem in theatre. And I knew that I could not leave the city and go into that lifestyle in the country. So it became like a conflict of interests. (I: That's right — in other words, everybody's dependence on the leader would become much greater?) Not good. That's not good. Then everything would depend, you see, on Peter's good will or on the charge that could be built up around the creativity. And I feel in the time we are now we're trying to build personal creativity as well as that kind of collective thing. That's very hard to do around somebody who is as stunning as Peter is. To develop a self is hard in that situation.' — (Palmer, interview, '79.)

'And you know when he went to Vermont the first time, I remember hearing a lot of cries that he was selling out, which often came from people who wouldn't for a moment have lived the way he was living under the privation that he was living in. Which made me very angry at the time. People who had no business opening their mouths on such a subject were talking about it, and I did once ask Peter how he felt about that — "You've been doing pieces in East Harlem, you've been doing things in the street, you've been where the battles are, where the city is, where the whole thing — how do you feel about leaving that aspect of your work out there?"

And his response to me — I hope I'm right on this — but I think I am, certainly my memory of what he said was — he said: "Well, I am a Christian and I don't believe that the mathematical chances of moving, usefully moving, one person in a crowd of a thousand are greater than the mathematical chances of moving one person in a crowd of six. That is, that the absolute is the individual effect on the individual." And he said that his position was that the bulk of people that you're dealing with in the city does not in those terms have any direct ratio to the amount of actual effect you have. I mean, I heard it not as a rationalization but as a point of very profound belief on his part. Certainly, an arguable one.' — (Shapli, interview.)

2. He had given such reasons for wanting to move out as early as '68:

'(I: I heard recently that you were thinking of leaving New York and going into a rural area. Why?) The stink. The thick column that you see when you come into New York, and

communal action in 'real America'[3] — with a group other than his '69 one — probably also was in his mind already, though for the moment he was keeping quiet about it.

Schumann does no more 'Crucifixion' from now on. Instead, in the springs of '70 and '71 he or his group without him, do 'crucifixion pageants' derived from *Cry*, in '70 outdoor ones, more political than religious, Bill Dalrymple on the 'Southern tour' of March-June, a more incitatory Resistance one, based on *Cry*'s 'building of Jesus' scene, Schumann a more pacific, plaintive one with local student recruits, in mid-April at Goddard and Cornell, where it was — on the flyer — advertised as a 'religious experience with a personal message.' A *Last Supper* and a *Crucifixion*, in '71, April 24, a similar one at a Movement demonstration in Washington, D.C. (for the four preceding, cf. supra, section on street agitation), and another indoors one, as part of a *Domestic Resurrection Circus* toured in New England, comprising some manner of procession of the disciples and possibly a Last Supper (whether it had a Crucifixion, I 31n't know), sufficiently important in the show, to make Elka think of the show as 'like a very elaborate version of the Easter show.'

(Schumann, interview, '79.)

Beyond these reasons there were two more important ones: the conflict between leadership and democratic collectivism in his group that on the '69 tour he had plastered over — he really had to leave that group and that predicament behind — and his having as artist outgrown the addressive-

---

the dirt under your fingernails. (I: Who would be your audience out there?) Trees. Farmers. We are not leaving the city so we can do social action theatre in new environments. We simply want to get out of New York because it's stinky and dirty. We'll live out in the country and return to the cities when we have to. Also this business of being a "professional protest theatre" doesn't seem good enough.' — (Brown and Seitz, *With the Bread and Puppet Theatre, Tulane Drama Review* #38, Winter 1968.)

'(I: That was kind of a major decision at the time to leave New York or was it not?) Well, mostly because we'd been getting all those lousy reviews — at that time he thought he was washed up in New York. (I: What was reviewed?) I guess when they came out for the *Cry*, he didn't like the reviews it got. He didn't feel they were glowing. (I: This decision in 1970 wasn't a very dramatic –) No, it was an opportunity, it was a job. He could go up there and live and take the kids out of the city.' — (Leherrissier, interview.)

Irene's remark about the lousy reviews is not as far out as one might suppose:

'We always felt that our audience was more worthwhile when it was an arbitrary collection of people from a lot of different walks of life, and not people that have gotten through these abominable artsy New York papers that are in charge of getting audiences. We left New York because we couldn't breathe the air there.' — (Schumann, in Rough, *An Interview with Peter Schumann, Dramatics*, December 1973.)

3. Cf. e.g. Michael Appleby's *Revolutionary Change and the Urban Environment* (in Priscilla Long's *The New Left*, 1969). Appleby calls for community action by sub-communities of radicals insinuating themselves into small rural and town communities to effect a 'pluralistic revolution', 'mobilizing small enclaves of radicalism in a variety of social locations, . . . changing people's consciousness, ... creating alternative ways of living . . . ' He later married a nun and went to Africa as a missionary. — (Ashley, interview.)

moralistic mode of street theatre and being hungry for a non-exhortative and more theatrical mode. Leaving New York effectively solved both problems. With minor variations, the same two problems in '70 caused a number of radical theatres to split up.[4]

The movement from New York to Vermont, moreover, was a general one. The state, originally a New York colony, was being invaded. On the one hand by hustlers with handsome Germanic instructors setting up ski-lifts and Alpenhütten motels and buying up real estate, on the other by intellectual types with maybe some independent income who figured that like Scott Nearing they could make it in the wilderness. When Schumann finally made it in Vermont, these transplants swelled his circus audiences and work crews.

His projects and enterprises that spring were multi-directional. The major factors of his situation were: life on the Lower East Side had gotten tough on his family (rapes and muggings, the small apartment, the Blacks hassling his kids in P.S. #122); the money he had secured for himself and the theatre from the '69 tour was running out fast; the crummy reception New York critics continued to give his shows contrasted insultingly with the esteem he had encountered in Europe in '68 and '69; agitational action in a radical perspective on the Big City crowd had to many in the Movement come to seem a poor alternative to insinuative action in the country by a combination of 'domestic resurrection' in the form of com-munes – an exemplary new way of life – and agitation, and Schumann was tempted by this viewpoint; his performances in fancy theatres for fancy audiences in Europe had left him with a bad conscience, but the touring way of life appealed to him; and the two perhaps most important: on the one hand, he didn't want to be dependent, as he had been touring *Cry*, on a big company (on 'actors' as he later misleadingly put it), and was in fact turning out a play involving almost no on-stage performers, and none of these actors or otherwise important, and not too many off-stage operators, but on the other hand, he was saddled with a very big company (eleven of them on $35 weekly salaries). Though the few remaining old-timers had left more or less permanently (Sherman and Ernstthal, the mainstays of his mid-'60s theatre, Levy, the energetic all-around worker for *Cry*), he had come back with quite a few late-'60s recruits hanging on, new French and German disciples were flying in weekly, former members that had stayed behind were dropping around.

His projects and enterprises, then, dealing with this situation, were on the one hand to establish the Coney Island operation as a semi-independent component of the Bread and Puppet Theatre, one for which he would furnish plays, masks, puppets, paintings and, commuting, the directing, and to run another operation himself on Cate Farm at Goddard,

---

4. Cf. Appendix X.

using Goddard students, and with the help of only a very few, maybe two or three regular puppeteers, trying things out there, performing around the area and on tours[5] (he had no intention as yet, this spring, of establishing a Bread and Puppet commune up there), and on the other, still as part of the Bread and Puppet operation, not as independent splinter groups of which at this time quite a few were trying their wings, to have sub-groups, run by lieutenants, go out on tours with his plays. The tourers would be out from under his feet, he would run the Coney Island operation without being part of the company there and free of day to day involvement, and at Goddard, notwithstanding the odd and perhaps misleading projection in an April 25 newsletter (cf. infra) of 'two companies at Goddard', there would be no company. Except that it was madly ambitious, it made sense as solution to the Crowd/Individual dilemma: the Individual (Schumann) extracting himself from the Crowd, and yet, using it, realizing himself as Individual.

At the same time, however, there was still something else in his mind: to recast the whole Bread and Puppet operation into the itinerant mold of the folk puppeteers that on the European continent from the Middle Ages onward with their families travelled from village to village, from fair to fair, playing for The People, though on the larger scale of a travelling circus with a tent. To some extent this fancy simply romanticized touring for himself and for the parts of his company cast out on the road under lieutenants, and justified the no-resident-company (and no-audience!) Goddard project. But, though it really conflicted both with his residency on Cate Farm, and with the settled operation at Coney Island, it was a sincere idea of his that he was serious about and it led on to his first two circuses ('70, '71).

A newsletter of April '70 enthusiastically and in the royal first person plural reports on these projects and enterprises:

'Mid March we moved to Coney Island – Hurrah! It's the old Boston Theater on 1205 Surf Ave. which used to be a people place where you had a movie and beer for 15 cents. We got there through the friendliness of Nathan's Mr. and Mrs. Handworker, Dick Levy and Marketta Kimbrell of the City Street Theater and the New York Shakespeare Festival. It costs only 4 hotdogs a year and we have a 1-year lease. And it belongs to Nathan's Famous Super Hotdogs Inc. The ceiling is leaking, there is no heat and hardly any light and water yet – but the place is ideal for us and besides Nathan's wants to help us find more light and

---

5. 'It seemed to me possible to have two companies at that point, you know. It's a little bit like now. I thought: I'm directing shows now, I can write them, I can make them ready, a lot more can be produced than what that little company that I have can perform and why not have two companies. That was the big idea. We go to the country and build up a new theatre with different ideals and different puppets and what have you and we make shows and take them to the big city – we have more space – we have free rent and we can do things here and over there we perform them in addition to, on this end, building up a different type of an audience.' — (Schumann, interview, August '82.)

16

water – no more Village Voice or other publicity necessary – the world is all there, especially kids, super-large families and old people. And that is what we want to do very much: do workshops with kids and with old folks (i.e. an old timer wants to do a professional Yiddish puppetry group production). And also we want to learn everything possible about ghostrides, carrousels, laughing ladies, etc.

Besides the workshops we will do 2 types of Fri-Sun short quick turnover puppetshows: right in the street under the awning, Punch and Judy in modern times political farces, kids stuff, dragon and sword battles, sweet bitter music and inside in the theater huge horrible puppet meetings between Mother Earth, Nixon, Uranos, Supercrook, Rats, Pigs, Lovers, Nightingales. These have to be short big spectacular pieces on reality, politics, war and love for 440 passersby (C.O.)

As I said there is a lot to learn. Coney Island is decadent and frightening, but it has a style, which is expressive and pretty real and close to the heart of the consumer. Yes we too need a laughing lady and certainly a crying lady and a gorilla transformation tent show. All that is a big human theme, material for truth. And the audience is like Mister Everyman . . .

Mid May we will all be back in Coney Island and will have at least 4 weeks for building a set of huge puppets which we started already, workshops and extensive rehearsals of the Coney Island business instruction amusement. We want to end up with 3 large 15 minute pieces for the inside theater. The outside productions should be directly out of weekday workshops. We want to play for a dime a nickel or nothing if possible. Rides and shows in Coney Island are now 25 to 27 cents, much higher than local kids can afford, but how we can manage without help I don't know yet. Our savings from Europe are being eaten up fast with 11 $35 a week salaries, petty cash, tools, celastic, the tent which we got for the new life pages 6 and 7, big car failure purchase, Bills mailtruck and 1 more travelling van.

Expected income plus the rest of the savings will allow 600 per month (that is what we are spending now per week) from May 15 till October 1st when we want to go on a Westcoast tour.

We may have some money from doing parades with Pete Seeger, demonstrating deadfish and wateraches in communities that live along the Hudson River. He is applying for a grant from the Council on the Arts. But they want to pay only deficits or museums or something like that, so we don't know yet.

In mid-June we will split into 2 crews again. One Coney Island, two Goddard.

Already last year when we were in Europe Jules Rabin (ex-puppeteer, anthropologie professor, ex-truckdriver) and students suggested a bread & puppet residence to the Goddard administration. In February the new college president Jerry Witherspoon invited us the puppeteers for meetings and discussions up to Vermont. A committee of faculty and students did the final agreeing, decision making and planning of details: we will move to Goddard in mid-June, be theater in residence, not hired salaried teachers, but doing our baking and puppeteering there with as much of Goddard and neighborhood involved as possible. We will live on Kate Farm, the barn is made into a workshop, food and more living space are available at the college if needed.

What are we doing in Goddard?

We the Schumanns and other old timers are ready for a bigger slower style of motion, air breathing and vegetable-growing included.

As a result of our European trip we said to each other: let's get a tent and move like a circus. We got the tent and it is a brown animalskin that grows every time we set it up. We got sledgehammers and an ax. We want to get 2 horses and a waggon and make a circus consisting of all creatures stilted gentlemen and the laughing lady from Coney Island. And we will move slowly from town to town and blow our horns. Years ago I travelled with horse and waggon through Austria and Bavaria doing fiddling and maskdancing by the side of the road. But the shows were solitary performances for trees rather than humans and the horse went lame and the waggon broke. Now we have a lot of stuff for the edge of any little town, choreographing the world makes sense now.

Life in Goddard will be a newborn life, featuring the hardships of early adolescence, hopes and aspirations are tremendous.

Let's not even talk about that. The barn is beautiful. John Kruse and his people are doing a terrific job on it. I want to build a Cathedral out of the barn. An event of people crowds and individuals sculpted in every material we can lay hands on, painted gloriously if possible.

Quite a few Bread and Puppeteers have started their own puppet and cranky-theaters: The Chickenlittle Theatre in France, Blackbirds in Maine, Eastbay-sharks and Moving Co. in California, Bob Ernstthal's theatre in Copenhagen, Murray's group in Washington and others.

Goddard will be such a step of not only new programs and new puppetry for all of us breadbakers. We have done politics, intense theatrework and our own style of carnival, inventing enough music to enjoy ourselves. In Goddard we will grow goodness I hope.

Peter Schumann
Bread and Puppets
(Schumann, *Bread and Rosebuds*, April 25, '70.)

Coney Island in a sense was Schumann's big chance. He finally had a definitely popular audience, the black proles and welfare clients of New York City whom he could address as he had by his street agitation six years earlier his Latino neighbors on issues of immediate concern to them, viz. *not* the war in Asia and he could amalgamate his high-culture ambitions as an Artist with a reasonable facsimile of the existence of a folk artist, a carney man's. Playing here was half-way street theatre. It was indoors but on the sidewalk, and by its posters, barker's spiels, sidewalk come-on music and in fact with some of the shows his theatre spilling over into the street, and it had a street audience — in fact street people — with their families — who in the middle of its amusements it surprised, who did not come to search it out.[6]

---

6. '(I: Now, you were there in Coney Island and you had this audience — street people — just came in and were there. Wasn't that an extraordinary thing for you and something positive?) Yes, it was. Yet, it seemed when we got there — it seemed a fantastic opportunity.' — (Schumann, interview, '82.)

But though a few fine plays — *Lamentation, Mississippi, Revenge, McLeod* — came out of it, i.e. were specifically designed and done there, the Coney Island project didn't really work out. The Schumanns, though especially Elka, Schumann being as reluctant to blame individuals as to praise them, tend to blame Bart and Brigitte Lane who more or less took

---

'Au Sud de Brooklyn, à une heure de métro express de Manhattan, Coney Island est le lieu de distraction favori des plus pauvres des New-Yorkais. Cette gigantesque foire qui offre des attractions de toutes sortes, manèges, stands de tirs, diseuses de bonne aventure, est aménagée sur une plage grise et sale, polluée par le mazout, où se déverse pendant les week-ends d'été une foule compacte de Noirs, de Porto-Ricains et de pauvres Blancs. Depuis une quinzaine d'années, les familles bourgeoises ont déserté ce quartier de plus en plus misérable. Tout près du métro sur la Surf Avenue qui longe la plage, à côté d'un stand où l'on vend des ballons et de la barbe à papa, se trouve le local du Bread and Puppet Theatre. Dans les premiers temps de Coney Island, c'était un "café-cinéma" qui passait des "Charlot". Devant le théâtre, une petite estrade: les acteurs y grimpent pour faire de la musique et annoncer: "Dans dix minutes, spectacle de marionnettes gratuit. Entrez!" Les vendredi, samedi et dimanche, ils jouent sans discontinuer toutes les demi-heures (en principe chaque spectacle ne dure pas plus de quinze à vingt minutes), de 3 heures de l'après-midi à 11 heures du soir, et la salle qui contient environ 400 places ne désemplit pas. Elle est installée rudimentairement: des rangées de caisses en bois et devant, un espace libre où les enfants peuvent s'asseoir par terre. Tout autour circule une vaste galerie où sont rangées toutes les marionnettes et d'où pendent de grandes toiles aux couleurs vives, peintes par Peter Schumann: des fleurs, un grand arbre, etc. Avant d'entrer dans la salle on traverse une grande pièce où se trouvent à droite l'atelier pour les enfants et à gauche une petite salle où l'on fait le pain. Pendant la semaine les marionnettistes se livrent à leurs occupations habituelles, fabrication de masques, de marionnettes, de bannières, d'affiches (sérigraphie), séances de musique, répétitions des spectacles. Le théâtre est toujours rempli d'enfants: l'atelier fonctionne en permanence.' — (Kourilsky, '71.)

'2. In June, Bread & Puppet began performing at Coney Island in a donated theatre previously used by an animal freak show. Coney Island has changed since I went there as a child in the late Forties. Even on the boardwalk half the concessions are shut down, though there are still masses of people. Everything is crumbling and dirty. The wax museum and pony rides have been replaced by fortunetellers. It's a place for the bottom poor. Black and Puerto Rican. On Surf Avenue, the barker across the street from the Bread & Puppet's Theatre was touting "Hollywood Horrors, *en persona*, not a movie!" Loud amplified voice, big comic-book-art posters of girls and gorillas. About twenty people had stopped. In front of Bread & Puppet several performers were playing quiet music; Peter Schumann did a tune on his toy violin. The building is painted with soft bright flowers, play titles, a recipe beginning, "BREAD: all you need is a grinder to grind the grain . . ." Here too, twenty people stopped. In the middle of the street a cop was teaching his horse to dance. The horse was good, the cop proud.

3. Bread & Puppet has moved away from the lefty-Village audience which followed them in the "peace churches," to another one of *Daily News* readers, television watchers living in the unrelenting ugliness of the New York ghettos. They have not patronized this audience with agitprop messages or an "attention-getting" pace. This is brave and honest. Pure, if you will.' — (E. Munk, *TDR Comment, Tulane Drama Review* #47.)

'A barker stands on Surf Avenue in Brooklyn. He is hustling Bread and Puppets at Coney Island, the amusement park where our rip-off society is most garishly manifest in the stuffed animals and cheap china that replace the dreams of the poor. Peter Schumann . . . had not grown up alienated by the commercial manipulation of mass tastes. Medieval

it over until, in '72, it folded, stayed there winters even (the amusement park closes down in winter) and did shows and workshops of their own in the community: their stuff was too slick, too commercial. The Lanes are probably as unfit to do art on their own as is anybody else that has worked with Schumann, but the problem wasn't there. Nor was it that he

---

pageants, public festivals did not seem altogether unreal to him; he knew that what is popular can also be aesthetically excellent. Surrounded by television's stale emotions we think the popular taste is hopelessly corrupt. It is surprising to us to learn that it needn't be scoffed at so much, rather, the honest needs it springs from should be recognized. (Black theatre workers are also aware of the necessity of presenting the beauty in the current popular culture. But this is precisely what middle class radicals find most difficult to do.) No other people's theatre has so closely joined the popular with the artistic imagination. That this can be done offers hope for the future and great delight in the present.

This union of popular tastes with revolutionary perceptions is an important goal for all people's theatres. Schumann recognized it first and has pursued it most insistently; this is his gift to the movement . . . . The Bread and Puppet's theatre in the Coney Island section of Brooklyn is a loan from the owners of Nathan's, whose hot dog palace stands across the street. The outside is decorated like a side show: Jenny, the flying lady; the thin man; the fat lady have been painted on its wooden panels. Across the top of the second story a huge clown face and torso with outstretched arms stops passersby. Schumann is perched on a platform outside the second story window playing "When the Saints Come Marching In" on his fiddle. On the street below a performer dressed in tails announces through a megaphone the performance of *The Bird Catcher in Hell*, a free puppet play, in just five minutes. He is supported by a young boy who keeps up a steady rhythm on a bass drum, a girl who bangs a gong and a fantastically costumed person from the play who does a slow Oriental dance on the street. It is Fourth of July weekend, 1971. The air is hot and rancid as only New York City can be. The Bread and Puppet Theatre has left its home at Goddard College in Plainfield, Vermont, traveling the 400 or so odd miles in a red and pink flowered school bus to make their Independence Day stand at Coney Island. The audience they collect is perfectly random, of all ages and races. Some have come especially to see the theatre, but most have just wandered over on their way somewhere else.

To combat the wheezing organ music and the barker's challenges from the shooting booths across the street, Schumann uses his own scratchy fiddle and his own barker. Competing with the gaudy colors are the equally brilliant colors of the theatre. But in place of the capitalistic need to get people in, get their money and get them out that contributes to the flurry of the amusement park, Schumann offers the experience of uncluttered time. In the first place, he is asking for a substantial commitment from his audience: the performance will take nearly an hour. More pertinent, his productions replace the capitalist's credo that "time is money" with a sense that time is unlimited, because only by ignoring its passing, in favor of close scrutiny of the events it reveals, will we understand what there is to know. Repetition is crucial to his theatre. When an action is important or when the puppets strike an attitude that is especially correct, the audience may watch it two or three times. The laconic pace of productions is another way the dismissal of life through the capitalization of time is combatted.' — (K. Taylor, *People's Theater in America*.)

K. Taylor's comment that Schumann did not mind commercial entertainment is precisely wrong: Schumann hates it.

'In spring 1970, the Bread and Puppet Theatre acquired an empty side-show house on Coney Island. They had made the break that most leftist/liberal groups have not been able to make, that is, they have moved away from preaching to the already converted and were able to go directly to the people. Coney Island. A remarkable choice! Where else do representatives from all layers of New York's diverse societies get a chance to rub shoulders?

didn't live in Coney Island, but first in Manhattan and then in Vermont, but went there to do a job, nor that he very quickly became involved in the Goddard operation (where a resident company soon aggregated) and in his circus project, and so just didn't have the time for Coney Island.[7] The question is why didn't he? In '70 he gave them story ideas that

---

Coney Island: for most foreigners the symbol of the "myths of America": all the garishness, sadness, hucksterism and joy in one place. True, Bread and Puppet Theatre seems to be a bit anomalous in that jungle. Their bright primitively painted building houses no sideshow or wax monsters, but countless puppets, costumes, props, masks, clay and a few dedicated young people. On weekends they put out a big sign saying: "Free Puppet Show" and perform continuously all afternoon and evening. People pass by, eyeing them suspiciously: "On Coney Island, something for free? Impossible!" And yet they have managed to amass quite a few loyal followers who come every day, bringing their friends: some have reportedly learned all the plays by heart and recite the lines aloud with the puppets.

These weekend audiences usually exceed 500 people a day. During the week the doors are opened most afternoons and youngsters are allowed to wander in and play with the clay and learn to make puppets (usually some adult guests can be found there too). A large sign on the wall is a recipe for baking bread and offers to give additional instructions in the art of bread-baking. During the shows the performers pass through the audience giving out pieces of homemade bread in their perpetual symbolic act of feeding the world.' — (E. Thalenberg, *Not by Bread Alone* . . . , *artscanada*, December '70-January '71.)

7. 'I remember Coney Island being sort of a problem. It became too — I mean Peter's idea then and also now is to sort of have a lot of things going on at once and I think I feel like he doesn't realize how complicated or difficult it is, so the thing in Coney Island didn't go easily at all. The people who — Bart made shows which were called Bread and Puppet shows which were — which he made and they were — I remember seeing one and being really embarrassed about how bad it was, and Chris Hartman had these other interesting things, very mechanical, and he had this slicker, commercial idea and he made a lot of puppets . . . at that time, I think without Peter . . . there would be all the conflicts that would be under the surface . . . people wouldn't get along.' — (Elka, interview.)

'I know Peter was really excited about that situation, about having something in such an unlikely place but yet a place where people go to see things and to get amused, but it seemed as though the things that were created for it were very fleeting . . . . And I know the people who were there had a lot of difficulty just with things like leaks and cold and filling up this — and the winters and — at the time it seemed more like a distraction for him to be running off to Coney Island to sort of pull that thing together because the company and the situation in Goddard wasn't at all super solid — there were a lot of people there who wanted a lot of different things and it wasn't an easy time. There were strains and people who wanted to do more independent shows and people who wanted to be directed, and it felt like that place wasn't really solved or resolved — and yet a lot of time was spent going to Coney Island — which was supposed to feel like another part of Bread and Puppet Theatre. But I think for most people in Cate Farm it just felt wholly removed and, you know, a completely other situation.' — (Elka, in Schumann, interview, '82.)

Elka clearly didn't think much of having Schumann off in New York in '71 and '72.

'The first set of shows were shows that I rehearsed with them and that I had made the puppets for. With their help. Then they started children's workshops. Bart Lane, especially, Bart Lane and Brigitte, Bart's wife, started children's workshops. And the children's workshops turned out to be the more important part of the Coney island thing, because these weekend performances didn't draw much audience. Whereas the children's workshop was pretty successful. They also gave performances. With the children participating in the performances. (Elka: I remember going down there. It seems as though — shortly, not too

21

weren't much good, and most of his shows there weren't much good either. In '71, he honored the Coney Islanders by doing his *Birdcatcher* there on July 4th — they didn't appreciate it and he didn't like their not appreciating it — but otherwise his work at Goddard on this play and on

---

long after we moved to Vermont, and watching the shows in Coney Island that Bart Lane had made. And they didn't — in my memory, they weren't children's shows, they were like very serious, taking themselves very seriously, copies of your shows, and I remember feeling so disappointed.) Yes, there were some shows of Bart's, other than the children's shows. (Elka: And then Chris Hartmann went down and they worked together.) The next year. Axel and Chris did a project there and they got a job from a man across the street who had a horror house that he wanted to revive, so they built him the puppets and things and the scary scene for that horror house. And they got a grant for materials from the New York Council of the Arts, I think. (Elka: I think the Coney Island project had a *couple* of grants. I think George Ashley helped get a grant maybe earlier. But I remember, that was one of the things that made it harder and harder to kind of *keep* it together, because it was — the people who were there were raising the money themselves — in ways that maybe you weren't interested in, you weren't interested in going after grants or whatever, and they were doing *more* of the work — you know, it was their *own*, and it seemed less and less any reason for it to be *one* group. Because it wasn't.) Yeah. Yeah.' — (Schumann, interview, '79.)

'Peter quit at some point and he took off for Cate Farm with Harvey Spevak. (I: After a month or two — that was in the summer of 1970?) He quit around the end of June. Took off for Vermont . . . . Axel Gros, Bart Lane and George were the managers of the Coney Island summer. Because I was a principal actor — and everyone else worked for free. I couldn't believe they did that. Everyone else worked for free, except for George, Axel and Bart. George and Bart were friends of mine and still are friends of mine — but Axel Gros wasn't. He was just this extremely macho guy . . . . We'd do all these things outside, inside. (I: You had Peter's — the masks and the costumes.) Yes, we had all the props and stuff. (I: And you were all living on Coney Island?) I wasn't, I was living in Manhattan with Arthur. (I: And they were living here and there?) They found this old house that was scheduled to be demolished, so they convinced them that they could stay there since they were doing this theatre program. It was an awful dump, run down and dirty — but they all lived out there and ate there . . . . (I: How did it feel to do theatre without Peter?) It was fine. There wasn't any real backbiting among the women there. That for me was a real plus. We got along real well, and there were problems with Axel, because he was such a fuckhead really, but he was somebody who liked to put people down basically, but we tried to just avoid Axel as much as possible . . . . He (Schumann) set us up. Basically gave us a whole bunch of shows and said keep the props and then split . . . . And then we did other dopey shows where we got people from the community at Coney Island to come. There was this one show where someone was going to be born. Peter — I don't even remember which show it was, but there was this one lady in the audience who had been like a mother of some of the kids who used to come around, and she was sort of — she was very engaged in work of the children and therefore wanted to get to really know us and she really did. I can't remember her name although I know people who do know her name, but there was one scene where a baby was going to be born and George said, "Oh, a birth. Is there a doctor in the house?" and Mrs. So and So would jump up from the audience dressed like a doctor in a white gown and she'd have one of those little mirrors on her head. One of those surgeon things, and she'd jump up with forceps in her hand and she'd yell "I'm a doctor" and she'd come running up and the audience would love that. She was obviously not a hippie. More square, but she was a good sport.

Then we'd do all these shows and we did them all summer. All the time. Maybe we

the circus, as well as perhaps personal considerations kept him away from there in '71. He put in a final summer in '72.

The basic fact was that Schumann didn't like Coney Island — we have seen that he considered it decadent and consumerist[8] — and wasn't, as he

---

wouldn't work on Mondays and Tuesdays, days off. All the other time we'd work. And we'd pass the hat and from the hat passing — I got a salary because I was a primary actor. (I: How much did you get?) I don't know — $10 a week. Not very much. But somehow I was able to manage on it with Arthur. I don't know how I managed but I did and the rest of them just split up the hat. They're just squeaking by really . . . . Bart — kept the workshops going for another two years at Coney Island but it changed complexion totally. (I: How so?) It became children's workshops and not a real performing thing. (I: And they did their own things not Peter Schumann's.) Sort of. Bart wasn't really good at making theatre so it was like this big flop . . . .' — (Leherrissier, interview.)

'My biggest — I wondered and I was always amazed, because when we were playing in Coney Island, it was very different than the street. How this was going to work for that crowd . . . the whole situation with Coney Island was that Bill came back with a ton of people and there was no work for them there, basically, and Peter was leaving, so we had a great mass of sort of socially interested young performers.' — (Konnoff, interview.)

'The work on the theatre building is now finished and we have workshops upstairs where it is much nicer and especially . . . much warmer! Besides the workshops at the theatre with both children and adults, we are now doing workshops in the psychiatric division of the Coney Island Hospital and this would be enough to keep both of us busy . . . . However we have now started working on a "Christmas Story" which we will perform both in Coney Island and Washington Square Methodist Church (between December 22nd and the beginning of January . . . .' — (Brigitte Lane, letter to Mary Brecht, November 27, '70.)

8. '. . . he finds the very term "popular entertainment" suspicious. "It suggests we are trying to appeal to mass audiences. It is not true, even if I would like to be attractive to people who live around here (Vermont) and not only to Goddard students." He does not agree with the terms popular and unpopular. "In fact it is the same thing that a piece of drama, a piece of Beckett, a piece of Shakespeare, or a piece of an Oldenburg Happening, or circus or carnival wants to do to people. It is uncritical to define that as something as flat as the word entertainment means. 'Entertainment' has a bias inside it, it is sort of the dress-up of it, and the appeal, and the success of that appeal . . . . It is hard to find the word for it, to say what makes people do these things. I don't know. I think people need to be attached to each other."

And the mass media today cannot do that. Even an amusement park such as Coney Island cannot do it. When the Bread and Puppet Theatre was working at Coney Island their theater was part of the amusement park. It was open to all the people. The troupe ran workshops with children and old folks and performed pageants throughout the park with their big dragon. From the small bandstand in front of the theatre, they called to the passing crowds in barker style: "Come on in! Free puppet show in ten minutes."

"Free" . . . Today's forms of popular entertainment have become just as commercial as the mass media and serve as a means of manipulating the audience in the direction useful to the moneymakers. Thus, even though the Bread and Puppet Theatre was part of the amusement park and the puppeteers had relations with other Coney Island showmen, their goal and their work were radically different:

"Some showmen came, they wanted stuff from us, painting, etc., and they taught us some tricks — fire spitting and sword swallowing. But they were pretty corrupt moneymakers, not very nice to deal with. They were certainly better at their things because

23

might have been during the '60s, willing to adjust his output to the people and conditions there, but on the contrary worked against them – to some small extent, perhaps, because the audience out there was mostly Blacks and Schumann isn't, I suspect, too fond of the American Negro; and he was in a phase where he wanted not to agitate but to show his vision of the essential reality of the human condition retaining all the obscurity attaching to visions and essences, and this made communication in an amusement park difficult. He hated the place and couldn't overcome his antipathy for the audience. But basically he got there too late. He was no longer interested in delivering a clear message and getting it across. And he was down on The People.

'And the barking was spliced with big puppets and with, maybe, little bits of performances – we just tried to make it as much Coney Island style as possible. And then the inside shows were hard to understand, esoteric – even *Mississippi*, even though it's about the shooting of a black man. It was done with distorted voice into a megaphone and whiney fiddle sounds accompanying it – very hard to understand, even just physically, hard to understand and in text, super simplistic and, I mean, it was fun for me to do it that way but I don't know if it was fun for the audience. We had some strong reactions from people out there. But it was certainly not the thing they wanted, or – it wasn't hand-clapping shows. They were not geared that way – we didn't want that. We wanted to see how that kind of material fares with people. It seemed to me very justified to do just that out there in Coney Island. I remember having discussions with the company, who wanted more outgoing stuff – more story-telling stuff – about how good in this hocus-pocus of Coney Island it was to open the door and people come in, sit still and show silent shows to them: that were totally unexpected and didn't do this trick, this overwhelming trick to them that they are used to. So to me, this first summer seemed very successful of what was done in Coney Island – very good – even though audiences were not very big, usually, and what the puppeteers did was, playing these few shows on weekends and doing workshops with children during the week . . . . See, we did that show (*Mississippi* (SSB)) and I remember talking with a black woman who very much agreed with the show and *did* understand it and telling me, furiously, why don't you make it about a kid from our neighborhood here. Do you know how many kids get shot by cops here? I remember that discussion – I mean, so I know it *did* come across somehow, you

---

they were out for commercialism, so their attraction was well defined to the point where people would come and buy this. We don't have that goal. If you don't have that goal, you end up with volunteers. It's very different. The audience is not the same. People came to us because they wanted to relax from the other things."

One has to have attended a performance of *Mississippi* and heard the silence at the end of the play, which contrasted so violently with the brouhaha outside, to realize the impact the Bread and Puppet shows can have on a "popular" audience, and by the same token understand why Peter Schumann dislikes the term "entertainment," which implies a kind of superficial pleasure, "meant for the skin." ' — (F. Kourilsky, *Dada and Circus, Tulane Drama Review*, #61.)

know, whether it provoked people or what it did to them I don't know, but there was an audience even if not a big one. But we certainly did *not* succeed to make a popular theatre. (I: Succeed – you weren't interested in that at the time.) Right. No, I *wanted* to make a popular theatre but I didn't want to do it with the established means and how one could make a popular theatre. I wanted to invent that – what that was – and I thought one could be as esoteric as one *wanted* to be. And still deal *with* the people who were there – and, as I said about silence and the *manner* of these shows – I felt very strongly that to not give in – to not open the door and come with a fantastic spectacle and loud clashes but to confront this very hectic scene of Coney Island with *this* type of slow motion theatre would be *strong*. And I think it *was* strong. And it wasn't that for big crowds – and that was what was not popular. But it was it to – for the small crowds that it attracted, I think.'

(Schumann, interview, '82.)

'3 short theatre pieces from Coney Island

Thanks to Nathan's hotdogs and ". . ."

we have a little theatre in Coney Island on 1205 Surf Ave. where we do short theatre pieces for adults and some for children during the summer season since 1970. We owe a lot to Coney Island. We try new shows, plus different ways of persuading our audiences every year. For us it's a place where we have to control our artistic endeavor and bridle our personal longing for infinite pleasures in puppetry in order to achieve some commonsense. Puppetry is made of big blue and certain white papermache hands, and one scratch on a S-string, and two pieces of pink canvas falling on a green garden of dwarf's noses. When these blues and whites and the weeds and cabbages of that garden swing all together, they are likely to tell a story, or rather to make up a feel-story, a story, that otherwise could not be told. You can easily get lost in the width and breadth of this glorious environment. But a Coney Island show is a cold water shower lesson for esoterics. Coney Island visitors come for the sake of the sun and the benches and cotton candy, etc. They don't allow you to dream just anything. Ideally you have to dream in solid terms of kitchen-and truck-driving experiences, and no less. We have to learn a lot of new dreaming. We have to make sense in a particular, unmistakable way, because the criticism that we get derives from people's lifes, not from their studies of modern drama, which they haven't started yet. I wouldn't exactly say that we have a naive audience in Coney Island. We certainly battle with the world's most thorough education in T.V. and movie kitch. But by now it seems, people have developed a somewhat ironical tolerance for those two dimensions to such a degree that they are not subdued by them any more and are almost ready for puppetshows.

Basically the idea of our theatre is to play for cheap. When we play for free, people suspect that the city or some other warmhearted institution tries to push culture and they watch our product in a bad mood, like wonderful under-privileged children, who sense the sparkle of dollars in humanitarians' efforts. And surely the spirit is free and culture is cheap. Since we live in an under-privileged nation, which suffers from the effects of a market designed to separate people, we don't even feel the lack of the spirit, we only suffer it. The sale of composition and serious thought is mixed with fun rides in Coney Island. People try very hard to be fast like the moon, to fly, or to witness the most extraordiainary event. And the spirit wanders through the job of the listeners and the observers. I think, people can't live without wings. And I think that is where our work is.'

(Schumann, draft of program notes for
The Coney Island Cycle, September, '72.)

One might describe his Coney Island failure as tragic. But the fact is that his other attempt of the period at a popular theatre, the travelling circus one, failed equally, and the Coney Island one at least resulted in those four good plays I have mentioned. These plays, like *Marriage and Revenge*, were about the American Negro. Significantly, all the plays made for Coney Island not on Blacks were trash. Totally free of the usual white man's all-god's-chillun-got-wings, they-are-like-children-but-they-sure-got-rhythm, etc. down-looking, those four plays represent a major human and artistic achievement: according the Afroamerican full dignity, they record the essence of his/her American position, subjection to terror and occasional response by helpless rage. This suggests the true reason for whatever failure there was: a group of white people, hippies in appearance, and, except for Schumann and a few others, in fact — the Lanes — not hippies but do-gooders — were trying to communicate to the black community. By '70, they couldn't but be rejected.

Schumann had not in '69, when Jules Rabin brought up the idea, wanted to go to a 'provincial place' like Plainfield, Vermont, and had turned it down, but Rabin (and then Appleby) apparently pursued the idea, and when February '70 interest was voiced from Goddard, not by the administration, but by the faculty and students putting pressure on the administration, it was an offer he could not refuse, and an interview with President Witherspoon in March settled the matter.[9]

---

9. '(I: So, when the theatre came back from the tour, then you decided to move to Vermont.) No, we didn't decide to move to Vermont. No. This was all other people's arrangements. This was initiated by Michael Appleby who went to Goddard College and took some kind of course there and asked around and found out that there was a real interest in Goddard — we had performed there several times — in having us be the theatre in residence there. He initiated that. (Elka: But the Rabins who had moved there previously had asked us earlier and we had told them very definitely we were *not* interested in moving to a little provincial place.) But the man who initiated that was Michael Appleby, and then other people like the Rabins formed a student and faculty group that pressed this, and I went up — we went up together to meet the President, and he invited us and that was *it*. And then we decided to accept and we came up, and as you know, we stayed for 4 years . . . But we must have gotten the invitation to go to Goddard early, early in the spring, because I remember at Easter time we went and did the *Difficult Life of Uncle Fatso* at Goddard and did a parade with the Jesus puppets, (Elka: And an Easter performance.) a sort of outdoor Easter performance, and the snow was just melting, and we also got sort of looked over by the faculty and were approved of by the school, to be invited to Cate Farm, to be this theatre in residence. That was our being inspected by Goddard and getting the approval. (I: So, how did you decide who would stay and work on Coney Island and who would go up? Which puppeteers?) We decided that only a very small group would come with us to Goddard and that the larger part of the group would stay on Coney Island. So

Just what the deal was is not clear. I somehow have not come across the piece of paper defining it. Was the Bread and Puppet troupe or group or was Schumann and his family invited? I suppose the group, with presumably — ? — some numerical limitation, its director to designate the ones selected. In the event, Schumann brought only his composer Spevak, a man

---

the people that came with us, after various consultations with everybody were Harvey Spevak, George — no, not George — Bill Dalrymple — that was it . . . (Elka: Another thing, just for the record, of our move out of New York City, when we had — when we had — when I think of it it was pretty important, too, that simply our children were getting bigger, our apartment with its rent of $23 a month was very nice, we were very lucky to have it, but when we got back from that big tour, it really was getting terribly small, and —) Plus, I found a young boy who pulled a knife on Solveig and took a doll from her. (Elka: That wasn't so unusual in that area. And I got held up. I'd gone to the bank. I was sort of the treasurer for the theatre and I picked up people's salaries at the bank once a week, and on one day, someone must have followed me and held me up with a gun in our hall. It was just before schools were out, and almost everybody else who was living in our area of the city had been robbed in their apartments at least a dozen — not a dozen, but several times. People just found out, they didn't even bother — like Bart Lane, he didn't even bother putting a lock on his door because he'd been broken into so many times, it was easier to just keep his door open. And everything had been taken, so when the invitation to move to Vermont came, at the end of this — *after* coming back from the big tour, it looked much more appealing that it had *before* the tour.)' — (Schumann, interview, '79.)

'The possibility arose last semester of the Bread and Puppet Theatre's coming to Goddard as artists-in-residence. The question was raised in the Governance Council, which referred it to committee. The committee took no action and failed to report back to the Council.

Meanwhile . . . the Puppeteers, freshly returned from a fabulously successful European tour, a bit of money saved up for the first time in their 8 year history, were in touch with us again: they were looking for a home; they had enough money to buy a place, but would still be interested in a relationship with Goddard.

In the absence of the Governance Council, a large *ad hoc* committee of students, faculty and staff was formed to meet with the Theatre. The troupe spent a weekend at the college, explored physical, financial and work possibilities here and, after meeting extensively with members of the *ad hoc* committee worked out arrangements satisfactory to all for their coming to Goddard in June for what will hopefully be the first of many years.

The arrangements, basically, are these: the troupe will live and work at Cate Farm, which will be remodelled this spring to meet their needs; they will have access to the food, health and educational services of the college; members of the Goddard community will have the opportunity of working with the Bread and Puppet Theatre in the preparation and performance of their theatre pieces.

Members of the Theatre will not have faculty status here and will not be paid salaries. Rather, they will welcome students and other members of the community to work with them in apprenticeship or partnership situations, creating puppets or musical instruments, contributing to the many other activities which go into the preparation of a Bread and Puppet performance, and to tour with the company whenever possible.

The Puppeteers will be at Goddard in mid-April to perform, to meet with students and faculty, to begin laying the groundwork for how people here might best relate to them. The troupe will return in June, will be based here and will be touring the Northeastern states, performing at country fairs, colleges, carnivals and the like. Students will be welcome to join them and also to participate in the preparation of pieces which will be taken on a six

described by Leherrissier (interview) as a 'sort of basically marginal person (with) mental problems . . . also gay', and by Sherman as on the '69 tour by his continual off-hour occupation by his own (musical) work and his non-participation in the group's social life exemplary for herself, and his lieutenant Dalrymple, whom he considered loyal and intelligent.

No salary and no teaching duties; free use of the fairly big farm house that the Schumanns moved into, of a smaller house 'with only about one room' (Elka, interview) that they moved to in '71,[10] leaving the puppe-

---

week tour of the West Coast in conjunction with the San Francisco Mime Troupe. The Bread and Puppet Theatre will be fully available to students here the second half of the fall trimester — and we hope — for a long time after.

Students who think they might want to work with the Theatre during the summer and/or fall are invited to join in their New York workshops for a few days to determine if they would, indeed, be happy with the troupe. Eunice Gray will be happy to put interested students in touch with them. Her telephone extension number is . . . .' — (Report of February 27, '70 of the *ad hoc* committee of Goddard College students and faculty on having the Bread and Puppet Theatre 'group' as artists in residence.)

'I was in the first Cate Farm trip, when we went up to decide whether we would accept the offer. Jules Rabin is the one who organized that, I think — the offer. And I can't remember the name of the man who was the dean or president of the college. I have that in my notes, somewhere. And we formed a group to go up and see what it was that they were offering — (I: They were at Coney Island then, basically?) Yeah. And it was hopeless — it was hopeless to work at Coney Island without any heat. It was a matter of desperation: Where to go? . . . and Peter's fortunes were really low, by that point. He had five children, he had no place of safety for his puppets. The Coney Island place had no heat; no security, to speak of; was a million miles from everything — as much as he liked playing out on the boardwalk and making shows there — it was not a place where you could effectively work twelve months of the year. Could not — at all. And when Jules got this offer tendered to Bread and Puppet: it was remarkable. So, we all piled into a Volkswagon — and we went up — I don't know how many we were, but probably 10, 11 people — and we went up and met with this dean or president and he talked about the facilities at the institution and how they would all be made available, and what the requirements would be — that Peter would teach one class or some such arrangement — and the Schumann family would get Blue Cross. And so, it was decided that we would go . . . and they were then secure. From that time forward, Bread and Puppet became secure. Now, is that a more important question about what changed or affected his work than some bedding up of available maidens? (I: But he had no salary up there.) He had a warm house, and he had food. (I: Food?) Food, yeah. They gave them — the entire core group of puppeteers and Schumanns were welcome to dine in the college hall or take chits. It was a very generous arrangement. Truly, he was, for the first time, secure. He had a roof over his head, big enough to house his family; he had a work place in that pig barn — though he had to shovel out pig manure, but he nevertheless had a place that was secure. It was cold up there, but he had a warm house, the pig barn, the chicken coop, where Harvey lived one year, and the barn. And food, the the Blue Cross. So, maybe he didn't have a salary, but he had security for the first time in his life. That may be a pivotal thing.' — (Ashley, interview.)

10. 'Our bedroom was maybe a little bigger than this (the Schumann's living room in Glover in '83, maybe 15 ft. by 15 ft. (SSB)) and then there was a kitchen that wasn't much bigger than this and then the children had a biggish room but there were five of them. Tamara had a little corner partitioned off and Ephraim moved up into the attic which the fireman said was a very dangerous place to get out of if there was a fire. But we

teers the bigger house, a chicken coop providing living space for two, and a big barn, unheated, providing work space, space for what was intended as a permanent sculpture exhibition, the Vermont Papier-Maché Cathedral, and eventually, a third floor performance space; grounds with land suitable for gardening, with a gravel pit suitable for some outdoor performances, and with a meadow generally suitable for outdoor performances; and apparently provision for food in the form of an allowance of chits good at the college cafeteria and good also, it seems, for bulk food at something like a college warehouse. The amount of these chits would have defined the size of the troupe the college had committed itself to support.[11] From '71 onward touring profits and gardening allowed Schumann to go beyond this limit.

There was a temporary influx of puppeteers in July and August to work on *Grey Lady Cantata #2* and on the travelling circus (whose tourers were *not* invited to return to the farm) but during the fall and most of the winter the Schumanns seem to have been pretty much by themselves: the group started building up at the beginning of '71 only, for another circus tour, then stayed big for the summer circus and *Birdcatcher* and a fall tour. The Cate Farm *commune* was a delayed reaction. In '70 the idea was 'Let them tour!' Once Konnoff in September had taken off with the travelling circus, Schumann worked with the students. Nicole Zand who in *Le Monde* in '68 had certified his status à propos of *Fire*, reporting (Zand, *Peter Schumann et l'éclatement du 'Bread and Puppet'*, *Le Monde*, November 12, '70) on a visit to Cate Farm in October, speaks of an 'éclatement': she paints a picture of the master alone with his innumerable puppets and paper maché figures, his troupe, a hundred strong, 'with his entire approbation' dispersed across the world from Paris to San Francisco, his dream occasionally surely of a 'world entirely evangelized by his strange

---

were so relieved to have a place where we could shut the door, where we weren't in the general kitchen, where we had our own kitchen. We did share meals, at least supper meals.' — (Elka, interview.)

11. 'Food and more living space are available at the college if needed.' — (Schumann, Newsletter, 'Bread and Rosebuds,' April 25, '70.)

'Food, yeah. They gave them — the entire core group of puppeteers and Schumanns were welcome to dine in the college dining hall or take chits. And the chits could be used to take food out of the commissary. You could turn in three chits and get a 50-pound bag of flour. You could turn in one chit and get twenty-five bananas, or whatever. Elka used to save them up for the circus. She used to save up those things rather than spend them so that the workers on the circus could be given chits to go eat. Because it meant that you didn't have to cook, clean, serve and clean afterwards for a whole bunch of people. They could go and eat at the dining hall and then come back. That didn't work out because they didn't come back fast enough. They felt they were workers, they were entitled to an hour off for lunch. Peter always thought they could eat while they were shopping, or something.' — (Ashley, interview.)

29

puppets,' but

'De l'aveu même de son fondateur, les acteurs – les monteurs de marionnettes – peuvent bien passer, les poupées restent et se multiplient. Ce sont elles qui forment avant tout la compagnie.'

If there was to be a commune, its membership would be of his choosing, and would be such as not to dispute his leadership. They would work.[12]

---

12. Elka, discussing the fine mask-making of '72/'73:
    'But I think it was partly that – well we had a bigger place to work in and better working conditions so that when you're working with celastic and it's fine work you're close to it and if you're in a small shut-in area then you can't do it for so long – and out in the country we did a lot of the building in the summer so you could do it outside and get – you know no trouble from the fumes, and also to have – I mean in New York there was a crew of people that, who were dedicated and hard working and became quite skilled at things. I think in the country maybe there – maybe in the city there were just too many other, if not distractions then just, you know, transportation and people having to maintain their own apartments and so on. In the country it was just – when people did enter the theatre, when they really could just be totally immersed in the theatre work and – I'm not – I mean Bill Whelan was one of the members that was living there so he could really devote himself.' — (Elka, interview.)
    Ashley, an occasional visitor from the city in the fall of '70, has defined Cate Farm then as 'a place we were working uninterrupted by any need to do anything except work,' and the settlers of '71 as 'willing workers at the shrine.' — (Ashley, interview.)

30

3. Slow death of his street agitation, January '70-May '72. Big city crowd audience replaced by small towners and college students. Shift from Movement participation to independent action.

After a few more participatory protest actions in New York City in January, February and March, as if to protest that he wasn't out of it by any means, Schumann's agitational focus shifted away from the nation's twin power centers onto his new locality and home state, and at the same time turned diffusely national, extending to Ohio, Georgia, Connecticut, his essential shift not this geographic one, however, but the attendant social one to the neoteric parasite class of college students and to the proud boobs inhabitating plastic America, small town USA. The small town is country, and the country, sucking on the supermarket tit and servicing the industry that has been grafted on the land, is way ahead of the big cities: XXth century. Schumann was wrapped in a German fiction of Bodenständigkeit, rootedness in the soil, but even so the negative feedback got to him. College trains a fictive elite for cooperative submission to the corporations by reducing them to tolerance for the ignorance taught them by high school. His agitational but paid-for forays to the campuses exposed Schumann to the drain of their vacuous self centeredness, many little whirlpools, confirming his worst suspicions about the state of humanity, and the more so as a college had become his own environment and his group collegey. More negative feedback. But in fact this negative feedback fed into his production during this period. As regards his agitation in Northern Vermont, he conceived of himself as making his stand known to neighbors, though to the people there he was either one of those college fellows or a New Yorker.

His feelings at first had been:

'The young audience gets into it easiest, but we work with various kinds of audience. It makes sense to be where things are happening, but we find they happen in Vermont too, on a smaller scale. We did something during the Laos invasion, also on Fourth of July and Thanksgiving, things like that. They're pretty slow, these Vermont people, but it works somehow. Not that they're different, they just don't show much of what they feel.'

(Schumann, on the phone to a *Washington Post* interviewer, *Washington Post*, May 14, '71)

But the slow Vermonters soon slowed him down (in fact he ran out of gas):

'In New York we were really . . . more politically involved than we are up here.

31

When we moved to Vermont, and we came into village parades with our anti-war ideas, and we are telling them what we think about Cambodia or Laos or what have you, we made a lot of enemies there, very fast. And it changed our ideas about how to get to people a little bit . . . it didn't make too much sense to push a political point . . . too much . . .'

(Schumann, in Sterritt, *Many-sided Bread and Puppet Man*,
Christian Science Monitor, February 9, '73)

'De onderwerpen van de stukken veranderden town we up het land gingen wonen. Dat kwam door de nieuwe interesse in tuinieren, in de aandacht voor bomen en groei. Once houding van radikale stadsbewoners, die altijd het gevoel hadden dat ze iets moesten bevechten, werkte daar niet. Plattelandsmensen, en vooral de boeren van Vermont, willen niet voorgeschoteld krijgen in war voor politiek ze moeten geloven. Lanzamerhand ging het beter, we hebben veel geleerd, we zijn nu in de gemennschap opgenommen, we worden nu vask voor optredens gevraagd in dropen waar ze alleen maar de meest armzalige banale vormen von Amerikaanse kultuur hebben. Het is een goeje ontwikkeling voor ons. Het betekent niet, zoals veel mansen denken, dat we geen politiek theater meer zijn. Maar politiek op het platteland is heel anders.'

(Aafke Stenuis, *Gesprek met Peter Schumann*,
De Groene Amsterdammer, June 14, '78)

'The Bread and Puppet Theatre still performs in the streets. Since 1970, on Saturdays and Sundays during July and August, they take part in parades in cities and towns of Vermont. Behind the flag of a veteran's organization, between a nurse's float and a fire engine, comes the Bread and Puppet parade with a giant Uncle Sam, the troupe's band, a moon float drawn by oxen, papier mâché globes, suns and stars carried by children. Uncle Fatso and his moveable fist, 'Peace', a puppet of two V-shaped fingers, red birds on stilts, a dragon whose body is made up of dozens of children, banners, white birds, etc. This array is as spectacular for the people of Vermont as Macy's parade is for New Yorkers, and familiarizes sceptical onlookers with the Bread and Puppet message, in an otherwise very conservative region.'

(Dupavillon and George, *Bread and Puppet Theatre*, Paris, 1978.)

On January 24, having just barely reestablished a foothold for his theatre in New York, before he even had the Coney Island place, he participated, doing *King Story* with the 'revolutionary' ending in which the people win (Jacoby and Beaver, *Exciting Theater for Sinclair, Guardian*, February 14, '70), along with the Revolting Theatre, Marilyn Fletcher's Burning City Theatre and, the sponsors of the event, the Pageant Players – decidedly left groups – in a loft benefit for John Sinclair, anti-war actionist on whom a long jail sentence for possession of marijuana had been inflicted: as though going out of his way not to withold himself.

In February 1970, for the first time since December '67 (as far as my data go), we again find the Bread and Puppet in the streets of New York City: Uncle Fatso appears on page 28 of the *New York Times* of February 17, '70: 'Protest Chicago Trial: Demonstrators Marching from City Hall Park yesterday to Foley Square to protest series of contempt citations given by Judge Julius J. Hoffman'. 'Judge Hoffman was depicted in effigy in the vanguard of the parade' — the egregious Hoffman had found the 'Chicago 7', on trial for having in August 1968 entered the state of Illinois with the intention of inciting to riot, guilty of contempt. Uncle Fatso's detachable left fist, with cuff and a bit of black boardroom sleeve, was carried separately on a pole to which was affixed a sign 'The true administration of Justice'. I think I discern an Uncle Sam-hatted puppet behind Uncle Fatso on the cover of the February 28, '70 *National Guardian*, which has it that besides an effigy of the judge, probably Uncle Fatso, effigies of a rat and a pig were carried, and confirms the Black Panther cry of 'Power to the People!'

According to the *New York Times*, out of the 3000 participants, 10 were hurt, 15 arrested: the fairly peaceful march to the courthouse was followed by a demonstrator-instigated riot — the kids starting throwing snowballs, some of them icy, and other objects at the cops and these retaliated. The proximate cause seems to have been anger at a Red Squad or FBI cop taking pictures. Beyond this, however, goverment throughout the U.S., led by Nixon's administration, had been taking a harder line. The march was directed not only against the Chicago 7 citations, but also against ongoing New York City Black Panther hearings. Though the February 16 mob apparently had few if any Negroes in it, the relevant background to its support of the Black Panthers was the murder, December 4, '68, of the Black Panthers Fred Hampton and Mark Clark in Chicago, by 14 police officers, led by Cook County State Attorney Hanrahan: implementing the FBI Cointelpro campaign against 'Black hate groups', and acting on FBI information. Out of nearly 100 shots fired, according to the *New York Times* (November 14, '82), when that Chicago Black Panther apartment was invaded, only one could later be traced to the attacked Negroes — though the police, trying to cover up, had bored nails in the apartment door from the inside to make things look different. The cause Schumann was acting in had shifted from the war to the homefront. He was not involved in the riot, though, only in the march:

'The New York demonstration in support of the Conspiracy folks on February 16 went great, up to a point. About 2000 people gathered in City Hall Park for a short march past the federal courthouse to the city criminal courts building, where the N.Y. Panthers are being framed and tried. Bread and Puppet Theater took a vigorous lead; they had some very clever large mobile puppets depicting the judge and the heavy 'hand of justice,' and they took off, tootling and drumming away, and led the march past the courthouse to the criminal courts building. So far, so good. Then — there was nothing for people to do, except stand around.

And so the dreary old collegiate pranks started up again, the same old story we've seen a dozen times — bait the cops, take your hate out on them, pelt them with snowballs and chunks of ice. Yell 'Off the Pigs!' Wow! Revolutionary tactics all! The cops, few in number, were under orders to remain disciplined, and they were, up to a point – they took the snow and ice stolidly from our revolutionary youth (very very young); but many cops were seething inside, and they in turn let loose their hate later with their billyclubs as they shoved people back away from the courts building. And so the afternoon went, with sophomoric skirmishes up and down in front of the courthouse for an hour or two – ah, sweet revolution!

Well, we pacifists screwed up again – we had no imaginative peaceful tactics to involve people after the march. And so, with nothing planned and nothing to do – no rally, nothing – the crowd joined with the ice-throwers and pig-callers.

Movement brothers and sisters: If we want to win cops to our side, we can't vilify them and pelt them with chunks of ice. Not only do we cause reaction and hate among the cops, but we turn off the public whom we supposedly want to attract. The 'violence' of our movement, small as it is, is counter-revolutionary, if by 'revolution' we mean working towards a more just, loving, humane society, a revolution away from the violence of Vietnam and social and racial oppression at home. Our 'violence' adds only to reaction in the country and stimulates tendencies towards fascism.'

(Kiger, (P.), The Same Old Story, WIN, March 15, 1970)

But this, until discrete appearances in '78 and '80 and a triumphal equally pacific return in 1982, was, as far as my data go, among his last agitational forays into the streets of New York.[1]

His attitude toward his own politics at this time is indicated by his publication as one of his little comic book journals ('Bread and Puppet Press', February 1970) of (in G. Tabori's translation) my father's *Parable of the Burning House*, the poet's defense (as I see it) of his association with possibly sinister movements, a poem ending:

'So much for Gautama, the Buddha,
But we, too, should stop cultivating the art of tolerance,
    and cultivate the art of non-tolerance instead,
    making manifold earthly suggestions, giving
    practical lessons to people to help them shake
    off their human torments.

---

1. There apparently were some additional street parades in March: 'downtown and midtown conspiracy parades, G.I. Coffeehouse Fort Dix, benefits at Alternate U. and Pageant Players Loft and one time Brooklyn College.' — (Schumann, Newsletter, *Bread and Rosebuds*, April 25, '70)

George Konnoff (interview, '83) speaks of 'a few parades in Manhattan', among them one with the Grey Ladies, ending at City Hall, not part of any national set of demonstrations, but on the war issue.

According to Konnoff (interview, '83) a resistance Easter pageant derived from *Cry* (cf. infra) intended for Central Park was snowed out, and according to Kourilsky ('71) Schumann had on invitation from the 5th Avenue Peace Parade Committee prepared something for a Hiroshima Day (August 6) march that did not take place because it was refused a permit. (In effect, there was no parade. There were some small rallies, one in front of the Riverside Research Institute and one outside the offices of the Atomic Energy Commission. Three students were arrested for 'obstruction'.)

To those who persist in pestering
us with
irrelevant
questions,
WHEN IT IS ALREADY TOO LATE,
who can see the approach of abominable bombs,
yet keep asking what exactly we have in mind,
or what we imagine the shape of things to be,
of what will happen after the cataclysm
to their piggy banks or Sunday pants –
well, to those
I have nothing to say.'

In April '70 (April 17) he did an Easter show at a rock and politics week-end, 'America is Hard to Find', at Cornell University, dedicated to Father Daniel Berrigan, S.J., on the lam. The FBI were trying to get the Father to begin serving a three year jail sentence for the destruction of Selective Service records – he, his brother and 7 other Catholics had on May 17th '68 burned 600 individual files of the local draft board with homemade napalm, prepared from a recipe in the U.S. Army's Special Forces Hand-book. Father Berrigan put in an appearance and gave a speech. The Feds let him speak, and when they tried to arrest him afterward he had dis-appeared:

'I think that what is delicious in retrospect is that I made my escape through a dramatic troupe, the Bread and Puppet Theater, by borrowing one of their tremendous, marvelous Stonehenge-type puppets, a puppet, as I recall, of one of the twelve apostles, and proceeding out of the hall bobbing beneath this tremen-dous papier-mâché and burlap figure, and getting into a panel truck, and getting away (Berrigan, in the *New York Times*, January 21, '71, excerpt from a taped message to the actors in his play, *The Trial of the Catonsville Nine*.)

Uncle Fatso leers grossly from the front page of the June '70 *Cornell Alumni News*:

'The Festival went on with the Bread and Puppet Theatre symbolically linking the Seder to the Last Supper. The similarity between a promise of sanctuary made to Dan (Berrigan (SSB)) and past promises made – and broken – to another was heavily suggested.'

(Jack Horowitz, *Catonsville 9 Go Underground, WIN*, June 1970.)

Schumann had knowingly abetted the criminal's escape.[2]

---

2. '. . . it was a large rally in a gym with thousands of students at the height of the anti-Vietnam business, I don't know which year – and Daniel Berrigan – we planned to do a Crucifixion show as a pageant, with the disciples and the Jesus puppet marching into the crowd, doing a short performance of crucifying and, I don't know to what end, what really happened at the end of that show. And the story with Daniel Berrigan was that he was looked for by the FBI – he was in hiding – he was under – supposedly to be arrested, but he had let people know that he would appear at that rally. So the whole backstage area

The idea of Dalrymple's Southern tour (mid-March '70 to sometime in June) was to hit the G.I. coffee houses,[3] which made it Protest in intent. It was also the first tour with a tent, brown, $60 \times 30 \times 20$, seating a hundred, so it was a first stab at travelling circus. They used the tent occasionally, and may have played at some coffee houses, but mainly it turned out a college campus tour, Princeton, the University of Maryland, Emory in Atlanta. The Nixon gang had invaded Cambodia — Nixon announced it May 1st — and there were 'student strikes' at colleges in protest. May 4th, the National Guard killed some students at Kent State University in Ohio, and the strikes then protested against these killings as well.

The touring Bread and Puppet got involved in these protests in Maryland and in Georgia.[4] Kelly Morris, then of the Emory drama depart-

---

— the whole sides to the gym where we set up all our puppets — were full of FBI agents, who were easy to identify, because they were the only folks around that had striped suits — three-piece suits and ties. They were quite stupid that way. So they were all over the place and everybody knew who they were. And then some friends of Berrigan discussed with me the possibility of sneaking him in. And that was the plot. To bring him — no, sneaking him out. That he would appear and then the trick would be to have the puppets — close to the stage somewhere, to get him into a puppet and get him to a door inside a puppet, where they would have a car prepared to take him out before the FBI could lay hands on him. Because we felt that they wouldn't — and they have proved they don't arrest people in front of thousands. So they would do it the sneaky way, right after he steps off. And so that's what we did. At the height of his speech we milled our puppets closer to the stage and snuck him into one of them and milled around until we came to a door. And they had a car there and got him inside it and he got out of there. And the same night people stole Uncle Fatso — that was the funniest part of it all — at that show. And somebody saw them going through town with him and made them bring him back.' — (Schumann, interview, '82.)

3. 'In the south we had parades because, right when we arrived at the campuses they started rioting and we got involved in that ... It (the University of Maryland campus (SSB)) was a very big place. It was huge and they burned the R.O.T.C. building, they really had a heavy scene there, and we were half way, we were sort of *caputured* by the Movement and also leading in a way and we couldn't leave, and we were being gassed and people were hiding in our can all night, and yet we were still doing shows ... Somehow, especially in Emory, we got credit as provocateurs. We were asked to lead a march to the dean's office, which we did, we were asked to do a parade to downtown Atlanta that ended up at the courthouse ... these smaller political or — less developed than in New York — SDS members and war resisters, you know, asked us for help on the spur of the moment group parades and things like that, while at the same time, of course, a lot of students on the campus were almost having a panty raid, it was fun and games for them. So it turned out to be a time of a lot of activity and so I guess we were helpful.' — (Konnoff, interview, '83.)

4. Military Intelligence noted the projected appearance of the Bread and Puppet Theatre at a 'Free Spring' Festival to be held March 21 in Fayetteville, N.C. — apparently an event designed to subvert trainees at nearby Fort Bragg. The Intelligence report, apparently drawing on FBI information of '68, says the Bread and Puppet Theatre is affiliated with the Youth International Party. Files are good, if rigid memories.

ment, wrote a letter to Erika Munk who had recently become editor of the *Drama Review*:

'The Bread and Puppet became a center piece of the strike. They pitched a tent on the main quad; periodically, bread was baked at the ATO frat house. Their tent was perfectly placed (against administration wishes; I spent much of the week fending off the vice-president and deans until finally it would have been inflammatory to remove the tent, so identified with the strike had it become.) B&P was truly a band of professional outside agitators, in the best way. I would guess that their presence and activity doubled the size of the mass strike march around the campus, so attractive were the huge figures, drums, and horns. They were crucial in drawing audiences for Leslie Morris' outdoor anti-war dance. They prevented many (most) of those occasions of idiotic trivial violence which spring from boredom after mobilization and energization. They had a hell of a lot to do with the size and shape of the whole week, which was the fullest and strangest in Emory history, I think, and they effectively disarmed administrative opposition by being aesthetically unassailable. They were just good at what they were doing.'

(K. Morris, *TDR* #47.)

And though in the *Great Speckled Bird*, a student publication there, of May 18, 1970, we see photos of the Bread and Puppet new *See Yourself as You Really Are* parade, a beautiful or beautifully masked girl in a lazy knit shawl and flouncy skirts carrying a well-proportioned piece of glass reflecting brick walls, black and white loungers, etc., through the streets, head high, chin up, sign of Schumann's veer into a post-agitational phase, we also see the row of persistent-faced Vietnamese Women in black, the front one with a naked baby doll cradled in her naked hands, Uncle Fatso, cigar in hand, tie out of his black coat in the old Yankee dissheveled small town character fashion, followed by gas masked carriers of hand printed picture signs, and further Vietnamese Women carrying, stretched out between them, picture banners with carefully hand-written and printed texts: 'NAPALM IS formed by stirring a powder and gasoline to form a jelly. The powder, an aluminium salt, is derived from acids . . .' Schumann is not there, but his group is still up to his old tricks. Dr. Fiser's (or Fizer's?) – of Harvard – clinging fire, a long way from Prometheus, really interested him.

Schumann had intended to join the touring group at the end of April with the new play, *Difficult Life*, and a 'large pageant' (Schumann, *Bread*

---

5. According to Schumann, interview, '83, the girl with the mirror – 'blue mask . . . some girl with long hair doing the job with a nice dress on' – was first used in a parade in New York in the garment district – probably one of the March '70 parades – and later in Toronto – probably in August – was part of a larger parade each time which 'was confined to the street' whereas 'that little group with the mirror went around freely outside of the parade', and 'related people to the parade by showing them themselves: 'What do you say to this woman?' – a gentle intensification of the agitation and a parallel in his street agitation to what Schumann with reference to his indoors theatre of the early '70s has called a 'pseudo-narrative frame.'

& Rosebuds, April 25, '70). I don't know if he made it, but according to Konnoff (interview, '83) they performed a pageant derived from *Cry*, centering on the incitatory Building of Jesus scene.[6] I don't know if this was the 'new version of the Easter pageant' Schumann in mid-April did at Goddard and Cornell – he seems to have done a more innocuous version there, but this version in any event was an outdoors one clearly qualifying as protest street agitation. Perhaps his lieutenants were a little more caught up in this student movement than he. I don't know of any demonstration of Schumann's of '70 protesting the Kent State killings, but when, ten days after these, some black kids got killed by the police in Mississippi, he reacted immediately with a Coney Island play, *Lamentation* (cf. infra). Perhaps he was a little disgusted by the campus reaction when the war hit 'their own'.[7]

The way things happen, Schumann's accommodation to the realities of Vermont middle America – really more an accommodation to the realities of the '70s, and ultimately not an accommodation at all, but expression of his own development as thinker, person and artist – at first took the form of an attempted integration of protest: an antiwar participation in the 1970 Plainfield Independence Day parade. He may already have participated in July 4th parades in Maine in '68, but otherwise this was Schumann's first participation in a patriotic demonstration, the more sincere for its protest form. Photos in the Bread and Puppet Theatre files from a 'short-lived local newsletter' (Elka), accompanied by tolerant references, show his new Miss America, all stars, stripes, makeup and glamor leading one of his traditional gloom puppets – black shroud and cowl, ashy grey or burnt face mask – as a prisoner, and someone in one of his old grotesquely grim masks obnoxiously intruding on what appear to be the wounded but flag-carrying youthful veterans of the revolutionary wars common in patriotic commemorative defiles, but who in fact may be Bread and Puppeteers also, they and the intruder adding up to some subversive comment.

He, in '79, remembers a 'short parade from Plainfield' of theirs, 'set up in Cate Field', and a show called *Pursuit of Happiness* or else *The Declaration of Independence*, or possibly (Schumann, *Puppen und Masken*, chronology) *The Spirit of '76* or *America's Heritage*, done in Plainfield. Avram

---

6. 'It had the elements of building Jesus, with musicians. It had sort of . . . you wouldn't say the highlights of (*Cry*), but it was the show in pageant format we took south and taught these students all the parts. There were large movements of beasts out of the end of a football field type of situation. Using the landscape and –' — (Konnoff, interview, '83.)

7. Cf. Richard Schechner, *Guerilla Theatre*: May 1970, *TDR* #47 (1970) in Appendix XV. Unlike Schumann's agitational theater, this 'guerilla' theatre never got anywhere: for the good reason that it was impracticable. Note the coward's violence it was to comprise – the forcible action on onlookers, the blood and gut props. Note also its grotesquely false 'realism' – the dialogue. It was in both respects the opposite of Schumann's street theatre. Schechner was an academic and did this macho stuff mainly with students of his.

Patt read the Declaration of Independence while (or before) *A Man Says Goodbye to His Mother* was performed: both in front of a giant mask called *The Pursuit of Happiness* (and later *The Godface*). They had firecrackers thrown at them. The Peace Hand was also in the parade. Apparently this ambiguous participation in July 4th inspired the '70 *Circus*, and it seems to be at the origin of the American theme of many of the pageants that later on terminated his annual *Circus*.

The Bread and Puppet also participated in the Huge Anniversary Festival Historical and Patriotic Parade (awards for best float, bands, marching units) of July 26th (Good Neighbor Day) at the La Barre Centennial Celebration.[8] It was his first use of flower banners (Schumann, interview, '79). I doubt he or his group attended the following barbecue dinner, honoring mayors and official families of surrounding cities and towns, but they may have watched the demolition derby later that evening. At the August 16-21 37th Festival of the Puppeteers of America at the University of Connecticut — he took his *Grey Lady Cantata II* there — he augmented his fellow puppeteers' resentment of his arrogance (disdain for them) by having the bad taste to put on *King Story* in front of their host's ROTC building: participation in the college protest movement.

The only other street agitation I know of for '70 was the work of his lieutenants. There was that southern tour of Dalrymple's. George Konnoff as 'acting director' took a Bread and Puppet contingent to the Toronto Underground Theater Festival that August and put on an outdoor performance of *Reiteration* there. Pascal Ortega took another contingent to the Shah's Shiraz Festival of the Arts during July and August:

'Peter wasn't interested and said to Pascal: You handle it. Pascal said: I'll take care of it. I'll get together a crew of people to go to Iran. And Pascal said: Okay, you, Margo, and Bill and Harvey and Maurice and Warren — who was in Europe. We were seven people — George Ashley. First of all, we got there and we saw what kind of country we had walked into. Some people already knew. Others, who didn't read the newspapers didn't know much about — oh, there's some country over there with a king. And there we were, living in this horrible place where, every step, people were offering you Coca-Cola, giving you hotels with swimming pools, and treating you like you're a movie star and all around you is the most horrible poverty — like slaves. And it was very shocking and we felt horrible. We would take food out of the restaurant and give it to beggars on the street and that felt stupid, too, but we did it, and Harvey wanted to leave . . .

---

8. 'Barre, Vt. used to be a communist stronghold in the twenties or thirties. And then it was Italian stone cutters, unionizing and doing all kinds of mean things, and riots in the streets and Emma Goldman coming to speak, and all kinds of interesting things, and now it's a very boring, middle class town with no events whatsoever politically. Conservative and — we did scenes about the war in Vietnam in the Ethnic Parade and got almost stoned and so — they hated it. This "Judge" (the "In God We Trust" Judge puppet (SSB)) was part of that.' — (Schumann, interview, December '82.)

we had been there quite a while, because we gave ourselves time to rehearse. And a lot of trouble getting the puppets which got waylaid by Air France airport — and finally, the morning that we were supposed to open *Fire*, Harvey said: I'm leaving. The rest of you can decide what you're doing. And he was the person we had chosen to direct the show. We spent the whole day in conference — and Erika Munk was there — sort of as a witness — she felt like she would need to protect us in case anything serious happened — politics. So she sat in on our conferences — all day — what we were going to do. Harvey was determined to leave. And we spent the whole day trying to persuade him to stay — we realized that we couldn't abandon the puppets, because — (I: What was the argument about?) He didn't want to talk. He had cast the I-Ching and the I-Ching had told him: Retreat. Besides that, from the day we were scheduled to do our first street show and they came with the announcement: You are not allowed to do the street show because of the place that you have chosen — which was at this lovely little park across from the street where the Queen will be driven on her way to see a show — and if she should see you doing a street show it would be very, very bad. We will have to arrest you. So we all got scared. (I: Harvey knew this street show had been interdicted?) Yeah, we all knew that. We all — now, everyone remembers this differently. What I remember is that everybody in the company except George Ashley got scared of this threat. George swears he was not the one who was brave. But I swear that he was. We got scared that they would arrest us and we were sitting in the dressing room immobilized. We had, by this time, decided to stay and do *Fire*, but I was to read a manifesto before every single performance that one of the people wrote that said: We made a mistake by coming to this festival. We realize that we are performing for some of the very same people who have arrested — we had more information about what was going on because people at the festival would pass us pieces of paper wrapped up in Kleenex that would give us lists of writers who had been imprisoned — writers who had disappeared — and other writers who had protested against the first group and who had also been imprisoned. Anyway, so we're immobilized, sitting in the dressing room — scared — and George, like the man the Roman Senate, would say the same thing over and over again — the guy who said: Carthage must be destroyed. He would just say: Pick up the puppets. Stand up. Go outside. We're going to do the parade. And I swear he said this like twenty times until finally we did it. So we got on the puppets and were marching down to the place where we were going to perform and a limousine pulls up and picks up Bill Dalrymple, who is inside the Great Warrior — therefore not quite able to protect himself with that thing on his head — grabs Bill, throws him into the car and drives back up to the TV studio which was our headquarters where we were going to perform *Fire* later that day. And we were marching single file and a couple of minutes later Bill appears — he was an extra-ordinarily strong person — so I guess they just brought him back to the TV studio; they didn't hurt him and they let him go and he joined us again. This may have happened a second time, I'm not sure. So we did *King Story* and they did not arrest us, because that — (I: On the street?) In the park where the street was — the road where the Queen was going to be driven by. (I: This was the *King Story* version where the people win — are not slain?) Yeah — they were slain. Yes, yes. I'm not certain — I think we only used that other version during the '69 tour. We had a lot of trouble rehearsing the show. We spent about a week trying to rehearse it, not with ourselves, but we needed a translator in every country – you need a translator . . . Well, it was very, very interesting – you need so much to translate the narration and we must have found three or four or five different people and they were very willing and eager to do it and then we would get to the line 'And the King was afraid'. Oh, I can't say that because the only word in Persian for King is Shah and if I say the Shah is afraid, you'll never see me again. I'll lose my job – I'll be killed. We finally found someone who was willing to say that. Anyway, it was great, the street show. We'd walk into the parks and you'd just see a couple of children – see nobody and you'd start to beat a drum and suddenly there are a hundred people all around you, grownups and children who adored the show. And we did it on different days and different places. The only other time that we were harassed was the students said: Oh, you did it in the park so would you please do it here at the university campus – which was where we were living. And the way they harassed us was: it's very hot there and they have gardeners there watering the grass constantly. They had instructed one of the gardeners to – every time we put down one of the puppets to turn the hose on the puppets – so we had to keep moving till we finally found some sort of patio and did it. (Sherman, interview, '79.)

By the fall of the year – out in Kansas where he was trying to pull a tour of his first circus (and of other shows) together – he was telling an interviewer:

'The message of Bread and Puppet has changed over the years, however. Originally it had a politically oriented theme, but now the experience has become more of a religious type. Schumann believes that theatre is a form of religion. He says it gives a message or a sermon and it allows the actors to reach for the purity and the ecstasy of the things in which they participate.'
(Sherman, *Bread and Puppet Players: A 'Religious Experience*, *University Daily Kansan*, Kansas University, October 5, '70.)

In the Goddard Trimester Calendar of the spring of '71, Schumann says the Bread and Puppet Theatre in early February '71 did 'two demonstrations in Montpelier protesting the invasion of Laos, the second one with a large contingent in masks depicting the faces of war: death, prisoners, business as usual' and in the chronology of his *Puppen und Masken*, 1973, we find listed for the winter of '71 'anti-war vigils with masks in Montpelier'. The *Barre-Montpelier Times-Argus* of February 3 reports on a February 2 vigil, undertaken, apparently as an independent response of Schumann's, immediately following the Nixon administration's announcement of the escalation:

'In sub-zero weather yesterday afternoon, seven members of the 'Bread and Puppet Theatre' of Goddard College in Plainfield marched through the streets of Montpelier protesting United States involvement in Laos.
Dressed in pitch-black robe with hoods, and grotesque, gray masks, six of the protestors marching in single file through the downtown business district clicked castanets, but otherwise remained silent.

The leader of the procession, which lasted more than an hour, carried a bell, which was ringing throughout the march. The last in line carried a bass drum with the name of the group painted in vivid colors on its front.

The number two man in the death march was dressed in a white robe and hood, and carried a sign with only the word 'LAOS' painted on it in big black letters on a white background.

There were no disturbances, but the drummer was nearly struck down by a passing car, as the driver honked loudly at the marchers as they crossed the street in front of the Grand Union store.

The driver of a passing panel truck yelled 'big deal, big deal,' but got no response from the silent marchers, so he turned around and continued his harassment. He again yelled, 'big deal, big deal.'

Montpelier merchants and shoppers were seen peering out of store front windows, but few came outside to see what all the commotion was about.

Montpelier High School students had just been released from school for the day and were heard shouting such things as 'trick or treat' and 'go home Goddard' at the marchers.

One person commented, 'Those kids won't be yelling those things when it's time for them to go to Vietnam, you can be damn sure of that.'

One elderly gentleman standing on the corner of State and Main Streets in the Capital City commented, as soon as the protestors marched by, 'I'd like to throw them all in the river.'

He did not identify himself and did not bother to discuss the matter with the protestors, but added, 'I don't know what they think they're gaining by this.'

A state employee who had just left his office in the state office building called the protestors a 'bunch of wild Indians' while another one gamefully leaned out of his third floor office window and yelled, 'What do they know about Laos that we don't.'

Several legislators, who heard the downbeat of the bass drum from inside the state Capitol were reportedly watching the march out the State House windows and making comments like 'What is this, Halloween in February' and 'It's just those kids from Goddard trying to cause more trouble again.'

After marching from the Capitol and through the downtown business district of Montpelier, past several churches, including one where a funeral was taking place, the marchers passed the VFW hall, where veterans peered out the windows with drinks in hand. The seven protestors returned to their two foreign-made cars in front of the State House and quietly departed the Capital City.'

(*Marchers Protest Our Laos Involvement,*
Barre-Montpelier Times-Argus, February 3, '71.)

The white figure in the line of black ones on the front page photo makes for an excellent composition, the contrast of its white to the black supplemented by the softer and rounder outlines of its draped sheet and its smaller size: it wears a Vietnamese Woman mask and carries a sign 'Laos' – I wonder why the *Times-Argus* reporter thought it was a man. Oddly, the small line of cowled and death-masked marchers in front of the clapboard fronts and poor but neat small town stores looks more forlorn than not unsimilar processions in the Lower East Side had looked in photos of

New York City demonstrations.

The second demonstration, on February 10, apparently more elaborate, was part of a nationwide series of demonstrations (instigated by a February 5-7 student conference at the University of Michigan) supporting the conclusion of a peace treaty analogous to the 'People's Peace Treaty' (negotiated during the preceding December in North Vietnam by representatives of the National Student Association, a treaty not too distinct, it seems, from the peace treaty proposed at that same time by the North Vietnamese delegation at the Paris peace talks). Here again Schumann is in the student peace movement.

That spring also he made what was until June '82 his last large scale street contribution to the Peace Movement: he took his family and a large Bread and Puppet group to Washington, D.C. for the April 19-May 2 'Spring Offensive to End the War', and on April 24 did a parade and put on a pageant, an Easter pageant, comprising a Last Supper and a Crucifixion (with, as in the '72 *Stations*, singing of *The Lord is Risen*), characteristically for this phase of his agitation not doing the pageant in the assigned place, but by itself, where the Movement would not be providing the audience: a contribution, not a participation. This was evidently not the 'revolutionary' Easter pageant with the building of Jesus in it.[9] Neither the *New York Times* nor the *Village Voice* mentioned his appearance.[10]

---

9. `(Elka: ... the peace march in the spring of 1971, the last big one that was held in Washington, D.C. I think our whole family went down there and the whole theatre – it was very big.) That's right. We slept in a church. (Elka: the whole busfull (of people – and you took the *Fire* masks – you sort of did a pageant, Last Supper and Crucifixion.) It was rehearsed with a lot of people in Washington. (Elka: There was a *parade* first with lots of people when we got there, I remember that, in the basement of the church. And then – the action was built up into a parade and the pageant. And the pageant was – the Last Supper with the singing of *The Lord is Risen*. (Elka: And the white *Fire* masks setting up a table) Yes. It was very *lost* – the pageantry and the parade also. It was – (Elka: The pageant was going on during speeches and no one watched (laughs).) We decided *not* to perform on the stage that they wanted for us, so we decided to do it directly under the column out there – I don't know what the building was – the Capitol. (Elka: The Capitol.) So it was off to the side and it was noticed only by people who were interested in it (laughs) – it was to *no avail* to those people, didn't make any difference. But for us it was good to do. It was our last production in the anti-war – well, later on, *Cambodia Story*. (Elka: I think it was important.) Yes, as far as war in Vietnam demonstrations, this was the last big one, really.. when did *Cambodia* happen? – about '72 or something. (Elka: In December and January, that's when you made *Laos* and wasn't that as a reaction to that?)' — (Schumann, interview, '79.)

Photos in the *Boston Phoenix* (April 24, '73) and in Schevill's *Break Out*! show the disciples standing in front of the Capitol: in the Ark for All in the *Phoenix*, at table in Schevill, their columnar figures repeating the Capitol columns behind them.

10. 'A large crowd of young people, which the police thought numbered 30,000 or more, gathered at the Washington Monument for the dusk-to-dawn rock concert. Some of the youngsters became disgruntled with the program which was two hours late in beginning, but there were no arrests. A few youths were treated for drug overdoses.' — (Naughton, *200,000 Rally in Capitol to End War. New York Times*, April 25, '71.)

He had intended doing something else: a thoroughly political deriva-tive of his '70 *Domestic Resurrection Circus* entitled *The Domestic Resurrec-tion of King Richard the Last*. (Cf. my account of the Travelling Circus infra.)

I don't know why he didn't do it. Apparently he used (Nixon) masks intended for this show in the parade.[11]

One of the places that had invited him on a college tour with his Easter Service circus in the spring of '71 was Kent State University – on the anniversary, May 4th, of the National Guard intervention. (Allen) Gins-berg was invited also, which to me sounds like policy and cleverness: religious soothing was called for, but religious in a way not suspect to the youngsters. I pestered what I consider a beautiful disembroilment of memory out of Irene Leherrissier who at that moment, being Schumann's girl friend's girl friend and a great person and a fine performer anyhow, had a slightly privileged position in the company:

'. . . but I do remember one for me – the most intense demonstration we ever did was at Kent State on the one year anniversary of the killings of the students, 1971. And we went with the ark – Peter had just made the ark at that time, you know, the big cloth thing. Banners that are like sails and then he has like a band that people sort of make a formation like a ship, and then they fold it on the out-side of them so it's like this ship that's carried by human feet . . . It's nice, it's blue. And at the side of the ship there are all these prople in the water. And the tree – the big sail is the Tree of Life and people and food and animals hang off of it. Blue and white. It's quite beautiful, but in that particular demonstration, Peter had me ringing this bell. (I: Excuse me, but what happened? You took a bus up there?) No, we were invited. The administration decided they wanted to have it be cool for the first anniversary of the slaying so they invited us and Allen Gins-berg . . . They wanted to make the students think that they weren't reactionary, so the students at that time were like real reluctant to talk about it, what had happened to them a year before. I sort of found out later – there had been a lot of dirty dealing there, like one of the guys who was the president of the senior class had been a class official all – first, freshman, sophomore, junior, senior, and at the beginning of his senior year he – it was right after the slayings, he had been busted by the class vice-president who turned out to be a nark. It was really weird, and they were scared to talk to anyone. We established ourselves as pretty normal, trustworthy people and they talked to us.

---

11. Schumann told a *Washington Post* interviewer (*Washington Post*, May 14): 'We weren't sure what we would do. We brought a lot of puppets and masks and then tried to find a theme that made the most sense to us. Finally we settled on a parade.'

The cover of Henry Lesnick's *Guerilla Street Theater* has a picture of a demonstration with half a dozen black dressed figures with tall masks in the likeness of Richard Nixon, broadnosed, lips compressed, a fat brutal face in the foreground. I have never seen this mask. But it looks like one of Schumann's and Part VI of the book lists a photo of 'Bread and Puppet in Washington, April 1971'.

The *Community Video Catalog*, Vol. I, #1 of the Winter of '71 lists a 10 minute video film '*Bread and Puppets*. Street theatre during April 24, 1971 mass anti-war march', but I haven't seen it.

44

It was really intense, because we all went up to the top of this hill where they killed the kids, really, in the boat — it was at night, we had torches, and I had this little bell and I was dressed up and I was holding the donkey, it was a puppet, I was holding the front thing, a donkey head in the front, and I had to ring this bell and just say in a very conscious way the names of the four slain students, and it was terribly powerful.

Okay, so Allen Ginsberg was going around going um, um, what I always wanted to do — and I just feel like — the guy is good theatre but at some point — well, in that particular instance he really bothered me because I thought he was showing off and not being appropriately personally removed from the seriousness of the situation. I felt very strongly at that time that I certainly could have been one of those kids, there was no reason why I wasn't except I didn't happen to be there. I would have been at that demonstration had I been there and how were they different from me at all? Not. So for me it was really serious. (I: How long did that service last?) Oh, God, maybe half an hour or 45 minutes. (I: And that's all the puppet theatre did there?) No, I was like ringing this bell and Peter had the disciple puppets and — you know, those big, high ones that he used for *The Cry*, and he had them roped up and maybe knocked down — I love the way Peter suspends time. (I: Simultaneously or after?) While I was ringing the bell. (I: But there were only four names. Did you say them over and over and over again?) Yes, that's all I said, over and over, but it was like what I said. (I: And you said it in a conscious way. What do you mean?) Well, like I wouldn't do it in an actorly way at all, but I was an American who could just as well have been one of them, that we were keeping in mind what it was we were saying . . . He just wanted me to say their names over and over. He just said: "Keep saying their names." (I: Did he say how?) No. But I remember — this was after the Coney Island summer, like the spring after the Coney Island summer. We did Coney Island in 1970, this was the spring of 1971. I remember in the Coney Island summer we were doing a show, *Mississippi* or something, or maybe it was a Cambodia show — that was at the time of the invasion of Cambodia, and we were out on the sidewalk singing, "Oh, Mary, Don't You Weep, Don't You Mourn", and I think I probably started having too much fun and he looked at me very sternly and he said, "Please don't forget what you're singing". And that was something I ingested and very much kept in mind . . . Okay, so there were two things we actually did. There was the evening thing and then there was the day-time thing. The evening thing is when we went with the boat and the torches, and we were singing maybe, "Oh, Mary, Don't You Weep, Don't You Mourn". It could be — I don't remember exactly what it was we were singing but we just sang, over and over — I don't know, in a kind of beautiful way but also very sad. It really was — when we went there, we said, okay, so here we are at Kent State. I remember going up to students and trying to talk to them about what had happened at their school and they really did not want to talk about it. So the students didn't really want to talk at all. They told me later that so many people had come to interview them and this and that that they were just really basically — they didn't want to talk about it anymore, so then for us to do this thing, like this torch parade — and the torch parade was really my idea and Peter's. I would say primarily mine. I was very much into keeping the art sense at that time, which is something I still like to do. You know, commemorating the anniversary of a person's death. We were invited there for that occasion but I felt that it wasn't enough for us just to perform, that we really had to do something very special about those people, and Peter immediately thought so, and I remember from my Catholic childhood we did lots and lots of candlelight processions and things, so I remember saying to him, well, why don't we do a torch parade or something, and he liked it, and he said, well, okay, here's the ark. there was a sculpture there at that time which was metal, kind of one of those ugly modern things and it had like bullet holes and stuff on it. It was weird — and the students — they didn't want to talk to us, but then when they saw that we were not just going to come there to exploit them in any way — I remember one student taking me on this walk and she brought me to see the sculpture and she said, "Well, do you see it?" And I said — and she didn't really tell me what I was going to see there, and I said, "It's hideous." And she just put her finger like that and there were the holes.

So then we did the torchlight thing, and Tanith Noble — anyway, so I was remembering walking across the campus and it was a very emotional time, and I got this idea in my head — "May your spirits fly easy", so I told it to Peter, and he said, "Okay, so let's put those words down somehow". So Tanith and I went to town and we bought a piece of cedarwood and we carved those words into the cedarwood together — so then — so we did the art thing, and — (I: One question — the singing and your saying those names, was that simultaneous?) No. (I: What was the organization?) Probably we sang in the procession and then when we got there there was the name saying and the business with the disciples going down — maybe there were roped up, lots of times rope was put around them and they just went down. I love the way Peter suspends time, he really dares to . . . No, let me just say — okay, there were two things — let me define it. There was the procession of the torches and the ark and we went on a long procession up to this hill where one of the students had been killed, and then we basically — we went there, maybe we sang something and then just ended, blew out the torches and put the thing down and then were quiet and left. Then the next morning was the business with the bell and the name saying. (I: What was in the evening then?) The ark, the torches and the singing. So then in the morning — (I: After Ginsberg in the evening.) He really didn't do something after. He was sort of doing something simultaneously. He was doing OMs, you know how he likes to do OMs — he was trying to get the students to do them and he was practically haranguing them into doing it, but it was these midwestern kids and they really didn't want to. And he has a way of making people feel silly, I think, which is another thing altogether, but he was sort of saying, "Come on, say OMs." No, he wouldn't do it like that but it was almost like that. I sort of got angry at him for that.

In the morning again was a big procession and either we went to the hill or we went down there by the sculpture where the students were actually shot down, and the students started crying, Stefan . . . So say you had a bell — ding, ding, ding, and I was just saying the names — doo, doo, doo, doo and again, doo, doo — maybe 100 times, 150 times, 200 times, I don't know, but a lot of times. While the disciples were getting roped up and then knocked down. It took a long, long time, and I felt that it was . . . They were like roped up — 12 of them maybe, and all bunched together, maybe to even protect each other, and somehow they'd all have to go down . . . Could be the airplane came falling down, I don't really remember that part too well, but the students started weeping, and I felt — like the boys were crying and the girls were crying and it just felt like it was very — it was good that they did, because they were basically trying to get rid of it and put it down in their memories, probably . . . So that was nice. That for me was the most poignant demonstration." (Leherrissier, interview, '79)

In including these commemorative services under the heading of street agitation, I am obviously straining the concept. But this is how in fact things get strained and twisted — and develop — or decay — in life and in the mind. All of Schumann's appearances during the early '70s on campus, supervised islands of tranquility, or at the contrived and commercialized profoundly conservative small town festivities contrast with his combatively pacifist big city exploits of the '60s, but there is both an inner continuity — for instance, commemoration of the dead — and an outer one, of means and techniques.

Just four days later, May 8, he was back in Montpelier protesting again: at an anti-war academic poetry reading (by faculty and students of Norwich University and Goddard College) in front of the State House, the high point of which was the reading of a poem by Eugene McCarthy, U.S. Democratic Senator from Minnesota, *My Lai Conversation*, phoned in from his Washington office:

'The Goddard Bread and Puppet Theater performed one of its grotesque allegories on war — a performance that frightened some of the children and set the curs who were napping on the lawn to snapping and barking at weird papier-mâché figures stalking about to the funeral beat of a bass drum." (*The Barre-Montpelier Times-Argus*, May 10, '71)

It was *King Story*. Police harassment was confined to citations for overtime parking. The crowd, largely of sympathizers, was sympathetic. The demonstrators had a picnic after the meeting.

At the end of the month, the Bread and Puppet Theatre got first prize for their contribution to the May 29 Hardwick Spring Parade, in which they henceforth participated more or less every year. We may presume their contribution was non-political. Schumann beat the drum on stilts, blowing a bugle at the same time.

That fall (September/October) he toured his first piece on the Attica prison police riots, *Whitewashing* (Cf. infra), on New York State campuses: he is appalled by the student ignorance and apathy: they are unlike the '60s students:

'We were amazed to find out that the students at Goddard did not know what had happened at Attica. (Elka: You found that during the tour, too.) Well, tell it as it *is*. We found out at Goddard, kids in Goddard did no *know* what Attica *was*. And then we took it to New York State, into the vicinity of Attica, and we found out *there* that students did *not* know — and we tried to find 42 people to stand in for the men that were shot, and women, at least 42 women standing in for the women to represent the families of the people who were killed, we never *found* them. We could never, at *none* of the universities find people to volunteer, and then we did a *big effort* — at every university — to *talk*, every puppeteer walking around personally and telling people about Attica and inviting them to help us stage this event. That was *impossible*. And — partially the reason was that people were not *knowledgable* enough about what had happened; they did *not* know — the thing did not come across which we thought of as such a big important event. It had not. So politics in America had really changed. The youngsters were completely disinterested in politics. (Elka: So before that you thought that usually the students were fairly — they knew —) Yeah. Until that time, going to the universities was — sort of taking your *chances*, you've got your subject and you've got to justify *why* you played what piece and what it is good for and you get into discussions of that sort and the people were up and interested and thoughtful and discussed with you — and from that tour *on* the opposite was true. They did *not care*. (Elka: So from then until now, it's still like that.)'

(Schumann, interview, '79.)

This disgust with one of his two post-'60s protest audiences, the students, has become total a year later:

'I don't believe in changing politics or the world through the stage. A political argument there isn't even truthful, because the audience isn't participating. We are not a revolutionary theater . . . I'm bored with playing at colleges. Young people are the most unrewarding audiences. They are liable to be blasé, know it all, have seen it all before. Our ideal audience is a cross section of everybody, from children to grandpas, mixed socially and racially.'

(Schumann, interview, *The Ann Arbor News*, Sunday, October 8, '72.)

In November he is back in with the other half of his post-'60s protest audience, the small towners, protesting (November 5) in Montpelier against the explosion of a nuclear device planned for the following day on Amchitka Island:

'A street theater representation of Uncle Fatso dropping an atom bomb on the world marked a demonstration in Montpelier yesterday against the plans to explode a nuclear device on Amchitka Island today.

About 40 persons, most of them from Plainfield and the Goddard College community, took part.

Demonstrators with large signs protesting the blast on the Alaskan Island began to arrive in front of the Federal Building in Montpelier at about 4 p.m.

They arrived in groups and then took their place in a line that walked in a circle on the sidewalk in front of the post office entryway.

The demonstrators were careful not to block pedestrian traffic going to or from the post office or passing along the sidewalk by the building.

About 15 minutes after the first demonstrators arrived, trumpet fanfares and a bass drum could be heard down State Srreet in the direction of Main.

The Bread and Puppet Theater Group, whose bus broke down just outside the city, had to walk the last half mile to the site of the demonstration.

As the puppet group walked down Main and State Streets they stopped periodically, to give short performances.

One of the group wore a large grotesque papier mache head referred to as

48

Uncle Fatso. Uncle Fatso was outfitted with a tall red, white and blue hat, such as is worn by Uncle Sam.

A papier mache globe was referred to as the world. On the globe were depicted pictures of women and children in tranquil settings.

The barker of the group told people on the street that they were about to see a preview of what would happen today if the bomb in Alaska is exploded.

To the sound of a drum and a cymbal, the Uncle Fatso figure strode up and struck the world down with a huge papier mache fist.

Persons along State Street heckled the troupe and told them to go away. At the site of the demonstration, a few persons gathered to argue with the demonstrators and the puppet group about their reason for being in Montpelier.

At the Federal Building, one man asked the demonstrators why they were there and then asked them why they didn't leave the country or get a job.

He left a few minutes later and got into a police squad car that was dispatched along with two policemen to watch over the demonstrators.

The police on the scene did not speak to the demonstrators. They stayed at a respectful distance and were apparently there just in case of trouble, but there was none.

Most of the passersby ignored the demonstrators and simply continued on their way. Persons in the post office building talked among themselves about the demonstration but few persons questioned the demonstrators about their purpose.

On the opposite side of State Street were two men in sympathy with the attempts to stop the blast, but one expressed dismay at the form that the demonstration took.

He explained that he could never take part in such a demonstration. He would not want to be associated with the group across the street even though he was in partial agreement, at least, but not with the form of the demonstration.

Another man standing with him said that demonstrations were a very limited way of getting action from Washington. The only way to make any impact on the government is to follow up a demonstration with letters of protest to government officials.

The demonstration was the idea of Jules Rabin, a teacher at Goddard, and Mrs. Anita Lander.

Rabin stated that the idea came to him Friday morning when he made a call to Mrs. Lander and asked her what they could do to stop the explosion.

She suggested the demonstration, he said.

As it became darker, the demonstrators sang verses of 'We shall Overcome,' quietly. At about 5 p.m. the demonstration ended and the participants melted away into the night.

(Barre-Montpelier Times-Argus, Grotesque Bomb Protest in Capital/Troupe Heckled Despite Sympathy for Cause, November 6, '71)

It was probably not unrelated to his perception of student response to *Whitewashing*, when after his return from his third European tour, he at the end of February '72 started a 'political theatre course' (Schumann, letter to puppeteers, February 23, '72) extending into April:

'I want to do newspaper nonsense and political smalltime theatre-pieces, suitable

49

for lawns, street-corners and assembly halls of any style, with George (Konnoff), Mark (Dannenhauer) and whoever else will be here plus Goddard students, till April 14. In June George will take these new pieces plus some old ones and hire 10 people with the money that's left in Coney Island and do it all there for the length of the summer.'

(ibid.)

'. . . experiments in quick representation and interpretation of daily news, something we felt was needed at Goddard: the latest on the war, Nixon's addresses to the nation, eastcoast water pollution and little people's plights in this society. We ended with a Monday lunch newsservice at the Goddard dining room and ran it till the end of the winter trimester.'

(Schumann, Bread & Rosebuds, November 1972.)

'We were obliged to the school somehow, so I did a lot of work at the school. Like, for example, I did a program, one year, of weekly political news services. Little puppet shows that we performed every noon during lunch hour in front of students . . . "News ideas" were simply newspaper stories with one or two rehearsals, hand puppet shows we made out of them, and small puppet shows with a narrator, usually, to bring it across to the students.'

(Schumann, interview, '79.)

'When Peter got back (February '72, from his third European tour (SSB)) there was some other things going on. We did decide to start trying to build some new political street shows and the way we went about that was we advertised that we were going to do a theatre production in the Goddard cafeteria every Friday at noon, and we take the newspaper and we'd create shows every week out of the newspaper, poisoned grain sent to Iraqi peasants who can't read "poison" and things like that. And, though March sounds early to me, there was a movement to have some kind of People's Fair in Burlington and we put together a whole bunch of shows and Laos was a show that came out of this workshop. Newspresentation and barking, you know, standup street stuff.'

(Konnoff, interview, '83.)

This remedial education program (in a mode going back to Russian and German agitprop theatre of the '20s and WPA work of the '30s) resulted in two shows done as street shows locally, Hallelujah and Laos, and in a show, McLeod, done at Coney Island that summer.

'To other demonstrations in New England we took two pieces from our political theater workshop: Hallelujah (Uncle Fatso's effects on the world) and Laos (a refugee's report from the Plain of Jars.)'

(Schumann, Bread & Rosebuds, November '72.)

Laos was done in front of the Montpelier Statehouse April 15th, at Amherst on April 21st, and variously thereafter. Both pieces may have been done in New York, in Washington Square Park, when the group was there to do Stations, May 22 to 28:

'they also performed three short political pieces in Washington Square Park and one short piece during St. Clement's Sunday service. (They were denied a police permit to perform in Central Park.)'

(Towsen, The Bread and Puppet Theatre: The Stations of the Cross, TDR 55.)

Hallelujah, which later became the regular opening of his circuses, was done, following Bread and Puppet protests against renewed bombings, in Montpelier and Burlington on May 4th and a vigil anent the same in Montpelier on May 8th and at a 'People's Fair' in Burlington on May 13th. The Montpelier demonstration of November 5 ('71) had apparently comprised its germinal idea. It may then have been done during the summer at Coney Island, was done as part of a *Coney Island Cycle* at Papp's place in September, and in later years occasionally as street play in Europe. *Hallelujah* (cf. infra) had a positive, upbeat, almost joyous accent, *Laos* (cf. infra) was dignified and restrained. Nothing outré or jarring about either.

'Later in the spring we all got upset by Nixon's announcement of the mining of Haiphong harbor. What could we do? How can we contribute and add ourselves to which forces to influence sick old decisions? Rhetoric and political exclamations don't seem to carry much weight in the streets of Vermont. Whatever may be the smartest way to get across unpopular views of U.S. politics up here, we needed to express our solidarity with the people who were struck. With the help of Goddard students we vigiled for three weeks in front of the Federal Office Building in Montpelier during lunch hour. Our drama was a sign and a mask and a banner. Our harvest was ambiguous silence, distinct disapproval and the occasional joining in of acquaintances and strangers alike.'

(Schumann, *Bread and Rosebuds*, November '72.)

'*Laos* was a very tender little musical street show, it wasn't as loud and clear and persuasive as *Man Says Goodbye* or *Story*. A white demon mask was either first made for that or first used for that — the Vietnamese Woman sat on a chair and two people, two gentlemen in tophats, held it in front of her. It was first done to be played in front of the State House in Montpelier. It was performed a lot that year.' (Schumann, interview, '79.)

'*Laos* had a little symphony of instruments, nails and bass fiddle and this was all orchestrated as a prologue. There was a red curtain. There was a woman in a Vietnamese mask hanging up clothes, laundry, some lengths of fabric, and there was a little house à la *Christmas Stories* with those little puppets said "hi, how are you?" or something like that. (The Vietnamese Woman during this prologue did not speak: Konnoff, operating the hand puppet above the curtain, would do the conversation between the puppet and her (SSB)). And then there was a break and there was a large oriental looking demon mask (held by) two guys — white and black. But much more like those dragons you see in Chinatown, you know, they were those chow — those temple dogs that are very stylized, with the big teeth. They come out from behind that red curtain and I think the operators have a gas mask on and rubber gloves, you know, something to make them look real strange, and they — she sits down, and I put the mask in front of *her*, and then — she's got nails, hidden, and sticks her gloved hand out of the mask . . . and drops these bolts or nails into a tin can. And at this point I had a *narration* part with some flip cards, drawings of waste land, just sort of desolate landscapes, with words on them, which were some information we had gotten — how many, what quantity of bombs had been dropped for every man, woman, child, more bombs than were ever dropped in World War II, one of those kinds of texts. I don't remember the

exact sequence, but it went in sequence with her dropping these bolts into the can.'
(Konnoff, interview, '83.)

Hallelujah (hallel-Jah: praise ye Jehova), quickly made,[12] like the *Good Man* at the '70 circus, was a flipover show, though perhaps initially not always performed that way:[13] flipping over strung-up naive illustrations, the narrator in appropriate tones, pointing to them, would deliver the text (this much an old European carnival format for the telling of Enquirer-type horror stories with a moral), while a performer would perform naive actions illustrating the facts successively evoked, each illustration followed by appropriate music. Schumann had substituted the fruitful earth for Jehovah as object of praise: successive evocations of its good qualities when properly treated were followed by ones of the dire consequences of improper treatment, pollution, etc. The illustrative actions are performed by a young, beautiful girl also representing the world, Uncle Fatso would join her for the bad part and to drum whirls would knock her out with his detachable fist. Since this was done as a comic action and the whole thing was done very lightly, *Hallelujah* effectively was not protest at all, but fun, a joyous celebration of nature qua man's benefactrice.[14] In this way,

---

12. 'I wrote a few stories into my notebook and I talked with Bill Dalrymple and asked him which one do you like, and he said, I like *this* one, and I made the woodcuts – the rest was just rehearsing.' — (ibid.)

13. 'This pageant is strongly anti-war and pro-ecology. The style is bold and theatrical. As a tinny band scrapes through a skating waltz, the musicians sing 'Hallelujah', and an actor in tophat on a tall ladder flips colorful banners inscribed with proclamations. At the word 'Sun' he feverishly waves a cloth sun as if it were a semaphore flag. The atmosphere is soon poisoned by a proclamation, 'But when you put fire to the world . . .' On cue, a puppet Uncle Sam marches out like a huge mechanical toy, followed by an actor crouching inside a disembodied menacing hand of Uncle Sam.' — (Mel Gussow, *Theater: Bread and Puppet Troupe, New York Times*, September '72.)

14. 'The only success of the evening is the third and final piece, entitled "Hallelujah or St. George and the Dragon or Laos", a series of tableaux with no narrative content at all. It is just as simple-minded as its predecessors: it tells us that generally the world is a nice place where green things grow and "the grandpas and grandmas sing hallelujah". But, if you rain down fire – here a puppet in a red-white-and-blue star-spangled hat comes on and some bombing ensues – "the world will cry and the children will die". In this playlet, however, the simplicity becomes charming. Each brief tableau is introduced with one line of narration, repeated in four languages; the girl in granny glasses who rings a bell and speaks in French is particularly winning. For each line, a woodcut is unveiled; the woodcuts are large, and most of them are beautiful. For the words "it will grow", an extra set of banners, depicting flowers, are unrolled from above. And the American villain is a Bread and Puppet masterpiece, familiar from other productions: a huge head with a bloated red face, with a huge fist attached clutching a cigar all worn by one performer, while another performer follows wearing a second huge fist. In spite of the magnificent hideousness of this figure, the bombing is not very forceful – the independent fist runs around a little bit, clutching a little airplane, and that's about it. The prevailing impression of the piece is one of gentle joy. As an indictment of American foreign policy it is a failure, but it is quite lovely all the same. And its loveliness is very closely connected to the aesthetic of amateurism and child-like-ness from which the company's infuriating limitations also come. — (Novick, *Child-like but not a dummy, Village Voice*, September 14, '72.)

52

made the same year that Schumann dropped Christ's message, the parables and beatitudes, whose suspect nature its perversion into resistance propaganda in *Cry* may indirectly have brought home to him, from his Easter show (*Stations*), and stopped celebrating His birth, it foreshadowed the positive pantheism of Schumann's mid-'70s circuses, which it introduced, enlarged by the repetition of each line in as many different languages as speakers of them available made possible, and by the music's augmentation by a choir. It was the first of three ecology street shows of this period, *St. George and the Dragon* and *He Who is Rich* being the other two (cf. infra). It was also the first of a series, '72-'79, of musical plays in which image/action alternates with music/song. I have always strongly disliked *Hallelujah*'s naive cheerfulness. Its naiveté is camp.

Laos was apparently Schumann's last street protest against the Vietnam war. But the war was winding down[15] and Schumann had stayed the course, though his street style had softened. He had taken the shock effect out of it.[16] August 8 (*Times-Argus*, August 9, '72) he appeared as St.

---

15. On January 27, '73, some two weeks after the last American bombings of the North – Christmas bombings – the foreign ministers of the two Vietnams and the U.S. Secretary of State Kissinger signed an Agreement on Ending the War and Restoring Peace in Vietnam that Kissinger and Le Duc Tho had initialed four days previously (in a villa in the Paris suburb of Gif-sur-Yvette owned by the French C.P.). The last American soldier left Vietnam two months later.

16. 'Much has happened in the meantime (since the mid-'60s (SSB)). No revolution took place, trade flourishes, moon flights flourish, Nixon flourishes. And it seems evident that if we don't succeed in reaching the more numerous masses of people and discussing questions of illumination with them – moon, butter and the right way to live – we shall only remain useless. To understand the motivations of men, to move them by these motives, to learn to move, to press into one's materials until it vibrates, to pluck music from pieces of wood, to walk slowly. To let neighbours know.' — (Schumann, *Puppen und Masken*, November '73.)

The gentle *Laos* and the positive, good-humored *Hallelujah* exemplify the not-only-no-but-also-yes-saying kind of work Schumann in the spring of '72 (Schumann, *Touring Europe, Silo*, Spring '72), having brought up, in his fashion, the hermeticism of the two *Grey Lady Cantatas* he had just returned from touring, calls for:

'The question is: why do we take our Vermont produce to as distant places as Poland, France, Sweden, Germany and Switzerland? French problems need French orators. Polish plights need Polish theater responses, not U.S. import. When we took street and Vietnam theater to Europe in '68, the understanding was that we had shaped American troubles – or our own troubled minds and the suppression that we all suffer from the top – into useful models of protest. The situation has changed. People who took to the streets in '68 are now working hard to gain sight and take constructive singing and screaming lessons for better, wider revolutionary goals. The discussion of this society from U.S. culture has started. Movement has to be everybody, not a few. American Everyman and his wife and kids and associates pretend to live fine and need to be understood by their blues.

The classical No-saying demonstrations have run out of texts and wits and guts. We need Yes-theaters as much as No-theaters now and generally we need things that last beyond the ridicule of the Washington DC spirit.

There are no models. And we certainly don't want to be a model for anybody. What you do has to be, as specifically as possible, you yourself, your neighbourhood, your taste

George – probably the ecological St. George of that summer's abortive Coney Island *St. George* – fighting the dragon at the Marshfield Community festival, along with two tri-sports vehicles ridden by Mervin Wells and Ansell Quintin, vehicles entered by the Winooski Valley Cabins, Houghton's Esso, Metcalf's Rubbish Removal and the Marshfield Garage and Construction Company, the 4-H Cloverettes, a racing car, the Marshfield Fire Department's 2 trucks, and a church float reading 'Break Bread with Peace', and many other entries.

The street protests of the spring of '72 were the end of his street agitation *sensu strictu* until at the end of the decade he came out on the streets again on the nuclear issue and on issues relating to food production. (He continued to do street shows on his European tours,[17] but there they were more edification than agitation.) They were not, however, the end of his political theatre, and in '73, in fact, the Bread and Puppet even still turned out some new street theatre pieces, two of which, *The Tragedy of the Soaring Price Index*, good-humoredly linking up with one of the three or so topics of conversation of country folk, inflation – the others being the weather, and, at that time, apparently, the oil crisis – and *He Who is Rich*, an ecological drop-out piece, however were not Schumann's work but respectively the Zalooms' and Konnoff's, and one of which, a revision of his second treatment of the Attica police riots, sometimes called *Attica*, though designed as street version, seems not too suitable for the street and seems to have been rarely if ever done there – it, like the others, was suppressed by the New Jersey authorities, when the Bread and Puppet were going to do it there.[18] (For this play, cf. my section on Coney Island pieces infra.)

He Who is Rich was a flip-over skit with pictures by Schumann. ·

---

of government, your understanding, your own teeth, your awareness of it all. It won't help anybody to advise bugles and drums and big puppets as a recipe for anything.

Living and producing in such different systems as West Germany and Poland educates our work, frees us from rumors, defines our paths. It's good to be back, though, and to continue on Cate Farm.' — (Schumann, *Touring Europe, Silo*, Spring '72.)

17. He did *King Story* and *Hallelujah* on the streets (in Athens at the University) during his winter '75/'76 European tour – in Greece, North Africa, Switzerland (Schumann, interview, '79); and during that tour also, in February in some Tuscan towns, e.g. at an occupied factory in Pontadera on February 11, or *King Story* in Pistoia on February 4; and during a later tour, in Tuscany again, in October (Catalogue, Bread and Puppet/Masaccio exhibit, Florence, December 16, '76-January 31, '77): supported in this, I suppose, by the communist and/or socialist municipal governments in Italy – as the Living Theatre obtained support from some Italian municipal governments during the '70s. *King Story* was done as street show during two '78 European tours, e.g. in Copenhagen in May and by a small group of Bread and Puppeteers in Barcelona in October: as first part of a street show program comprising also *Dead Man Rises* and *Hallelujah*.

18. They had an agreement with the North Jersey Cultural Council, as part of a New Jersey summer 'Fun in the Parks' program – for $7,000 – to do ten shows in small Bergen

'. . . this show that I did with paintings that Peter made. *He Who is Rich* is Uncle Fatso's political show . . . It was sort of this panorama of *Attica* pictures and bombs and the message was — sort of a drop-out-and-go-to-Vermont message. I know the last picture's with crocuses and green mountains — and the test was "leave them alone." ' (Konnoff, interview, '83.)

The Tragedy of the Soaring Price Index (in the Lions of Inflation and Bulb-head Family masks of which, not entirely due to Schumann, the shoulder-resting bulbhead masks and all of Schumann's mask making reached a sculptural apex) was put together by Paul Zaloom and his wife Catarina for the Hardwick Spring Parade of '73:

'the parade wasn't totally — well, it was satisfying, but it wasn't something we would continue. It wasn't real clear. It had this family (the Bulbhead Family (SSB)), and they were used as a family, and with the baby carriage, and, as much as I recollect, different people that had signs saying "gasoline 65 cents worth" or "money" or this and that. And there was a scene where these lions (the Lions of Inflation (SSB)) on the backpacks would attack and gobble up some people. I don't remember who they gobbled up. I don't think it was this family, because they were playing more the excessive ugly Americans, or, you know, overweight middle class. They were in ugly clothes. And we were trying to — I mean, we were tying up with Hardwick — for some reason it's harder to think about infla-tion now that we have more of it, but it was during a bite, you know, some kind of economic — that's what it was, the first big gas hike, which, you know, was in a little area like Vermont, on everybody's lips, you know, the weather and income tax and all these kinds of things.' (Konnoff, interview, '83.)

Zaloom, out of this, then

'did a show that *he* was more responsible for, that was slapstick, indoors, with these lions chasing this housewife around. It was never performed publicly (though, according to Konnoff, they took the lions along on that New Jersey project (SSB)). We'd have open houses, but it wasn't taken out. A lot of times — Peter doesn't usually — his puppets go too far if he doesn't direct the show.' (Konnoff, ibid.)

'And the short new plays performed . . . in recent months do reflect a continued political interest . . . Among the new products is a poetic and bitter . . . The

County towns. The Council cancelled the tour after two shows, saying the shows were not suitable for children, were not funny and were more than moderately political: 'Their satirical pieces on ecology, war, and Attica (the New York prison) were brilliantly done', the director (of the program) said, 'and it is obvious why they enjoy an international repu-tation. But the sense of unrelieved gloom was hardly what we were looking for in "Summer Fun" '. — (New Jersey newspaper, July '73.)

'And then they threw us out of New Jersey. We had big meetings with their lawyers and there was mothers out there with shopping carts and signs saying 'Keep the Kids Away' I knew we were going to get kicked out of New Jersey. When we showed up there, the first thing — that was actually one of the most — I felt more attacked there, more likely to have gotten beaten up than any other place I've ever been in.' — (Konnoff, ibid.)

But they hired a lawyer and got most of their money.

Theatre of Uncle Fatso presents "The Whitewashing of the Dirty Sheets of Attica." And there is a hilarious play dealing with the common man's most urgent plight: *The Tragedy of the Rising Price Index*, wherein the Gods of Plenty are eaten up by the Lions of Inflation, who then escape from the circus and gobbled up The People of America.'

(Rough, *The Bread and Puppet Theatre. Interview with Peter Schumann,*
Dramatics, December '73.)

The reason Konnoff remembers so much of this '73 activity is that he was in charge of much of it, Schumann having pretty much in the name of Letting the Kids do their Stuff, withdrawn from things in '73 (cf. infra), including also street agitation. Thus Schumann was not along on the New Jersey parks tour. The touring group billed their presentation and, though surely the name 'Bread and Puppet Theatre' appeared somewhere, themselves as 'Theater of Uncle Fatso.' Its name was created in '72, in conjunction with the Bread and Puppet's Goddard 'puppet theater information service', to categorize Bread and Puppet street theatre. In '73 it had two alternative programs offered to sponsors and handed out to audiences:

'SECOND PROGRAM

"THEATER OF UNCLE FATSO"

Uncle Fatso is our fat old American boss-puppet of many purposes, built in 1966 with the help of many children on 100th St. in East Harlem in New York City.

These and other short street-theater pieces put together under the title "Theatre of Uncle Fatso" are dedicated to all those persecuted by Uncle Fatso, to the dead of Attica and the dead and the refugees of the Plain of Jars in Laos.

We will present a selection of the pieces below.

HALLELUJAH Uncle Fatso's effects on the world.

WHITE WASHING OF THE DIRTY SHEETS OF ATTICA on the 1971 prison riots in Attica State Prison, where 43 men were killed by the guns of the National Guard.

LAOS a refugee report from the Plain of Jars, where 15,000 people used to live.

KING STORY legend of a good king and great warrior.

TROUBLE Uncle Fatso's fist turning against himself.

THE TRAGEDY OF THE SOARING PRICE INDEX on inflation.'

The Theater of Uncle Fatso was gone by '74. As so often happens, here also a line of endeavor and form of activity were institutionalized, i.e. well-organized, distinctively defined, given clear and distinct shape, identity and name, just when they were about to go out of existence, reaching an apex at their vanishing point: the distinct identity thus suddenly emerging in fact a perversion of what they truly are, i.e. have been (as when Ronnie Davis and Saul Gottlieb in '68 set up the Radical Theater Repertory). The owl of Minerva spreads its wings at twilight.

The Vietnamese people, represented by the Vietcong and North Vietnam, had defeated their native oppressors and the latest imperialist sponsors of these, the U.S.A. and Schumann had done his bit to help them. September 25, '77, he and his group were among those joining a charitable outfit calling itself 'Friendshipment' in welcoming the representatives of the new and 149th member, admitted four days earlier, of the United Nations, The Socialist Republic of Vietnam, at the Beacon Theatre, an old-timey Egyptian and everything else movie palace on upper Broadway. The place was crowded with the faithful, outside the cops were watching Vietnamese refugees reminding the celebrants of the new concentration camps. Dave Dellinger, an ancient peace combatant, goateed and bulky, his syntax weak as ever, but very loose, and a Mrs. Cora Weiss, affreuse juive if there ever was one, chairman of Friendshipment, congratulated the American people on their opposition to the war in Vietnam, and proposed that further debts of gratitude be imposed on the Vietnamese, viz. that money be given them. The Movement, present in the hall, ancient now and causeless, applauded our friends and itself again and again, moved. The small suited men from Southeast Asia, one of them a pretty lady, were moved onto the dais, where they sat discretely in the odor of the new order. The Lucha girls presented their version of a Chilean poet's ode to the right to freedom. The Bishop of South Dakota presented a minstrel group doing 'Freedom'. I had come to see Archie Shepp and Peter Schumann fit in, but between me and them there were still some more offerings, notably Pete Seeger, so I left. I did see a line of Bread and Puppet mask figures, wondrous beasts, snake dancing through the auditorium, their mutate faces well meaning, and later heard that 15 Bread and Puppet performers had ended the show (which itself ended the Anti-Vietnam War Peace Movement) with the deer pursued and killed by the hounds released by the butchers, prayed over by Margo Sherman in the white mask of the Vietnamese Woman, resurrected by Schumann on stilts, or rather with a flag salutation to the representatives of the new government.

He was in New York to warn, by his play *Masaniello*, against the tendency of successful revolution toward dictatorship and terror. Two and a half years later, in February '80, when the revolutionary Pol Pot's regime of terror in Cambodia had been reduced to some jungle enclaves, and the war of Vietnam, in the meantime become a client state of the 'Soviet' Union's, in Cambodia – part of the Russo-Sinese conflict – was in its second year, Schumann contributed a show, *Cambodia* (cf. infra) to the cause of Cambodian relief.

An individual's political commitments, rationally considered with due regard to larger context and further developments universally turn out tragic and comic. This goes for as little as casting your vote for the Republicans or Democrats. But abstinence tends to be less productive.

In an introduction to a little book (*Puppen und Masken*, Frankfurt, November '73) on his '71 *Birdcatcher*, Schumann summed up the Vietnamese War as exhaustion of America's soul analogous to the death of Germany's under Hitler:

'During the times when emperor Johnson ruled in the American land, and the dirty war became known, people went into the streets and protested. And that's what we did too, as much and as visibly as ever we were able, sometimes with 100 helpers, with marching tears and enormous noise, with 50 wardrum puppets and 49 peaceblossom masks, with a grey airplane on sticks that made snowwhite prisoners of war collapse on the pavement.

This war was not as far away as it at first seemed. Human, American arrogance, deepseated Gemütlichkeit and contempt for pain, hidden civilized cynicism unexpectedly came to the surface. And similarly as the revelation of national horrors did not destroy the famous German soul, did not destroy German self-contentment (Selbstbewusstsein), nothing Grandiosely National happened in the USA either. There was no natural recoilment when Alice Herz, Roger LaPorte and Norman Morrison made an offering of themselves, publicly ignited themselves with torches and burned to death. And similarly as Germany's poor unfamous soul at that certain time died, and the private story of a mass murderer attaches to the nation as its future prehistory, the American soul exhausted itself in this smaller war, and the great warlord will not again recover from the deathblows that he intended to give others.'

4. Deperdition of Christian observances. Offerings of the eviscerated story of Christ's birth, puerilized for popular audiences which it insults by its now dominant ridicule of the common man, but otherwise still in the well known accepted form, are relegated to others: his death, now told without his teachings, after an initial politicalization à la *Cry*, is importantly commemorated, but contrarily and incomprehensibly, as crime of humanity. (*Stations of the Cross*, 1972.)

Schumann seems to have cooked up a new *Christmas Story* in '70, i.e. to have written up and settled, in the process horribly expanding, the dialogue of the old one and to have substantially stuck with the result up to the Christmas season of '73, when he quit doing it. His next treatments of the story, *Ave Maris Stella* of '77, *Washerwoman Nativity* of '79 were radically different, merely using the story as vehicle and made statements not particularly relating to it, let alone traditionally attached to it. A script in the archives marked 'fall '72' appears roughly the one used '70-'74: roughly because it fixes the previously improvised talk along the hand puppet burghers and between them and Herod, Prof. Sauerkraut, Kings, the soldiers, and though it is easy playing hand puppets behind a screen to follow a dialogue script, it seems doubtful to me the players would have followed it exactly. Of this talk there is an interminable amount, all quite foolish: the humor appreciated in teenage friends and the glee and giggles at which among them are the seal of conspiratorial intimacy: humor without wit; and the heavy gag of many Jewish turns of phrase only served to get it closer to the lowest level of TV humor.

In the first scene the narrator introduces the couple (embarrassed humor *à propos* of the bride's pregnancy) and a clownish Herod makes an out-dated (Johnson era) speech up-dated by announcing taxes – on which the broad American audience Schumann has in mind addressing can agree with him – rather than war. Scene two is the crankie-narrated travel of the couple with donkey to Bethlehem, fixed in format in Schumann's story from '63 to '77. Scene 3 shows them in Bethlehem, turned down by people, accepted by cattle, scene 4 shows the three kings and a dancing comet, scene 5 the three kings' arrival in Jerusalem and audience with King Herod (again with loads of heavy folksy humor in the silly hand puppet-burghers' dialogue), scene 6 the angel's advice to the kings not to return to Herod with the news of Jesus, scene 7 his/her announcement to the (funny) shepherds, scene 8 Herod's being 'furious', the people's being scared, Professor Sauerkraut advising Herod to have all the kids in Bethlehem killed, Herod's phoning the corresponding command to the 'Third army', scene 9 the army's arrival in Bethlehem and the Savior Angel's prevention of the massacre. The end is a candlelight procession of Mary, Joseph, Donkey, Kings, Shepherds, with the Soldier giving the couple his helmet to be used as cradle. ' 'Neath the Vine and Fig Tree' is sung:

> 'And every man 'neath his vine and fig tree
> Shall live in peace and unafraid
> And into plow shares beat the swords;
> Nations shall have war no more.'

There is no adoration scene, the baby is not in the script, but probably appears as doll in the concluding procession. I.e. we get People vs. Despot, but no Christ. But the crucial change from the '60s *Christmas Story* is the interminable exposition of The People or Ordinary Man as bunch of silly, selfish and cowardly comic individuals: that was how Schumann showed them in the '60s, too, but it now is ironically the play's main point, ironically, because it is the result of Schumann's determination to please the audience so pilloried.

He put out a real effort to do the play locally in '70.[1] He didn't do it in the U.S. in the winter '71/'72, but Elka's Dancing Bear Theatre and a host of subsidiary and splinter groups did do it, though strictly as hand puppet show, and in their own adaptations: he was on his third European

1. According to an account of his activities in the winter of '70/'71 in a Goddard College catalogue, the Bread and Puppet in the fall of '70 offered *The Christmas Story* to half a hundred colleges, receiving only two replies, both negative, but nevertheless presented the show, mostly for free, 'over 20 times' from December 6, '70 to January 29, '71, e.g. in Middlebury, Spaulding High School in Barre, Waterbury Hospital, St. Johnsbury Academy (Schumann, *Puppen und Masken*, 1973, chronology): after doing it in the Cate Farm barn (ibid.). He was this winter, he sais (ibid.), working on a version 'für die Strasse bei Schnee und Kalten Wetter und für die Supermärkte.'
'Elka: (In) the winter, the *Christmas Story* was done – that's when we played in the public schools in Vermont and got into all that trouble for singing *Everyman 'Neath His Vine and Fig Tree*. That was blamed for being peace propaganda – and also played it at Middlebury College and at the St. John's Academy, to a meeting of the drama clubs of high schools of Vermont (the State and Regional Secondary School Theatre Conference, sponsored by the New England Theatre Conference, the International Thespian Society and, last but by no means least, the Vermont Council on the Arts (SSB)) and there it was a *big* success. Do you remember that – with, I think, the students joining in with the soldiers and all? I remember you telling me about it.) At St. Johnsbury? Oh, yeah, that was a lovely bunch of high school kids – yes. From Rutland, and later on they invited us to see a show there that was sort of done with the technique of the *Christmas Story*, with the little puppets acting with big masks. It was very nice. They did a *Noah's Ark* performance.' — (Schumann, interview, '79.)

tour, showing off his new Vermont plays — this is when he established his status as an important American artist in Germany — and he performed it with fair assiduity there — he had so far not shown it in Europe — and it was a success.[2] The new arrangement was repeated in the winter of '72/'73: the little companies doing little versions in Vermont and new England generally, Schumann doing the big version, this time in New

---

2. While one subsidiary company, the Trompetters' Blackbird Theater did its version of *The Christmas Story* (and other Bread and Puppet plays), Goddard students participating, on Cate Farm and in the state of Vermont and in Montreal, and another one, Elka's Dancing Bear Theatre, did another version of it as well as hand puppet plays at Vermont schools (Schumann, *Puppen und Masken*, '73, chronology), altogether, according to Elka's newsletter of November '72, 'seven different *Christmas Story* productions (being done) by former Bread and Puppet members in Italy, France, Canada and the U.S.', he performed his own big standard version. It wowed them in Basel and Zürich in December '71), and in Karlsberg they liked it so well they forgave him the modernization of the star of Bethlehem to the Mercedes emblem, the Bethlehemites' portrayal as 'tückisch klatschsüchtige and provinzielle Spiesser' (the image hit home there!), and Herod's shouting of 'Durchhalterparolen' (shades of Goebbels! — he was delivering a Johnson speech) into the crowd; and the Swedes, in January '72, preferred it to the slow *Mississippi*.

The *Badische Neueste Nachrichten* of December 27, '71 enthusiastically spoke of the show at Karlsruhe as 'von einer schon fast verloren geglaubten theatralischen Naivität.'

'Die theatralischen Mittel dieses einzigartigen Theaters, das ohne jede Allüre in Lumpen geht, diese Mittel sind von einer bestrickenden Einfachheit, sind von so grosser Kraft, dass ein grosses Auditorium atemlos einer Geschichte zusieht, die es schon zahllose Male gehört hat. Nicht nur zusieht, sondern sie weiterdenkt bis in alle Konsequenzen hinein. Denn es ist eine Geschichte aus unseren Tagen, die da gespielt wird, gespielt in fast heiliger Heiterkeit, einer fröhlichen Trauer darüber, dass der Mensch so ist, so geblieben ist, die Weihnachtsgeschichte immer wieder wahr werden lässt.' — (*Ku*, Basel, December 23, '71)

'In der Mitte ist ein blauer Vorhang gespannt, rechts davon steht eine kleine Kasperlibühne. *Peter Schumann*, der Leiter der Truppe, greift zu seiner Geige, er intoniert eine Melodie, die wie ein altes Weihnachtslied klingt, und dazu singt er von Frieden und dass man die Schwerter in Pflugscharen umwandeln soll . . . Schumann übersetzt das Lied und fordert zum Mitsingen auf, er bittet auch um Verständnis für die etwaigen Sprachschwierigkeiten seiner Leute, die heute zum erstenmal auf deutsch spielen.

So hat für einmal das Gute über das Böse gesiegt, und die Kinder sind sichtlich beeindruckt und erleichtert, dass der böse König Herodes sein Vorhaben nicht ausführen konnte. 'Kinder erschiessen, das darf er doch gar nicht!' sagen meine zwei entrüstet, und auf ihre bedauernde Frage, warum denn das Jesuskind jetzt fortgehe, vernehmen sie erstaunt und mit grossen Augen, dass es in die Welt hinausgeht zu allen Leuten. 'Das is ein schönes Theater, da wollen wir alle Tage hingehen!' lautet ihr abschliessendes Urteil. Und wirklich, es würde nichts schaden, wenn alle Tage viele Menschen diese Aufführung besuchen würden. Als respektlos, wie angekündigt, möchte man diese Weihnachtsgeschichte eigentlich nicht bezeichnen; respektlos behandelt werden darin ja nur die bösen Figuren, der König, der Soldat und die selbstsüchtigen Bürger, und die haben es nicht anders verdient. Inwieweit die Kinder die verschiedenen in dem Stück enthaltenen Anspielungen auf heutige Gegebenheiten erfassen können, hängt von ihrem Alter ab; stellenweise richtet sich die Aufführung doch mehr an die Erwachsenen; doch hat sicher jedes der Kinder zumindest einen negativen Eindruck von der Figur des Soldaten erhalten, und das ist schon etwas.' — (*Die Tat*, Zürich, December 17, '71.)

'It is a fun (rolig: entertaining, amusing) performance which in a miraculous manner eventually becomes a little (en smula) gripping.' — (*Svenska Dagbladet*, February 1, '72)

York:[3] where it was not a success: and in the winter of '73/'74, Schumann taking his version to Europe with him for his November/December '73 tour, others doing theirs in New England, except that he didn't show it in Europe very often ('sometimes' he says in '79), and when he came back and saw that others were taking care of it, he decided he wasn't going to do it this winter in the U.S.

This was it as far as he was concerned for the *Christmas Story* so-called, though there were little off-spring groups still doing it in at least '74,[4] Elka's new group, the Hardscrabble Theatre may have done it for another year or two around Glover. He did celebrate Christmas — at Goddard — in '74, but by one of his *Grey Lady Cantatas*, the 5th (cf. infra). Set to music, with Bach's gloriously upbeat *Jesu Meine Freude* following Tallis' tragic *Lamentations of Jeremiah*, and the action correspondingly going

---

3. The Dancing Bear Theatre did a smaller version in Vermont, the churches of Thetford and Montpelier, in Waterbury Hospital, in schools at Warren and Middlesex, in Newbury and Plainfield, he and the Bread and Puppet main group did his during a ten day presentation of *Simple Light* at St. Clement's Church Theatre in New York City (some of the Vermont presentations listed may have been his, also) (Schumann, *Puppen und Masken*, '73, chronology). The Show Business reviewer, a Ms. Wasserman, did not like it too well:

'. . . a sketchy and incohesive script, including many unnecessary anachronisms, interfere with what would otherwise be an excellent children's play about the Nativity.

Opening with a long, laborious pronouncement of each of the '"begats" in the bible — accompanied by the crash of cymbals and a parade of masks — the production does not promise to be particularly exciting. However, after this extraneousness is dispensed with, the play begins, and for a while it is very effective. A narrator relates the legend, assisted by the masked and caped figures of Joseph, Mary, and King Herod, and by hand puppets behind a curtain to represent the townspeople. However, as Joseph and Mary begin their journey, the play begins to talk down to the audience. The couple eat peanut butter and jelly sandwiches; Herod drives a Cadillac; and the people call themselves good Christians. Soon, the production becomes so involved in cheap jokes that the story is lost. Individual scenes are still good but they are no longer tied together and the grotesque satire of King Herod becomes so much more important than the action, that Joseph and Mary are forgotten altogether.

It is unfortunate that the Bread and Puppet Players found it necessary to resort to tricks to get laughs, for with so many talented performers and such an excellently executed multimedia concept, there is no question that they are capable of much more.' — (*Show Business*, December 28, '72.)

4. 'I think some people must have been part of the theatre, must have existed at that time, because people were traveling while I was doing the Christmas event at Goddard. Some people were traveling, I remember that, because I had a hard time to have a company for what I did at Goddard. (Elka: People were doing the *Christmas Story* with Marc (Estrin) and Mary (Eldridge). And they traveled pretty far. They went to Appalachia.) Yeah. Down south, yeah.' — (Schumann, interview, '79.)

'Mark Dannenhauer and Mary Eldridge, who live next door to us, have their Northeast Kingdom Puppets and do kids' shows around the state, complete with dancing bear, Punch and Judy and toy piano. At Christmas time they put together the old Bread and Puppet *Christmas Story*, and with other experienced puppeteers played in Pennsylvania and Vermont from Thankgiving till New Year's' — (Elka, *A Newsletter*, Glover, Vt., February 7, '75.)

from dark to light, it was implicitly far more of a celebration of the Christ than his *Christmas Story* had become, but since it had neither the Christian story nor the Christian figures in it, rather was a St. George and Dragon story in which the White Lady saves the Grey, the message was Bach's and just what salvation Schumann was celebrating was totally open, a mystery.

Though no doubt some of the versions done by the sub- and splinter-Bread and Puppet groups, at least the first time, in the winter of '71/'72, tried for a little bite and political significance, by and large, these derivative versions, especially those done in the States, were specifically adapted for children, i.e. further weakened and diminished the play beyond what Schumann had already himself wrought in this direction with his '70-'73 version, cutified it for Plasticland's kids, notably by going easy on the Bethlehem child-murder attempt.

---

5. Elka on her Dancing Bear *Christmas Story* of '71:

6. 'My first crew was all women. They were all — Helen Rayburn was in it, and there were about four women who were — we were quite a small crew. And part of my idea was to try to — was to do a small version of the *Christmas Story* that I felt we could handle and do it on a very — in a kind of a low-key way so that it wouldn't frighten little children.'

On her shows, fairy tales and Christmas shows, with the Dancing Bear and the '75 ff. Hardscrabble Mountain Theater (both all-woman groups): 'What I was trying to do was to just bring good small puppets to small children, you know, a good small puppet theatre to small children in a way where there wouldn't be a lot of hassle about things being too big or too bulky or — we tried to make the stage small enough so it would fit in a classroom and we tried to be very punctual and tried to leave things neat and — I don't know. It was partly a reaction against the Bread and Puppet's sort of grandiose looseness and also the fact that it's a much bigger thing and often it's much more splendid and terrible then and often scares little children. So I wanted very much to do something very limited, something that wouldn't scare the children or scare the teachers and it wouldn't make people hostile but where people would says, 'Oh, how nice', and I think we succeeded a number of times . . . I really was thinking I wanted to do something that would be acceptable where we lived. And all our kids were going to public school so I — and when Bread and Puppet would come and do a show, I mean, there would be — the Christmas show is a great — when it was well done and together and all it was really a great, moving show, but it would have these very scary — I don't know if you'd call them dark, but horrible monsters, King Herod, and then references to the Immaculate Conception that I felt was really — in a public school situation it's the kind of thing that they'll never ask you again after that, because that's too religious or too — (I: What are those references in Peter's piece?) Well, in the *Christmas Story* it begins with describing the Conception, Mary's conception and how the neighbors just — (I: The Annunciation.) The Annunciation, but that she also was big with child and her husband thought about putting her away and then did take her to home and then — and I think they give the story a great — much more depth and beauty and everything, but I know in the school situation something like that — it's just too good — too, you know, too strong and the monsters are too scary and there are all these things. And the whole way the company would come in would often feel very threatening, I think, to the school situation, which isn't saying the show is bad. It's just saying the school system is so inflexible and you know, structured. But I think I felt a real kind of — like I wanted to do something which would be neat and small and fit into people's ideas of puppet shows but also do it for small children and not deal with — not deliberately avoid terrible — not

Schumann did no more 'Crucifixions' after he left New York. Instead, in the springs of '70 and '71 he or his group without him, do 'crucifixion pageants' derived from *Cry*, in '70 they do outdoor ones, more political than religious, Bill Dalrymple on the 'Southern tour' of March-June, a more incitatory Resistance one, based on *Cry*'s 'building of Jesus' scene, Schumann a more pacific, plaintive one with local student recruits, in mid-April at Goddard and Cornell, the Goddard one as he remembers it in '79, an 'Eastern performance', as Elka in '79 remembers it, a 'parade with the Jesus puppets', the Cornell one, according to *WIN*, 'symbolically linking Seder and Easter' but both possibly comprising a Last Supper and a Crucifixion. In '71 they put on a similar show — 'the Last Supper with the singing of *The Lord is Risen* (Schumann, interview, '79) and 'the white *Fire* masks setting the table' (Elka, ibid.) — at an April 24 Movement demonstration in Washington, D.C. (for the four preceding, cf. supra, section on street agitation), and another indoors one, as part of a *Domestic Resurrection Circus* toured in New England, comprising some manner of procession of the disciples and possibly a Last Supper (whether it had a Crucifixion scene, I don't know) sufficiently important in the show to make Elka think of the show as 'like a very elaborate version of the Easter show.'   (Schumann, interview, '79.)

From '72 onward, these pageants are replaced[7] by a spectacle created that year, *The Stations of the Cross*, performed in April at Goddard, in May and June elsewhere in Vermont (at the Northfield High gym, May 19th, at Bennington, June 4th in the Memorial Building in Burlington, where it was, on the flyer, advertised as a 'religious experience with a personal message', then in Montpelier) and in New York (at St. Clement's Church, May 22-28). Elka (interview) says he did it again in '73, but I have no record of this. In the spring of '74 it was without Schumann, with Carlene Fernandez rather than he in charge of the music — which involved recruiting singers locally and getting them to learn the songs — taken on a tour of some southern states, and Schumann took it on a tour of Vermont and to Montreal, Quebec and Boston, and for three performances at the Washington Square Methodist Church, to New York as well, and at the

---

avoid death or anything like that, but certainly there's enough children's material. But I never thought of an ideology.' — (Elka Schumann, interview, '83.)

7. '. . . the spring of '72 . . . was when the Easter show became *The Stations of the Cross* . . . within the telling of these stations, you tell the story of Easter . . . . And it was good for our Easter stories to have a more permanent form that could be used and could be used again every year. There wasn't the need anymore to make a new Easter story every year like we had done in New York. We really tried hard and with different ideas and we really rehearsed and we worked with new puppets, and with new ideas and with different fashions of doing it every time we did it. Which was fun. And then — and at that point it was good to find a form. I didn't want to do any new stories after *Stations of the Cross*, I just wanted to continue that.' — (Schumann, interview, '79.)

end of '75, as section of a *Domestic Resurrection Circus* to Europe and to North Africa (where it offended the Muslim as it had the renegade Catholic students in Quebec), but apparently the circus was often or mostly done without it, as it had been two of the three times he did it just before the tour in Vermont. Except for some very bad and ill-attended performances April 24-27, 1980 at the Cathedral of St. John the Divine, managed by Larry Gordon (Schumann was in Europe), these are the last performances of *Stations* I know of.

The 'Stations of the Cross', originally tourist attractions for Roman Catholic pilgrims to Jerusalem, in the later Middle Ages sculptural displays scattered inside or around Franciscan churches, a meditative circuit of which would procure the visitor the same indulgences a pilgrimage to Jerusalem would, are fake. Nos. 3-4, 6-9 are not in any of the Gospels, and No. 5 is different: Simon is pressed into service by the guards to help Jesus carry the cross, he doesn't volunteer. But what is more amazing than the invention of the particulars of the whole walk with the cross is that their story of the last day of Jesus wilfully disregards the striking incidents reported by the Gospels. Schumann may not have been aware of this free adulteration, but I suspect he liked it.[8] The music Schumann picked to go with the untraditional story is equally untraditional.

Heading for the Hardwick Spring Festival Parade on the Bread and Puppet bus in late May '71, Elka and Schumann were enamored by some hymns that Margo Sherman and her boyfriend of the moment Larry Gordon were singing, *New Britain* (or *Amazing Grace*), *Northfield* –

> 'His own soft hands shall wipe the tears
> from every weeping eye;
> and pains and groans and griefs and fears
> and death itself shall die.'

'It was overwhelming to hear that – you were all very much enjoying learning that and doing that, and it sounded really great, much better than ever after'.
(Schumann, interview, '79.)[9]

---

8. '(Elka: (The Stations of the Cross) tell . . . the same story (as did Schumann's *Crucifixions* (SSB)). In traditional, in Catholic terms, the Stations of the Cross is just as definite a form to tell Easter as the saying 'Crucifixion'. The Stations of the Cross – within the telling of these stations, you tell the story of Easter.' — (Schumann, interview, '79.)

9. 'For the last two years some of us had learned Sacred Harp or shaped-note singing, under the influence of members of the New Hamburger commune in Plainfield. We had tried some of the hymns before in our DOMESTIC RESURRECTION CIRCUS but felt that we should employ this beautiful music much more. We had developed compositions for nails on tin cans, 1-gallon container fiddles and washing-machine-agitator horns, during music workshops earlier this year, and we have done Easter shows, Crucifixion pageants, wars, Sermons on the Mount since 1962. From this background and with the help of a lot of singing friends, we built the FOURTEEN STATIONS OF THE CROSS, celebrated Easter at Goddard and took our lastest Easter Story on tour there-

The music of the hymns published in *The Sacred Harp* of 1844 was the native American music that, in the viiith chapter of his *Life of the German Composer Adrian Leverkühn*, Thomas Mann's secondary narrator credits to a German immigrant to America, prefacing his account of it by:

'es lieg(t) im Wesen dieser seltsamen Kunst (music (SSB)), dass sie jeden Augenblick imstande (ist), von vorn zu beginnen, aus dem Nichts, bar jeder Kenntnis ihrer schon durchlaufenen Kulturgeschichte, des durch die Jahrhunderte Errungenen, sich neu zu entdecken und wieder zu erzeugen. Dabei durch(läuft) sie dann dieselben Primitiv-Stadien wie in ihren historischen Anfängen, und (kann) auf kurzer Bahn, abseits von dem Hauptgebirgstock ihrer Entwicklung, einsam und unbelauscht von der Welt, wunderliche Höhen absonderlicher Schönheit erreichen.'

Sacred Harp's being such a recreation *ex nihilo* of the medium must have recommended it to Schumann, himself recreator *ex nihilo* of a medium.

---

after, engaging and rehearsing new choruses of shaped-note singers wherever we went.' — (Schumann, Newsletter, *'Bread and Rosebuds*,' November '72.)

After that first encounter with Sacred Harp, the Schumanns or perhaps just Elka began 'meeting weekly either at the New Hamburger or (at) people('s) in Plainfield, or they came to us' (Elka, in Schumann, interview, '79) – singing, learning the hymns. One gets the feeling that it was Elka's enjoyment of and involvement in this work that sold Schumann on this music. It's really too pretty for Schumann. When Omar Shapli saw the show, Elka was conducting the choir (Shapli, interview) – something that Elka when I interviewed her in '83 with characteristic modesty omitted to mention. In '58/'59 she hadn't made it as a dancer with Schumann but here was something she could do – and not just, like her hand puppet kiddie shows at this time on her own, but with him. What probably spoiled it for her (she had just, in October '71, broken up one affair of Schumann's, but he was now getting into another one, with Carlene Fernandez), was Fernandez' involvement:

'I think she got involved in the *Stations of the Cross*, I remember. She did the music for that and she either – I don't remember if she described herself as a music student, but I know she played piano and would often just play the piano. And if things had to be figured out musically or something rearranged – she played the toy piano in many of the pieces and she would know how to put things in different keys, but she wasn't a great pianist or a musician but I think she just took that on herself and would be given that job and when Peter didn't go on tour – I mean Peter had been doing the music mainly for the *Stations of the Cross*, staying out of the show – then Carlene took over that part.' — (Elka, interview.)

But she was still in '74-'76 very much involved in Schumann's musical work, and not just, as she says, singing, but rehearsing the singers and conducting them:

'I would love to be able to play an instrument well enough to really be crucial to a music group and for a while with singing I felt really important – not important myself but as an important part of the music, which was important in the show, and that's, I find out, a really – (I: Why didn't you work on it?) When we moved here it was – I don't know what would have happened if we'd stayed in Plainfield where the chorus was and there were more opportunities to sing more. I guess I was never – not that good that I would be really, like, oh you've got to come to this rehearsal, you've got to be in this. And after a while it didn't seem worth really the effort of the drive and all that. I was in the Bach cantata *Jesu meine Freude*, which was just a wonderful, wonderful experience though.' — (Elka, interview.)

The play normally was done recruiting the singers locally and training them hastily.[10]

10. 'In *Stations of the Cross*, we tried to recruit singers to join the chorus, we had the music printed up ahead — books that we have many copies of still — and we sent that to the schools where we were coming and we tried to work with the music departments and the choruses that were there, so our chorus could be augmented by singers from the place, and it worked pretty well.' — (Elka, in Schumann, interview, '79.)

'NOTES TO ANY SINGERS FOR STATIONS OF THE CROSS

1) Most of the songs we transpose to lower keys. The starting notes are included in the cue sheet. Sometimes we sing NON NOBIS where it's written.

2) In all the Sacred Harp songs men's and women's voices can be on any of the parts. If you have high men's voices, have them sing either of the upper parts an octave below the women.

3) You don't need to learn the whole *Easter Anthem* on page 7, only the short segment 'and did he rise'. We usually sing the *Eastern Anthem* before the show, so if you have the time to learn it, great.

4) If it seems like too much to learn, leave out MON COEUR on page 12.

5) NON NOBIS, IDUMEA, and THE LORD IS RISEN should be memorized. There is another verse to IDUMEA:

> Waked by the trumpet sound
> I from my grave shall rise,
> And see the judge with glory crowned
> And see the flaming skies.

6) DUANE STREET and NORTHFIELD are sung very, very fast.

7) Excerpts from KEDRON, page 27, are sung a few times throughout the show as indicated in the music.

8) We will rehearse other chorus parts, as indicated in the cue sheet, when we arrive.

9) The way it goes: The show is a dramatization of the Fourteen Stations of the Cross. A station is announced, we sing a song, and the rest is "dramatized" in image and feeling with large puppets and people. The images with the music reflect the style. The chorus sits off to the side of the staging area, generally at a long table which at one point becomes the scene of the last supper — twelve chorus members get inside of twelve disciple puppets. The chorus is the center of attention at many points during the show and is always visible, so chorus members need to be serious and focused. But the whole is also somewhat informal.

Because of our schedule our rehearsal time will be much shorter than we would like, so the more you can study and rehearse the music on your own the better. We are looking forward to meeting you all.'

Schumann regretted that the singers for the New York performance 'were not much at ease'. They had been recruited in Washington Square Park at some outdoor political shows Schumann did there just before he did *Stations*. But apart from facilitating tours, the casting procedure made it less unlikely that the singing would be like what in Schumann's mind originally the music was: personally involved creation by autodidact amateurs — a mode he has tried to keep alive in his own work.

The book, *The Stations of the Cross/Bread and Puppet Theater* (1974) was beautifully illustrated by Schumann, Christ a white line drawing at the various stations beset (and/or aided) by black figures, the male ones by their cloaks and hats Puritans.

The way Schumann used the music, bursts of songs encapsuled each scene of the play, his second, after *Grey Lady Cantata I*, of '67 to high-culture and respectable (though in this case pre-classical rather than classical) Western music, his first real play — extended, with a story — to music, the first (with *Hallelujah* precursor) of a series to choir, and the first (after *Hallelujah*) to use the music in this divisive manner, separating the scenes. The effect of this was to suppress line, story and development, and to make the show a disjunct series of actions, each a solitary unit of a title, an image and a song: the more so since not even Catholics know the stations anymore (so that the story is not separately present to mind, connecting up the scenes), and since the sentence passed on Jesus does not lead up to the walk, and the walk not to his crucifixion.

Using for him a large mask, originally, in '70, called the Pursuit of Happiness, and used in the July 4th *Declaration of Independence* parade, he added a character — in the role of a witness — to the story appearing in his Easter shows for the first time, God. (The Lord had first shown His face in Schumann's theatre in February of 1970 in *Emilia*.) He added an extensive prologue — thirty minutes out of a total seventy or so — in fanciful form leading up through Jesus' messianic activities (a love affair with the world) and arrest to his presentation in court.[11]

---

11. 'The entire piece, which is played without an intermission, lasts about seventy minutes: It consists of a prologue of about thirty minutes duration, followed by the fourteen separate stations of the cross. At each station, the narrator rings a bell, shows the audience a drawing depicting that station and announces the station. Each announcement is followed by the chorus singing a hymn (or part of a hymn).

The story which is told without any dialogue, is at times simple and literal, but at other times seems dense and apparently symbolic. While spectators are often puzzled by the "meaning" of certain images, Schumann conceives of the story as "a pure, clear thing" — something that can be understood on its own terms and not a plaything for the interpretative mind. He feels that the audience has enough to do just absorbing everything that is happening and that the spectator should be able to tell the "story" himself after seeing it. The puppets, props, and acoustics share an interior relationship that is independent of any symbolic framework.

This "narrative with mute action" is essentially a series of images punctuated by various acoustical effects. Schumann explains theatre as "the impact of sound and visual elements on the spectator, and not transcendental poetry put into dialogue." the visual effects achieved — closer to Happenings than to traditional plays — derive from the fantastic puppets and masks that Schumann designs . . .

The Stations of the Cross reveals a costume continuum that stretches from the performer in street clothes to a 10-foot puppet, concealing a performer. The performers appear and re-appear in different roles, sometimes as stagehands, sometimes as actors, sometimes wearing a mask and costume and sometimes inside large puppets. Christ is represented both by an actress who is onstage throughout the piece, and by a large (about 18-foot) puppet carried on during the eighth station. A performer wearing a mask and a complete costume may appear quite similar to a large puppet, but the movement of the human body underneath the costume makes it less distant and more real. In all cases, there is no attempt at hiding the falsity of the presentation; the mechanics of puppetry are an integral part of the production . . . .

'A few notes on the flute are heard. A large, spheroid-shaped puppet, which covers the performer from the waist up, enters from backstage. The performer's arms are outside of the puppet, and she is ringing a bell as she goes to the chair and sits down. The puppet is mostly green in color, and we can now see that it represents the Earth.

The choral singing of William Byrd's "Non Nobis Domine" is heard from behind the audience:

> Non nobis, Domine, non nobis,
> Sed nomini tuo da gloriam,
> Sed nomini tuo da gloriam.

As the singing continues, a man enters the performing area from the center aisle. On his back, he carries a large face mask, which he slowly nods to each side of the audience. He is followed by a woman (Christ) confined inside two large, clasping hands; another woman helps carry the hands. As the rest of this procession enters the performing area, we see a man in the mask and costume of a worker, several other performers, a chorus of twelve draped in robes made from white sheets and a few men dressed in suits and top hats.

As the singing ends, the chorus and musicians sit in the chairs provided for them (stage right) and all of the other performers except Christ go to the edge of the performing area. The large face, which might be seen to represent God, is set up in front of the backdrop with one of the large hands on each side of it.

Christ and Earth spin around in place to peaceful, humming music. The music becomes less peaceful and more noisy as the chorus begins striking nails together; it reaches a climax as the chorus beings drumming loudly on tin cans with the nails. It ends abruptly with a loud cymbal crash.

In the silence, all of the performers simultaneously breathe out loudly. they then say "thank you" to each other.

The lack of dialogue heightens the aural effect. Traditional instruments – violin, bass, flute, horn, drum, cymbals and trombone – are played, but more unorthodox means of music-making are also employed. This includes the chorus drumming tin cans with nails and Schumann playing a saw with a bow as if it were a violin.

PERFORMANCE AREA:

The Station of the Cross is basically a flat piece that does not try to use the space environmentally. Although there is no stage or curtain, a proscenium relationship between performer and spectator is maintained.

At the rear of the performance area hangs a flowery pink and green backdrop. With two exceptions, all exits and entrances are made to and from the backstage area behind the backdrop. A chair, which serves as a focal point for much of the action, is in the middle of the space. At stage right are about fifteen chairs, arranged in three rows and facing the performing area. Together at stage left are a drum and an easel; the easel has a large pad of paper on it and a bell hanging from it. On the floor as the play opens are three groups of painted, toy-like models, a foot or two high and apparently constructed from papier-mâché. One group is of soldiers with rifles, another is of peasant women with babies, and the third is a group of civilians in Western clothes. The lighting on the performance area (the audience is in darkness) remains constant throughout the piece except for the occasional addition of spotlights.' — (J. Towsen, *The Stations of the Cross, Tulane Drama Review* 55, September 1972.) (Copyright J. Towsen 1972.)

Christ covers the large face with the sheet she has been wearing. She is now seen to be wearing a patchwork quilt as if it were a robe. There are several household objects attached to the quilt, including kitchen utensils, an orange, two flashlights and two small plastic bags of water.

The narrator, a woman dressed in a black and gold showman's suit, comes to the center and does a fast tap dance, after which she bows to the audience and says "Good evening, ladies and gentlemen . . ." She returns to the easel and drum (stage left) where she will remain throughout the performance.

The worker (stage right) drops his big, heavy sack on the floor.

A man wearing a mask with the word "SUPER" on its forehead enters and crosses to the chair. He shows us twelve separate pieces of paper, each with a word on it, and places them on the chair, while the chorus makes an eerie "ooh" sound that we might associate with ghosts. The words are: "ah", "way", "can", "pop", "room", "any", "no", "blah", "magic", "what", "do", and "ooh".

The worker hits his sack with a large sledgehammer; a cloud of dust rises from it. The worker and "SUPER" exit.

A high-pitched screech is heard from the narrator and then from the chorus. The neighing of horses sounds from behind the backdrop, and then two men wearing horse-heads and heavy wooden clogs pull in a large wooden box; a man in a death mask is at the reins. The chorus covers its eyes as Death picks up all the models of soldiers, women and civilians and throws them into the wagon. Death takes a rope from Christ's feet and whips the chair (and the words on it) several times.[12] He exits with his horses and wagon.

---

12. '. . . it was a tremendously effective thing, and I remember Elka was directing the chorus in that and she was out there conducting. Strong musicality was a part of that. Again, talking about alienation effects, one that really stuck in my mind — in fact, I've stolen it on occasion sometimes in my own work because it struck me so vivid — the flogging of the Christ. Margo had her hands tied and held above her head. One of the warrior figures came out with a thong of some sort, a leather piece, and instead of miming the flogging of Margo, brought out a chair, a simple chair, I think it was just one of the chairs the people were sitting on, and began to beat the chair right next to her, but beat it very hard, full force. I don't recall her doing any attempt to mime imaginary blows or anything. But it was startling, because what we were seeing was a fragmentation of a beating. We were seeing a human being vulnerable, a woman playing a man, playing Christ in fact, and with no attempt to explain things through the facial expression again. But somehow a very moving and concentrated facial expression. And next to it, a figure of great violence manifesting real, not imaginary violence on the chair. And it somehow, you know, your mind simply put — it was a montage. You saw this, you saw that and such a simple resolution and yet so original and so much better than Peter Brook and his flogging sequence — you remember the hair dragging across. I mean, that to me is a very good example — comparison . . . my God, what a brilliant directorial touch. It was a beautiful, tremendous effect. And yet that's it. I mean, it was a touch, a directorial touch and you saw the touch and you were impressed by it, you admired it, extraordinary imagination. I think, you got much of what Mr. Rice was aiming for in that scene, or what — you know, what you saw was a director at work. Watching this other thing I wasn't aware of that at all. It wasn't imaginative enough for you to be impressed by the direction. That's again part of the throwing away. You didn't have to see wow, how imaginative, how inventive this was. It was a natural and simple, almost anti-theatrical statement that was superbly theatrical in its effect. And that to me is typical of Peter's work at best. One of the things that makes him so

Christ raises her arms high above her head as three large puppets slowly enter. Unlike the other large puppets we will see, they are topped, not by a puppet head, but by several figures of people arranged to represent a crowd. As each crowd-puppet passes the chair, the performer's hand emerges from within and wipes the chair with a handkerchief. They exit, but Christ's hands remain above her head.

Three men wearing helmets march in noisily. to the command of "de da, dit dit dit-de da, dit!" one of them ties a handkerchief and a rope to the chair. There is a pause, and the narrator rings a bell.

Narrator: "The First Station of The Cross: He is condemned to death." The chorus sings the first line of "Kedron": "Thou Man of grief remember me."

One of the soldiers shoots the chair with his rifle, and it falls to the floor; another soldier has yanked it to the ground with the rope. Christ drops her arms and looks under the sheet at the hidden face. To the command of "de da, dit dit dit," the soldiers march out.

Christ picks up the chair. A woman wearing a colorful robe and carrying a basket full of paper flowers enters and stands on the chair.

A large gray cross with a reptile-like head is carried in and connected to the ceiling by a pulley system. It can be seen to resemble a prehistoric flying creature and/or a modern fighter-bomber. To dramatic music from the drum and bass, a padded strongman fails in an attempt to lift the cross. He leaves in embarrassment.

Narrator (rings bell): "The Second Station of The Cross: He is made to bear His cross." Again the chorus sings: "Thou Man of grief remember me."

Christ successfully pulls the cross to the ceiling as the flower lady sprinkles her with flowers.

A large yellow puppet enters and sits on the chair. He points at Christ with his large yellow puppet hand. He keeps pointing as Christ lies down on the floor.

Narrator (rings bell): "The Third Station of The Cross": the chorus sings "And did He rise . . ."

Christ stands up and nods and smiles at the chorus. The yellow puppet exits.

"SUPER" places a small table to the left of the chair. Christ sets the table with a tablecloth, an orange and a cup of coffee, all of which are taken from her quilt robe.

A large blue puppet — apparently Mary — peeks out from behind the backdrop. Christ waves to her.

---

extraordinary. You know, there's so much theatre and theatrical form that relates to itself, it's incestuous. We do things because, you know, the critics will tell you which influenced what, and so forth. Peter is one of the few strong theatrical artists whose main influences seem to me to be the world around him. And his theatrical devices are ways of viewing that world and taking elements from that world and showing it to us in a somewhat lopsided way so we can look at them better. And for that he sometimes does make use — I'm not trying to portray him as some sort of, you know, a primitive — he obviously is enormously sophisticated in terms of his awareness of theatre and of art and all these other things. But it isn't the functional route with him. He has it available to him if he needs it. And when he has it he more often than not throws it away.' — (Shapli, interview.)

Narrator (rings bell): "*The Fourth Station of The Cross*: He meets his mother."
The chorus sings Orlando di Lasso's motet "Mon coeur se recommande à vous":

> Mon coeur se recommande à vous
> Tout plein d'amour et de martire,
> Au moins en despit des jaloux
> Faictes qu'adieu vous puisse dire.
> Ma bouche qui savait sourire
> Et compter propos gratieux
> Ne facit maintenant que mauldire
> Ceux qui m'ont banny de vos yeux.

Mary exits, and Christ goes from the table to stand in front of the large face mask.

Down the center aisle through the audience, a man in a suit and top hat enters on a child's bicycle. He honks his horn, puffs on a cigar and nods to the spectators and performers. When he reaches the performance area, he gets off the bicycle and bows ceremoniously to the performers, who applaud him in turn. As he bows to the audience, the narrator rings the bell and . . .

Narrator (rings bell): "*The Fifth Station of the Cross*: Simon helps him carry the cross." The chorus sings "Thou Man of grief remember me/Thou never canst thyself forget."

The man gestures as if to speak finally but, suddenly noticing his watch, realizes he has to leave. He rides off backstage, beeping the horn and waving goodbye. (This and the scene with the strongman provide the only real clowning in the piece.)

The sheet is now removed from the face and held before it by the large hands.

Narrator (rings bell): "*The Sixth Station of The Cross*: Veronica wipes His tears."
The chorus sings "Wondrous Love":

> What wondrous love is this! oh! my soul! oh! my soul!
> What wondrous love is this! oh! my soul!
> What wondrous love is this!
> That caused the Lord of bliss
> To bear the dreadful curse for my soul! for my soul!
> To bear the dreadful curse for my soul!

The flower-lady is sitting at the table, which now has a bucket of fire on it. The sheet is removed from the large face mask, revealing two tears under the eyes — they are the two plastic bags of water that were previously seen on Christ's quilt robe. The tears are briefly illuminated by the two flashlights hanging from Christ's robe. The face is again covered by the sheet, and the flower-lady exits with the fire.

A man wearing a suit and a head-mask topped with a king's crown enters, singing the scales more or less in tune to the bass. He sits at the table as a man wearing a red-nosed mask resembling a dog enters on all fours, to the loud panting of the chorus. The dog holds up a white rag (or handkerchief) which the king grabs and examines. He shoves the dog away to the wailing of the chorus and then tears the rag in half. He exits.

Christ lies down on the ground.

Narrator (rings bell): "*The Seventh Station of The Cross*: The second fall." The chorus sings "And did he rise . . ."

Christ stands up, nods and smiles at the chorus, and then stands on the chair. The three crowd-puppets enter. A hand comes out of each of them and waves to Christ, who waves back.

Narrator (rings bell): "*The Eighth Station of The Cross*: He speaks to the women of Jerusalem." Christ gestures vigorously with her hands above her head, as if she were speaking, as the chorus sings "Northfield":

> How long, dear Saviour, oh how long
> Shall this bright hour delay?
> Fly swift around, ye wheels of time,
> And bring the promised day.
> Lo, what a glorious sight appears
> To our believing eyes!
> The earth and seas are pass'd away
> And the old rolling skies.
> His own soft hand shall wipe the tears
> from every weeping eye;
> And pains and groans, and griefs and fears,
> And death itself shall die.

The crowd-puppets (the women of Jerusalem) wave once again to Christ and then exit. Christ comes down from the chair and stands in front of the large face.

To the sound of several cymbal-crashes, the Great Warrior enters and sits at the table. He is a large (about 10-foot) blue puppet with a gray head topped by a crest of spikes; he carries two swords, each with the world "hallelujah" on it.

A very large (about 18-foot) puppet representing Christ is carried in, trembling to the sound of Schumann's violin, and laid down on a mattress.

Narrator (rings bell): "*The Ninth Station of The Cross*: The third fall." The chorus sings "And did He rise . . ."

The Christ puppet is mounted on a ladder with two men inside it, as the flower-lady strews paper flowers. To a mournful tune on the violin and bass, a large blue puppet (Mary?) enters and kneels before the Christ puppet, which bows back, holding its hands in supplication. Christ stands under the outstretched hands of the Christ puppet.

Narrator (rings bell): "*The Tenth Station of The Cross*: He is stripped of His garments." The chorus sings "Thou Man of grief remember me/Thou never canst thyself forget."

"SUPER" takes a tie and a pair of socks from Christ, shows them to the audience and then places them on the table: he takes Christ's boots and puts them on the floor.

Narrator (rings bell): "*The Eleventh Station of The Cross*: He is nailed to the cross." The chorus sings:

> Thou Man of grief remember me
> Thou never canst thyself forget

Thy last expiring agony,
Thy fainting pangs and bloody sweat.

Oh come mourn with me awhile
See Jesus and Mary by His side
Look how patiently He hangs
Jesus our Lord is crucified.

The chorus exits backstage. The huge cross is let down from the ceiling, and the Christ puppet is tied to it, as the narrator loudly beats the drum and the flower-lady sprinkles her with more paper flowers. A dozen large puppets (the chorus) representing the disciples enter slowly from behind the backdrop.

Narrator (rings bell): "*The Twelfth Station of The Cross*: He dies." The chorus-disciples sing "Idumea":

And am I born to die?
To lay this body down?
And must my trembling spirit
Fly into a world unknown?

All is still as "SUPER" slowly removes his mask and vest and puts on a red cape. He points at the Christ puppet. Christ goes behind the sheet to the large face mask.

Narrator (rings bell): "*The Thirteenth Station of the Cross*: He is taken down from the cross." the chorus-disciples yell "AAAh" loudly for a few seconds.

To the loud banging of empty paint cans against the floor, the Christ puppet is taken down from the cross. The cross is laid on the middle of the floor, and each side of the crossbar is broken in half. The Christ puppet is laid on top of the cross, and the sheet is placed over them. One at a time, the chorus and all of the other performers remove their puppets and lay them on the grave of Christ. The puppets are now in a pile in the middle of the floor, and the performers are standing to the rear of them.

Narrator (rings bell): "*The fourteenth Station of The Cross*: He is laid in His grave." Everybody lies down on the floor except for two or three musicians and the narrator.

After about twenty seconds of silence, the narrator begins softly singing "Hallelujah, the Lord is risen" to the music of the violin and bass. The other performers slowly rise and join in the singing, which grows louder and louder. Finally, horns, cymbals, drum and trombone join in, practically drowning out the singing. The loud clamor ends abruptly upon the conductor's signal.

The performance is over, the applause is very enthusiastic, and bread that was baked on the premises is given out to the audience. Most of the spectators are slow in leaving, with about half of the audience still there twenty minutes later.'
(J. Towsen, *The Bread and Puppet Theatre/The Stations of the Cross,
Tulane Drama Review* #55, September '72.)[13]

His invention of the imagery was guided by a very simple principle, not

---

13. Copyright J. Towsen 1972.

used by him in any other show, contrariation: the images would oppose the text, thus perhaps forcing viewers to consider matters more closely, possibly arriving at some view or experience reconciling image and word.[14] The result was an appearance of burlesque, surrealism, even dada, of meanings private to Schumann – one could invent one's own. He related as freely to the story as its inventors had related to the Gospels, or the Sacred Harp musicians to music. Thus perhaps telling his audience that the story of Christ was what you made of it. On the whole, however, his imagery was upbeat and cheerful[15] – there was clowning even – so that even without the rousing ending on *Christ is Risen*, the performance raised the woeful story to a celebration of spring, or, since the Prologue ended downbeat – with a crash like that terminating *Cry*'s Last Supper – gave it the traditional form of Easter masses, woe, then joy.

There was nary any politics in the show – it was reduced to an action involving the little Johnny puppets in the prologue: you were not told what cross humanity is bearing. The shark-faced plane identifying that cross as war and warlike greed was there, but the crucifixion was not imaged, so the point slipped by. And Jesus correspondingly appeared not – as in Schumann's shows hitherto – as representation of oppressed, victimized, suffering humanity, but as its victim, the individual tortured by the crowd, a generalization of the Gospel accounts' absolution of Pilate (and in one of the Gospels even of Herod) and indictment of the crowd – 'Crucify Him!' – 'Give us Barrabas!' He turned the Church's Jewish crime into humanity's. The play was done in churches, but by the idiosyncrasy and levity of its imagery unlike the '60s *Crucifixions* could not be done as *participation* in the community's celebration of Easter, but only as an individual's celebration of it. This also was a withdrawal from the crowd, paralleling that of his street agitation's at this time.

The New York Times and the *Village Voice* both loved it, for its child-like serene joy, though, in the words of Feingold, 'the cognitive specifics kept eluding' them. Even Sainer, who in '69 had hemmed and hawed at *Cry*, when he saw *Stations* in '74, gave it his heartfelt approval.

---

14. The cross is light for Jesus, not heavy; he does not bear it; whenever he is said to fall, he rises, smiles; he does not meet his mother; Simon decided not to help him bear the cross (Schumann may here be thinking of the legend of the Jerusalem shoemaker who became the Wandering Jew); he does not weep (his father does); Veronica does not wipe his tears, but a king tears up the handkerchief; he is not nailed to the cross; he does not die: he joins his father; he is not laid in his grave, instead everybody else dies (lies down on the floor); and Jesus is a woman.

15. 'The lightness of touch, the color. There was a lot more humor in *The Stations of the Cross*, whereas, I don't remember humor in the Crucifixion plays, and there were softer colors. The fact that Peter was living in the country was clearly having an influence on his work, then . . . the chorus, for example, wore costumes that had bright colors – woodblocks, with words on them, but in addition to that, there would be a patchwork of bright colors – like red and blue – with little hats, again, with red and blue and bright colors – I, myself, was wearing a pink costume.' — (Sherman, interview.)

5. March 1970. The first play in the post-agitational mode, *The Difficult Life of Uncle Fatso.*
A goodbye to the city and its agitations,
a detached look at the world.
Uncle Fatso the slimy despot
has almost become just one of the guys.

Schumann's experiences during the *Cry* tour and a catalytic visit during its summer break to the Puppentheatermuseum der Stadt München[1] made him want to do 'mechanized theater,'[2] theatre by mechanical contrivance disposing with humans. *Difficult Life* was the proximate result of this wish to sweep his group off his stage,[3] and his only piece of mechanical theatre, attempts '70-'72 at marionettry proving abortive, though individual

---

1. 'Founded by Ludwig Krafft in 1939 . . . German popular and artistic puppet stages of the 18th, 19th and 20th century, including a Max Jacob stage. An important section on Chinese shadow figures, Wayang figures and Siamese rod puppets.' — (*Puppentheater international*, Berlin, 1980.)

   '. . . a marvelous museum. It's one of the most beautiful museums I know. It's an amazing museum. They have collections of a lot of different forms of English and German toy theatres and home theatres. In the last century there was a lot of theatrical work done in people's homes. Families played theatre for each other . . . . With cutout things that were mechanically moved — with imitations of big, Italian-style proscenium stages, in cardboard or wood, and with Kasper Puppen — but very elaborate stages, quite frequently, with this depth and this scenery painted and wings and so on — and they have beautiful examples of that. Everything from mechanical puppets that they just — on cranks — very limited movement — just things passing by — dogs going by, people going by, preacher coming in, audience coming in, animals and — to scenes, melodrama or other bourgeois little theatre ideas — plots. Terrific collection.' — (Schumann, interview, '82.)

2. '(Elka: We didn't come back and think we'd go to Vermont. We came back and we found out we lost the Courthouse and we searched desperately for weeks if not months, to find another place for the theatre to work in, and you *very* much wanted to do your new show, which was not going to have any people in it at all, just mechanized theatre, inspired by the visit to the Munich puppet museum, where there were many, many examples of mechanized theatre, and you had had enough of all these personality, prima donna clashes and everything else. (I: Just one-man?) No, not one-man theatre but everybody backstage, pulling strings and nobody in the show at all.' — (Elka in Schumann, interview, '79.)

3. 'I hated *The Cry of the People for Meat* by the time we came back from the European tour — I remember that — and during the performance in New York, where we did our last performance of it, I felt: What am I doing here working with actors? I have no interest in this — with all this performing. Do you remember that? (Elka: Yeah, I remember that.) That's not what I want to do. I want to work with puppets — with things that move — (Elka: And have no personality clashes or — *Uncle Fatso* was really — I think succeeded in what Peter wanted to do. It didn't want to have anything to do with personalities or people's acting.)' — (Schumann, interview, '82.)

devices stayed with him, cf. *Joan of Arc* ('77) infra. Much as he hates to admit it, the human performer is essential to what he wants to do. The idea of mechanization was not technological only, however, but served him for statement and style, and in this way the Puppentheatermuseum may have been catalytic for his work of the period beyond *Difficult Life*, somewhat as the Manteo puppets were beyond *King Story* and the Christmas and Easter shows.

The little — perhaps 5-10 inches tall — string-operated doll puppets and objects for *The Difficult Life of Uncle Fatso* were made in the Bank, and apparently also the roll-up curtain, the background Vermont landscapes,[4] and the box-tower bridge stage for it — columns of the touring prop crates with boards over them from which to operate the strings moving the dolls and toy objects.[5] One of the *Cry* beast masks was colorfully painted for a head for the Chinese New Year's dragon-bringer-of-good-things — who in other plays had been the bringer of Jesus, but here brought on the beautiful womanly essence of natural Vermont; three or four dummies were made, henchmen or yes-men but essentially proletarian slobs, good-for-nothing hangers-out; a big black mask[6] to represent charitable Night, the Black tidal wave of riots engulfing the City, and the end of cities as habitable places; and Sara Peattie made a clumsy beautiful colorful sun lampoon to represent the damned life and beauty of this earth. But in the main, work for this play provided its — simple, as Schumann emphasizes — mechanisms, consisted in giving the little figures joints and arranging for their

---

4. 'Well, we have those landscapes that were done in the Bank — terrible weather — Bart Lane was there, working on them very hard. I never knew how he lived. I mean, I thought he would die, it was so cold in that Bank. The horse was over in the corner standing knee-deep in used hay, and infections in its feet and everything, and there was no heat . . .' — (Ashley, interview.)

5. Schumann thinks of *Uncle Fatso* as attempt to create a distinct impression of a 'theatre'. The boxes as such were not important:

'What was important was that with *Uncle Fatso* and with *Grey Lady Cantata #2* even *more*, we had a stage that allowed us to do what marionette plays and puppet plays can do to imitate a *theatre*, to be on a *small scale* what a big *theatre* is, sort of.' — (Schumann, interview, '79.)

6. A huge black face with an open mouth through which word signs could be suspended and a body of black fabric that could gradually be lowered and spread to cover most of the stage.

'(I: And what was your idea in that with this black thing swallowing up the city? What did it stand for?) It was a good-natured face. It was not an evil — (I: It could have been just night as far as I was concerned.) Right. (I: Maybe not.) (Elka: I think it certainly had the connotations of this is the time of riots in cities — of the chaos kind of all over, engulfing.) But I think it was ambiguous as that. Definitely it was a night scene where the light got darker as this dark face covered up people, and because it was a black face, a black person's face, it had that other connotation. (Elka: There was also a finality about it; the words that came out of its mouth were "good night, bye-bye", and then the last of it was "that's all.") That's what it was, "that's all"? That's what it said? Well, that says it.' — (Schumann, interview, '83.)

string operation, fixing up the dummies with strings so the puppeteer inside Uncle Fatso could make them gesture, arrangements for making a landscape heave in a live fashion from below it, and stringing up various things so they could be pulled up on or across the stage.[7] Leherrissier (interview) thinks rehearsals were at Christ Church in Brooklyn. It was done at Spencer Church March 4-16, together with *Lamentations* and 'crucifixions' (Schumann, Newsletter, '*Bread and Rosebuds*', April 25, '70). These performances bridged the gap between the Bank and the Old Boston Theatre. There were mid-April showings of it at Goddard and Cornell, Leherrissier (loc. cit.) thinks, perhaps mistakenly, there were showings at Washington Square Methodist Church, the *Daily News* for April 25 mentions showings at WBAI's Free Music Store at 359 East 62nd Street on April 25 and 26, and there had been a show there on April 24 as well. It was taken to Atlanta in May, and on a tour with the circus August ff. – I know of a showing in Ohio. But because of the intricate and heavy stage and the delicate staging it wasn't too suitable for tours or isolated showings and did not survive for long in the Bread and Puppet repertory.

It was an enchantingly beautiful, delicate show focused on the contrast between Uncle Fatso, a human-sized though bulky personage, but very large indeed – 'in another world' – relative to the tiny colorful world within the box of the stage, a world ignored by him, a world towards which he did not so much turn his back as his shoulder, grossly seated out front, below (at a table, reading a newspaper, drinking beer, smoking, surrounded by smaller cronies, dummies. The tinyness of the constituent living parts of this world,[8] in the minute, intermittent, but, in all, incessant movement of Reality, seemed an aspect of reality per se, not a scenic device but an ontological comment. Uncle Fatso and his cronies – the livingly dead, sadly stupified, the integrated but out-of-it, their cruelty – or meanness – merely an aspect of their dumbness, unthinking rather than vicious[9] – were achromatic and essentially unmoving: a contrast to the

---

7. 'I was down underneath the stage. I would do all these things through a little trap door. I would appear or set puppets up or twirl different things – it was a jerky part, and basically I was bored, I was fed up with that. I didn't want to do that stupid show. I hated it.' — (Leherrissier, interview.)

8. 'All these tender and violent movements of little puppets and – events were confronted with Uncle Fatso and his cronies sitting at a table having a good time, playing cards and drinking and being served – it was a *living* room contrasted with a cityscape, and with the world.' — (Schumann, interview, '79.)

The Living Room/World contrast is crucial to Schumann's work during this period, cf. *Emilia, Grey Lady Cantata #2, Simple Light* infra: the Home intrudes – after *Difficult Life* as an isle of safety – into the world of his theatre of the '60s.

9. '(I: It was called *The Difficult Life of Uncle Fatso*. What is –) The "Difficulty" was mainly in that he didn't perceive any of this – of what went on in the world. So the world went on – in the first scene, as some dark, big event in the form of a dark face eating every-

color and changes around and behind them. It was a contrast of size that made sense. For one thing, it signified power bearing down upon the world. For another, one could think of it as a researcher's enlargement of a constituent but alien element within the scene: after all, the little people up there shared humanity and weaknesses with the stand-out powers out front: these were not totally alien — the difference was a purely relative, perhaps even just subjective difference in size. But then there was also another point: the world was formally alienated: shown *as* something small and distant; and this seemed a comment by the author Schumann, namely a recommendation of Stoic detachment, probably adequately reflecting his true inward change of attitude at this time (possibly not as yet quite known to him himself), marginally verging even on an identification with Uncle Fatso and Uncle Fatso's cronies: his detachment, of sight and distance, in the end not so different from theirs, that of blindness and of a caught-up part.

The play ends with a violently destructive action by Uncle Fatso, the rage of the dumb (a new perspective, in Schumann's oeuvre, on the violence of war, really a pitying one): not an enjoyment, not negative living, as in *America Hurrah*. This sudden commotion, the previous slow and rare routine gestures of Uncle Fatso and his cronies, and the movement of people and vehicles on stage were all mechanical: though, of course, especially the movement of people in the toy world. The only properly organic movement in this play was that of nature — hills, the sun, night.

The show — 'slow motion dance in four landscapes' — proceeded in four scenes: (1) *July Fourth 1968 (Uncle Sam's Birthday even 60th Birthday)/*

---

body up. And then the pastoral scene and then the giant falling out of the sky scene — but he sits and reads his paper and drinks. And, even the end of the world — uninfluenced even by that — and then jumps up and — you don't agree? (Elka: I saw it very differently. I was in the band when it was being done in New York and I remember that — at a certain point seeing he is gross and terrible and disgusting and very pathetic and tragic — that darker aspect of his came through very strong — in the streets when he's marching along he's just a caricature and very — you know, something you throw tomatoes at, but in this theatre piece he was just — he was like Frankenstein — like somebody who was sort of caught into a horrible body and a horrible situation that he couldn't get out of and ended up destroying everything, including himself . . . he would end up — I mean, it was like a self — you know, annihilation of everything — but there was something very sad about him — he was really — he was — you know, like a raging beast that was locked up inside and ended up destroying. . . . But the way he was used in the scene — I mean, being so gargantuan compared to this little, delicate world, very tenuously held together with cardboard and string, but a very sweet little world. All these little scenes from the city and the landscape and all — and then this big, sort of bluh, bluh — you know, with the beer and the newspaper and the partially comical waiters stumbling in and having some interaction with him, but — and he isn't just — he isn't just the villain he was a victim it seemed to me.)' — (Schumann, interview, '82.)

Happy Birthday Uncle Fatso — an aggressively political, but meaningless title (nobody remembers what it refers to), which does, however define the gathering of Fatso and his cronies out front, the play's frame, as a self-celebratory occasion, a birthday, (2) *The Tree* — named for its blue and white backdrop, the rather beautiful Tree of Life I quoted Leherrissier on à propos of the Kent State anniversary, first used in *Difficult Life*, then in various '70 Coney Island shows, later as sail of the circus Ark for All, (3) Vermont, (4) *The Sunset*. 'Because of the way the play had developed there was no plot or main character or anything, but it did just sort of merge — the scenes merged from something sort of light —' (Elka, in Schumann, interview, '82).[10] There was a text, taken from a late-'60s hippie poster, adulterated form, Schumann thinks, of a 'text dated 1692, found in Old St. Paul's Church, Baltimore' (*Tulane Drama Review #47*); recited (actually spoken from the wings) by a tiny figure in scene 2 (according to some, sometimes in scene 3 rather than 2), making of scene 2 an annunciatory transition from the first end-of-the-city to the third glory-of-the-country scene. The text expresses Schumann's newfound Stoicism and explains his retreat to Vermont:

'Go placidly amid the noise and haste and remember what peace there may be in silence. As far as possible without surrender be on good terms with all persons. Speak your truth quietly and clearly, and listen to others, even the dull and ignorant; they too have their story. Avoid loud and aggressive persons, they are vexations to the spirit. If you compare yourself with others you may become vain and bitter; for always there will be greater and lesser persons than yourself. Enjoy your achievements as well as your plans. Keep interested in your own career, however humble; it is a real possession in the changing fortunes of time. Exercise caution in your business affairs, for the world is full of trickery. But let this not blind you to what virtue there is; many persons strive for high ideals; and everywhere life is full of heroism. Be yourself. Especially do not feign affection. Neither be cynical about love, for in the face of all aridity and disenchantment it is perennial as the grass. Take kindly the counsel of the years, gracefully surrendering the things of youth. Nurture strength of spirit to shield you in sudden misfortune. But do not distress yourself with imaginings. Many fears are born of fatigue and loneliness. Beyond a wholesome discipline be gentle with yourself.

---

10. 'For me, *Uncle Fatso* was a real find. I took a long time to work on that, so it's possible in the bank we did nothing but that. Because the work was very slow — very unsimilar to other shows. Took a long time to find it. And, yes, there was something very new. (Elka: Yeah, I agree, and very, very — I've tried to describe this to you many times because I feel that very strongly — that as in many of the pieces that came later, there was such a sort of a ready made way to do things and a lot of it consisted of drum rolls, cymbal clashes, things pointing — sort of there's this, there's that, part I, part II, beginning, middle — and *Uncle Fatso* was very amorphous and very — yeah, it just created a whole other world that you could enter and see.'

Elka loves Schumann's pieces of this period for this openness, organicity, imaginative freedom, poetical quality, contrasting them to his pieces of the late '70s and early '80s which she thinks tend to turn out dry and mechanical.

80

You are a child of the universe, no less than the trees and stars; you have a right to be here. And whether or not it is clear to you, no doubt the universe is unfolding as it should. Therefore be at peace with God, whatever you conceive him to be, and whatever your labors and aspirations in the noisy confusion of life keep peace with your soul. With all its sham, drudgery and broken dreams, it is still a beautiful world. Be careful. Strive to be happy.'

Elka describes the play:

'There were four main scenes . . . interrupted by — interspersed by scenes between Uncle Fatso and his cronies . . . And the first scene was the city . . . with the cars moving and the little scenes inside the houses. (Schumann: a drinker with a cup . . . a father-son or some double figure spinning . . . a woman with her handkerchief waving bye-bye)[11] and then as the light dims the face comes out (Schumann: and the crowds come in on the floor) . . . crowds come in with signs saying "Hunger", "Air", "Dirt", whatever . . . and then as the light dims the face comes out (Schumann: (and) drops words out of its mouth on the crowd) "Good night, Bye-bye", and then the last of them was "That's all" — a big black face that swallow(s) up everything. The second scene was the landscape . . . the little speaker . . . the little lady walking her dog and the text, ending with the horses with the nude riders, galloping in and across. And the next one was the nude scene (Schumann: with the moving hills (with) various loving couples (on them), (but) the majority of the nudes are sort of relaxed in reclining positions or sitting, lying, different arm positions — very . . . gentle) ending with the dragon — moving, coming in with a girl on it . . . (Schumann: very beautifully dressed with a beautiful mask, riding on the dragon) — entering — oh, and the little boat! — the little boat coming in (Schumann: In front, over the stage. . . . The girl gets delivered on stage by the dragon and then . . . gets wrapped into a landscape. She keeps spinning and spinning and the landscape wraps her up. All the way, from top to bottom.[11]) (And in the fourth scene there is) this strange globe that Sara Peattie made a globe of pieces of cellophane . . . tied together and inside is a light bulb . . . pieces of colored cellophane . . . This has been hanging in the scene the

---

11. 'A car kills some of . . . the little figures. They ascend very slowly to heaven. From under a large Uncle Sam hat emerges a small Uncle Sam who is shown the tenement floor by floor. From the top he is dumped into a passing dump truck.' — (Whittaker, *Bread & Puppet's entry in FUT relaxed, mysterious*, student paper, G. & M.U., Toronto, August '70.)
12. Anique Detolle, a French girl who had joined the group in Ste. Baume in the summer of '68 'would wear like this blue dress and blue mask and have her golden hair sticking out and she would stand there and sort of twirl around' (Leherrissier, interview) . . . 'they'd walk around her and then carry her off because she would be all bound up, she couldn't walk off. That was sort of awkward, but okay, what are you going to do.' (ibid.) But touring *Uncle Fatso* with other pieces in the Midwest that fall, George Konnoff had the idea of having another French girl, Tanith Noble do it in the nude: 'So she rode in on his shoulders, and they didn't tell any of the puppeteers. She was stunning. And she stood up on this stage and she spun around. At last she was clothed with the crankie that wound up her body. But it was so beautiful, you know, and Peter loved it actually, he freaked out, he really did. (He) wasn't there for that but he saw it later (he joined the tour in Ohio (SSB)) and he just went Ah! And Elka just said: "Well, everyone has nudity in the theatre now and you really want to be like everyone else." '

whole time but pretty high up and in this last scene the globe is very slowly lowered and as it's lowered the lights very slowly dim. From behind the backdrop – this is a very eerie touch – somebody throws articles of clothing over the backdrop so you don't really see what they are, a sock, or a shirt, or something that's sort of thumped down there. (Schumann: The giant falling from the sky.) A piece of clothing falls; it doesn't flutter and it doesn't fall fast – sort of in between. And these little figures that have been in the first scene – they're probably up there the whole time, just you don't see them – they are lowered – hung over the back curtain ... on strings. And at the same time the crowds, these crowd puppets holding up little signs, they're being pushed from the wings by poles across the stage, I think from (both) sides. And the dragon that had brought in the woman in the previous scene and has just sort of slumped at the base of the stage, opens its mouth and these (crowd) figures fall into its mouth. (And) the others just fall down ... until they are on the ground. And the light is dimming the whole time. And there is a little sound (talking high-pitched and with a little sound) to this. And at the end of that scene, Uncle Fatso gets up and just smashes everything around him.'
(Elka in Schumann, interview, '82; Schumann, ibid. and in Schumann, interview, '83.)

He gets up violently, turning over the table, and staggering around smashes the bare light bulb suspended from the ceiling that has been illuminating the show: an amazingly shocking denoument.

The action out front, a barely stirring action, was the sad birthday party. Uncle Fatso reading a newspaper much of the time, smoking his cigar, drinking beer, his dummy cronies drinking beer also. In between scenes, a slightly comical waiter stumbles in, bringing beer, at some point a birthday cake. Uncle Fatso rumbles unintelligibly, the cronies (all voices are done from off-stage) say 'Okay. Okay. ...' The rumblings, the 'Okays' and Uncle Fatso's gestures from interlude to interlude progressively become more violent. The depression finally irrupts into destruction.

The show as here described makes pretty good sense both politically (some or all of the tiny urban demonstrating crowds were black) and personally, but, a perceptual feast, it carried its sense visually, meanings were delayed side effects. E.g. that the smashing of the light bulb was the end of the world – presumably in an atom bomb war – was quite inobvious, though emotionally the image is with one other – a black sun in a late '70s pageant – the best Schumann ever found for this. The night engulfing the city in scene 1 and the tiny nude love-making couples – Maillol sculptures in miniature – on the erotically heaving green hills in scene 3[13] were equally grand trouvailles. It was an obscure show. As is

13. The first nudes in any show of Schumann's discrete expression of his belated '60s-style sexual liberation. Ashley, speaking of them and of nudes in the '70 Movement Papier Mache Cathedral:

'It was an explosion of, for me, saying, where are all these tits and asses coming from in

essential to art, in all three cases the symbolization was stirring and was rendered ambiguous by multiple reference: the giant's rage was that of any big, dumb deep-down resentful slob and also stood for the cataclysm of the final big bang. The nudity and the fucking were Carnal Life but also the lovingness of the land. The Night was cultural decline (including both city dirt and the violence of the time – '70 – when the Weathermen went underground), Negritude, and an expression of sympathy for lost humanity.

The play was not reviewed in New York. The two Toronto reviews of it I have seen when Konnoff took it there in August were fairly negative – unimpressive setting, childish.

---

his . . . he was creating a large number of naked ladies, all very voluptuous and all very much Elka Schumann, I assumed. It's the first time I remember them. And I remember that they all looked like – at that point, now, I'm saying to myself, he's fucking all of these young girls – or some of them – or one of them – or whatever – and yet he is making naked ladies that are all Elka Schumann. Huge bottoms, thighs, breasts – and obviously he had an eye for a nice young maiden.' — (Ashley, interview.)

6. The challenge of Coney Island. The need to be clear. Quickies for the masses and four great Black shows: *Lamentation, Mississippi* (March-June '70), *McLeod, Revenge of the Law* (July-September '72).

To fit into the local rhythm, the shows had to be brief. They were general-ly 10-15 or perhaps 20 minutes long. A show might be repeated a dozen or several dozen times daily over a weekend. Schumann sketched out ideas for a dozen or more of them, and at least half a dozen of these were developed into plays, but two of these plays (*The Grey Lady from Manhattan/The Grey Lady from the Island of Manhattan*[1] and *On an*

---

1. '*The Grey Lady from Manhattan*

The Grey Lady from the island of Manhattan

A grey lady lived on the island of Manhattan
And the sun dragon brought the sun to the
island of Manhattan.
And the sun dances around her house.
And in the morning the shepard brought
his sheep to the island of Manhattan
And the sheep grazed on the grey
ladies lawn.

. . .

And then all the neighbors of the grey
lady came by to say hello.

. . .

And a troubador with a dancing bear wandered
Over the island of Manhattan.

And they put on a dance for the
grey lady.

. . .

And then a dark cloud appeared in the
sky over the island of Manhattan.

And the dark cloud grew bigger
+ bigger.
And then the dark cloud covered up the
sun.

Island Far Away, or *The Speech of Super Professor*, a variant of *Speech²*),
were apparently never put on, at least not *The Grey Lady*. Of four that
were done, two were equally slight ones, *Marriage and Revenge of the*

> And then the troubador + the dancing
> bear went away from the island of
> Manhattan.
>
>   . . .
>
> And then the grey ladies neighbors
> said goodbye + left.
>
>   . . .
>
> and the Shepard & his sheep went
> away + were never seen again on
> the island of Manhattan.
>
>   . . .
>
> . And then the grey sky dragon appeared
> over the island of Manhattan.
>
>   . . .
>
> And then the grey sky dragon flew over
> the grey ladies house.
>
>   . . .
>
> And then the grey sky dragon
> flew away with the grey lady.'

Apparently he had in mind following this up with doing a whole series of 'Grey Lady from
Manhattan' plays, an idea later realized as the *Grey Lady Cantata* series. Essentially the
play, an anti-city play like *Difficult Life*, opposes the figure of a weeping lady to the deity
of amusement parks, the Laughing Lady.
2. In Act I, sir Moustache introduces the Professor to the TV audience. In Act II, the
Professor — speaking to a cheering seated audience of three or four, seated with their backs
to us, masks on the backs of their heads, in hats and 'outrageous' costumes 'if possible' —
enumerates the ills that 'a great number of our young people are concerned about' — pollution, lack of parks, inferior education, 'inadequate' health, 'alienation' between the races
and generations in 'our great cities' — and affirms that of all nations, this nation, being 'so
fortunate to be so rich' has the power and ability to do away with all these ills and others,
but that 'the quality of spirit that each one of us needs, that each one of us hungers for must
come from . . . the god of heaven' who will address them in a moment. In Act III, the god
(Uranus) appears, introduces a 'great favorite of us all', Mother Earth, he and she proceed
to flirt, dance with one another to some 'schmaltzy waltz', she feels sick, she is ('already')
going to give birth, the Great Warrior comes out of the Professor's stomach 'with a rope
for umbilical cord' (there is a doctor in attendance), shouting and slashing the air with
his sword, and takes the mike, 'I want this nation to be at peace and we shall be' (but a
placard simultaneously announces 'Unjust War'). I don't know what was to happen in
Act IV, except that the Great Warrior 'fights the elements and is swallowed by the
Great Green Dragon'. Irene Leherrissier gave or was to give the Professor's speech. Music
was or was to be provided by cello, drum and flute.

Statue of Liberty,[3] 'just a farce' (Schumann, interview, '79) and a fairy tale, *Tristan and Isolde*,[4] but the other two were beautiful shows, *Lamentation for Phillip Gibbs and James Green/killed in Mississippi May 14, 1970* (its title on the sidewalk billboard), and a slightly later show on the

---

3. Napoleon (played by one of the new French recruits, Claude Roche) is given birth by Uranos and Gaea, is chased out of Russia where he has killed the Grey Lady, but rebuilds his fortune by building the Statue of Liberty and selling her to an American millionaire, Mr. Schmaltz Sr. Installed in her place she equitably saves the lives of a shipwrecked immigrant, Mr. Everybody, and of Schmaltz Jr. who while on the beach with his mom has gotten into the water over his head. Jr. is so grateful he makes her his wife. Mr. Everybody, contrariwise, who on hitting the shores of the New World, changing masks, has turned black, has the bad grace to begin to feel ungrateful, and in fact conceives the dastardly plan to blow her up. She catches him in time, however, and vengefully decides to reveal her true identity. Her hubby helping her shed dress, breasts and torch, she stands revealed as the horrible Great Warrior (the Statue of Liberty, in fact, with her heavy, menacing, steel grey and spike-crowned head, looks a little like the Great Warrior), sword in hand. She proceeds to kill not only Mr. Everybody but the whole Schmaltz family as well. According to Kourilsky, '71, a sign 'Don't trust the Statue of Liberty' was circulated in the audience at the end of performances.

Robert S. Collier, a Negro, was convicted June 14, '65 with three others on charges of smuggling dynamite from Canada to New York as part of a plot to blow up the Statue of Liberty and other national shrines to 'dramatize the plight of Negroes.' he did 21 months in Lewisburg. After he got out he applied for a job as a city recreation officer, but the Parks Department in January '68 after a 'careful examination' determined that he was not 'qualified' (New York Times, January 13, '68). I at the time had the impression that he qualified.

4. A puzzler:

'. . . just a very slight lyrical movement piece with a tiny little bit of narration in it. Not more than one sentence, the whole thing, (not really) about' Tristan and Isolde, 'because I don't think it told any of their story.' — (Schumann, interview, '82.)

'. . . the classical love story about the guy who falls in love with this girl and then there's a tragic ending. Isolde was dressed all in white and she had a long dress that extended quite a way from her, and then a beast came and I think that was Tristan. There were love scenes where they would embrace. It was like almost an erotic thing. They were sort of loving each other. I thought that was nice. And then somehow there would be like a transformation thing. A king would come and ring a bell. Then they'd ride off on a little cart with the beast drawing them. It was like all of them were very quiet – blue light – and it was a very pretty piece.' — (Leherrissier, interview, '79.)

'It was *Tristan and Isolde* done Bread and Puppet style. It started out with a prologue in hell with the Red Man, and he sets up the Tristan and Isolde. I think (the prologue) was taken right out of *Faust* . . . abbreviated – Peter . . . looked that up . . . The Tree of Life was the main backdrop, and then it had (side) curtains, so you looked *into* – so there was a (contained) performance space. It really filled up the *space*, so it was very *pretty*, you know – a *lot* of paintings – a rich looking space. Blue. And so it was easy to frame things in there and light it so the shows were bright. *Tristan and Isolde* was this fairy story: started out in hell, and then there was a big birth scene done with a parachute and a baby carriage and with Isolde being pulled forward, and she's sitting on top of the baby carriage and parachutes are stretching out in all directions and there are beasts crawling there and pulling when she arrives next to them, with Carlene (Fernandez) playing a lot of fairy tale music. Probably the flute. We had flute players, toy piano players and we had a lot of musicians. The same mask that was used in *Dead Man Rises.* Then the witch or the Grey Lady puts a

86

same event, *Mississippi*. They also, still in '70, did *King Story* and *A Man Says Goodbye* (Konnoff, interview, '83), and probably still others, as the confused memories of *Tristan and Isolde* suggest, and with 'little bits of the circus' (Fernandez, interview, '83) that Schumann was working on, and that he may have briefly returned to Coney Island in July to work on with Konnoff, put on something listed in Kourilsky, '71 as *Bread and Dragon Circus*, a parade at the Bronx Zoo, with trumpets, kazoos, cymbals, bass drum and Dragon, in which Fernandez was Strong Man, 'stuck with muscles'.

*

Lamentation was Schumann's immediate response to the *New York Times* coverage, May 16th, of the killing in Jackson, Mississippi, two days before, of two young Negroes[5] by the highway patrol.[6] I imagine that,

---

curse or threw the curse on. Different people try to court or break or to reach her. That's where the dancing bear was in there, Axel (Gros) and the dancing bear tried to break the curse, and some machos tried to break the curse, and finally — who in hell broke the curse? It was the Great Warrior. Came out and wiped out the witch and *maybe* took the Great Warrior costume off — turned the witch into the pope, and then the pope turned around and married the two of them. It's vague to me how the curse was broken, but — (I: What *was* the curse?) Well . . . it wasn't a hundred years of sleep, but it *might* have been. Oh, it was more like a glass mountain, you know, it was like that. She couldn't be approached. (I: Was there a political point to the thing?) No. It was a fairy tale. It was well received. Short, like the others.' — (Konnoff, interview, '83.)

'Tristan was played by Claude Roche and he wore this mask that had a trumpet mouth and he mimed most of what he did and my flute was his voice . . . Isolde was poisoned by the witch and Tristan came and found her. There were some beasts in that show. They were like her watchdogs. I remember a glorious ending where everyone sang Gloria . . . And Bart Lane directed that much of the time.' — (Fernandez, interview, '83.)

5. 'The two youths — James Earl Green, a 17-year-old senior at Jim Hill High School in Jackson, and Phillip Lafayette Gibbs, a 21-year-old junior in prelaw studies at Jackson State — spent most of their days working or studying — and, friends said, had little time to be militant.

Young Mr. Green, a star miler on the track team, who hoped to go to college, worked six hours a day after school and most weekends in a grocery store for $12 a week plus tips to help support his widowed mother, three younger brothers and sisters.

Mr. Gibbs, who was born in the hard-scrabble hill town of Ripley, Miss., and received much of his education in Wisconsin, was married and had a son who will be 11 months old tomorrow. He was described as a fine student who had hoped to be a doctor until shortage of money made him switch to law.'

6. There had been some minor disturbances in Jackson involving students at the (Negro) Jackson State College on May 12th and 13th and the National Guard had moved in. On the 14th, according to the *New York Times* of the 15th, the police had 'battled protesters' — presumably student protesters against the Kent State slayings — 'on five other campuses', but there was no protest that Thursday in Jackson. But sometime in the morning of that day, some police officers had the impression they were being fired at from a women's dormitory on Lynch Street. The Highway Patrol responded by a barrage lasting some 7 to

given Schumann's probable sensitization by his Coney Island audience, the harmlessness of the victims provided the inspiration, but the disproportion of the public reaction in the U.S. to instances of the police and vigilante regime of terror that the American Negro has since Emancipation been subjected to for now over a century to the public reaction to the Kent State killings of May 4th[7] may also have gotten his arse. His first outrage translated into a non-narrative concatenation of symbolizations symbolizing essential aspects: the affectively essential aspects. Such a first reaction is apt to be vitiated by the normal drawback of the lack of intellectual control over immediate reactions, namely that one grabs for one's habitual forms and categories. A second reaction then may possibly be affectively both more effective and more adequate to the event, but is apt to be narrative, more closely descriptive, and thus further removed from the essential. *Lamentation* was that first, *Mississippi* this second reaction. (Schumann the following year had a similar two-beat response to the Attica event.) *Lamentation* thus, though it is about an instance of the State's repression of internal dissent from the war abroad, still has Schumann's focus of the '60s on that war: parallels the Jackson events with it.

Nobody remembers how *Lamentation* went, but there is a short account of it, probably by George Ashley, entitled *Earl Green, 17 and Phillip Gibbs, 21, shot in Mississippi*. It lists as puppets Uncle Fatso, five Negro woman puppets, three standing and two sitting, i.e. presumably, dummies, wearing the Vietnamese Woman masks from *Fire* painted black, three big Vietnamese Lady puppets, i.e. performers with the *Leaf* White Lady masks on top of their heads, a Big White Face and a Big Black Face, a Grey Lady with Tear,[8] a Negro Cleaning Lady, i.e. a performer dressed

---

12 seconds, from about 30 to 50 feet, using ammunition that kills deer at a hundred feet. All the windows were shattered. There were nine wounded besides those two killed. Green had been walking down the street in front of the Jackson State dormitory, Gibbs down it on the other side.

7. 'A planned walkout by students and teachers to protest the slaying of two Negroes at Jackson State College in Missippi forced the closing yesterday morning of George W. Wingate High School in Brooklyn as antiwar demonstrations and other protests continued at many schools here.

The slayings, which occurred on Thursday, came in the same week as the fatal shooting of six Negroes during disorders in Augusta, Ga., and gave rise to new demands by demonstrators and others that the Board of Education close all city schools for a day of mourning next week.

City schools were closed on May 8 in memory of the four students, all of them white, killed at Kent State University in Ohio and in a general protest against violence.

A Board of Education source said that the board would consider the new demands early next week. However, it is known that some of the five board members are of the opinion, or leaning toward the view, that the May 8 closing was intended to honor all victims of violence and that a second closing would serve no constructive purpose.' — (Leonard Buder, *School is Closed to Balk Walkout, New York Times*, May 16, '70.)

8. Schumann (interview, '79) calls *Lamentation* a 'solo Grey Lady show'. The Grey Lady mask differs from his dominant female figures of the '60s, the Vietnamese Women and

in black dress with a black mask, big celastic or paper maché hands and a broom, a group of Big Soldiers and a single Big Soldier, this one without a gun, a dancer in a black dress with a black mask and big hands, and three of the small 'Johnny puppet' soldiers.

Tin cans filled with nails, a violin, a cello, a little piano, presumably a toy piano, a bass guitar and cymbals are listed as musical instruments.

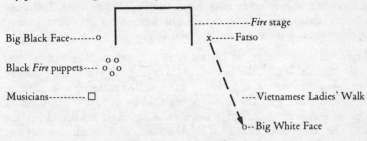

The 'Vietnamese Ladies' Walk' in Ashley's sketch pertains to the first of *Lamentation*'s three 'sequences', but otherwise the sketch seems to indicate setting and places for all three: a curtain or other division stage-right and another one, up-stage, stage-right, and next to this, center-stage at the rear, a smaller stage formed of three black curtains, with a fourth curtain (not indicated in the sketch) that may be opened or closed, at its front. The musicians are up-stage, stage-right, but otherwise placing seems by a simple left-right black-white symmetry, black stage-right, white stage-left, visual equivalent of the playlet's parallel between Vietnam and Jackson May 14th, a symmetry not broken but affirmed by the action in the inset box stage in the second or middle part of the sequence, the crying of the Grey Lady: she represents the suffering of mothers black or white.

(1) Light up on Uncle Fatso, smoking. Sun – probably Sara Peattie's Chinese lantern, cf. *Difficult Life* – in over the Black People as first part of text is read. The text probably was the May 16th *New York Times*

Ladies, by a lack of expression that, working out as sorrowing, makes her a figure representative of passively suffered suffering as a permanent state. *Lamentation* is apparently the first play in which she weeps, her tear a glass chandelier pendant slowly descending from her eye on a string. He conceived her as his counterpiece to the amusement park Laughing Lady:

'Die Arbeit an *Grey Lady Cantata (II)* begann damit, dass wir eines Tages über einem Laden in unserem Viertel eine weibliche Reklamefigur entdeckten, die ständig lächelte und durch Federn angetrieben, lächelnd auf und ab wippte. wir beschlossen, einen Zyklus von Stücken zu machen, in deren Mittelpunkt eine immer weinende graue Frauenfigur stehen sollte: Grey Lady war gekommen.' — (Schumann, interviewed by Gregor Laschen, *General-Anzeiger*, 22./23. Jan. '72.)

report, *Two Negro Students are Killed in Clash with Police in Jackson.* Fast rattling of the tin cans. The Vietnamese Ladies, probably roped together, their hands tied, either emerging from the wings just below Uncle Fatso or stationed there to begin with, are pulled down-stage toward the Big White Face stage-left. When they are about midway, the Black Cleaning Lady, coming out behind Uncle Fatso crosses to the Black People. She starts sweeping slowly when they reach the Big White Face. Light out over Uncle Fatso, sun's light out, bright light on Vietnamese Ladies. Cymbals and soft mallets. They die. She is sweeping.

(2) Light on in *Fire* stage, its curtain drawn. Single soldier without gun opens the curtain. Inside, the Grey Lady is crying. The three little Johnny soldiers cross the *Fire* stage, probably string-pulled rather than carried, in the light of a flashlight. The group of big soldiers crosses it (probably in the opposite direction), pulled on dollies. The single soldier closes the curtain. The action is accompanied by slow rattling of the tin cans, off and on. It concludes with reading of the remainder of the text.

(3) Light on in the sun over the black people. Cymbals, soft mallets as: the two standing black people are slowly taken down by the kneeling Black Cleaning Lady. 'O Mary Don't You Weep, Don't You Mourn' sung to violin, cello, bass guitar, toy piano. Words (?) come out of the Big (Black?) Face as the black dancer dances slowly.

Possibly afraid that the audience wasn't getting *Lamentation*, Schumann, still in '70, probably in June, replaced it by an adaptation of *A Man Says* to internal repression, *Mississippi*, a puppet play in seven scenes preceded by a short spoken text, a synopsis of the May 16th *New York Times* account,[9] with dialogue — not spoken by the operators of the respec-

---

9. 'A barrage of police gunfire left two dead and several wounded yesterday. All the casualties were black. The highway patrol refused to comment. The university was closed. James Gibbs, aged 17, worked six hours a day to help support his widowed mother and three brothers and sisters. Phillip Green was married and had a son who was nine months old the following week.'

Note the generalization resulting from the absence of specification of place and time, but also the retention of the 'black'.

'Oh that was done several ways. For a while there was a fellow working with us who would introduce it, this black story teller, O Shake A Leg. And then, I think, the way we did it most was, Irene, I think, or some person, clearly read it on the microphone, either in a blackout or a near blackout, so it was presented, that newspaper text was presented *cold*, – so I think, yeah, it was nearly very understandable, and also quoted as a piece of history or fact or newsprint. — (Konnoff, interview, '83.)

When Kourilsky saw it, it was preceded by the announcement, 'The show is dedicated to (est un hommage aux) two black students killed at Jackson State University May 14, 1970' – rather than by that generalized text.

When Munk (*TDR comment, Tulane Drama Review* '74) saw it, the reading of the text (which she does not mention) was preceded by an announcement 'This is not a spook show

tive puppets, but displayed on signs held up by 'an unmasked kneeling man who held up large strips of paper' (Munk, *TDR comment*, *TDR* #47), like the musicians in front of the stage, but on the other side, and also recited through microphone in a pseudo-operatic manner[10] by a male and a female speaker next to the musicians. The structural principle of the play is repetition: probably inspired by *Reiteration*, though in this play it serves not for punching home the moral demand (none is made) nor for the presentation of alternative responses, but — though equally also as a purely formal, rhythmic device — for the development of the exposition and for inclusion of complements: the needs of the mother, supplied by the son, are multiple, the agents of repression parrot its instigator, both the (white) dissenting student (Kent State!) and the black non-dissenting student (Jackson) are killed.

The Mother was done by a Grey Lady with Tear in a blue robe. The Son, the Teacher and the students (in Scene (4) the People) as well as the two men bringing the Mother her dead Son (puppet minus operator) were all done by the disciple puppets, the Son by a Negro one (in a red robe), the Teacher by one wearing a tophat and a sign 'teacher'. The soldier was the grey, spiked soldier puppet with the built in gun (Munk: 'a steely grey soldier whose mask is at once skull and helmet'). The play went as follows:

I) flute call
    doorbell
    mother: seated at a table covered   come in
    with a white table cloth — there
    is an extra chair, empty)
    son: good evening, mother
    mother: good evening, son

---

or a funny show, but a serious show in seven scenes. We are going to ask the children to keep quite.'
'Spook show' seems infelicitous.
10. '. . . murmuré, extrêmement lentement, les voyelles démesurement allongées, au point qu'il est rendu pratiquement incompréhensible. Les voix sont accompagnées par des sons doux, lancinants, provenant d'une sort de cor (qui n'est autre qu'un agitateur de machine à laver) et d'une flûte (un tuyau d'orgue) et par des coups tres sourds frappés sur la grosse caisse . . . la voix liberée du souci d'articuler clairement, exprime avec les instruments de musique le sous-texte, tout ce que cachent ces mots très ordinaires.' — (Kourilsky, '71.)
'. . . spoken over mike in a weird, drawn-out, incomprehensible way, accompanied by washing machine agitator, trumpet, creating muffled, hollow, unintelligible sounds.' — (Bread and Puppet script of *Mississippi*, in K. Taylor, *People's Theatre in America*.)
'The written dialogue is paralleled by large, slow gestures and by eery sounds from a washing machine agitator horn and an organ pipe flute; these are like the sorrowing behind ordinary words, made audible.' — (E. Munk, *TDR comment*, *TDR* #'47.)
Munk either missed the recitation or had forgotten it when she wrote up her account: suggesting to what extent it had a musical function.

son:	here are $5
mother:	thank you
son:	. . .
mother:	the rent is not paid
son:	I will go again
mother:	thank you
son:	good by, mother
mother:	good by, son

II) flute call
doorbell

mother:	come in
son:	good evening, mother
mother:	good evening, son
son:	here are $5 more
mother:	thank you
son:	. . .
mother:	the light is not paid
son:	I will go again
mother:	thank you
son:	good by, mother
mother:	good by, son

III) flute call
teacher and students file
in and sit down (on 6
chairs facing the teacher
seated on a 7th)

teacher:	what did you learn?
son:	I studied hard, I am tired.
teacher:	try again
son:	yes.
teacher	good

IV) president:

we have enemies far away.
they are bad. We will
go into their country
and shoot them

$\frac{1}{2}$ people:	yes
$\frac{1}{2}$ people:	no[11]

---

11. Scene 4 according to Munk:

'Uncle Fatso, monstrous, comes on. Booming noises. I AM THE PRESIDENT. Cymbals and drums. WE HAVE ENEMIES FAR AWAY, THEY ARE BAD, WE WILL GO INTO THEIR COUNTRY AND SHOOT THEM. Two groups of puppets have entered. Bowing slightly, the group on the left says NO, on the right, YES. Crashing noises.' — (Munk, *TDR comment, TDR #47*)

'Scene 4. La scène est vide.

Entre Uncle Fatso qui se place au centre, gesticulant dans tous les sens. Beaucoup de bruit. Cymbales. Grosse caisse. "Nous avons des ennemis au loin. Ils sont mauvais. Nous

V) soldier trembling	the president says we have enemies far away; they are bad; we will go into their country and shoot them
students:	no
soldier:	be quiet
students:	no
soldier shoots; one student falls[12]	
VI) enter soldier	
enter son	
son turns to go	
soldier shoots; son falls[13]	
VII) flute call	
doorbell	
mother:	come in
enter two men carrying son (empty son puppet)	
man I:	he is dead
man II:	he is dead
mother:	he is dead?
men:	yes
men exit	

---

irons dans leur pays et nous les tuerons." (Le texte est dit très vite au micro sans être montré sur les pancartes.) Entrent trois étudiants côté cour, trois étudiants côté jardin. Les uns disent "oui" les autres "non". Noir. — (Kourilsky, '71)

12. Scene 5 according to Munk:

'A steely gray soldier whose mask is at once skull and helmet marches in THE PRESIDENT SAYS WE HAVE ENEMIES FAR AWAY, THEY ARE BAD, WE WILL GO INTO THEIR COUNTRY AND SHOOT THEM. The students have entered, saying NO. BE QUIET. NO SHOOT. One hard sound made by a hatchet head hit with a rivet. The students bend forward gently, like reeds, and leave.' — (E. Munk, *TDR comment, TDR # 47*)

'Scene 5. Même dispositif que pour la scène 3.

A la place du professeur est assis le soldat. Entrent six étudiants (le fils ne fait pas partie du groupe). Ils s'asseoient sans s'incliner. "Le président dit: Nous avons des ennemis au loin. Ils sont mauvais. Nous irons dans leur pays et nous les tuerons."(Cette fois-ci le texte est montré sur les pancartes). "Non! – Taisez-vous! – Non! – Tirez!" Le soldat tire (bruit sec, métallique). Un étudiant au premier rang tombe lentement. Les cinq autres se penchent sur lui. Noir. Refrain.' — (Kourilsky, ibid.)

13. The end of scene 6 according to Munk:

'The son enters. The sound again. As he slowly goes down, his forehead touches the tip of the soldier's bayonet in a gesture of sacrifice and defeat. Dark.' — (E.Munk, ibid.)

'Scene 6. La scène est vide.

Le soldat est seul, debout, côté jardin. Entre le fils côté cour. Le soldat tire. Bruit sec, métallique. Le fils tombe. Noir. Musique douce, lancinante (flute et cor). Refrain. (From '*O Mary . . .*' according to Kourilsky there was a refrain also at the ends of scenes I and II.) — (Kourilsky, ibid.)

mother cries. crystal tear
slowly rolls down her face
toy piano:[14]

O Mary don't you weep,
don't you mourn.

Schumann with *Mississippi* achieved an extreme simplicity and clarity of
words and action, going beyond the simplicity and clarity of *A Man* even
and making the fullest use of what in these respects his street work of the
'60s had taught him, and did so by a sacrifice of the esoteric symbolism of
Lamentation (compare the killings in the two plays) and of its complexity
(parallelism of Jackson and Vietnam, the synthesizing image of the Grey
Lady, the actions of the Black Cleaning Lady): for the sake of coming
across to his Coney Island audience made the sacrifices I have quoted him
supra (Part V, section 2, September '72 draft of program notes for the
Coney Island Cycle) deploring.

So doing, he came up with a hit, the Coney Island audience responded
to *Mississippi*.[15] Though *Lamentation* had been a masterpiece, *Mississippi*

---

14. 'Flute. A bell. The mother is sitting at the table. COME IN. Two students bring in the
son's body, mask and robe empty on a pole. Low drumming. The robe is bright red against
the white and blue painted backcloth with its figure of the tree of life. HE IS DEAD? HE
IS DEAD. The body is laid on the table. The mother bows her head slightly above it.
There is a gleam on her cheek under her eye. A jewel tear very slowly falls from her eye
into the air between her face and the corpse. Turning, it is held by the light. Toy piano.
Silence ' — (E. Munk, ibid.)

'Scene 7. Meme dispositif que pour la scene 1, une chaise supplementaire cote cour. La
mere est assise pres de la table. Clochette. "Entrez" '. — (Kourilsky, ibid.)

15. 'I remember scenes from that show, it was very quiet and it was a wonderful thing we
did that summer. We performed *Mississippi* on the 4th of July in 1970 — I think 26 times
in all ... It was a very short little piece but it was very clear and succinct. Coney Island
was going wild on that 4th of July, but inside that theatre ... there was a realm of solemn,
very quiet, people would cry during the show. And then you would go outside again and it
was like (makes noises). (I: Black people?) I would say mostly. Very few white people go
to Coney Island, even then.' — (Leherrissier, interview, '79.)

'It knocked people out. I loved that. It made the people coming in with their cotton
candy off the boardwalk, quiet. It actually stopped them from talking ... But when was
the last time that you were truly moved by something that Schumann did? I think the last
time was in Coney Island when he did *Mississippi* and I was observing — and there again it
was a feeling of being removed — I was watching the fact that he could dominate the feelings of these people who came in from the street, who knew nothing about what they were
going to be seeing — a television generation of children and adults who were eating hotdogs, and he stopped them from talking. A very brief piece, but nevertheless he did stop
them. So I — but even so, I wasn't caught up in it, I was observing the reactions of others.'
— (Ashley, interview, May '82.)

On Coney Island reactions generally:

'They were very positive. I mean, we did get in fights but we were in a very good
position to — when we did things like *A Man Says*, you know, people would sometimes
verbally attack us ... but that was really always very easy to deal with. When we did
things like *King Story* inside, we'd often get people who would relate to the puppets, you
know, run in crazed or drunk or both, just, you know, respond very strongly, get involved

94

also was one, and in fact in spite of its simplicity and clarity retained the artistic opulence, the mystique and the sacral-ritual reverberations of its predecessor: by the stateliness and grandeur of its puppets, by the rhythm of its repetitions, and by the musical doubling of the sign-displayed speech. This mystic and aesthetic opulence, for the one brief moment of Schumann's production marked by *Mississippi*, balanced by simplicity and clarity, was to take over during his Cate Farm period (as it already had in *Difficult Life*) at the expense of simplicity and clarity. His masks and shows became beautiful and obscure.

I would say that a good many among Schumann's devotees of the '60s — but how many were there of these? a few hundred people? a few dozen? nothing like the followings of the great popular musicians, even the esoteric ones, or film actors and actresses, or even film directors, ballet and theatre stars — came to feel that the last of his New York productions, *Cry, Mississippi, Uncle Fatso*, were also his last great theatre pieces, the last to equal, or almost to equal *Fire, A Man Says Goodbye, Dead Man Rises*. These people are apt to be New Yorkers and to have been, during the '60s, in or close to the Peace Movement, or at least pacifists and/or 'philosophically' anarchists and vaguely leftish, so their judgment is apt to be clouded by nostalgia and resentment at Schumann's leaving New York. Still: they had been moved by the clarity, directness and power of the moral stance of his work of the '60s in a way no subsequent work of his moved them, and felt that this was indistinguishably effect of content and form, and so regretted not only a loss of message and stance, but of artistic quality as well.

'(I: You haven't been truly moved by anything Schumann has done since?) In several years. (I: In several years. The pageants, no?) The pageants are — yes — the pageants are moving, they're beautiful. But they're almost a given. That if you're outdoors with 10,000 people and you're at dusk and there are green mountains around you and the blue sky and clouds and a sunset and music sounds in a certain way outside and the deer come through the forest and there's huge pyres and 28-foot puppets and — who could not be moved? They're wonderful. But in structuring — content — in a discernable way of dealing with material. There have been interesting works. *The Story of One Who Set Out to Study Fear*

. . . In the shows where we were asking for silence, we quite amazingly in some ways, *got* it. Which I think, the length and the concentration helped that a lot.' — (Konnoff, interview, '83.)

Schumann dropped *Mississippi* after its spring of '70 showings in Coney Island, but then took it along on his winter '71/'72 tour to Europe. At some of the presentations of it there, the falling teardrop was illuminated with a flash light, adding to the abstraction provided by puppeteering a pseudo-narrative ('the mother cries') gesture of 'monstration'. Its reception in Europe was mixed, but e.g. the reporter from the Kölmer Stadtanzeiger (January 19, '72) thought of the Bonn performance 'Ergreifenderes auf der Bühne ist kaum denkbar.'

was an interesting kind of thing. But when was the last that you were truly moved by something that Schumann did? I think the last time was in Coney Island when he did *Mississippi*. (I: What has changed in his work or what is gone? What is the element that did move you previously?) Well, that comes back to what is his art and what makes him totally extraordinary. It's very hard — I can't think of a way of expressing it. I mean, the man who made something so absolutely clear and simple as *Dead Man Rises* or *Fire* or *A Man Says Goodbye*, is not the man who's making — well, it's true, none of them used any kind of scenery, proscenium — anything. They had a clamp-on light or a flashlight — a light that was held over the character — others are a little more sophisticated, they don't seem to work as well. (I: *Simple Light*, for instance, you thought was less powerful than the previous things. *Cry of the People*, you thought, was still a huge success.) Oh, that was a huge, monumental work. Yes, I loved it. (I: Artistic success — and moving.) Complete in every way. (I: But what is it that sold you on him, that attached you, that pulled you in?) I don't know — you remember the *Johnny Comes Marching Home*, when he used for the first time the strobe light, which was already, by that time, fairly exhausted as a device — nevertheless, that was a powerful piece. (I: If it was not the political or message, per se — because *Dead Man Rises* does not have one, does it?) No, it doesn't have. I suppose it has some kind of Christian message that I wouldn't recognize . . . I think maybe you've got two good words. Intensity, which at times would reach ferocity — as with Margo being shot down; as in the *Chair* piece where it was unrelenting, the driving of those chairs, beating on the floor. (I: Ferocity is the word that you used here — to intensify intensity. So: "as though a ferocity had gone out of the man.") Has gone. At some point. Maybe then. Maybe at that point, after that — after going up to Vermont. Why does he live there? It's so terrible'. — (Ashley, interview, May '82.)

When in scene 1 of *Uncle Fatso* we see demonstrating crowds, of Blacks and others, swallowed up by a huge black face, we are seeing Schumann put outside of himself what he had been a part of: he may have thought he was saying goodbye to the City, but he was saying goodbye to his participation in life. He returned to being an outsider. In the city he belonged as much as anyone can belong in a city. When during the later '70s people around Glover and in Vermont 'accepted' him, they accepted him as an institution. Not as a neighbor.

Schumann's next and last three Coney Island pieces were made for the summer of '72:[16] two good Black pieces, longer than the earlier ones,

---

16. 'When we got back to Cate Farm (from the touring of *Stations* (SSB)), Coney Island problems were waiting for us. Bart and Brigitte Lane had run children's workshops there since 1970, both in our Nathan's hotdog theater and in Coney Island Hospital (they also did big puppet parades in New York City and Harrisburg, Pa. for the Catonsville 9). Now a crew from Cate Farm was ready to take over and do a summer's work of short pieces for which no advertising was needed but rather a band, a barker and an open door. This year's program included *Harvey McLeod, Revenge of the Law* and *St. George the Dragonkiller*. After showing these new pieces at Goddard, we started in Coney Island in July, ended in September, then took the plays to the Public Theater and later to a few other

lasting about thirty minutes, *Revenge of the Law, Harvey McLeod (An American Tragedy in Eight Acts: The Story of Harvey McLeod)*, and a silly ecological piece, *St. George the Dragonkiller.*[17]

Harvey McLeod was 'based on the murder of four persons and the wounding of seven others in a Raleigh, N.C. shopping center (in) May (of 1971), by a janitor named Harvey Glenn McLeod, who then took his own life' (*New York Times*, September 6, '72), or, as Schumann puts it, was 'about a black man who went crazy and shot a lot of people. Somebody who was unemployed and went crazy'. (Schumann, interview, '79.)

'came together pretty easily and quickly. We decided to build a marionette stage and we wanted to go to Coney Island, and we wanted to do shows that were — addressed politics and dealings, and somebody came up to — on a rehearsal, because we still had this experience with newspaper stories — quickly enough, we were talking, Peter decided to do this man's story, and, very *quickly*, because we had actually *more* help, and we had a lot of people to rehearse the show and a lot of people with talent to put into it, built these almost cartoon picture show characters, a little bigger than life size, limited in gesture, moved somewhat by marionette work, because the idea was that we thought that in Coney Island we would

---

places in New York State.' — (Schumann, Newsletter, *Bread & Rosebuds*, November '72.)

'All three are 20 minute pieces, which lend themselves to be played Coney Island style, at intervals all afternoon long, introduced by a barker and a musical band, playing out front in the street until a crowd is collected and then the play can start. They will continue through Labor Day weekend.' — (From an accounting intended for Goddard students and faculty by Schumann of Bread and Pupper Theatre activities. Probably written during the summer of '72. Bread and Puppet Theatre files.)

The two Black pieces, together with *Hallelujah* instead of *St. George*, under the collective title *The Coney Island Cycle* had a brief run in New York City, at Papp's place in September, were shown at Goddard October 7, and in Ithaca, Utica and Cobbleskill, New York, October 11, 12 and 14. These were the last showings of *McLeod*, I believe, but *Revenge*, revised, was done in the States and in Europe in '73, cf. infra.

17. The king's daughter is about to be sacrificed to the land-devastating dragon when a simple man of the people, St. George, decides he is tired of the dragon's air- and water-pollution (and chicken stealing) and ups and fights and kills him, making king and people happy, getting rid of pollution and winning the princess' hand. The Great Warrior as Savior.

'It didn't work. We wound up almost with that conclusion. I think we wanted to do a fairy tale because (like) the *Tristan and Isolde* it filled a need for us and the audience, and we tried to rehearse *Saint George* down there, we didn't really build — we built the other two shows in Vermont, and we were just going to build the fairy tale with these people (the Lanes and others down in Coney Island (SSB)), and work with them. There wasn't enough time, or — it just wasn't happening, so we never did do it — I mean we *tried* to do it a couple times, but — we tried to re-rehearse it (for Papp's place in the fall (SSB)) — we got Joe Papp to book it, and the idea was that we would try to do *Saint George* again, with *puppeteers* now, you know, and wound up doing *Hallelujah*. It's just a title and not a show.' — (Konnoff, interview, '83.)

We note that Konnoff didn't consider the Coney Island people *puppeteers*.

have *less* people and would do more movement, we would like to get away from more people, but still have more *movement*. I did the narration of the text that Peter wrote, that drew or pointed to the fact that this fellow was being sent down this road. He had blackouts, which we played on a tin horn, and had a lousy time at work, a lousy time, period, and he just burst and got shot. That was the end. It was *not* in contrast to *Revenge of the Law*, which is in the same frame and looks a lot alike and even uses quite a few of the same puppets. It was much more left open to however you want to look at this situation. Blame him or blame these workers or blame who? Which is I think a point that we were even feeling or kicking around a bit at that time. These occurrences happening that were horrible and senseless, but — if you just read them, and then you buy the next paper and you see it the next day, and to do something theatrical with it. Or to make a show with it. It was what we decided to do. And *that* — *because* of those reasons — was received in Coney Island — It was a much different season (from the 1970 one (SB)), without this big gipsy band of performers which we had in the past, which just generated, in a way, a different kind of excitement. It was much easier to get audiences the first year at Coney Island than the second. It (*McCloud* (SSB)) was not as clear to them (as) *Revenge of the Law*.' — (Konnoff, interview, '83.)

I.e. the black audiences in Coney Island didn't much go for *McCloud*: whereas *Revenge* had strong responses, positive and negative. They didn't know how to take it. That in some way it might relate to the murders of Malcolm X, King, the Kennedys did not occur to them. It wasn't apt to occur to any spectator.

'It was done on a framed proscenium stage with a bridge — it was built from our puppet boxes so that a bridge could be spanned across the stage — it was framed on the sides and (that made a) fairly small stage, and the puppets were early bulb-heads — heads that were sitting on the shoulders of the operators — there was a black man and his wife and a doctor and a grocery store owner, from whom he bought the gun, and a boss, and very strikingly different backdrops for each scene. There was a scene at home with his wife, which said that he didn't have a job — and a second scene in his job — no, it must have been the other way around — one on the job and then he loses the job in a boiler room — that was what that boiler room was painted for — and then a job — running home because his wife was having a baby and the baby died; the doctor came too late, something like that. And then, some kind of desperation scene of himself alone and then, when he goes to a grocery store, buys himself a gun — but in a very easy manner, like buying cheese — and then, a shoot-out scene in the street with a backdrop that had cars and street crowds and houses and in front everything was done with tiny little puppets and he just came in shortly, as this sort of a giant, compared to the little people — and then a banging and a tipping over of all those little puppets . . . In style it's like the *Revenge of the Law* show . . . Oh, (and it) also had a dog in it. He always was sitting there with this dog — funny dog on strings, operated from the bridge. (I: What was the bridge for, by the way, for those puppets?) For the dog . . . And probably for the shooting scene — puppets on strings that then flew off.' — (Schumann, interview, August '82.)

98

'HARVEY McLEOD
A TRAGEDY IN 8 SCENES

'a gunman fired repeatedly into a crowd at a suburban Releigh shopping center today, killing 3 shoppers and wounding 8 others before killing himself with the weapon'

New York Times, May 29, '72.

Scene 1 (home)

Harvey: No nature, just garbadge. Birds fly away and grandma dies. I am 22, but my head is old like a rock. Go away dogs. Leave me alone.
Mother: Hi, little man, go to work.
Harvey: Work is bad.
Mother: No
Harvey: Yes

Scene 2 (school)

Harvey: I'll sit in my job all day long. I hate it. I don't like it. I hate it.

Scene 3 (home)

Harvey: This is my wife
Wife: I am his wife
Harvey: We live in Raleigh
Wife: And we will have a child
Harvey: I will get the doctor.
Wife: (sings) I am alone
              I am alone
              I am not here
              I am not there
              I am in America
              O my feet have walked from the ocean
              O my feet have walked from the ocean
              The sun stops now
              And the moon looks fine
              And my child will be born in the eveningtime
              Oh ah ah ah ah ah ah!
   (drums)
Harvey: Where is the child?
Wife: It is dead
Doctor: Yes.
Harvey: Oh!

Scene 4 (street)

Friend: You are wrong
Harvey: No
Friend: Really, you are wrong.
Harvey: No, I am right
Friend: Ha! ha! ha!
Harvey: (pulls knife)
Police: Off to jail Mister

Harvey: . . .

Scene 6 (store)

Customer 1: Butter please
Storekeeper: Yes
Customer 2: Raisins please
Storekeeper: Yes
Harvey: I want a gun
Storekeeper: Yes

Scene 7 (street)

Harvey: Leave me alone dogs
   Leave me alone
Shoppers: Good morning Mr.
   Good morning Miss
   How are you?
   How are you?
   Good morning
   good morning
   good morning
   good morning
   goodbye.
    (Boom! Boom! Boom!)
    (People fall, then Harvey shoots
    himself, Police arrive)'
    (Bread and Puppet script of *Harvey McLeod, A Tragedy in 8 Scenes.*)
 'The *Harvey McCloud* and *The Revenge of the Law* shows were not a happy find for me — even Elka didn't like them — and that was, for the first time I did a dialogue play and I wrote the dialogue. And I put it into a band — there was a little outside band, very different from bands we had before — that also did the announcements in between scenes and did the dialogue for the puppets on stage, in a way that I hadn't done before. Very concise little dialogues inside each scene, contrasted with sort of singy announcements in between the scenes. And for me that was a real find and I wanted to use that style and make many shows like that — which I didn't succeed to do — it was just a couple of shows. And then *Joan of Arc* was again a little bit like that. But other shows that came were not like that at all. Like *Grey Lady Cantatas* were very different.'

On Coney Island and at Papp's place, Schumann played electric fiddle in

---

18. '. . . the Bread and Puppet seems to have a hard time figuring out how to make the most of its magnificent puppets in a theatrical context. The best scene . . . has no dialogue at all. "Act V — jail", says the narrator. There are slow drumbeats and the curtains part, revealing Harvey sitting in his cell facing us. He slowly looks around, then bows his head, and the curtains close. The scene works because it simply lets us see, without interference, the magnificent image of grief that is the Harvey McLeod puppet. But even so, its effectiveness is limited, because we have already been looking at this image during four previous scenes when there was little else to look at.' — (J. Novick, *Theatre. Childlike, but not a dummy, Village Voice*, September 14, '72.)

the band, 'three musicians, two of whom wear battered looking tophats' (Novick, *Village Voice*), and mostly announced the scenes. Konnoff did the dialogue, sometimes announced the scenes also.

The Coney Island '72 *Revenge of the Law* was Schumann's second treatment of the event:

'Forty-three citizens of New York State died at Attica Correctional Facility between September 9 and 13, 1971. Thirty-nine of that number were killed and more than 80 others were wounded by gunfire during the 15 minutes it took the State Police to retake the prison on September 13. With the exception of Indian massacres in the late 19th century, the State Police assault which ended the four day prison uprising was the bloodiest one-day encounter between Americans since the Civil War.'

(Preface, *The Official Report of the New York State Special Commission on Attica*.)

A good many of the guards and civilian employees taken hostage were injured by the prisoners — two or three died of these injuries or were killed outright. One or two of the prisoners were killed by other prisoners. 54.2% of the inmates were Negroes as of September 9th, 8.7% were Puerto Ricans. But the uprising was a Black affair.

Neither the uprising nor its bloody repression seem to me in the normal course of events to have been avoidable, though perhaps the uprising could have occurred elsewhere or slightly later or earlier. What made the negotiations with the rebels virtually hopeless was the ultimately non-negotiable issue of amnesty and the fact that the prisoners had no collective decision-making procedure for arriving at a single set of demands or accepting any compromise on them. Conceivably, with better will from the authorities, the rebels could have been tricked into surrender — divided and defrauded. The liberal deploring of the event and of Rockefeller's refusal to 'go to Attica' comes down to regret at violence instead of deception having been used. The uprising and its repression ended the Black Liberation Movement of the '60s.

Most every society so far devised produces a substantial body of persons living in misery or near it. A significant number of this class are apt to engage in crimes of violence and in the limited categories of crimes violating property rights that their disadvantaged condition enables them to undertake. Terrorism is indispensible for containing this crime at a culturally tolerable level. Incarceration under near-intolerable conditions is a necessary part of this terrorism. The crime cannot be eliminated unless the misery is. Whether the misery can be eliminated, I don't know: it seems doubtful to me. Given the crime, the terrorism is indispensible. It does not seem desirable to me that either should disappear while misery persists: the crime is a manifestation of spirit, the terrorism is necessary to contain it.

What shocked Schumann was the unanswered cry from the lower

101

depths. He saw the insurrection as a drumming — an alarm. He saw it as an appeal for help. And he saw this appeal answered by a wiping of the Blacks off the sheets of accounting.

He immediately[19] got up a show, a 'happening', and under the title *Attica* put it on at the little theatre he had fixed up in the Cate Farm barn on September 16th,[20] three days after the prison had been retaken (an

---

19. 'The day after Attica. We made (*Whitewashing*) right the next day and performed at Goddard that same evening ... The heads may have been made that day, because I remember that the heads were done just like this (snaps fingers). Chris (Hartmann) and Axel (Gros) were very fast with celastic ... A few days after Attica happened, we made the things for *Attica* and we performed it at Goddard.' — (Schumann, interview, '79.)

20. 'Attica, the Bread and Puppet production based on the Attica State Prison massacre, was performed September 16 at the Haybarn Theatre.

As in all Bread and Puppet productions, the imaginative beauty of the masks permeated the setting of the play. They were visually arresting enough to hold the audience's attention quite a while, but not by any means enough to overcome the lagging tempo. The 10:30 P.M. choice of time contributed to the number of nodding students that could be seen.

On coming out of the theatre, the same response could be heard again and again, "too long ... too played out ... O.K. so-you-know-they're-hanging-out-the-linen-they-don't-have-to-do-it-for-fifteen-minutes" kind of thing.

The non-verbal tempo of the piece ... that total absorption of every gesture, complete unto itself, was just not made accessible enough to the majority of the audience. The frequent interruptions of people coming in late and the stage door being opened and closed by an uncostumed assistant took its toll in boredom and restlessness.

As the play was about the recent massacre at Attica State Prison, they obviously couldn't have had more than a few days to put it together; and it showed. The force that managed to survive the dragging pace is evidence enough of the potential of the piece. The nature of the deaths was aptly conveyed by the draping of the bodies, the staining of the shrouds with the blood-red reality of violence, pain, and terror, the not-quite-successful attempt at whitewashing our consciences of it, and the sharing of the karma that the unknowing audience partook of when eating the bread. If the tempo of the play had been speeded up, the impact of this context would surely have been made more immediate ... especially to a late night crowd of played-out Goddard students.

The hazily delineated ending was in grand B and P style. You're just left looking at the stage knowing somehow that there's nothing more to be resolved, and with what came before withering itself away back into your consciousness.' — (Chris Kadison, *Attica, The Paper*, Goddard, September '71.)

'The Space Patrol, a drug rescue service of the Environmental Center, has been started again this year at Goddard. The student Space Patrol will be working with the college's doctor, nurses and an ambulance service.

There was an organizational meeting in the library on September 17, Billy Copeland from the Montpelier Crises Center will speak at the library well on September 27 at 3:00.

Mark Adams, the organizer of the Space Patrol, hopes to get enough people interested in the drug situation. If enough people join, says Mark, there could be a person on duty in each campus every night to assist anyone having drug induced problems.

The aim of the Space Patrol is not to take the bummed-out person to a hospital where he could be hassled, but to talk with him and try to relieve his anxiety.

Concerning other drugs, Mark commented, "The community needs to develop a con-sciousness about heroin."

Mark also related some sound tips concerning drug dealing: "This is a warning to people dealing drugs — only two people from Goddard were busted last year — and it's

event the most disgusting part of which was the wholesale systematic beating of the subdued Negroes by sheriff's deputies and by the guards[21]). In October (October 1-14), now under the title *The Whitewashing of the Dirty Sheets of Attica*, he took this first version with other plays on a tour (arranged by NYSCA) of N.Y. State college campuses.[22] This was his

---

important not to deal to people outside Goddard." ' — (Jay Onady, *Space Patrol Soars Again, The Paper*, September '71.)

21. E.g.:

'National Guardsmen in the yard to evacuate the wounded testified they saw correction officers, troopers and sherriff's deputies strike inmates with nightsticks during the strip searching. One guardsman said that as he helped carry out an inmate who had been shot in the groin several troopers came over and hit the inmate with nightsticks. The inmate screamed in pain, the guardsman recalled, and a trooper responded: "Fuck you, nigger. You should have gotten it in the head." ' (*The Official Report of the New York State Special Commission on Attica*, '72.)

22.'. . . even though we took *Birdcatcher* along, the reason – the first reason for (the tour) was *Attica*.' — (Schumann, interview, '79.)

'And then after that, there was a New York State tour, a horrible New York State tour. We consider as the low point . . . anybody ever having a bad time on a tour, we always compare it to the New York State tour. Is it as bad as that, or worse? One night stands in all those different colleges in New York State. Staying in motels, eating junk food, performing very often in places and colleges where they were not at all interested.' — (Sherman, interview, '79.)

I have quoted Schumann supra on his shock by his student audiences' unawareness and indifference as manifested by their unwillingness to participate in the happening or to discuss the event. The participation was called for on a handbill:

'WHITEWASHING OF THE DIRTY SHEETS OF ATTICA
(an event for audience participation)

WE NEED: 1) TO REPRESENT THE DEAD BODIES OF ATTICA:
42 UNIDENTIFIED MALES TO LIE ON THE FLOOR FOR THE DURATION OF THE PIECE, ASSUMING ONE POSITION AND NOT CHANGING IT DURING THIS TIME

2) TO REPRESENT THE GENTLEMEN OF ATTICA (politics, corruption, efficiency) 10 PEOPLE TO DO THE WHITE-WASHING

3) TO REPRESENT THE BEASTS OF ATTICA (blood and guns): 8 PEOPLE

4) TO REPRESENT THE FAMILIES OF THE DEAD: AS MANY WOMEN AS POSSIBLE.'

(Program for NYSC tour, October 1971.)

Konnoff didn't think the reaction was that bad; but he identified the play's effect as catharsis:

'I think it was mixed. I think some places weren't much better, but what was *asked* was to have as many people as possible lay down in the *lobby* or wherever we were *doing* it or out*side*, and some places a lot of people *did* that. And some places, they were more hesitant, but it was a celebration of this event. I don't know how you would expect them to react a week afterwards. It was more like a church service or a burial. I was – I felt good doing it and I didn't feel that there was any like real adverse lack of or, you know, or heckling or

third topical work after *Lamentation/Mississippi* and the 2nd version of *Birdcatcher*: theatre, that unlike *Fire*, which was merely occasioned by a current event, and unlike *Speech/Chairs*, which merely used one, had a current event for its subject matter, a turn of his theatre not to the topical, but to the representational: relatively non-topical plays of the period like *Difficult Life* and *Emilia* differed in the same way from *When Johnny Comes Marching Home*, and *Grey Lady Cantata II* from the *Bach Cantata #140*.

'. . . it consisted of a bunch of ugly oversized janitors with bulbheads dirtying white sheets with blood, ketchup, and washing them out and hanging them up. But there was more to it – I can't describe it.'   (Schumann, interview, '79.)

As in the case of *Lamentation/Mississippi*, this first reaction was followed by a second, again perhaps because the first one hadn't been effective. Sometime in '71 still, he wrote the more descriptively narrative *Revenge of the Law*, put the show together in the spring or early summer of '72 on Cate Farm and played it at Coney Island July-September, and still in September, introduced by 42 stark portraits of black men done by Schumann, Rockefeller's victims, hung in the lobby at Papp's place.

'Ladies and gentlemen:
   We now present to you our tragedy in 9 short acts *"revenge of the law"*, conceived from newspaper reports or events in the year of our Lord 1971.

First act: *the governor's office*

Act 1

governor: good afternoon! This is a good country, it's not a bad country. Bring me a cup of coffee please! (Please notice that I said please)
witch: (coffee)
governor: I am a good governor. Everything is fine
(knock, knock) Hello, come in!
mailman: hello, I am the mailman. It's raining outside.
governor: still, it's a nice country.
mailman: certainly
governor: a letter from my wife!
mailman: yes, indeed.
governor: thank you, I am quite happy and I see that everything is fine. There are a few problems in our country, but else everything is fine.

curtain

---

being impassive, it was just a matter of a bit of maybe nervousness or some people maybe didn't want to *lay* down in their clothes, I don't know. But in all, talking to people, after the show, when we performed, it was – you know, it was important to *them*, you know, and they were affected by it, and they really felt they got some emotional feeling, or something that you *do*, other than – I think the first reaction was to run down the street and trash things, like they did in New York a bit.' — (Konnoff, interview, '83.)

In Act 1 you saw the governor in his office, you witnessed the arrival of his daily mail, and you learned that he lives in a good country, and that everything is fine.

Now in the 2nd Act we take you to cellblock 1, in a prison of the same country.

Act 2

prisoner 1: I am cold!
guard: you are bad, that's why you are cold!
prisoner 2: I am hungry!
guard: you are bad, that's why you are hungry!
prisoner 3: I can't sleep!
guard: That's because you are bad!
prisoner 1: Don't push me!
guard: Yes, I push you!
prisoner 2: Don't kick me!
guard: Yes, I kick you!
prisoner 3: Leave me alone!
guard: No!
voice: Telephone!
guard: For me?
voice: Yes!
chorus of prisoners: no more, no, no, no, no more, no, no, no more, fight back, fight, no, no, no, no, no more, no.

curtain

In Act 2 we showed you the prisoner's hunger and cold and sleeplessness and the guard's righteousness, and you noticed, that the guard received an important telephone call, and you heard the prisoners shouting.

Act 3 is again in cellblock 1, in the same prison.

Act 3

prisoner 1: you fight with a gun and I fight with a spoon (he knocks down guard). Now I have the gun, and you take the spoon.

curtain

In Act 3 you saw the fight of the gun and the spoon. You saw how the gun was defeated and how the spoon was victorious.

In Act 4 we will be back in the governor's offices.

Act 4

mailman: Your highness, it is very dangerous, they took hostages, they will kill them, they want to see you, they want to talk to you.
governor: No, no, I will not go.
mailman: You will not go?
governor: I will not go!
mailman: What shall be done?
governor: shoot them!
mailman: shoot them?
governor: Yes, shoot them.

curtain

In Act 4 you heard the latest news development, as reported by the mailman, and the governor's reaction, and his decision to shoot.

Act 5 takes place in front of the prison, in the street.

Act 5

people: (loud) shsht!
national guard: (steps in)
woman: please do not shoot!
national guard: we have to!
woman: no!
people: no!
national guard: (exits) shoot!

curtain

In Act 5 we presented to you the people in the street and the national guard. You heard a woman's plea and gunshots in the distance.

Act 6 will be back in cellblock 1, in the same prison.

Act 6

(prisoners falling, gunshots)

curtain

In Act 6 you heard gunshots and you saw prisoners falling. Now, in Act 7 we will be back in the prison again.

Act 7

(Black angel covers body of dead prisoner with white sheet. Witch brings bowl of blood, beast smears blood on sheet.)

curtain

In Act 7 the prisoners were dead and the Black angel visited them, and the dragon of revenge smeared them with blood.

Now in Act 8 we will be back in the governor's office.

Act 8

Mailman: the prisoners are dead, the hostages are dead, the throats of the hostages have not been cut. 42 men have been killed by the guns of the national guard. The families of the dead cry and moan.
governor: They broke the law, that's why they died. I am the governor, I will conduct an investigation to find out the truth, and the truth will say, that I am right. send condolences to the families of the hostages who died.
mailman: yes.
governor: send flowers, also.
mailman: Yes.

curtain

In Act 8 you heard the mailman's report, and the governor's announcement of an investigation.

Act 9 takes place in the home of one of the dead prisoners.

Act 9

Black angel: (leaves)
woman with dead body: (sits)
chorus: wake up dead, wake up, wake up, wake up,
   wake up dead, wake up, wake up, wake up,
   wake up, wake up dead, wake up.

light and curtain

This is the end of our short tragedy in 9 Acts *revenge of the law.* We thank you for your patience, and ask you to remember the prisoners who died, and the prisoners who survived.'

(Peter Schumann, *Revenge of the Law.*)

Rockefeller was a legless dummy seated on an office chair, string-operated from a bridge. The Coney Island audiences,

'. . . whether on one side of the fence or the other would react very strongly, would sometimes leave during the show, or would really get on this puppet of Rockefeller, would use this to vent some of their spleen.'

(Konnoff, interview, '83.)

"Revenge of the Law," an eight-act play by the Bread and Puppet Theater, is an eight-panel tragic-strip — a sequence of pictures framed in a box set. Wearing bulbous masks, the actors may look like cartoon figures (there are also a few people-size puppets on strings), but the play they are performing is as earnest and as mournful as a dirge.

Dialogue is sparse and mostly spoken by a narrator. Bread and Puppet is not a theater of words, but of images. The sentiments are basic. Things are "good" or "bad" with no middle ground of ambiguity.

"Revenge of the Law," one of three pieces in "Coney Island Cycle," which Bread and Puppet is presenting through Sunday in Joseph Papp's Public Theater, is a stark reminder of Attica — a conscience-struck primer lesson.

A puppet labeled The Governor, his face as expressionless as a slab of granite, sits complacently in his office and ignores the violence around him. Forty-three men die "by the gun of the National Guard," and the Governor intones in slow-emotion, "They broke the law. That's why they died." If it were performed on the steps of a real governor's office, this drama might be an incitement to rebellion. In Martinson Hall — converted for the occasion into an adult puppet theater — the work seems somewhat removed from reality, but it is still jolting.'

(Mel Gussow, *Theater: Bread and Puppet Troupe,*
New York Times, September 17, '72.)

Both Novick at the *Village Voice* and Gussow at the *Times* found it boring:

'Well? Of course the Bread and Puppet Theatre is amateurish and childlike. To be amateurish and childlike is the basis of its aesthetic. This is evidently what these people *are* — this is what gives their work its integrity, its consistency, its strange purity. And it is unfair to characterize them by quoting from their dialogue: they are not essentially a verbal theatre, they are a *puppet* theatre. A few of

107

the characters in their current program are life-sized puppets dangling on wires; most of them are live actors inside immense molded headpieces. The voices of the puppets come from a narrator, sitting at the side of the stage and speaking through a microphone. These large, stiff, ponderous creatures, with their unchanging expressions, encourage — practically demand — a slow tempo and a simplicity of utterance. And some of these puppets, in their grim way, are beautiful: they have a primitive grandeur, an Easter Island magnificence.'

(Novick, *Childlike, but not a dummy, Village Voice*, September 14, '72.)

Sometime between October '72 and the summer of '73, Schumann by a synthesis of *Whitewashing* and *Revenge*, eliminating Rockefeller and *Revenge*'s telling of the story, restoring *Whitewashing*'s symbol-language and doubling it by backdrop panels, created a third version, a street version, with a perhaps sort of upbeat ending, sometimes named *Whitewashing* etc.:

'There's very little text. I sang the text which was just the information that Peter wrote down — it was just straight information, the date, how many people were killed. . . . It had this Angel of Death (apparently the Gentleman Angel from *Grey Lady Cantata II* (SSB)) — soldiers marching, and then this Angel of Death comes in with the one prisoner and his drum. He comes in and plays the drum and the soldier or the guard lines up over here and the guy plays the drum till he gets exhausted and the drum sticks fall down, and he stands up to the guard and the guard shoots him. He goes down slowly, a black woman — the same mother mask was used in *Revenge* — comes out and does a dance with this Gentleman Angel with a big cigar, dressed up, and dances him down, destroys him or whatever. That's the end of the show. They do the whitewashing scene (from *Whitewashing* (SSB)). Then when that's over, the mother comes in and the mother gets in a fight with the Gentleman Angel and takes him down. I call it a dance. It looks more like a dance, but what the movement was was to end up on top of him. I mean they're both not moving but she's taking him down.'

(Konnoff, interview, '83.)

(1) A woman shows the white sheet and waves it like a flag.

(2) 3 grotesque gentlemen in tophats step in front of a black screen. They carry a garbagecan, a drum, a bucket with water, a bowl of blood, a gun and the white sheet.

(3) The gentleman angel with black wings and business suit enters. By two strings which he holds in his hands he guides the black prisoner of Attica to the drum.

(4) A woman on a ladder that holds up the black screen says; "it is dark as you see" and she and a man who plays a shakuhachi turn over the black sheet and show a white screen on which black prisoners behind bars are painted.

(5) The prisoner drums. His oversize hands are guided by the gentleman angel. When he stops drumming, one tophatted gentleman takes one of his hands and throws it into the garbage can.

108

(6) The white screen is turned over showing another white screen on which the same black prisoners are shown falling.

(7) The prisoner drums again. The tophatted gentleman takes his other hand and throws it into the garbage can.

(8) The white screen is turned over again showing the same scene with the prisoners dead on the ground.

(9) The prisoner drums once more with his bare hands, the drumsticks are taken from him and thrown into the garbage can. The last screen is turned over, again showing the black one of the beginning.

(10) One tophatted gentleman lifts up a gun, one snaps a finger and the gentleman angel guides the prisoner until he falls dead on the drum. Then another tophatted gentleman hands the sheet to the gentleman angel.

(11) The gentleman angel covers the dead prisoner with the sheet. A tophatted gentleman hands him a bowl of blood. The angel sticks his fingers into the blood and smears it on the white sheet on the prisoner's body.

(12) The the 3 gentlemen in tophats hang a laundry line, wash the sheet in the waterbucket and hang it up to dry.

(13) Then the man on the ladder plays the shakuhachi and the woman sings, and the 3 gentlemen take away the garbagecan, the bowl of blood and the gun.

(14) Now the mother puppet is brought in by the same players who did the 3 gentlemen, without masks playing snakepipes as they operate the puppet. She falls on the dead prisoner, then gets up and attacks the gentleman angel and fights with him until they both die.

(Schumann, *The White Washing of the Dirty Sheets of Attica*.

The integrated use of these panels is perhaps the only case in which Schumann realized his ambition to have paintings be as important an element of his theatre as the sculpture of the puppets and music. It helped him virtually to eliminate verbal text. He did a lot of painting and not much theatre in '73.

They performed it on Cate Farm, then as part of a 'Theatre of Uncle Fatso' program took it on the frustrated summer of '73 New Jersey 'Fun in the Parks' tour I have spoken of supra. Its two showings shocked the audiences and were the reasons why the sponsoring authorities stopped their tour.

Changed around some more, they took it along on their November/December '73 tour to Europe with *Simple Light*: the pictures in George and Dupavillon's *Bread and Puppet Theatre* are of a performance of this version at the Theatre de la Commune, in Aubervilliers, a working class district of Paris, during this tour – though the accompanying text is that of *Revenge*.

Both *Revenge* and the street version of '73 are about the repression of resistance, or more precisely: about the maintenance of an appearance of normalcy by the stifling of protest. Societies at most times appear to most

109

every individual living 'in' them as 'normal', namely as reasonable structures allowing reasonable people to live reasonably satisfying lives, each of these perceptors blaming themselves and/or peculiar circumstances for the fact that in their case this is not so: that appearance, however, is a tenuous artifact laboriously created and maintained by (ideological, political) authorities – by means of misrepresentation and terror. Both versions of *Attica* are about the creation of this discrepancy between appearance and reality – or about the distress it causes sensitive perceptors. The '70s were a return to the appearance of normalcy. In the '60s, the veil had been, momentarily, rent. The play is not about life in prison, nor about the maintenance in subjugation of the very poor by means of prisons, a crucial problem for governments and ruling classes, sometimes because there are very many of the very poor and they have been congregated in such large numbers that they constitute a real threat to the social order, sometimes only because although there are not that many of them, at least not in urban aggregations, there is always the very real danger that some systemic malfunctioning of the social system may make a significant proportion of the poor very poor. The apparatus of intimidation has always got to be working. But poverty has not been much of a concern of Schumann's. He wants the drumming of discontent to be heard.

7. The first Vermont winter. Liberated from the compunction to make sense, Schumann cuts loose with mysteries: a eulogy, shielded from the spectators, to the sweet mystery of domestic life (*Emilia*) and two crazy happenings; and commences a show of a huge mass of nudes, with which as setting one of the happenings, *Genghis Khan and the Women*, gaily concludes the first year in the country on a note of utter despondency.

His three major projects of the Cate Farm years, short plays for the black masses, delightful but insinuative travelling shows for the white, enigmatic and tortured but beautiful plays for himself, kept Schumann busy the first summer on the farm, but once he had packed his troublesome old followers off into the Western wilds with a busload of masks and rags (Konnoff's Western circus tour, cf. infra), in September, things were delightfully quiet – for the first time in years. No tour in the offing – the deal with Goddard kept the wolf from the door. He repeated his Thanksgiving show, the third, putting it on with Goddard students, twice in the Goddard Library well, once at Putney School, according to a 'Bread and Puppet History' of Elka's of December '70, with some stilt walking, the first in the Bread and Puppet Theatre. He himself first appeared on stilts the following May, in the Hardwick Spring Parade. And December 6-January 20 he put on twenty local Christmas shows (Goddard Spring '71 Calendar). In mid-winter also, he rehearsed *Grey Lady Cantata #2* (cf. infra) with new performers.[1] But otherwise things were quiet.[2]

---

1. There had been a considerable afflux of students to his 'workshops' when he first came, in the summer of '70. They had made his puppets for the circus and for the first *Grey Lady Cantata* and done the performing in the cantata. His expectation of their availability had been an important reason for his coming there. This winter he found out he'd been wrong:
'we were surprised how little interest and what a kind of weak reaction and reception these workshops got. For some of these things that were offered there would be no students or maybe five the first time and maybe none the second time. I don't know if it was the distance that Cate Farm was from the college or the general lack of interest, or what, but it wasn't a booming success.' — (Elka, in Schumann, interview, '79.)
So he had to get a new crew of performers for the cantata, and when he put on *Emilia* (cf. infra) here in February 'absolutely nobody came – two people came, two ladies that travelled all the way from Massachusetts – to see the show. That was our audience for *Emilia*.' — (Schumann, interview, '79.)
2. Most of us have more than one mood at a time, a surface one and a basic one. His basic mood was, as always, despair:
'When a dog is ill, he is given elixir from the sap of a telephone pole. When a little girl is sick she is loved a lot by an enormous grandmother. When the world is sick, the old grey bugs and the old grey worms that have been here from the beginning of the world, leave,

He got heat into his workshop space there before the end of the year, but the barn otherwise was too cold to rehearse or perform in. He had to abandon attempts to rehearse his Thanksgiving show in it. This gave him the idea of doing small scale pieces – pieces that could be rehearsed and performed in a space as small as that workshop space – probably the major reason he called them 'minor'. He worked on these – *Emilia, The Quest, Genghis Khan and the Women* – and at the same time embarked on a huge project: a permanent exhibition of paper maché sculptures in the big barn – 'a large quantity of small figures meant to cover the whole ceiling and the walls of the barn' (B. Lane, letter to Mary Brecht, November 27, '70.) – that would make its interior the equivalent of that of a cathedral, structured by sculptures, *The Vermont Paper Maché Cathedral*. The sculpture could be done in the barn workshop and in the house.[3]

'In the waning rays of the autumn sun scores of plaster casts spewed forth hundreds of paper-maché figures for the first paper-maché Cathedral of Vermont, with the help of many students, sometimes to readings of poetry, Doyle and Twain, sometimes with hot wine . . .

In the newly heated workshop in the Cate Farm barn plastering, pasting and painting continued, plus a new project – the building of many large music instruments, horns of garden hose and fiddles of gallon tins. All this work came together to produce, in late January, the Vermont's First Paper-Maché Cathedral

---

and find themselves a new place. Only there is no new place, because God makes the world smaller and smaller every day. He makes nebulas and comets and light years and stardust, and the world shrinks, until only a pea-sized world is left, and on that, not even the old grey bugs can find enough place.' — (Fable of Schumann's from a book of fables he sent out to friends that Christmas.)
3. 'And – every Thursday they were having the Papier Maché Conspiracy – (I: What do you mean by conspiracy?) That's what they called it. In those days, remember, they were having the – the hippies were all calling – The Great Bread Conspiracy – it was a useful word, meaning nothing. Every Thursday he had these forms that he would make out of clay, and then we were making papier maché prints from it – copies from it – and everybody had to do that on Thursday. And he allowed me a payment. He allowed me to take one away. I made twelve and I got to take one away. And those he was staple-gunning on to the interior of the barn. When they were made out of papier maché, the rats were eating some of them.' — (Ashley, interview, May '82.)
'The paper maché for the cathedral was a workshop. We read Dostovievski, somebody read *Crime and Punishment*, I believe. (Elka: People brought their favorite poems.) No, there were some novels. I think it was *Crime and Punishment*, and I learned to know a lot of the people, Paul Zaloom and – that later on came into the theatre. We did a paper maché workshop. I made the plaster casts that people had to lay out, so there were a whole lot of plaster casts there and we made a big pot of hot wine and then in the evenings people came – I don't know how it was organized, maybe twice or three times during the week, in the evenings people came and we got a lot of paper maché done, and then the next day when the work would be dry we found out how many of them were messed up. Maybe the wine was too good, or something, but I remember having as much work afterwards.' — (Schumann, interview, '79.)

Exhibit in the Library Well. A week in the mounting, it culminated in a midnight event titled: GENGHIS KHAN AND THE WOMEN.'

(Schumann, in the Goddard Trimester Calendar, Spring, '71.)

Though he did, after this exhibition start installing the sculptures in the barn, to an, according to visitors such as George Ashley, impressive, even overwhelming effect, he not too long after abandoned this project, the cathedral remained unfinished and after he left Goddard, the mice ate the sculptures. I suppose, partly Goddard didn't seem worthy of the monument, partly he was too busy the following winters:

'By the time I got going I got the sense that we wouldn't stay there very long. I stopped: I had used a wheat paste as paste and then the next winter the mice got into it and ate up most of it. What's left is hanging in the (Dopp Farm) barn, but the mice are still working on it.'   (Schumann, interview, December '82.)

He is cagey as usual about what theme the installation was going to have. When I asked him, he said the color brown was the unifying feature, when his son Ephraim interviewed him for me, he just said '. . . it wasn't very coherent'. He told Nicole Zand it was going to tell the history of the world.[4] Ashley, when he saw it in the winter of '70/'71, was astounded by the quantity of voluptuous nudes in it. Its intended theme seems to have been the major one of Schumann's sculpture and dance in the late '50s and one in the early '70s again preoccupying him: the opposition individual-crowds, as type feature of the human condition in a representation of Humanity. But in Elka's reticently dry description, the projected *VPMC* instead sounds like a preview of his '81 *Chapel of the Condemned*: a vision of a humanity gender-split for sexual transgression in agony awaiting last judgment.

---

4. '. . . ajoutant des clous de girofle ou de la cannelle au vin chaud. Il est une sorte de patriarche retrouvant avec délectation les rites d'une vie chrétienne primitive. "Voyez, dit-il, en ouvrant la lourde porte de la grange, ici je veux faire une cathédrale de papier mâché, j'en ai jusqu'à l'été prochain, je ferai cinq à six mille statues qui couvriront les murs et les toits et qui raconteront l'histoire du monde."

Pour l'instant, quelques centaines de ces statues ont été achevées et assemblées pour composer des scènes qui évoquent les portails de cathédrales romances; personnages assisis, hommes qui tombent tête en bas, couples se penchant sur un enfant, madones, monstres, saints, dieux, diables.

"Je ne sais quel est le sens de ces scènes, dit le maitre d'oeuvre. Mais quand tout sera fini, il y en aura un". On pense à ces "demeures inspirées" dont parlait Pieyre de Mandiargues, tant cette cathédrale du Vermont évoque le palais fantastique du facteur Cheval, construction géniale que l'on édifie pour soi, loin des routes et des voyeurs.

Il est des artistes qui veulent oeuvrer dans le marbre ou dans la peinture; Peter Schumann, lui, a choisi le papier mâché, encollant des milliers de pages du New York Times ou du Desvoir, de Montréal, avec un peu de farine et d'eau pour donner à un quotidien une forme impérissable! Et, paradoxe: au lieu de solliciter les éloges des critiques new-yorkais et une place de choix dans le monde du théâtre, il va passer des mois a édifier une oeuvre que presque personne ne verra.' — (Nicole Zand, *Peter Schumann et l'eclatement du 'Bread & Puppet', Le Monde*, November 12, '70.)

'The paper maché sculpture was made in the fall by the puppeteers and Goddard students during several "paper maché poetry readings" (books: LeRoi Jones, favorite modern poets, Mark Twain, Sherlock Holmes, African tales, etc.) in the Cate Farm workshop and kitchen. And by the puppeteers over several weeks. A good number of the figures first finished were mounted inside the barn, where they were originally intended to go; later, since the higher wall spaces could not be reached without scaffolding, they were piled up on the barn floor. The figures are in high relief, made of 3 to 6 layers of newspaper and brown paper glued with wallpaper or flour paste into plaster casts of original clay models made by Peter. When dry they were gessoed, painted very fast in brown with details roughly added afterward in darker brown and black. The effect is of hard sculpture, old, weather-worn and solid. The figures, single and in groups, are mostly naked humans in different attitudes: standing, sitting, kneeling, lying. There are some beasts, some interiors with beds, tables, chairs. Hard to say how many, but well over 150, maybe almost 300.'

> (Elka, A description of: *Vermont's First Paper Maché Cathedral*,
> and *Genghis Khan and the Women*, March '71,
> unpublished, Bread and Puppet files.)

Emilia, the result of 'very intense work' (Schumann, interview, '79), was like *Difficult Life* staged as 'theatre' and like it was obscure, in fact deliberately and formally obscured. Out front, a witch rocking a cradle inspired by Griffith's like action-frame in *Intolerance*, had the framing function of Uncle Fatso and his Cronies in *Difficult Life*, like him given one significant but symbolic gesture concluding the play. Behind her, a 'second stage' (Schumann, interview, '82) 'inside this hazy-colored, hidden-by-clear-plastic living room' (Schumann, ibid.), was seen through a transparent (shower) curtain, drawn most of the time, and through a rear window of this living room (the plastic curtain pulled aside for this) one saw additional 'outside' action, the larger world: perceived through the lens of domestic life: together, these two worlds were put into the perspective of time's and self-reproductive life's continuance by the old woman with the cradle out front.[5] The schema was an articulation of that of *Difficult Life*, in which the frame combines the function of frame and representation of a living room, and in which the living room is also the larger world of power politics and the large world glimpsed behind it a world of domesticities – and the schema was the same in the *Grey Lady Cantata* made the preceding summer, though here in the form of consecutive action: party – outside world – death and resurrection. These technical and conceptual specifications may be misleading: like *Difficult Life, Emilia*

---

5. 'Performing some of these minor pieces in New York equals a delicate transplant of one small breast-of-Aphrodite-shaped hill-of-Vermont to a Lafayette Street linoleum floor, with special care taken for particles of dynamite, horizontal morning light mixture, sounds of affectionate kitchens, visits and appearances, of birds and beast and definitely the rumblings of imminent horror and war.' — (Schumann, program notes to the New York Performances of *Grey Lady Cantata II* and *Emilia*, called "two minor pieces" '.)

was a beautiful, mysterious play, and, unlike it, a very intimate play. It was put on, to practically no audience, February 6 and 7, in the heated workspace in the Cate Farm hay barn, February 24 to March 7 at Papp's place in New York, and again, the last time, in the hay barn, on April 16.

Sue Bettmann, a Goddard recruit, played Emilia, Schumann's second individual after the Grey Lady in that *Grey Lady Cantata*, again a woman, though now down to earth, a housewife and mother totally involved in her home and family. Sue wrote a script of the play which also, through no fault of hers, is misleading in that the action in the 'outside world' – war, demonstrations, a son's getting, once again, drafted, another's returning from the war wounded – in the script has a prominence it didn't at all have to the spectator, simply because, seen through a shower curtain and through a window at some distance behind it, it was indistinct, something that, though it surely was not Schumann's deliberate intention, fit in very well with the displacement of his focus to domestic life. Attending the play one felt one had an insight into domestic life.

'Throughout – soft, slow bass drum beats.

1 Old woman with raven sits with Emilia (in crown and ring) who rocks cradle.
Bells
Large face in window. Light on it dims up and down again.
Bells
Old woman takes crown and ring, Emilia gets up into room and draws shower curtain, turns on light. Ties children to waist.
2 Lily leaves. Grandpa, Josephine, Hattie, Emilia and children do washing of clothes, hanging laundry line, gossiping, all singing and moving in slow motion. Motion and sound stop. Emilia switches out light, draws back shower curtain, and starts washing dishes.
3 In window, Roy and Lily meet, converse and walk off Hand puppets Mr. Parmigiano and Lily meet. Mr. P. proposes. Lily runs into house and James Allen (soldier) comforts her. Mr. P: Revenge!
James Allen's parents at home. James enters, says he must go away, exits, singing.
4 Emilia draws shower curtain, turns on light. Josephine and Hattie leave. Lawrence enters. Fast action and conversation. At door: pretzel salesman, Girl Scout selling cookies, flower girl, Watchtower lady, Rapid-Sure-Fire Delivery Service (breaking bottle of . . .), etc., etc. Mr. Parmigiano, the landlord, and his lady, Alice, enter and exit as does Lily.

In window 2 boxers (puppets) fight and the cop puppet chases them away. All exit but Grandpa.
5 Grandpa sits alone.
Grandpa: Emilia! Emilia? . . .
Bells
6 Emilia enters, turns out light, draws back curtain. Grandpa and Emilia exit.
Roy enters cautiously, Lily behind him. They bow to each other and begin dancing. Hattie appears in window, hands Roy a letter and withdraws. Roy sends letter; sadly embraces Lily and leaves.

Lily sits on bench weeping. Emilia enters to comfort her.
Bells. Plastic tube.
Face appears in window.[6] Emilia, startled, falls to her knees in fright. Count of
10. Emilia gets up, switches on light, draws shower curtain. Laurence, Grand-
pa enter; Mr. Parmigiano and Alice enter.
Mr. P. sets up toy plane. Fast action and conversation.
Knock at door. Roy enters, says goodbye, leaves.
Mr. P. plays long piano interlude. Grandpa keeps time. All others immobile.
Knock at door, Roy enters, with one foot bandaged, on crutches. Silence. Mr.
P. and Alice leave.
Roy takes Alice's seat. Emilia turns out light and draws back shower curtain.

7 In window – hand puppets – James Allen (singing softly, heigh di, heigh do,
heigh da) comes to White House, *knocks.*

Man in tophat:	Hello
James Allen:	James Allen
Man:	Have you been here before?
James Allen:	No
Man:	You must got to war
James Allen:	Where?
Man:	Far away
James Allen:	Why?
Man:	Because
James Allen:	Yes sir. (exits singing)

Same exchange twice more except in 3rd intervals: caterwauling, only
Lawrence reacts, throwing cans and cursing.

| James Allen: | Because of my many wounds I can no longer serve you. |
| Man: | You may go. We have no further need for you. James Allen exits singing. |

Witch comes through front of stage to stand at window while White House is
changed to James Allen's house. Then steps back.

| James Allen: | (singing, comes to empty house) |
| | Hello? Anybody home? Is there anyone here? Exits singing softly. |

8 Witch approaches window as house changes back to White House, then sits
down by cradle again. Crowd puppet passes in front of White House. All hum.
Emilia goes through door, takes away White House, comes back. Family goes
through door, hand puppet crowds in window. Sound fades, Emilia goes to
cradle, receives crown and ring from witch. Women sing: Emilia, Emilia,
Emilia.'

(Sue Bettman, script of *Emilia*, written February 6, '71, Bread and Puppet files.)

'. . . And *Emilia*, I think, had this same similarity to *Uncle Fatso* – this show
behind the plastic – of being – creating a very fragile but very believable world –
and something that – you really couldn't put your finger on it. It had very little
structure and very little you know, no real plot or anything. But it worked. It fit

6. The face in the window in scenes 1 and 6 was in fact the Pursuit of Happiness mask of
Schumann's '70 4th Parade and show, here God's face – the Godface, as which in '72 it
reappears in *Stations of the Cross.*

together, like a very organic whole . . . A very dreamy, muffled show with sort of flashes of clarity in it. It was played behind an old crumpled piece of, sort of what must have been not really transparent plastic, but sort of a translucent milky plastic and a curtain would be pulled open and shut. At the beginning of the scene the curtain would be shut and you would see the show, most of it, through the plastic. In the front was the old witch who was haggard, very stylized, wrinkled gray face, and the costume that goes with it has a hump back so it's a real old, haggard, hump back witch . . . It was a family scene. Behind the cloudy plastic was Emilia in her bathrobe and surrounded by all these little dummy children that were tied to her waist and a grandpa reading the paper who'd just sort of grunt and make — a lot of it was very unclear because you were seeing it through the plastic and because the text was deliberately — people didn't speak lines. They just grunted and the grandfather kept calling, 'Emilia, Emilia, (grunt sounds),' kind of incoherent, and she was cooking or sort of bustling around the house like a har-rassed housewife, but in a very gentle sort of sweet way. And then there were other characters and two of them — one was a young man who was Chris Hart-mann, very tall, with his blonde hair, and he had a mask, I think, Murray's face. And he had kind of like a uniform. He had an army coat or some kind of army uniform on and he was going off to war and a pretty young girl was saying good-bye to him, so one of the scenes was where he went off to war, sort of kind of lingering at the door exchanging confidences and kissing — and then he was going off and she was sad. But the other people would come in with like a — not a chaotic, violently chaotic, but a sort of amorphous scene of people milling around and bumping into each other and snatches of conversation. And then, in the back-drop is a window, a cutout window — and I can't remember if that was cut out of cloth. I don't think so. I think it was a real window frame that was set in there and then sometimes the action of the people would start and attention would go to the window and a little white house would appear there, and a lot of little puppet people, probably mainly from the *Christmas Story*, and they were protesters . . . and at the end of the show they somehow pushed the white house, which was just a plain white house, but it represented the White House, they either pushed it over or pushed it out . . . But it was just in a tiny little, in a very small space and then between these scenes the witch would rock the baby but Emilia would come out and in the end the witch puts a crown, a very pasted-up-together crown of costume jewelry and sort of pasty things and she puts that on Emilia's head . . . when Emilia joined the witch she sort of went through a barrier, a real . . . the first impression of the (witch's) face was of she's sort of frowning and looks very — probably looks evil, but she would be played in a very ancient trembling way so maybe you felt more pity for her. But she felt like some ancient, ancient being . . . somebody who wasn't threatening but was kind of protective . . . (the cradle) seems somehow to be connected with Emilia's role as this mother, harassed mother, but the witch was taking care of her child . . . (I: Did you think it was a nice home?) (Laugh) I think it was supposed to show — I mean, maybe this was an earlier Washerwoman type of an ordinary woman doing ordinary sorts of tasks of keeping the house together and barely succeeding because she would — I think part of the thing — it wasn't carefully written out and choreographed, who interrupted when, but it was a sort of she's constantly bombarded with grandpa trying to get her attention, and other people, neighbors come to borrow a cup of flour and ... she's fussing with her children and trying to stir a pot and then trying to answer all these things. But it wasn't done as a pointed picture of the role of the housewife ... the *Grey Lady Cantata* is much more poetic and all, but it also somehow shows the ordinariness of things. Maybe it wasn't new that way but it was more realistic than the *Grey Lady Cantata*.

(Elka Schumann, interview, '83.)

'... behind that window it varied between God appearing in the window and little hand puppets going to the White House. And the inside story was simply family matter. With washing — there was a washing scene, there was a homecoming scene of the son who had gone to war, a goodbye scene — that was about it. I think that was about the whole ingredients of that thing. But it was very much about that woman who rocked that —'

(Elka, in Schumann, interview, August, '82.)

'It was a show about an old and a *young* woman. A mother-figure that was played by the mask of the *Witch*, that was called The Witch, who was acting like an ancient — oh — woman from fairy tale books. Rocking a cradle. And that woman gave a crown to a young woman, to a fat, heavy-set woman, to a woman in the likeness of — she was played by Sue Bettman. (Elka: Who played The Witch?) Maybe I did. If I was in it, I played The Witch. I think I did play it a few times. And then it was like a family story of this — of a woman with household chores and laundry hanging and some gossips coming in and meeting her and the son of hers who had to off to war, and then the war story and the son's story could be seen out of the window of that woman, performed by little hand puppets. There was a backdrop with a window, a window and a door were needed in this show, (the door for) entrances and exits, (the window) for a puppet stage (behind it). Also, I believe the Big God Face appeared in the window.'

(Schumann, interview, '79.)

Elka liked the show and its 'translucent dreamlike quality', but she didn't, we can see, much like Schumann's picture of home life as something harried, disorganized and hectic — and indeed, Schumann's warmly appreciative description in the program notes to *Emilia* of his Cate Farm home life that winter notwithstanding (cf. supra), his home life scene in the *Grey Lady Cantata II* the preceding summer had been caricatural and a note of his (cf. infra) on the *Grey Lady Cantata III* of the following winter equates 'comic everyday life' with concentration camp living — nor did she much like his portrayal of the housewife at the center of it, though she appreciated it was an appreciation. Schumann defends his mask for fat Emilia by saying he had wanted to make her face 'very real and not easily good or sympathetic' (Schumann, interview, '83), but Elka doesn't buy this:

'It's a very narrow, a long narrow face with a very pinched nose. It looks very snobbish, disdainful, looking down the nose at people. The ones that we have I think are all painted fairly realistically, you know, sort of light and pink cheeks and some of them have had eyelashes added. Do you remember Kenny in the circuses doing his women in a very slinky, very, I guess transvestite way? He used that mask quite a number of times.'

(Elka Schumann, interview, '83.)

It's hard being married to an artist. Schumann has always loved his family and having a home, but during the Cate Farm years, at any rate, he felt crowded by it, which went as much with his being then in his later '30s as with his preoccupation then by the individual-crowd opposition. *Emilia* by technical means distances us from the 'larger world' reflecting Schumann's detachment from politics and society at the time, his self-removal from the crowd and juxtaposes home-family to it as essential, valuable reality. But a margin of unease nevertheless attached to the intense feeling for this reality that *Emilia*, I thought, the obscuring curtain not being an arbitrary device but having the effect of a cocoon, shielding the home from an outside which included us, projected in an actually profound way.

Emilia is crowned out of the cradle and wedded to time: Schumann's accolade to the homemaking mother, the regenerative power beyond politics and history. The play's obscure ending with the mock crowning of a harassed housewife signifies his progressive detachment from the political struggles of the Resistance and presages his coming attempt during the second half of the '70s to give to this detachment the form of a pantheist affirmation of life.

Nobody remembers what *The Quest* (sometimes referred to as *Tristan Quest*, a 'happening', first done in January or February '71 at the Goddard library, then, for children, at the same time as *Emilia* at Papp's place and at Middlebury College on March 12, and done as parade show at Burklyn Manor, West Burke, Vt. in June) was about.[7] I saw it and loved it, and remember nothing about it except that it was an enigmatic and beautiful turmoil of rituals and children, and that it was done inside a plastic tent-like covering.

Emilia and *The Quest* are two of the most beautiful shows of Schumann's I have seen. The tent, a tepee, in and out of which, below us, as I remember it, *The Quest* was done, worked as formalization of mystery, just as the plastic screen separating *Emilia* from the audience did, though

---

7. 'I think there was Genghis Khan in it and the eating of a heart, the devouring of a heart, and various fights of important historical personages, and again a *tent*'. — (Schumann, interview, '79.)

'I think it was — I mean, not a minor piece, but they didn't work on it long ... something to do with a ladder and a parachute and a bunch of people in it, including kids. (I: Was there a tent in it?) Well, it was *like* a tent. By being on — in the ladder when something was draped over it. You see the plastic around it. Or an umbrella. Not an umbrella — either plastic or a parachute, and, you know, a little confrontation, and a hurray. (I: A confrontation between?) Genghis — somebody bad who I think was Genghis Khan, and then somebody is good.' — (Konnoff, interview, '83.)

'I remember that there were shoes coming down from heaven. (Elka: And skis, a death mask on skis.) (Ephraim: That's what the old skis were used for!) Avram was Death on skis. The audience was given instruments, spoons and forks — at certain times they were invited to *beat* these instruments. There was a *tent* in the show. I doubt that there was a story line to it. — (Elka: It was like a long happening.)' — Schumann, interview, '79.)

119

in this case the mystery was the grace and delicacy female ordination gives to a household, while in *The Quest* we un-understandingly saw mystery as such, an incomprehensible event, viz. the life of others, perceived, perforce, always, as quest for God knows what, comic, for sure, in its glimpsed futile directedness, ridiculous in fact, but beautiful because it is an adventure. In *The Difficult Life of Uncle Fatso* this same Ordinary Life, seen as mechanical busyness in a living world, had been accorded the mystery of an amusing, miniature and intricate and very much working mechanism, the appeal of innocent seriousness in play. The three plays are in fact philosophic eulogies to domesticity. The divorce rate doubled in the U.S. from 1966 to 1976.

Genghis Khan and the Women[8] a 'complicated show' that 'took a lot of work' (Schumann, interview, '79) was given a one-time midnight showing (after an 8 p.m. run-through) in the Goddard library stairwell on January 30 ('71) that was at the same time a show of the figures that had been made for the barn cathedral.

Walls and ceilings of the space were covered with nudes, single, in small and large groups. This representation of humanity, dead and/or living, was complemented by four huge, figure-covered, suspended world globes, one for each side of the space. Some of the worlds were festooned with tiny blinking Christmas lights. Here and there along the side walls couples and trios — families, lovers, friends? — of life-size dummies were seated, their arms around one another. Along the wall facing the audience was a representation of The City, stacks of creosote-painted cardboard boxes, lit up within, their interiors painted as interiors and peopled by small figures, above it a dim sun. Files of horses and women, the horses paper maché, the women sketched on paper towels, seemed to be hurrying toward it. A manner of ramp, a huge board slanting out of the city to the center of the floor, seemed to connect the action of the play to it. Above it and its sun hung large homemade horns, suspended from a balcony, somber-colored.[9] Behind the audience, below suspended bells, a bedded dummy woman is attended by a dummy woman.[10] Five musicians (top-hats, etc.) are seated by the wall to the audience's left, entrances are from

---

8. I follow Elka's account, Elka, *A Description of: Vermont's First Paper Maché Cathedral, and Genghis Khan and the Women, a happening in the Library Well of the Pratt Center done January 30, 1971 (the 8 pm version)*, March '71. Bread and Puppet files.

9. '. . . horns, of lengths of stiff hose and iron pipes, ending in celastic bells or gallon tins or washing machine agitators. The mouthpieces are either from bona fide trumpets, or hand whittled wood . . . painted in . . . uneven shades of brown with design.' — (Elka, *A Description*, etc.)

10. 'The dummies were made by stuffing old left over costumes and assorted clothing with crumpled newspapers, sewing, stapling or pinning the separate parts together, sometimes over a wooden frame, and topping them with large puppet heads.' — (Elka, *A Description*, etc.)

its right. The space for most of the performance seems to have been dark, with the action illuminated by a spotlight, operated by a musician for the first scene, subsequently by one of the play's figures, that of Mary, like the other performers masked, in white.

Part I (the division into parts is mine) was in the nature of a Christmas play, though, like the remainder of the play, ridiculous and surrealist, with the birth of the savior broached but not reached, the Herods of all ages appearing in the guise of Genghis Khan, Schumann's ideal hero of the '50s, the Savior as St. George slain by the Dragon, and none of this certain. Mary enters on a donkey pulled by Joseph, she is followed by the three kings, the procession crosses, exists, returns and crosses again, leaving Mary by the city and the horns, facing the audience. Rattling (of tin cans) and high sharp notes: footwear, shoes and boots, fall one by one from the balcony. Three, four or five Shepherds and a Doctor (stethoscope, white coat) have entered. Mary, the musicians and they rummage through the footwear, the Shepherds leave with it, reenter with a pile of shredded newspaper which they dump on the floor. During the remainder of Part I, the Doctor, mumbling, moves about examining the dummies, occasionally is consulted (comic dialogue) by one of the Shepherds. Rattling, loud noises on the mike. The Shepherds, lit up by Mary, to some musical accompaniment roll about in the newspaper 'voluptuously'. Blackout, music stops, the rattling gets louder.

(Part II.) The spot, still held by Mary goes on again, illuminates the Shepherds still rolling. Death, rather than the Annunciatory Angel, enters through the elevator door: in skull mask and black raincoat, on skis and holding ski poles, a small siren around his neck. During the remainder of this part of the play he is slowly skiing about, in a low voice counting 'left, right' as he moves. Police whistle. A sigh on the microphone. Genghis Khan enters, a huge royal figure wrapped in blankets and parachute silk, red haired, his face painted, his giant brown celastic right hand raised in a gesture of command. The Musicians, Shepherds, Doctor fall on their faces in worship. A gesture from him allows them to rise. In a lengthy work process ceremony a page divests him of his ornamental garments, down to his long johns, dresses him in armor. To the tune of 'For He's a Jolly Good Fellow', another herald or annunciatory figure enters, the Circus Director, a young woman in tophat and tails, playing the fiddle on horseback. A Knight, to clanging of metal, his horse prancing and rearing, follows her. He rides about, St. George looking for the Dragon. Like Odysseus Achilles in Scyros, he finds Genghis Khan a woman, covered up to his neck by a huge naked female torso that has been put on him. Genghis Khan in a falsetto denies having seen Genghis Khan – apparently that's who the Knight had been looking for. The Knight leaves. An interlude: the Bear is made to do tricks while the Doctor plays the tuba and Death skis. The bells are rung. The Knight reenters. Death sounds his siren. Combat of Genghis Khan (who has come out of his disguise) and the Knight: Genghis Khan kills the jolly good fellow. Music of slow discordant scales. To bass violin and heavy breathing on the mike, while Genghis Khan engages in loud arguments with Mary and with the breather at the mike, the reentered Circus Director has the Bear do more tricks and Death, followed by the tuba-playing Doctor who hereby apparently is applauding Death's recent success, the slaying of the Knight, make a tour. The Shepherds gather around the dead Knight and after a moment in stances of mourning, slowly divest him of his armor, finally pull him away.

(Part III.) To 'The Blue Danube', everybody approaches the horns hanging above the city, and lighting cigars and blowing the smoke into them, make them smoke. The pall above the city. Then they play the horns. The sound is loud, but muffled and mournful, a hooting and wailing, with a few shrill, piercing sounds. This continues for a long while. Blackout.

The abortion of Jesus. The victory of a barbarian over a knight. The victory of the city.

As in the '70/'71 circuses, the play's tragic outlook is masked by hilarity, ridiculousness, buffoonery. This form of spoof and silliness is also, though there it is low-brow and childish rather than 'surrealist', that assumed by Schumann's *Christmas Story* at this time, but whereas the *Christmas Story* continues to be uplifting and the circuses and also the *Grey Lady Cantatas* at this time end on — however ambiguous — notes of uplift, *Genghis Khan*, though as experience for those attending it it was a groovy party,[11] is down all the way. Somewhat as with *Difficult Life* where the message was that the end is approaching. But the play came across as lyrical and serene and the evil in it as comic.

Schumann uses the term 'happening' to indicate the absence of a story. *Genghis Khan* was 'surrealist' in the sense of a free use of affective visual (and mostly incidentally also auditory) metaphors, metaphors relating not by semantic but by affective correspondence. E.g. the Shepherds rolling in the shredded newspaper, Death's moving on skis, the victorious combattant boisterously arguing with other performers. But there were semantic metaphors working by association of ideas, also, e.g. the Circus Director's relation to the combattants (gladiators, wild animals) or the representation of expected birth and of cure from illness and thus, in the context, of the

---

11. 'For the first performance, actually a runthrough, there was a small audience, mostly friends and acquaintances, and several small children who were noisy at first but quickly became very quiet and attentive during the show. For the later, actual performance, the audience was much larger, ca. 100, so it was very crowded and hard to move. The students got very turned on. Kazoos, tin cans and nails and cigars were distributed and many joined in the music and action, especially with the shredded newspaper and the parachute. People said it was very groovy, freaky, and far out.' — (Elka, *A Description*, etc.)

savior's birth, by a doctor; and the representation of a self-poisoning city by smoking horns was, because the city was right there too, perhaps not a metaphor at all, but to the extent it was — the horns standing for human vocal mechanisms conceived as made for making music — was semantically metaphorical also.

8. The Circus. Panorama of human existence
for a broad American public. Development from
romantic conception of travelling circus,
'70/'71, to local spectacle, '71. Development
from one big show to one-day-cycle of
entertainments, '70/'71-'74. Development from
escapist warning in re the urgency of dropping out
(individual salvation) to representation
of cosmic resurrection, '70/'71-'74.

Immediately upon his arrival in the country, in June '70, Schumann
started out on both of his other two long term projects, the Grey Lady
cycle and the travelling circus: starting 'rehearsals on very different experiments that ended up with – that was later called the *Grey Lady Cantata II*'
(Schumann, interview, '79), and building puppets for a July 4th parade
with their use in the circus in mind: 'they were meant for the circus, all
these puppets, the Howdy Doody and Domestic Insurrection...'
(Schumann, interview, '79). *Grey Lady Cantata II* had its premiere in
August, the first *Domestic Rescurrection Circus* in September.
    The idea of a circus apparently came to Schumann as a reaction against
the performance of *Cry* on the European tour in regular established
theatres with their habitual audiences: fancy or bourgeois, at any rate not
popular and expecting and paying for art, not merely, like circus audiences,
entertainment (and excitement, skill and beauty). He wanted to be independent of these mausoleums and these culture cravers. A popular audience
was the aim.[1]

---

1. 'Nous avons appris beaucoup de choses pendant ce voyage, et à tous les points de vue
... Une des choses les plus importantes, c'est que nous ne voulons pas jouer dans les
théâtres; dans les salles des autres, nous n'avons pas touché le public que nous voulons
attendre: c'était trop cher; et nous n'aimons pas le professionnalisme et l'artifice du théâtre.
Ce que nous voulons faire, c'est changer notre théâtre en cirque, nous voulons construire un
cirque, et voyager avec une tente, comme font les gens du cirque – ça c'est un de nos projets
les plus sûrs, quand nous serons rentrés aux U.S.A. – pour toucher tout le monde, pour
pouvoir apporter le spectacle à tous. (Du Vignal: Que joueriez-vous dans ce cirque?) Nous
essayerons d'y apprendre à faire un théâtre plus populaire, un théâtre de marionnettes, et un
cirque comme le cirque d'autrefois. Les anciens cirques sont morts, parce qu' ils n'étaient
pas assez bons. Nous voudrions faire quelque chose de différent, nous voudrions inventer un
nouveau cirque avec notre matèriel ... Mais notre intention, c'est d'atteindre d'autres gens
... la foule qui viendrait au cirque; vous savez, cela fait partie de nos buts.' — (Schumann,
interview accorded Philippe Du Vignal, November '69, reproduced in *Theatre* (date?),
under the title *'Peter Schumann ... des vertus plus simples et plus profondes'* apparently from
some issue of *l'Art Vivant*, perhaps that of December '69.)

The idea of a traveling theatre — Dalrymple had taken the new tent along on his March-June '70 southern tour and had apparently even sometimes performed in it — also enters into it, in part in turn probably due to the idea of a Real America to be reached (in sufficient numbers) only outside of the big dehumanizing cities, by traveling, in part due to Schumann's childhood ideal of the unintegrated vagrant artist, in part perhaps simply to his having been able to support himself by theatre only by touring. The idea, note, even if we identify humanity as community of man, is the opposite of the idea of a community theatre. It is the Romantic idea of the artist as stranger.

But the circus format is also in his mind, (1) the excitement, the shoddy — unslick, patently unreal — glamor, (2) the gestures of presentation — by fanfares, drum-whirls, ringmasters, m.c.s — in the menage, (3) the variety show, the diverse multiplicity of stunts, beauties and marvels. The presentational mode of circus connects up with an idea important to him during this period, that of 'non-narrative narration', an indicative frame that is part of the show. The variety show form of circus, given the impact of Coney Island (and perhaps, from his childhood, of midsummer county fairs) on Schumann, connects up with the idea of an amusement park, and with the ideas, first of being able to accommodate a variety of shows with different orientations and appeals — more aesthetic, more crude, more personal, more traditional, more political, more religious — within a single show, without shocking any expectations, and, second, of being able to get Everything in, the scope of human existence, birth, life and death, and thus being able to achieve, the diversity notwithstanding, by means of it, a unity, the true unity of life.[2]

'As a result of our European trip we said to each other: Let's get a tent and move like a circus. We got the tent and it is a brown animal skin that grows every time we set it up. We got sledge hammers and an ax. We want to get 2 horses and a waggon and make a circus consisting of all creatures, stilted gentlemen and the laughing lady from Coney Island. And we will move slowly from town to town and blow our horns. Years ago I travelled with horse and waggon through Austria and Bavaria doing fiddling and mask dancing by the side of the road. But the shows were solitary performances for trees rather than humans and the horse went lame and the waggon broke. Now we have a lot of stuff for the edge of any little town, choreographing the world makes sense now.' — (Schumann, Newsletter, *'Bread and Rosebuds'*, April 25, '70.)

2. 'Puppeteers are carnival people, conceived at country fairs, born in garbage cans, married to dancing bears and committed to a fullsize job of exaggerating up-to-date plights and catastrophies, celebrating glorious particles of dust in the evening sun, and demonstrating pain and greater tender love which are at the heart of the world. In the year of Our Lord 1971 we continue working on our circus, your domestic resurrection circus, where the whole unabridged universe will be brought to your attention, our monstrous human fate explained, master Death exhumed, lady World materialized, little U.S.-man with his disqualified liver recommended to your neighbourly compassion and proposed for your latest urban renewal project.' — (Schumann, *After-Words* to *Theater Pieces for the Inside*, dated

'Circus' was to afford him the opportunity of coating as Entertainment a presentation (1) of his critical attitude toward modern life and toward modern America in particular (and would in this respect replace the moral challenge of his political street demonstrations), and of (2) his personal metaphysics, an inner relationship of life to death that could be conveyed by a birth-life-death sequence or structure and – as part of it or independently – by a dance of death. Both attempts failed '70/'71, so that he abandoned circus, but in '74 he found the circus format that during the following period allowed him to achieve (2), though only because he now conceived that personal metaphysics as a religion, but he again failed in (1), and abandoned this attempt during the latter half ('77, '78) of this following period.

And finally there was the obvious idea of doing by (Schumann's kind of) puppetry the kind of thing done in circuses: acrobatics, magic, juggling, clowning, trained-animal performances. But this, the most obvious part of the concept of circus – which later on defined the circus proper part of his circuses – then was apparently the least important to Schumann: there was relatively little of this in his '70 circus. That though bent on appropriating this popular performance form for himself (as he had appropriated the medieval Christmas show, the Oberammergauer crucifixion show, the dance of death presentations, and in his street parades the masked processional of the Church and of carnival, and as he was (in '72) to appropriate the Franciscan Stations of the Cross displays) he would simply disregard the actual nature of the thing, is characteristic of Schumann's use of folk art: it is, for him, a personal artistic mask of convenience. He proceeded likewise when he responded to the big knightly

Vermont, February '71, in the program notes for the New York City run of *Emilia* and the *Grey Lady Cantata II* of February-March '71.)

'Whatever was done in Cate Farm in 1970 was consolidated into a show that lasted about two hours ... The idea of the '70 and '71 circus was to have what now is pageant, side show and circus – and have it in one. Have them together in the show. And part of that was a dance of death. We felt that that had to be part of it – so that was the form of the circus, that all of these things converged and split from it. So they came from somewhere, arrived there, performed and marched out. But it was one piece – it was meant to be one piece. (I: But that one thing, was that a circus in any strong sense?) Only in that there were singular acts instead of one ... disconnected-from-each-other acts ... (The dance of death) was an important part. That was the ambition of the circus, to be an allembracing representation of everything from being born to dying to pains in between ... to find a form that would allow anything from the silliest kind of fun making as is done in the circus to a service of some usefulness to people who died or have true reason to be very sad is meant to be what is achieved there. So one has to create a lot of different pieces ... to be able to do that – to make such a broad reflection. I would say that the *goal* of the thing is to be a truthful – a project (?) for a big form for a cyclic play such as other cycles in theatre...' —(Schumann, interview, August '82.)

I suspect that when Schumann mentions 'other cycles in the theatre', he has Bayreuth and the *Ring der Nibelungen* in mind.

Sicilian puppets: their mechanics didn't interest him; and, in fact, likewise also when he cast his whole art into what he called puppetry by derivation from the popular art of hand puppetry, dropping the essential feature of it, the puppet's dependency.

Though sometime in late July or early August on a visit to Coney Island, he worked on some circus ideas with Konnoff, who was to tour the circus, perhaps on this occasion setting up the Bronx Zoo *Bread and Dragon* circus parade – rehearsals didn't start until after the August 21 performance of *Grey Lady Cantata II*, when 'George' Konnoff came with his Coney Island crew. 'I think that was early September and you had a very intensive, I think maybe a two or three week rehearsal period with him on the circus' (Elka in Schumann, interview, '79). Though the work had actually started in August, this was still not much time to spend on such a big and new type project. The name of the show at this time was going to be either *The Domestic Insurrection* or *The Domestic Resurrection Ship* (or, perhaps, *Circus*) – depending, Konnoff told a student interviewer, on 'how political they got by the time they put it on' (McClellan, *Bread and Puppet People, Playgod*, January 28, '71). The *Domestic Resurrection Circus* was done once on Cate Farm meadow, the performers coming out of the tent, and then Konnoff took it on a cross country tour to California. What its name – later changed to *Our Domestic Resurrection Circus* – means to Schumann, he doesn't say. Presumably, that insurrection makes sense only if it's for the sake of a rebirth (as in the case of the American Revolution), but also that you have to change yourself before you can aid a rebirth of society, and perhaps: that renewal has to start on a community level. It may also have been a declaration to Elka that on Cate Farm family life wouldn't get eaten up by Bread and Puppet life.[3]

3. '(I: Why "domestic" and why "resurrection"? Why "domestic resurrection"?) "Domestic" because it is domestic. That is, the immediate concern of any artist, I assume, is to deal with the immediate – with the domestic surroundings – the as domestic as possible surroundings, and "resurrection" because one has to steal that term from the religious clubs, or from the religious traditions and can't allow it to belong to that category of mankind. It has to – it's applicable. It's a term that can be profaned – that can be used outside of church and Christianity. It doesn't belong to them, it belongs to all of us. (I: As an event in individual lives and also –) Yeah. As a necessity in communal life as well as a – even if just a provocation – a provocational idea, in an individual life. There's no description of a realistic – a biological resurrection attempted, right, we are not telling a fairy tale, we don't have that. But we are calling this – what happens after all the elements that we used in the show *die* – that what follows that death – that picks all that up again – we're calling that the resurrection – in imitation of the religious folks who created that . . . I guess the main thing about that term, "Domestic Resurrection" is that it was to be the title for an all inclusive cyclic show that wants to – has the ambition to include everything. To make details of life be part of larger communal or larger than individual events. I don't know how I came across that – to call it domestic resurrection. I think it probably came from just a quick notion of reading the Declaration of Independence where there's a reference to "domestic insurrection" and Domestic Insurrection in the first circus was a puppet. And a

127

Apparently it was a slapdash make-shift show — 'the puppet people roughly maneuvred, organized and pulled together a spectacle that was like a live cartoon ... the result of painstaking, meticulous labor' (McClellan, loc. cit.) — given some external shape as Show-for-the-Queen by an initial entrance, starting the show, of Pamela MacDonald, the singer Schumann got at Goddard, as Cleopatra, at the head of a parade of all the big puppets around the meadow. Ribbons tying her to Eric the Red and Ethelred the Unready are cut and they fight for her, and the circus funny business — Man Mountain Dean, a girl as muscle man with Uncle Fatso's big shoes which leave her and walk by themselves, a hobby horse number by Leherrissier — is performed for her. She subsequently sings the narration to a flip-over book parable, *The Man Who Could Only Walk Straight*, a parable defending Schumann's change of direction after *Cry*. But its underlying conceptual structures necessarily compatible with one another, seem to have been primarily a three-part Birth-Life-Death structure, secondarily a History of the World structure on a Christian schema, but without *Cry*'s Christian elements. There was a Birth Scene with people coming out of a Womb Bag topped by one of the *Difficult Life* copulating couples, a *Consumer Cycle* scene may have been intended as depiction of life, and there was a musical chairs Dance of Death scene, the contenders for the chairs wearing 'neutral life' masks on the backs of their heads, and Death successively snatching up the chairs — and a Garbageman taking out the chairless, taking them back into the tent. The Garbageman puppet first appears in this circus. As for the History of the World structure: the show, after the parade, seems to have started with a *Mother Earth Waltz*, followed, probably, by a scene involving Satan, First Woman, God and an Angel of Death (the Gentleman Angel, a somber, watchful kind of angel, then used in *Grey Lady Cantata II*) and a slaying of Abel in the presence of Mr. Schmaltz from the Coney Island *Revenge of the Statue of Liberty*, and seems to have ended with the *Pursuit of Happiness* scene performed for the Plainfield 4th of July: *A Man Says Goodbye to His Mother*, with readings from the Declaration of Independence, the current reality of America contrasting with its promise. A finale was tacked on to this: Paul Revere and running, flower banner-waving, white-clad puppeteers (an element of the show from the spring of '71 onwards) bring on the saving Ark for All, the magnificent, blue and white gigantic dry-land sailboat, having for its sail the Coney Island Tree of Life curtain, and the audience — salvation of the elect! — is invited into it for a parade sailing it around the meadow to the tune of *The Storm is Here*.[4]

---

puppeteer questioned me about that puppet — or about the demonstration of domestic insurrection. Why not "domestic resurrection"? And I think I picked up on that.' — (Schumann, interview, August '82.)

4. '. . . the first and only use of audience participation by the theater. At the conclusion of

I.e. the World History issued into and to a large extent was American history. Schumann crammed American allusions into it, an ending not with Hell or the Last Judgment, but with the New World Kingdom in the Wilderness, the ending Americans feel it has, as well as American satire, e.g. a *Domestic Insurrection* scene: the giant chickenesque Howdy Doody puppet's laying of various patriotic emblems, Easter eggs with American flags on them, etc., perhaps after a victorious fight with Uncle Fatso (America the Good vs. America the Bad), and there may also have been a scene with demonstrating crowds derived from *Difficult Life*, complementing the topical political reference of the *Pursuit of Happiness* scene.

Apparently, there was still another element, a critique of Modern Society in the form of essentially tragic game rituals, one a critique of Marx's original object of critique, the division of labor, and a critique of consumer-orientation: an *Assignment of Jobs* (my name for it, I don't know what it was called) routine, in which social roles are distributed and assumed, and another that was the *Consumer Cycle* — I don't know what either consisted of in that first circus. The *Game of Musical Chairs* dance of death may have been conceived as critique of competition.[5]

---

the Circus an ark was formed around the audience, and they walked around the meadow chanting 'The storm is here,' between the ropes and banners. In retrospect this gesture seems dated, and in fact seemed so at the time. I moved into the ark to guide a blind friend, but the words stuck in my throat painfully. I could not chant and merely felt awkward in another refuge of the self-elect and burned at the willingness of my friends to be so.' Goldensohn, *Peter Schumann's Bread and Puppet Theater*, '77.)

5. '(Elka· I remember all these puppets parading around the big meadow as a parade for the circus, and then the circus itself had sort of the theme of Tristan and Isolde. There was a queen, played by Pamela MacDonald and she had hearts, she had long ribbons that went to the hearts of Eric the Red and Ethelred the Unready, the knights that fought for her hand.) And big Mountain Dean. (Elka: Acts came out and performed for her.) (his) feet broke off and walked by themselves, across the meadow, giant feet. Elka: and Irene did the little horsey trick. There were these tricks in it that were just for fun, but then they were done for the queen.) It was all a takeoff on American History, a lot of it was about the terms of the Declaration of Independence. Like the act that was *Domestic Insurrection*. (Elka: That funny chicken puppet with the body made of hoops that went along and laid eggs and Solveig went afterwards and picked the eggs up in a basket.) It gave birth first to a little Easter Bunny — it laid an egg, and then the little girl with the basket came and found that egg that was another little item of Americana, it had a flag painted on it. (Elka: Miss America . . . the girlfriend of Uncle Fatso . . . was hopping around with him and dancing with him. There was a birth scene. That was an important part in that it was repeated in the next couple of circuses, including the 1974 one. A big bag and people coming out of the bag and being spanked on their backsides, and Happy Birthday had been sung, and they were given a mask.) A big box with hands in different positions and everybody picked up a different hand and did different jobs with different hands.' — (Schumann, interview, '79.)

'. . . a bit of the ideas at that point was much more to do a circus that presented the history of the world. So it started out with a pageant and arrival of several larger-than-life heroes and heroines, Cleopatra had a big part in this show. Everybody tied up to her on

129

The circus was a bitter pill of politics coated with the sugar of fun and silliness:

(1) circus funny business done for a presiding lady
(2) world history in the Christian perspective: promise of paradise, grim reality of a last judgment
(3) American history: promise of beginnings, grim reality of present
(4) a birth-life-death cycle image of life
(5) a critique of modern civilization (in the form of game rituals)
(6) word-unto-the-wise parables
(7) a straight-out offer of salvation (a sail on dry land).

---

strings. And she sort of floated in, and the strings were out and the performers, animals . . . a Goddard woman (Pamela McDonald (SSB)) who had quite an immense voice (did Cleopatra). And from there — there was an orchestra, there was a birth scene, happy birthday under the sack with a copulating couple, being born, and — there were a lot of scenes that were collections of people in just face masks that were more like crowd scenes that said "yes", "no", "hunger", accompanied by the musicians. Almost no slapstick, clown material was in it, the circus part, very little of that. Ending up in doing *Man Says Goodbye to his Mother* . . . There were a couple of absurd entrances. One entrance was introducing Man Mountain Dean — one of the girls in the company who had fake muscles and had the big Uncle Fatso shoes and she made an entrance. So it was a bit of that, but not really — not *scenes* that are built around dancing bears and things like that. Uncle Fatso had several entrances. There was a mask that had four masks on one person's head (joined together with elastic (SSB)) and they came out of the tent and just spun around while music was being played, and disappeared. (I: You said "a history of the world?") That's what we had hoped to *arrive* at, but I don't think we did. Yeah. There was a dance of death. With chairs. Two rows of chairs were set out and it was done much like musical chairs. You know where one is eliminated. (I: Skull masks?) No. Life masks. Very neutral masks. The music would play something like a violin, because we had Pascal (Ortega), we had a cello, and flutes, and we had an electric guitar, we had quite a few musicians. They would play a round and Death would pick a chair up, and they would be without a chair, and they would be escorted out — into the tent. Pamela, who was the queen at the beginning — (there was) a parable that she would sing. There were several parables. There was a parable of the man who couldn't bend, a straight man, honest man, so he couldn't get home, he could only walk straight, couldn't bend his back — he had to go all around the world before he could get back. (I: These were sung?) Right. And (done with) flip paintings. Some of the ideas of this first circus were to do parables and celebrations of things to make mock of them or make points by treating them in a theatrical way. *Man Says Goodbye* was the end of the show and then the Ark was set up and we invited the audience into it . . . We really did put it together to do it at Goddard once, and then we left, on tour, so it never . . . Peter joined us, I think, in the first show in Princeton, he came down and we rehearsed it some more, and I would have to say that it was not something that the company was really at ease with, because we didn't work on it very much with Peter.' — (Konnoff, interview, '83.)

'The whole performance was a strange conglomeration of characters and peculiar abstract situations. They included: the fable of the Good Man Who Could Only Walk Straight and met with considerable difficulty, then came Satan, the First Woman, God and the Angel of Death which made an interesting foursome, the slaying of Abel in the presence of Mr. Schmaltz, the infamous Uncle Fatso (a big chicken with very nice legs, who cocked and cooed and left very patriotic eggs with stars and stripes on them), then the consumer

The circus funny business seems to have clustered at the beginning, the critique of modern society at the end, but otherwise everything was loose ends, hints and superimpositions.

If the show had any message, it was carried by its ending and by the ending's relation to the preceding and was Drop Out! for the Salvation figured by the Ark in spite of its being in opposition to Judaic-Calvinist doctrines of the Chosen 'for All' was a Se Sauve Qui Peut: get out of this mess! — as Schumann had gotten out of New York and out of the Resistance Movement. It was the opposite image of that of Jesus as Resistance Fighter in *Cry*. There was no message of insurrection, but neither was there — effectively — one of resurrection — of an escape not only from the death of alienation of 'modern civilization' but into a gentle blue yonder in which the tree of life would flourish, and where, as it said on the Ark's blue galleon prow-head, 'kids' would (the word actually was 'should') 'be allowed to grow up and live a good life'. For the tune was *The Storm is Here*, and the circus's Christian world history schema, shorn of the promise of the figure of Jesus, allowed no such future — though this became clearer as Schumann reworked the circus in '71.

The circus tour didn't pan out. That is, the tour didn't, but the reasons seems to have been the circus, not — the circus was not the format of the whole but just one show among others — the other shows (e.g. *Difficult Life*). Konnoff thinks that though Schumann came out (to Kansas) to help them fix it up, the circus just wasn't presentable[6] — also, it couldn't be

---

cycle evolved and we were confronted with people in their roles in modern society including a housewife, businessman, garbageman, an Aunt and an Uncle who all played our society's last game at musical chairs and were consequently thrown out to the dump.

The musicians were magnificent and played diversified arrangements to fit the array of scenes and contrasting excitements. Mother Earth Waltz, which was written by an orchestra member, was one of the best pieces.

It was all topped off by a mass race to meet Paul Revere who descended Cate Farm hill, sounding his trumpet in an attempt to call us together in a moment of great danger so that we might not miss the domestic resurrection!' — (Ian McClellan, *Bread and Puppet People, Playgod*, Vol. I, #1, January 28, '71.)

6. 'Well it didn't work out. It sort of started falling apart. You know, at the seams. One thing, one thing was the show was not under our belt enough, and I didn't feel, or felt later that I didn't have enough of a handle on it to be a sort of assistant director to keep it together or make changes or improve things because I just was . . . I wasn't at ease with it. Plus, we were eighteen people in the school bus and were ill prepared for it. We were exhausted already from the summer, and all the personal problems and things like that became really difficult, when you are driving the long distances that we were driving, our work was spotty, and we had a huge amount of shows and the bus was really overloaded and we had the circus tent. Now I'm friendly with some of the people who I had a hard time with but I think at that time it was really sticky, and I made a decision half way through — we did this circus in Denver or Boulder, no — Lawrence, Kansas, and I didn't want to do it anymore. I didn't feel that I had a handle and yet I had *Fatso*, which I felt very good about, and *Fire*, and the little shows, and it made more sense to try for me to — it

131

felt more comfortable just trying to hold that together and to cut down the company to nine people. So I gave people *notice*, which of course . . . well, once I did it I *did* it. (I: In Kansas?) Yes. It was not received real well. Well, it was a little unclear too because our tour was supposed to end in California, and we had a chance of extending it, so what I did was I said, I don't want to do this circus after California, which was the first projection of when the tour was going to end. But I'd like to go on with nine people from San Francisco and work with them. (I: Not all of those nine came back to Kate Farm?) No, there was no *offer* to come back. See, that was a strange time, too, (in) that Peter wasn't really offering to run the company the way it was in New York because they'd have to *live* at the farm and that was not explored yet, and he invited a few people back, so it did leave a lot of people who . . . because the company had grown sort of out of his hands anyhow. Bill's company wound up staying in Coney Island, were never encouraged to be a part of the company because it never – you know, couldn't offer them any likely livelihood, didn't have enough work, so, yes, a few people went back, and by that time Peter had gotten some nasty letters about the tour from different people. And that was – I don't know what. We never talked about it a lot. He was worried, and – worried about getting his puppets back, too. He really didn't know – well, not that he didn't know what was going on, but, you know, it definitely – things weren't going on as planned . . . So, I decided not to go back or – he offered to let me keep *Fire* and perform it, and I decided not to go back. Maybe I thought I was going to get spanked, I don't know. I had hepatitis, by the way. But Pascal took the puppets back, and I kept the bus. (I: And did *Fire*?) Didn't do *Fire*. No, I didn't want to keep it and do it that way. You know. No. I didn't want to stay in California. So, I did, I left for Spain. And I spent quite a bit of time in Spain recuperating, going to bullfights . . .' — (Konnoff, interview, '83.)

'Then at the end of the summer we had a tour to California. We went to Kansas. (I: What did you call yourselves?) Bread and Puppet. Kansas and Colorado and California – did quite a few shows there. (I: How did you get there?) We bought a bus and it must have been about 15 people (I: You must have made some money to buy a bus.) Probably Peter paid for the bus. I'm not sure. And George managed the tour and Pascal Ortega was there and Hillary Rawlings, George's girlfriend who was this very woman's lib. Somewhere in Indio, California we blew a rod in the bus. We blew the rod in the desert and all this smoke came out and George's little boy was there and we left him in the bus in the hysteria of getting out of the bus and we had to run back and get the kid out of the bus – he was asleep – and then these guys offered to fix the engine if one of us hippie girls would sleep with his nephew. Cause he had never gotten a girl.

Well, Sara Peattie was there and she said very emphatically, "I don't know about this. I know what's right and I know what's wrong and this is wrong." She said no way would we be doing this. So then Hillary decided she would volunteer, and she told all of us little bourgeois girls a lesson about we were whores inside of a private relationship anyway, so what difference did it make really. Next thing we heard – this was the time of the Manson murders – right at that time – the next thing we knew, we went to Pomona, the next thing we heard, George (inaud.). They stayed behind so Hillary could turn the trick for this guy, and we were all extremely agitated by this whole thing. They were arrested. (I: For what?) They thought they were the Manson people. They had seen two men and a woman leaving the area and thought they were them. Hippies. Then they let them go when they found out they weren't but in the meantime Hillary didn't do it because George figured he didn't want his girlfriend sleeping with the nephew of the garage guy. (I: Narrow minded bastard. So was the bus fixed?) Yes, we got the bus fixed, paid the money. And we did shows in Pomona and that was okay, but it wasn't too great. The shows weren't that terrific. I don't remember what shows we did. I think we did *Uncle Fatso* on that trip . . . We did *Uncle Fatso* on that tour and other shows also, little ones. But the students were unresponsive, they weren't really very together. Nothing like the French kids a couple of years before. It wasn't that great.

squeezed into the tent.[7] But the real reason for the debacle rather obviously was that the circus didn't add up, didn't make any point – Schumann had slapped it together too quickly, didn't know as yet what he was doing. Plus, maybe was a little too anxious to get rid of all these people he had loaded himself with for and on that European tour: sent them out on a leaky boat, left another bunch on wintry Coney Island, where, testing their nerve, they would evaporate.

Schumann reworked the circus that winter of '70/'71 – Nicole Zand has him 'revoyant les textes' in late October or early November, and he himself evokes his preoccupation with it later in the winter – in January '71 – in the program notes to his double header (*Grey Lady Cantata III* and *Emilia*) at Papp's place (February/March '71) – 'our circus needs a meadow and a tent' (a remark, however, that probably mainly meant they didn't need Papp, didn't really *need* him.)

He took this reworked version, a 'very different show' (Schumann, interview, '79), for one thing, apparently redesigned for indoor showings on a college circuit, on a tour in the spring of '71, with two dozen puppet-

---

Then we went up to San Francisco ... So then I went to see these friends in San Francisco who had moved there from New York and I go so freaked out in San Francisco I didn't stay around for the little shows we were going to do there, with the Mime Troupe, on our own. I took the first plane I could back to New York. I got terribly nervous in San Francisco. I was just convinced that the city was going to go into the ocean while I was there and I really didn't want it. That was October 1970 ... (I: And the others were still on that tour?) What actually happened was they never did do any shows with the Mime Troupe because there was some disagreement between George and them, I don't know exactly what the details were. (I: And they came back later, all of them?) They didn't all come back to New York, some of them stayed in California, some of them went to France. They just dispersed.' — (Irene Leherrissier, interview, '79.)

7. Konnoff had the tent along on the bus. (Schumann, interview, '79) recalls performances of *Fire, King Story* and *Grey Lady Cantata II* in the tent, in September, at Cate farm, just before the tour. They did *Fire*, for which an enclosing frame had to be set up, 'a lot' (Konnoff, ibid.) in that tent, also *Difficult Life*, which Konnoff improved by introducing a naked woman (as essence of Vermont – of Nature) into it, a change enthusiastically applauded by Schumann, and *Mississippi*, but

'We explored like getting another size up. We couldn't really do a circus in our tent, not a circus, you could do sideshows or *Fire*, but, you know, it wasn't – it was a much larger tent that you're dealing with if you wanted to go that way.' — (Konnoff, ibid.)

They played only college campuses:

'(I: So why didn't you actually try that and set it up outside of town somewhere, get a town permit, set it up in the fairgrounds, do a parade?) Gee, I don't know. I can't think of any reason why not. Well, we definitely didn't try it on that tour for just *weather* reasons. We walked right into winter all the way.' — (Konnoff, ibid.)

How they dealt with this problem when they set up the tent on campus grounds, I don't know. The big jet blowers with which the big (locally provided) tent that in November/December '73 on a Theatre National Populaire sponsored tour they did *Simple Light* in Lyons, France, 'were no good for a puppet show. They make a lot of noise! It's loud and – it turned out to be not a great environment for the show.' — (Konnoff, ibid.)

eers, doing shows in March in Providence at the 'Rhode Island Festival: Theater '71', at the Emmanuel Church in Cambridge, Mass. in April, at Kent State University in Ohio on May 4th, on the anniversary of the 'Kent State slayings'. Elka (Schumann, interview, '79) thinks they did it at Drew University also, 'went down the east coast'.

He sorted out the show, splitting it up into a History of the World (Part I) and a circus (Court of the Queen of Sheba, Part II), in Part I casting out the specific American references that his July 4th parade had inspired in the '70 circus, substituting for them a Christian religious framework with a parade of the disciples (whether there was a Last Supper and/or a Crucifixion, I don't know — Elka saw the show as a 'very elaborate version of the Easter show before it became *Stations...*' and thinks the Last Supper may have been in it (Schumann, interview, '79)) and with an apocalyptic ending that was a kind of Last Judgment, in Part II realizing the circus idea more fully by more skits actually like what is done in circuses, e.g. a ringmaster cracking a whip. He elaborated the Show-for-a-Queen frame by complementing the watching Queen of Sheba of Part II, in black and with a black mask, by a watching woman in white, with a white mask, in Part I, the light figure (in the perspective of Christian transcendency) watching the dark show, the dark figure (in the perspective of mortality) watching the light show. Inspired by Konnoff's use in the western tour of '70 of a nude in the *Difficult Life* Vermont scene, he had the performer — Sherman who had joined the tour in Rhode Island — change from light to dark as part of the show, nude at the transition point,[8] which the police chief supervising the Kent State University showing thought "the most beautiful thing he had ever seen" (Levy, interview, '89), but which Elka didn't like at all.[9]

---

8. 'I, as the white woman, Peter said, I want you to change character entirely, and go from a white woman to a black woman in the second part of the show. You have to be black and I want you to take off all your clothing. I had to drop snow on my head while Herod was eating, take off my mask and blouse and my skirt. I wasn't wearing any clothing under that. And I just slowly put on a black skirt, black shirt, and ... And in fact, we tried this out — in the spring of '71 they did a little tour that included Boston and Rhode Island. I joined them for Boston and Rhode Island, Kent State. Boston is where we tried this out first. A church in Boston ... And then I had to get into a black costume and pick up the donkey and watch the second part of the show which I think had circus acts in it. I think that's when there must have been circus acts, yeah. Lots of very funny circus acts. And in those days the circus acts were still very, very funny. (I: And what mask did you have as a black woman?) A Negro mask, a Negro woman's mask. Somber. A character like this would use either a white woman's mask that was black, painted black, as if it had been burned, or else a Negro woman's mask. And I don't remember which one we used that time. She was sitting and watching. The very end was to bring her up to the center and do *A Man Says Goodbye to His Mother*. It's possible that we had approached a place in which there was a soldier, so that it would be easy enough for me to come and join him and I think that's what we did.' — (Sherman, interview, '79.)

9. '(Elka: I was so much against it. I thought that was such a bad idea ... that I can't

134

The show as a whole wasn't circus anymore: the circus had become a separate, identifiable part within it. It may not even have been called 'circus', but only *Domestic Resurrection*.

'Can you imagine a contemporary theater company dramatizing the history of mankind? This is exactly what happened at the Emmanuel Church when the Bread and Puppet Theater staged DOMESTIC RESURRECTION.

In DOMESTIC RESURRECTION both the old world and the new are demonstrated. The birth of civilization is depicted by a group of actors under an earth-colored fabric. Slowly the mound swells and is "planted" with little trees and houses. The First Woman then dances with a ludicrously large and red Satan, to the accompaniment of an onstage chamber ensemble. A series of similar vignettes interlarded with snippets of vaudeville and mime[10] chronicle the saga of man to, perhaps, a mythic point in the future where the world ends. The Evil People are cast into hell, represented by many, many small dolls falling from a dizzy height over the nave of the church.[11]

The awesomeness of the nether-world is further suggested by a slow, candle-lighted procession of gigantic puppets, enhanced by loud, eerie organ music. The Good People, the peacemakers who have found heaven, are discovered seated in a gallery over the heads of the congregation.[12]

Our domestic resurrection is likened, in part two of the evening, to the court of the Queen of Sheba, beginning with a brass band parade, the Queen is entertained with puppet animals, a fire-eater, a juggler and all manner of circus acts. There is also a horseback joust between Ethelrod The Unready and Richard the Lion-hearted.

The performance concluded, spilling out of the church, with a street celebration – the Floating of the True Ark. The congregation (it couldn't be called an audience), was invited into the Ark – a block-length of fabric painted midnight blue and white. Puppets with the same colors hoisted a huge mast and the Ark

---

remember when it was.) It was a changing of a woman from a white woman into a black woman by stripping into the nude and then redressing herself into black, including a mask of a black women. (I: And was this not a major structural element of the show?) It was tied into the event – that's right. (Elka: But one of your ways of placating me was saying it's done so incidentally that nobody hardly even notices it's happening. It wasn't a big, central –) No, it wasn't done in the ring, it was done outside of the ring. But there were several things coming from the outside, so –' — (Schumann, interview, August '82.)

10. Apparently including a revised *Consumer Cycle:*
'. . . a parade of *things* around the circus perimeter with a tray with, or not even a tray, a coke can, a beer bottle, different – whatever was around, you know. Different *drinks* and plastic bags of food. It was just – done like they were very important.' — (Konnoff, interview, '83.)

11. 'Harvey (Spevak) on the organ and airplane attacks, (with) babies being dropped out of the sky and bouncing all over the place, (and) Herod breaking wood for a sound (effect).' — (Konnoff, interview, '82.)

12. '. . . a group of some 30 dummies – they were not dummies, we had asked people to sit with these big masks, sort of up-and-quick-quick-made masks that had tophats – people, whom we had to find – sitting up in the gallery, doing slow motion hand clapping for some of the scenes.' — (Schumann, interview, '79.)

proceeded to the intersection of Newbury and Arlington singing "The storm has come."

. . . Is it credible that youth, who will not receive bread during regular services, will do so at a dramatic presentation? And an even headier speculation – can the theater provide, for some, salvation? The Bread and Puppet Theater says, "Theater is a form of religion. It is fun. It preaches sermons and it builds up a self sufficience where the actors try to raise their lives to the purity and ecstasy of the actions in which they participate." Perhaps, when the last church has shut its doors, every town will have a Bread and Puppet Theater.

(Donald Colucci, *Theatre/Bread, Puppets and Salvation, Boston Review of the Arts*, April 15, '71.)

To make up, I would say, for the shift from the political to the religious of the toured circus, he had planned to intercale, between its Cambridge and Kent State showings, at a Movement demonstration in Washington, D.C., April 24th, a contrariwise quite non-religious but highly political version of it, *The Domestic Resurrection Circus of King Richard the Last*. It would have opened with Nixon's (rather than Uncle Fatso's) dance with Miss America, Howdy Doody, the Domestic Insurrection chicken, would have laid her patriotic eggs for him, then the circus would have been performed for him and Miss America, and the dark part of the show, introduced not by a nude but by a G.I. angel with snare drum, would have followed: the White Ladies pulled into King Richard's mouth (as into the Big White Face in *Lamentation*), 'deadly marches' involving the Shark Soldiers, the Great Warrior, a chorus of skulls, the Great Warrior's slaying of the White (Vietnamese) Ladies. The four- or three-face Spinning Dance of the First Woman would have introduced the final Ark for All and *Storm is Here*.[13] But he did a Last Supper and Crucifixion instead.

---

13.   'THE DOMESTIC RESURRECTION CIRCUS OF KING RICHARD THE LAST
1. DANCE OF KING RICHARD THE LAST AND MISS AMERICA
2. ARRIVAL OF FRIENDS: HOWDY FRIENDS,
                    GENTLEMAN ANGEL
                    DOMESTIC INSURRECTION (HEN AND LADY)
                    SATAN AND FIRST WOMAN
3. 100 CRAZY DANCES FOR KING RICHARD THE LAST, INCLUDING: CONSUMER CYCLE DANCE, STRONGMAN DANCE, HARMONY DANCE, NYC DANCE, DANCE OF THE NEW WORLD – COLUMBUS, MAYFLOWER, SLAVESHIP –, THE LAST DANCING BEAR DANCE, KING RICHARD PEACE DANCE, DANCE OF POLITICAL SPEECHES MEANING NOTHING, DANCE OF GENERAL FEAR, ETC. ETC.
4. THE ARRIVAL OF THE G.I. ANGEL WITH SNARE DRUM
5. THE WHITE LADIES OF VIETNAM PULLED INTO KING RICHARD'S MOUTH
6. FOUR DEADLY MARCHES: AIRPLANE
                         GREY SOLDIERS
                         GREAT WARRIOR
                         CHORUS OF SKULLS

Taking time out in May to make the puppets for and to stage the second of his three major shows of this period, the new *Birdcatcher*, and to perform it in June, he during a three week 'workshop' on Cate Farm, July 10 ff., with about 30 puppeteers — puppeteers, older members of his group, rather than students, not easily plucked out of their curricula, had taken it on the road that spring — performed the toured circus. Audiences were invited to see different parts of it. He retained the tour's White Lady/Nude Woman/Black Lady frame, incorporated elements of the abortive Washington, D.C. circus, eliminated again the Christian references, and increased over the previous outdoor version, the utilization of the landscape by processional approaches over the hills. He put in on twice on consecutive days, now called *Our Domestic Resurrection Circus*, July 30 and 31: redesigned as again an outdoor show, but now not for travelling. It was now about 3 hours long.

In his mind, the retained salvational — rather than insurrectionary: it's a withdrawal — ending with the Ark for All and *The Storm is Here* was a third part of it, but I fail to see any concept to this three-part structure. Part I, *The Door of Heaven*, a 'mythology for worried man', again has aspects of a World History according to the medieval schema — from the expulsions from paradise of Satan and First Woman, in the medieval view though not in Schumann's the two sources of earthly trouble, to the Last Judgment, which is set to chainsaw and combines aspects of the Bethlehem child murder and of an air attack in Vietnam: the schema Birth-Life-Death of Earthly Man. Its middle part, Life of Earthly Man (my designation, Schumann thought of it as Review of the World), takes the form of American history. Part II, *The Circus of the Queen of Sheba*, divides into the circus proper, or 'silly circus' as Bread and Puppet people later came to refer to this part, and a sequence of the three not so circusy game rituals that already in the '70 circus made up a critique of modern society, the *Job Assignment* scene, the *Consumer Cycle*,[14] and 'modern society's last' *Game of*

---

7. DESTRUCTIOIN OF WHITE VIETNAMESE LADIES BY GREAT WARRIOR
8. SPINNING DANCE OF THE FIRST WOMAN
9. THE STORM IS HERE AND THE FLOATING OF THE ARK.'
(mimeographed outline, dated April 24, 1971, Bread and Puppet Theatre files.)
14. 'It was a circular type of piece. People in masks were stationed in the form of a circle and one thing would happen to one person or persons in the circle which would cause a reaction in the next person and so this reaction would continue around the circle. Let's say the eating of something, and then it being thrown away, the garbage man would pick it up and he would take it and dump it somewhere and somebody would go rummage through the trash and find it again and this kind of thing. It was *Consumer Cycle* and that changed and changed and changed to try and find the right way that it should work and it was always very hard . . . the beginning of the *Consumer Cycle* with masked people who would wear masks on the backs of their heads and sit in chairs and really react as a group, like everybody would follow everybody else. (I: The same thing in sequence?) Yeah. It was like everyone was just followers. No one would seem to be thinking for themselves, that

Musical Chairs, a dance of death, a *Domestic Insurrection* scene in which Howdy Doody chases Uncle Fatso intrudes into this sequel, and the sequel is followed by the concluding *Pursuit of Happiness* (*A Man* + the Declaration of Independence), two contrapositions of Bad and Good America.[15]

---

kind of situation, and somehow they were led almost in that vein into this Consumer Cycle. They were just consumed into this role of using things and everybody then gained their role without exactly deciding or choosing their role in life, but they just followed along and did what they were told to do . . . everything would end up at some point being dumped and the garbage man would come and pick it up.' — (Fernandez, interview, '83.)
15. 'Our DOMESTIC RESURRECTION CIRCUS is the mythology of worried man.

In the first part (The Door of Heaven) the Old World will be demonstrated, the phenomenon of Mankind and Man-unkind.
While Angels sing sweet Cello and play Piano.
The Grey People are watching Paradise.
The First Woman and Satan are smashed by the Archangel;
Cain kills Abel and Death covers the Limbs of the Earth.
Then you will witness the Dance and Labor of the Womb and all Happy Birthdays of all Pink People. But Satan collects their faces. But then Diogenes with his little rattling Schaefer's bottle-cap Lantern looks for Man and finds Woman, and the Lord is risen and Irene claps her hands and dances the Dance of 3-Face and the Devil collects the Pink People's Faces.
First Woman washes us all, makes us sit on our Chairs and has us watch the World outside, and the World drives by real fast: N.Y.C., A&P, Robbery, Dogshit, Peace and Harmony, Mayflower, Slaveship, Miss USA and a Slice of War and phony Peace.
Then the big Indian Chiefs will be upon us, and a good pipe of tobacco should be lit at this time.
And Snow-woman walks.
Oi-Oi-Oi-Oi-Oi-Oi-Oi.
White Trumpets hike over the Mountains, White Ladies of strange Faces are pulled into King Herod's Mouth, big Sound is bad and hurts our ears and an Airplane arrives and Babies fall from the Sky and the White Ladies die.
(Now the dogs will bark but the people shall be quiet.)

THE CIRCUS OF THE QUEEN OF SHEBA

The First Woman will now change into black and will distribute the Bread until the Queen and her Court arrive.
You will see the Sword-Battle of Ethelred the Unready and King Richard the Lionhearted, King Richard II's Love and Disaster, Man Mountain Dean's Fight with the Dancing Bear (or not), the Appearance of the Three Kings from the East, the Strong Man, Bird and Beast, Lion, Elephant and Cockroach, Summersault-Lady, Handstand-Man, and other incredible Acrobats, Little Dragon and One Big Dragon.
Then the Queen in her gracious Manner will distribute the Jobs of Modern Society; Housewife, Consumer, Uncle Joe, and Aunt Mabel, Fido the Dog, Snowwhite, Free Delivery and Free Enterprise, and such.
The Consumer Cycle can be brought to your attention.
But Domestic Insurrection rushes in and chases Uncle Fatso and lays its important Eggs. They eat them and they get sad and that's the end of that.
Because now you see Modern Society play its last Game of Musical Chairs, and their Chairs are taken from them and the Garbage Man wins. And a Man says goodbye to his

138

There was no circus in '72 or '73. With men like Schumann the reason that he was busy with something else is inapplicable. He was doing *Stations* in the spring of '72 and spent the summer addressing himself to the big city crowd at Coney Island, and with Elka went to visit his widowed mother later in the summer, but *Birdcatcher* hadn't precluded the

---

Mother and the GI Angel appears and Paul Revere rides over the Hills, calling us all together in this Moment of Great Danger that we may not miss Our Domestic Resurrection.

THE ARK

Oi-oi-oi-oi-oi-oi-oi-oi-oi-oi-oi.
The Storm is Here.
Oi-Oi-Oi-Oi-Oi-Oi.
The Storm is Here.
Oi-oi-oi-oi-oi-oi-oi.
The Storm is Here.
etc. (7 times repeated)
And finally for your Enjoyment and Enlightenment we will float the True Ark for you.
The Ark is driven by the demons of the troubled Waters of the Earth and the Ark will not know where to drive to.
And it will stay here.
And no swimming lessons will follow the performance.
The water is green grass.
The wind is the symphony orchestra.'

(Schumann, *Our Domestic Resurrection Circus Program*, July 16, '71.)

'. . . there was the beginning, the way there always is, of pageantry and a lot of flag waving and arriving at the circus area, the way there usually is. Then there was the parade of the characters — there were big figures who came out, Snow White and there was Saint George, the dragon slayer and there were others who took place.' — (Levy, interview, '70.)

'I was a white woman, white outfit, white mask, white hair. And Pam(ela MacDonald) was dressed up as some other kind of character. She was my husband. We gave birth to a lot of creatures, and there was a canvas, burlap, and a lot of people coming out and getting born, and being slapped, and being wished all kinds of good luck. Prior to this, there may have been a dance between Mother Earth and the God of Heaven. Probably there was some Greek mythic beginning, then there was the giving birth to all these characters. Then there must have been events that involved all these characters, and would go on for quite a while. And then it would lead up to a big, horrible destruction scene, in which there was a King Herod puppet. A white door was always very prominent in this play, people locking the door, getting hit on the head, singing happy birthday, stuff like that. King Herod is eating a long white piece of cloth, this would be hundreds and hundreds of yards long. And this white cloth, the other end of it is attached to the hands of those same Vietnamese lady puppets that were used in Fifth Avenue parades several years before. And they are approaching from the barn and down by the river and long strings are attached to their arms, and he is eating it, eating, eating, eating. The airplane is arriving, the grey airplane is arriving at the same time. Somebody else, I don't know what kind of character it was, but it was very essential to have somebody drive up on a motorcycle to get the horrible noise of the motor of the motorcycle . . . he was eating these ladies. And then I think they fell down because the airplane was arriving and the motorcycle . . . all this was going on. This was

circus in '71, and the circus had had precedence over Coney Island. And in '73 he wasn't doing much of anything. The reason for that, that he was dispirited, may in fact help to explain why there was no circus in '73, but still doesn't explain it for '72.[16] He had variously permuted its conceptual and theatrical elements over a period of two years, overall separating them and giving it more structure, but what still eluded him was the trick of imposing on it an effective identity, an overall unity of effect and message without losing the basic virtue of the concept of circus, its allowance of variety – the variety that would allow him to sugarcoat his politics by silly circus and thus be able to communicate politically with a broad American audience without turning them off – as '70-'72 the Vermonters had been by his street agitation – and on top of that to slip in his views on life and death. The underlying reason for this, I would say, was that, the way he felt, he really had nothing to tell these people: at most, something to show. On the one hand, they were the opponent, the Crowd opposing the Individual, the same crowd that had betrayed Hyperion. (He got this feeling off his chest '72/'73 by making it the subject matter of his third Big Play of this period, *Simple Light*.) On the other, his over-arching conception of life as birth-life-death cycle wasn't working for him as an artistic

---

using, all this was arriving from different directions. And the end of the first part ended with this tremendous amount of destruction right in front of him. All the ladies falling down. The airplane probably landing on them, and this eating and eating.' — (Sherman, interview, '79.)

'Then there's the parade of the big white Vietnamese Ladies crossing the field and coming to the center and a plane comes and when the plane is overhead, the death masks come out with chain saws and saw wood and break wood, until there is a big heap of destruction, and Uncle Fatso drives in with a car to observe the devastation and he comes out of the car and that's when the Consumer Cycle begins, I think, a little scene of how garbage is brought to people and used and then it's more garbage, garbage keeps piling up . . . It's the housewife – the delivery boy brings the garbage to the housewife, she prepares it, she gives it to somebody else – it gets passed around – then more garbage. Not just food, all kinds of things. Just so there was a big heap of trash.' — (Levy, interview, '79.)

16. He still intended to do a circus at the beginning of the year:

'I want to work on the circus with all forces available, all of you and as many students as possible. I want to finish the papermache cathedral, build a big set of hand-waving cheerleaders for our sunset horizon, Winoosky puppets on rafts, adoration of the peepers-puppets, horses and related beasts, some in papermache, some in celastic, some in cement. Musically we will need a) a string quartet b) a you are my sunshine bugle band 3) nondescriptive wind orchestra. In other words: I want to do a piece of landscape, something that cannot and need not be moved and belongs right here – a day, with greenfields sunshine and bread and butter. Didn't I say that before, that we should build a real big Kitsch like Oberammergau featuring everything – even some 100 dances for King Richard the Last? So, that's it. This is going to be the first year, however much of it we get finished.' — (Schumann, letter to puppeteers, February 23, '72, Bread and Puppet files.)

'I kind of remember that Peter didn't want to do a circus, and of course people would ask him for a circus – but he didn't want to and it didn't happen.' — (Sherman, interview, '82.)

tool in giving the circus structural unity: because he had as yet not integrated it with his view of World History, of the larger fate of humanity in any way that would make it useable as a message. It was caught up in the medieval schema of a closed, finite World History. Thus the Ark for All salvation at the end of the '70/'71 versions of the circus dangled. It related (as '70s message of turning off and dropping out, not as '60s message of resistance), to the circus' critique of 'modern society', but not to its evocation of or structuration by that cycle. (What eventually, but not yet in '72 or '73, furnished him the conceptual tool for integrating that cycle with humanity's history, was his ecological concern, the concern first forcibly expressed in the *Hallelujah* of '71/'72.)

When, after three more years, he had overcome the basically negative view of humanity and history that the '60s had left him with, he (again with old puppeteers, rather than students[17]) put on another circus: in a form and with a concept that at least for the three or four years following seemed to him suitable for communication with a broad American audience, the Cate Farm circus of July 27 and 28, '74. It was now a noon-to-dusk affair, repeated on consecutive days, consisting of four separate parts that have remained the same since: *sideshows*, short skits repeated, except while the circus itself was on, through the afternoon, the work of puppeteers other than Schumann, though Schumann furnished ideas and masks and in some cases directorial assistance; the afternoon circus proper or *silly circus*, fun and entertainment comprising also satire on American history, performed in a central ring, lasting perhaps an hour; a *musical puppet play*, i.e. a puppet show to a composition by a classical composer, *in a Christian manner* or perspective focused on individual death and salvation, lasting somewhat less than an hour and performed after the circus; and a concluding *'pageant'*, i.e. a puppet play in choreographed processions of large groups of puppets extending over the landscape, a representation of human history – perhaps with special references to American history – sometimes rather a representation of modern civilization, lasting perhaps an hour, concluding at dusk.

There were three sub-elements that Schumann with some more or less minor variations also retained thenceforth: the *presentation* of a presiding

17. '. . . there was a certain, I think, sentiment, in that circus which made it a little special, like people – this was going to be the last circus and you know I want to, you know, swallow the whole thing, do everything I can and make it a good circus. There was a lot of building compared to what the previous circuses had been as far as masks and costumes, a lot of foreign people arriving at the farm just to do the circus and – not all Europeans but people from around the United States that people had met on tours or whatever, a lot of different people coming to work on the circus. I think it was the first taste of really doing a circus that involved a lot of people and – working on it and the fact that there would be a large audience and the fact at that point a lot of advertising was being done to try and get people to come and make it a big extravaganza.' — (Fernandez, interview, '79.)

patronal/matronal deity, a giant puppet, by an onrushing, flower-banner-waving group of white clad puppeteers (the white uniform of *Cry* was retained for all circuses from the first onward), imaging the meadow's bursting out in spring, either (as in '74) with the august Pursuit of Happiness head of the July 4th '70 parade (rebaptized the Godface for the '72 *Stations*), or with the buddhaishly smiling oriental face of the pretty Domestic Resurrection Deity, brought in, erected, and danced around while it is made to turn; a performance, in many languages, of *Hallelujah*; and *a celebratory conclusion of the pageant* and of the whole event, in '74 still the Ark for All and *The Storm is Here*, in later circuses a bonfire and dancing around it (as though in celebration of the summer solstice) by the puppeteers and masked creatures, normally led up to by a mass torch light procession from afar bringing in a nighttime equivalent of the more solar initially celebrated presiding deity, a Moon.

The patron deity, even when it wears the stern God-face, has the pantheist aspect of an incarnation of nature; the *Hallelujah* that of a (pantheist) glorification of the natural world; and the concluding celebration that – also pantheist – of a 'pagan' celebration of the natural world.

The pageant, prefigured in the '70/'71 circuses by the concluding Ark for All – its announcements from afar by Paul Revere, its advent over the hills, its circuit – and by the White Hornblower puppets' announcement from the surrounding hills of the Last Judgment ending of the summer-of-'71 circus's first part, *The Door of Heaven* – and first used, as isolated theatrical element only, however, in the prologue of outdoor performances of the '71 *Birdcatcher* – was the crucial discovery of the '74 circus:[18] a combination of the circuses' (and of earlier street parades') white and blue with the *Birdcatcher* prologue's red processions. Schumann concentrated in it (relegating other elements and conceptions of the circus to preceding parts) visions of humanity's history as recurrent cycle of birth, life and death integrated into and sustained by an ever renewed nature (the medieval Christian one-time cycle changed into a pantheist recurrent cycle), a message, but now neither Christian nor Resistance, of hope-despite-all, and a prognostic of resurrection – not just of individual

---

18. 'I guess that the circus we do is a little bit like the gigantic pageants performed all over the United States on pieces of American history, although I haven't seen them. It has to do with just creating a big outside attraction for the people in the area.' — (Schumann, September '73, quoted in Kourilsky, *Dada and Circus TDR* #61 (March '74).)

'I'm told that there is a lot of historical, especially wild west and western history, western states history, Texan and so on, history performed on a very large scale with horses and wagons, covered wagons and cattle, and many, many people. That there are quite a few places in the states where such things get performed, many of them. But I've never seen it. (I: In other words, you didn't just mean July 4th parades?) No, no, no, no, no. There are pageants in America . . . like town centennials or whatever.' — (Schumann, interview, '83.)

salvation (to undertake which the Ark for All had exhorted all). The matter of salvation — through right living — was relegated to the musical Christian play. And the matter of Resistance was concentrated in the silly circus: the silliness of which now served not or not only to soften up the audience so they'd swallow social criticism and high-faluting ideas, but in the pageant's perspective made sense as ultimately comic aspect of the day to day everlasting struggle between good and evil.

The crucial theatrical feature of the pageant was its manner of integration of the natural setting with the show. From '75 onward, Schumann didn't use it just as a background — the starry heavens above a Central Park Shakespeare — nor did he make it a theatrical element, a backdrop or the equivalent of *Difficult Life*'s heaving-hills-of-Vermont tarpaulin, a scenic element. Instead of integrating the setting with the show, theatricalizing it *by* the show, as he had done, for instance, when he presented *Cry* against a mountain background in Ste. Baume, he integrated the show with the setting, left its character of Nature — actual nature, locally present but by the use made of it generalized into Nature per se. He adapted the pageant, both in terms of what it represented, e.g. warring armies, and in its choreography, to the topography, so that it would be something perceived as taking place in nature, and in such a manner as to bring out the intrinsic qualities of the setting qua Nature or at least those which from his pacifically pantheist viewpoint were the essential ones, something to which the gentle Vermont landscape tends to lend itself, viz. the easy commerce of hills with sky, the harmony of day's transition into night (crucial feature of the pageants), the reposed outlines of the distribution of masses, the natural and enduring productivity of the grass roots, in short, bringing out the aspects of nature making it the potential of man and trustable, no matter how strident man's colors (e.g. red) or how weird his antics (e.g. war): a mother watching the sometimes uncouth play of her children and easeful bearer of a womb that could bring forth more of them. Not e.g. anymore the pretty girl that in *Difficult Life* had represented the essence of nature, an urbanite's perception. To place his theatre in nature in this way, as formerly in his street agitation he had placed it in the City, was a theatre man's theatrical achievement. The underlying ideology was the ecological movement's. The trick was to make the pageant's processions not seem to reach out and draw in the setting, but to come out of and go into it.

The '74 circus was a first attempt at the new form. As is indicated by Schumann's trying to get Goddard College to sponsor it,[19] it was not yet

---

19. 'Ladies and Gentlemen:

    One of our most ambitious projects in the last few years has been the production of a couple of versions of *Our Domestic Resurrection Circus*. Next summer we want to redo this piece, widen its scope and intensify its performance.

conceived of as community festival, as a joint celebration in which the audience would figure as congregation served and represented by the performers, this being, for Schumann, its peculiar form during his next creative period and the way he surmounted the individual-crowd opposi-

---

I propose some six performances (two Friday through Sunday weekends) in mid-August in the big meadow on Cate Farm. The event would depend on good weather, even though some of its parts could be presented in the haybarn and in the Cate Farm Barn, but the most spectacular appearances of puppets would need the Winooski, clay-pit hill, mosquito bomber hill, the meadow and the sky.

I envision that the circus will last all afternoon and evening, will include exhibitions along walks in the area, musical sessions in the woods, giant birds descending on trees, a sunset happening on the west horizon, etc . . . Also food and drink, which can be a source of income for the producer.

I hope that Goddard College will want to be the producer, that is, carry the burden of advertising the show through hand bills, letters, posters etc. and in return take 50% of the income (suggested popular admission price $2) (I think the show should be advertised intensively state-wide but also east-coast-wide through schools and press contacts – maybe the Vermont Council on the Arts could be interested in matching the expense for publicity.)

The Bread and Puppet Theater will start work on the circus in January or February. Then during the A session of the summer trimester we will offer two afternoon rehearsals and two morning building workshops for students. During B session building will merge with rehearsing (circa 4 times a week for up to 20 students).

The Bread and Puppet Theater will use or raise its own funds for puppets and prop building materials with the understanding that it will own the show and its artifacts. The producer will have to provide publicity, parking, and if necessary seating (if the audience exceeds 400 people it would be wise to rent bleachers. Depending on how wide the publicity reaches, camping grounds may have to be found).

These are a few basic ideas, quite undeveloped and improvised as yet. But we are dreaming about a giant puppet circus with beasts crawling out of the woods and gods and over-life-size politicians appearing on tops of hills since we live on Cate Farm. We have tried little bits; experimented quite a bit, and thought a lot about it. And now we are ready for it. For the students who participate, there won't be intermediate or advanced course sessions in puppet-technique, but rather the full involvement in one big production from the beginning to the end for one full trimester. For the Bread and Puppet Theater there will be the first step of the realization of a dream, a summer event, that by its nature belongs here, makes sense here, and wants to grow to be part of this part of nature and society.

We also hope that we will be able to interest the other performing forces at Goddard to help create the production.' — (Schumann, Letter of September 27, '73 to the administration of Goddard.)

'(Ephraim: Was the work done with students?) Some students, not many. We weren't so happy with the participation of Goddard College. There wasn't much. We tried, we had workshops for all kinds of things and some people came and not much stuck to us. Goddard had its own path and was not too interested. We tried several times to involve them in the larger sense, to have them *organize* the circus and they were not interested in that. We wanted them to be the *sponsors*, to advertise it, to make money on it, to have concessions on it – we proposed all that to them – luckily they were not interested, because it was much nicer without all that, but we offered it to them.' — (Schumann, interview, '79.)

'. . . the Domestic Resurrection Circus . . . evolved (at Goddard) as a college-oriented spectacle. Once Schumann and company moved to Glover – where a natural amphitheater allows at least 5000 people to comfortably watch the proceedings – the circus developed into a state-wide spectacle.' — (Susan Green, *The Free Press*, week of August 12-19, '78.)

144

tion dominating his thinking during the Cate Farm period as well as his theatre's presentational-representational mode. That it was not that as yet is indicated also by its pageant's having as yet the Ark for All and not yet the bonfire dance ending: while the ending with the Ark addresses the circus to humanity — 'all' — on the one hand, and to those electing to opt out of 'modern civilization' on the other, the bonfire ending addresses it to a community in presence, inviting them not to escape, but to celebrate humanity's endorsement by nature. Yet the integration of the ending into the pageant — of the Ark's blue of hope with the pageant's victory of the red of war over the white of innocence — a patriotic triad — constituted a step in that direction: the meaning of the Ark ending was no longer let's escape all this evil, but: in spite of it there is hope: and in this there was an acceptance of the community as it is and the expression of a feeling of oneness with it. The new form was incompatible with travelling and indoor performances (though Schumann later attempted both), and the '74 circus was conceived of as stationary local show[20] — which is basic to the idea of community communion. The '74 pageant, finally, though it achieved integration into the landscape present, was part of the particular piece of countryside it was placed in, did not achieve its universalization: presumably was not designed to. The photographs show this: it was simply the result of making use of the physical features — riverside, forest edge — there: as another scenic theatrical element: instead of making use of spatial extensions, perspectives and of the relation of land and vegetation to sky. Nature figured in this pageant as intimate — then and there — not as encompassing matrix. Cate Farm meadow's delimitation by barn and river might have worked against this. And the '74 silly circus still, like the '71 silly circus, divided into a silly circus proper and a sequence of game rituals that included birth-life-death-cycle and dance of death elements — besides a concluding *Door* sequence in the birth-life-death pattern, entrance of the performers into the show as Birth, a variant (*Show of Hands*[21]), less

---

20. 'Our *Domestic Resurrection Circus* will be an effort to find a new way of doing circus that is more human, that is not merely a collection of superlatives, of extraordinary feats, arbitrarily mixed together, but something that becomes a story of the world circus. We don't use circus techniques: the heaviest acrobatics done in our circus is a somersault. Or the horse is done by somebody putting on a horse mask. In that respect, it's only a parody of a circus ... I guess that the circus we do is a little bit like the gigantic pageants, performed all over the United States on pieces of American history, although I haven't seen them. It has to do with just creating a big outside attraction for the people in the area. It's a piece that shouldn't be traveled, something we want to perform where we can integrate the landscape, that we can do with real time and real rivers and mountains and animals. It's something that is seen in the woods, up there in the hills, back here in the river. I guess it would be called an "environment"!' — (Schumann, interviewed September '73, in Kourilsky, *Dada*, '74.)

21. '... there was a box of hands from all over these building years, many different hands with different expressions, that were not attached to any puppets, and one of the scenes

critical, more appreciative, of the *Job Assignment* scenes of the earlier circuses as Life, an exit dance in robes with death motives as Death — elements later exclusively carried by the Christian musical play with respect to the individual and by the pageant with respect to humanity, or entirely absent.[22]

---

from that *Circus* was to be a performance of different tasks, like lifting up a stone, climbing a ladder, doing laundry, reading the book, looking at a star, ironing as on an ironing board with different hands.' — (Schumann, interview, '79.)

22. 'In the summer of 1974, when Schumann decided to leave Goddard and free himself of the burden of a communal company, he set up a weekend called the *Domestic Resurrection Fair and Circus* as both a retrospective and as the occasion for the creation of a massive work, the *Circus* itself. Many old pieces were shown in the afternoons: *The Dead Man Rises, Hallelujah, Mississippi, A Man Says Goodbye to His Mother, King Story, Theater of Uncle Fatso, Life and Death of Prisonman.* The *Circus* itself contained parts of earlier circuses, notably the central parricide of Uranus, here appropriately enough the keynote of domestic insurrection — a comic version of the archaic revolution. This insurrection is resurrection, a primal validation of life by Love, the conquest of death, the circus, the big show.

Where the structure of *The Dead Man Rises* (and other short pieces) is based on concentration and exclusion, the *Circus* is expansive and inclusive: as Schumann says (in conversation, November 1974), "The circus doesn't make sense. It is the opposite — show-offy, and it makes its own rules. It is more amateurish, a collection." This is not to say that the work is without structure, but rather that it is episodic, its frame is enormous, the range of movements and type of puppets is broad. The large puppets move among masked and robed puppeteers, small puppets, costumed clowns, and tumblers.

The general pattern of the 1974 *Domestic Resurrection Circus* is that of a dance of life. It begins with birth, the birth of "the people" and of the Circus Director, which is followed by a circus with life on show, and concluded by the triumph over death. The beginning is solemn, with the entrance of the God mask from the *Easter Show*, an enormous face supported on poles, that is sorrowful and transcendental and vaguely Asian. "The people" are born by being hauled out from under a tarp by the Devil and his Helpers. They emerge with signs that read War and Peace, Law and Order, Rags and Riches, Guns and Butter, Day and Night, Sun and Rain. The polarities are all ridiculed with slapstick as each set emerges. The playing is so broad that it crowds attention away from the Devils's Helpers and the Gray Lady on the sidelines who are intended to provide a framework of suffering and regeneration, but who remain a kind of passive iconography alongside the fun.

This sequence is followed by a dance of giant puppets, Uranus and Mother Earth. They are about 20 feet high, grotesquely ugly, and seem a nightmare of drunken parents careening out of control. Mother Earth complains of feeling ill after a short waltz, and a doctor drives up, climbs a ladder to treat her and delivers her of Zeus-the-Circus-Director, who moves the ladder over to his father, knocks off his head, and completes the skip-rope version of the Theogony. The cheerful parricide then proceeds to conduct the circus acts that follow. Daddy is dead and we can all have fun, so we have jugglers who drop everything, tumblers who fall, weight-lifters who die trying (Hubert Heaver), magic acts, dancing bears (Ethyl and Butane), with a group of Two Penny Circus clowns who egg on the audience with a polished style that is in sharp contrast to the ineptitude of the parody circus acts that are all show and bluster. In this primal revolution, life simply bursts forth and the new Daddy remains a child.

After the Circus proper retreats, the finale begins, a convoluted allegorical dance of life where the figures go through a series of stations that suggest growth, initiation, taking on the values of civilization, death, and some kind of resurrection. Each puppeteer, in the role

The *Hands* part of the circus' *Door* sequence differed significantly from the earlier *Job Assignment* scenes by giving a poetic though in its progression from star to ironing[23] to gravestone tragic picture of lives. The earlier

---

of "the people" enters through a door set up in the middle of the field, and goes through a series of stations that signify the process of a complete life. Each is given a face mask, climbs a ladder to look at a star (which dangles from the end of a telescope), works at an ironing board, pays homage to a little house with a family of tiny puppets by placing a stone on it (a funeral gesture?), visits the Gentleman Angel who shows him his face in a mirror, gets his Dance of Death costume, and disappears through the door he entered. The death dance is peaceful, with none of the expressionistic exaggeration of the medieval form that celebrates the triumph of death. When the last puppeteer is through Death's door they all knock it down, and carry off, standing on the door, a figure wearing a robe bearing the words "All People." This is done to a wildly rollicking tune called Charlotte's Wag that is the appropriate music for this easy triumph over Death. The order born from such transcendental mayhem is clearly some notion of a human community, and not a pious mystagogy. The *Circus* is an elaborate celebration of life with a nod to death and the evil, a divine low comedy that displays, in Kafka's phrase, "a great careless prodigality." ' — (Barry Goldensohn, *Peter Schumann's Bread and Puppet Theater*, '77.)

Charlotte's Wag:

© Sid Blum

23. The particular chore in the *Hands* scene — there may have been others — exemplifying how a person's life settles down to doing chores — was a woman's household chore. I.e. there is an appreciation of working women, though particularly housewives, here. It was first expressed in *Emilia* of '70 (cf. supra) and later — '78/'79 — by his creation of the figure of The Washerwoman (cf. infra). Elka thinks she was instrumental in the emergence of this figure and thinks of a character she contributed to the '74 circus as significant stage in the development from Emilia to the Washerwoman figure:

'. . . in the '74 circus I know some of the things Peter was saying, he was going to go out and find a character — I'm not sure he was saying it then but I had the idea of a character being a simple, I guess the prototype of the Washerwoman and I had these different articles of clothing, a short sleeved brown shirt and then a sort of tucky kind of maternity blouse that was printed checkered fabric like patches, but printed on, not real patches, and then an apron and this skirt and I somehow thought of all these things being laid on some-view that people's life generally consists in going through the gestures of a social role — a specialization — job — foisted on them by Society and weakly accepted by them, foreclosing their realization of human potential, at least for the moment no longer seems Schumann's dominant or only one. It was Schumann's view when in the mid-50s he decided he wasn't going through with letting himself be schooled as professional sculptor. I have quoted his friend Starosky to the effect that Schumann's objection to modern society ('civilization') focused on this alienatory aspect of it. The view ties in with his predominant focus, during the early '70s, on the crowd-individual opposition. It reemerges in his work *(Diagonal Man)* toward the end of the '70s. The view of *Hands* accords with his mid-70s willingness to celebrate with a community of fellow sharers of tragic individual fates doing their job as he does his the transcendence of individual tragedy in the nature-cradled recurrence of the birth-life-death cycle.

The sideshows served partly to eliminate irrelevances from the main show, Schumann's own, the circus-play-pageant sequence, partly to relieve his puppeteers' discontent at always doing Schumann's thing, not their own and the resulting pressures from them on him. They effectively, over the years, proved to his puppeteers that they were incapable of doing their own thing. The circus sideshows, at least the ones I have seen, have, for ten years now, been dismal: imitative (of Schumann), crudely naive, witless, graceless and inept. Among the '74 sideshows: a *Potato Dance* that Elka had worked on, a show of Nancy Kendall's with Sacred Harp music, *The Potato Eaters*, done with the Schumann kids by Paul Zaloom, Sir John Casey's *Water Show*, done by the bank of the Winooski: the River spirit emerges from the waters in a big and very heavy fiberglass mask made by Bill Whelan, an experiment, and Sir John in a wrinkled Red Demon mask throws a pail of water at him as little cardboard boats with perhaps little straw huts on them burn in the river, their crews of nudes copulating on the sand dunes under a big head suspended from a tree, its body a blue flowered tent. (Schumann, interviews, December '82 and '83.) There was also a sideshow by the master himself, more or less his last attempt at marionettry, done with child-size stuffed dummies, *The Golden Shoe*.[2]

---

body and not trying to look like a beautiful young girl with long, long hair, but trying to look very dumpy and ordinary and that this character would be doing these very home — you know — homespun, ordinary tasks like hanging out the laundry or housework or whatever. And I think I did that. I wore it and then the mask was picked out, or the mask is one of the black faced, black women's faces.' — (Elka Schumann, interview, '83.)

24. '(Elka: There was a lot of preparation made for (the '74 circus) because we conceived of this format of having afternoon sideshows going at the same time and you had written all these texts, pages and pages and pages of stories that you had pinned up all over the place so that people could look at the stories and pick out a story and you would then find the puppets and you would rehearse with them and hardly anybody did that ... These little

148

The circus' Christian musical play was *Jephthah*, to the music, simplified as to its orchestration and sung by Marc Estrin's Plainfield Community Choir, of the oratorio of the same name by Giacomo Carissimi, the 17th-century developer of the oratorio proper, i.e. the oratorio unaccompanied by dramatic action:[25] done in the Cate Farm clay pit with its 50 ft. walls: a play on filial submission and acceptance of fate,[26] derived from the story of Jephthah, a good general though the son of a whore, who as reward for a victory pledged to Jehovah whatever would meet him at his door on his return, which turned out to be his only child, his nameless daughter, greeting him with drums and dancing, and who slew her, fulfilling his contract – the morality of the Jews and mine – though allowing her a two months' delay in the mountains by herself, from which she returned, a properly obedient daughter. Do your duty and be mindful of God, a life well lost is life gained.

Sir John Casey out of old lumber had built the junk ghost of a castle on

---

shows seemed to swing between you having a lot of control over them and determining what the content of these little shows are and kind of ordering, directing it much more, and then loosening up and then other people taking much more independent paths of directions. In a way it seems like an attempt to find a happy medium between too much control and not enough control and too much looking for a theme.) Lots of them I didn't like. (. . . even though you chose the theme, but here people had their own puppets and used them.) Well, I was working with such a big group and working with people with lots of the puppeteers in the company, the necessity arises that people *have* to do their own directing, and the circus is a very good time to put in that kind of broad reaching-out to different people's directing, and that's been done every year, with the other people's directing jobs included. It isn't always satisfying. It isn't what I would like to stand around or to stick with or to leave as it is – it's very unhappy that it's only a few performances.' — (Schumann, interview, '79.)

25. 'It was not incidental music. It was a very, very close collaboration . . . As I was working on that music, I had it on tape when the score was not available to me. I really learned it by heart and it was, to me, a very overwhelming piece of music, a powerful piece of music. I really wanted to bend into it and have that music come out and not disturb it with activities. I think we did something that was very sparse, not great or overwhelming so the music could come through. The major effect of that performance was really that of stillness because it was in a strong place, in a gravel pit into which we had hung all therse *Simple Light* faces, so they were hanging there in the gravel pit above the castle and that was mainly what you saw visually. Then the other movements were seldom, infrequent and with long stills and slow motions in them so there was, I feel, no disturbance with the music. That was the thing that I would have loved to pick up again and do again. It was also so special for that place I don't want to do it anymore (laugh) . . .' — (Schumann, interview, '83.)

26. 'The strongest thing in the story is not even the biblical story. The strongest thing in the Jephthah story is the acceptance of the daughter, that she accepts it, that she doesn't protest it in contrast to Iphigenia or other women figures who suffered that, and the way she accepts it and walks into the mountains to think about her fate. That's, musically, the high point of the thing.' — (Schumann, interview, '83.)

the pit's desert bottom, and the great crowd masks from *Simple Light*, strung around the pit here and there provided the basic audience. The Prophet, a large crude mask on a tripod with an aura of branchlike wig, mutely spoke from the left. The general had been doubled into the black figure of a magician (Margo Sherman) and into a white-robed, white-masked soul astride a small black beast. This soul's ears had been cut open, for the general 'listens, but he doesn't listen', and as the tale's words were sung by the chorus grouped at the right beneath a small junk-tower on which sat the bearded narrator, the general would take the Hebrew words, writ on fabric out of the Prophet's mouth and pass them through his soul's ears. The daughter, Schumann, her face the sweet face with the long hair that had been the Mother of God's eleven years earlier — Schumann's face for stilt walking since a parade in '71 — met him tall on stilts in red clothes, but left for the hills, her fate announced, small, dressed in white — stiff, bulky jersey — her face changed, crooked, an asymmetrical face. (Schumann, interview, '83.)

Schumann had done the rural Uncle Sam on stilts in parades, and later regularly did him at the conclusion of his silly circus, leading his group around the arena, but this is only for show: for art and for his heart's delight he goes on stilts — ever longer — in drag, a subtle business, as more than Angel he is like Jephthah's daughter the graceful virgin, the aethereal moonlight, we might say (he is all in white), that is all that in his renun-ciatory moods he would allow of dark carnal love, Isolde beyond the sword: an ideal of womanhood. I might add that these woman stilt dances of his, featured in subsequent *Circuses*, are all that he has allowed himself as fulfillment of his early ambitions to be a dancer; that they are superbly beautiful; and that as his stilts have grown longer, they have become the only true circus acts at his circuses, the only ones done for real, i.e. requir-ing skill and skill of the sort at the heart of circus and delighting the people, viz. pushed far enough to enact something at the evident edge of the corporeally humanly possible, a human miracle. All his other perfor-mers have been forced to just fool around. Also it's a dangerous business, especially for a man with a bad back, and Schumann in fact has injured himself stilt dancing. His dance of welcome for the returning general in Jephthah inaugurated a period of stilt puppets in his theatre, often birds.

The Pageant was the combat of the obviously vicious and evil, in fact hellish Red with the obviously benign (but here the first to attack) as-sembled White and their victory over them in combat: death of the White, the puppets fall into the grass: all this as part of Nature, mind you; the victors withdraw, the dead lie there, but lo and behold! from afar a ship comes sailing! all over the meadows green! and the fallen rise, that is the white-clad puppeteers emerge from the white recumbent rags and celastic and join the miraculous progress of the heavenly ship — it is the colors of northern summer sky and clouds: no doubt to some appropriate

150

song of praise. Hardly *The Storm is Here*: this is a resurrection.[27] It is in fact a development of the resurrection that the combined radical and hippie factions of Schumann's group in '69 for a while, till Schumann again got rid of it, imposed on his *Cry*; a development by way of the resurrection of the puppeteers at the end of the '72 *Stations*, rising to sing *Christ*

---

27. This 'first big pageant' (Schumann, interview, '79) started with 'a tiny little act . . . , where (Paul Zaloom as Bob the Butcher, wearing the first of the White Horse Butcher masks) was playing a drum in one corner of the big field where the pageant was performed. Dressed all in white, to start off a scene that consisted of some animals, Nancy Tyndall, playing a shepherdess, with four sheep heads mounted off sticks around her, so she could spin with them, and somebody else playing a ram — two people playing a ram. Then there was a Little People activity with an umbrella and three white masks — everything was in white with a little bit of black in it . . . These are two big tiny little scenes that preceded large entrances of big things that came. And started off the pageant in the green field underneath the hill where people were sitting.' — (Schumann, interview, December '82.)

(. . . There was a drummer, a part of the White parade that came in. White Drummer drumming. Then — and a little flag waving, a white flag. Then the sheep dance and some other strange group with umbrella approaching from different directions. That was the introduction to a giant parade that consisted of simultaneous parades that went all at the same time, white parades . . . the next thing must have been the white — the appearance of white. Probably horses — there were different orders: horses were in a military order but not physically attached to each other. They had a certain routine to do — that involves forward motion, stopping, prancing, hind leg movement, turning, advancing again, and so on. Abreast movements, I think. And then, there were single file movements of women that were attached on a long string, followed by a Great Warrior. A different Great Warrior — a white Great Warrior — that was used behind them, driving them forward. It was that — it was an abreast line of horses, or the single file women, with several — not just one Great Warrior, maybe, but several similar characters following the women — the line of women . . . One deep line of Vietnamese Ladies tied to each other by one white rope and then a group of Vietnamese masks also, but I don't think they were — I don't know where they marched because right behind them was a Great Warrior, a white Great Warrior with two swords. And then further towards the west was a row of horses that were walking abreast. But there was another group, the Indian Chiefs . . . And, out of another direction, the Indian Chiefs. The timing was delicate — there were things that had to converge at the right moment, in the right place — so I don't remember in what way that was achieved, but there were signals for people to start. And everything came from a different direction, so that the whole field slowly became filled with these white figures. And only after that was pretty well done to completion — where we wanted that arrangement — is when the red people started coming up — because they moved much faster, and they were much more consolidated. They had only one big movement. And that was the carrying in of the big Yama (the King of Hell in *Birdcatcher* (SSB)) on a tripod and the rousing and loud movements of all kinds of red figures: Dragons, Demons, etcetera, that would carry him, but also surround him — and that also included the big Demons from *The Birdcatcher* — all of that would push forward and set up a battle order at the end of that — on both sides and behind Yama, who was lifted up at the end of it. Then, when all that battle array came to a halt, the battle started, and that consisted of several moves of Red against White and White was first — in the form of the biggest Indian Chief. He was taken down; then came other chiefs slowly came down, then the Ladies came down, and etcetera. All by different sections of the Red fighting different sections of the White . . . The horses approached in abreast line over the meadow and the *Birdcatcher* Demons would approach the line of horses with their spears and seemingly pierce them and the horses would rear and fall, then

151

Is Risen. But its significance is now neither the combative and communal Resistance one of '69, nor the religious and individualistic one of '72, but a new one combining aspects of both, placing man and his history into the self-recreative cycle of a cosmic life.

Schumann's eventual grandiose concept of 'circus' and his equally grandiose concept of a 'pageant' in 1974 emerged from the scattered fragments of Schumann's magnificent concept of 'circus' as one all-enveloping big and brilliant and funny show in which the prestidigitation of artifice would create the fictive image of the utmost human skill and daring (essence of the circus, the jugglers and acrobats of the Middle Ages in Christian bloodlessness recreating the heroism of the gladiators) and as a weave of the gay, laughable and childlike, a scatter of small springtime marsh and meadow wild flower delights that drape and almost hide the dark shapes, breaking through, of Life's contours, dark because by their creator by no means bereft of the lineaments of the death of which life lives, the succulent rot of summer, fall's decay, winter's recurrent quietus, the death of each of us, the deaths of commonwealths, the death of disintegration, the death of death-dealing intent, the death of thought. This emergent concept of 'circus', first realized, approximately in 1974, was that of a sequentially structured cycle of entertainments, guiding the common man from a catharsis by harmlessly gay foolishness down into the somber valley of tears of finite individual life, grimly contained by the demand of painful right action, and up again to a truer purification, both grim and gay, by the contemplation of the Larger Movement in which the living dies and the good is defeated by bad, but both go on: the concept of a theatre of nature showing the true eternity of the procreative sacrifice of the fecund and in which human life, a matter of combat, and like other life, seen at a distance, would appear very light, almost a dream recalled.

The circuses up to and including the one of '74 had all been small affairs, travelling or stationary had a college student zero audience, did not have THE PEOPLE or THE AMERICAN PEOPLE for an audience, and though perhaps fresher and by a raw innocence more beguiling in their 'silly circus' parts than later ones, dragged along a pretty heavy load of

---

another devil would come running, but it was an arbitrary thing that happened. There was no choreography to it other than that they had to be killed. Whereas, with the Butchers (spring of '75 onward (SSB)) there was a whole dance made out of the struggling between the Butcher and the horses . . . Then, when everything was down, the Yama stuff, yelling and screaming, running off and at that point the boat would start. All the liberated people – the people who had died and left their costumes in the field – ran off and dressed up in blue and came out with the Ark – out of the gravel pit that was on the side of that field. That was the final movement, and then that boat travelled to the river – little boats were set into the river . . . it ended up with setting little paper boats with candles into the river – that then would float off into the river.' — (Schumann, interview, '83 and Schumann, interview, December '82.)

incriminatory political charges and complaints, and all, even the '74 one still, lacked somewhat in identity — the audience got a whiff of this and that — 'affirmation of Life', say — but really didn't know what was going on: the fun and the Jeremiads didn't add up.

9. *Grey Lady Cantatas.*

These 'cantatas' are a series of five plays (*Grey Lady Cantatas II-VI*, 1970-75[1]) focussing on the travails of a single Grey Lady, an elderly woman: an individual, Schumann's first puppet-representation of an individual, though as yet only The Individual, not A Particular Individual. the first one, *Grey Lady Cantata II*, could be viewed as a 'cantata' in a sense derived from the 17th century Italian use of the term — a 'declamatory narrative or scene in recitative, held together by a primitive aria repeated at intervals' (D.F. Tovey, *Encyclopedia Britannica*): speechless, without dialogue, scene titles or verbal narrative, its voice the image of the figure of the Grey Lady, who actions (more or less) alternate with bits of music, the same piece of music, vocally or instrumentally rendered, at first discordantly, progressively more melodically, a complete and melodic rendition of the whole piece[2] introducing the dance that concludes the play.

The musical development of *Gray Lady Cantata III* similarly had the form of a progressive coming-together of the tune, which Schumann may have thought of as form analogous to that of Bach church cantatas in which the successive movements are founded on the same chorale tune. But the term 'cantata' in no way applies to the later cantatas.[3]

---

1. The *Bach Cantata#140* of 1967, was called a 'grey lady cantata' only in retrospect, and differs from them in having a lot of Grey Ladies in it instead of focusing on an individual one, as do II-VI. The idea of the grey-lady-as-heroine format goes back to the Coney Island 1967 *The Grey Lady of Manhattan*, a playlet that may never have been performed.

2. 'After the whole thing was over and she dances with the Angel of Death, all the people in the company had to rapidly change into Ladies and Gentlemen costumes, there'd be knocking at a door, knock, knock, knock, and somebody would come and open the door and there they would all be, dressed up in outrageous Lady and Gentleman costumes, and we would have to walk up to the stage and like a small town glee club, plus the instruments, we would have to sing the whole song very sort of righteous and pompous and ridiculous.' — (Sherman, interview, '79.)

3. 'Sometimes it is unfair to describe a show as if it was a concert of the different operations of puppets or of the different possibilities of what masks and puppets can do, and an experiment for that. The *Grey Lady Cantata (II)* and . . . the first *Circus* were more musical experiments than anything else. The *Gray Lady Cantata* was based on the five notes that comprised the little tune by Thomas Tallis and we just tried to use that as the only sound — plus a very few other sounds like the jug (the "narrator" pseudo-narrated on a jug strapped around his neck (SSB)) . . . The *Grey Lady Cantata* happens to be something that has very limited improvisational possibilities. It's really a tightly woven and composed piece where every little move is very rehearsed and strict. It isn't a cantata. The word 'cantata' was simply chosen because of that one song. It doesn't really comply with (the rules that a musical composition has to comply with besides being basically *a cappella* in order to be a cantata (SSB)). But the composition of the piece was as organized as a cantata or as any classical piece of music — slow, fast, largo, and fast again. (Elka: What was fast in it? There was almost nothing fast.) Yes, these were very contrasted, if not extremely strong

154

'Rehearsals on very different experiments that ended up with — that was later called the *Grey Lady Cantata ‡II*' (Schumann, interview, '79) had been done when Schumann first settled at Goddard, in June '71 (ibid.), but most of the work was done in July and the play, one of his longer pieces — according to Sherman, interview, '79, about 40 minutes long — was first performed the last evening of the August 16-21 Festival of the Puppeteers of America at the University of Connecticut in Storrs, Connecticut. It was done again in September in the Cate Farm barn, and then, 'But with a new crew', after tryouts February 12, '71 in the Cate Farm hay barn, in Spaulding High School 'the early morning and evening' (Goddard Trimester Calendar, *Educational Resources*, for spring 1971) of February 19, in New York City, with *Emilia*, February 24-March 7, '71,

---

differentiations in the speeds, but the scenes *were* organized that way — in that how crowded they were, how slow they ran, how long they lasted, so the whole organization is more or less from a musical standpoint.' — (Schumann, interview, '79.)

The musical interlude of *Grey Lady Cantata II* was a tune by Thomas Tallis, with words by Harvey Spevak.

(The Word of Mouth Roundbook, '73)

in Boston and Providence and at Kent State University in Ohio in March and April, and, after various performances in the U.S. and Canada during the remainder of '71, was taken on a tour to Europe, where it was performed as first part of a program, the second part of which was *Grey Lady Cantata III*, December '71-February '72. It was Schumann's first Vermont production, 'a result of the work with students' (Schumann, interview, '79), both as regards the puppets built for it — the Gentleman Angel, a stylistically (as well as technically, it was a backpack puppet) new type of puppet, namely an enigmatic one, a figure of divine detachment corresponding to Schumann's new-found own, a Purple or Sunset Beast, indicative of nature's grandeur and indifference to human suffering, new Grey Ladies, one-headed, the heroine two-handed, the others hand- and arm-less — and as regards the 'experiments' with these and the first two performances. But most of the students were unavailable for the American and European tours and the New York City run the next year. Regular, i.e. old-time puppeteers replaced them. 'Most people from the *Grey Lady* group (performing in Connecticut) were students who I never saw again, who did just this job' (Schumann, interview, '79.)

Like *Difficult Life*, the play just before, *Grey Lady Cantata II* was made for a stage imitating a theatre (Schumann, interview, '79): framed and elevated, the performance space a curtain-sided box, with a (grey, cross-pulled rather than as in *Difficult Life* roll-up) curtain in front. Schumann later sees this staged theatre as the non-narrative equivalent of a narrative form (we might say it provides an indicational form), as yet radically absent in *Cry* ('69), first broached in *Difficult Life* ('70).

'the difference is that the *Uncle Fatso* events (in *Difficult Life* (SSB)) all these tender and violent movements of little puppets, were confronted with Uncle Fatso and his cronies sitting at a table having a good time, playing cards and drinking and being served — it was a *living* room contrasted with a cityscape and with the world. In the *Grey Lady Cantata*, there was a narrator with a little band who, instead of telling a story, rang a bell that made a large blue puppet open a curtain, and then inside the curtain you would have insights into either landscapes or living rooms, so there's a big difference between that *situation*, that was *created* there: the *narration* which wasn't a real *narration* but rather just the occasion for it, the moment before such a narration happens, was the situation of the *Grey Lady Cantata*. There is a same situation as in an old fashioned picture-story-telling event where a narrator has a stick and a fiddle and points with the stick to the picture and flips it over when he is finished telling that. The *Grey Lady Cantata* was very much like such a picture story, with a picture of an inside, populated by Grey Lady Puppets. The narrator who always was a narrator without telling a story about it, we didn't use any words for that, would progress from one scene to another in the manner of a narrator. That was something I very much *wanted* and that I tried in different ways with this *Grey Lady Cantata* and with other things, several productions later on.' (Schumann, inteview, '79.)

This gesture of communication, the showing of something, is characteristic
156

of his work of this period, in a radical shift replaces his '60s mode, exhortation.

The play was framed, visually presented, by the combination of a little band, cello and violin/drum, stage-right and two Blue Lady puppets stage-left, the performer of one of whom, Avram Patt, a new Goddard recruit, by banging a metal pipe mounted between his puppet hands against metal pipes mounted on the stage announced scene openings, the performer of the other opening and closing the curtain between scenes. A concluding song and dance, the singing sedate and formal in contrast to the fragmentary and discordant musical interludes, the dance gay and stately, in contrast to the play's stark depression, the dead heroine one of the dancers, similarly framed the play, pointed to it as theatre – Kourilsky saw this finale as alienating device, saying, 'look at how we do it, it's only a show, it's not real': 'Suddenly, after the death of the Grey Lady, a group of 'rejoicing' ladies and gentlemen in fancy dress enter and blast out a song . . .' — (Kourilsky, *Dada, TDR* #61.)

It was staged using strings, but whereas in *Difficult Life* ('70) both objects and some puppets (little Johnny puppets, the crony dummy puppets), and in *Revenge of the Law* ('72) a dummy puppet, in *McLeod* (72) a dog were moved by strings, in *Grey Lady Cantata II* eventually only things were so operated: in the first scene.[4] This was to make the point how insecure the solace of comforts is these days – they can fly away at any time. But the effect was to enhance the play's image of passive suffering.[5]

Three grey and black backdrops – the play was all in grey, black and white – were used, at least in the '71/'72 productions. One was used for

---

4. '(Elka: were marionette techniques used in the bigger shows?) No, it's *wrong* to say that. It's the other way *around*. *Grey Lady Cantata* (II) was conceived of as a marionette show, with a bridge, it was built that way. Then there were strings *left* at the end of the show. It was started off *entirely* as a marionette show with the Grey Lady strung on strings, and later on we decided *not* to do that, but to put *people* into the puppets, then we ended up using *some* strings. The coat of the young man was operated from a bridge, the airplane was operated from a bridge, the blanket was operated from the bridge, so just a few objects were left to be operated from strings . . .' — (Schumann, interview, '79.)

5. J. Schmidt, a Lukacs-quoting, i.e. neo-Marxist German reviewer objected to this:
'(Das Stück) zelebriert das Todesurteil das Krieg auch und gerade für die, die ihn nicht wollen, bedeutet: die Unterlegenheit der Menschen, die gross sind, unter dem Bomber, der aus der Spielzeugkiste kommen könnte; die Ergebenheit eines Manschen, der sein Schicksal nicht in die eigene Hand nehmen kann. Besonders diese Ergebenheit wird sinnfällig. Vieles, zum Beispiel der Soldatenmantel des Einberufenen, schwebt den Figuren an Bändern entegegen, als sei es der Himmel, der es schickt.' — (J. Schmidt, *Lady in zweierlei Grau*, review in a Hamburg, Germany, paper, January '72.)
'Die Strippen . . . die der Himmel hier knüpft (was wörtlich zu nehmen ist; der Lady schwebt das Totentuch genauso marionettenhaft entgegen wie ihrem Sohn die Kriegskluft), lehren allzuviel Schicksalsergebenheit. Sie lehren nicht und niemanden, sein Schnicksal in die eigenen Hände zu nehmen.' — (J. Schmidt, *Des Teufels*, review of Hamburg *Grey Lady II* and *Grey Lady III* showings in the Frankfurter Rundschau.)

the interior scenes showing the Grey Lady's routine life (Scene 1) and her death (Scene 6), this one showing her shitty little house's interior, her 'gute Stube' — painted window onto landscape with cloud, nail-hung double portrait of the two old sisters, flower in vase on chest, lamp hanging from ceiling. One backdrop bare except for distant trees, her house with the long furrow of a road leading to it and a solitary airplane peopling the grey sky for the agony that is her life, was used for her flight into and back out of nature (Scenes 2-5). The third one, totally bare, just grey, was used for the last scene, her post mortem fling with the courtly Angel of Death. The clash in the interior scenes of the two unrealities of painting and of three-dimensional puppets is shocking. In some productions of *Grey Lady Cantata II* apparently the landscape backdrop for the Grey Lady's flight was moved progressively further away, to indicate her motion, which would have been an application of Schumann's ideal of an *active* use of painting as theatrical element.

Schumann told the story of the play in the program of its New York City production. The following in footnotes supplements his tale by stage directions of September '70 and by the appropriate sections from the stage script of March 1972.

'The Grey Lady is at home.
The son sits in the corner.
The gossips are there for a visit,
drinking Schaefer's beer and Ballantine's
ale and eating nothing all the time.
Behind them is the Black Angel (I don't
think anybody knows who he really is).
Jesus, the flower pot tips over!
The gossips are so surprised.
Their hats fly up in the air.
And they go on eating a lot of nothing,
drinking a lot of beer.
And the spoons disappear out of their
hands and the beer cans jump away from
their lips.
Let's go, they say, and they all go.
So the chairs go away too and the
fancy sofa and the table goes away too.
And the man puts on his boots and his
stupid dangerous coat and he says
goodbye to his mother, and that's it.
And the Grey Lady cries and the Angel
leaves.
So the Grey Lady is left all alone,
only a little bird flies through the
window.[6]

'1. *Home.*
Gossips, Angel,
Man, Grey Lady
sit Drink Eat
Flowers fall
Hats fly
Dish and spoon exit
Gossips exit
Table & chair exit
Man says goodbye
Exits
Grey Lady cries
Angel exits
Bird flies

6. 'Home. Gossips sit around table. Grey Lady sits. Son sits. Gentleman Angel sits. Coat

And away she goes with the little bird and she comes to a white little house in the middle of the fields.	2. *Landscape.* Bird flies Grey Lady enters
She is tired.	Sits
She sits down.	
And an airplane zooms through the air and many women with baskets come into the field and they work and sing a nice song.	Airplane flies Women & baskets Walk Turn Sit Sing
But more airplanes zoom around and everybody is afraid.	Airplanes fly All look
Suddenly a horrible noise comes down on them and that's death and they	*Dragon Smoke &* *Loud Noise*[7]

---

hangs. Big Woman Blue 1 is out front, hits chime for beginning and end of every scene. Big Woman Blue 2 opens and closes blue curtain. Band sits in front, on the side. Two fiddles. Maybe a cello. Drum. Birdwhistle, etc.

FLOWERPOT:	Clash! (tips over)
HATS:	(Fly up)
GOSSIPS:	deedle deedle deedle deedle deedle deedle deedle deedle deedle
GENTLEMAN ANGEL:	(smokes)
GOSSIP 1:	(smells flower, flower flies off)
GOSSIPS:	deedle deedle deedle deedle deedle deedle deedle deedle deedle dee
GENTLEMAN ANGEL:	(smokes)
BEER CANS:	(fly off, one after the other)
BLACK LADY:	(exits)
GOSSIP 1:	(exits)
GOSSIP 2:	(exits)
GOSSIP 3:	(exits)
GOSSIP 4:	(exits)
CHAIR 1:	(exits)
CHAIR 2:	(exits)
CHAIR 3:	(exits)
CHAIR 4:	(exits)
GENTLEMAN ANGEL:	(smokes)
TABLE:	(exits)
SON:	(puts on boots)
COAT:	(wraps itself around son)
GREY LADY:	(hands son knapsack)
SON:	(embraces Grey Lady)
COAT:	(pulls son out)
GENTLEMAN ANGEL:	(bows, exits)
2 CHAIRS:	(Clash! tip over)
GREY LADY:	(cries crystal tear)
LITTLE WHITE BIRD:	(dwuit dwuit dwuit dwuit dwuit dwuit dwuit (flies around)

CURTAIN'
(Stage script, *Grey Lady Cantata II*, Scene 1, March 1972.)

7. The two instrumentalists put on death masks and one of them does a drum solo – when Schumann did it in Toronto, the reviewer thought it 'terrifying'.

159

all get wounded[8]
It hurts a lot but she crawls away[9]
Then the sun sets[10] and the sky turns pink.
And the sun is like a beautiful big animal.[11]

3. *Landscape*.
Hands and Grey Lady
Sun sets
Grey Lady rises
Leaves

---

8. This is the end of Scene 2.
   'Between Scene 1 and Scene 2 band plays three times:

BUM! BUM! (soft)

Outside. Fields.

LITTLE WHITE BIRD:	dwuit dwuit dwuit dwuit dwuit dwuit dwuit
GREY LADY:	(feeds bird, bird exits)
LITTLE BLACK AIRPLANE:	hmmmmmmmmm hmmmmmmm (jugsound done by Big Woman Blue 1)
GREY LADIES:	(enter with buckets, sit down, sing)
AIRPLANE:	(continuously through end of Scene 2)
GREY LADIES:	(up)
ASHES:	(thrown on Grey Ladies)
LIGHT:	(fades away)

CURTAIN

   Band put on skullmasks. One flickers the light, one swings a tincan rattle and one drums full blast until sound of police whistle.'
   (Scene 2, stage script.)
9. '. . . a plain of prostrate dying women with two gigantic hands groping to emerge from the morass' — (Gussow, *Peter Schumann's Giant Puppets Provide a Spooky Experience, Village Voice*, February 25, '71.)
10. End of Scene 3.

'STRANGE BIRD: tooh tooh
GREY LADY: (gets up, crawls out)
   Fields, very little light, which slowly grows.
   Grey Ladies on floor, hardly moving. Buckets on floor.
STRANGE BIRD: tooh tooh
PINK SKY: (comes down)
SUNSETBEAST: hooooooooo! (done by one or two washing
   machine agitator horns)
   (head of beast, then curtain)
   Band pull red sheet over their heads and continue
   hooooooooo! after scene 3 and during scene 4.'
   (Stagescript, Scene 3.)
11. End of Scene 4.
   'Pink sky.
SUNSETBEAST: hooooooooo! (enters, lies down, turns head)
   Band continues hooooooooo! until scene 5 starts.
   (Stagescript, Scene 4)

CURTAIN

160

And the Grey Lady crawls through the woods
Among the worms and the snakes.
And that little bird flies down to her
again.
But it falls and the worms carry it away.
And the Grey Lady keeps dragging herself along[12]
Until she comes home.
Her sister is there and she helps the Grey Lady
to lie down in her bed and she dies.[13]
But it isn't so bad.
Because the Gentleman Angel is there and he
asks her for a dance.
And they dance together.
The Grey Lady and the Angel with the black
wings for a long time.
And the whole world makes music for them.
And that's the end.'[14]

4. *Woods.*
Wind blows
Sun rises
Grey Lady crawls
Bird falls'
(Stage directions,
GLC II, Cate Farm,
September '70.
I don't have the
stage directions
for the remainder
of this earlier
version.)

---

12. End of Scene 5.
    'Pink sky. Wind. Falling leaves.
PINK SKY: (moves up, exposes woods behind)
GREY LADY: (crawls across)
WORMS: (follow her)
LITTLE WHITE
BIRD: twuit twuit twuit (falls into worms)
WORMS: (drag away little white bird)

CURTAIN

BAND: Bum!
(3 times) Bum! (soft)'
    (Stagescript, Scene 5)
13. End of Scene 6.
    'Home. Bed. Sister sits.
GREY LADY: (crawls in)
SISTER: (helps her up, puts her to bed)
BLANKET: (covers her)

CURTAIN'

    (Stagescript, Scene 6)
14. End of Scene 7 and of the play.
    'Home or Heaven. Gentleman Angel sits. Grey Lady dead.
GENT. ANGEL: (bows)
BLANKET: Gong! (flies up)
GREY LADY: (gets up)
FANCY LADIES
& GENTLEMEN: Knock! Knock!
BAND: Come in
FANCY LADIES
& GENTLEMEN: (enter, sing:)
    The sun it rises in the day and in the evening

The reviewers saw the show as a show about war. The Americans, generally quite impressed, saw it as a horror show, the Germans – as Schumann had conquered the French intelligentsia in '68, with *Fire*, so he won over the German on his '71/'72 tour with the *Grey Lady Cantatas II* and *III* and with *Birdcatcher* – saw it as realistic portrayal in Kabuki form:

'. . . the huge puppets, wearing what looked like rotting shrouds, moved to the slow dirge of eerie sounds – distant foghorns, bird whistles, the thumping of a bass drum, and the cry of dissonant fiddles and the clang of metal against metal.'

(Leo Seligsohn, *Eerie puppet show, Newsday*, February 25.)

'Imagine the ancient stone heads on Easter Island having bodies. Suppose them transformed into papier-mâché puppets eight to ten feet tall. Picture these puppets moving as if they were in some prehistoric slow-motion silent film. This is hierophantic theater, as old as time, as young as the infancy of man. To see *The Grey Lady Cantata* as performed by the Bread and Puppet Theater is rather like waiting in the mystic whispering groves of Delphi to hear the oracle speak. Despite the primordial trappings, this virtual dumb show is as contemporary as tomorrow's bombing raid. It is a cantata of death, an immensely said and strangely affecting tale of the wartime slaughter of innocents.

Glass Tear. The show begins amind the banal frivolity of a beer party. A group of the Grey Lady's giddy friends have come into guzzle Budweiser and Ballantine's ale. These are not puppets, but men and women wearing decadent, citified masks. At the sound of a funeral chime, which is actually two lead pipes clanged together by the agent of fate at the side of the stage, the beer cans are whisked away. The guests leave and the stage is occupied by a puppet father and mother and a masked son.

The father looks much like Churchill and he smokes a white cigar, but the black wings on his shoulders signify that he is the Angel of Death. The mother, or Grey Lady, is the *mater dolorosa*, a woman of sorrowing countenance, possibly the mother of Christ; her huge supplicating hands resemble those of a pieta. She sends her son off to war and we feel that she knows he will be killed. A single glass tear slowly descends her right cheek. *Blare of Music*. A white dove of peace chirps

---

goes away. The moon it comes up in the night
and fades away in the morning light.
GREY LADY: (dances with Gentleman Angel)
BUGLES &
DRUMS: tuh-tuh. clash. bum!'

(Stagescript of March 1972, Scene 7.)

15. '. . . this text that came out of it was supposedly out of a meeting where all of the students who were working on it said "What does it mean? We can't do the show." So he had to write this rather – thing which looks much more like poetry than a description of the play but then everything was all right after that, nevertheless.' — (Konnoff, interview, '83.)

briefly, but flies off as a black widow spider as a model plane wings its way with a searching deliberateness across the rear stage-curtain. We see the bomber's victims-to-be, other Grey Lady puppets. They sway and huddle together in mute terror. We feel their pain all the more accutely because, like wounded animals, they cannot articulate it. Think of Picasso's *Guernica* unfolding in slow motion and you have the image of these women dying. The evening ends with a jolly blare of music. The Black Angel and the Grey Lady wheel to the music – a Totentanz, the dance of death . . . for anyone who wants to seek out and comprehend the deepest well-springs of drama, it is an hour well spent.'

(T.E. Kalem, *Dance of Death, Time*, March 8, '71.)

' "Grey Lady Cantata" hat zwei Hauptfiguren: die grosse tragische Puppe der grey lady – und einen schwarzberockten Herrn, der rotwangig die Zigarre pafft hinter einer familiaren Tischgesellschaft. Mit einem fliegen den Tanten und Cousinen der grey lady die Tassen und Teller davon; man erhebt sich betreten. Dann weht es Tisch und Stühle hinaus, und auch der Schwarze erhebt sich paffend. Als er sich wendet, sind auf seinem Rücken die schwarzen Flügel des Todesengels zu sehen. Indessen schnürt still der Sohn die Militärstiefel; die graue Frau nimmt Abschied vom Soldatensohn. Weint. Grosse Glasklunker am Bindfaden aus dem Augenschlitz der Puppe.

Das Schicksal der verlassenen Frau, nicht das des Soldaten: ihre Welt und Visionen. (Denn "Soldatenleben" findet ausserhalb der Realität statt.) Ein zwitschernder Vogel empfängt sie im Freien, wo Bauersfrauen beten. Banal wie das Böse selbst ein Spielzeugbomber. Es splittert. Mehr Krach ist nicht nötig, credite expertis. Zeitlich verschoben, wie eben solches Unglück zum Bewusstsein kommt, setzt das Schlagzeug-Bombardement ein. Später die Niedergemähten. Diese grossen, grauen Puppen sind ganz andere Leichen als Schauspieler sie vorstellen könnten. Über die Niedergemähten schnuppert der Kopf eines beast, Ungeheuers. Dann ein grausiger Sonnenaufgang: der Auftritt des beast, des Tiers aus dem Abgrund mit prächtigem Fell. Flucht der Frau. Hinter sich einen verknäulten Strick herziehend, in dem sich der Zwitschervogel fängt und stirbt. Mühsam schleppt sich die grey lady ins Haus, legt sich. Der Schwarzgeflügelte klopft an und lädt zum Totentanz.'

(Th. Hardtmann, '*Grey Lady Cantata', Theater Heute*, February '72.)

'In der zweiten Kantate der "Grey Lady Cantatas" (die erste mit ihren hundert grossen Puppen konnte in einem Theaterraum wie dem Malersaal nicht aufgeführt werden) wird gezeigt, wie ein Sohn in den Krieg muss. Der Vorgang des Abschieds wird in mehrere theatralische Bilder zerlegt. Einmal im Bild der unheimlichen Verschreckung und Isolierung: einer im Raum versammelten Gruppe werden an Fäden die Tassen und das Obst aus der Hand gerissen, die Stühle rutschen aus dem Raum. Dann in dem Vorgang der Zurüstung: die Uniform baumelt ebenfalls an Schnüren, legt sich wie von selbst um die Schultern des künftigen GI, der dann mit befremdlicher Geduld seine Stiefel zuschnürt. Schliesslich in einem erschreckend schönen Bild: zurück bleibt die Mutterpuppe. deren Riesenhände eine ohnmächtige Trauer ausdrücken – aus einem Augenschlitz der grossen Maske rinnt an einem Faden langsam ein glitzernder Glasscherben heraus. Das Bild einer Träne.

Mit so geduldig einfachen Mitteln arbeitet die Truppe stets. Bei einem Abschied werden im Hintergrund die hingetuschten Leinwandvorhänge nach und

163

nach entfernt. Ein immer distanzierteres Bild der Landschaft erscheint, immer mehr in die Vogelschau verzerrt. Zwischen Figuren, die sich aus der Gleichentfernung zuwinken, wächst eine traurig unendliche Entfernung.

Man mag das, wie das in manchen Besprechungen geschah, als die Darstellung einer fatalistischen Ohnmacht denunzieren. Doch wahrscheinlich übersieht man damit die dialektische Wirkmöglichkeit, die die Aktivitäten nicht auf der Bühne dem Zuschauer vorweg und damit abnimmt, ihn stattdessen vielleicht gerade durch die Ohnmacht ausserwirklicher Bilder auf eine Wirklichkeit verweist, die für ihre Zwangsläufigkeiten nicht die Mythen des Theaters, sondern die des Alltags bemüht.

Das Bread and Puppet jedenfalls macht sich für die Unübersetzbarkeit der Wirklichkeit immanent theatralische Übersetzungsmöglichkeiten zunutze:

Puppen, zu Gruppen zusammengeschweisst, füllen langsam die Bühne. Im Hintergrund wird plötzlich ein kleines schwarzes Flugzeug sichtbar, das den Illusionsgrad eines an einem Faden baumelnden Kinderspielzeugs hat. Die Szene verdunkelt sich, und über die Puppen rieselt Sand – ein Bild und ein Geräusch, das mit den konzentrierten Mitteln des "armen Theaters" schlagartig auch die sonstige Verlegenheit des Theaters annonciert, das sich den mörderischen Luftkrieg in Vietnam immer noch aus projizierten Wochenschauausschnitten holt.

Die Aufführungen sind das Ergebnis einer eindrucksvollen Konzentration, wie sie sich sonst nur in der Tradition des japanischen Theaters entwickeln konnte. Doch hat das Bread and Puppet, nicht vom Zwang einer langen, quasi akademischen Tradition belastet, eine rauhe Spontaneität.'

(H. Karasek, *Traumatische Genauigkeit, Theater Heute*, February '72.)

Grey Lady Cantata II, a reworking, in Schumann's Cate Farm period mode, of *A Man Says Goodbye to His Mother*, has no moral implications, it shows something. It returns to the original theme, the mother's suffering, dropping all concern with resistance, and depoliticizes it even further, focussing not on the war causing the suffering, nor on the guilt of waging it, but on that suffering.[16] The thinking by which he got *Grey Lady Cantata* II from *A Man* is an interesting example of artistic thinking: he thought: the mother of the killer IS the mother of the victim; and: killing the mother's son, the killer kills the mother – lyrical abstraction going to the essence of the matter. The instigation was his prior use of the Grey Lady figure in a play on the deaths of mothers, *Bach Cantata #140*.

---

16. This reorientation of concern makes *Grey Lady Cantata* II seem to Schumann quite unrelated to *A Man*:

'. . . in the *Grey Lady Cantata* #II the idea had been originally to use only one of them (only one Grey Lady (SSB)) and then I got stuck with the rehearsals, and then all the others came into it. But I remember that the scene – the play was meant to be what the first scene was and that was about one grey lady and her son leaving and the food leaving and the cups and spoons leaving and the table leaving and the chairs leaving and the room emptying itself – that was the idea for the play, I remember. And then when working on it with Goddard students who behaved *silly* and were *difficult* to deal with, I abandoned that and put other scenes into that – added more characters. (I: To your mind, that theme does not relate to *A Man Says Goodbye to His Mother*?) It doesn't really, no.' — (Schumann, interview, August '82.)

164

State, son and soldier have almost disappeared from this play. A woman lives, war wounds her, she is alone in nature, death obtains her, her death a wedding to the cold world. That it's war that does her in, a point that Schumann somehow was stuck with making, seems almost irrelevant. The power of the play is in its image of the indifference — only set off by the friendly little bird — of nature to man: so that when social relations fail him, killed by materialism, cut off by war (the son's being drafted), turned negative by war (the old lady attained by a bombing raid), he has no recourse. The angel in this play is no longer a savior angel, but is like Malamud's angel Levine and like the angels in Richard Foreman's early plays, a Jewish, Cabbalistic, or a Gnostic angel, the Lord's eye, more logos than love.[17] He is truly a figure out of a dream, incursive and over-determined, and this adds to the eventual paradoxical opulence of the play, but his indifference repeats nature's.

Though the thought of the play is aethereal, a thinking-of rather than a thinking-about, a thought of the suffering individuals undergo, and its substance the emotion attaching to this thought, and though its seminal images were simple pictures — them sitting at the table, she lying in the woods — in the play as staged, the play of imagery turned out in the realm of the grotesque. The puppets were no more grotesque than they had ever been, but the simplicity of conception no longer disciplined their perceived appearance into naivete: because the direct address of the whole to morality was gone. And they were even more grotesque in their juxtapositions: a bizarre dance series of tableaux realized the childlike images of the childlike tale, itself the dress of a feeling: a triplicity giving the play unit, power and strangeness, and the qualities characteristic of Schumann's work of this period, secretiveness[18] and artistic opulence.[19] Dropping his essentialism of the '60s, he was cutting loose.

---

17. 'He's not a consoler . . . To me, he's a representative of death, death in the form of a gentleman — of a fairly nasty gentleman . . . like a funeral director.' — (Schumann, interview, August '82.)
18. We must make allowance for the obtuseness typical of the people papers get to review plays, but even so cf. e.g. Seligsohn in the February 25, '71 Newsday: 'The plot, if you can call it a plot, dealt with the relationship between the puppet symbols. The grey lady, a mother perhaps (or was she death?)' – 'a vague and obtuse work . . . the group . . . fails to create any real empathy with the audience. A printed program tells the story . . . but even the writing is obtuse.' — (M. P. Kelly, Bread, Puppet Theater Fails to Communicate, Times-Union, Albany, October 11, '71.)
For the New York City performance, at any rate, the program with the play's story was handed out only after the performance:
'After the performance, a program is distributed with a childlike scenario of the plot. The scenario elucidates some of the drama. Without it, you may not always know what's going on. I mistook worms and snakes for branches and twigs, and the "Black Angel" for the father of the house, although I wondered why he had wings on his back.' — (Gussow, New York Times.)
'Das ist nicht so eminent wichtig, ob der Zuschauer die Story kriegt, ganz kriegt. Viel

Thus the opening scene is a scene of odiously trivial conviviality, meaningless lives conjuncting in consumption of things – continuing the treatment of the same theme in *When Johnny Comes* and *Eating and Drinking*, both of '68 (and already in *The Ceremony of The Things* of '62/'63), the theme of the self-alienatory and asocial materialism of modern civilization, contrasting with the loving sociability of the simpler Good Life (*Fire*, '66, *Emilia*, '71). But in the staging of it, as shown by photos of the Paris production, it turned out surrealist: pretty ladies in satin, bare armed, masked within their tresses to be pretty dolls, a male Negro woman, grim-faced, like an American houngan below his/her Afro, a hippie clown, maskless but with Lincoln's beard and tall-hatted, the Gentleman Angel out of Wodehouse, and the Grey Lady out of Schumann's childhood, her head, snitched out of a potato, at an angle – the soldier-to-be son a normal young kid half-invisible in a rocker in the background. The scene shows the kid's alienation from the scene, but also Schumann's.

The play was perceived as a play about war, but Schumann had thought of it as a play about the Grey Lady, about an individual person and a real one, though also about the ordinary women that survive wars, and though he thought he had not succeeded in bringing his woman down to earth, he thought he succeeded more in this with *Grey Lady Cantata II* than with later *Grey Lady Cantatas*.[20]

---

wichtiger ist, dass die dargestellten Bilder zu Bildern seines Inneren werden, dass sich in ihm etwas regt, aufgerissen wird. Wir haben die Erfahrung gemacht, dass, wenn es uns gelingt, ihn gleich und gleichsam an den Augen in unser Spiel zu ziehen, er richtig sieht. Der Zuschauer soll zuschauen, ruhig und lange und genau hinsehen, wir lassen ihm die Zeit. Dann wird er auch verstehen: WAS DA VORGEHT, GEHT AUCH IN IHM VOR.' – (Schumann, interviewed by Gregor Laschen, General Anzeiger, 22./23. January '72.)

19. Konnoff, up at the farm, getting his western tour into shape, fresh from the Coney Island operation, was shocked by this change when he saw the September performance at the Cate Farm barn. He liked the piece, but didn't approve of it:

'Well, it's more of a personal thing with me and Peter. I'd get on a track like Coney Island track – and I'd come and see something totally different and I'd get *confused*. I mean, it was – it was a great movement piece and there were fire extinguishers going off, and it was much different than – you know, I was on a *Man Says Goodbye* kick, I mean, I was more into the direct –' — (Konnoff, interview, '83.)

20. It's the 'story of a single grey lady, her relationships, pains, death and funny resurrection' — (Schumann, *Bread and Puppet Theater/The Grey Lady Cantatas*, undated, Bread and Puppet files.)

'Grey Lady Kantaten sind Kammermusik eines jetzt entstehenden, noch unangepackten Menschen, sind nicht für Jahrmarkt oder Meinungsaustausch gemacht. Grobes materielles Leben, Bier und Gold fallem vom Tisch, fallen aus einem dicken Mund. Aber diese schwarzen Hüte und Schmerzensbereiter sind verdammte, und der lange Krieg ist kurz. Denn die grauen Frauen bleiben immer da, und immer, während Kaiser und Fettmölche Geschichte und Europa und Amerika gemacht haben sind sie dagewesen. Die Kantaten sind aus langen und kurzen Tönen komponiert, aus Grau und Weiss und wenigen Farben.

Schumann's intentions emerge from a comparison of *Grey Lady Cantata II* with *Bach Cantata #140* from whose crowd of Grey Ladies, a crowd without individuals (the puppets were multi-headed), lashed by the storm of war, Schumann had extricated the single Grey Lady of *Grey Lady Cantata II*, and with *A Man* whose abstract mother, mother and just that (so that the force of the play lay in the essential identity of its two mothers, and the role of the mother in it is in the loss of a son) reappeared in *Grey Lady Cantata II* as an individual who happens to have a son that is drafted, with a story and fate specifically detaching themselves from those of her likes, other women like her suffering the same blows, and distinct from her very own sister's story and fate a singling out of *the* Grey Lady that would have been even stronger had Schumann not, perhaps to accede to his student crew's desire for parts, desisted from having the other Grey Ladies be dummies on strings. Not only that motherhood is no longer her defining identity, but three other things characterize this individual and distinguish her from Schumann's female figures of the '60s: she suffers suffering not as a supervening fate, consequence of cruel war, but lives with it, it seems part of her nature (and that being an individual involves suffering seems a point essential to Schumann at this point); she puts out a heroic effort to survive in spite of adversity, may not be a Resistant, but is a Survivor; and she is a real person, not an idealization, a point carried both by the backdrops and by her earth grey appearance — in fact she struck me as one of the women from Schumann's past, the little grey women on the farms and in the grey garrison towns of eastern Germany: we see a real person in real space.

'I remember that I wanted to make something much sparser, with less staging, with less pure Grey Ladies, less contrast. I tried, already, from *Grey Lady #II*, on, through the others, to individualize the Grey Lady, to do *more* around — create little traits and stories out of them, make them look more flesh and blood. But I don't think that succeeded, that thing. But still it came out strongest in the second *Grey Lady Cantata* — then in the others it *didn't* happen. It did not come as strong in any other than the second one, where it really did feel like the story of that one woman.'

(Schumann, interview, August '82.)

The second *Grey Lady Cantata* (III) was put together a year and a half after the first one, in November '71, just in time after a few local performances[21] to be taken on Schumann's first return to Europe since his '69

Ihre Frechheit verdanken sie unserer Frechheit, ihre Langsamkeit der Schönheit der Natur, ihre schwerwiegenden Ereignisse der Wahrheit, ihre Traurigkeit (?) den Schmerzen der Vietnamesinnen.' — (Schumann, draft of program notes for the European tour of December '71-February '72, with *Grey Lady Cantatas II and III*. Handwritten, Bread and Puppet files.)

21. *Grey Lady Cantata III* was 'built, created and rehearsed', according to Elka's January '73 Bread and Puppet theatre chronology, in November '71, shown November 7 and 14

appearance there in the guise of Resistor at the head of a band of splendid hippies: as though to assure, by providing a third piece deviating from the pieces he had done on that tour, notably *Cry* in the same manner as the two others he was going to show – *Grey Lady Cantata II, Birdcatcher* – or one that would eke out the new image of him provided by these two Vermont pieces, that he would not be mistaken for simply a political agitator with artistic talent, a concern having the more weight for him as Germany rather than France was the tour's center of gravity. But it was probably as important for Schumann, if not more important, to provide a rectification of the impression produced by *Grey Lady Cantata II*, that it was about war, a mere rework of *A Man*: to point up that, though the miserable Goddard students he had had to work with on that piece had forced him to put in a whole bunch of Grey Ladies, it dealt with an individual's life – to make clear what these cantatas were about.

His puppeteer Leherrissier had been working with her old man Arthur Binder on putting together a recitation to music by Binder of poems by the less than mediocre German poetess Sachs – Irene dancing and miming, Arthur croaking the poems in his Yiddish German (which actually, when he and Irene did their piece at the east 9th Street Bread and Puppet off-shoot, turned out not a bad delivery at all) – partly under the aspect – Sachs belonged to the Berlin Jewish bourgeoisie and barely made it out of her murderous fatherland in 1940 – of a reference to the 'holocaust'.

Schumann picked up on the idea, decided to do his next *Grey Lady Cantata* on the final solution.[22] Of the two poems he picked out, *Oh Nacht der weinenden Kinder* and *Sieh Doch, Sieh Doch*, only the former relates to this subject matter. *Sieh Doch* tries to present the image of an individual's city garment expanding (cracking?), strained by a deep breath he/she takes straightening out (rising like a candle into the night), but Sachs fucked it up among other things by having the individual saying 'Ah', which is said on an exhalation and normally is a sigh rather than an expression of discovery. For a while he tried to use *Oh Nacht* as a Raven's onstage song in the concluding scene, but apparently soon abandoned the

in Burlington, November 22 in the Cate Farm haybarn, sometime also in November at the Union 32 High School, and was taken to Europe around Thanksgiving where with probably its first scene omitted it was shown as sequel of *Grey Lady Cantata II* until the end of February '72.

Schumann was probably speaking more of *Grey Lady Cantata III* than *II* when, in the spring of '72, after the tour, in an interview given to the Goddard student paper he said:

'Life and style of the tour were determined by the nature of (*Grey Lady Cantatas II* and *III*), with the need for constant rehearsals and changes, arriving at some kind of conclusive form only in our last performance in Paris.'

22. '(*Grey Lady Cantata III*) was about the holocaust.' (Schumann, interview, August '82.) '(It was based on) a poem on a concentration camp – poem by Nellie Sachs, the poet who has a whole book of poetry about concentration camp pictures and images . . .' — (Schumann, interview, '79.)

attempt, I think probably because it broke up the musical development, based on Binder's music for *Sieh Doch*.[23] So as it turned out, the play had nothing to do with Jews, Germany or persecution. In a general way it is about escape from confinement (possibly the frightening aspects of confinement), but it is specifically about an escape from confinement by a grotesque world, a party world as at the beginning of *Grey Lady Cantata II*, though the party is of a nightmare sort. I don't think the play's imagery was stimulated by *Oh Nacht*. The words of *Sieh Doch*'s incidental

---

23. Two prima donnas were fighting for the songs:

'Susan Bettman did this Grey Lady thing and I sang. I was like the curtain guy. I was out front and hitting the part. Margo was furious. (I: What was she doing there?) Nothing. Well, first she was going to do the *Night of Weeping Children*, and Peter had it worked out where she was going to be in this big bird costume, blackbird, and there were going to be little ladies from *Johnny* on the floor and she was going to flap her wings and gradually knock the puppets off the stage, right? But it didn't work out, so we had to kick it out. She got so furious, she said to him. "Well then, Irene has to share her part with me." And he gave in. And I said, screw this junk — I'm not going to give her my part because her part gets kicked out. Forget it. So do you know what happened? One day I arrived at the theatre at 6 o'clock to do an 8 o'clock show and Margo was wearing my costume prepared to do my part. I went to Peter and I said, "Get her out of that costume, Peter." And he said, "I can't." I said, "Why not?" "She said she'll never work with me again if I do it." I was like nuts. I really went crazy. She couldn't sing. At that time Margo hadn't learned to sing on pitch, which is why she really had to kick her out of the *Night of the Weeping Children* thing, because she kept screwing it up. So he had to kick it out because it was always out of key. So I sat out in the audience, you know, and she was going to do my part. I had a great part. I would move the curtain for the scene and then I'd sing the song at the end. It was one of the better parts. Susan Bettmann had the other really good part. So she did my thing and she didn't sing the song well at all. She was off key and some of the audience started booing and it wasn't me. She thought it was. So what I did — I would come to the theatre at 3 o'clock in the afternoon and get into my costume so I could be in it before she would show up. She wanted to take turns with me. I said forget it, no way. You can't sing the song number one and why should I do it? And Peter said to me, well, if you can get here and get the costume ahead of her, okay. So then I started saying, it's a real grown up way of handling things. So then I started saying to myself, this is ridiculous. So I would get out of my costume after the show and I would hide it. But then one day I came and I found she had found it. And had put it on. And I said to her, "Look, I'm going to tear your hair out if you don't cut this crap. Just knock it off. Get out of my costume." And so she had a big fit to Peter and finally Peter had to tell her to knock it off. But it was like he really didn't do anything to stop it. It was so stupid. He was like a baby. "What can I do?" ... This was when we had gone abroad. We had to kick out Margo's part.' — (Irene Leherrissier, interview, '79.)

'Arthur had written — he had taken many of Nelly Sachs' poems and he wrote — set them to music. And he sent them up to me and Irene and asked us both to work on them. So Irene and I were working on these songs and Arthur came up and worked with us and then — we sang them for Peter and he chose two of them that he wanted to have in *Grey Lady Cantata*, and we used to take turns singing the songs on the tour. There were two songs. For a while Irene sang one and I sang another one and then I sang the one she was singing and then I got sick and, we each kept getting sick, we were under a lot of stress doing that show. And finally Mark Dannenhauer ended up singing the songs during the last part of the tour, which was in France. Nancy.' — (Sherman, interview, '79.)

comparison of glassy shop windows to the broken eyes of ravens may have started Schumann on an unrelated series of associations. But he didn't get much from the poems.

He used *Sieh Doch* with Binder's music, as he had Spevak's strophe with Tallis' in *Grey Lady Cantata II* for a series of musical interludes in front of the curtain, fragmentary, distorted and discordant ones on violin used as 'country fiddle' at first, more complete, instrumental and sung ones, next, finally a full instrumental and vocal rendition in tune, violin and cello on one side, a curtain operator, who was also the singer, on the other.

The story of *Grey Lady Cantata III*, which like *Grey Lady Cantata II* took about 40 minutes, closely parallels that of *Grey Lady Cantata II*, except that it is now very far away from *A Man*, there is only one Grey Lady, the surrealism of *Grey Lady Cantata II*'s staging has invaded it and taken over, its imagery is fantastic and grotesque, as well as pointedly frightening, and winter is coming. We first (in a scene dropped when the play was done as continuation of *Grey Lady Cantata II*) see the Grey Lady covered by a giant protective hand which moves up and disappearing uncovers her rocking a baby: a raven crows outside the window. A number — seven in the script, apparently more had been prepared and fewer were actually done (Avram Patt apparently contributed greatly to their creation) — of slapstick scenes, separated by blackouts and country fiddling, but not by curtains, follows. Boisterous, grotesque figures[24] — three Uncle Fatsos, in suits, with big grey and/or black and white faces, over-lifesize masks, and a Mouth puppet who by a single word, followed by 'Bum! Bum!' gives a title to each of these scenes — have crowded into the Grey Lady's room and, under a portrait that in response to the antics keeps changing its expression, successively looking mean, happy, gentle, interested, fine, concerned, curious, carry on with one another and with ancillary characters that keep entering and leaving, a 'coquette', a messenger, a witch, 'the masses', a clown with a necktie made of banana peel, an assassin. The nasty, jovial party culminates (Scene 9) with the entrance of the assassin who is promptly assassinated by the clown, and with magical vomiting of gold by one of the Uncle Fatsos' heads the head

---

24. '. . . men in oversized masks, big, grey sort of rough masks like city guys, rough guys, landlords, slumlords, those kinds of people. We've used them for different roles. We used one of them as the boss in "St. Francis" recently. You could use one as a cop. They're vulgar uncultured people, and these guys are sitting there.' — (Sherman, interview, '79.)

These characters, and they only, speak, but only rudimentarily: 'Blah! Blah!', 'Yes!' 'No', 'Bye', 'You are welcome!', 'O.K.' The Mouth: 'Country Fiddler!', 'Bum! Bum!', 'Friendship!' 'Bum! Bum!', 'Inspiration! Bum! Bum!', 'Messenger! Bum! Bum!', etc. The 'masses' say the alphabet.

The nightmare slapstick genre of this scene is unique in Schumann's work. It identifies the world of The Individual — the Grey Lady — as grotesquely odious conglomeration of crowd ('the masses') and pseudo-individuals (the grotesque 'guys').

rising into the air for this stunt.[25] The curtain is closed and the last part of *Sieh Doch*, 'but man has said *Ah* and rises, a straight candle, into the night', is sung with cello and violin. When it opens again (Scene 10) the bland and sedate but in the context of the other men there perhaps sinister Gentleman Angel, ravens perched on his head and shoulders, as well as a hump-backed Witch, lying on the floor, have joined the company. The Grey Lady's eyes have been joined by strings to those of one of the men, the gold-vomitting Uncle Fatso's.[26] The Witch, responding to 'Ah!s' from both of them, cuts the strings, the ravens crow, everyone exits (Fatso and the Grey Lady backwards): through a window we see the Grey Lady with her baby, the big Hand and the ravens outside, where the Witch, catching two ravens, joins the Grey Lady's eyestrings to them. Curtain, 2nd '*Ah!*' We now (Scene 11), against the background of three successive landscapes successively further away, in our view, switched by the Witch, see the Grey Lady pulled across by the ravens, and off, the Witch and the Hand remaining and on the instigation of bell ringing by a North Star repeatedly acknowledging her further departure into the distance — we don't see her, we see the succession of landscapes — by the waving of handkerchiefs. The ravens pull the Grey Lady back in and fly away: the Grey Lady leaves the scene and comes out in front, and being offered his chair by the cello player, becomes a watcher. Curtain, third '*Ah!*', Grey Lady joining in. What she sees (when the curtain is again opened, for the final scene) is the fleeing in front of a fourth landscape, of tiny Madonna-like puppets, from a flock of ravens, a big one and a bunch of small ones, pursuing them.[27] The fourth landscape is removed by the Witch, and the Grey Lady against the bare background moves back into the scene with her baby and is met by the descending Hand which — the Witch tying the baby to it — rising, takes her baby away: at which the full *Sieh Doch!* is sung — as though the baby were man, who, having said 'Ah!', rises like a straight candle into the night, or as though the Grey Lady's relinquishing the baby had been her 'Ah!' and her child's ascension hers. She does not weep. She claps her hands and snow starts falling: 'first a little bit, then a whole lot, a whole snow-storm, light grows!' (script, *Grey Lady Cantata III*, March '72) and to bright light on the stage, a big white landscape moves in.

---

25. It was lifted by strings from a 'bridge'. The big hand and the small ravens were also string-moved.

26. Or, more probably, not to his eyes as the script has it, but to his mouth — as Elka (Schumann, interview, '79) remembers it.

27. 'There was a scene in which I had to be a gigantic black bird who would fly very slowly across the stage. And there were little things on the floor that were being knocked down or being destroyed by the big black bird . . . We had a lot of little Madonnas, those little doll puppets. They were set up and the big black bird would go across the stage — in the beginning, it was to sing a song, eventually the song was cut — and either push out of the way or knock over the women. It was all about the women, the effect of the war upon the women.' — (Sherman, interview, '79.)

It's a beautiful story in its own right, an image poem, and totally obscure.[28] But it seems a gentle story, the party a clowning, the flight into the country a finding of refuge, with a happy ending, the death-or-whatever at the end a rise into liberty, the old lady dry-eyed. Yet this also seems dubious, for the images, abducting or pursuing crow-ravens, eyes that are tied, reaching hands, are cruel, and the party is brutal, the flight a flight and a flight into nothing, and in the end the child is lost. And what the lady is penultimately watching may indeed be the shunting of the Jews into the extermination camps, the trains for which in 1943, when the war was being lost in Russia and the 2nd Front was expected, had precedence over troop trains.[29] It may have been in Schumann's idea [30] and in this play to rise above such horrors (as in *Grey Lady Cantata II* the war) even while showing them: by showing the destruction of individuals as a salvation. But *Grey Lady Cantata III* was perceived as was *Grey Lady Cantata II*, as a horror show, a perception that probably read his mind more accurately than he did in thinking he had surmounted horror, if in fact he thought not only that the plays expressed such transcendence, which I think he did, but also that they expressed his state of mind: which it is by no means necessarily the case that they did. Intelligent watchers of the play confounded the ravens, dark announcers of winter, birds of bad luck, with crows, the greedy thieves that, mistaking them for lasting jewels, pick out small children's eyes — kraah, kraah.

'Eine staccato gespielte Folge von slapstick-Szenen bietet die verhexte Welt, die Kreig führen muss: Bäuche und Biergesichter in Uncle-Fatso-Zylindern machen in Kultur (come, fiddler!) und lachen sie aus; die "Gesellschaft" ist lustig. Aus Schnappshälsen: "friendship!" Geldsegen; the witch kauert und lauert und besorgt ihn, "the coin". "Argument": einer wird niedergeschrien. "Assassine": einer wird niedergeschossen. Bumm.

Dann blättert die Hexe eine Reise von Landschaften — ein bemalter Vorhang um den anderen — hin, und jetzt sitzt und singt grey lady als Zuschauerin im Proszenium vor einem Guckkasten-Theater. Wir sind die grey lady. Die Landschaften der Hexe sind krähenbehackte Angst-Landschaften, eine Mutter-mit-Kind-Puppe gerät in neue bombardements, ungezählte winzige Mutter-mit-Kind-

---

28. Schumann in re the toured *Grey Lady Cantatas II and III*:
   'There was no ultimate product but a working program in which as diverse audiences as possible had to do a great share of the job; viewing and listening attentively in a new, unorthodox way, for which there could not be an introduction or guideline.' — (Schumann, *Touring Europe, Silo*, spring '72.)
29. The concentration camp theme of the poem is paralleled by the Grey Lady's imprisonment in comical everyday life. She flees through landscape into snow.' — (Schumann, *The Grey Lady Cantatas*, undated mimeograph in Bread and Puppet files.)
   To Schumann, then, comical everyday life was a concentration camp.
30. He oddly remembers the play as
   'about a little doll, a little man, similar to a Johnny puppet, but a standing man, and some hands coming down from heaven, and a woman giving birth' — (Schumann, interview, '79.)

Puppen werden zu Paaren getrieben von Feuerwalzen und Verteidigungs-
ministern. Eine Hand vom Himmel erreicht schliesslich das baby der Mutter-mit-
Kind-Puppe. Es ist die Hexe, die das Kind an diese Hand bindet; das Kind wird
emporgehoben. Die Augen der Mutter erblinden unter schwarzen Krähen. Zuletzt
sitzt die Hexe in der Mitte und wird eingeschneit.'

(Th. Hardtmann, *Grey Lady Cantata, Theater Heute*, February '72.)

Jürgen Schmidt continued his neo-Marxist critique, coming down heavy
on *Grey Lady Cantata III*: for its flight into mythologizing, distorting
abstraction, inaccessibility.

'Die Unbedingtheit und die Totalität dieses Verfahrens entsprechen der
Unbedingtheit und der totalität der Not, um die es in der "Grey Lady Cantata
2" geht; mit ihr demonstriert die Gruppe künstlerischen Materialismus: Dank
seiner werden die Grundlagen und die Macht der angespielten Ideen plausibel.
Entsprechend "urwüchsig" (Georg Lukacs) ist das Spiel. Alle sinnlichen Nei-
gungen und Begabungen, die Theater wecken kann, sind in ihm geweckt.

Und werden nach der Pause, während der "Grey Lady Cantata 3", zugunsten
eines univerständlich kompakten Eigenlebens der Figuren, die da bemüht werden,
wieder verleugnet. Bemüht werden unter anderen eine Handvoll Krähen und eine
Hexe. Die setzt der Lady zwei von den Federviechern an die Augenhöhlen, dann
ruft sie eine himmlische Hand herbei, legt das Kind, das die Lady in ihren Armen
trägt, in sie, und lässt sich schliesslich Körbe voller Papierschnee übers chaotisch
maskierte Haupt schütten. Die (Premieren-) Zuschauer reagieren irritiert und –
auf die einzig theaterzulässige, nämlich umwundene, Weise – aggressiv. Sie
erwehren sich spürbar solch "pseudokritischer, abstraktverzerrender, mythi-
sierender Wesensart" (Lukacs), die des Teufels ist anstatt des Menschen.'

(J. Schmidt, *Des Teufels, Frankfurter Rundschau*.)

'Nach der Pause wirkt die gastspielende Truppe, als habe sie das Bekenntnis
gewechselt. Ihr Spiel wird zügiger, die Begleit-musik der beiden Streicher vor
dem linken Proszenium absurder. Realitätsbezüge, die die angespielten Ideen und
ihre Macht materialisieren könnten, gibt es keine mehr. Statt der Not des Krieges
widerfährt der grauen Lady ("Grey Lady Cantata 3") der magische Einfluss
einer Hexe, die ihr zwei Krähen an die Augen setzt und das Kind, das sie in den
Armen trägt abnimmt. Statt dessen legt sie es in eine vom Bühnenhimmel herabbe-
schworene Hand.

Was angespielt wird, ist bestenfalls erratbar. Vielleicht ist es ein Wahn oder die
Furcht vor mythischen Mächten, die uns unzugänglich sind und die uns
unzugänglich bleiben: So improvisiert die Bühne auch ist – die Lady und die
Hexe, die Krähen und der Himmel, die sie beleben, führen ein Eigenleben, das die
Zuschauer vom Geschehen ausschliesst. Entsprechend wächst ihre Ungeduld oder
ihre Hilflosigkeit; entsprechend zwiespältig ist der eindruck, den die beiden – zum
ersten Male in der Bundesrepublik aufgeführten – Cantatan hinterlassen.'

(Jürgen Schmidt, *Lady in zweierlei Grau*, Hamburg newspaper, January '72.)

Schumann though he had failed with *Grey Lady Cantata III*, this time not
because of the student puppeteers, but because of Binder's music and
Sachs' poem:

'The concepts weren't so good. The second one with Nellie Sachs' poem was a

173

rather feeble choice. And, a poem is okay and then the music is already much less than that – but I never came to terms with that. That was fairly arbitrarily and artificially put into that. That was not a good theme to use . . . The thing was stuck a bit with the music of Arthur Binder and with Irene's performance of that, so I never got – it was never finished. It was just a sketch, no more.'

(Schumann, interview, August '82.)

Right after his return from Europe, though, he expressed some moderate satisfaction with the two first *Grey Lady Cantatas*:

'Theater is the inside by way of the enlightened outside. God is the word. Theater is the flesh and the rosebuds of the word. Frantic, hectic language, well done, rare and medium conversations are all finished. Snowgardens and horse's silence are above us, we sit here, we are well surrounded, the tongue will slip, the mouth will overflood and tiny truth will slip through our gestures, and we'll address the nation with little bits of bla-bla-bla and little bits of oi-oi-ois and little bits of words.

We are not finished with language, we are just starting it.

We live in US shambles. We are not representatives of US shambles. We eat waste, we are not the stomach of it. The US Imperium on its deathbed has the strange effect of growing rosebuds out of decaying limbs. Dead body US will finally grow a culture to live by. Our organizations are called "consoled suffering" and "thirst for wedding the impossible" and "that simple light may rise out of complicated darkness".

We are still up and generate movement of No-sayers. We are still the complaint department for the Unyielding – at least we respond as closely as possible to stinking newspapers, invent styles for screaming now and do problem-parading when needed.

Life is good. Snow is good. Slush is good. Every day is good. We have to build real places of thought, alterplaces for wounds, which can't be touched by pity. We have to be good happy walking man and woman on our path and create distinct pieces of recognition for the spoiled and the hurt. We have to do that, we can't live as solo-gardeners and get away with it.

So, last year, we made 2 grey lady cantatas, 2 small wondrous tales ending in resurrection. The stage is built from the boxes which carry the puppets, plus some poles and curtains.

We worked hard on the grey, on the real nature of it all, chairs, cups and people speaking the language of the width of a generation, unfancily, unmotorized, unshortened motions of a quarter-day scope. To fully do that grey, interrupted by 2 times trembling pink cloth for sky, and one time beast red wrapped like a dead flag over the band, that was our grey lady job. And so, with ashes falling and noises dropped incessantly and partaking in this true world, we headed towards disaster, end of good, very assuredly great disaster. Only, we did not let it happen, but instead we ended by blasting out our petty sunshine-moonshine hymn, full of rejoicing ladies and gentlemen and we made a resurrection for the fun of it. That's what we called 'grey lady cantata No. 2'.

Grey lady cantata No. 3 is another slice of resurrection. (Life is short and unless we get resurrected right away, we have no chances ever at all. Backers (Bakers? (SSB)) and puppeteers are technicians and doctors of such practical

174

resurrection and exalted realities. We can put you into the barrel of our Sunday afternoon resurrection ray gun and shoot you right into the heaven of the brightest whitest snow of Vermont or anywhere!)

(Only we need listeners, snow and dust sound listeners, tiny crackly listeners, plus onlookers in the spirit of perfect vision. The story is definitely the audiences' job, not ours. We have no free delivery of interpretations, librettos, symbols, special philosophies. We have a physical fitness apparatus of colors and other wonders of perception. Audience does the sport, the skiis and knapsacks of theater.)

Grey lady cantata No. 3 is about the great 'A's of the German poetess Nelly Sachs. She says: aber der Mensch (stuck, mutilated, poor) hat 'A' gesagt ... It's shining yellow and tremendous this 'A'. Again we shall strike the lower depths of our grey ladies' fate, saturated with American poison, with all this stuff that we know, this brittle sour life and sour shame in capitalist America. but the 'A' sticks and we believe it. The 'A' is sung, set to music by Arthur Binder. And then the snow starts falling and the light from the snow almost blinds you and you see for a split second a large white landscape, signifying snow, finish, hurrah, curtain. Thank you very much. Goodbye.'

(Schumann, *Forward*, unpublished mss., possibly an intra-company summation, dated Cate Farm, March 9, '72.)

The *Grey Lady Cantata #IV*, also called *The First Garbagemen Cantata*, a 'project with Goddard students featuring the combined Goddard College and NYC sanitation departments, a bus ride and God' (*Bread and Puppet Theatre/The Grey Lady Cantatas*, February 25, '75), 'finished ... as a book of drawings' in February '72 (Schumann, letter to puppeteers of February 23, 1972, Bread and Puppet files), performed to a melody from A. M. Bach's *Notenbüchlein* (ibid.) April 24-May 5th, '74 at St. Clement's Church in New York City and during the Cate Farm circus that year, July 27-8, seems lost in the troughs of memory. The Bread and Puppet *Grey Lady Cantatas* chronicle kiddingly summarizes it as

'The Grey Lady's life as operated by the sanitation department. With this delicate guidance she succeeds, and ends up reunited with her clan.'

Whatever the story, apparently the Grey Lady was in the spring of '74 emerging from her isolation of the beginning '70s.

Schumann remembers of it only that the Garbagemen, proletarian figures and in-view stagehands in his circuses since '70 or '71, did a lot of furniture moving in it, that there was a group of Grey Ladies in it, and that for each scene it had a text narrated, to the turning of a flip-over book, by himself (who also played the violin) wearing his old Mother of God mask, 'so that for each picture there was an in-between little scene with a dancing bear, with a bird in a cage that was fed' (Schumann, interview, '83.) – the bear had Christmas lights mounted on him.

'*Grey Lady Cantata #V*' was the name of his '74 Christmas offering to Goddard College and was performed there at the end of the year. It consisted of a first part to Thomas Tallis' *Lamentations of Jeremiah*, sung by the Word of Mouth Chorus, and of a second to Bach's *Motet (Cantata?)* *#40, Jesu meine Freude*, sung by Marc Estrin's Goddard Community Choir. It was done in the 3rd floor Cate Farm hay barn theatre with no new puppets and with a lot of Goddard students – only Goddard students, because he just then 'had a hard time to have a company for what (he) did at Goddard' (Schumann, interview, '79). Schumann, as White Lady, on stilts for his entrance up two flights of stairs either with a horse strapped between his legs or mounted on one operated by another puppeteer – 'I couldn't see too much because she (the Vietnamese Lady mask (SSB)) was on my head and had a wig that came down' – did a 'sort of St. George fight' with a dragon.

After some action to words by Jeremiah and music by Tallis, Jeremiah arrives, his donkey cart loaded with his baleful Hebrew words, Death keeps his Angel flying (he is pushing him on a swing above the scene), the Riders of the Apocalypse (the Bread and Puppet *Grey Lady Cantata* chronicle says) are riding, the Grey Lady rises through a trap door and is attacked by a dragon – the White Lady, to *Jesu meine Freude* rides up and saves the Grey Lady, the whole concluding with a 'procession that was all light. (Peter) had all the lights turned on (and) used only white puppets for (the) procession' (Elka, in Schumann, interview, '79), 'this long procession that just moved very, very slowly from the stage and the light got brighter and brighter' (Schumann, interview, '83). Possibly the disciples, possibly also Jesus – redressed in white? – were in this procession – the Bread and Puppet *Grey Lady Cantatas* chronicle says 'the chief characters of the Christmas legend' were in the show:

'The horror of our history is lamented hopelessly in the first part. The second part takes the joyous beat of Bach's music and transforms it into a vision of light and harmony.'

(Bread and Puppet *Grey Lady Cantatas* chronicle.)

While this show seems outside the sequence of *Grey Lady Cantatas*, called one chiefly because of the heroine's being a Grey Lady, the preceding one, *Grey Lady Cantata IV*, seems in that sequence, seeing as how *Grey Lady Cantata VI* seems a further development of it.

His first performance event in '75 was the *Grey Lady Cantata VI*, a sequel to the *Grey Lady Cantata IV* of '74 and the last of the *Grey Lady Cantatas*,[31] done – 'one week rehearsal, one week performance'

---

31. 'Glover, Vt. – Paris, France, 1975. A new French-American venture, with music by the Bread and Puppet municipal garbage band. Featuring Garbagemen, a burning house, a dragon. Further adventures in the life of the Grey Lady, lovingly attended by ageing members of the Paris sanitation department.' — (Schumann, The *Grey Lady Cantatas*, mimeograph in the Bread and Puppet files.)

(Schumann, interview, '79) – in Paris in March at the Théâtre de l'Aquarium:

'Christian (Dupavillion) put it together in something like three weeks, I think, because you just told him you wanted to do it, and he found the theatre and he found the people to work with you and it was very successful and it made some money which you very much needed at that time. That was about the first thing that we did – that you did that made money.'

(Elka in Schumann, interview, '79.)

In fact, by Elka's reckoning, the Bread and Puppet Theatre made $616 on this play, the fee having been $1050, and expenses $334.

As Dupavillon – I believe it is him – tells the tale, it is a charming fairy tale, humorously surrealist:

'On stage, a white backdrop portrays the interior of a house. A white curtain is drawn over the window. In front of the backdrop is a flagpole with a lowered red, white and blue flag. Stage right – the M.C., Peter Schumann, has a series of instruments (bass drum, megaphone, violin and bell) and signs to announce each scene. Stage left is the space for the Garbagemen's band, with a miniature piano.

A bell rings. The M.C. announces, "The Grey Lady Cantata – beginning of the first part."

Onstage, a Foreman (with a mask, a cane and a felt hat) calls to the Garbagemen. Coming from the audience, stage left, seven Garbagemen (wearing caricatural masks and the green caps of the N.Y. Garbagemen) enter, clumsily carrying chairs. They reach their places and tune their instruments (piano, horn, lute, etc.). The Foreman raises the flag while the band, standing at attention, plays the anthem (a march from Bach's *Exercises for My Daughter* first hummed and then played by the Garbagemen).

On stage, the Garbagemen pose for a photo, grouped around the Foreman sitting near the flagpole.

The Grey Lady enters from behind the backdrop. The Garbagemen seem surprised. The Foreman asks the Grey Lady to sit down. A Garbageman brings a harp. The Grey Lady pretends to play it, accompanied by a Garbageman playing the lute.

First chore: cooking. A Garbageman brings a saucepan on a stool. Showing little cards that say "salt", "peas and onions", three Garbagemen take turns pouring bottle caps into the saucepan. The kettle tips over, and simultaneously a Garbageman drops a tray full of metal objects. The Garbagemen go back to their places.

Second chore: sweeping up. A Garbageman gives the Grey Lady a broom. While the band plays a tune with appliances (a vacuum cleaner, a coffee grinder, a hammer, etc.), The Grey Lady sweeps the stage.

Third chore: the rock. With a rope, four Garbagemen directed by the Foreman drag a rock from downstage right to center stage.

The Lady tries to lift the rock. When she does lift it, it falls to the ground. The Lady collapses, accompanied by the clatter of the tray full of metal. A Garbageman opens the curtain on the window. The Lady is lying down. A Garbageman puts down an oil lamp and another puts a white pillow under her head.

177

Two Garbagemen stretch a blanket over the Lady's body.

Night falls. It is dark. A flashlight trained on the window allows us to see the moon and stars going by, to the sound of bells. The sun appears, with a clash of cymbals. The M.C. announces "The Middle". Two Garbagemen change the backdrop, which now portrays a house and a tree. The Lady gets up and sits on a chair near the door of the house. A Garbageman brings her an attaché case while another takes off her shoes after tying strings to them. Smoke comes out of the chimney of the house. Pulling the strings, a Garbageman makes the shoes walk. The Garbagemen, the Foreman and the M.C. wave to an imaginary person walking by in the shoes.

The Lady leaves. The Foreman holds an inspection. The Garbagemen stand at attention and salute comically.

A horseman (a Garbageman riding a broomstick) gallops in. After playing a tune on a toy trumpet he gives the Foreman a message.

The horesman rides off. The Foreman reads the message and gives orders. Four chairs are placed onstage as if they were car seats. Four Garbagemen sit down and pretend to take a trip, making the sounds of a motor and miming gear changes, bumps and sudden stops. A backdrop behind them is turned to show a moving countryside. Darkness, then a light bulb dangling over the downstage area shows us a multi-colored dragon that appears from under the backdrop, beating its wings. A Garbageman grabs a piece of red cloth in the dragon's mouth that represents a flame. The dragon disappears, the lights go back on and the Garbagemen in their car return to the Lady's house. The M.C. announces, "The beginning of the end". The Garbageman attaches the flame to the roof of the house. Directed by the Foreman, the Garbageman throw wads of paper at the house. Two of them shake the backdrop.

A new backdrop shows the house on fire and the tree falling down.

A siren gives the signal for a lunch break. The Garbagemen sit down wherever they are to eat and drink. Another siren immediately ends the break. The Foreman gives the order to clean up the stage. Garbagemen sweep and vacuum while others pick up the wads of paper. Pulled by a string, a miniature boat crosses the stage. On board, an angel waves a trumpet. A trumpet is sounded behind the backdrop. The Lady appears, tied up and held by Garbagemen. She manages to undo the ropes and take off mask and grey dress. Underneath we see a White Lady standing on stilts. The backdrop is white.

To a Scottish tune, "None Such", played three times over, the White Lady dances. Behind her the Garbagemen clap their hands loudly and dance. Blackout. The end.'

(English language synopsis of *Grey Lady Cantata VI* in
Dupavillon and George, *Bread and Puppet Theatre*, '78.)

We see the mutual involvement of the Grey Lady, now a delicate little Netsuke figurine of a beggaress (probably not truly a beggaress: the ghost of a Lady) with a small, mysterious band of musical workmen-dwarfs (there are seven of them) who are tightly disciplined by a bizarrely mondaine, slightly sinister operator: she comes upon them unexpectedly; they seem to test her; they put her to sleep; they fight a dragon or don't fight it: steal from it fire and burn her house down; they have and don't have a lunch break; she has been taken prisoner by them, she frees herself; she reveals herself, turning into a pretty young girl, yellow-locked, a gauzy bride, dancing. There are elements here of *Snow White*.

Perhaps Schumann is telling us how he liberated himself from one obsession in favor of another – how he became an optimist. The Grey Lady here *really* resurrects, as Lady Resurrection (The White Lady), not just ambiguously as in *Grey Lady Cantata II*. And she is not out in the cold any longer. We might view this show as Schumann's act of purging himself of the negativities of the preceding years of retreat from the '60s. But it's hard to tell where a man is at (though not as hard as where one oneself is at): Schumann was also exchanging the realism of those years of reconsideration for fantasy – as exemplified by the figure of that girl in white, Jephthah's pure daughter sacrified, savior of the Grey Lady (enduring woman), now that Grey Lady herself. This White Lady with the face of the Lady of Mercy becomes Schumann's Savior Angel in his circuses of the mid-'70s, who thus, we might say, turning the third around, secretly is the Grey Lady, the tough little grandmother whom, when I was young, I saw digging potatoes out of Prussian fields and in Northern Bavaria at evening time lugging enormous bundles of dry twigs back to the farm for kindling, at heart the grand, merry old dame of my father's *Unwürdige Greisin*, his grandmother.

What happened during this extended experiment with the Grey Lady theme seems to have been somewhat the following. Schumann started out somewhat disgusted with his heroic ideal figures of the '60s – notably those ethereal ladies. He decided he would do somebody real – not bucking the system, not representing any principle, but just trying quietly to get through life. He picked for his figure a tough little old lady who gets kicked around a lot, in no way resists, doesn't wear her "sufferings" as aureole – and who cannot be defeated because she gives all the way and instantaneously: there is no opposition in her. When she first appeared, people took her as image of passive-undergoing-of-"fate" and of the suffering of sufferings by "the people" and Schumann wasn't about to nay-say that. But her subsequent development, the shenanigans in *Grey Lady Cantatas IV-VI*, suggests she stood for more than that: survivorship, maybe, and/or the rationality of accepting things as they are – and/or the handsomeness of the modesty of not creating too much of a stir when things go badly with you. The secret of the matter – one Schumann hardly even liked to let himself in on – was that this anti-Mother Courage of his was in all her enormous commonness and peasantness his Ideal, her modest, decent way to be for him the way to be. This meant that obscurity was essential: so he wouldn't give offense to himself (let alone to his admirers and followers). Not wishing to propose as saint the arch-typical acquiescer, he felt more than free to play games, and so kept up a five year humorous dialogue with himself – the *Cantatas* – on minor questions relating to acquiescence and its deplorably obvious reasonableness and even beauty. Over the years the little old lady grew more cheerful and more involved with people. But by the time this happened, form had pretty much taken over from content. The obscurity — a fun-loving obscurity — had become total. The form started out batty, but in *Grey Lady Cantatas II and III* wasn't yet everything — was just a device assuring his privacy. But then pure playfulness took over. The irony of the whole thing was that starting out with a decision to deal with something real and down-to-earth — non-moralistically — ideas aside — he ended up with a totally fantastic figure involved in fantastic adventures.

The Grey Lady theme turned out abortive: the kind of self indulgence in Schumann's second creative period that *Leaf* had been in the first. From *Grey Lady Cantata IV* onward he frittered the theme away. The figure during his next productive period is replaced by the Angel in White (saving the Grey Lady in *Grey Lady Cantata V*, coming too late to save her in the '75 Circus *White Horse Butcher*), and during the later '70s by the Washer-woman — a cheerful fighter and an insipid idealization.

10. A vision of satan's earthly kingdom becomes a very pretty show.

President Nixon's pardon of the war criminal Calley in the spring of '71 inspired Schumann, sensitive to the moral and political challenge, and perceiving that its analogy to the birdcatcher Kiyoyori's pardon by the King of Hell presented an opportunity to portray the world as hell, further motivated, perhaps, after the severe achromatism of *Grey Lady Cantata II* and the Black Coney Island plays of '70 and the restrained color displays of all his plays since the vividly blue first *Birdcatcher* of '65, by a hunger for vivid color and associating hell with the intense red of fire, and, last but not least, perhaps, being just then intensely aware of himself as a sinner in need of pardon, finding the subject personally most relevant, in spite of the heavy workload of a tour of his circus in March and the revised presentation of it coming up in July, found time for doing not just, as he first thought of doing, a small 'puppet news service' hand puppet treatment of the case but a new version of the *Birdcatcher*, in a splurge of creative energy making most of the masks for it and putting together all within the month of May and the first few days of June — having earlier made woodcuts for the ornamentation of the costumes, and these having, for the greater part already been made during his absence on that tour by Elka. The textual revisions were minor: the interpolation of two excerpts from Nixon's announcement of the pardon into the lines of Yama the King of Hell, the insertion of bloody combat passages from the *Iliad* into a demoness' sportcast of Kiyoyori's fight with Yama's minions on his arrival in hell. But the masks and costumes, both, but especially the costumes, were sumptuously elaborate[1] (for the first time in his theatre), and he restaged the play entirely[2] from a small, contained, lyrical one into a large, highly theatrical one, with, this time, explicit topically political allusions, in particular also adding an extended (wordless) prologue,[3]

---

1. '. . . it was also a very elegant show. It was utterly elegant . . . This was the first time that they had spent such time and consideration in creating wonderful costumes — dyeing the reds, all different shades of reds, woodcuts, it was very, very beautiful. Pam, who was one of the narrators, created for herself some extraordinarily long fingernails — and a headdress.' — (Margo Sherman, interview, '79.)
2. '(I: So it was a completely different show.) A *completely* different show. It had no other similarity other than the technique of a dancer who danced not by music but by text, and in the first *Birdcatcher*, I was that dancer and in this one I worked with Sue Bettman on that dance — Sue Bettman performed that.' – (Schumann, interview, '79.)
3. 'In the spring of '71 when lieutenant Calley appeared in court for the shooting of women, children and old people, and the American Nürnberg reached its apex with Nixon's demonstration of sympathy for Calley, we experimented with drums and handpuppets on a representation of the case and soon were reminded of the Birdcatcher play.

which, whenever the play was presented outdoors, as it was originally intended to be,[4] had the form of a pageant, of choreographed converging processions and individual displacements across the landscape, the ending of his '70 circus with the advent of the Ark across the meadows apart, his first pageantry. He showed it first locally in June – June 3 and 5 on Cate Farm meadow, at Marlboro College June 6, on the Plainfield soccer field June 18, at All Souls Church, the first indoor performance, in Brattleboro, June 19 – then – which during those first years, at least, in Vermont was his standard operating procedure, and not for the money, but where else was he going to get a grownup audience? not in Boston! – in New York City: June 30 and July 1-3 on Sheep Meadow in Central Park (where its sumptuousness and the joyousness though not the picnicking atmosphere of the occasion contrasted with the protest assemblies so often held here during the '60s), and, June 24, 26 and 27 and on the 4th of July – a special gesture of Schumann's to his poor – on Coney Island.[5] It competed with *Swan Lake* and brass ensembles at the July 20-22 Saratoga Summer Convocation on the Arts, and August 2-4 in French translation 'ajoutait une note prestigieuse au programme des manifestations' of the Quebec Summer Festival. The Quebec visit was extended to Toronto, there were showings at various Vermont colleges (Goddard, Windham, Castleton) and at Drew University in New York in August and September, a two-

---

We then built it, ornamented it with nuggets of Nixon sayings, and painted it red . . . It also seemed to us that the bodies of the dead children should be there from the very beginning – even before the fable was told. And so we invented pink shadows who gently buried the decapitated doll babies in sand hills and planted flowers in them.' — (Schumann, *Puppen und Masken*, Frankfurt, November '73, my translation.)

4. '(Ephraim: I remember the show being done – I think I remember that you wanted to do it in a pageant way. In that summer – did you try to change the show from a mainly inside show? (Elka: It was created as an *outside* show.) (Ephraim: . . . in that summer of rehearsing, the demons would come in from the forest on the far side, remember? And when you played in a theatre, they couldn't – the show was pretty different.) That's right. Yes, well, the whole *time* of the show when we did it originally, was conceived of as a pageant, that's true. Because these long walks, these musical events, the whole prologue of shrouded figures, humming, and working in piles of sand – all of this took a long time when we did it outside, and later on. (Elka: The entrance of the Madonna also was very slow.) The blue Madonna? (Elka: The *red* Madonna.) — (Schumann, interview, '79.)

'*Place of Performance*. The '*Birdcatcher*' was rehearsed on a meadow and as long as the weather permitted was performed outdoors. The Drum demons (in the Prologue (SSB)) come from afar, out of a forest or from behind buildings. The Madonna, too (also in the Prologue (SSB)), arrives from far away.' — (Schumann, *Puppen und Masken*.)

5. 'Schumann is perched on a platform outside the second-storey window playing '*When the Saints Come Marching In*' on his fiddle. On the street below a performer dressed in tails announces through a megaphone the performance of *The Birdcatcher in Hell*, a free puppet play, in just five minutes. He is supported by a young boy who keeps up a steady rhythm on a bass drum, a girl who bangs a gong and a fantastically costumed person from the play who does a slow oriental dance on the street. It is 4th of July weekend, 1971. The air is hot and rancid as only New York City can be.' — (K. Taylor, *People's Theater.*)

week tour of it with two other pieces to New York State colleges in October, and before Schumann took it along on his December 14-February 14, '71/'72 tour of Europe, he showed it some more in Vermont (Goddard, U. of Vermont, Union 32 High School), at the same time putting out two new important pieces, *Attica* in September, *The Grey Lady Cantata #3* in November, and, October-November, making the masks of a third, *Simple Light*.

The text[6] of the slightly anti-Nixonized and for the sake of song and dance Homerized kiyogen follows. As usual, but especially during this Cate Farm period's turn away from the '60s — during which what sparse texts there were had been at one with the sparseness of the performance style — it is miles away from the performance: another kind of thing. The kiyogen, shouldering the elegant Noh, partaking of its tree-in-winter poetic precision and of its clear view of the living as groupuscule within the vast and turbulent lasting population of the dead, but rude and cynical refusal to take its stand with the dead, mockery of art's aristocratic arrogance, is well suited to Schumann's combination of refusal of art as privilege with a hankering for redemption by it. But that hankering is strong, and as in '65 he had used the text as pretext for a containedly Noh evocation of the elegantly cruel life in our blue air, so in '72 he used its sober justification by political topicality and moral outrage as occasion for a grandly theatrical[7] bicolor[8] vision of man's world as conflagration of raging greed running amok in the earth's silently benign photosynthesis. When then the play had to be performed indoors and the green was gone, it turned into a vision of man's inner hell.

'Prologue:[9]

Red curtain with two Hands of Yama.

---

6. Published in English and German in Schumann, *Puppen und Masken*, Frankfurt, November '73) I give the English version infra.

7. 'And *The Birdcatcher in Hell* was terrific because in that case he dropped the pose of reality and really developed the theatrical aspects that he was so good at. Because he was really good at — but he always rejected it the same way that he rejected money and success and all that. But in that case I remember the show was *very* theatrical, and he just went hog wild in it and it was terrific — just great. It was because he accepted his own theatricality. But theatricality, in the old days — being theatrical — was on the same level as making money — which is on the same level as sex, which was just no . . . It was a big, big place and it was gigantic — they had this enormous Yama that had to be hoisted up on pulleys on the ceiling and it was all this gigantic — not stadium-size — more like doing it on a basketball court. And it was very bright.' — (Ernstthal, interview, '79.)

8. '. . . making it in red, opening it up to red — the idea for the red was the green meadow — to place something red and pink in a giant green meadow on Cate Farm — that was the — make it big, put long parades in it — make it a giant, open thing. And, just the whole elaboration of it, plus the politicizing of it — much less concentrated than the first version.' — (Schumann, interview, August '82.)

9. 'In the middle a red curtain with Yama's hands. At each side of the curtain, three tin

Enter 3 pink-shrouded Gardeners.
Enter Bird riding on Beast.
Enter Flower-Madonna ringing bell. She transforms
  3 Gardeners into 3 Little Demons. Exit Madonna.
Bird shapes Little Demons. Beast exits.

---

drums. Out front three half circles with buckets of sand, lying next to them three Pink Shadows. The Ancient Ones bring a tree, a hoe and a watering can. The Pink Shadows build small hills of sand. Into them they plant headless dolls, and into their necks they plant flowers that they pick off the tree and then water. The six Big Demons sail to their drums like ships. Then the Bird Demon screams and rides in on a green Dragon, fries the puppet bodies in his frying pan, and the Dragon devours them. The bell rings. The Madonna in Pink Blossoms arrives, drapes her garment around the Pink Shadows lying on the ground, pulls them out of their covers, and the Bird Demon raises them up from the ground and teaches them flying motions. Drum-crescendo.' — (Schumann, *Puppen und Masken*, Frankfurt, November '73: my translation from the German.)

Since he kept changing the play in Europe, this would describe just one variant of the prologue. E.g. mostly there would be no 'Ancient Ones', the three pink shadow cadaver-gardeners miraculously rewarded by the status of demons (an image of civilizations reared by war) would bring their own implements.

In the prologue to Schumann's piece, three robed personages are growing something. The 'something' is three rubber dolls without heads. Each doll is planted in a pile of sand. Then one of the robed actors puts a flower in each doll's neck hole, another waters the sand around each doll and a third hoes it. All the time they are making a subhuman humming sound. Are they bees? Anyway, they are as intense as they are unlikely. The choice of props and the order of activities seem completely off-the-wall, out of Schumann's imagination, or even constructed from the contents of a local garbage can. Their combined sense, however, is undeniably growth and nurture. A hell beast appears; each doll in turn is fried over a fire made of waving strips of red cloth and then devoured by the beast.' — (Kent Taylor, *People's Theater*.)

'Bäurische Lemuren schaufeln an drei Beeten; aus den Beeten steigen verhüllte Wesen, die kopflose, nackte Püppchen pflanzen, darüber stecken die Lemuren grüne Zweige: Auftritt einer Höllenprozession ganz in Rot; rote Höllenfahnen. Vorn haut ein Dämon die Püppchen in die Pfanne, brät sie und gibt sie einem zweiten zu fressen. Eine Aufstellung paukenbewehrter riesiger Rinds- und Schweinsköpfe säumt die Scene.

Auftritt einer Mantelmadonna, umschmeichelt von Dämonen. Hier setzt Deutung ein: die bäurischen Lemuren dürften fluchbeladenen Schweiss des Angesichts tellurisch dargestellt haben. Die Mantelmadonna betrifft die Beete. Auf den Spuren ihres Rocks entspriessen der Erde vieräugige hässliche Wesen, von den höfisch buckelnden Dämonen wieder in den Boden gedrückt, wieder aufsteigend, etc. Der König der Hölle wird angesagt. Seine Erscheinung: ein roter Vorhang, flankiert von zwei riesigen Händen. Vom Schnürboden senkt sich ein Elefantenkopf, der sechs, sieben Fratzen enthält.' — (Th. Hardtmann, *Der Vogelfänger in der Hölle*, Theater Heute, February '72.)

'Das Hauptstück, wahrscheinlich, des einwöchigen Gastspiels des New Yorker "Bread and Puppet Theater" in Bonn war "The Bird-Catcher in Hell" (Der Vogelfänger in der Hölle). Es war vorgestern im Bonner und gestern im Godesberger Haus der Städtischen Bühnen Bonn zu erleben.

Eigentlich gehört ja das, was dieses radikale Theater aus der Delancey Street New Yorks produziert, auf die Strasse. Immerhin aber: Tournee-Erfahrungen mögen mitgewirkt haben, dass sich eine solche Produktion auch einem konventionellen Bühnenraum einpassen lässt, zumal im Bonner Haus, wo das riesige gähnende Schwarz der leeren dunklen Bühne die Illusion eines finsteren Platzes vermittelte.

Enter six Giant Demons. They start drumming.
Enter Gentleman-Narrator and Demoness With Long
   Fingernails-Narrator.
Enter Yama, the King of Hell, rising above red curtain.'

Enter Yama, the King of Hell, rising above red curtain.[10]

Aus dem Dunkel kommen monotone, zikadenähnliche Schnurrgeräusche. Vermummte Gestalten knien nickend vor Beeten. Erst weiss man nicht, was sie dort tun, dann erkennt man: sie holen Sand aus einem Eimer und schichten daraus kleine Berge auf einer Platte auf. Inzwischen kommen weither links und rechts bunte Phantome mit Fahnen über ihren grotesken Köpfen, riesig gross reihen sie sich an den Seiten hinter Benzinfässern auf. Auf den drei Beeten im Vordergrund sind aus der Erde drei kopflose kleine Puppen gewachsen, ein Zirkusansager mit rotem Zylinder ist vorgetreten und ruft in ein Sprachrohr. Die Phantomgestalten beginnen ein immer härter, lauter werdendes Trommeln auf den Fässern, während sich mit grellem Geheul ein Riesenvogel und ein Höllenhund heranwälzen, der in enervierender, von Trommelwirbeln untermalter Monotonie nacheinander die Püppchen frisst. Eine Mutter-Kind-Popanz wandelt heran, dreimal entsteht unter ihrem Riesen-mit Hilfe des Vogels und des Hundes eine Kreatur, die zu leben beginnt. Eine monumentale Teufelsfratze steigt aus einem roten Vorhang empor. Aus dem Zuschauerraum klettert der Catcher auf die Bühne. Er "nimmt an der Hölle teil", erst gehetzt, dann mit einer Maschinenpistole schiessend.' — (H. G. Kraemer, *Woche des modernen Theaters/Eine Antwort auf das was in der Welt passiert/'Bread and Puppet Theatre'* mit *'The Bird Catcher in Hell'*, German newspaper, January 19, 1972.)

'(I: What was your major impression of the spectacle ... what was the color of it, the feel of it?) Red. Violets. Extreme — there was a scream — Mark Dannenhauer riding on the back of the beast — he was a red bird riding on the back of a beast and as the beast went walking, "Ahhhhhhhhhhh!" It was a slightly different scream, but — It was horrible and beautiful.' — (Sherman, interview, '79.)

Kiyoyori the Birdcatcher at least in indoors performances was waiting in front of the stage during the prologue.
'. . . at Coney Island the musicians were hidden behind a red curtain; their banners were visible swaying slightly above it. When the same production was done several days later in Central Park, the musicians were not around at all. Schumann had sent them behind the trees at the far end of the Sheep Meadow. There they began a slow stately procession toward the playing area. It took them at least fifteen minutes to reach the stage and by then the play was well in progress. They became visible first out of the corner of an eye: prehistoric beasts swaying across the field.' — (Kent Taylor, *People's Theater.*)
The original prologue was a pageant and the arrival from afar of the Demons, with banners, flaming red, at first slow in the distance — I saw it in Central Park, where elsewhere one glimpsed the movement of the kids' baseball teams in their colorful uniforms — was overwhelming: their horror materializing as they came near.
'. . . the first performances at Cate Farm — out of doors — it was gorgeous. And then they started work on — But it was quite different when it was done in this enormous field with the puppets coming up, red — red — giant red puppets coming up in green trees . . . It started big, like in Central Park . . . — (Sherman, interview, '79.)
10. '(Yama) was used on a tripod — he had two 2×4s that extended from his chin onto the ground about 8 or 10 feet. And then another 2×4 attached to the *top* of his head in the back that was operated by somebody behind the curtain, to push him *up* into a straight

The play:[11]

YAMA   Gentleman-Narrator with megaphone
Yama, the King of Hell, comes forth to stand at
   the meeting of the ways.
Yai, yai, where are my minions?

DEMONESS
Haaa . . . here we are.

---

position. So he was lying down and when this moment came, he was pushed up above a red curtain that was in front of him. His hands were mounted on the two *sides* of that curtain, so his hands were present at *all* times. In *some* performances, that is. In other performances, *all* of it came up. All of it was *down* first. (I: You mean the curtain was flat?) The curtain and the hands were *down*. And then were *up* together with *him*. In theatres, when we performed it later, we used often a rope system. We had him strung and we *pulled* him up instead of having him pushed up. But basically he consisted of this giant head with a mane, a wig, that was full of little reliefs and sculptures that dangled around him, and two painted hands . . . the curtain *holders* – the curtain was his *body*. In the middle of the curtain was a *hole* that acted as his belly and as his mouth, with which he ate the little birds or the little people. (Elka: He also *trembled* . . . He would be shaking when he talked. Everyone would shake.) That's right. He would really be *excited*. (Elka: The arms didn't work, though, did they?) They did, yes. They did not gesture speech, but they moved according to the head movements.' — (Schumann, interview, '79.)

'Yama's head moves above the curtain somewhat like a sunrise or sunset. When he speaks, head, head ornamentation, hands and curtain shake. The big demons are very slow, their banners and costumes are meant for the wind. The Madonna and the Ancient Ones also move very slowly.' — (Schumann, *Puppen und Masken*.)

'. . . the God of Hell, a gigantic gorgon-like head . . . rises majestically on creaky pulleys above the red curtain. 'Everything in the Bread and Puppet Theatre is allowed its own noises. The pulleys creak because it would be violate to oil them.' — (K. Taylor, *People's Theater*, on the July 4, '72 Coney Island performance.)

11. '*Instruments and voices.* Musical instruments in the *Birdcatcher*. 6 tin barrels, struck with soft mallets. 3 rubber hose rattles (for the Pink Shadows). 1 bell (for the Madonna). 1 violin (for an Ancient One). Several cymbals and gongs (for the entrance of the Demons in outdoor performances). Voices: Mr. Narrator has two voices, a quiet, almost amused one for the Birdcatcher, and one screaming through a bullhorn for Yama. The Lady Narrator, responsible for the Demonesses' text, utilizes a large repertory: song, Sprechgesang, screaming, moaning, etc. The Madwoman sings and croaks the text from the *Iliad* in distorted sounds, accompanied by an Ancient One on the violin. All the performers together constitute a choir and for their slow exit sing a high tremulous 'I'. The rattles of the Pink Shadows correspond to the grasshoppers, birds, wind and traffic noises that attended outdoor performances.

Gestures and dance. The Small Demons and the Bird Demon have a rich scale of movements, long and short positions, many speeds, they run, leap, fall, crawl, etc. The Birdcatcher is a mime, small, gay (lustig) and precise in his gestures, whose beat is set by the Narrator. The Madwoman acts as dancer for the voice of the Demoness. Her gesticulation is alternately interpretative-descriptive and reflective-suffering. The long beginning of the play is a dance that needs a great space and large distances. The playing area lies between the tin drums to both sides of the curtain and the 3 half-circles in which the Pink Shadows sit (i.e., during the Prologue, lie (SSB)).' — (Schumann, *Puppen und Masken*, my translation.)

186

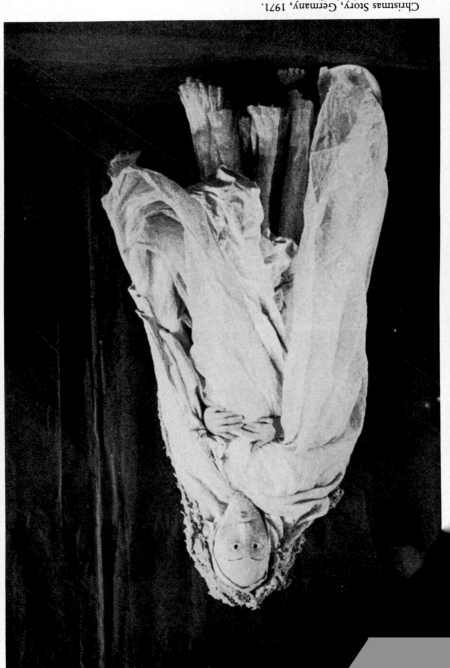

Christmas Story, Germany, 1971.
(Photo: J. Kaltenbach)

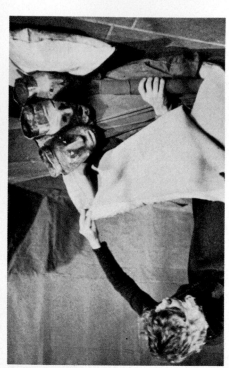

Christmas Story, Germany, 1971.
(Photos: J. Kaltenbach)

The Stations of the Cross, St. Clement's Church, New York
City, 1972.
(Photos: P. Moore)

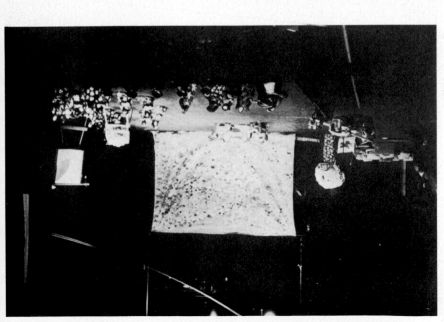

Above: The Stations of the Cross, St. Clement's Church, New York City, 1972.
(Photo: P. Moore)

Right: The Stations of the Cross, Christ (with two operators) and Mary, 1972.
(Photo: Rif)

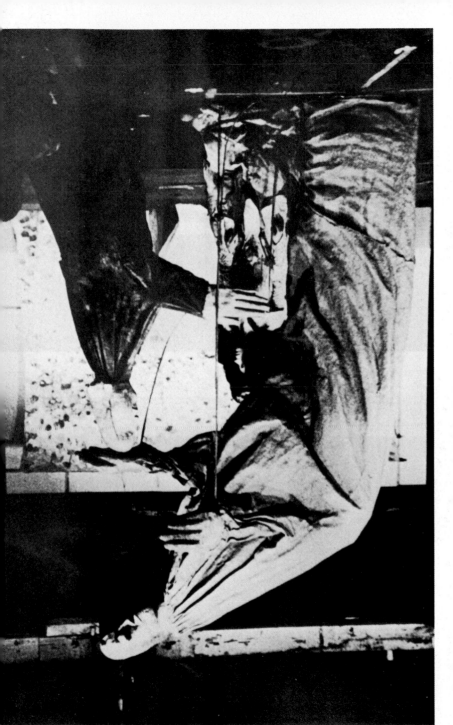

The Stations of the Cross, 1972
(Photos: P. Moore)

The Stations of the Cross.
(Photo: E. George)

Peter Schumann, Coney Island, 1972

Coney Island, 1972.
(Photos: P. Moore)

Coney Island, May 30, 1970.
(Photo: F. McDarrah)

The Story of
Harvey McLeod,
Coney Island,
July 3, 1972.
(Photos: P. Moore)

Grey Lady Cantata III, Nancy, France, December 1971 –
February 1972.
(Photos: E. George)

YAMA   If any sinners come along, set upon them
    and drive them off to hell.

DEMONESS
We tremble and obey.

Enter the Birdcatcher, Kiyoyori.

BIRDCATCHER   Gentleman-Narrator, no megaphone[12]
Ladies and Gentlemen, let me make one thing
    perfectly clear.
All men are sinners.
What have I to fear more than the rest?
My name is Kiyoyori the Birdcatcher.
I was very well known on the terrestrial plane.
But the span of my years came to its appointed close:
I was caught in the wind of impermanence:
    and here I am, marching to the sunless land.
Without a pang
I leave the world where I was wont to dwell,
    the temporal world.

Whither, oh whither have my feet carried me?
To the six ways already I have come.
Enter Beast with sign.
Why, here I am already at the meeting
    of the six ways of existence.

Long crying Oi-oi-oi-oi-oi-oi-oi.
He trembles, kneels, covers himself with dirt.
Oh, shit!
I think on the whole I'll go to Heaven.

DEMONESS
Ha ha: That smells like a man.
Why, sure enough, here's a sinner coming.
We must report him.
Please Sir, here's the first sinner arrived already.

---

12. '. . . the title character is played by a smallish actor wearing a pug-nosed face mask. He
introduces himself with the statement: "Let me make one thing perfectly clear." Then
the narrator takes over his dialogue, leaving him free to gesticulate jerkily.' — (K.
Taylor, *People's Theater.*)
    'Susan Bettmann's mime was just stupendous. Peter taught her her part. It was not
Chaplinesque in any way, but it had some of that free spirit. I remember thinking of
Charlie Chaplin although it didn't remind me of him. And she moved like a dream. Everything was in order.' — (Leherrissier, interview, '79.)
    Sherman (interview, '79) also says the Birdcatcher was mimed — as 'a little man who
was sort of proud of himself — thought he was pretty terrific — and didn't have a sense of
morality about killing.' Schumann in '65 had danced him. But he thought of Bettmann's
mime as dance.

YAMA
Then bustle him to Hell at once.

DEMONESS
I tremble and obey.
Listen, you sinner.
Hell is ever at hand
    which is more than can be said of Heaven.

ALL DEMONS
Humph!

DEMONESS
Come on now, come on. Yai yai yai.
Battle ensues between armed Demons and Birdcatcher.

DEMONESS
And so they fought in the likeness of blazing fire.
Achilles held a long spear uplifted over his head
    straining to stab.
Kiyoyori caught him at the onslaught and broke his
    knees like pliant willows.
Then the wide-powerful Kiyoyori struck Isus in the chest
    by the nipple, dragging him out of his
    gilded chariot
    to be tramped in the fury by his own horses' hysteria.
Retrieving his sword, he struck Hector beside the neck
    at the collar-bone and the double-edged blade
    plunged full-length inside.
He dropped to the ground face downward,
    and the black blood flowed, and the ground
    was soaked with it.
Pedacus rose up, the spear still lodged
    in his right shoulder, only to receive
    a more vicious blow between navel and genitals,
    there where beyond all places
Death comes most pitifully.
Atreus, at the sight, sprang —
Kiyoyori struck him as he came onward
    in the forehead over the base of the nose,
    and smashed the bones,
    so that both eyes dropped bloody
    and lay in the dust at his feet.
Atreus in all his strength dropped suddenly
    to the ground, let fall the spear from his hand,
    and his shield clashed over his limp body.
Three little Demons and Bird exit.

And there Kiyoyori in the huge pride of his strength
  rages irresistibly and gives way to no one,
  neither man nor god.[13]

Let me tell you, you're showing a great deal more
  spirit than most sinners do.
What was your job when you were on the terrestrial plane?

BIRDCATCHER
I was Kiyoyori, the famous birdcatcher.

DEMONESS
Birdcatcher? That's bad. Taking life from morning
  to night. That's very serious, you know.
I am afraid you will have to go to Hell.

BIRDCATCHER
Really, I don't consider I'm as bad as all that.
I should be very much obliged if you would
  let me go to Heaven.

DEMONESS
We must ask King Yama about this.
To Yama   Please Sir.

YAMA
Well, what is it?

DEMONESS
It's like this.

---

13. 'Another scene that was added after you saw it, when we took the show to Europe —
originally, when Pam (as the Demoness Narrator (SSB)) narrated the show she had to
sing a slaughtering passage from the *Iliad* and when she was no longer doing it Peter
created a character for me to play and a scene which was that passage — slaughtering
passage — which was then acted out. We — did not act out, we did it as an aria, Peter and
I. I created a character that was the village idiot who was witnessing the whole show —
Birdcatcher in Hell — and had a bucket of ashes. Wandered onto the stage in the very
beginning — an idiot character — with a bucket of ashes and sat down and watched the
whole show and then at one point the show stopped — and came and sang about the
slaughter. And Peter, who was playing an old man, walked nearby accompanying this aria
on a violin. — (Sherman, interview, '79.)
  'Margo had made up a new part for the *Birdcatcher* which was this insane lady — she
loved the part, and she did that . . . It was a character that was unrelated to the rest of the
action. She would just sort of wander around, having little tantrums Margo-style. Margo's
thing. (I: What happened to her Crazy Lady part?) She kept it and just made it crazier and
crazier. Peter loved it.' — (Leherrissier, interview, '79.)
  Pamela MacDonald, a good singer, one of the Goddard recruits, who had in the States
as Demoness Narrator sung the combat description on the tour was replaced by Leherrissier who — like Sherman — couldn't sing: so Schumann gave the Iliad piece to Margo:
who croaked it. But Margo is a 'trooper': her scales-practicing during the tour helped
drive Leherrissier into one of her breakdowns. The students weren't as available as the
hippies, so Schumann made do, maneuvred, played A off against B, stroked egos.

The sinner says that on the terrestrial plane
   he was a well-known birdcatcher.
Now that means taking life all the time.
It's a serious matter, and he certainly ought to go to Hell.
But when we told him so, he said we'd entirely
   misjudged him.
What had we better do about it?

YAMA
You'd better send him to me.

DEMONESS
Very well.

To Birdcatcher   Come along,
King Yama says he'll see you himself.

BIRDCATCHER
I'm coming.

DEMONESS
Here's that sinner you sent for.

YAMA
Listen to me, you sinner.
I understand that when you were in the world
   you spent your whole time snaring birds.
You are a very bad man and must go to Hell at once.

BIRDCATCHER
That's all very well.
But the birds I caught were sold to gentlemen.
*Two Hands of Yama sink to the ground, revealing 4
   seated Gentlemen in tophats and jackets.
Then hands are raised, replacing red curtain.*[14]
So there was really no harm in it.[15]

YAMA
Falcon is another kind of bird, isn't it?

DEMONESS
Yes, that's right.

YAMA
Well then, I really don't see
   that there was much harm in it.

---

14. The gentlemen Kiyoyori sold his birds to are the backers of Yama. 'When the red
curtain is raised, three human-sized, pink-jowled capitalists in tophats and tails are revealed
to be literally behind the scenes. Capitalists in formal dress recur sarcastically in nearly
every production. They are reminiscent of nothing so much as the angry cartoons that
appeared weekly in the *New Masses*, and the truth of this image seems undimished by the
decades.' — (Taylor, *People's Theater*.)
15. The gentlemen fed Kiyoyori's birds to their falcons.

BIRDCATCHER
I see you take my view.
It was the falcons who were to blame, not I.
That being so, I should be very much obliged
    if you would allow me to go straight to Heaven.

DEMONESS
Then the great King of Hell, because,
    though on the Hill of Death
        many birds flew,
        he had not tasted one . . .

YAMA
Come, take your pole.

DEMONESS
He cried.

YAMA
And here and now give us a demonstration of your art.
Then go in peace.

BIRDCATCHER
Nothing could be simpler.
I will catch a few birds and present them to you.
Enter Beast with gun in mouth. Birdcatcher takes gun.
Beast exits.

DEMONESS
Then he took his pole, and crying:

BIRDCATCHER
To the hunt, to the bird-hunt,

DEMONESS
He cried,
    and suddenly from the steep paths
    of the southern side of the Hill of Death
    bird-whistles
    many birds came flying
Little puppets on strings are lowered over red curtain.
Then swifter than sight his pole darted among them.
Birdcatcher dashes about, aiming and shooting at little
    puppets, which fall to the ground and are replaced by
    others on string, also shot.[16]

---

16. 'Foot-tall people puppets represent the small birds whose bodies are fed to the rich men's hawks. The bird catcher shoots each one as it appears over the red curtain. They fall in a heap on the floor and are fried like the dolls were in the prologue.' — (Taylor, *People's Theater.*)

BIRDCATCHER
I will roast them,

DEMONESS
He cried.
And when they were cooked,

BIRDCATCHER
Please try one,

DEMONESS
And he offered them to the king.

YAMA
Let me eat it, let me eat it. Well!
Yummy, yummy!
I must say they taste uncommonly good![17]

BIRDCATCHER *to Demons*
Perhaps you would like to try some?

DEMONS *yelling and screaming*
Oh, thank you!
I want that bit! No, it's mine!
What a flavor! *Exit*

YAMA
I am uncommonly concerned about your case and I decide
to add an extra-legal ingredient to the review
process. I personally will decide your case once
the review procedure is exhausted and before you
ever serve a day of your sentence to hard labor
for life.[18]

BIRDCATCHER
I am very much obliged to you, I'm sure.

*Four tophatted Gentlemen file out; first takes gun and
places it on pillow, second puts military coat
on Birdcatcher.*

DEMONESS
You shall catch many birds, pheasant, pigeon, heron
and stork. They shall not elude you, but fall
fast into the fatal snare.
So he, reprieved, turned back towards the world.

---

17. 'The god of hell wants to taste a bird and it is handed back to him through a hole in the curtain. The curtain, manipulated by its two holders, becomes the god's great, greasy mouth; it chops greedily at the bird.' — (Taylor, *People's Theater*.)

18. A Nixon quote. 'Gerade in der gewollten anachronistischen Uberschneidung, die die Nixon-Sätze als Fremdkörper in Text erscheinen lässt, liegt die spezifische politische Wirkung.' — (D. Herms, *Mime Troupe, . . ., Maske u. Kothern*.)'

Third Gentleman in tophat puts army helmet on
  Birdcatcher's head.

DEMONESS
But Yama, loathe to see him go
  bestowed a jewelled crown,
  which Kiyoyori bore respectfully
  to the terrestrial plane,
  there to begin his second span of life.[19]

Fourth Gentleman in tophat plays long roll on snare
  drum, while Birdcatcher marches out in goose-step.[20]
Everyone wails with high, tremulous sound. Giant
Demons step forward and form line across stage.
Four Gentlemen in tophats and Birdcatcher step between Giant Demons.
Everyone takes long, slow bow.
Demoness and Birdcatcher, arm in arm, slowly come across
  to stage center and take long, slow bow.[21]

---

19. Der Vogelfänger in Stahlhelm und Soldatenmantel mit Gewehr wird sogar ausgezeich-net – in dieser Hölle.' — (Hardtmann, *Der Vogelfänger, Theater Heute.*)
20. Second of the three allusions I know of to the Nazi era in Schumann's work – that, rather than Prussia, being the goose-step's evocation to him and audiences. The first were Uncle Fatso/Johnson's German accents in the '65, '66 *Speech*. The third the goose-stepping of squadrons of business men and German accents in the speech of their leader in pageants of the late '70s.
21. There were two alternative endings:
  'Back on earth the birdcatcher is dressed in military uniform and decorated by the rich men he serves. He parades before the audience carrying a sign that identifies him as Sergeant Calley. (The sign changes from performance to performance, after all there are any number of names to choose from.)' — (Taylor, *People's Theater.*)
  '*Later version of the ending.* The birdcatcher, in helmet and soldier's coat, marches to one of the heaps of sand. The Bird Demon presses him to the ground. The Madonna dresses him in the (pink) shadow skin. As Pink Shadow he shovels the sand back into the bucket. And the Madwoman drags him to the red curtain, puts him under it and herself slips in behind him.' — (Schumann, *Puppen und Masken,* my translation.)
  'Aber auch (der Vogelfänger) wird zu Boden gedrückt. Das lemurische Ritual beschliesst die abziehende Prozession der Schweine – u. Rindsköpfe. Der Kreislauf des Ewig-Gleichen und Schrecklichen...' — (Hardtmann, *Der Vogelfänger, Theater Heute.*)
  'In 1971, First Lieut. William L. Calley Jr. was convicted of murdering 22 unarmed civilians, including women and children, in the South Vietnamese hamlet of My Lai. He was sentenced to life at hard labor, but actually served three years under house arrest at Fort Benning, Ga.
  Today, Mr. Calley lives near the Army post in a quiet section of Columbus, Ga., and works six days a week at the V.V. Vick jewelry store, which is owned by his father-in-law. Customers say Mr. Calley, 40 years old, is the store's most popular salesman. He married Penny Vick in 1976, and the couple have a son, William Laws Calley 3d, who was 3 last month.
  Mr. Calley refuses to talk to the press. He can be seen driving his Mercedes-Benz or Ford Granada around Columbus or working in the yard of his three-bedroom brick bungalow on Hilton Avenue where he has lived since 1977. — (*William Calley Jr., New York Times,* July 10, '83.)

Birdcatcher in Europe apparently was not nearly the success the two *Grey Lady Cantatas* were and Schumann himself seems to have been dissatisfied with it. He repeatedly on programs substituted the *Cantatas* for it, and kept changing it. Transposed to the indoors, the prologue's child burial lost its bucolic veneer of gardening, the curtailment or suppression of its pageantry changed the dreamlike materialization of the demonic powers into an abrupt presence or irruption, a change not only of presentation but also of politics, and the play's red opulence which in a natural setting was an antagonistic complementation, became the visionary monochrome of an otherworldly hell, a stage designer's artifact. But the main and real reason why the play didn't quite work seems to have been the political stuff: the gun, the helmet and the marching, the Nixon quotations. It rudely reduced the fable to allegory and didn't go with the theatrics. There was no question for Schumann of cutting down on it: he tried to render it more effective.[22] For him the problem was the other way around: the spectacle overwehelmed the politics.[23] The play is remarkable in his oeuvre for (and

---

22. '. . . *the Birdcatcher in Hell* was not a show that had — it didn't work for me as far as meaning goes. (I: Why not?) It worked in those other areas. (I: Why did it not work?) I don't know. I think it was that — I felt that he was trying so hard to get the war into the show — the war in Vietnam. He tried to get it in and he couldn't, really . . . The speech worked itself, but something, some urge to be political for me did not come through in that show. And I felt that what was more successful in the show was the visceral experiences that the audience received through the extraordinary use of sound and color. (I: Those visceral experiences would be?) The screaming, the horror, the drum beating, the appearance of those red demons. (I: But the visceral experiences would be mainly horror?) Yeah. (I: Terrifying. I'm trying to remember what I experienced. Okay.) And I do remember that when we took it on tour to Europe, Peter must have begun to feel that the show wasn't working and he kept on trying to change it unsuccessfully, more and more we would have a choice of doing *Birdcatcher* or *Grey Ladies 2* and *3*. He would say, I'm going to do *Grey Ladies 2* and *3*. Of course when we had a chance to do both the programs we did both. — (Sherman, interview, '79.)

Elka felt his changes were making the play *harder* to understand:

'Do you feel — I was in the show and saw it while it was in America, and then it went on tour to Europe that following fall and winter, and then I saw the French movie of it, made for TV, and you told me about the changes that were made in it, and that show seemed to get more and more *stylized* and abstracted and hard to understand, and I wonder if you think — ' — (Elka, in Schumann, interview, '79.)

23. 'Ich weiss gar nicht, ob ich alles richtig wiedergegeben habe. Denn die Faszination, die auf Auge und Ohr eindringt, macht alles, was da geisterhaft und gräulich, makaber und naiv, symbolvoll und rätselhaft geschieht, zu einem komplexen Erlebnis. Die Riesen-Masken, die lumpigen Pludergewänder, die grellen Stimmen und das gespenstige Dunkel: was passiert da eigentlich?

Es hebt wie ein Geisterritual an, Ritual-Opferszenen mischen sich mit Horror-Märchen-Szenen, die Reflektion des Publikums ist ständig in Fluss; wenn es zu lachen beginnt, fällt es gleich darauf in verunsichertes Schweigen. Dann und wann bietet sich die Szene wie die grell-phantastische Unterhaltung der chinesischen Oper an, bald erinnert sie an das mystischmakabre Höllische von Hieronymys Bosch. Mal kommt alles ganz naiv, oder es

its politics indeed swamped by) its theatricality and opulence, both blatant in its flaming redness — what my father called 'culinary opulence': 'ein Blick in die Hölle, appetitlich gemacht durch prächtige Masken und Puppen' (Hardtmann, *Der Vogelfänger, Theater Heute.*)

Though this outburst is surely significantly situated in his life curve also[24] it is as though Schumann had suddenly felt himself liberated from the severe restraints of the white Vermont winter (which he loves). *Birdcatcher* was a splendid operatic production, gorgeous. But its luxuriance is sentiently the equivalent of the semantic scintillation (Georg Lukacs's term — 'Schillern') of the first two *Grey Lady Cantatas* (death as salvation), of the groovy-party form of the end of the world in *Genghis Khan*, of the unclear vision of matters of life and death through the cocoon of domesticity in *Emilia*, of the oppressive obscurity — 'complicated darkness' — of human struggle in *Simple Light*. Schumann is not on the ball. He is indulging in art during this period, and delighting in mystery.[25] The play's colorfulness, intricately devolutive and ornamented, painted masks and elaborate and

---

gibt Theatertricks, die zwar einfach aber wirksam sind. Für unsere Aufnahmefähigkeit ist alles auf des Messers Schneide, mürbemachend bei aller Faszination.

. . . In einem interview hat Peter Schumann einmal gesagt, das Bread an- Puppet Theatre wolle mit seinen selbstgemachten Stücken und selbstgebastelten Masken und Kostümen eine Antwort geben auf das, was in der Welt passiert. Wirkt es wirklich so demonstrativ? Oder ist es doch eher die radikale Abwendung von der konservativen Theater-Mache, was uns anzieht?' — (H.-J. Kraemer, *Eine Antwort auf das was in der Welt passiert*, 'Bread and Puppet Theatre' mit 'The Bird Catcher in Hell' German newspaper, January 19, '72.)

24. The gossip has it that when he made it, an affair of his with a lovely young French girl, scotched by Elka in the fall of '71, was at its high point. The play's hell's fire is (also) that of intoxicating but for him at the same time poisonous illicit sex. Schumann's directing of the part indicates a certain sympathy for the birdcatcher.

'Most all of the woodcuts and the shields and the reds, the masks were all these devils with erections in some kind of combat, fighting on the backs of women. They weren't full of madonnas and Jesus. They were full of Peter. I mean, he's had couples copulating and all but he's never had that graphic a scene of a devil with an erection. On the costumes, on the shields. Repeating. Each one done by hand. The costumes were lighter red, and then we would paint darker red on top of the lighter red, or we would print lighter on top of darker — but that didn't work so good, it was easier to print darker on top of lighter. Birds and devils and musicians (wore those costumes) . . . Symbol of virility and also of oppression. They seemed to go together. On one level it was Calley and My Lai and on the other hand I saw it as a reflection of some of the sexual conflicts that he was — (as a) self-critique — maybe self-critique — unless it was just the unconscious doing its work.' — (Levy, interview, '79.)

25. He defended obscurity by calling for active audiences. E.g. à propos of *Birdcatcher*, to a Swedish interviewer:

'Jag vill att publiken skall vara medlevande, aktiv vid mina föreställningar. Inte sitta stum som franför en TV-apparat och ta emot en pjäs som en färdiglagad sötsak. Ja ställer krav pa askadars aktiva lyssnande — pa samma sätt som modern musik gor det.' — (Schumann, 'ledare för den världsberömda' Bread and Puppet Theater, interviewed in a Swedish paper, January 4, '72.)

elegant costuming, its oriental musical effects and grandiose operatic choreography overwhelm its 'j'accuse'. The references and moods of his puppets always went beyond the lessons of Schumann's allegories, but once he had left New York, his staging did too: was directed to support these moods and references rather than the allegories and their lessons.

His father died during this tour.[26]

26. 'The guys who were having us in Hamburg – they hadn't signed the contract, so they ... when the puppeteers got there, they invited them all to a restaurant and they wanted them to eat and they basically ended up getting Peter drunk which he did from time to time, get drunk. (I: I heard that he drank a little beer with dinner.) Not true. He likes to drink vodka too. He sneaks it because Elka disapproves of it. Oh boy, people don't think he gets drunk, huh? (Interviewer off mike) ... who told you that? That's amazing. No, he certainly does get drunk from time to time. Particularly when he starts acting funny and his little fey routines. So anyway, what these people did was they succeeded in getting Peter drunk, they got him to sign a contract for less money than he had originally agreed to. As soon as they had his signature on a contract – they had been wining and dining him in the restaurant for like two hours or something – as soon as he signed the thing, the guy turned to him and said, oh, yes, by the way, your brother called, and if you hurry, you can catch the last train to Freiburg. Your father has died. So Peter just jumped up, and went running out. And Murray grabbed the guy by his throat and started strangling him. So the puppeteers had to all pull Murray off – he's a very volatile guy. He's a very smart guy, although sometimes his emotions get in the way. And then Peter stayed away. Well, the first couple of days we were in Hamburg, Peter was at his father's funeral ... His father I think died on New Year's Day or something like that.'— (Leherrissier, interview, '79.)

11. *Simple Light.* Der Einzelne und sein Eigentum vs. the crowd spirit.
Summative goodbye to the '60s.
Let's cultivate our gardens.
Obscurity as form of asociality.

'. . . du kennst ihn, da du kennest, jugendlich,
Des Guten Kraft, und nimmer ist dir
Verborgen das Lächeln des Herrschers
Bei Tagen, wenn
Es fieberhaft und angekettet das
Lebendige scheinet oder auch
Bei Nacht, wenn alles gemischt
Ist ordungslos und wiederkehrt
Uralte Verwirrung.'

(F. Hölderlin, *Der Rhein.*)

During the late fall and early winter – October, November – of that very productive year 1971, just back from the New York State campus tour that convinced him that the young to whom he was addressing himself then, the college students, had lost the idealism and enthusiasm in his experience marking them during the '60s, that the frivolity of Goddard was not an exception, and getting ready to leave in December on a European tour, his third, that would show him if the enthusiasm over there for his work was holding up, and busy for that tour adding (in November) another *Grey Lady Cantata (GLC III)* to the first, shifting the accent of the repertory he was bringing away from the topically political, Schumann, utilizing the troops he had assembled for his European onslaught, indulged in an orgy of plaster cast mask making 'for an as yet unidentified show' (Schumann, Bread and Puppet chronology, *Puppen und Masken*) – 'a big mask building project of a very different kind. It was some kind of renaissance in our theatre, some kind of new mode of sculpture' (Schumann, interview, '79). Above his desk while he was making the puppets (Elka, letter, March 6, '85) he had pinned a photo for inspiration.

Like the demon heads made for *Birdcatcher* the preceding May, and like the Bulbhead Family masks made (probably) in '73, they represented the demonic in man and – by the many multiple-face masks among them – man in crowd form. He continued work on the masks after his return from Europe, the following spring, but it wasn't until after the Cate Farm harvest – 'freezing and pickling, canning, storing vegetables and apples; bottling cider and beer; drying apples, mint, corn and making jellies and

197

juices from wild grapes and berries' (Bread and Puppet Theatre history, January '73) — that he actually got down to working — with Goddard students, in the 'ice-cold' barn — on the play, in October-November '72: 'rehearsing' with:

'black plastic which we had discovered on the farm as something useful for the garden. And a material that wasn't very expensive, was available at lumber yards

— and we liked the shine and the body of it, and the sound of it, so we did a *lot* of experiments with that black plastic, people underneath it, and moving in it, and these faces on poles, a little bit of light and out of that we made something that was like a story of geological events in the world and not so much a human history (Elka: I remember the rehearsals because it was late in the fall and it was very, very cold and you were having *such* a hard time with the rehearsals. You were coming back all mad and frustrated and not getting anywhere. I remember when you came once and said that you'd discovered the title for it. I don't know if *you* made it up or if someone else made it up, but it had been part of the difficulty of the show — was that we couldn't think of a title.) The title was from a letter-like essay that I wrote before — about our life on Cate Farm.'

(Schumann, interview, '79.)

That Simple Light May Come from Complicated Darkness was first tried out in the barn November 9, 10 and 11, '72, had 'workshop' showings at Windham College December 7, 8, 9, a run in New York City at St. Clement's Church Theatre, December 12-22, was toured in New England in January ('73) – it played January 13-15 at the Loeb Drama Center in Cambridge, Massachusetts, was presented by the Copeland Colloquium January 20-22 at Amherst – and was taken on a European tour at the end of '73, November-December.[1] The Amherst version was billed as the '3rd revised version', so the New York version must have been a second one, revised from the original one.

The Windham College 'workshop' showings were typical: the show (like the '72 *Stations* which it was even bigger than) was so big its cast had to be locally complemented:

'Amherst people will have the opportunity to participate in a most unusual style of theatrical presentation this month. The Bread and Puppet Theatre, a New York drama troupe under the direction of Joseph Papp of the Public Theater in New York is coming to Amherst College to conduct workshops in theatre which will be open to everyone of high school age and older in the Five College area. The workshops, beginning January 17, will culminate in three performances of *'That Simple Light May Rise out of Complicated Darkness'* . . . Professor Eugene Warner of the Amherst College Dramatic Arts Department, from whom more information can be obtained . . . emphasized that all interested people are urged to come to these workshops, and especially musicians – cellists, woodwind and trumpet players, and so forth.' (Amherst student paper.)

'(Ephraim: It was taken on tour with *Christmas Story* and *Revenge of the Law*.) That must have been a *big* company, for that. (Elka: It *was*, 25.) Could be, but I remember we took on at least 20 people *each* place where we went, and that they were very *big* and sometimes were *horrible* rehearsal periods, to produce the show. It was sometimes very hard to train people into it because training time was too short to tell people *what* we were doing, we just told them what to do and we just rehearsed with them, and they got – they *complained* and they hated it and they didn't want to do it and we had trouble finding people in Berlin for it – so it was horrible, absolutely horrible – at the end of that *tour* we decided to stop the theatre. (Elka: *You* decided.) Yes. (Elka: Was *Simple Light* the first *major* piece where you had a built-in – you know, you had – you depended on such a large number of volunteers to make the show possible? (Ephraim: Didn't *The Cry* . . .?) No. *The Cry* was self *contained*. But we *did* include other people quite frequently. (Elka: But we didn't depend on them.) We didn't depend on them. (Elka: But in *Simple Light* you really *had* to have those people, otherwise you couldn't use the puppets.) *Simple Light* couldn't be performed without another 20 people.

---

1. He was twenty performers short on this tour and they were with great difficulty recruited and trained in each place they performed. He had had the chutzpah to ask Goddard to pay for twenty students to come on this tour – pay their travel expenses – and had topped this by making this request in the form of an offer. He was turned down.

(Ephraim: So it was the only show that was really like that?) At that point, it was the *first* show that was like that. That depended so much on a *large* number of volunteers and sometimes *that* was the problem that we – they knew that we had a contract, that we got paid and *they* wanted to be paid too and we just couldn't afford that – the expenses of touring and of having to bring some of that money back to the farm to be able to continue, didn't allow for paying 20 other people. So – (Elka: But most of them didn't perform with you longer than the few days that you were in that town.) Nobody ... they only did for the few days, but it meant a lot of rehearsal time. (Elka: And I think also you conceived of this tour as being a thing where you would go to one place and work with a group of people intensely and then perform a lot of times and it turned out to be all – not all – one-night stands, but very much travelling – new rehearsals.) Yeah, it was an awful tour.' (Schumann, interview, '79.)

My account of the New York showing, written in the winter of '72/'73, follows:

The Bread & Puppet Theatre provides a homemade program book, a series of 12 woodcuts on its cover, the successive states of a 'Vermont' landscape, the hills constant, but a more or less of black clouds in the sky, covering the sun or not. The sun becomes progressively more prominent in the strip, but there are also more and more big black clouds very near it. Inside, a table of contents, part I in 19 parts, part II in 8, each scene has a title. In the show, the scenes tend to go over into one another and some scenes seem displaced, others missing, but I shall try to correlate these titles with a brief account of what I remember seeing. The show took between 2 and 3 hours. We are seated on the floor, in a shallow horse-shoe, at one end of an assembly hall or gymnasium. First, an oppressive nightmare:

> In visions I saw in the night
> When sleep falls on people
>
> A secret word came to me
> and my ear received of it a little.
>
> Fear and trembling overtook me.
> My bones were frightened.
>
> (Job IV. 12-19.)

(1) *Rocky Mountains*   Heavy-duty black plastic covers the floor, buckled like a field of congealed lava. The theatre is dark. A performer shrouded in black illumes a not too bright light hanging from the end of a pole and slowly, raising and lowering the lantern, moves over the black surface which responds by a golden glitter. The light illuminates only the sector of the lunar surface just underneath it. The lantern carrier's ir-

regular searching has the air of a trepid voyage of discovery or of an apprehensive check-up, but one's impression is perhaps rather that a dead, or, worse, morbid, world is disclosing *itself*. Some movement begins to manifest itself in the landscape which now takes on the aspect of a swamp in which gaseous bubbles are forming. Very gradually, the movement becomes more definite, slow heaving billows, faintly phosphorescent, on a black ocean of Poe's. The movement becomes more agitated, the protuberances and excrescences grow taller, it grows violent, a tossing and threshing, monstrous basalt monuments have arisen, we are witnessing the birth-pangs of evil, liberated from death, or/and the emergence of creature. Obscure figures have been congregating in the background. Cricket noises.

(2) *Original crawling*

(3) *Voices of the people*

Several densely compacted black groups of hooded figures, moving from place to place, revolving, one of them under a giant mask in the shape of a shield, consisting of many faces like warts and perhaps of other signs. Little by little, moving like a giant paw, it gathers the individuals in. Perhaps it is a collective face, the face of the faceless shrouded individuals. Finally it covers them all. At first there is silence, then gentle wails, at the end the wail is in unison. Vox populi is a cry of anguish. I first saw this powerful image in *The Difficult Life of Uncle Fatso*. There the devourer was the night of urban anarchy.

(4) *Single man's fate*

A lighter face mask, double life size (Sara Peattie), rises from within the black group. The covering mass mask is gone. The group shatters: the individual wearing the large light mask stands alone. Lounging, they stone him (with loose wads of paper). The figure collapses by stages, tiny under its mask, all face when it is down. A black figure (the first individual was black too, but one didn't think of him that way) pounces forward with a knife, drives it into the floor in front of the martyr, the others approach crawling, groping for the knife blindly, the group reforms, the knife is somewhere within it. The tragic-faced figure again rises above the crowd. They gather round it, a scream, they scatter, the Individual is standing, knife in his hand, hand in the air. He performs a Japanese knife dance. One of the

(5) *Story of a knife*

(5a) *Confused ambitions & power of contrast fight complicated*

201

black crowd is carrying a sword. They fight a grand
noisy duel. A scream. The faceless sword fighter
agonizes. The tiny knife wielder is the victor. There
is a brash noise: folding chairs are being thrown on
top of one another to the rear, stage-right. Everyone
falls prone, then gets up, all flee to the rear.

(5b) *Birth of
Johnny*

One of the black hooded figures comes back out
with the knife, fastens it to a rope dangling from
above. A grey witch – her wig made of a mop – is
huddled at the edge of the space, stage-right. One of
the 'Johnny-figures', named for their role in the
spring 1968 *Johnny Comes Marching Home*, this one
a foot-high figure of a seated, hatted, stocky
middle-aged man in office black and white, is advanced toward us by a cooing ('Johnny, Johnny . . .')
black crowd, carrying it like a baby. It is deposited
down-stage center, under the knife.

(5c) *T.V.*

A most complete apartment, centering around a television set, including among its many normal-sized
furnishings a toilet bowl, is rapidly put up around
Johnny, dwarfing him. The black figures form a
circle around, sit on the floor. A tiny puppet pops
out of the television set, says something. The apartment is rapidly dismantled.

(5d) *A whole Johnny
population
arrives*

A stooped witch advances onto the stage chuckling a
robot chuckle. She is carrying a rope. To the sound
of a cello, she fastens the rope to the rope with the
knife and sets the knife swinging above Johnny (ask
not for whom it tolls). Black crawling figures push
forward a long line of Johnnies. The cello is playing,
the knife is oscillating above the crowd of small
figures.

(5e) *Knife depos-
ited in a
local grocery*

A black figure comes out, detaches the knife, lifts its
arms, a vast ball, perhaps a many-faced mask, descends to it from the rafters, the tiny T.V. Puppet
pops out and the knife is handed to it to the sound of
trumpets.

(6) *Story of soup.*
(a) *Hunger,*
(b) *Stone soup
cooking,* (c)
*Feeding of
populace.* (d)
Soup spilled

A soup pot is taken out of the ball, held up and
fingered by the reassembled crowd of black figures,
stirred to the sound of trumpeting and operatic arias.
The assembly of Johnnies is salted (shades of Chaplin), then they are spoonfed from the pot. The witch
advances with a narrow white door, places it out in
front of the line of fed Johnnies. The black figures

gather in two chorus lines this side of it, around them. On kitchenware instruments they play a repeated melodic-rhythmic sequence, as one, then another black figure enters through the door (opened by the witch, I think), each carrying an additional Johnny figure. Admiring exclamations as each enters. The little Johnnies are admired. They are figures of 'ordinary people.' The two blacks reenter, take out the two babies to 'bye-byes' from the choruses. (Somewhere in this scene, I guess, the pot gets dropped.)

A firing squad of Johnnies faces seated female Johnnies. The giant Uncle Fatso — tophat, cigar — in the role that I first saw him in *The Difficult Life of Uncle Fatso*, enters. His movements are soft, small, meaningless, there are many of them, he is continually in small motion, he has the expression of a joker, amused. A female black slightly behind him at his side, seated at a desk, continues to dial a telephone frantically . . . The female Johnnies, seated as though at a bridge party, in front of the firing squad, are gathered up by a mad executioner, a large puppet whirling about frantically, picking them up under his swirling black cape, throwing them through an opening in the cape to a polyp that disposes of them: a kneeling group of the blacks, squeezed together, its arms outstretched toward the corpses flung them. The executioner thus clears the stage. The shooting squad Johnnies are removed by others in an incidental manner. (First appearance of Simple Light? I didn't notice the small figure in white until the 12th scene, cf. infra.)

A duel-dance of approach between a creature with a giant grey bent head, its face at a right angle to its neck, and a long tapeworm, 4 or 5 performers covered with black plastic sheeting, with a similar head. The worm, over and over, its many feet tapping heavily, advances toward and retreats from the other creature. As they approach one another (fife music), a naked arm with outstretched naked pale hand slowly, weakly extends from each as though the creatures wanted to touch, effect a union, but the hands never join, the arms pull back as the moving extended figure moves away from the other again, the hands disappear. The effect is amazingly pathetic. A giant black figure, its head that of a Christ, advances and retreats between them at the normal to their cross-stage dance. Lights off.

A slight figure in white is out front in the dark. She is lighting herself with a flashlight. There is a white veil over her face. The lantern suspended from the end of a pole is by another performer carried toward the rear, illuminating a row of giant puppets with even more gigantic heads. A chorus of semi-laments, quasi-Gregorian, a peaceful indecisive wail, starts. One perceives by the light at the rear, in front of the giant standing puppets still other figures, each with a row of half a dozen or more heads, only slightly smaller than the heads of the giants looming above them. Then more figures in front of these, a third row, even lower down, with giant double heads, near the floor. All the puppets are swaying to the ecclesiastic wail, each order of magnitude in its own way. The giant standing ones are bobbing faintly. The self-illuminated white figure in the foreground is seated with its back to us. It seems to be praying. All three rows of puppets advance very slowly, almost imperceptibly toward it and us. We see that the giant upright figures have several faces melting into one another. The whole pushes forward like the edge of a forest or like a giant street parade. The wail is growing more rhythmical. They all stand and chant and sway, now well lit, black. Their wail turns into something like a hunting shout. It stops. Silence. Hands emerge, rising from each figure, slender-fingered. Cricket noises. All the giant figures and faces, all three rows, start to decline slowly backward. The wail has set in again. It is in unison now. The faces disappear from sight on the floor. Again in silence, the now headless indistinct black figures, joined in the church of death, crawl away in darkness, back toward the rear, melting into the darkness to the crinkling sounds of their dragging plastic garments. A trumpet or a tuba sounds rawly.

A banner with a winter tree and a half moon on it is unfolded and held, stretched out between two poles. Two standing projectors illuminate it from the front of the stage. In front of it, two black figures engage

(b) *Lovers' love*	in combat. They finish, and a succession of couples, each couple actually a single performer with a large mask on which a male and a female face are joined, emerge from behind it, while handfuls of snow (shredded newspaper), thrown over its top, drift down. The coupled lovers advance to the mournful notes of something like a bass viola – perhaps a cello – in large dance steps, slowly, bending their knees deeply. They kneel, each couple convincingly a couple. They join hands, embrace. A moon mask slowly rises above the banner (on which there is also a moon). A white figure, who has been there all the time, approaches, lifts off the lovers' double-faced masks one by one, and one by one hands them back over the banner. The shrouded performers leave slowly. The banner is gathered up, removed. White figure off.
(16) *Great walk*	Black figures promenading to tones I thought those of a tuba.
(17) *Drummer's diversions*	The lights go on and the black figures, a little grey in the light, stand revealed. One of them comes out of their crowd and begins to move about banging a spoon on a cookie tin in a two-figure rhythm of command and execution. Commanded, the other black figures turn their heads toward him like blind people listening, having become aware of him, trying to locate him. On the command of execution, they rush toward him. Each time they scurry and gather, he has smoothly moved on. Finally they corner him. Is there a scream? The crowd disappears.
(18) *Pure demon* (a) *Dance* (b) *Fight* (c) *Message torn*	A personage, by its mask a Japanese demon, emerges, the body performed by one person, dancing sinuously, the head by the carrier of the mask, the hair by a third who carries the wig. It fights another figure, triumphs. The figure in white, with a white right hand twice life-size, presents a message to it. To 'ohs' from the chorus, the message is taken by hands coming out of its mouth. The hands tear up the piece of paper to expressions of horror. The white figure smites the demon by a gesture of raising her big hand in the air. It dies in agony ('aieeee, aieeee . . .'). All leave.

Part II

(1) *Simple Light goes someplace else*

Simple Light, the figure in white, enters with a grey Vermont landscape carried in behind her, walks from it, turns, sits and looks at it. She gets up, she and the landscape leave. This is repeated with another picture, of another landscape. A tiny person, her face uncovered, with some elegance draped in the black of the play, a red ribbon sash diagonalling her from her black tophat down across her chest sits with quiet demureness, watching. It's Sara Peattie, a performer and an actress of considerable power. She's the Captain. I believe she also did the Individual in Part I, scenes 4 and 5a. A door is brought out near Sara watching. Simple Light has left. Behind the door, in a file, performers holding cloud cutouts on sticks. Chairs are put out for a party. There is a knock on the door, the Captain gets up and opens it, the Clouds file in, greeted individually by the Captain in different ways. They sit down, have tea and conversation, the reseated Captain, their host, watching in a kindly manner. Sara gets up, touches one of them on the shoulder to indicate it is time for them to leave, opens the door, bids them goodbye individually, they leave. The chairs are removed. The scene, definition of a captain, explanation of his relation to the weather, *clue* to Schumann's stage poetry, is his tribute to Sara's tranquil charm. Sara returns to her chair, Simple Light enters, sits down opposite. They sit. Sara guides her out (Schumann: 'to the boat').

(2) *Big boat's movements on the sea*

A wild scene, shouts and movements, various figures, a big mask with wide bands of black plastic stretching out on both sides like wings, perhaps the storm, a giant black figure (wall/mountain/oak: the sea?), waving its horizontally held double hand high up. In the middle, Simple Light and the commanding little Captain who is shouting orders into a big megaphone. A flag is waved wildly. A group of figures are on their backs in the foreground, flailing their arms and legs in the air. The storm subsides, apparently subdued by the Captain. All off.

(3a) *Arrival in the new world*

A procession. A donkey, a performer under a covering with a two-dimensional donkey head on a stick

(3b) *Parade of house builders*	and another stick for the donkey's front legs, is followed by Simple Light, cradling a red baby-angel-doll. With her, her little husband, a small dainty fellow, also in white, with white face makeup and a white tophat, walking, bowing, holding his head, moving his arm with a faintly and amiably ridiculous grace. To the cricket sound of something like finger tympans and/or little bells, he, successively taking them out of a saddle bag on the donkey, distributes on the floor three small paper cutouts of houses, drawn as though by a child, Simple Light's angelic hand puppet blessing each in turn. They seat themselves on the floor with their baby, behind one of the houses. They sit quietly. She is absorbed in the baby, he in her.
(3c) *Hurricane Frieda*	A black figure, wearing a grey businessman's hat wanders about among the houses, leaves, returns with a helmet on instead of the hat, resumes wandering, again leaves. The little Captain enters, hands dignifiedly folded behind her back, also wanders about around the houses, inspecting. There is a rising sound of beaten pots and pans from the black chorus seated around. The woman and her husband seem afraid. The first, first hatted, then helmeted figure, returns, the orchestra clanging frantically, and wildly flails a black plastic sash. The sash overthrows two of the houses. Simple Light's home is spared. Quiet. (Little bells). The Captain and the Storm go off. Business and war are the forces that wreck homes.
(4) *Simple Light's Poverty* (?)	The family is still seated. Singly, one after the other, the black figures come out to them and each in turn puts pale naked hands softly on the couple, until there is a dark rim about the family, all the hands slithering gently on their white clothes. Simple Light is petting her baby. A humming little car is led up to them on a string, the family rises and follows it out. He is leading her ceremoniously, as at a floor parade opening a cotillion ball. She is waving goodbye delicately to the figures – their hands are again hidden.
(5) *Simple Light's Courage* (?)	The black figures remain there in a kneeling, crouching huddle. They are half covered over with a shroud of black plastic. A white giant smiling mask emerges from the heap, the shroud its garment. The shroud is arranged around the mask, half revealing,

207

half framing it. A horn blows, the giant starts trembling. It stands in the crowd of its body, trembling. They carry it off, like a cadaver, over their shoulders. A drum is thumped.

(6) *Growing forest* (?)

To the sound of the drum, tall poles on small cement plaques are placed about the stage, filling it. From each of them dangle a large mask, at the top, and, reaching down to the floor, a broad band of black material. The masks hanging like enigmatic moons, they stand.

(7) *Trembling of swords and men* (?)

The drum falls silent. Flashing lights and wailing horns: the forest at night? Cries like of owls from the performers. Large, though among the tall poles small, fanged beasts filter toward us through the trees. Agitated by the beast-performers, the bands of black start shivering. Trees and beasts. A violin. The passive masks above them, Simple Light and her husband are seen wending their way through the woods followed by a dancing bear. (I suppose she was carrying her baby.) The forest noises subside. Simple Light and her husband have left. A giant white figure in the rear (Simple Light grown gigantic?) is slowly moving up and down as the forest is, with some awkwardness, the poles having to be inclined to take off the masks, deprived of its foliage, only the bare poles remaining standing. The giant white figure. Brightly lit, center stage to the rear, a white door.

(8) *Door opens (hopefully)*

I have forgotten what happens here . . . except that a parade of circus clowns and acrobats, all in bright raggedy clothes, enters from the rear of the audience, dancing and joking, doing tricks. They pass through the door.

*   *   *

The world is a harsh dark place moved by evil. Men are cruel and lust for power and/or foolish and avid for food:

And now remaineth faith, hope, charity, these three: but the greatest of these is charity.

the loving simplicity of some holds the faint promise of a better world.

*   *   *

The play is very dark. It does not figure the world as arena in which the powers of Evil and Good, dark clouds and bright sun, do combat, but as evil in substance. Matter is evil, a medieval view, making the origin of good a problem, the solution of which, if the existence of good is recognized, as it is in this play, would seem to require extra-mundane and supernatural intervention. Thus the Christ: between Rome and Israel, the West and Asia (Part I, scene 9)? Simple Light is supposed to[2] rise out of complicated darkness, but there is in the play no image (cf. Act I, scene 10) of the complication of darkness giving rise to simple light. The simplicity of the pure heart and the complexity of the greedy world of cruel masters and foolish slaves stand as absolute opposites. An altogether exceptional phantom of simplicity = purity = goodness is a visitation in the laboring turmoil of Act I. In Act II we find it established in the world's darkness, leading a charmed existence in the midst of its terrors, almost oblivious of them. Simple Light is isolated in a nighttime world. Somehow her courage, but it seems more obliviousness, soothes the antagonism that rends the world and complicates it. At the end, her mere existence projects a future of universal light, and a bright parade of simple entertainers, come from nowhere, gambols through the white door of her vision. I suppose that Schumann thinks of the complicated vale peopled by ordinary people as suffused by a faint light – some goodness in every soul – and thinks of the figure of Simple Light as symbolic incarnation, concentrate, of this common goodness. But this thought is extrinsic to the show, which seems to despise and condemn the very complexity of the world from which goodness might arise. Whatever magic matter may possess appears here as black, and the simplicity of the good individual not only excludes an origin of his or rather her goodness in a complex act of self-purification – Simple Light is a miracle – but denies the goodness of partial goodness. The ideal is Franciscan, but the stance is Dominican – Savonarola's. But as the Image told Eliphas:

> How can a man be just before God?
> Or be pure before Him that has made him?

> Lo, there is none of His servants that is without blame,
> And His messengers He accuses of foolishness:

> How much more those that live in houses
> Based in the dirt and made of clay,
> And who are eaten by worms!

> (Job IV, 17-19)

---

2. The German title in *Puppen und Masken*, 1973, is *Das einfache Licht, das aus komplizertem Dunkel scheinen kann*. If, as seems likely, this rendition of the title is Schumann's or had his accord, Act I is to be taken as a statement of historical fact, Act II not even as representation of hope, but only of the envisagement of a possibility. The English title is either an incomplete sentence, or bad English, the 'That' a mistake, in the form intended by Schumann 'May simple light arise from complicated darkness' – the expression of a wish.

The play is very dark. When the stage is lit, the illumination is feeble. Much of the play is placed in darkness. A lantern, a flashlight, a floor-projector momentarily cut out a small volume of light in this darkness, which appears in itself the real light of the world:

> For like the coming of morning, darkness is to them:
> For they are familiar
> with the terrors of the dark.
>
> (Job, XXIV, 17.)

The naked hands startle by their contrast with the faceless draped figures. The greys and browns have been thronged out by black, a manner of invisibility. The figures melt into the night. We might speak of a virtual disappearance of the performer in this play, little more than a piece of material or the carrier of a mask. The masks, quite divorced from the bodies under them, are enormous. In no previous play of Schumann's were these strange dead effigies so dominant. The disappearance of the performer is a deindividualization of the represented world. The individual is disappearing in this play in another way also: the masks often have more than one face, sometimes are compactions of many faces running over into or disappearing in one another. Sometimes they have faces covered with smaller faces. Sometimes they are series of heads. Cities and countries are the human units (Act I, scene 12). The white husband and woman and the red baby are very much units: but they are hardly human. If they were, Schumann could have cast Sara Peattie in the woman's part.

The large masks in this play often, as do actors in other theatre, wore identifiable single expressions, in the performance sometimes reinforced by the gesticulation of their carriers. In earlier productions, they tended to look more like elemental principles and forces, but their relative personalization here works out rather as an absorption of the types of individuality encountered in the syndrome of complex darkness than as infusion of saving light into ordinary life's horrible meanness, more as introduction of terror into pity than of pity into terror. Death in Schumann's work seems to be arrogating more and more of the functions of the living, such as expression.

His art continues to grow wonderfully. The images now *emerge* into metaphors — or don't — the metaphors merge to form a story. The images, ever splendid, have grown autonomous of their imputable metaphor, and the story or thesis has become so cisted, to its very core, with local growths of ambiguity, pity diffusing terror and terror pity, that it exercises no constraint on the flight of the imagery loosely shrouded in remnants of disposable metaphor: a liberation of the immediate picture (sound comprised). The liberated images, become veritable dances, support more stylization of the movement patterns of their component parts; the movements of the individual figures, seeming more attentively and firmly worked out and rehearsed, differ more definitely.

210

In keeping with their metaphorical function, the images used to tend to follow one another in discrete succession as separate scenes. They now often loom up before their predecessor is quite done, in sinuous overlap, visual opera. Schumann's power seems more *in* the spectacle, less an outside driving force.

* * *

Simple Light employed puppets, but in fact was not a puppet play but a very big dance with masks, and both as regards the dance — choreography and type of movements — and the masks was a return of Schumann's to his dance ambitions of the late '50s. Both the dance and the masks focus on the opposition between individual and crowd — rather than on the opposition between good and evil. The many-faced King of Hell of the '71 *Birdcatcher* has become the Crowd; Simple Light is the extract of the Normal Life and Domesticity celebrated by *Emilia*, not moral principle. It's a female principle and there is some strong suggestion that she is Christ — the Christ of *Stations* of '72 was a woman. The choreography was reminiscent of the New York *Totentanz*: the mask substituted, as in it, for the skilled display of the individual dancer. The death-and-resurrection or rebirth theme with which Schumann, at least on the level of consciousness, at the end of the '50s started his productive career (and this theme, note, can be extended to an endorsement of the death of the individual by socialization) is absent from this play: the darkness of civilization does not per se give rise to any simple light redeeming it.

Of the two scripts I have, a 'January 1973 version' and a 'January 1974 version', the former underlay the December '72 New York and the January '73 northeast showings and I presume the latter similarly underlay the European version(s). The New York performances seem to have both added to and dropped things from the '73 script, as well as made some transpositions, while the ones done in New England just dropped scenes shown in New York and present in the script, but as far as I can tell, the versions shown did not conceptually to any significant extent differ from this script, and the script pretty much tells us what was seen in New York, i.e. the sense it made to Schumann, its intended meaning.

On reading the ' '73 version' stage script (reproduced infra), one soon realizes that it does not make any story evident and in fact barely even gives glimpse of any kind of logic of action or development: Schumann was relying on the visual spectacle itself (phenotype arising from the script's genetic code) to yield a development with its own kind of sense. It is equally evident that he was not only concerned with choreographing movement,[3] but did have very specific points in mind concerning the

---

3. 'The whole show consisted of such movement ideas of puppets and only the little bit of story that goes with it. It's hardly a story. It depends all on those noises and movements

nature of Man, of Society, of History (cf. e.g. 6-8, the great detail regarding the handling of the Johnny puppets): points he presumably hoped the visual spectacle would make and the audience would get.

ACTION	LIGHT	SOUND
1. ROCKY MOUNTAINS Puppeteers lie under black plastic sheeting and slowly raise it up and down when peepers begin, gradually building up speed and height until plastic is making storm sounds and the people inside are standing. Violent plastic motion. Plastic is whipped away and packed off stage, revealing a burlap bag moving with small, quick movements on the floor, which gradually moves off stage too. All figures dressed entirely in black.	One 150W lamp moved on a pole by by one puppeteer over different areas; light slowly grows up.	Peeper sounds (high, short sounds on celli) begin when all is quiet. Peepers fade out.
2. ORIGINAL CRAWLING. CROWD People crawl from plastic to backstage center to pile up on top of each other, slowly building the mass to standing position, then rocking it.	Same.	Low humming begins.
2. (A) VOICES OF THE PEOPLE Round crowd face is brought in. Mass moves around with it, first slowly, then faster, breaking off into small, tight groups and rejoining the main group again.	Same.	Same.
3. SINGLE MAN'S FATE. SINGLE FACE Single face mask is brought in through the mass and raised above their heads. All advance to center stage. At clash, group falls to the floor, away from mask, splitting to 2 sides, and crawls into 2 groups, immediately beginning to throw balled up newspaper at the Single face. Single Face slowly sinks to the ground as it's hit.	Same. Light grows to full: 4 150W lamps on poles: 2 on tall poles at stage front sides, 2 on short poles at front stage center.	Hum quiets down and stops. Cymbal clash.

that these puppets could do. It was just an organization of those kinds of movements that could be made so the contrast of groups acting and than an individual puppet coming out with, say, such a very specific dance and movement was pretty much — the composition of that was what that whole thing was. — (Schumann, interview, '83.)

ACTION	LIGHT	SOUND
4. *STORY OF KNIFE: ANTIQUE WAR*		
Knife is planted stage front center by man from orchestra. 2 groups crawl to knife, hands outstretched towards it. Hands grab knife, raise it up till groups become one group standing again and backs up to the Single Face which has also risen up as the group approaches. Single Face grabs knife, brandishes it, sinks down behind group.	Same.	Silence.
5. *PUPPET:* 'Confused ambitions and power of contrast fight complicated war without result'. Group splits away from Single Face, now crouched low and wielding knife. Half the group runs to UR to set up several rows of chairs, half runs to UL to pick up the Puppet, bass drum and bugle. Puppet, waving a sword in its right hand and waving a banner in its left, advances (see 'Sound' for step description).	Full light.	'Ai, ai, ai' from puppeteers.
		Step forward on 'Ai', down to ground on 3 'booms' from drum, stand up on bugle call: 'Ta ta-ta, ta-ta, ta' Pizz. on cello for Arm, low gurgling laughter from Face alternately. Drum beat.
At the 4th step, the Puppet's right arm, madly waving the sword, breaks away from the puppet and fights the Single Face. At 3rd pass, Big Hand puppet enters and screams. Arm falls slowly to ground, whimpering: Single Face puts a foot on Arm's chest.		
On drum beat: Chorus (half of the group of puppeteers) throws the chairs into a big pile, puppeteers collapse on the ground. All rise, strike the puppet, and start gibbering very fast in high voices, softly.	Same.	Drum beat. Drum beats.
6.(A) *BIRTH OF JOHNNY: JOHNNY'S LIFE AND DEATH*		
All head for BL where little Johnny puppet is brought out. He's hanging down into the ( ) which becomes a road, forming	Full Light.	Soft High Voices.

---

4. 6 (A) and 6 (B) are only partly readable in the mimeographed 1973 script.

constructions for him to pass over, through,
around and under. He is advanced to C.
(   ) placed under the knife, which has
been placed on a (   ) just above the
floor, some (   ) tickle (   ) Johnny's (   )
Hands of puppeteers (   ) their
fingers. Group gets (   ) talking (   )
and rapidly and goes out (   ) and SL.

6. (B) *T.V.*

Group brings in a lot of furniture ( ) sets	Falsetto talking,
up around knife and Johnny. All ( ) in	loud.
front of that 'scene' Miniature ( ) set	
amidst furniture. Ha puppet ( ) in	
screen, saying, 'Hi, Hi!' On ( ) hi',	Silence.
all put their arms up ( ) the ( )	
On second 'hi', ( ) stick	
their hands out from their sleeves & wiggle	
their fingers, then put their hands back in	
their sleeves and take their arms down.	
Puppet goes out. Puppeteers get up, talking	Loud falsetto
again, strike the furniture, leaving Johnny	from puppeteers.
under the knife.	

6. (C) *A WHOLE JOHNNY POPULATION
ARRIVES*

From BL, Johnny puppets are handed down and	Same.	Celli – tune:
passed over to the right; the puppeteers on		start solo. add
their stomachs, forming a line all across		canon, improvis-
the stage, line up the puppets in front of		ations and chimes
their faces and slowly push the puppets for-		on alternate
ward, stopping when they reach the single		down beats.
Johnny. The Witch has meanwhile attached		End on D.
a string to the knife and is at DL pulling		
the string to make the knife swing.		

7. *STORY OF SOUP* A) *HUNGER*
    B) *STONE SOUP COOKING* C) *FEEDING
    OF POPULACE* D) *SOUP SPILLED*

Witch takes off the knife and picks up a	Same.	
soup pot. Puppeteers get up. 'Stomach'		
(grey burlap bag) is set up, with 2 arms		
sticking out of it, which receive the pot		
and spoon from the Witch. Stomach starts		
singing opera aria. All pick up Johnny	Arias – all join
puppets and try to eat from the spoon,	in.
crowding up and finally knocking down	
Stomach. All leave to get instruments.	

ACTION	LIGHT	SOUND

8.*A NEW UNCLE FATSO AND HIS*
SECRETARY

Witch brings in door. Puppeteers with instruments form semi-circle around it. Music. Door opens and a puppeteer brings in Johnny. Music. 'Fancy Lady' puppet is brought in. Music. 'Mrs. Johnny' comes in, Fancy Lady goes out, under the skirt of one of the puppeteers. Reactions from chorus: 'Hey, oh, ah', etc. Puppeteer at door sets up 2 Johnny puppets at the feet of the 'band' puppeteers SL.

Light column:
Light only on front of stage.

Sound column:
1. plastic flute:

2. Toy fiddle:

3. Tin flute (same as (1).
4. Mandolin (same as (2)).
5. Drum (same as (1).
6. Nails: 4 fast beats.
7. Sticks: 3 fast (ta, ta-da).
8. Iron rods: 2 beats.
9. Garbage can lid: 2 beats.
10. All voices: 'Uh-oh'.
11. Witch: 'Come in'.

Cardboard car on a string is pulled in across stage front L-R by first and last of 'band' puppeteers in semi-circle. Knock on door. Witch: 'Come in'. Megaphone announcement: 'It's Henry!' Door opens and puppeteer brings in small Johnny seated puppet, amid cheers and comments from the chorus. Puppet is set by the other 2 seated puppets. Repeat 3x (different names and entrances). Last 4 puppets are brought out as a group and spilled all over the stage, then set up. All sit down. One person goes to BR and opens door to admit Uncle Fatso, who enters smoking his cigar and wiggling. Chorus trembles slightly. Secretary appears at SL carrying in a desk, chair and telephone. She dials a number. Trembling stops. The door at C opens and closes as 7 Johnny soldier puppets are brought in and set up in a line facing SL. Door opens: the 2 puppeteers enter with a little puppet of a woman and child: they imitate the puppet's pose. Witch puts down door, grabs the puppeteer 'child' and pushes him down, grabs the 'mother' puppeteer and pushes her down.

Sound column:
Car sound: voice through megaphone.

Bass drum beats.

Intake of breath from Chorus.

Bass drum build-up.

Silence.

Music – slowly and in the minor. Long 'Oh' at the end.

ACTION	LIGHT	SOUND

9. *ARMY EATEN BY DWARF. THE PRO-*
PHET'S COMING – SIMPLE LIGHT'S
PROPHET

All split. Prophet puppet is swung down from SL and is slowly pushed back and forth, its hand outstretched across the stage to touch the out-stretched hand of the Hand puppet on SR. The Dwarf (single face mounted on black plastic) rushes in between them before they've come too close, covers over the Johnny puppets and sends them flying toward the Hand puppet, whose many reaching-grabbing hands grab at the little Johnnies and hide them off stage R. When the last puppet is gone, the Dwarf rushes out, and the Prophet and Hand puppet approach each other. 'Dead Body' puppets (Johnny-size puppets) are 'swum' in by pup-peteers who are lying on their backs and creeping forward, and are placed between the big puppets. The puppeteers roll out to SL and join in Prophet.

Lights dim slowly.

Chimes begin. Drumming of feet. High, long tones on clarinet saxophone.

10. *GENTLE TIDE BRINGS FORTH*
SIMPLE LIGHT

The Sweeping Puppet appears from BC, sweeps forward, covers 2 of the Dead Body puppets and takes them out to the back. Comes for-ward again, taking out 1 puppet, and again to take out the last puppet. Sweeping for-ward again, the Sweeper brings Simple Light along behind it. When they reach DC, Sim-ple Light rolls out onto the floor from under the Sweeper's black plastic.

Lights quite low.

Drumming with feet, and sax continue.

Blackout.

Silence.

11. *WHOLE WORLD MOVEMENTS*
TOWARD SIMPLE LIGHT

Simple Light sits in the center front of the stage playing a flashlight over her body. From the back of the stage, the tall crowd puppets (a dozen or more) move slowly forward, chanting, until they have nearly reached Sim. Lt. She stops them with a cymbal clash. She stretches up one arm, takes hand out of sleeve. The puppets do the same. The hands disappear (and arms) again, and the puppets slowly sink to the ground, whence they are crawled out backwards (Their faces forward, the puppet-eers hidden) to the back of the stage. Sim. Lt. in her place reaches out her arms after them.

Simple Light's flashlight. Light slowly dims half-way up.

Lights dim down.

Blackout.

Murmuring chant begins slowly and grows louder and more rhythmical.

Clash. Murmur stops. Peeper sounds from orchestra begin.

216

| ACTION | LIGHT | SOUND |

12. RISING MOON (FIGHTERS' FIGHTS, LOVERS' LOVES)

In the dark, the Moonscape screen is set up SC.
A dimly visible puppeteer walks across the stage
blowing a deep celastic horn. Puppeteers come
from behind screen in pairs doing fighting gestures, and disappear behind screen again. Then
each pair reappears slowly carrying in the
lovers – double faces. They sit down in front
of the screen. A white single face – Moon –
appears over the screen, and slowly goes out.
Sim. Lt. gets up, goes to the lovers, one by
one, she takes the masks away from them and
hands them out over the moon on the screen.
As each mask is taken away, the pair holding
it gets up and splits apart and each person
walks, a random but deliberate medium-paced
walk around the stage. Sim. Lt. sits down by
the orchestra FR. The moonscape screen is
struck, and the whole stage is gradually
filled up by walking figures.[5]

Light column:
Lights dim
up slowly.

Lights dim
up slightly.

Sound column:
Celastic horn.

'Moonscape
Sonata', long
chords on celli.

---

5. We here encounter Love: not in the play's light section on family life, but in its dark historical section, as fifth of the darknesses (note of December '73 to Paris spectators, cf. infra), 'darkness by the light of the moon', squeezed between the darknesses of too timid converts ('all people marching together') and the darkness of false prophets, 'drummers who fool people and turn out terrible demons'. Thus also in his *Disquiets, Poisons and Shouting* (publ. May '72) he had identified it as state of magic poisoning, and in his '65 *Leaf* as moonlight inducing a tremor, but here it is presented as demonic and among the things we must extricate ourselves from. In fact, he had thrown himself into making the masks for *Simple Light* immediately after, on a tour of New York State campuses, a love affair had turned 'complicated': a meeting was called in the group to censure Schumann's carryings-on, 'leaving a Grey Lady', Elka, on the farm; and Elka had over the telephone given him an ultimatum to which he submitted, unceremoniously, gossip has it, letting the young lady off at a bus stop, no longer a member of the troupe. The paeans to domesticity in *Simple Light*, Part II, reflect good resolutions of 1972. But the fact that the description of scene 12 stands out by being remarkably poetic suggests Love's extra-familial pull on Schumann was still strong. The scene was powerful in performance also: Carlene Fernan-dez who saw the fall of '73 rehearsals in the Cate Farm haybarn thought *Simple Light* was a love story. 'In a way to me it was a love story . . . I mean I saw it too as not just as a love story but surrounding that all the complications of the world . . . and the hope was that simple light may rise out of this complicated darkness. (I: But you thought the love story was the focal point?) I don't know, just for me it was.' (Fernandez, interview, '83.) The scene shows love as state of truce between individuals normally antagonistic, but even so as darkness of the soul, better foregone for its element of poetic spirituality. Schumann in one of his little self-printed comic newspapers *(Sugar I)* in '74 listed Aphrodite as #2 among the '7 major celestial spirits' that 'support my work': preceded only by small children, and well ahead of pipe and beer (#s 7 and 6). His report on the state of his relationship to her, at the time of his return from the New York and northeast showings of the play, in the

219

220

ACTION	LIGHT	SOUND

13. DRUMMER'S DIVERSIONS

All are walking. One figure on a chair, hidden till
now, beats once on a tin drum. All stop. He moves,
beats the drum again. All heads turn to him. He
moves, beats. All go to him. He moves, beats, heads
turn. He moves, beats, all go to him. This is repeated until the drummer and the group are really
running. At the height of this accellerando, the
drummer runs to a corner where the Demon is lying
(UR), picks up the Demon head. Another figure
picks up the Demon's hair, and a third simply plays
his hands by sticking her hands out of her sleeves.
The rest of the puppeteers run screaming 'Ai, ai, ai'
to DL, where they sit and pick up tin drums,
and drum madly for the Demon's advance.

Full light. — Drum (tin).

Puppeteers:
'Aiiiiiii!'

14. END OF DEMON

Demon advances several steps at a time —
the head makes a gesture, then the hair, thn
the hands. Pause. When the Demon reaches
the chorus, the hands grab one chorus member
and shake him into doing a jumping dance
until he falls exhausted on the floor.
Simple Light gets up, holding a large white
hand with a scroll of paper in it, and slowly
approaches the Demon, whose hand comes out of
his mouth to grab the paper. He looks at it,
turns it upside down, then tears it up. Sim.
Lt. reaches up and hits him on the head with
the white hand. The Demon, with loud cries,
falls (in his 3 parts) to the ground. Still.

Drumming from
chorus: screams.

Bass drumbeat.

February ('72) issue of his paper, one entitled *Sauerkraut*, suggests she is still the major inspiration.

Simple Light's evocation of love, the union of two, a black ovoid in the wash of the moon magically freed of divergence, is Schumann's third and last. It is both the inversion of and identical with his first evocation of it seven years earlier as the slow dance of parallels in white minutely modifying the angles of their proximity. These evocations are linked in progression by the second (of 1970, in *Difficult Life*), the opposite of both, love as a body formed of two, pulsing in the heartbeat of a larger body, the world of sunlight and dirt, a cyst within it. He made the first when he was 31, the last when he was 38. As though in an uphill run, the second is close to the third, and between them there are the figures of nude young women, appearing twice, briefly. The shortness of this sequence, a record of three loves, its progression reflecting love's changes in a man's lifetime, contrasts with the extension throughout his work of images of man exerting his power over men in subjugating combat, the two sequences disastrously linked with it by images of women suffering male brutality.

ACTION	LIGHT	SOUND

15. SIMPLE LIGHT'S DANCE

Sim. Lt. Pauses, then begins to sing her tune, moving slowly in circles. She repeats the tune and starts moving a little faster, until finally she is dancing around the stage. Gradually the chorus joins in, after carrying out the Demon, first with voice, then dancing too, until the stage is filled with dancing figures. Cymbal clash! The group all comes together around Sim. Lt. cymbal clash. The group splits apart. Cymbal clash. Sim. Lt. does a somersault. End of song, lots of cymbal clashes, everyone takes off his face cover and bows.	Full light. Blackout.	Cello I begins with Sim. Lt., doing pizz. The other celli gradually join in, arco. Cymbal clash Cymbal clash Cymbal clash Clash, clash, clash.

PART II THAT SIMPLE LIGHT MAY RISE OUT OF COMPLICATED DARKNESS

1. TWO LANDSCAPES (SIMPLE LIGHT GOES SOMEPLACE ELSE).

A grey and white landscape is walked in on 2 poles by 2 black figures. Simple Light walks in front center of the landscape, shining her flashlight before her. At C, Sim. Lt. turns out to the audience and goes to sit in a chair DC placed there; cardboard Clouds are raised above the landscape, then lowered. The landscape is folded up and all walk off with it to SL. This is repeated once (different landscape); then Sim. Lt. walks in with the white door, the Clouds lined up behind her (behind the door).	From black, light dims up to full on the 2nd landscape.	mandolin and motorcycle-fiddle duet from 2 musicians at SL – one chord before each landscape and one before the door is brought in. Cymbal clash from Sea Capt., seated DR.

2. CLOUD PARTY

The musicians from SL leave their instruments and bring in a table, some chairs, and cups and bottles which they arrange as for a tea party, next to the Captain DR. The Captain walks around mumbling to herself. One of the Clouds knocks on the door, and the Capt. opens the door to welcome in all the Clouds. They all chatter as they come in and sit down. Silence. They take one sip from the cups. Chatter. The Capt. thanks them all for coming, and shows them out the door again. The musicians strike the furniture and the door, and Sim. Lt. and the Capt. sit facing each other on the 2 remaining chairs. Silence, for a moment. The Capt. offers Sim. Lt. his arm,	Full light on front stage. Half light on front stage.	

222

ACTION	LIGHT	SOUND

and they get up and walk slowly and courteously
to the back of the stage, where the double Boat
puppet stands. They bow to each other; Sim. **Half light**
Lt. goes behind the Boat plastic, and the Capt. **on stage.**
takes up her station on SL side of the boat.

3. SEA JOURNEY

Capt. calls out a command through the megaphone. **Dim** · Shouting and
The Boat begins moving (the black plastic hang- **general** · cries from all,
ing down from the double faces) as if in a high **light.** · shipboard
wind. Shouts from all the puppeteers in the · phrases, prefer-
boat. A chorus of black figures lying on the · ably. Repetitive
ground in front of the Boat, roll like waves. · cello patterns
Different characters appear from behind the · and chimes.
Boat (Army helmet man, Fedora hat man, banner
waver, etc. – all with hats) and then dis-
appear. Waves roll out, Boat slows down and is · Police whistle
backed up against the back wall, where it stops. · from Capt. All
· sounds except
· celli die out.

4. HOUSE AND HOME

Joseph (figure wearing Joseph mask from *Christ-* **Same.** · Bottle Cap
mas Story, and Shepherd's blanket) appears from · shaker.
behind the Boat leading the Donkey, followed by
Sim. Lt., who carries the little Angel handpuppet, and the Sea Capt. They make a parade in
a circle to DC, where Joseph stops the Donkey.
From the Donkey's saddle bag, the Capt. takes a
wooden cutout house and sets it up on the floor.
Sim. Lt. flies the Angel over the house, and
from behind the house makes a sunrise-sunset
with her flashlight. Then the parade goes out,
and Sim. Lt. and the Capt. sit down behind the
house, home, and play with the little Angel.
Storm enters (black figure waving black plastic) · Chorus DL be-
and dances around, almost knocks over the house. · gins beating on
Little group in front huddles together. The · tin drums, in-
Storm goes out, and the little group in front · creasing to a loud
goes to sleep. · crescendo as the
· Storm increases
· in intensity.
· Celli join in on 1
Celastic 'Johnny'-size car is pulled in by a · note. Decrescendo
black figure, stops in front of the little · as Storm goes
group, picks them up and they all file out be- · out. Billy blower
hind the car to UL. · (car sound).

223

ACTION	LIGHT	SOUND
5. GROWING FOREST		
Puppeteers push in the forest puppets in cinder blocks. When all the faces are set up, the puppeteers go toward the back of the stage.	Light dims slightly.	Cello peepers.
6. STORM		
At UR, beast heads are thrown down from a bridge to the crowd of puppeteers below, who put them on and then crawl slowly through the forest until each one is crouched next to one of the trees. They begin to tremble the black plastic of the trees slightly.	Lights flicker on and off.	Screeching from horn mouth-pieces, high cello tones, sax and clarinet sporadically.
7. DANCING BEAR PEACE AND HARMONY		
From UL enter Capt. leading the Dancing Bear and Sim. Lt. playing the toy fiddle. They walk, dance, slowly through the forest, collecting beasts in a mass behind them, and exit slowly UR, where they help the beasts take off their masks.	Lights flash on and stay on, dimmed.	Screeching stops. Silence. Toy fiddle from Sim. Lt.
8. DOOR		
Dancing Bear, Captain and Simple Light set up the Captain in the Sheep-Shepherd puppet. Dancing Bear and Simple Light give bread to the puppeteers, who go out to the audience to distribute it. Simple Light picks up the white door and opens it for the clown as their parade from the back of the audience reaches the stage. Dancing Bear dances. Sheep-Shepherd spin slowly to the clown music like a carrousel. The clowns bow one by one to the audience and to Simple Light and go out through the door. The last clown, dressed in white satin with a white tophat, tips his hat to the audience and makes a funny face. Blackout.	Lights dim up.

Blackout. | Clown music begins softly from orch. and at back of auditorium if possible, and grows louder as clowns reach the stage.

Sound stops. |

Simple Light, the script makes clear, was very much an intellectual product: not only intended, but structured as a statement, a concise and elaborate one, of what Schumann was *thinking* at the time. The play had been conceived as embodiment in a bunch of sculptures of emotions and of a vision and had acquired shape in 'rehearsals', guided — I do not doubt Schumann's recollection of '83 — by choreographic considerations in response to the appearance of those sculptures when worn by people: as dance of puppets; but the power controlling this ontogenesis and structuring its product was a philosophy of history. That the play was such a statement is to me as remarkable, given Schumann's anti-intellectualist stance and pose as simple puppeteer and simple evangelist of simple truths, purveyor of simple light, as that it was pretty much inoperative as vehicle of the statement, conveying at most dim abstracts of its major points.[6] Schumann structured it to tell in detail what he had in mind *and* to prevent the audience from getting it: made of it a complicated darkness. Unlike *Cry*, the '60ish call to resistance of which it repudiates, so that it stands as Schumann's final break with the '60s, resolution of a three years' inner struggle, it stated — but only marginally communicated — Schumann sabotaged the delivery of the statement, aborted the message — not a history of the world, but a philosophy of that history: e.g. the false Christian prophets are fused with the false prophets of resistance. Its meaning, so far as I can make out from the text of the script, consisted of the following propositional functions, easily convertible into propositions:

Part I *(That Simple Light)*:
the emergence of humanity as a homogenous coherent Crowd, not unlike the Beasts in *Cry of the People* (1-3);
a Hobbesian state of war of everyone against everyone in which heroic individuals define themselves (4-5);
a pacification of universal combat by ideology in which the Individual is redefined as member of the crowd (the Johnnies), as citizen of a modern commonwealth (6-7);
the emergence of Brutal Repression/The State as product of competition for survival (soup!) in this civil society or commonwealth (or as the December '72 program had it by the 'progression of democracy') (8);
some kind of rule of death, crisis, abysmal malaise as essential state of modern reglemented society (9);

---

6. 'Warning: The list of numbered titles — which are really working-titles used by the Puppeteers during rehearsals, in order to identify the phases of the play — will not necessarily make the play more understandable.

We did not start our production with a written story or interpretation of secret story-outlines.

We built the masks first, got the black plastic next, developed sound and movement from there, and finally ended up with the present sequence of events.

We make the play. The plot is the audience's job.

What we have in mind is the theme of the piece: 'That simple light may rise out of complicated darkness.' Part I ends with simple light defeating the demon, dancing happily.

Part II shows more detailed adventures of light in the darkness, journeys, stays and seemingly unsurmountable dangers.

The end is a white door and everybody's free passage through the white door.

. . . The importance of story-telling and puppetry is little in the face of hunger and mutilation. That little importance is important. The master plan of all the little importances together has a name: liberation, light, the good life . . . (Schumann, *Warning to Audience* in program of *Simple Light, Copeland Colloquium*, January 20-22, '73.)

The *Copeland Colloquium* of that year dealt with the question(s): 'What's Worth Doing? To be or not to be political?'

arrival of a propheted savior (Simple Light) — a mode of understanding? a spirit of love? the person of the Christ? persons of good will?: in reaction to the suffering and carnage historically associated with power-ruled and reglemented competitive society, and with modern society in particular (10);

a tentative conversion of men to this spirit, this conversion itself, however, of a collectivist, reglemented sort (Schumann's judgment of the 'revolutionary' counter-culture youth movement of '68/'69; and/or of the historical role of institutionalized Christianity) (11);

the demonic rise of falsely converted men against this spirit (12-13);

a miraculous victory of Simple Light over this demon of the crowd that has usurped simple light by adulteration (14-15).

Part II *(May Rise out of Complicated Darkness)*:

friendly communion with nature in the voyage through life (1-2);

the troubles in life arising not, even when seeming to, from any recalcitrant nature but from man (3);

the home/family, though its bliss is vulnerable to external forces, as goal (4);

living nature and its panic aspects (5, 6);

nature's being truly man's friend and in need of protection (7);

joy of innocent life (8).

This philosophy of history in Part I pinpoints 'mass man' or collectivism as the historical evil, and reglemented cooperation (even as in a modern democracy — or as in a Cate Farm Bread and Puppet Theatre pseudo-commune?)[7] as false solution to the problem of competition for survival.

---

7. Schumann in '73 did think of the Cate Farm Bread and Puppet 'commune' in terms of the play: as a complicated darkness from which, he was still hoping, though this hope was soon to disappear, simple light would rise:

'What we learn from being in Vermont is new and strong and happy, when it's good; and when it is bad, it represents the aches of communal dragging along.

Since we occupy ourselves with puppetry proper and improper, New York City and company, with their worthy and dirty problems, are not lost to us. We have not withdrawn from them successfully, we have them inside us, it seems forever, and we reach them ever so often by flowered school-bus and during rush hour. But we have now found a spot, where we may grow at the pace of garlic and homebrew.

. . . To manage cooking, carpentry and consumption is not easy. To try to be friendly, but poorly educated in civilities is uneasy. To insert time and archangel's modesty into an unknown body of mixed-up creativity — life and invisible acting inside sculpture — is difficult. We need horse's fun and enough play for great exaggeration. We need a common tune.

Three years ago, we went away from New York City to be simple. Now we live in the meadow's green, on the Winooski River, in great cold, in thunderstorms and befriended by clouds, it seems, and we live in complicated darkness. And accordingly our new puppet show is called: THAT SIMPLE LIGHT MAY RISE OUT OF COMPLICATED DARKNESS! (Schumann, *Vermont Puppet Theater's Desire*, draft of a statement, July 18, '73, Bread and Puppet files.)

This competition, rather than the resulting violence, is pinpointed as the problem.

Part II indicates the true solution: not any organization of society according to Christian or neo-Christian ideals – any such organization or the struggle for its institution apt to generate the evils indicated precedingly – but self contained, even closed-off family life in and with nature: a state troubled and endangered not by nature, if nature is properly appreciated, but by man. Whether this is Candide's retreat to his garden, or the suggestion that generalized domestic bliss is achievable by humanity is not clear: it appears the former, however: resignation. There may also be the point here, relative to the Individual/Crowd theme, that the private individual in the family context is the true or real individual: to hell with history.

The 'January '74 version' stage script, probably the one of the November/December '73 European tour, differs in a number of respects from the 'January 1973 version' one.

Thus the crowd turns on the Crowd Head rather than as in the '73 I 3 on Single Face, i.e. Schumann now identifies the first of 'antique' form of the individual as leader, as himself function or product of the crowd. This Crowd Head rather than Single Face, as in the '73 I 5, outduels the Kabuki sword fighter: the heroes are themselves men of the crowd rather than as e.g. in Homer's misrepresentation heroic loners. In the end, now, both parties to the heroic combat of antique war collapse: the inconclusiveness of classic war is pointed up. The Whole World's Movement toward Simple Light ('73 I 11) has now been so amalgamated with the first part of the following '73 scene ('73 I 12, first part, 'Fighters' Fights') that Simple Light now comes to prevail over the world's false conversion to it not by the force of its simple but imperious appearance but by the falsely converted world's internal divisiveness (in line with which, 'Single Head' puppets – killing off one another – have been substituted for the 'Tall Crowd' puppets of '73, though this may be a change of name only). The inciter of what I considered the 'spirit of the crowd' in the '73 version, namely the drummer ('73 I 13) who by inciting the concerted hysteria of the crowd generates within it the demon that rejects Simple Light's message, now is himself fostered by Simple Light (she feeds him), a subtle point concerning the dangers of however benign reformism. In the '74 version, the ideal household that the second part of the play is about and counterposes to the movement of history of Part I is troubled not only by external dangers – by which it is now more seriously beset, e.g. the home is destroyed, not, as in the January '73 II 4, spared – but by problems intrinsic to it: a new 'Work' scene suggests that work may be a problem; a new 'Cop scene' that the household may cause scandal inviting persecution by the authorities.

Schumann apparently during '73 pondered the content of *Simple Light,*

227

thought about what he had been saying, and changed the play accordingly, i.e. conceptually and not just formally or aesthetically (the only other kind of change discernible being one toward more humor). The changes seem to add up to a more realistic and even cynical, hence perhaps more pessimistic appreciation of the world's potentials for the Good Life, and toward a more decided identification of the Crowd as the crucial evil.

At the end of '73, Schumann, quite in the spirit of these changes, guided his European audience in an even more densely obscurantist manner than he had his student audience in January, jovially making a mystery of the first part of the play which he now thinks of as as 'circus-type show' (Rough, *The Bread and Puppet Theatre*), and in the kindly manner of an overbearing grownup talking to foolish children steering them away from the contestible allegory of its second part:

'Part 1

In order that Simple Light may rise out of complicated darkness, we have to demonstrate the ways and the aspects of darkness.

The First Darkness is the darkness of the beginning, in which 25 puppeteers dressed and hooded in black give a show of geology: the growth and final destruction of the Rocky Mountains. The music for the first part of this section is called *The Adoration of the Peepers*, and is based on the sounds of tiny frogs in the wet grass on the Winooski River in Vermont.

The Second Darkness is very early History with a multiple face and the rising of a single face, followed by old-fashioned war.

The Third Darkness is modern times, our friend Johnny, his furniture, his life and his involvement with Uncle Fatso and the disastrous consequences of it, and finally the appearance of Simple Light, who is a woman in white, and is brought forth by a puppet called Gentle Tide.

The Fourth Darkness is all people marching together.

The Fifth Darkness is the lovers' darkness by the light of the moon.

The Sixth Darkness is the darkness of the drummer who fools people and turns out to be a terrible demon.

The Seventh Darkness is the end of the first part and is Simple Light's dance in spite of all darkness.

Part 2

The 2nd part of our play is the story of the return of Simple Light. Simple Light gets up early and takes a walk in the morning sun. It starts to rain and she stops at a house where the captain of a big ship gives a party for the clouds. It is most enjoyable, the clouds leave happily and the captain invites Simple Light to journey with him on his ship. They cross the ocean together, and Simple Light marries the captain and they have a little child and they get a little house. Everything seems to be fine. But when Simple Light and the captain travel away to visit relatives, a hurricane comes and breaks their house. There is no more home for Simple Light and she stays away. And the world grows darker, and darker until it is covered by a gigantic forest. Then the people yell and scream for Simple Light to come back! But she cannot return. The forest is too thick! Then the people cut down the forest and call her again. In the meantime her child has

228

grown up to be a dancing bear and Simple Light plays the fiddle. So she returns, and the people are glad to see her again. And Simple Light makes a pasture with a shepherd and sheep and a ram and she builds a house so big, everybody fits in it. And she opens the door. The end.' (Schumann, explication of *That Simple Light* ... to audiences at the Théâtre de la Tempête, December '73, published in George and Dupavillon, 1978.)

The message of *Cry of the People* ('69), summing up, at its end and apogee, Schumann's agitational and hence communicative phase, was relatively overt, that of *Simple Light*, summing up his retreat from that historically oriented reformist/revolutionary position, is cryptic. The visual impact of the contrast between the darkness of the struggles of mass and individual in surging conflict (Part I) and the lightness of the individual braving life in a family context (Part II) probably sufficed Schumann as communication. But in fact the piece was intricately ideological, an intellectual construct expressing a philosophy of life. Schumann (in September '73) protested[8] that he was still aiming at a simplicity facilitating communication, the street show form, was still 'open hearted', but in fact his notion of communication has shifted radically to a non-rational mode, a mode in which meaning is up for grabs and either gets lost or is what the spectator wants or, as the case may be, does not want.[9] The true test of theatrical

---

8. 'It wouldn't be fair to say that we are doing two kinds of shows ... There are shows like *Simple Light* that probably also want to be as simple or as good as a street show and don't quite succeed. The material used is too complicated, the forms are too abstract and too pure to lend themselves easily to the streets, even though I would like very much to perform *Simple Light* outside as a street show. We are trying to stay pure in our vision and in the forms we are using, but, on the other hand, we want to be sure that we don't get stuck in a cold, abstract art atmosphere that doesn't convey anything to anybody but a good intellectual friend. Certainly we want to be broader. So we try for simplification, or you might call it openheartedness. Story is something we are very much searching for, but we don't start with it. We are starting from forms – pure musical and movement ideas – and then we proceed slowly to something that, we feel, becomes understandable, becomes communicable.) — (Schumann, interviewed by Kourilsky, in Kourilsky, *Dada*, '74.)
'(I: As the puppets grow more meaningful to you and your players, don't they also become more obscure for those of us in the audience who cannot know what they mean to you?) Maybe. But on the other hand, I think things gain their life from being real in themselves, rather than trying to be a poster design for clarity. Meanings cannot be painted on puppets. There isn't first a thing, and then the psychological explanation for it in our plays. It's the job of the audience to do that. We are not the ones who do something and then are also the interpreters of that which is being done. We do the thing as clearly to ourselves as possible. To find the missing link, that's the piece of work somebody else has to do. That's the real audience involvement.' — (Schumann, in Rough, *An Interview with Peter Schumann, Dramatics*, December 1973.)
9. 'Il faut mettre à part les marionnettes de Peter Schumann, ces visages, ces faces humaines élevées au-dessus de draps noirs ou portées comme des masques. Ces "puppets" parfois d'une intense beauté sont en soi des oeuvres d'art. Pas tellement naïves, elles. Qui vont plus loin que la simple démonstration de langage. Qui transcendent la technique

simplicity is translatability, by the spectator, into simple verbal statements.

From the Gentleman Angel in *Grey Lady Cantata II* onward, the mysterious puppets have multiplied in Schumann's output. Liberated from a moralistic street-agitation-stimulated if not -enforced semantic discipline, affirmed by European fame in his self esteem, in his very ideology – e.g. the philosophy of history of *Simple Light* – become radically suspicious of his audiences, the popular audiences he continued to want to address, unwilling too clearly to communicate this distrust (or even antagonism) to them, Schumann in his puppetry from '70 onward from going marginally esoteric became centrally esoteric.

Schumann had added a narrator to the final version of *Simple Light*. The '74 script has him turning the page of a newspaper at its beginning. But it was only a joke: the performer, under the name 'Ritz Carleton' a figure in the play, turning pages of the *New York Times* (Kourilsky, *Dada, TDR* '61), announced scenes by barking: Schumann was addressing the play to dogs. Schumann thought of the function of this narrator as alienatory in my father's sense:

---

d'expression, si éblouissantes soient elles. Et particulièrement, et surtout ces visages collectifs élevés de la fin du spectacle, ces visages du foule dont le multiple regard traverse les réalités immédiates, exprime une expérience spirituelle capitale, entre l'extase mystique et la révélation de la mort. Par ces marionnettes, Peter Schumann met en scène non pas des individus dans le siècle, mais l'humanité accomplissant son destin à la face de Dieu.

Car il n'est question que de cela dans ce spectacle au titre un peu rebutant, "Que la simple lumière peut surgir de l'obscurité compliquée" : de l'affrontement de l'homme et de Dieu.

Quel dieu? Celui des chrétiens, avant tout. Le "Bread and Puppet" a beaucoup joué devant les églises. Son animateur est pénétré de culture biblique et la "simple lumière" trouvée, perdue et retrouvée dans ce spectacle est une allégorie messianique.

La troupe montre même une nativité, et un retour de Christ qui réalise la prophétie du loup fraternisant avec l'agneau. Mais ce christianisme a des côtés orientalistes. "Le Bread and Puppet" a certainement médité le bouddhisme, les grandes religions d'Asie : cela détermine jusqu'à la forme du spectacle, jusqu'à une philosophie du geste, héritière des théâtres chinois et japonais. Peter Schumann accorde la prééminence au message chrétien non sans une fusion oecuménique préalable. Il se conforme à toute une démarche spirituelle des jeunes communautés marginales américaines ; jusqu'à friser un néo-scoutisme gênant . . .'
— (B. Bost, *Présenté par le T.N.P. à Villeurbanne/le 'Bread and Puppet Theater'*, French newspaper, probably Lyonnais, November 8, '73.)

'Cela dit, j'étais plus sensible aux pièces du "Bread and Puppet" directement en prise sur la guerre du Viêt-nam contre laquelle Peter Schumann et ses compagnons n'ont cessé de manifester qu'à cette parabole un peu obscure parfois, d'un syncrétisme vague, christiano-bouddhique pour l'essentiel, accommodée d'un pacifisme oecuménique qui ne parait pas sans naiveté. Si l'idéologie reste quelque peu confuse la cérémonie qui la porte est, elle, d'une telle force d'incantation, si troublante avec ses clochettes tibétaines de l'élévation, ses rythmes martelés sur des boîtes de conserve, ses lumières, ses ténèbres, ses paroles de poupées géantes et ses clowneries funèbres et dépenaillées, qu'on communie volontiers avec le "Bread and Puppet" dans le pain de seigle que les compagnons de Peter Schumann, à la fin du "mystère", rompent et partagent avec nous, dans le style d'apôtres puritains et burlesques qui est le leur . . .' — (J.-J. Lerrant, *Présenté par le T.N.P. : le 'Bread and Puppet Theater'*, *Le Journal de Lyon*.)

'Something is demonstrated in the show, and then at the end, instead of staying with the demonstration, we say — obviously we are just actors. It's like pouring water on what was done, it's like taking away the impression that people may have collected and saying, okay, this is the end of the theatre piece. That is also what the narrator is used for in *Simple Light*, to constantly step into that development and to say "the spectacle" so that the person doesn't get too involved with it and has a chance to step out of it. I think what Brecht tries to do with his manner of speech in theatre would be what people call "Verfremdungseffekt." But in this case, it is done with simple means; with more directness.'

(Schumann, quoted in Kourilsky, *Dada, TDR* '61.)

But this quote suggests that he actually had in mind an effect opposite to that intended by my father: not to make spectators think about the relevance of the play to their conduct of their lives, but to tell them 'it's only a play'. The barking narrator was Schumann's way of saying 'I might as well bark as try to tell you anything'. It's a tragic image.

12. A celebration of Nature's eternal return, driven by love. Spring of '72.

A small celebration in the spring of '72 shows Schumann's allegiance to the *Simple Light* program — family and nature. Sometime after their 240 gallon maple sap harvest (six gallons of syrup), in March, 'when the ice started breaking on the Winooski River' (it runs by Cate Farm), he 're-hearsed the breaking of the ice', but 'could never get it into performing shape' (Schumann, Newsletter, *'Bread & Rosebuds'*, November '72). Konnoff (interview, '83) also thinks it never got performed. But apparently something related to it, *Marriage of the River Winooski and Lake Champlain*, was performed that spring — as a 'celebration of spring' (Schumann, interview, '79) — at Burklyn Manor in West Burke, Vermont, a 'pageant, with lots of kids and lots of movements in it, parading over a huge area' (Schumann, ibid.) and with someone in armor dancing on stilts (Schumann, ibid.) — probably the first theatrical use of stilts in the Bread and Puppet Theatre.[1] Its story with charcoals by Schumann, was published as a birthday gift to Solveig Schumann in the October '72 issue of Scripts under the title *The Story of the Love and Marriage of the River Winooski and Lake Champlain*.

'the river says:
i am King Winooski and my heart is blue.

the travellers say:
we are travellers from far away.

winooooski: please take my heart to the Lady Champlain.

Travellers: Yes indeed, your majesty.

the Lake says: i am the Lady Champlain and my heart is blue.

there are 3 fierce gentlemen at the door

what are their names?

their names are: ice, north wind, and snow.

what do they want?

they want to marry you

---

1. The plot has echoes of *Tristan and Isolde*, and materials of the '71 *Quest* or *Tristan and Isolde*, and materials of the '71 *Quest* or *Tristan Quest* seem to have gone into the play.

'It's a beautiful huge estate on a brow of a hill and we did *Tristan and Isolde* in a big — in a big area. I remember going, starting in one part of the gigantic lawn and going around and the final part was done in front of — right in front of the entrance to the house. And it used quite a lot of kids who did — who represented the plants that start growing in the spring, I think.' — (Elka Schumann, interview, '83.)

o what shall i do? . . .

i don't know.

travellers: here.

Champlain: what?

t: we bring you King Winooski's heart

C: Oh!

3 fierce: Revenge!

and the 3 gentlemen go to their king

and winter says: i am the king and i am strong. Bring me my armour and my sword. Go and capture the Lady Champlain.

3 fierce: Yes!

Travellers: O King Winooski.

Winooski: What?

T: Winter has captured the Lady Champlain!

W: Where?

T: There!

Winooski: Bring me my armour and my sword.

And he finds Winter and they fight. But Winter is stronger and he wins. And he puts ice over the King Winooski, and he sends december and january and february and march . . . but in april West Wind blew in Little Grey Cloud and Little Grey Cloud poured rain on the King and the sun licked a hole in the ice on the King and the King felt his strength and he lifted up his arms and he broke the ice, and in all his power and glory he travelled on to marry the Lady Champlain.'

13. Goddard period puppet and mask making.

The masks Schumann made during this period — not quite the same as those he used: most '60s most-used masks remained in use, though with the exception of the Grey Lady mask in much diminished use, and used much less than new masks — in the aggregate were significantly distinct from those made earlier and later. They may be said to be more theatrical and expressive; as expression of their maker's mood — something else than the character of the puppet they express — they more often than the earlier or later masks convey anger, fear, revulsion; and they have more shape or sculptural definition, not infrequently a complex, sometimes even elaborate, in some cases a geometrizing one. He tended more than earlier or later in his mask making toward representations of the negative in man and in man's existence, greed, brutality, vice, meanness and the retrenchment, poverty or depressed state of the soul; there are few if any of the physiognomic representations of the ideal or good frequent and perhaps predominant in his work of the 60's.

Whereas the key word for Schumann's mask sculpting and puppet building during the '60s is 'severity', and during his Dopp Farm Glover period, from the fall of '75 onward, the terms 'austere' or 'light' and 'gay' seem indicative, his output during this period invites terms such as 'opulence' and 'ferocity'. He is letting himself go as a mask sculptor, his masks are complex, and more often than before and after the faces he makes have ferocious expressions, and even when they don't indicate ferocity on his part, a violence of judgment on men and the world — e.g. the non-ferocious Garbagemen. There is significant experimentation, notably involving diverse attempts to sculpt celastic over clay, not just mold it onto it, also fiberglass masks. While the '60s output visually is dominated by a series of severe figures representing suffering man idealized — male man at first, Jesus and the disciples, then female man, the Vietnamese Women, the Vietnamese Ladies, the Grey Mothers with Babies, the Grey Ladies — the Cate Farm output visually is dominated by three outpourings of grotesques representing the demonic in man: the finely finished and richly painted Bulbheads (at which he arrived via the severely powerful Negro blockheads of his Coney Island shows as stylistic transition), effigies of malice and hypocrisy, the cancerous red hellshapes of his new *Birdcatcher*, ornamented and decked out, effigies of torturing man and of the rampant, conscience-less prick, and the pullulating faces and distorted bodies of *Simple Light*, effigies of ruthless competition and of man's perversion by society.

The fact is that the very expressive, interesting, well made masks and puppets of this time — in some abstractly aesthetic sense the best he's ever made, and some of them seeming full of thought — lack of the power, the universality and the strike at the essential of his masks of the '60s: which 'qualities' reappear, it seems to me, only with his animal masks and puppets of the following ('Dopp Farm') period. The masks are too strange to mean much: heart and head are not at one in Schumann's hands. The Grey Lady with or without Tear is perhaps the emblematic figure of the period: but she is New York's gift to it. The Godface sacrifices majesty to blandness. The Gentleman Angel is weird: but stands for what? His obscurity does not release uncontrolled vibrations of response: it disrupts emotionally significant intake. Similarly for the *Simple Light* figures.

Two sets of puppets make the feebleness or shallowness of Schumann's splendid puppetry sculpture during these years particularly evident because – in totally different ways – they are so near the grandeur of the major New York period puppets: one set which emerges fully in use and in numbers only during the following period, but the first exemplars of which come into being in this one: the 'Garbagemen', proliferating for the fourth 'Grey Lady Cantata' of the spring of 1974, which is also the 'First Garbagemen Cantata', and the black Negro 'bulbhead'-type masks for the '72 Coney Island Black shows. The 'Garbagemen' have individuated faces and symbolize the ordinary and real adaptation to work in a life dominated by work, and by work in the modern sense: holding down a job (one which in the case of the 'Garbagemen' happens to consist in physical labor). They fall short of grandeur only because Schumann could not help a weakening infusion of contempt for them that undercut conveyance both of the infinite worth to a man of his own individuation (no matter how stunted or ridiculous) and of the tragedy and heroism of a life spent on holding down a job, i.e. reluctantly doing something perfectly meaningless. The Negroheads convey subjugated men's resilience and stubborn integrity: but by a smidgin of excess of stylization are bereft of humanity. Schumann by then is telling us that the cost of dignity may be too high: a point well worth making: but his full breath is not in his telling of this: the statement is enfeebled by incidentality.

As before, masks and puppets were made in rushes, in large batches of different ones and of sets of like ones, with relatively few being made in between. The rhythm is not only an interior one of inspiration. It also relates to the seasons: the outdoors is better for work with acetone; indoors heated workspace at first was not at all, then only in a restricted way, making work on very large masks or large puppets difficult, available; student labor was available only during the academic year. The interior rhythm to some extent depended on ideas for shows associated with images of puppets, but to some extent also, feelings not uncharacteristic of this period that he really didn't have anything useful to say to people probably sometimes prompted Schumann to throw his energies into a focus on making puppets rather than shows, e.g. in '73: as during the '50s frustrations by dance probably prompted irruptions into sculpture.

There were some paper maché masks, but by and large Schumann stuck to celastic. Isolated experiments with fiberglass (by Bill Whelan) – a half dozen masks, if that many – were not pursued: like a puppet head of plastic wood Schumann essayed in '72 or '73, the masks seem to have been too heavy.[1] Though there was some important work of a new sort directly over clay, my impression is that on the whole, work from plaster casts was more important than at any time since '63/'64 – possibly even a majority of masks and heads may have been made this way, and the reason seems to have been not so much to make many masks from the same clay mold, but to maintain better control of the final product.

Due to the availability of some talented individuals, notably Bill Whelan, working steadily on Cate Farm, the first – and apparently only – innovations in work with celastic occurred during this period. These were of two sorts, both of them in work directly over clay, and both involving sculpturally modelling the celastic rather than merely applying it to the clay: which is why they required talent. One was a use of tiny pieces of celastic (apparently sometimes molded with tongue depressors): making up for the distortions normally resulting, because of the multiplied overlap, from the use of small pieces, by pushing into the clay (thus distorting it: it has to be extra soft for this method).[2] Apparently some use of the acetone

---

1. À propos of a secondary Uncle Fatso puppet which was made for *Hallelujah* and/or for parades:

'So I built, off and on, new Uncle Fatsos. This one, I think, is built from fiberglass. I tried fiberglass once. It's awfully heavy, so we gave up.' — (Schumann, interview, December '82.)

This was not his first reaction. He pointed out to a Swedish interviewer some *Birdcatcher* masks made out of a fiberglass-like new plastic ('Fibreglas liknande, ny plast'), saying 'See how light they are!' (Länstidningen, November 29, '71) – but perhaps he was being ironic. Konnoff (interview, '83) thinks Bill Whelan probably joined them when they were working on *Birdcatcher*: so these *Birdcatcher* fiberglass masks may be among the earliest.

2. 'Marie Antoinette (is) part of the Bulbhead series . . . A double chin, ugly monster lady . . . the head must have been built together with the other Bulbheads. It's the same style of work, and I'll bet I did them all in a row – because I had celastic workers. Very good – people who at that time had made an art out of that – how to use that celastic – and were extremely skillful. And these are made as if in a plaster cast, but they're not. They're made directly over clay . . . they have more detail than a lot of things that were made in plaster casts. So the people who were best at that, I think, were Bill Whelan – he was a puppeteer with us; very good was Carlene Fernandez; and Barbara Leber and then, later on Genevieve Yeuillaz. She did quite a bit of our good celastic work too. But I think the best ones were really Bill Whelan and Carlene. (I: What made them so good? What's the difference?) Their work? Any material – whether it's masonry or whatever it is – it takes more than just the knowledge of how to swing the hammer. You become sensitive to your material – that's what sculpting is all about – to be sensitive to clay – and some sculptors prefer clay to plaster and to wood and what have you – or stone to wood. You can understand the piece of sculpture that's made in clay as a celastic worker and then really get that piece of sculpture. Or you can muddle it up – make it wishy-washy – make it terrible – lose

236

bath of the celastic was associated with this technique; and/or the celastic was left in the bath longer than normal, making it extra soft. Results as fine as or finer than those obtained by sculpture into a plaster cast were

---

all its characteristics in the process – you can misunderstand how the eye is built – you can misunderstand the indentations around the nose – you can change the whole character of the mask by misunderstanding what's there in the clay. And these people had it. They looked at the thing – they saw it – and they could do the real thing. And I really – and I worked with them – we worked together on this. They did most of the work, but I came into it and helped them to see it and to get it. (I: Does it matter how big the pieces are? And where you put them?) Yes. It's much more work to do this – with tiny, little pieces – and takes a long time – they spend a lot of time on each little piece. A lot of care. It's not just plastering the thing on. After you put it on you remold what you have underneath. See, with any sculpture, when you add something to the original you lose the original. You really lose it. You make something new, whether you like it or not. You add a thick skin of something over it – like putting a coat on something. Just as a face with a hood on it isn't a face any more, the same thing is true of a piece of sculpture with papier mâché or something on top of it. But with learning and understanding the original, you can get to reproducing that – to adding that really evenly on it and even emphasizing some of the crevices and things, to get more of what there is. (I: How many layers would there be – of celastic?) One. We will always choose a celastic that's the right weight for that size. So if we do a very big size – it depends on the purpose of the puppet – there are puppets that are very big and we did them with very thin celastic. Much too thin for the real – to get a real strong, supported surface out of it. But if it's a mass of things – if it's like thirty masks in a row, then we often say that's okay if they break, we'll make other ones – the same kind. And actually, it's a nice character with all these folds and wrinkles that they get from being handled and getting little cracks in the celastic. But with these things we said, okay, let's make it perfect – let's make it like a cast – let's really sculpt them – until they are finished, and not just that I sculpt them in clay and then it's just a technical job. So these people were really lovingly involved in really fine, delicate craftsmanship. The best we ever did with that material. So all these heads, then – that stall in the museum – were made this way. — (Schumann, interview, December '82.)

'. . . what I used to try to make my work good was the idea that when you're putting on celastic you need to resculpt the mask, I mean the clay with the sculpture that's there. And by using large pieces, number one you're not going to get as strong a finished product as you do with overlapping. It makes for more strength because you're having double thickness more often of the celastic material, and when you're trying to go over curved surfaces you can't use large pieces because you'll get wrinkles in the celastic. So it's a matter of what area you're covering whether you're going to use a small piece or a larger piece. Also, for small details in the eyes, around the mouth, or in the nostrils and so forth, you also usually need to use small pieces to get the detail and after you've laid the celastic over the surface you have to press the edges down – of the celastic – to make them make a nice connection to the next piece. And if you have two thicknesses the layers are going to have – I don't know – it's not going to be one level surface. You're going to have like a step effect as you go from one piece to the next. So by actually pushing into the clay and re-creating a smooth shape you come up with a nice, much nicer surface, which is like the original piece of clay. And you can actually feel the clay moving underneath when you're laying the celastic on and that's why it does feel like you're almost resculpting the same piece because you can really feel the clay moving . . . you couldn't be afraid to feel the clay more and push it because it really wasn't going to go anywhere, you know. (I: Well, you lose the shape, maybe.) Yeah, you might be fearful of that but it really wouldn't happen if you had a clear idea of what was underneath.' — (Carlene Fernandez, interview, '83.)

obtained by the small-piece technique: the 'resculpting' of the mask in the celastic more than making up for the flattening of features normally resulting from working on top of the clay. The other innovation was a use of very large pieces — apparently sometimes a single sheet for a whole mask — making effective use of the resulting wrinkling.[3] The thinness and therefore weakness of the resulting mask seems to have been a drawback of this technique. These techniques gave the mask maker some artistic independence from the maker of the clay molds, Schumann. The employment of these techniques '72, '73 probably related also to an increased openness of Schumann's to this. Only the smallpiece technique seems to have been retained (though not in a dominant way: it was time-consuming) during the following periods (Carlene Fernandez and Genevieve Yeuillaz continuing to do work of this sort).

The only other work process innovations I have heard of for this period (or any other) were some devices for making one-piece plaster casts of very large and heavy clay molds: supports for the clay-plaster combinations allowing their partial removal so that the clay could be scraped out (from underneath and from the sides) without moving the plaster cast.[4]

---

3. Concerning the 'Mailman' of Revenge of the Law (summer '72), later, hat and moustache added, the 'Drum Major' in Woyzeck ('81):

'That looks like a job by Bill Whelan. Bill Whelan, besides being good, was — actually — Bill Whelan did something else with celastic that was interesting. He took a whole sheet of celastic and wrapped it over the face. And then squeezed in on. Very different from other ways of doing it. And he got very good results. This one is made like that — with two or three pieces. Very big things, and then he squeezed them in. But he was a painter and he was very sensitive to the result. So he could do that — he's the only one who could ever do that. (The celastic) is soaked in acetone. But he could do it with a big piece, and he would arrange the wrinkles that you would necessarily get from that so that they would service the sculpture. He was very good at that. And there are several heads that you have that he did (like that), and it would take him only a fraction of the time that other people needed to make a head that way.' — (Schumann, interview, December '82.)

'When Bill Whelan was doing the celastic on the Simple Light puppets, he discovered that if you're really, really good at it you can use a large piece and get it to really take the shape of the clay. And there was a lot less waste and you have a much smoother texture.' — (Sherman, interview, '79.)

According to Konnoff (interview, '83), the heads of all the Black puppets in Revenge and McLeod were made by the big-piece technique.

4. '. . . the building of the puppets (for Simple Light (SSB)) was difficult, because the puppets were very big. But the trouble was that the clay pieces were very large and we had to invent some way of plaster casting them in one chunk, so what I did is I had some . . . system, with two tables underneath the molds, and then after the mold was cast, I pulled the tables away and climbed on my knees and dug out the clay. That was the only way. We couldn't lift up these things, it was too heavy to lift it up from these giant molds, so we devised it so we could pull it out on the sides and climb underneath and pull out the clay, and it did work, they didn't break, we got 'em all out. So they are pretty — the molds are really beautiful. But each mold was only used for one or two puppets at the most.' — (Schumann, interview, '79.)

There were four technical innovations in the area of mask and puppet construction: 'bulbheads', backpacks, crowd masks, string operation.

'Bulbhead' masks are called that because they tend to have the shape of bulbs, but the term more specifically refers to enveloping puppet heads resting on the wearer's shoulders and strapped on by straps passing through his or her armpits. The resulting figure is neckless, head and body are one and move as one. One of the things that inspired this type of puppet was Schumann's observation that fat people trying to see something to the side tend to move their whole body, not just turn their heads. His bulbhead figures are normally stocky – he has the performer stuff his or her custome. The '65/'66 puppet construction innovations had tended toward dance: this one tended toward abstraction of a real life movement type. He had made heads resting on the shoulders earlier – e.g. the 'Big Mask' of *Totentanz* – but during this period turned out quite a few, the earliest ones – Negro heads of '72, perhaps already '70 or '71 – abstractly bulb-shaped, the later ones – those of the 'Bulbhead Family', e.g. the '73 'Gods of Plenty' – made by the small-piece celastic working technique – elegant variants on this shape. The drawback of this head is that the wearer can't see much: his or her eyes are several inches away from the eye slits.[5]

Backpacks are wooden structures for the 'inside operator' of a puppet to strap to his or her back with a peg protruding to above their (the operator's) head: the puppet head is attached to the peg. The idea seems to have been less new gestural opportunities for the head – in fact, these puppets seem to have a distinctive – not uninteresting – heavy-shouldered rigidity – than increased freedom for the arms. But the backpack put the puppet's sleeves up too high and so in fact constricted arm movement.[6] Neverthe-

---

5. '(Ephraim: The Bulbheads didn't have anything inside ...) No, it was a mask that fit over the head of the player and rested on the shoulders and was strapped around the armpits. (Elka: Almost impossible to see – it was like being locked up in a room.) Yes, *those* masks are *difficult* because the eye has to look through holes that are some four or five inches *away* from the eyes. In the face mask, your eye is near the hole that is cut for it, but with these masks vision was very limited.' — (Schumann, interview, '79.)

6. '(Elka: Can you describe how the Gentleman Angel was made? That was a new type of puppet.) It was a puppet that was built on a backpack. I think there were several of those tried out at that time, just trying to build oversize puppets that would be operated different from the Grey Lady, which was mounted on a simple little stick and the operator is inside ... (Elka: And your hands are busy holding the puppet.) Your hands are tied. So these puppets like the G.I. Angel and Gentleman Angel or that large Black Man, we tried backpacks. Those are stiff backpacks built from 1×2s that fit your back, are tied around your hip and around your shoulder, and the head of the puppet is mounted on a stick above your head. This means that the arms are hanging from a shoulder piece that is on – underneath the neck of the puppet, attached to your backpack. If you imagine this, you will realize that the sleeves are a little bit in the wrong place for your own arms. (Elka: laughs) (Ephraim: But it wasn't such successful – you didn't try making puppets like that again.) Yeah. I did.

less, such puppets continued to be made after '70, e.g. the big 'Drummer Demons' of *Birdcatcher* ('71), or, according to Konnoff (interview, '83), the 'Lions of Inflation' ('72, or, more probably, '73).

The Crowd puppets he made for *Simple Light* ('72) developed from the tiny multiple-figure 'Demonstrators' paper maché sculptures used in *Difficult Life* ('70) (themselves going back to the only slightly larger 'Johnny puppet' group sculptures of *When Johnny* of '68) and the crowd-headed life-size puppets — puppets whose heads consisted of a group of small figurines — of *Stations* ('72). They consisted of serially arranged masks on a stick carried either horizontally or vertically by a single operator shrouded in black plastic:

'. . . there were two different group effects, one of a group of masks that was really like a relief that moved in itself, like a piece of sculpture that came towards you because they were mounted on upright sticks, the faces in the crowds on upright sticks topping each other, lots of faces on top of each other, and they walked suspended by different sticks carried by different people in black disguises, so they came towards you as a relief effect. And then there were puppets that were mounted not on uprights but horizontally so they had a very different effect, mounted in different head positions, straight ones and leaning ones, but horizontally, with a single operator (under them).'   (Schumann, interview, '83.)

Other Crowd masks were puppet heads consisting of grotesque congeries of symbolic faces.

In the case of the Crowd puppets with many separate heads, because of the wood supports of these, in the case of others among the big *Simple Light* puppets because of constructional peculiarities, and in both cases because of the free draping of the black plastic, Schumann here got away from the idea of puppet bodies as like human bodies, an idea inappropriate to Crowd puppets of any sort *per se*. This led on to the subsequent development of the distorted (elongated) bodies of stilt puppets, the abstract shapes of kite-type puppets, animal bodies generally and their impressionist rendition, skeletal bodies and banner bodies.

Operating puppets, whether life-size dummies or less than hand-size pin-jointed figurines, from strings, whether pulled laterally or from an overhead 'bridge', was part of Schumann's attempt, '70-'72, at a 'mechanical puppet theater' dispensing with actors and with visible crew. The results of string operation of small figurines (*Difficult Life*, '70) were

---

Several puppets were like that. The same system was used for the red demons in the *Birdcatcher*. They were also on backpacks. A little bit different, but similar. (Elka: It limits the movement.) Yeah, it does limit the movement. (Elka: — very, very much. It's just a way to hold a big puppet, to mount a big puppet on a person and the arms are free: but they can't really do very much — beat a drum, or hold a — hold something.)' — (Schumann, interview, '79.)

probably theatrically too limited to encourage much use. String operation of dummies – near-completely eliminated, '70-'72, from several shows for which it had been intended as major *modus operandi* – probably yielded results theatrically inferior to live puppet operation because dummies were not the kind of puppets called for (their gestures clumsy, dead), and for some reason Schumann was unwilling to go into jointed marionettes (made of rigid elements): perhaps feeling their movements would be *too* mechanical. String operation was used only as isolated, minor device after *Difficult Life* (in which not only toy figurines but also life-size dummies in front of the stage were string operated).

Schumann first started walking, e.g. in local spring festival or Fourth of July parades, and using stilt walkers in his circuses, during this period, but stilt walking became important and special puppets were built for it only '75 ff. when it became an important feature of his 'silly circuses' and circus pageants.

The first puppets Schumann built after his second Europe trip, at the Bank, January-February '70, were the 'little figures and cardboard boxes' (Elka, in Schumann, interview, '79) and 'life-size dummies' (Uncle Fatso's cronies) for *The Difficult Life of Uncle Fatso*. Some of the figures – smaller than the Johnny puppets, perhaps 5-7 inch dolls – were string operated from a bridge, some from the wings:

'One was a drinker with a cup, so there had to be a string going into the top floor of the cardboard building that made it possible that the drinker drank. Then there was a father-son or some double figure that was spinning. Then there was a woman with her handkerchief waving bye-bye – it was not hard to build – the arm built separately and then a pin was built into the shoulder so it moved – very simple.'   (Schumann, interview, '83.)

The performer of Uncle Fatso, seated, 'had a lot of string collected that operated his cronies, running through the side of the arms, through a hole in the fabric.' (Schumann, interview, '82.)

The dummies, out front, not melting into the background as in *Fire*, were a new departure for him both technically and stylistically. They were real life – real American life – figures: sequel to the 'petty bourgeois' Johnny puppets of '67, predecessors of the working-class Garbagemen of '70 and following. Their inertia (they only had a few simple arm movements) signified they were qua cronies dummies: that Uncle Fatso moved them was meaningful, even though not apparent to spectators. That they were string operated was itself not visually important: but their rare, heavy, identically repeated movements made a visual point.

'They were very roughly made. They were also painted differently from masks until then. They were just painted, just a pink smear. Just smear a coat of pink on them and red lines into it for markings. So the sculpturing is very rough, hardly

241

any elevation for the nose, like that, and then the rest is just smeared on with red marks on the pink surface.' (Schumann, interview, '83.)

There was a Night puppet made for this show: a big black open-mouthed Negro face with indistinct features — good natured, Schumann thinks (Schumann, interview, '83). It appeared suspended in a corner of the stage, words (signs) came out of its mouth and then its body — black fabric — as lights dimmed, slowly was spread by its operator over the stage, gathering in the little figures.

At Coney Island, during the next few months, nothing much of importance was built. He painted a blue Tree of Life curtain for *Lamentation/ Mississippi* that later that year became a sail (that of the Ark for All), and gave a glass tear to the *Mississippi* Grey Lady mother, counterpiece to the maniacally rocking biddies on the funhouse roofs, but generally used puppets he already had, notably his armless 'Disciple' puppets ('6-8 ft. tall, red or ochre burlap bodies, yellow or brown faces' (Elka's script, *Mississippi*)).

The gaiety of the Tree of Life curtain marked a departure for the theatre. It went with the folksy come-on music they played on the side-walk. It didn't go with the gravity and formality of the Black plays. But there was a general attempt to make the Coney Island shows seems entertainment. This was new for the Bread and Puppet Theatre, but in the parades — e.g. the 4th of July parades — and the circuses and in their puppets, cf. e.g. Miss America and the Peace Hand (infra), henceforth became a persistent strain. During the '60s only children's shows had been done as entertainment (e.g. the '66 and '67 *Chicken Little*). The tree — behind a low white fence, its white branches all broken out in white flowers, the trunk at the right edge of the print, the flowers filling the print — was lyrically exuberant: the exuberance of life.

The Coney Island *Lamentation* of '70 had Negro masks in it, partly 'Vietnamese Women' with their masks painted black, partly a big black mask (either worn by somebody or positioned by itself upstage), and two black face masks, one a dancer's and one a broom-wielding woman's. Some of the disciples had been gentlemen of color, Schumann had given life mask replications to black kids in *Chicken Little*, the Night that swallows the city in *Difficult Life* had been obscurely Afro-American, but now he was getting into ethnic abstraction.

Mixing clay from a Cate Farm quarry with New York clay, and exploiting to the hilt the initially ample supply of student 'workshop' labor — ten of 'em — he irrupted in a shower of puppets as soon as he hit his new location, during the two or three weeks before the July 4th parade in Plainfield. The new puppets, generally first used in that parade and in a Centennial Parade at Barre, Vermont on July 26, were intended for an outdoor circus, and typically, I would say — there were others, e.g. strap-on horses — were of an 'effigy' type: to be carried by often visible operators, for display. They tended to be fantastic, not streamlined for quick and easy 'reading', for interpretations of their — especially their moral — significance, but idiosyncratic: though they generally related to the theme of America and American history. In construction, most were not too dissimilar from the giant center pole puppets of '65/'66, but some were built on backpacks.

Among these new open-space, parade, circus arena or pageant masks and puppets made in the two weeks before the 1970 Plainfield July 4th parade: the Big Godface, Godhead or Godmask,[7] a giant Black Man 'backpack' puppet (paraded before the circus of later that summer, but not used in it), a 'backpack' G.I. Angel, a giant Howdie Doodie puppet, whose hat could 'fly off', the Domestic Insurrection puppet, a giant Chicken, at the circus laying various eggs, the Peace Hand, Miss America, the Blue Face (made over the same base of stone and clay as the Godface, but different from it) that served as (prow)head of the Ark for All, and — Schumann thinks of the Ark for All as a puppet — the Ark for All. And probably the 'In God We Trust Judge' used in the Barre, Vt. Centennial Parade of July 26 ('70).

Schumann printed his first flower banners at this time, used them in the July 4th parade, made some strap-on horses (apparently of a hobbyhorse type) used in the circus, and made the first of his Garbagemen and used him in the circus. More were made for the 'First Garbagemen Cantata' alias the 'Grey Lady Cantata IV', and then used in the circuses 1974 and following:

'The Garbagemen idea came from these Goddard College garbagemen, from the maintenance crew at Goddard College. The first one I made was really a portrait of the Goddard College maintenance men. And then — they were good natured and we liked them and they were very nice people so we wanted that characteristic in them.'

(Schumann, interview, '83.)

---

7. The Godhead mask was initially called the Pursuit of Happiness because the Plainfield parade led into a show (possibly also called *The Pursuit of Happiness*) consisting of readings from the Declaration of Independence followed by a performance of *A Man Says Goodbye to His Mother*, and the Godhead mask was in the parade, strapped to the last marcher's back, and was the background for the readings. A different face of god peered through the window in *Emilia* ('71), but the Godface received full dignity (and probably its name of Godface) in the '72 *Stations* as God the Father: against just the mask — Christ attaches bags of water under its eyes and later bites them to make them leak: god weeps to see his son crucified.

This Godface subsequently ('74 following) was often the face of the deity to which by a Maypole dance around it the Bread and Puppet circuses and/or their pageants were dedicated, a deity seeming to represent nature or summer. Sometimes this deity, however, had a female face, that of the 'Domestic Resurrection Deity'. It has been oddly difficult for me to determine when one face or the other — two different theologies would be implied — was used, or even which one was used normally. I don't know when the Goddess was made. Her head is said to be of fiberglass. If it is, she was most likely made in '73.

243

The D. L. Chicken:

'(Elka: that funny chicken puppet with the body made of hoops that went along and laid eggs . . .) . . . it was a *big*, big face, painted in purple, with *lots* of wrinkles in the face and a *tongue* sticking out of its mouth. And then for a dress it had some kind of garbage material that was mounted on wire hoops that were shaped like a ball, so it got bigger and bigger and then smaller on the bottom, and it could collapse, to something very small, and it was used like a chicken – it had the noises of a chicken.' (Schumann, interview, '79.)

The Peace Hand:

'(Elka: It was just cut-in-half celastic.) Picture: two little figures, a little boy and a little girl doll were made and they were stuck on wires that stick through the extended fingers of the Peace Hand, the forefinger and the ring finger, inside, so they could bounce and dance around on top of those fingers. (Elka: The Peace Hand is put over the performer's head . . .) Yeah. Right. And the performer is draped into a shroud that is painted like an American flag, with just stripes, and that surrounds the operator. The operator holds the piece *and* operates those little dolls that are dancing on top of the fingers.' (Schumann, interview, '79.)

Miss America, who danced with Uncle Fatso:

'. . . pink faced, not very big, maybe a little bigger than a Grey Lady, but with a red and white or red and pink striped dress.' (Elka, ibid.)

She has a Mae West face, made up, a bold expression of a slight perhaps-smile, a draped dress (over a presumptive slim body) sewn to the head, with stars on the blouse, red stripes on its skirt part, a modish, red and white striped head covering (*Vogue*, but 1920s/30s). She is ten feet tall or so. Like all of Schumann's puppets she has force, the force of sex for sale.

The Ark for All:

'It's nice, it's blue. (A) big cloth thing. Banners that are like sails and then (something) like a band that people sort of make a formation like a ship, and then they fold it on the outside of them so it's like this ship that's carried by human feet. And at the side of the ship there are all these people in the water – and the tree – the big sail is the Tree of Life and people and food and animals hang off of it. Blue and white.' (Leherrissier, interview, '79.)

The hull is also the water in which those that did not save themselves are drowning. The sail, the Tree of Life curtain I have mentioned,

'is so big, that when the wind – the only way to hold it up is all these guide lines, but what the people on the guide lines do amounts to weight on the person who holds the mast. So the balancing of the pole itself becomes a tremendous weight for the people who carry the mast.' (Schumann, interview, '83.)

On the long blue Pursuit of Happiness prow-head, between its long nose and its tight mouth, it says, inscribed in darker blue, 'kids should be able to grow up and live a good life'. The ship is evidently America-according-to-its-ideals.

The 'Judge's' big, bulbous, light grey head, 3-4 ft. tall, narrows above his simian eyebrow projections into a grey three-pointed wattle or cock's comb, and below his tiny light grey slit of a mouth (nicely curved, though) instead of a chin a heap of finger-like warts grow out of his face. The long narrow column of his nose is imbedded in a deep vertical fold. His round eyes stare out in clear but perhaps unseeing sight. On his right cheek, in white, 'In God', on the left, 'We Trust'. His costume – he is perhaps 11 ft. tall – continues the shape of his head to make him grow downward, bottle shape, his neck a widening black cravatte, below it, in narrow, gathered folds, a slightly shiny black robe: the soberly threatening ensemble by an odd inspiration given a touch of finesse by white lace down his front.

Schumann made additional single headed (and two handed) 'Grey Lady' puppets for the August '70 *Grey Lady Cantata II*. The Grey Ladies had been mostly multi-headed non-individuals in the '67 *Bach Cantata #140*, used in a crowd, though one had had a solo musical part. The individual Grey Lady, used by herself, had emerged in Coney Island, in *Lamentation/Mississippi* and perhaps in other shows there, and was the center – though she had a sister and sometimes was part of a village group of working Grey Ladies with baskets or buckets – of *GLC II*, again with a glass tear. For the same play he made a Purple Beast that was to fill the stage – 'the only thing it did was it came in and it lay down' (Schumann, interview, '79) and needed an operator for each of its four legs; two Blue Lady puppets with yellow hair and red or pink lips, their heads mounted on top of their operators' heads, serving as part of the frame of the play, one as musical pseudo-narrator, a musical jug strapped around the operator's neck, who signalled scene changes by striking a steel pipe mounted on the puppet's celastic hands against steel pipes fixed to the set, the other as curtain operator; and the 'backpack' Gentleman Angel, perhaps eight or ten feet tall. He is a staid, portly figure, all in black: tuxedo, rosette in lapel, white handkerchief in breast pocket, white lace gloves, black shoes, neatly trimmed black hair, and a receding hairline, with black crow or raven wings, not too large, that stand straight out from his back and look more like insignia of function than functional. His large, full, red-veined pink face is thoughtful, but by no means painfully so. He has a tiny, pursed mouth and short straight eyebrows, an elegant paunch under the loosely fitting tux jacket. He is an observer, really, more than a helper or censor, neither doer nor sufferer, and though indubitably not evil, yet not marked by his presumable position on the side of the forces of the Good, a mysterious, faintly ironic figure a far cry from the Grey Lady whose kinship to earth – plain dirt, ashes – is, especially next to him, manifest in her lack of color and the lumpy, cloddy shape of her head, body and hands.

Grey Lady Cantata II had been initially set up as a marionette show, with a bridge, and with the Grey Ladies worked on strings, but during rehearsals this plan was abandoned, though some objects – a blanket, the young man's coat, an airplane – still flew through the air on strings.

During the next 8-9 months, Schumann's mask/puppet output was again relatively low, but during the '70/'71 winter[8] he with student help turned out a great many small plaque-mounted, half-relief paper maché figures by whose installation the barn was converted into the *Vermont Paper Maché Cathedral*: an exposition that opened in January – I quoted Elka's description of the part of it that made a set for *Genghis Khan* (V.7). Like in his later *Masocchio* and *White Horse Butcher* exhibits and *Chapel of the Condemned*, this impermanent art (not made to last, besides which the mice ate it, the art with the most savory glue first) was designed for en masse installation in an architectural context: not like most sculpture since the Renaissance designed as individual works of art, semi-independent of their surroundings. The difference in his mind between it and his puppetry sculpture was chiefly its immobility.

A closed-lips face mask, perhaps one of the Napalmed Women masks, repainted (Schumann, interview, '83) – 'thin-nosed' (Elka) – Elka wore it as a school teacher in some show and dislikes it – that the titular young housewife heroine of *Emilia* (January '71) wore, is important to him apparently because he thinks of Emilia as transition from the Grey Lady (woman 'passive in history' never quite individualized in the shows she appears in) to the active and cheery Washerwoman. It was the first appearance in his work of woman not as angel, sufferer and/or mother, but as woman in the household – everyday woman. The real significance of the mask in his work, however, seems rather to be that it presents its bearer not as a universal type or principle, but as a particular individual. For *Emilia* also, he made the flat plaque-mask of a God Father. The short

---

8. Konnoff, à propos of the unfavorable response in '71 of Coney Island audiences to *Birdcatcher*, notes a trend, '70/'71, toward a 'pastoral' style:

'to *me* his *puppets* were starting to change at that point, too, a bit. When I would come back and see Vermont puppets there for a period of time, early, before *Birdcatcher* got going, they were getting very pastoral, and he had been doing this black and white city cutouts and stuff for a long time and it seemed to be a need for a time to readjust living there and still doing shows. The celastic work and the painting were getting more delicate and refined. Well, of course, it's a great contrast with Grey Ladies which are these moldy – or not, you know, there's not a lot of time trying to detail or sculpting anything in there. (I: What puppets are you thinking of?) Well, there's a whole lot of puppets that I haven't seen used a lot. They were built in the early days of Cate Farm and they were very large female masks. You know they had no backs but they were huge. They never got used in any shows.' — (Konnoff, interview, '83.)

Konnoff associates this 'early Cate Farm pastoral' trend – distinct from the trend represented by the *Birdcatcher* masks, also divergent from the '60s more achromatic and simple style – with the early '71 *Genghis Khan* and *Emilia* shows.

curly chin beard and hair frieze of this fourth Godface of Schumann's suggest solar affinities – the Big Godface of '70 had unequivocally been not a nature deity but the God of the Word – the word before it was Light. God Father was pink skinned and grey haired and had a river flow rippled moustache. His eyes were closed. But he wasn't blind, just not in need of inspection – nor of active interventions. He looks into Emilia's window blindly.

His next important set of masks – by their opulence different from all of Schumann's previous masks, by the craftsmanship expended on them a reversion to his German days – were those for the second version of *Birdcatcher* (June '71): a large set of red, very elaborately shaped and very elaborately painted and drawn-on masks, except for the chief one, Yama's, made in plaster casts, intricate and fantastic and, oddly, not very expressive masks, indicating evil neither as disposition nor as locus in a moral universe but as a pseudo-natural function. Some were of fiberglass. Schumann may have made the molds (and the woodcut prints for the costumes) before he left on the northeast tour and painted them in May when he returned. Schumann had almost no time to spend on them. This makes of the making of these many, well-finished and elaborate masks something of a mystery. The explanation seems to be that they are to a much greater extent than any previous masks the creation of others, notably Bill Whelan. Elka, while he was away, dyed the fabric for the prints (mostly in coffee and tea grounds): sewn onto the red costumes of the big drum-beating puppet demons and the small masked-performer demons, and made into banners.

'Seven different kinds of masks and puppets were used in the *Birdcatcher*.

(1) *Yama*. A heavy, man-high head, the eyes, ears, nose, mouth and chin of which consists of demon's faces (Dämonenfratzen) and are painted with landscapes and city and people scenes, mounted on a movable tripod, about 5 meters high, decorated with a wig of red-tinted hemp rope and with about a dozen of small devil puppets and reliefs, fastened in the wig and that shake with the head. Yama's belly or body is the play's red curtain, held up by Yama's hands on long sticks, and with a hole in the middle, a maw, through which Yama devours roasted birds.

(2) *Six Drummer Demons*. Over-life-size heads and garments on wooden structures that are fastened to the back of the operator ("backpack" puppets (SSB)). Also fastened to the operator's back: flagpoles, 4 meters long, with flags that fly in the wind above the demons' heads.

(3) *Kiyoyori (the Birdcatcher) and three Ancients*. Full face masks with fabric wigs. These and the half masks were modeled in clay over the face casts of the performers, then duplicated in plaster, then laid out with celastic in the negative of the plaster cast.

(4) *Bird demon and three small demons*. Half masks with fabric wigs (for voices and quick movements.)

(5) *Birds* (caught and roasted by the Birdcatcher). Several 10-15 cm. tall, full

figures of women with children, men in holiday dress, old people. Played by the bird demon over the upper edge of the curtain.

(6) *Madonna*. A $2\frac{1}{2}$ meter tall whole figure, mounted on a stick. There is room for two people inside the puppet. Her dress is put (by the performer who also carries the bell) over each of the Pink Shadows in turn, the shadow garment is taken off inside the Madonna, and in this fashion one after another of the three little demons is born (entpuppt).

(7) *Four fine gentlemen in tophats*. Full head masks that fit over the heads of the performers and are fastened to their shoulders.'

(Schumann, *Puppen und Masken*, '73.)

In addition there were the three gardeners in pink shrouds (the 'Pink Shadows'), the Beast on which the screaming Demon Bird rides, the She-Demon narrator with long fingernails, the 'Madwoman', and a male narrator (tophat, cane, no mask).

'the demons, the big demon heads were made in plaster casts because I wanted very fine sculpture for them. They were made a bit like demons from Tibetan temples – they looked a bit like Tibetan oversized demons with these big teeth and with elaborate painting on their faces. All their faces are painted with landscapes – there is a lot of detail on them. So that must have taken *some* time. (Ephraim: You made all the little masks also.) Yes. There were quite a few of them, because we made much more than what we actually used in the show. The little masks were also made in plaster casts. The only thing that was made directly over clay was Yama, the big head. I remember it was (made) very fast. I made the head ... operated by somebody behind the curtain ... he was lying consisted of – the eyes are faces, the nose is a face, everything is faces, in *sculpture*, and then, in addition to that, everything is painted over again so that there is more detail again in the painting than in the sculpture. The eyeballs have demons inside them, and the horns have little stories painted on them, and so on.'

(Schumann, interview, '79.)

'Yama was used on a tripod. . . he had two 2×4s that extended from his chin onto the ground about 8 or 10 feet ... another 2×4 attached to the top of his head ... operated by somebody behind the curtain ... he was lying down and when this moment came, he was pushed up above a red curtain that was in front of him – his hands were mounted on the two sides of that curtain, so his hands were present at all times. In some performances, that is. In other performances, all of it came up, all of it was down first. In theatres, when we performed it later, we used often a rope system. We had him strung and we pulled him up instead of having him pushed up. But basically he consisted of this giant head with a mane, with a wig that was full of little reliefs and sculptures that dangled around him, and the two painted hands that were also built, the curtain holders – the curtain was his body, in the middle of the curtain there was a hole that acted as his belly and as his mouth, with which he ate the little birds or the little people. (Elka: He also *trembled*. There was a shaking. He would be shaking when he talked. Everyone would shake.) That's right. He would really be excited. (Elka: The arms didn't work, though, did they?) They did, yes. They did not gesture speech, but they moved according to the head movements ... The Red Madonna was an old puppet from New York with a baby in her arms, a life-size puppet that had very faint sculpture and detail, and was just painted over something that was very rough in outlines. (Elka: And mounted on top.) No mounting. (Elka: No mounting, but it was held at head level. The figure was held high.) Yeah, somebody put a stick inside her. (Elka: and the skirt came down from the figure. And there was no loose movement — there was no movement of the puppet at all.)'

(Schumann, interview, '79.)

Yama, the sun's son, but as the first mortal also the first of the dead, by prerogative of priority presides over the spirit world. He is in the Glover museum now, all red, 20 ft. tall or so, his fifteen foot arms horizontally extended, the red people and fire and devils that, painted or sculpted, are all over his face and hands making his actually white skin red. The Demon faces, with tusks and horns, make up his face: he is a coral growth, the incorporation of all the spirits of evil — of all the evil in men. If he could be said to have any expression at all, however, one would have to say he was smiling.

Due to a tour and the summer circus there was a hiatus in puppet making in July-August '71, but then, in a day or two in mid-September, as Schumann remembers it — 'Chris (Hartmann) and Axel (Gros) were very fast with the celastic' (Schumann, interview, '79) when in response to the Attica prison uprising he put together a 'happening' about it entitled *Whitewashing of the Dirty Sheets of Attica* (performed September-October '71), he built for it 'a bunch of ugly oversized janitors with bulbheads' (ibid.) to wash those sheets. The story of the three or four shows he did about this uprising is unclear, but at any rate in the scipt of one of them entitled *Whitewashing* etc. there are no guards (which is what I think he has in mind when he speaks of 'janitors'), 'gentlemen in tophats' clean those sheets. I think he misremembers and is actually speaking of the guard in *Revenge of the Law* (summer of '72), a subsequent version, and/or of the several guards in *Attica* (summer of '73). They have bulbheads. There is a Negro prisoner with detachable hands in that *Whitewashing* script: whether he had a bulbhead or not I don't know. More or less all the male figures in *Revenge* and *Attica* had them, i.e. head masks resting on the shoulders tied under the arms and perhaps around the hips, and the Negro prisoners among them had ones that were distinctly bulb-shaped: the classical bulbheads. These masks are very strong. The 'ordinary man' or 'The People' never had more dignity in Schumann's theatre than in these Negro figures — rebels.

Revenge and *Harvey McLeod*, the two Black Coney Island plays of '72 had 'all new puppets and new curtains' (Elka in Schumann, interview, '79), their puppets 'slightly over-life-size figures with big bulb masks and very, very strictly controlled movement — sometimes strings on the hands; and some bridge operation' (Schumann, ibid.). There was a string-operated dog in *McLeod*, and strings were probably used for its shooting

249

scene — 'for little puppets on strings that then flew off' (ibid.). The hands, the head and the chair of the 'Governor' in *Revenge* were string operated. 'Several of the prisoners were represented by tripod figures (dummies, I take it (SSB)). The attempt was made to make them look as realistic as the performers (Konnoff, interview, '83). Etienne George's photos of the Paris (November/December '73) version of *Attica* show the 'Governor' and the 'Mailman' as legless torso-dummies — presumably string operated, though no strings are visible. According to Konnoff (interview, '83) a bulbhead mask was made for the Negro mother appearing at the end of this version: 'very much like the other (*McLeod* and *Revenge* Negro masks (SSB)). It's got very lipstick-painted lips and the hair is sculpted. And there is a black armature that you got in that had celastic hands.' (ibid.) According to Konnoff, also, the Negro bulbheads of *Revenge* and *McLeod* were made by the large-piece celastic sculpting technique.

According to the chronology in Schumann, *Puppen und Masken*, '73, it was in this fall of '71 also that he started to make the next important set of masks after the *Birdcatcher* ones he had made earlier that year, for *Simple Light* (first performed December '72), continuing this work during the summer of '72:

Other work during the summer: more Dancing Bear Theater, parades in local towns, FIRE ... workshops and performances in Wisconsin and Vermont, banner-printing, poster-printing, Punch and Judy, KING STORY, and a lot of mask and puppet building for THAT SIMPLE LIGHT MAY RISE OUT OF COMPLICATED DARKNESS — our new hope and problem child since the summer of '71 when the clay masks were started, plaster molds cast, celastic and paper maché worked into the negatives. Between then and now we never stopped building these large puppets, mounting them on poles, rehearsing their movements and sounds, tackling with storms and silences, composing growth of rocky mountains, finding the history of a pot of soup, groping with masses and hordes of puppet faces aroused, and finally seeking a light bulb's victory over darkness. I hope it's true. I hope the light bulb will win, and hope is SIMPLE LIGHT's theme song.'

(Schumann, Newsletter, *'Bread and Rosebuds'*, November '72.)

'... a big mask building project of a very different kind. It was some kind of renaissance in our theatre, some kind of new mode of sculpture — what *Simple Light* was about. Different ideas for crowding up faces, the difference of individual faces and crowded-up faces — so there were faces that were strung up in the horizontal, and faces that were strung up in the vertical. Towers of people and houses of people and big balls of faces. That, and the use of black plastic ...'

These plastic-soma'd puppets stand apart in his oeuvre: much more, even, than the monstrous Grey Ladies and disciples of '66/'67, they were by their abstraction designed not for theatrical gesture but for dance motions and dance effects, and specifically for group movements and the movements of individuals relative to groups: as though Schumann had decided

250

he was now sufficiently in command of his medium to realize an adequate choreography for *Totentanz*.

'The whole show consisted of such movement ideas of puppets and only the little bit of story that goes through it. It's hardly a story. It depends all on those noises (of moving plastic (SSB)) and movements that these puppets could do. It was just an organization of groups acting, and then an individual puppet coming out with, say, such a very specific dance and movement was pretty much – the composition of that was – what the whole thing was (about).'

The performers for the most part were shrouded and veiled black figures (the opposite of the white clad in-view operators he had employed since *Cry* of '69). They were the faceless members of 'the crowd'. But there was also a considerable number of individualized and very particular – though conceptually almost unidentifiable – puppets, large and peculiar. Citing their names from the 'January '73 version' stage script: a (round) Crowd Face mask, a Single Face mask, a Kabuki puppet (its sword-carrying right arm detachable and operated by a separate operator: in this version it was to carry a banner in its left, in the '74 version a distinct operator was to follow it with the banner), a Big Hand puppet (the script of the '74 version speaks of a Neck puppet, but it may have been the same one), a Prophet puppet,[9] a Dwarf puppet,[10] a Sweeping puppet[11] (in the '74 version replaced by or called the Gentle Tide puppet), a dozen or more Crowd puppets,[12] several composite two-operator Lover puppets (a mask

---

9. 'That's a head that's built in a position with a stretched-out neck going up at a right angle.
   Then there's a stick attached to that angle, a long stick with black plastic attached to that. (The stick) was an elongation of the body, so (the puppet) was the shape of a flying figure that way. It was moved by lots of feet that did some kind of stomping, drumming on the ground. And then finally a hand came sticking out of the puppet, an arm, and did something.' — (Schumann, interview, '83.)
10. Possibly the puppet operated by Bill Whelan:
   'Mostly the black plastic was used for noise, to make sound in the puppets and mostly it was hanging straight. But then there were some puppets where the black plastic was bundled up and crumpled up – sort of an undesigned kind of chaotic kind of a costume – and some hand was sticking outside of it. (One) puppet for example was not molded around the operator so what (he) did was he held that stick and then – but in a very disorganized fashion – he did nervous little jagged movements that sort of moved the body of the puppet and created noises.' — (Schumann, interview, '83.)·
11. '. . . with a single head and one arm – a piece of black plastic with an arm sticking on it and a stick and she was a Sweeping puppet that could do only one job and that was a to and fro one, always in the same direction. She couldn't change direction because she didn't have any backside to her. So she did sort of a diagonal run and with that run the fabric would go this way, then the operator would swing the fabric to the front and run backwards, and it would fly with the wind, the wind blowing into it that way. It was like a large pumping motion.' — (Schumann, interview, '83.)
12. The term in the theatre's parlance sometimes refers to single-operator puppets whose head, above their black plastic body, was a row of individual faces mounted on a rod held

consisting of two joined half-heads, separate garments for the two operators, one with a left, one with a right sleeve), a two-faced Boat puppet, Forest puppets.[13] A Pekingese-style white Demon mask with an open-toothed mouth, that in *Laos* (February/March '72) had been hand held by two people over the contrastingly (*Fire* mask) masked face of a woman seated in front of them, was used in *Simple Light* also. There was a turning Sheep-Shepherdess Spinning or Carrousel puppet developed from a Spinning First Woman of the '70, '71 circuses, a performer with 3 or perhaps 4 masks around her head: a masked and parachute silk-costumed performer turning with a horizontal cross over her shoulders, at whose draped arms' ends were attached, loosely, so they could bounce, masks of sheep. There was a variety of the small paper maché 'Johnny puppets', single figure and group sculptures, a tiny 't.v.' hand puppet and a small Angel hand puppet, a Stomach puppet (a bag, burlap in '73, black plastic in '74, with arms sticking out of it – variant of Schumann's Munich Womb puppet), cardboard cutouts of clouds, a celastic toy-size car. The heroine of *Simple Light*, Simple Light, simply had white gauze over her face.

Schumann (interview, '82) thinks of his Crucifixion puppet masks as in a Renaissance tradition, mentions Piero de la Francesca à propos of them. Oddly, to my mind, this is also how he thinks of his *Simple Light* puppets, contrasting them in this regard not only to the Grey Ladies but to his earlier masks. But whereas in the case of the Crucifixion puppets he seems to be thinking of the masks' coloring, in that of the *Simple Light* masks he has the features in mind:

'The kind of sculpture that was used was new, the crowding up of faces in great masses. What was new for me too was the type of face that was made for it. It's

---

in some cases horizontally, in some vertically, the heads vertical or at an angle in either case. But masks from *Simple Light* that now in the Dopp Farm museum are labelled 'Crowd masks' are grey, stone-colored, compacted-together faces in heaps – seeming colonies of faces – along the lines of the mask of the red 'Yama' – or series, their expressions sensitive, watchful, indicative of neither thought nor purpose, but of feeling only – primitively, reducedly sentient. The earlier kind of 'crowd puppet' had been used for instance in *Stations* in the spring of '72: '. . . off and on, in circuses, for example, and other shows, a crowd appears, that's a person shrouded, in burlap, let's say, and on top of him, worn like a head mask above the head, a tiny little group of sculpted people. On one of them an arm can move with a mechanical inside string pull and raise a flag up and down. And on one of them, I think, a hat goes up.' — (Schumann, interview, December '82.)
13. '. . . a face that was mounted upright. This one was a tall one that was played on a pole with fabric underneath – with black plastic underneath, in a high position, probably. It was a group mask that was not used solo. It was only used with others – it played the Forest. One job that the big puppets had was to create a forest. They were made like trees. On a single stick, with some black plastic hanging from the bottom of this mask, down the long stick. They were either held by people or sometimes put into concrete cast blocks that held them upright. (I: This was part of the forest.) Yeah. A tree in the forest.' — (Schumann, interview, December '82.)

252

very different from what I had done before, these relaxed Renaissance Italian faces that I like. They are very different from the Grey Ladies or . . . the faces of the years before. They sort of have the harmony and the relaxedness and sort of well proportioned features. (I: In *Simple Light?*) Yeah. They are not grotesque. They are not expressive that way. They are very quiet. I don't remember it now, but I think Piero de la Francesca is sort of the classic I can think of. Yeah, probably I saw a good book on Piero de la Francesca. It's very possible.'

(Schumann, interview, '83.)

Though Schumann may in '73 have made some new masks or puppets for his fourth European tour at the end of that year – for *Attica*, the revised version of *Revenge*, or for *Simple Light*, apparently also changed from its northeast showings at the beginning of '73, he apparently made nothing important for these or for any other shows that year. But I suspect that it was in the spring of '73, rather than in that of '72, that he made the bulbheads of most of what now in the Glover museum is entitled the 'Bulbhead Family' – though Marie Antoinette and George the Third, for instance, may have been made in '74 or even '75. They were made by the small-piece celastic molding technique and were beautifully finished, patina'd, painted. They, like the (according to Konnoff, backpack) 'Lions of Inflation', exquisite and elegant like them, and made the same way, were first used in a spring parade of '73 (*Tragedy . . .*) and in a New Jersey parks show derived from it. The 'Bulbhead Family' was used in the '75 and '76 circuses but not much otherwise – in no important play. The Lions were not again used, I think. The exquisite sheep heads of the Shepherdess-Sheep Carrousel or Spinning Puppet, of *Simple Light* and of the pageant of the '74 circus – stylistically belong to this group also: sculptures that simulate the glory of a sculpted substance.

Six of the small (5-6 ft.) but very big headed (their heads make up about a third of their height) members of the 'Bulbhead Family' are now, misdated '1976', assembled in the Glover museum, all sort of giddy-silly and very jolly looking, tiny tongues protruding from their generally tiny mouths, the yellowish white of their (I believe lacquered) faces shaded by a hectic red, wearing a variety of small ridiculous headgear on their bald pates and more or less funny vagabond's dress-up suits of unmatching jackets and pants on their slim boyish figures, whose trim is in sinister contrast to the false sweetness of their faces.[14] George the Third and Marie Antoinette – Bulbheads named for their parts in the '75 and '76 circuses Bicentennial shows – form a separate couple in the museum. Around 7 ft. tall, they are corpulent, even fat, and their heads are, like the Bulbheads'

---

14. '(I: To me they look real nasty. Sort of sly and overly sweet.) Yeah. That was sort of the idea. To make a real mean set of – I saw them as clowns and I just wanted to have a great variety of them to have – with some similarity, in that they would all stick out their tongues and all have little horns, hidden or not, and all big double chins and wrinkles and fat and all that.' — (Schumann, interview, '82.)

generally, large and shiny, the features imbedded in the pig-face surfaces: small features. They also are jolly looking. She has tiny, he has small white hands. Not far from them (dated '1975') are the Lions of Inflation, 4 large open-mouthed yellow cat faces, laughing, jolly also, but ferocious, their pink mouths' interiors showing the faces of people they are in the act of swallowing: in the '73 *Tragedy of the Rising Price Index* they ate up the (Bulbhead) Gods of Plenty. The faces in their mouths are those of 'Bulbhead Family' people. And a little way over, dated '1974', are the Spinning Puppet sheep, whose heads are among the most beautiful 'masks' Schumann ever made, red-eyed, with marvellously abstracted skull shapes, concave planes abutting in delicate ridges as though sutured with the characteristic fragility of bone, an interplay of curves within the dominance of planes — curling nostrils and ear snails growing out of the skulls' lines. They convey the sculptor's secret pleasure in the delicacies of speciation on this harshly rich planet. Schumann in '82 was not sure whether they were made from plaster casts or by the small-piece celastic sculpturing method directly over clay. I would say probably the latter.

'72/'73 was also the time of experimentation with fiberglass masks, e.g. the head of the 'Doctor' in *Woyzeck* ('81), also used for 'Papa' in *Diagonal Man* ('82).

During '74 Schumann did paper maché sculptures for his show *Meadows Green*, and made a set of 'Garbagemen' masks for the *First Garbagemen Cantata* of the spring of '74.

There are 14 Garbagemen in the Glover museum, in a group, all stocky, most a little paunchy, man-sized, fully dressed from boots to caps — they all have green, black-visored caps with something like crossed hoes in a white circle as insignia on the green and all wear work gloves. There are slits to see through in their flesh-colored, sometimes more grey, sometimes more yellowish head masks: middle-aged men's faces with tightly compressed lips. Their black eyes *stare*. Expressions of slight superiority have imprinted themselves on their fleshy faces — 'Well! What do you want?!' These masks rest on their wearers' shoulders which eliminates neck movements — fat people, Schumann observes, tend to move their heads and bodies together: but in their case it gives their movements a slight inertia of recalcitrance, perhaps in Schumann's view not untypical of American workmen. I mentioned Schumann's claim that the earliest, of 1970, were inspired by the Goddard College maintenance crew, and that he liked these men, that they were 'nice'. The Garbagemen don't look nasty, but they by no means look accommodating. Perhaps this reflects his experiences at Goddard after 1970.

He did some building for that summer's circus, especially, it seems, for the pageant associated with it, which was on the theme of a fight between the (bad) Red and the (good) White. Yama and the Demons from the second version of *Birdcatcher* were used for the Red, and the Vietnamese

Women and Ladies for the White. The new puppets were mainly for the White side: one-operator, i.e. two-legged White Horses – a vertical stick attached to hose that goes over the operator's head and holds the mask, a horizontal stick, ending in a tail that is fastened to the vertical stick, white fabric carried by the horizontal stick – white birds, a white Great Warrior or several, white giant Indian Chiefs, and among them a particularly gigantic one, their leader, 'who couldn't walk – it was too big – it was a half-face mounted on some tripod. Mounted on a plywood sheet, I think. And that one was carried in flat and just erected – like Yama, also . . .' (Schumann, interview, December '82), and Hornblowers who 'were on backpacks – backpack puppets where everybody who wore the mask was a hornblower – an elongated tube that came from the mouth of the puppet which was shaped like a trumpet bell into the mouth of the operator inside his dress . . .' (Schumann, interview, '79). Also made for this circus was the mask of what from the '75 Dopp Farm circus onward became 'Bob the Butcher' or the Chief Butcher, in the '74 circus worn by the drummer, dressed in white, starting off the pageant.

The big white Indian Chiefs are in the museum, 8 or 9 of them, with 3 ft. high heads. 12 to 14 feet in all, white tubular figures with light gray print dresses, their shrouds joined to their heads, which are all different, but all have vivid, perceptive faces, their mouths slightly open and the eye shapes tensed, looking interested, but not aggressive, Schumann's fantasy of a humorous age with more time to figure things out in.

The white birds in the '74 circus pageant, as Schumann remembers it (Schumann, interview, '83), were the Gulls appearing in his pageants also '85 and following, his first kite-type stick puppets, with 'streamlined, three-dimensional heads, . . . very easy to run, . . . ideal for sort of almost a kite. Once you have them up they almost carry themselves. You can do it with one hand. They're not heavy anymore. The wind gets them.' (Schumann, ibid.) In their ease of handling they contrast with some puppets of this type made later, e.g. the angels with cutout, flat heads in *Washerwoman Nativity* ('79), whose heads are 'very difficult to manipulate or bend (Schumann means, I suppose, change direction with (SSB)).' (Schumann, ibid.)

Schumann appeared as 'Daughter' in *Jephthah*, done at the '74 circus, in two puppets, in his old Mary mask and dressed in vivid colors, dancing on stilts, and, without stilts, in 'a piece of white jersey fabric which is stiff so it can move bulky, in a bulky way' (Schumann, interview, '83) and a mask head operated on a short stick by one hand, the other modifying the shape of the garment, 'sort of a crooked head and asymmetrical face of a woman – or rather, the face is not asymmetrical, but the hairdo is so weird that – ' (ibid.). He used the same crooked face and dress as White Lady in the *White Horse Butcher* pageant at the '75 circus; and appeared as White Savior Angel in the Mary mask and on stilts, but in a loose, white dress, straddling a white one-operator hobbyhorse-type puppet horse in his '74 Christmas show (called *Grey Lady Cantata #5*) and then again as Angel of Resurrection in that same '75 pageant. His two *Jephthah* puppets were to my knowledge his first female impersonations and the stilt one of them his first performance as stilt puppet in a play (he had from '71 or '72 onward appeared on stilts, as a male figure, in parades), and they were, by way of his figure in the '74 Christmas play, the origin of one of the Bread and Puppet Theatre's more famous puppets, that Angel of Resurrection, first done in the '75 pageant.

For *Grey Lady Cantata #4* (= *Garbagemen Cantata*), performed as part of the '74 circus also, he made the first large set of Garbagemen (face masks and costumes): much used in later circuses.

A big fiberglass mask made by Bill Whelan was used in a sideshow, *The Water Show*. It wasn't used again: 'It was very heavy. (Bill) had heard it was such a great material and when he made it it was enormously heavy and felt very brittle. It wasn't a success.' (Schumann, interview, '83.)

14. 1973. The break with the '60s accomplished,
Schumann is exhausted, has nothing to say,
and therefore faces crises: in his family,
in his group and with Goddard. **1974.**
He solves his problems with his group and
Goddard by leaving them and figures out a
new message. Move to Dopp Farm.

During the '60s, Manhattan, from Harlem to Foley Square, had been his church where he had stood like a preacher opposing a stern 'No' to the war, a small war, a peccadillo, but to him the moral equivalent of the German Reich's second reach for Lebensraum, and the morality of it was what counted for him. Of New York's 8 millions only a small fraction had even seen as much as a picture of his puppets in the papers, but marginally and faintly their images engraved themselves on the town's image for those years, an image within which St. Patrick's Cathedral, say, is merely a building on 5th Avenue, a minor heaping of soulless dead bones, unrewarding to the inner eye, part of the background.

During his Cate Farm years, when he had given up his ministership, he failed by his circuses to extend his mission to the nation, and had to give up his outpost in the big city, his voice sorely inappropriate, defeated by distractions. His open air evangelizing was wasted, a lollipop on campuses, a nuisance in the small towns of his neighborhood, and anyhow was turning into a banal whine about the degradation of the environment. What he did achieve, however, was to wash his linen in public, namely by a number of grandiose and elegant tragic spectacles, red, or black, white and grey, or simple black, but all dark, embodiments of private anguish. This involved a certain amount of deception, with respect to which he figured as a con man, for his assembled people were working on the assumption that they were sweating in a cause not only his, and there was no such cause. There was the justification, though, that his private anguish corresponded to large, although perennial and unresolvable, issues – the intractability of which he was in fact stating, though he dressed this up in mystery and funny business.

Actually, he was working his way through a Weltschmerz that had sat at his heart even when he was young, in Germany, and that in his New York period had only been temporarily suppressed by an outflow of creative energy made possible by a fortuitous combination of circumstances, a good public cause actively pursued by many and his discovery of an art form appropriate to its support. Circumcircuited by his energy flow, the cancer became inactive. But in the favorable condition of inner and

257

outer stasis at the end of the '60s brought about by the simultaneous fade-out of the Movement and by his attainment of mastery in his self-created medium, the old ailment flared up and started burning him again.

He worked his way through it by going with it actively. Expressing it by the articulated wail of his *Cantatas*, his *Stations, Birdcatcher* and then finally *Simple Light*, he made it work for him.

Integrated, become his working heart, the tumor by early '73 had become a functional organ. But the self cure had been exhausting. And though, with *Simple Light* he had got his 'No' to his '60s 'No' off his chest, he as yet had no 'Yes', none, that is, whose power over him could mobilize his energies for artistic expression of it: the 'Yes' to Family and Nature of *Simple Light* wouldn't do, it was still too close to a rejection of negative alternatives, too much like just 'Yes' to a cop-out. He for the moment had nothing to say. So 1973 was an uncreative year for him.[1]

He fiddled with the New York/Northeast version of *Simple Light*, but produced only minor changes for its end-of-the-year tour in Europe. He revised *Revenge of the Law* into a street show. There are only two new very minor Bread and Puppet pieces that year, *He Who is Rich* and *The Tragedy of the Rising Price Index*, but both were chiefly not by him but by members of the group. There was some interesting puppet making, notably the Bulbhead Family, but, uncharacteristically, others did a good deal of the creative work on them; though I can see him turning to fine mask making that spring as outlet for a wandering, searching mind. There was no circus, no new *Grey Lady Cantata*. He did the *Christmas Story* in Europe a few times, but for the first time not in the States – he let sub- and splinter-groups do it. Coney Island was gone and he accepted *Stations*, made in '72, as definitive form of his Easter show. He toured it, for almost two months, in the spring, and at the end of the year toured *Simple Light* and some other shows in Europe. Otherwise, he painted, unlike mask- or puppet- or show-making, a solitary activity.[2]

His relations to his family, his group and his host, Goddard, had been troubled throughout this period, but this year the troubles became a crisis.

People tend to explain crises by the problems that produce them. This is almost invariably a mistake. There are always problems, but they become

---

1. 'You think there weren't any shows? (Ephraim: Yes.) (Elka: It's true. It's true. (Laughs.)) I think I lay on my ear in 1973 . . .' — (Schumann, interview, '79.)
2. 'I think of '73 as being pretty much dominated by *Simple Light*, including Bill Dalrymple's death, which was a big – he did a series of paintings on sort of the theme of Attica, Rockefeller and kind of telling the story in masonite sheets. (I: I've seen portraits of people.) And portraits, yes. He mounted those. Then these big – some of them are in the museum now – paintings that I think Peter thought of them as being for *Simple Light* but they are paintings that are mainly black with very small lit up scenes – a nude, or a tree. But there are at least three or four and I'm sure there were two or three times as many.' — (Elka Schumann, interview, '83.)

critical only when the will or ability to cope with them — I say 'cope' because problems are rarely solved — is weakened below a critical level. This is precisely what happened in Schumann's case in the course of '73 as regards his problems with Goddard and the group. And this weakening of the ability and/or will to cope was due to the inner vacuum produced in him by his finally having accomplished his break with the '60s and thus having lost the raison d'être of his production during the preceding 3 years, the driving force of denying the primacy of resistance, political activism.

The Goddard administration's continuing refusal to sponsor his activities or make arrangements facilitating his work with the students[3] and the

3. '(Elka: We were also, as a group, we were really looking for activities that would support our being in Cate Farm. You know, we had been invited to come there but it was a very open invitation — and —) We didn't have a teacher's salary. (Elka: We had no salary, it was very unclear what our relationship was. We weren't faculty, we had no salary but we did for a while try to —) But we were *obliged* to the school somehow, so I did a lot of work at the school. Like, for example, I did a program, one year, of weekly political news services. (Elka: As a whole group, and also as separate individuals, besides yourself, there were attempts at getting workshops going and different things. You offered a bread baking workshop. I know we made posters and Chris Hartmann made posters where we listed a dozen activities that we offered to students ... Do you remember other activities that we offered? I remember vaguely the bread baking one. I think there was also woodcut printing.) Banner printing. (Elka: And different kinds of puppetry. Puppet movement.) The political puppet theatre — (Elka: That came later.) That came later. But it was one of those workshops. (Elka: But it was all part of our attempt to give something back to the college in exchange for this, and we —) Well, we offered them *various* things. We also offered them a program where we would take students on a tour. That was a bit later, but anyway, we *did* offer it to them. We offered them a program of taking some twenty students to Europe — I believe it was with *Simple Light*, for *that* tour, and — (Elka: And did you have students in an earlier tour?) But they didn't come through with it, they never got organized to provide what we asked them to do. We asked them to pay for the trip for the students and to come up with some support for financing of such a program. But they didn't. So —————? and Paul Zaloom were the only ones that came from that big group of students. I was angry at the college at the time, I remember. (Elka: But another thing that we also did, I think quite conscientiously, and also was very beneficial to us was simply every show that was worked on at Cate Farm was performed at Goddard College at least once, and then often several times, for free.) And sometimes not at Goddard College, but on Cate Farm *for* Goddard College, *advertised* at College. (Elka: Was the work (on the '74 circus (SSB)) done with students?) Some students, not so many. We weren't so happy with the participation of Goddard College. There wasn't much. We tried, we had workshops for all kinds of things and some people came and not many stuck to us. Goddard had its own path and was not too interested. We tried several times to involve them in the larger scene, to have them *organize* our circus and they were not interested in that. We wanted them to be the *sponsors*, to advertise it, to make money on it, to have concessions on it — we proposed all that to them — luckily they were not interested, because it was much nicer without them.' — (Schumann, interview, '79.)
'Plus, even though it was wonderful to be in the country and to have all the space and all that — but underneath that surface, when Peter thought of doing things on a more permanent basis, Goddard seemed as flimsy and impermanent as anything, any rental that we had in New York. The College was constantly in crisis. So it didn't seem that great a

student body's general disinterest in his activities,[4] mitigated only by the sporadic and unreliable participation of individuals, aggravated by the time, loss and nuisance of students hanging out and/or wanting to be dealt with as individuals ('persons')[5] and/or wanting to be given creative opportunities without being willing to do the drudgery[6] had come to seem a

---

change from the very, almost intolerable thing in New York, which is that we hadn't had a place to work.' — (Elka, interview, '83.)

4. In the beginning, in the summer of '70, Schumann had a good response from the students:

'(Ephraim: So what was the workshop done in Cate Farm when we first moved? There was a workshop?) There was a workshop with students. (Elka: Very unwillingly agreed to by Goddard. I remember how difficult it was to get their cooperation in providing — you know, telling students about — and allowing the students to —) We had a workshop, a beautiful workshop. And we did a lot of puppet building, a lot of paper maché reliefs I made, and plaster casts ... There was quite a bit of building with the students.' — (Schumann, interview, '79.)

But then the response slackened off:

'(Elka: We were surprised how little interest and what a kind of weak reaction and reception these workshops got. For some of these things that we offered, there would be no students or maybe five the first time and maybe none the second time. I don't know if it was the distance that Cate Farm was from the College or the general lack of interest, or what, but it wasn't a booming success.)' — (Schumann, interview, '79.)

5. Konnoff (interview, '83), speaking of an emergent 'pastoral' style in Schumann's masks in the winter of '70/'71, thinks the change (to students) in the people working for him affected his style:

'I think he was working with a whole group of different people too, and a lot of them were or got a lot ... a lot of them have different kinds of commitments and interests in what was going on (than) in New York. They were students and that sort of thing, part of the relationships — some of them were smart and some weren't smart, they were there to be educated a little bit, you couldn't exactly step on them the same way that you could with — the commitment was that they had other classes too, it wasn't the only thing that they could do. Some of them were interested in ecology, some of them in metaphysics and — I saw, over the years, Peter dealing, like when we had open workshops, were doing a news show, and did it at Goddard every day. Quite a few people would come in and quite likely want to do something about Tantra Yoga and the newest levitation and I think that's just a technique that he learned how to — that — and it doesn't slow him down anymore.'

Ashley, à propos of Schumann's leaving Goddard in '74:

'I think he must have been tired of the hippies by that time. It was a perfectly revolting bunch of people at (that) school ... The student body was utterly awful. They were the left over — the worst of the left over hippies of the middle class — revolting. For instance, they had a swimming hole. It was absolutely mandatory that every student should swim naked. Therefore, when the Schumanns went clad they stood out, you know. They wore their clothes. The puppeteers, by and large, wore their clothes. But they were the weird ones. If you went to Goddard you had to swim naked — that's all. That was part of freedom: Everybody Will Swim Naked! And I think he probably didn't like it. I think by that time he must have been very weary of hippies and — ' — (Ashley, interview, May '82.)

6. 'The real work is in the daily routines, jobs, experiments and alterations on Cate Farm. We are now about 15 steady workers, and for lack of living and working space will start puppetry and life on a 2nd farm in Glover, Vt. this fall.

We work 6 days from 9 A.M.-5P.M. building, paper-macheing, sewing, cooking,

negative outbalancing the farm, barn and clay pit. When he left for Europe at the end of the year his contract had not been renewed. The administration was suspected of toying with the idea of getting a new artist in residence. (Konnoff, interview, '83.)

In his relations with Elka there had been a crisis in '71 and now there was another one – he had a new mistress. This, like actually the Goddard crisis, was not just a personal matter, but pertained directly (and, at least in one regard, negatively) to his work. Both put in question the feasibility of the salvation by retrenchment, the idea of which he had worked out for himself from *Emilia* to *Simple Light*: and his work depended, then as earlier and later, entirely on his having ideas to express about right and wrong that he believed in strongly. Elka went to live on the farm her parents owned in Glover, Vt. in the spring and stayed there with the kids through the summer.[7]

---

gardening, a wide range and mixture of crafts and preparatory petty labors and rehearsals, all culminating in performances. As members of the troupe get more involved in puppetry, and better at the tasks at hand, we find it harder to run benevolent workshops for students or other community members, whose skills cannot be fully incorporated into our productions. And since we are not a commune per se, but a unit geared to production and resurrected by production, we naturally apply our production minded criticism to the work students and other community members share with us.

We are always understaffed. There is always more work to do than we get done. There are, mostly all the time, simple jobs to do. That people, who wish to learn and to participate, can do. We do springtime parades and political pageants and marches at irregular times every year, where people can get involved with their heads and hands, with their political convictions or their classical instruments.

Our puppet plays are trying to give form to our thoughts and beliefs. We want to play for free as much as possible, but because of that, we constantly have to improve the organization of our daily doings, our spending, our bookings, our time schedules. And because that is such a full time job, we have a hard time at superficially instructing others, at entertaining non-essential workshops. To entertain non-essentially involved people. For a person who wants to inform himself, or to glimpse at or to feel out what we do, there are ample occasions for both: to watch and to participate.

For persons who are seriously interested in the art of puppetry we have to offer a number of apprenticeships, which do not necessarily entail travelling with us on our tours, but else mean 6 days 9AM to 5PM puppetry, garbage-burning and dishwashing included, and require a one-year commitment. For possible credits you have to check with the proper Goddard office. Since we are working class, we don't have the means to offer room and board for such an apprenticeship, but again, you can discuss that with your administration.'
— (Schumann, *Bread and Puppets*, mimeographed newsletter, beginning of '73, Bread and Puppet files.)
7. I suppose Schumann went back and forth between Cate Farm and Dopp Farm that summer. According to Fernandez (interview, '83), Elka and the kids moved up there in the spring, Schumann stayed on Cate Farm till the end of the summer. According to Elka he 'was staying more on Cate Farm'. — (Elka, interview, '83.) The impression Schumann, covering one half-lie with another, gave an outside visitor associated with the Vermont schools system was he spent the summer at Dopp Farm:
'During this past summer the company split into two operations, one moving to a new

261

He had not managed to establish a working commune on Cate Farm.[8]
His confidence in the importance of his work, not its artistic importance,
but the importance, given the capacity of his puppetry for expressing it
powerfully, of what he had to say, as measured not by its originality or
profundity — he is not a vain man that way either — but by the importance
of the evils it concerns and the scarcity of effective public objection to
them, is such that he had thought a working commune devoted to the

---

and smaller location on a farm in Glover, Vt., about 30 miles away. There, some of the
players concentrate on print shop work, and Elka Schumann continues to develop the work
of the Dancing Bear Theatre. This is a branch of the Bread and Puppet Theatre which con-
centrates on the 'Punch and Judy' kind of puppet show intended primarily for children . . .
Peter too spent the summer in Glover with his family, anxious to give the rest of the company an opportunity to develop new directions and a closer sense of community without
his frequently heavy handed leadership. He hopes his temporary absence has helped to
build a closer and more permanent company of puppeteers working and living together to
create a more communal product.' — (Rough, *The Bread and Puppet Theatre, Dramatics,*
December '73.)

8. As I suggested, Schumann, during the first half of '70, when he decided to move to
Goddard and then did, so he could retain his liberty to pick its members, kept his desire for
a commune under his hat, asking only two people (Dalrymple, Spevak) to come and stay.
By '73, when he was fed up with the crowd there, he more or less disavowed the ideal.
But that he had wanted one, and — apart from the ticklish point that he was going to tell it
what to do — how he conceived it is indicated by a letter of February 23, '72 he wrote the
puppeteers (and certain ones he then wanted there in particular):

'Dear Puppeteers,

I'll write to you together, because else I have to say the same things 10× over. It's a
good-morning meeting (20 below zero today!) or a state of the union message: My fellow
puppeteers, concerning our life on Cate farm several puppeteers have expressed a strong
desire to not come back, or rather to move somewhere in the vicinity and commute to our
claypit for occasional or regular working hours. I told Zaloom, Neetz and Marsino they
couldn't be on the farm because there is no place here and I told them that precisely because
I feel that the farm should be as much as possible a past-presence-future community of
friends, a place where the hopefully long term associates can learn the skills of neighbor-
hoodism and general friendliness toward dirty dishes and each other. If now Su and Bart
and Brigitte and Pascal and Marie Odile and — if I remember right — Sylvie, all tell me
they don't want to live on the farm, then, frankly, that sounds to me a bit like copping out
on me and Elka. Can you fairly consider our life in that respect? What are we left with
when you all tell us you don't want to 'live' here? Exactly with what we don't want, or
what we wish to get beyond, the youth hostel bachelor housing project with Elka and me
residing as Mom and Dad for good. Do you see that? I assure you we also like 'privacy' or
'our own life' and we realize as much as you do that there are sacrifices in communal enterprise. (And beyond that I feel that until recently Elka has carried the heaviest burden of
these sacrifices). The argument for communal living does not easily stem from physical
advantages — even though there are plenty. We need to learn such communal living for our
own sake and for the sake of the rest of the world. That we are not good at it is a healthy
challenge. Besides, I haven't seen anybody who is good at it, it's gruesome learning new
ways of thinking and going about things and it will be handsome only through lots of labor
and failure and friendship. But please, think of the theatre that way: once you are not confused anymore about that, once you understand that you want to do this kind of work with
me, understand also that for this kind of work we need our little worldwide communion

implementation of his work[9] would be feasible. In this he had been mistaken. In part, with the war going and then gone, and with man's place in nature (by '73) already at the center of his perception,[10] but not yet as participation in nature's eternal return (viewpoint of his next period's message), what he had to say during this period in fact lacked at any rate the practical importance, the bread kind of importance, needed to keep up the enthusiasm and discipline of the kind of people attracted to him.[11] And

---

that for bread's sake and for puppet's sake we can't change into a salaried private happiness enterprise where actors and other specialists assemble at rehearsal time and quit after the performance. As you know, that happens often enough anyway. So, for you who have stayed through enough of this, some wider deeper scope of relationship with the theatre should be possible.' — (Schumann, letter to (certain) puppeteers, February 23, '72.)

Leherrissier (interview, '79), speaking of the summer of '71, after the Schumanns had moved into their own little house (leaving the big one to the puppeteers), didn't think it was a commune because the Schumanns had their own kitchen:

'(I: What Margo Sherman said is that at this point – the spring of '71 – there was a commune at Plainfield, that Peter Schumann was trying the commune life style there.) No, they had their own kitchen so I wouldn't call it a commune at all. They had their own kitchen in their house and we all lived in a little extension house and had our own kitchen, or people lived in the barn or in the chicken coop.'

9. 'We are working on it communally in that everyone lends a hand in putting it together. I'm really the designer of it, the director of the show, so it is not in that sense everyone else's product until the performance. Then it becomes a communal property. The puppets themselves are not really a communal creation; they are clearly mine. But a lot of people are learning the crafts of it, and helping out. So that is the limitation of our group: that is like that.' — (Schumann, in Rough, *The Bread and Puppet Theatre, Dramatics*, December '73.)

'That is like that.' He could have been talking to his group.

10. 'Puppet theater is a public address-system and therefore a political instrument. Crying and song-singing can be quite wrong in this here American thicket. But politics are not necessarily the daily news. Some landscapes have to be exposed just as urgently as the cruelty of our economy; some facts, more wondrous than inflation, want to be attended to; and some truths, older than the US, want to blossom from the hearts of US puppeteers. The birds in the US wake up at 5 am and blow trumpets. And the meaning of the trumpets is the delicious harmony of the sky and matters of the planet earth, politics not included.' — (Schumann, *Vermont Puppet Theater's Desire*, July 18, '73, draft of a statement, Bread and Puppet files.)

11. Aware during this period that he didn't have a puppet-message 'as useful as bread' to give to The People, and sensing that his puppeteers sensed it, Schumann in exhorting them to keep up the good work had to demand Faith of them: not in him, but in the puppets: the puppets would come up with something: for they 'make God's music'. This in fact made sense for him since it was by working on and with his puppets that he arrived at the statements he made by his shows. But it was in fact a demand of faith in him:

'And besides all that, the validity of our profession is often dubious to ourselves. Sky and trees, birds and waters are aching. Politics fail people. No philosophy or spiritual guidance have managed to bring about peace. Our civilization reveals itself only now. Its mechanics, who once set out to improve our lives, turn out to be thieves and murderers, and the goodies we live on enslave obscure populations across the globe. Is there still time for puppetshows? Are we allowed love and bullshit? Are clouds and fire falling on us soon?

Holy Mr. Nobody appears in my dreams, leans forward (ever so gently) and says: get

in part, as the fate of his Coney Island and circus projects showed, his utterance was not effective either: neither the big city nor a broad American audience were reachable by it. But most importantly, a working commune devoted to doing his work was infeasible because people's egos wouldn't stand for it, at least not without creating serious trouble: essentially the individual's competition for survival that he had deplored in *Simple Light*. He tried to deal with this problem by giving more scope to people – letting them do their own shows (*He Who is Rich*), directing things (*Tragedy of the Rising Price Index*), working out their own parts (Sherman's on-looking witches), working on masks in more creative ways[12] (the Bulbhead Family) – or then, in '74, the circus 'side-shows'. A few people moved up to Glover in '73 to work semi-independently. But all this was too little and too late and went too much against his grain. He couldn't really let go. His very help to people limited them. Moreover, instead of a working commune something in fact more like an actual commune had by '73 evolved. A practically uncontrolled[13] influx of girl-

---

up, wake up, arms up, ears up, up rosebuds up! Quite a Mr. Nobody!

The ways and solutions that have been radically proposed and radically experimented with, are inefficient. We can't and we don't want to kill all those bourgeois uncles, small, medium, large-size Nixons, and then start socialism. First of all: they are big and real, we are little and esoteric. Secondly, when studying post-revolutionary societies, we find their achievements not only not exactly befitting the higher aspirations of the masses, but also not fulfilling our own yearning for a free and meaningful life within the regulations of citizenship.

We want full-size contribution. Our muscles and heads are wrong from the lack of perfect uses. What we enjoy, what we are able to truly perceive, we need to share and spread out. Our community with others has to have culture and guts, enough to be fun and expressive of everybody's wholeness.

The apparatus will fall apart one of these days. Then what do we do? What do we say to our neighbors?

Puppetshows are not tools for speeches, they are God's music, eternal hands, faces from inside. They can't be used.

Puppets moving, and we serving their moves. Puppets speaking our language, and us listening and sticking our thought into their words, that is our relationship.

What can a puppet do? See to it. Study its ways diligently, tickle it, shake it, walk it up-hill and down, deliver it, knock on a door, let it fall, rise!' — (Schumann, *Bread and Rose-buds*, newsletter, November '72.)

12. Techniques of celastic molding by which it has more influence on the final appearance of a mask (the mold for which may still be by Schumann) than normally. Also, some people – Bill Whelan – were allowed to make certain molds, for experiments at least:

'A group in the workshop was preparing the clay mold for a new Uncle Fatso head. They were experimenting for the first time with the use of Fibreglas for building masks.' — (Rough, *The Bread and Puppet Theatre, Dramatics*, December, '73.)

13. '(Elka: You'd come to Cate Farm with a small group of people with whom you worked, if not for a long time – some of them you had only known since the '69 tour, but you'd worked very *closely* with them and somehow there had been a mutual agreement, a desire to work together, but towards the end of this stay in Cate Farm – '73 and '74, people were joining the theatre you didn't know at all, friends of friends.) There were

and boy-friends had swollen the group even beyond the size that after the deflation[14] following the circus and *Birdcatcher* inflation the big shows of '72 had resulted in, and within this bigger group the hold of the work ethic and of devotion to Schumann's projects had weakened and the commune's social life[15] and doing your own thing had become important. There was no way for Schumann to go along with this, a commune to him was a monastery, and the only gospel around it could be devoted to was his.

---

people in the company that I didn't want *in*, that just had *slipped* in as boyfriends or girl-friends of somebody else and I did *not* enjoy that company at all. And that happens off and on.' — (Schumann, interview, '79.)

'I remember we had had this meeting about Cate Farm was getting so crowded. It was this very open policy where almost anybody seemed to come and move in. It wasn't quite like anybody felt they could walk in and move right in but they would ask can I join the company and if they'd ask Peter, "Could I join the company", he would often tell them to talk to the other people and see what they said. And the person would then go to some puppeteer, maybe someone who also had just recently joined the company and said, okay with you. Or Peter says its okay if it's okay with you, and then it would be interpreted as go-ahead. But anyway, at that point there were several pupeteers – I guess Mark Dannenhauer was the main one who wanted not to tour so much but to do more farming, more – do the sugar bush and planting. He collected a whole lot of literature on soil and conservation and – so he and another group of people moved up here (to Glover, in the summer of '73 (SSB)) and it was a way to relieve some of the house pressure off Cate Farm.' — (Elka, interview, '83.)

For Schumann the problem was who was there and what were they doing. Being surrounded by congenial co-workers, i.e. a followership, was as important as having a family. But for Elka, having to live with all these many – more and more – people was a nightmare:

'But I think the life in Cate Farm was – the having to deal with so many people and live with them and not being able to get away . . . towards the end, I think, before we moved away, our children made an adjustment to this kind of a life and kind of formed together with some of the other children there a kind of, a pretty sturdy little society of the kids and they began to like claim a part of the driveway for basketball playing and do things but I think for quite a while they really felt sort of sat on by the whole life of the theatre and those things that were happening there. But certainly our living situation was quite different there and it was just really small, and the many people who came – it seemed, you know, really hard to stop growing.' –— (Elka, interview, '83.)

14. 'That was actually a different group after the *Birdcatcher* because a lot of the *Birdcatcher* crew was gone. Either out of college or done with the theatre for whatever reason, had had enough, and it was, you know, like a new start and things I think had settled down into – living arrangements and the whole conflicts. Murray was gone. You know. Things had really made a transition. Sue Bettman was gone.' — (Konnoff, interview, '83.)

15. 'Our situation had become unsatisfying. People were too dependent on me and our community was too settled – people didn't want to leave it and others couldn't come because of that. It was like a club or any small, closed society after a while. It wasn't healthy for the work: you had to keep dealing with personal problems, with why people had joined the group and why they wouldn't leave, instead of with what you wanted to work on. An easier, looser situation has always suited our way of working best.' — (Schumann, interviewed by Malcolm Hay, *Our Domestic Resurrection Bread and Puppet, Revived. Alternate Theater*, May '76.)

He needed an exploitable labor force. In New York City earlier, the shared political cause and his puppeteers' ability to make or somehow obtain enough money to get by on on their own had in conjunction provided the solution. The solution to how to stay outside the System and yet get a lot of help. At Goddard the well-defined anti-war cause was gone, commitment had to be to his art and to a far less well defined only vaguely political mission. Workshops with students — with their own interests and scholastic obligations and mostly on pseudo-hippie trips — didn't generate the mobile, devoted and skill-acquiring labor he needed. On the other hand, settling puppeteers on Cate Farm, growing vegetables for self-consumption, and money-making tours didn't quite make up for what he didn't get out of the students — the college was good for only so much support, and local jobs were scarce or non-existent. The Cause being (at this time even in his mind) vague, the kind of people that would for the sake of art work their arses off and be committed were also the kind that wanted to do their own art. Moreover, to make the arrangement palatable, it had to have the aspect of a 'commune'. This was the real rub: he could not tolerate having the communality extend to the art. But then there wasn't really any 'commune'.

The resident group was his responsibility and its size was a financial problem not much diminished by horticulture.[16] Touring was the only way the problem could be dealt with. Now touring was something that as long as there were no people-problems Schumann liked and not only liked but believed in: it was the puppeteer's way of life. The big shows Schumann

---

16. 'This has been our third summer of gardening. We certainly had fresh food every day all summer long, from the first radish in late May until cabbage and corn season, plus a big freezer full of wonders, plus beets, squash, pumpkins, garlic, potatoes stored throughout late fall, plus tomatoes on the window sills, plus five bushels of apples sliced and strung under the ceiling, and more. We still have a lot to learn to provide for our large lunch- and supper-tables.

Since our cash is from puppet shows only, the schedules of garden and theater experience difficulties with each other. Our system of chores changes frequently. Our organization is as yet uninvented.' — (Schumann, *Bread and Rosebuds*, newsletter, November '72.)

'The 16 'hard-core' members and seven children have lived since 1970 in nearby Plainfield. Some 12 stay in a single family dwelling on a large farm . . . owned by Goddard. 'We have,' says Mr. Schumann, 'two houses. One is little, that's where I live with my family . . . In the same building is a second house, with more rooms, where the puppeteers live. And somebody has a chicken coop that's rebuilt . . . and it's warm, it's a good place . . . and there's another little room, in a barn. And then in the summer we have a big tent, and we can house more people that way, or in another barn, where there's some space.' A few members live in the town itself. 'We never imagined that the economics would be so disastrous. And that it would be so expensive, just living expenses. Even with . . . a lot of gardening. Between dentists and shoes and warm winter clothes and electricity and phone bills . . . it's disastrous, it's disastrous, it's just awful.' The group meets (the challenge) largely by travelling with their productions. 'We don't have any support, we live on the money that we make with puppet shows. So we figured last year we travel-

craved had big casts, however, that ate up the profits. He solved the problem (from *Stations* onward) by touring with less people than he needed, relying on the local recruitment of volunteers. But this not only limited tours to places where the volunteers were available, and to stays sufficient to rehearse them, but apart from the onerousness of continually instructing new people, made tours unpleasant by giving rise to a new problem: the volunteers, discontent with the hurried and mechanical rehearsals they were subjected to, especially when, as typically was the case, the situation had been presented to them as a 'workshop' one, tended to want to be paid: the troupe members were, why shouldn't they be?[17] Schumann, uneasy to begin with about touring for profit rather than or rather than only for spreading the good word, feeling bad about *having* to tour,[18] and disliking having to perform chiefly for audiences that could afford paying him what he needed,[19] grew disgusted with tours, and ended up hating the one at the end of '73. He resolved, during it, to disband the group and announced this on its return: they would still do a circus together in the

led probably . . . six months.' — (Sterritt, *Many-sided Bread and Puppet Man, Christian Science Monitor*, Feburary 8, '73.)

17. Cf., in my discussion of *Simple Light* touring supra, the quote from Schumann, interview, '79 on this problem.

18. 'What it was was that we had become a company so big and so unorganized, we were so undefined — who belonged to it and who didn't — that we found ourselves in the position of having to make a lot of money to support everybody, even though comparatively, when we compared our spending with other communes that we knew of, we were way lower and way cheaper in living expenses than the other people we knew of, in that area, with dentist and doctor and all that included, quite a bit of spending for at least 20 people. (Elka: 15 — on those tours.) Yeah, but count the people who stayed at home. There were at least 20 to be supported. So that was *hard*, and the money-making became important at that point — it had never been important at that point — it had never been important before, really, that was the first time it was a real issue — travel for money-making.' — (Schumann, interview, '79.)

19. 'In the middle of the European tour in the winter of 1973 Schumann announced that he would disband the company the following summer, because the communal company, too, had begun to impose its financial necessities and was shoving him into the pattern of the professional theater world which he was trying to avoid.

I don't like the general situation of theater that one gets oneself into when one becomes a professional recognized theater . . . and then responds to the channels which respond to that . . . that ask for that type of theater. In other words, when we go to perform both in this country and in Europe, we would very much like to perform for people cheaply, in our places rather than in the halls of fame of theater . . . but we end up playing in a lot of professional places . . . for bored high-ticket people. A lot of things happen that we don't agree with, but we do it because this is our contract. One gets involved in this and loses control of the creation of that place where one performs. Theater production as *we* understand it, is that one creates that place oneself. You don't assume that because one pays $3 what they see is theater. You want to be able to create a surrounding that you create for them . . . not one that is 'just there.' And that is not possible when you are part of an organization travelling and performing wherever you are invited.' — (Barab, interview, '74, *Country Journal*, Plainfield, Vt., quoted in Goldensohn, *Peter Schumann's Bread and Puppet Theater*, '77.)

summer, but that would be it. No more company.[20] This also enabled him to leave Goddard, which he decided to do at about the same time, though his wish to leave Goddard may also have been for something in his getting

---

20. '(Elka: After the *Simple Light* tour is when Bill Dalrymple was killed. He was on his way to do a workshop in a factory in Switzerland.) That's right. He was killed at the end of that tour. So there was a great confusion at the end of the tour. But already in France we had decided that this would be the last tour, that the theatre would disband after that. (Elka: How did you announce it? Did you just say on that last day that was going to happen? Or did you discuss it?) No, I discussed it with people. (Elka: Did you have support for this decision or were people dismayed?) I had only two people who were intelligent and were friends with me to discuss it with and that was Marc Estrin and Bill Dalrymple. And they both agreed. (Ephraim: You said you didn't want a theatre anymore?) (Elka: No – did you?) No. I wanted to disband a company that made its livelihood on doing theatre performances. I wanted to disband *that* company, and work again in theatre, and get a group of people together who wanted to *do* what they did – and then *maybe* make some money with that, but not be running an organization with the obligation of having to feed twenty people . . . but also around them the people who have been working in the theatre become more important – I guess, Paul (Zaloom) and Barbara (Leber) and Trudi (Cohen). (Elka: In 1973 those were all newcomers.) They were all newcomers. They didn't suffer too much from the split. *Nobody* did. It was good for them. It was a healthy move for *all* of them. It was like cold water on their heads. And it was *good* for them, they didn't have the problem of figuring out what their relationship to me was or anything like that, they just had to go on their own way. Lots of people started their own theatre companies and their own little groups. Quite successful ones.' — (Schumann, interview, '79.)

'For me, at least the way I understood that, from the other puppeteers who were working at the time, that there were certain people in the theatre who were hanging on, he had asked them to leave and they wouldn't, so he decided the only way to get rid of them was to dismantle the theatre.' — (Leherrissier, interview, '79.)

In fact, at the time the word was Schumann was through with theatre – would sculpt, paint. He may have thought so, momentarily, himself. But I doubt it. He probably intimated it to some because it made getting rid of them easier. And probably already had in mind a regrouping with certain ones – Leber, Bell, Cohen, Zaloom, maybe.

'I think it was Peter's thing. He wanted to change things and to disband. I think disbanded is a better word (than "dissolved" (SSB)), because he certainly wanted to continue doing everything he'd been doing. He just didn't want to – he didn't want this group that had . . . that decision came after they returned from *Simple Light* and I didn't know anything about it. It was a surprise to me . . . but I think Peter's feelings just got stronger and stronger at the tour and I think people came back knowing what his – about how he felt, and then he made a formal statement about it, what it was, that we would continue through the next summer and there would be the Easter tour to the south and there would be the big circus for '74, and after that the group would disband and we'd disburse the money that we had and disburse all the goods, except the puppets that – Peter got all of those . . . it was a pretty serious declaration but it wasn't impossible or like everything had to happen all at once.' — (Elka, in Schumann interview, '83.)

'. . . .there was, first of all, the big talk about this being the last circus. There wasn't going to be anymore Bread and Puppet so this is it. So there was a certain amount of – (Was that Schumann's own talk too?) Mm-hmm. Yeah. I think Elka mainly had those feelings and Peter was saying, "Yeah, this – okay, this is the last circus, okay, okay." ' — (Fernandez, interview, '83.)

268

rid of his people.[21] And getting out of the commune situation would allow for a rapprochement with his family, as would the greater isolation at Glover generally.

He, in fact, had Elka's parents to thank for the solution to his problems. Mr. Scott had bought the Dopp Farm up in Barton County – Glover the nearest town – in 1970. The Bread and Puppet Theatre – for a rent of about $1000. a year (Elka, interview, '83), 'just enough to cover taxes and insurance' – rented it from him in '73 to take care of some of the overflow on Cate Farm, and in '74 the Schumanns took it over, subleasing part of the house to two of the puppeteers (Mark Dannenhauer, Mary Eldridge) for another year. The Schumanns were Mr. Scott's tenants on the same favorable terms until 1976, when shortly before he died he made his daughter a present of part of the farm, with the house (and the workshed and giant barn, and the circus meadow, previously a gravel pit Mr. Scott had managed to exploit)[22] on it. (In '79 Elka sold the house, workshed and barn to the Bread and Puppet Theatre and gave it a 15-year lease on the circus meadow and the little pine plantation next to it.) So as of '73 Schumann knew he had a place to go, he didn't have to go back to the Lower East Side if he left Goddard.

His Goddard and group problems resolved by a fell swoop (Elka spent the spring of '74 also up on her parents' farm), Schumann, though now facing the problems of no puppeteers after the circus – and, as it turned out, not much else either: tools and household goods were divided up among the puppeteers, and so was what money there was[23] – could settle

---

21. '(Elka: And during that year was also when we rented Glover as a place for the puppeteers who wanted more independence, and wanted more autonomy as a place where they could live and work.) That had already happened, before we went on the tour. (Elka: that was part of this movement of people, more and more people.) It was *more* than that. We also felt this is enough for Cate Farm, we shouldn't accept these services any longer, we shouldn't be dependent on the college anymore, we don't want to offer them any more, and we want to *split* and we do one last *event*, and we offered them that last event as a source of money-making or anything they wished. They did not accept, and so that's what we did. So there was a circus there and after the circus we said bye, bye, and we went here.' — (Schumann, interview, '79.)

22. 'Elka's father, the lone-wolf, wine-connoisseur Time Inc. troubleshooter and correspondent – who had become such a contrast to *his* ascetic, back-to-the woods but still Marxist father – also decided to buy a farm, the Dopp Farm, which coincidentally was only forty miles north of Plainfield, in Glover. With his 260 acres he did do one thing differently from the counterculture, however, he set about mining his hayfields for gravel to sell to the contractors then constructing Interstate 91 where it swoops through town, thus providing his anticapitalist son-in-law with the supremely suitable stage setting he uses now.' — (Hoagland, *Let Them, Vanity Fair*, '83.)

23. '. . . and the puppeteers split the properties that the theatre had (Elka: And the money.) . . . and the money the theatre had made up until that time. (Elka: Down to everything.) Down to *everything* and that was it, and we started anew when we moved here. We didn't

down to work. And in fact, though '74 was a somewhat thin year, and started slowly, it was a year of promise, for he solved his main problem, the problem of what to say.

He in January '72 was one of 'Ten Independents', 'artists of strong and adventurous individuality whose involvement with life and the world is consuming, and who see form as their means for embodying and communicating that involvement, not as a more or less absorbing and even sensuously rewarding studio game' (Genauer, *Art and the Artist, New York Post*, January 29, '72) to contribute to a group show at the Guggenheim Museum – a Last Supper and a 'tophatted audience leaning ... over the ... balustrade' (ibid.), his first sculpture show I believe, other than the *Vermont Paper Maché Cathedral*, since 1962. Soon after his return from Europe, February 14-24 ('74) he had another show, entitled *Meadow's Green*, this one at the Goddard Library, redone, apparently, with a performance frame – there were curtains over the exhibits and Schumann playing the violin and Axel Gros as Dancing Bear guided the visitors from one to the other, unveiling them, on the occasion of a Bread and Puppet Theatre visit to New York to do (April 24-May 5) the new *Grey Lady Cantata #IV*, and again in September at the uptown Hunter College Arts Gallery in September: 'a weird showing of the art of paper-maché ... bizarre puppet creations, as well as dozens of smaller reliefs of figures' (*New York Times, Going Out Guide*, September 9, '74). In the summer there was the first circus since '71, the year's important event, since it was with it that he found the solution to what I just called his main remaining problem at the beginning of the year, that of what to say, namely that though Good always defeats Evil – as in his '72 spring show Winter defeats the River's love for the Lake – the defeat is never final because the struggle is cyclically eternal – there is always another spring; and at the end of the year he put together his *Grey Lady Cantata #5*, for a Christmas and goodbye offering to and at Goddard. Otherwise that year, he moved, after the circus, all his puppets to his and their new home and, with the help of Carlene Fernandez, the only puppeteer invited to come with him, which didn't help his other remaining problem, that of his relations with Elka, installed them as a permanent loan exhibit in his new barn.

---

even have tools at all anymore because the tools had been given up. (Elka: That's right. (Laughs) One person – Paul – got the table saw, we got the freezer.) See, we couldn't make the show without the freezer too easily, but without the chainsaw it was harder.' — (Schumann, interview '79.)

Part VI.
1975-'78. The Initial Dopp Farm Period,
or The Celebration of Nature.

The puppet factory on the farm, an isolated unit of production. Performance as community festival, ecumenical and ecological, a pantheistically religious celebration of the return of all things: a hosanna to living nature. Theatre as communion. Gesture: leading a congregation's hosanna to the world. Paradigm: the July 4th celebration. Contradictions: a communal work on a communal product; collective work on an individual's product; hope and the death of all things in the cycle of recurrence.

> 'O Hoffnung! holde, gütiggeschäftige,
>> Die du das Haus der Trauernden nicht verschmähst,
>>> Und gerne dienend, Edle! Zwischen
>>>> Sterblichen waltest und Himmelsmächten.
>
> Wo bist du? . . .
>
> Im grünen Tale, dort, wo der frische Quell
>> Vom Berge täglich rauscht und die liebliche
>>> Zeitlose mir am Herbstlicht aufblüht,
>>>> Dort, in der Stille, du holde! will ich
>
> Dich suchen . . .'

(F. Hölderlin, Bitte.)

Contents: Part VI

1. The nature of his work during the initial Dopp Farm period, '75-'78.

During this third period, Schumann is oriented neither toward moving the masses to action morally, nor toward dramatizing the human condition as he (glumly) perceives it, but toward communion in contemplation of shared fate, viz. individual extinction and obligation in the succession of generations. The overall aim is uplift.

'. . . und die zuerst
　　Das Mass verloren, unsere Väter
　　　Wussten es nicht, und es trieb ihr Geist sie.

Zu lang, zu lang schon treten die Sterblichen
　　Sich gern aufs Haupt, und zanken um Herrschaft sich,
　　　Den Nachbarn fürchtend, und es hat auf
　　　　Eigenem Boden der Mann nicht Segen.

Und unstät wehn und irren, dem Chaos gleich,
　　Dem gärenden Geschlechte die Wünsche noch
　　　Umher, und wild ist und verzagt und kalt von
　　　　Sorgen das Leben der Armen immer.

Du aber wandelst ruhig die sichre Bahn
　　O Mutter Erd! im Lichte, Dein Früling blüht,
　　　Melodisch wechselnd gehn dir hin die
　　　　Wachsenden Zeiten, du Lebensreiche!'

（F. Hölderlin, *Der Frieden*.）

The vehicle is what he calls 'circus', an annual local celebration in the landscape, to which in principle the community of all mankind, in practice the neighbors (widely conceived) are invited: to participate, by time, labor, money, performance or inwardly. The event is (is to be) a community gathering around spectacles. Of these, the elements of the circus, there are three, the ones first separated and defined in the concluding circus of the preceding period: the circus proper or silly circus, designed to purge of care and hostility; a morality play in Christian terms presenting the moral challenge presented mortals by their finite life, structured by choral interludes evoking the transcendentality of this challenge; and a 'pageant',[1] designed to place the crimes of mankind against man and nature that constitute the history of mankind and American history in particular and that

---

1. '5. A spectacle arranged for effect; esp. a procession or parade with elaborate spectacular display 1805. Since 1907 applied to celebrations of local history consisting of a series of representations of events and personages connected with the particular place.' — *(The Shorter Oxford English Dictionary.)*

define modern civilization in the consoling perspective of nature's everlasting bounty, natural life's self-regenerative — resurrective — power. These spectacles are complemented by evocation of the civic responsibility of men toward men, i.e. political skits (initially still part of the circus proper, then more 'sideshows') and by a sharing of bread and garlic.

Almost all of Schumann's shows during this period were designed for and first produced at these circuses. Of these shows, however, there are three, the afternoon shows *Carmina Burana* and *Masaniello* ('77 circus) and *Wolkenstein* ('78 circus), that seem not quite to fit into the category of morality play, and that do not quite have the format of those that do (*Jesu Meine Freude, Joan or Arc* and *Ave Maris Stella*, nighttime performances in the pine woods at the circuses of, respectively, '76, '77 and '78). I didn't see and don't know what to make of *Carmina Burana*, but *Masaniello* and *Wolkenstein* differ from the three morality plays by being not glorifications of Woman, but portrayals of male sinfulness, of the (not too successful) struggle to face up to the 'moral challenge presented mortals by their finite life', rather than of a simple and successful response to it, which latter is shown by those three morality plays, as by their predecessor, *Jephthah*. These negative morality plays (the ones about men) lack the concentrated inwardness and intimate form of the positive ones, they are epic, colorful, boisterous and large, in spirit and in form.

Unlike the pageants, the morality plays, both positive and negative, were for Schumann significantly if not primarily, experiments with music, and by the relative uniformity of their solution to the problem of according to music a powerful and self-contained yet integrated role, along with the pageants distinguish this period from the others. As Christian treatments of the challenge of individual morality, they complement the pageants' pantheist treatment of man's place in the world of nature: an eschatological pendant to their soteriology.

The pageants and the musical morality plays were Schumann's discoveries and artistic successes during this period: the silly circus or the circus proper, significantly accented by the presence of the Garbagemen, the acquiescent modern proletariat, was his failure: he failed to find an adequate puppetry mode for it, and he failed to attain the objective he had pursued since the circus of '70: to make it a vehicle for social satire, for a critique of contemporary America and/or 'modern civilization'. If he had succeeded, silly circus or circus proper would as treatment of Man in Society or of Man's Social Failure logically have lead up to and complemented morality play and pageant. To portray social life as a grotesque and fantastic comedy, whether hereby accepting or condemning the status quo, has in literature, painting and theatre been attempted frequently and often successfully: the idea is not outlandish. Perhaps Schumann is not lighthearted enough; and/or insufficiently vicious.

Schumann's work during the four years I have grouped into this period, though in '78 there were signs of change, was distinctively characterized by its positive outlook: the positive outlook given the circuses by the pageants. The man seemed actually cheerful! And not just because he was working well, etc., but in contemplation of the world. The rationale, as far as one could make out, was not just an analogy of the cycles of individual life, group life and of the life of nations with the seasonal cycle of life in nature, but his perception of a real and reassuring connection between man and nature: on the one hand, nature was bountiful and could be relied on to continue to be so, on the other hand, though man's political and economic aberrations were severe, civilization was not powerful enough either to destroy that bounty or definitively to cut man off from its benefits; and man's spiritual life could be counted on, the ill effects of civilization on it notwithstanding, to be perpetually regenerated by his relationship to the (continuing) life of nature about him, bound to affect him (in a sustaining manner) by his material dependency on it: this relationship being the chief or only and a sufficient source of spiritual health. This seemed the implicit faith and the message of his pageants during this period, though especially of the first three which presented the fable of the White Horse Butcher, the distinctive theme of this period, and was conveyed as much or more by their use of the landscape as/than by their fables.

His communicational gesture during his New York or '60s period had been confrontation with the challenge of a moral exhortation, during his Cate Farm or Goddard period, the presentation of a representation according to his views of what concerned him; it now became the offer of a joint consideration of how things stood in a large – and – comforting – perspective. His advice had gone from Resist! to Drop Out! to Keep up the Basic Values! – family, neighborliness, hard work, social usefulness, and though his two prior counsels still attached to this advice, they did so ancillarily and in the new form of a presumptive agreement on what was so and on what was right and what wrong. The audience now addressed was the community or neighborhood: which in principle was not bounded, extending not only to Quebec and even New York but to the whole world, but which, in terms of his assiduous cultivation of it was Nothern Vermont.

2. Puppets, masks, 1975-'78.

From a puppet sculpture in form tending toward elegance, in content veering toward the monstrous ('70-'74), Schumann during his first years on Dopp Farm jumped to lightness as form of gracefulness. The demons are gone, evil appears as white collar crime, as a meanness of the spirit by its heaviness contrasting with the gracefulness of what's natural. In the fourth year, the euphoria slips, there is a fall to the bland and pretty, terror and schizophrenia emerge. But the overall distinctive mood of the puppetry output of these years is gaiety and Olympian detachment.

There are more colors than previously, less black and grey, the colors are more delicate (with perhaps an initially marginal but growing tendency toward brightness and primary colors). The structures give an impression of airiness. The salient puppets and the new puppet types of this period are designed for natural settings: the circus arena and the hills surrounding it, the pine forest clearing in which at night the positive, or the forest-edge meadow in which during the afternoon the negative morality plays of this period are presented.

To a visitor of Schumann's circuses – the focal point of his production, with the 'morality plays' they comprised – during these years, certain puppet figures, recurrently appearing, stand out: the tall and slender White Angel of Resurrection, done by Schumann on stilts, in the repertory of images replacing the sturdily suffering Grey Lady; the gigantic but delicate, flower-bedecked Domestic Resurrection Deity; two figures framing the interplay (in the circus pageants) of some graceful herd of fragile, wild and innocent, white herbivores, typically deer, and of a dark band of men, criminal and disciplined, the 'Butchers'; the Garbagemen, dating from the previous period, but now only coming into their own, framing the silliness and politics of the 'silly circuses' with a small human ordinariness, counterfoil to fantastic and colorful, ornate and inoffensive huge beasts; and five huge white gulls, eerie and cold, visitors toward the end of the pageants, purifying the scene of ritual crime.

The bands, flocks, herds of diverse beautiful and harmless animals, birds of different species, deer, sheep, horses, cows, and fantastic, mythical or bizarre animals, solitary or in couples are distinctive to this period of puppet making. They provide an integral vision of nature – seen as harmonious and magical – not present in Schumann's earlier theatre, in which the animal kingdom had appeared partly in a perspective not too far from Disney's – the cutout donkey that was all poor Joseph could provide his wife with, the slum rats enacted by scampering slum kids, the huge pink Chicken Little chick, a dog on strings for a crazed nigger, the strap-on hobbyhorses of the early circuses, a 200-foot Chinatown dragon – or as something threatening – a throng of grey crawling beasts (on Dopp Farm

278

turning up as harriers and hunting dogs), a rushing crimson demonic bird with a demon rider, people-devouring smiling, elegant lions. A city-liver's anthropocentric and supercilious view. The sheep carrousel of the previous period provides an overture to the new vision: but it has as yet the character of a toy. These animals also provide a whole new set of movements and a new choreography. The new animals individually move in gentle abstractions of natural movements, and whereas his human crowds from *Totentanz* to *Simple Light* had moved in vicious and turgid agglutinations, the movement of animal herds now is choreographed as contrast to the drill-ground rigidity and brutal efficacy of the movements of their hunters, herders and butchers: by a geometry of sensitivity.

Three types of puppets are distinctive of this period: stilt puppets, kite or kite-like stick puppets, cutout puppets or puppets with cutout heads.

A stilt puppet is simply a stilt-walker, costumed and with a mask or puppet head, not infrequently, for angels or birds, with wings, attached not to the performer's back, but to his or her arms (or extensions of sleeves, or on sticks extending his or her arms), so that they enter into his or her movements. What makes it a distinctive puppet is that with the height of an over-man-size rod or pole puppet – the stilts vary in length from 2 or 3 to 12 or 15 feet – it combines the distinctive swinging movement of a stilt-walker,[1] and that its costume, while unlike the costume-bodies of rod or pole puppets of like height adapted to the human frame and firmed by a human body, also makes – or can make – use of the stilts' extensions of the performer's legs: providing a distinctive half-human, half-puppet silhouette.

The kite or kite-like stick puppet, carried aloft by two or more

---

1. 'Peter leads a hermetic existence, never discussing his work with anybody but his disciples; and one seldom meets him round about northeastern Vermont at the cattle auctions, the hunters' breakfasts during deer season, the demolition derbies at the country fair, where young farmer-loggers batter each other in junk jalopies, or at the tent for female mud wrestling, or the old-style girlie shows where "you can watch Sheba marry your next-door neighbor right onstage on the inside," as the barker on the carny platform likes to proclaim – all places where he could witness passions that would be new to him in the rural context and see new lusts unbuttoned and new faces. So, it was like him not to have learned about stilts simply by attending the nearest circus. Instead, while he was doing puppetry at Cate Farm, a visiting French mime (Claude Roche (SSB)) described to him how shepherds in the Les Landes district near Bordeaux traditionally used to stride on stilts over the rolling ground, stopping to rest against a staff with a seat fastened to it. The women herders even knitted in this way. And thereupon, Peter says, it occurred to him to adapt the craft of stilt-walking to puppetry. The accidental quality of his discovery, for a man who trusts and values accidents, made it feel all the better.

Stilts put Peter and his spectacles into an airier and more dynamic realm. His warriors became scarier, his angels more ethereal, his gods more awesome and supernatural, at the same time that his now super-abundant menagerie of animal masks ands puppet masks spread his field of concern to include the kingdom of nature.' — (Hoagland, *Let 'em*, '83.)

operators (the community of white-clad puppeteer performers reemerges into view during this period), normally a winged creature, bird or angel, is built with fabric surfaces or loose fabric suggesting, when it is moved along overhead, flight. The sticks or poles may be anywhere from four to twelve feet long. There is no center pole, and the sticks are uncovered.

The cutouts are in profile, of masonite, painted. While full-figure cutouts are rare in this period, there are two plays whose puppets have cutout heads.

The common character of all three kinds of puppets is their lightness, and a playful air to their fantasy.

The only distinctive trait of this period as regards materials is the use of wood — two-by-fours, saplings, branches — in the construction of puppet bodies: fabric-covered wooden frames carried by and/or strapped to the performers of animals, giving them backbone and body. Wood previously had been used chiefly either for the operating and carrying sticks, rods and poles, or as strengthening armature for puppets with large, heavy heads.

* * *

During the winter of '74/'75, Schumann was on his own up in Glover fabricating the paper maché half-relief figures of the story of the *White Horse Butcher*, among the little figures: a white winged horse and black-suited, black-hatted butchers.

He never did a winged horse puppet. Instead, when in the *White Horse Butcher* pageant of the '75 circus he as White Resurrecting Angel on stilts resurrects the slain white (wingless) horse — a development of his appearance in the '74 Christmas show as White Lady on stilts and mounted on a horse, saving the Grey Lady from the Dragon — the wings (made that winter by Carlene Fernandez) are under his sleeves, lace wings: a pair of wings that according to Fernandez (interview, '83) starts off the ensuing fashion of wings in his shows.

In May in California, for the first of his *White Horse Butcher* shows, called *Monument to Ishi*, he went into one of his punishing iconic orgies: a dozen or more woodcuts for Death or rather Dance of Death banners and flags,[2] according to him (interview, '79) his first, frequently used subse-

---

2. '*Banners and Flags.* Designs are drawn on pieces of untempered masonite (hardboard or utility brown board) about 3 ft. square. The part of the design which is to remain white on the banner is carved into relief using wood carving tools. Using a large rubber roller, the completed printing block is then inked with printer's ink to which a drying agent has been added. A piece of unstarched muslin or a bed sheet is now cautiously lowered onto the printing surface by two people holding the cloth by the corners. It is pressed onto the inked areas with hands and then rubbed with spoons, doorknobs or other hard smooth objects until the ink has come through in all inked areas. The banner is then removed and hung up to dry.' — (Th. Shank, *The Bread and Puppet's Anti-Bicentennial: A Monument for Ishi. Theatre Quarterly*, Vol. V, #19, '75.)

quently; three dozen or more delicate little triangular deer heads made directly over clay – the small ears erect, the black pupils looking at you seriously, mouths open in an unhearable remark, the white bed sheet bodies extremely long and ridge-backed, so that the herd, the twig-antlered heads extending the spines' horizontals, looks like wind-driven snow[3] four giant carton heads (furniture cartons) of Gods, the Gods of Greed, Stupidity, Cruelty and Pride, their faces those of cruel capitalists, disfigured by clownish noses, with square tophats of corrugated card-board, arrogantly pointing celastic noses, hinged, square mouths in which Punch and Judy might appear: they were pulled on carts, seated, their heads half their total height, or standing, their heads a third of their height (c. 15 ft.), dressed in black dress suits, white shirts, black bow ties; two dragons for pulling the Gods' carts, with carton heads also; a dozen hunchback witches with long hair of unravelled hemp rope dyed black, their masks, made in plaster casts, expressionistically modified Noh in style. These witches' masks had mostly been originally intended as masks for 'Butchers' and as Schumann had intended these to be bearded, he had left out their mouths: when you look at them you realize why these women turned witches: they resented nature's little joke in depriving them of mouths. Schumann decided to use these masks for witches because of their mute look. Up to then, Schumann had had only one witch's mask, made in '64 or '65. But I don't think he used these new witches' masks very much. There were 21 'Butchers' in *Monument to Ishi*: they wore no masks, they had celastic noses, black beards and tophats that had skeleton

---

3. In the '81 Glover pageant, they were very white and walked in a dense clump to the sound of bells as though a herd of sheep at Angelus. The long curves of their high backs are due to their main poles being saplings. The poles rest on the operators' heads, and the operators hold up the pointing, thirstily extended heads from additional small poles, little handles. Schumann has sacrificed a bit of young pine forest for their skeletons. — (The airily light skeletons of the deer, tundra animals, are in stark contrast to the rigid, crude, carpenter-angled and because of the abundance of the wood, relatively heavy cow-skeletons – a different animal.)

The sheets around the neck, presumably to see through, make a fine pattern. At that pageant they were all operated by young, reasonably pretty (of course invisible) girls – the master, when he can, assigns his puppets by correspondence. The deer were sniffing. They can raise their heads way up – nostrils 10 ft. up in the air. They did so in unison – then all collapsed sideways to the ground. Up, then slowly down sideways: a most graceful, a most gracefully sub-death. G. Himes in the February '78 Washington edition of the *Unicorn Times* describes deer in the '77 circus as having 'polished stump heads, charcoaled eyes, and twig antlers.' He speaks of them as 'reindeer'. The bells you hear actually are home-made chimes: 7 metal pipes of different lengths hanging from a pole riding on the left shoulders of two men walking one behind the other following the herd, striking the sus-pended pipes (three or four between them, the remainder in front of the front man) with ones in their right hands. The pipes are hung loosely by loops. Their intervals and sequence are thus easily altered. An ingenious instrument. Two men can also walk with two poles, one on each shoulder, the pipes hanging down partly in front of the front man, partly between them, so each can play a full set as they walk.

scenes painted on them. With the gods' carton box heads he reverted to a technique of '62/'64 – improvisationally, as a matter of expediency: I don't think he made further use of cartons in the sequel. The puppet stages inserted in them were a device going back to '65/'66.

Among the figures in the '75 circus: the dozen or so 'Garbagemen' made for and used in the *Grey Lady Cantata IV (The First Garbagemen Cantata)* of the spring of '74 and in the '74 circus (the first one or two had been made for the circus of '70); red stilted and winged birds, their wings on sticks extending their operators' arms, appearing only briefly, but made for this circus, importantly first used in the *Red Fire Bird Dance* of this circus' travelling indoors version at the end of the year; the giant 'Domestic Resurrection Goddess' (as presiding deity replacing the Father-God figure presiding over the '74 circus, whose head was the 'Godface' used in *Stations of the Cross* since '72), with its pretty pink fiberglass face and its hands of living branches, 'a beatific madonna with Buddha eyes, a Mona Lisa smile, and lightly rosed cheeks, her head and outstretched arms moved by eight-foot poles, her body consisting of four long white banners, each painted with a bright but simple oriental flower' (G. Himes, *Unicorn Press*, February '78 – Himes saw her in the '77 circus); 'Bulbhead Family' puppets used as clowns; five variously colored dragons, one of them large and green; a black man-high vulture with a small red head; a square-necked giraffe, probably made for the '71 circus, and if so, Schumann's first stilt puppet; the deer and witches whose masks he had made in California that spring; two gigantic white oxen; four white kite-type gull stick puppets, one of them enormous, its wing span around twenty feet, brought in at a run, swooping down and circling, this one apparently made for the '74 circus; a large white horse, built in the winter '74/'75, 'the first horse that had a body for two people to get in and built so that it was proportioned enough that someone on stilts could ride the horse, which was Peter – we put the bridle on the horse and really made it into a whole puppet by itself, just the cloth, a fabric body (no rigid sub-structure (SSB))' (Fernandez, interview, '83); the lace-winged white stilt 'Angel Resurrection' done by Schumann.

The Domestic Resurrection Goddess, now (undated) in the museum has a dress akin to that of the kite puppets, 3 vertical flares and sleeves like the wings of a glider plane. Her green neckerchief covers a small gasoline drum, placed horizontally over a sexagonal frame of 2×1s, perhaps 10 ft. across. The dress is suspended from this frame. Thin black poles hold up her hands: they connect with her arm poles. Her center pole up to her head measures about 16 ft., her mask is 5 or 6 ft. tall. Carried, she is about 25 ft.+tall. Her face, a full pure oval, has the serenity of a Noh lady's mask – pencilled eyebrows, a small nose, a small, cute pink mouth, elegantly rouged cheeks, but her hair is an oddly bushy disarray lending her a farm maid effect.

For the pine forest 'morality play' *Jesu meine Freude* at the July '76 circus he built 'quite a few' devils, but the rest of the masks and puppets were, Schumann thinks (interview, '79), 'possibly taken from what's hanging around in the museum'. But I noted: a white angel, six splendid Heavenly Body stilt puppets with flat flame-edged faces, three of them like suns, golden, three more, star puppets, one of them a small purple one, that were new to me. They have flat plaque heads (mounted above their operators') and slim costumes of fringes in the vivid colors of their heads, a combination making them linear and accenting their verticality, so that with them Schumann broke through into a creative exploitation of the stilt-puppet medium. By 'Washerwoman Nativity' (1979) he had them dancing, a further potential of theirs, fully exploited by '83: by Susan Dennison's dance as 'Black Demon' stilt puppet, a puppet in their stylistic genre.

The cutout figures for the '76 sideshow *The Mountain Man of Chile*, were except for Mary's donkey, the first he made:

'Just drawing on masonite, and you cut them out with a saw, and paint them and put some mounting on the back and hold them up and that's it.'

(Schumann, interview, '79.)

In another sideshow at this circus called *The Garden Show*, directed by Nancy Tyndall, but with set and puppets by Schumann, there were six White Lady rod puppets built according to Schumann (interview, '79), 'almost the first year' on Dopp Farm, i.e. in '75 or '76. They were the striking slender-headed, spindly-handed White Lady rowers in the August '76 New York City version of *White Horse Butcher*, but had for this show been converted:

'. . . this group of White Lady puppets were strange puppets because originally they had been built as rod puppets. Then we cut out the rods and mounted them on people's heads, but the fitting was so awkward that they could do only very few movements, so where the rod had been attached something was inserted to make it possible to wear them on people's heads. Then the vision was greatly impaired and the arms didn't quite fit because the rods were taken out of those arms also, so people now held on to these arms and these pretty awkward figures were quite beautiful . . . They were the attendants for a while of a White Lady . . .'

(Schumann, interview, '82.)

During the following winter cutout heads for the figures of a speechless musical play, *Joan of Arc* (opened February '76), very much picture heads – the play's visual relating to its musical dimension as illustration to text. The two-dimensional puppet heads (the puppet bodies' draped fabric more suggestive of motion than of body) function powerfully according to their pictorial nature. Joan was done by an unmasked performer, her face draped in white, stood out. The poor people of this world about whom the play initially seems to be were represented by small, horizontally string-

283

pulled figurines on the floor – the 'Johnny puppet' idea of '68, the string technique of '70 *(Difficult Life)*.

I know of no new masks or puppets for the '77 circus pageant, but for the 'negative' (or male) 'morality play', *Masaniello*, at this circus he built a variety of things, some of them of new types. He built 5 giant center pole puppets, stylistically new, colorful playing card personifications of social powers, but technically more or less like the center pole puppets of '66, 'way too heavy' (Schumann, interview, '79): the Queen of Spain and the Grand Duke of Naples, both blue faced and blue handed, each manipulated by five visible puppeteers; the pole puppet of a general, perhaps 12 ft. high, with the (green) mustachio'd face of Stalin and a single, sword-holding arm; a magnificent, only slightly smaller two-faced but one-headed puppet of an ecclesiastic functionary, priest in front, a red devil with prints of dollar bills around its neck on the other side, the priest's praying hands a separate Praying Hands puppet; and a super big, perhaps 16 ft. tall puppet, Our Lady, the true one (not 'my' Madonna), with a lace-framed golden face, her dark golden hands holding a baby. He'd made a black giant Madonna previously, and he made a green one subsequently. With these giant Madonnas of '77-'79 he finally exploited the full emotional potential of his processional puppets – 'Jesus', the 'Disciples' – of '63/'64 and of the Catholic Easter time processions that, with church statuary, had inspired them. The green Madonna with child, only slightly smaller than the bronze one, around 18 ft. tall, its shallow, perhaps six inches deep, but high, perhaps three feet high, head on a neck perhaps 4 ft. long, now stands in the Dopp Farm puppet museum, her green baby, its arms curved, lying on top of her large – perhaps 3 ft. long – green hands' uncurving fingers. Her dress is in varying greens. Her head, hands and baby are grass green with small five-petalled white flower stars here and there in the meadow. She is handsome, her face almost naturalistically 'painted' – sculpture, but as though flat and in a painting – her expression very vivid, awake, almost challenging. A head-kerchief is draped with some offhand coquetry around her not unhandsomely mop-fringed face. He also made his first all-wood puppet (except for the head), a Death Man, as tall as Our Lady (they dance together), his head perhaps 3 ft. high, but shallow, perhaps only a foot deep – narrow, black nostrils, stumpy white teeth, hung on his 12 ft.+center pole, all bones, strung-together pieces of wood, his limb segments peeled branches, his chest crate slats, a barked piece of wood his pelvis, his flat feet all toes, 1×2 slats a foot and a half long. His backbone pole is carried by one operator, two others each with two smaller poles moving his limbs – he moves like a jiggly marionnette, toy-like, but is frightening, his expression pitiless, ruthless, regardless.

In *Masaniello* also there was a set of masks not previously used: two or three dozen yellowish, light- and dark-grey (shaded), anguished-looking, about 2 ft. tall 'People's' masks, hand-held in front of the face by Masaniello as 'sinner', hand-held in front of the face and moved in unison by a crowd of performers, the 'masses'. These hand-held and -moved masks were a new device, used again in the '79 *Washerwoman Nativity* and, in a sword dance, in *Swords and Ploughshares* ('81) – their use distinctive not of this, but of the following period.

In the winter of '77/'78, puppeteer-less again on the farm, he made his third set of cutout puppets, i.e. of puppets with cutout heads in profile for *Ave Maris Stella*. In this play, resuming tentatives of '70 and '71, a group of Blue Ladies and a bird of paradise messenger were operated by strings from a bridge.

The next summer ('78) he built the many colorful Wolkenstein heads, portraits really, likenesses, his first, really, other than for some Nixon face masks of '71, of different sizes, some for dummies, used in the circus *Wolkenstein* that summer. Some of them were mounted on a demon's chin, at more or less right angles so the mask could be either a Wolkenstein or a demon mask. The actual mask is a double mask, and Schumann seems to have thought of Wolkenstein's 'outside' face, the portrait one, as ancillary to his 'inside' face, the demon face, face of the demon within him: which, the way the mask was used, was not visible to spectators.[4] A rare occurrence in his theatre, someone else's puppets were also used in *Wolkenstein*, 'tincan puppets' Michael Romanyshyn had made, 'tiny, little junk puppets' (Schumann, interview, '83) 'sort of imitations of Sicilian puppets – tin cans and wood and so on. They had battles on the table.' (Schumann, interview, December '82.) There were stiff, square chested white knights on spindly stilt legs and red horses in this circus' pageant, horned crimson demons with funnel mouths,[5] going back to the backpack Hornblowers of '74, a red demon on stilts, and, apparently – according to a Glover museum note – the Skeleton Death from *Masaniello* rode on a giant Skeleton Horse, made for this circus. This horse is one of Schumann's

---

4. '(Schumann, looking at photos:) – it's a *Wolkenstein* demon. These are portraits of Wolkenstein that I made underneath the demon face . . . the mask of the poet is on the chin (of the demon) – underneath the demon. So the real mask that people see – people never see this because it's used this way. See, the face of the demon is here, and the horns and the ears are here. And then underneath that demon is that Wolkenstein portrait. Inside demons. Here you see the sort of funnel-shaped mouth of the demon, and the nose is peeking over a bit – so the whole mask goes that way'. — (Schumann, interview, December '82.)

5. 'A lot of these Horned Demons have Wolkenstein portraits on the bottom of the horns. I wanted to create a whole blasting, big sound by having people blow these tubes that go into these funnel-shape amplifiers – we did that as part of the pageant. There were different ideas – of mounting them in the forest, and then, eventually they were walked on sticks, with a stick carrier and a bugle blower – a horn blower. That was their first use – I think they got only used in the June 10th ('82) parade again.' — (Schumann, interview, December '82.)

great puppets. Its essential frame consists of a backbone pole about an inch and a half across, about 12 ft. long, and two vertical poles tied to it, one 5-6 ft. long, near its rear end, one 3-4 ft. longer than that going up to the head. It has a ribcage and a tail. It is light and airy — made for motion (and is therefore not sculpture: which captures motion). Its head is almost wistful, its nostrils are withdrawn with something approaching but not quite disdain. Skeleton Men, jointed wood puppets in dance-of-death robes, arms and legs hanging loosely, jiggling when they were walked:

'. . . wood structures, their arms and legs are hanging from little braces that go up from a pole, and the head is not attached, it's just sitting on top so they can dance around. (Elka: It's sort of like a marionette, the joints and all, that's carried from the bottom instead of strung from the top.) And the hands don't get any operation, they just dangle around and move, and make that thing dance. For dresses, woodcut prints are used that are strung from the shoulder. That is one type of puppet that is used — for the last *two* years (i.e.: since '77? (SSB)).'

(Schumann, interview, '79.)

Their center pole is 7-8 ft. long, lifted up, the tops of their small black hats are 10-11 ft. above ground. They are made of crate wood, with jointed legs and arms, two- or three-toed feet. When marched, they are normally alternately raised and lowered, the bobbing of their white black-pitted heads and jiggling of their arms and legs a Hampelmann dance. Their costumes are ponchos of, front and back, black on white death-image/word prints, a costume first used in the '74 circus.

The first 'Washerwomen', peasant-costumed female performers with face masks, were in this show also grappling with the devils for Wolkenstein's soul, but they didn't come into their own until the next period.

3. Settling in. The country.

Schumann's situation once in August ('74) he had taken himself and his busloads of puppets up to his in-laws' farm was defined negatively by — as in June '70 — the absence of puppeteers (Mark Dannenhauer and Mary Eldridge were up there, more or less doing their own thing, also Carlene Fernandez, who got busy, once, which took weeks, the barn, dating from the Civil War, four stories high, over a hundred feet long, a thing of splendor, had been emptied of the hay in it — they ended up with a 14 foot stack — helping him install the puppets in the barn),[1] but this time also by the absence of a local pool of voluntary labor: there was no Goddard across the hill. He was really, though this turned out to be the case only until the next spring, on his own. And he was really out in the sticks, no Goddard library to perform in, no Goddard students and faculty to perform for. (Also he had no status, not even that of a 'resident artist', to his farmer neighbors he was just a weirdo foreigner from New York City. The farm had until five years before in a small way been worked by an aging couple as a dairy farm and for maple sugaring. The Schumann family during the years following in a still smaller way kept up the maple sugaring. But this was a long shot from making him a farmer.) Of course, a number of the puppeteers settled in the area, not in Orleans County, but in little towns not far away, kept themselves afloat.[2] And he still had good will and a name at Goddard — did his Christmas show there with students. But still.

---

1. 'I was there pretty much alone. Kenny Eisenbraun came for a period of time, like for a few weeks, and worked. At the beginning — I mean, after the move to Cate Farm, all the puppeteers helped move to Glover, all the stuff and busloads and, you know, people helped clear out the barn so we could put puppets in and a lot of sweeping (laugh), moving old machinery out and that kind of thing, then everybody left and I stayed. And I started working on the barn museum . . . Setting up the museum. A lot of it is still original from what we originally did. Mark Dannenhauer was living there with his little family and he did some of the setting up of the barn and the more heavy duty things . . . And Peter helped some. I mean, of course, Peter pretty much laid out the design. Like, "I think the red stuff should go here, and all these colors should go in this section," but I pretty much set up their arrangement and mounting on and stuff.' — (Fernandez, interview, '83.)

2. 'George, Barbara and Alexis live by S. Woodbury, doing small puppet shows in Vermont schools and Boston streets most successfully, as the Puppet Co-op. Sara and John Bell worked with them in the fall, now Sara's back at Antioch, and Paul Z. has joined them. Avram Patt has started the Barking Rooster Theater (with Carlene Fernandez, Trudi Cohen, and Margo for a while (she's in NYC now, in Chaikin's *Seagull*) and friend musicians.) They've performed in Appalachia and NYC, besides the Plainfield Grange, where most of their work has been premiered. Mark Dannenhauer and Mary Eldridge, who live next door to us, have their Northeast Kingdom Puppets, and do kids' shows around the state, complete with dancing bear, Punch and Judy and toy piano. At Christmastime they put together the old Bread and Puppet Christmas Story . . .' — (Elka, *A Newsletter*, February 7, '75.)

287

Dopp Farm is outside the place – a dozen or so houses along the highway, a nice big 'old-fashioned' all-round grocery store, a roadside diner, a taxidermist – called Glover, with a grade school and a town hall off somewhere – far enough so a modern person wouldn't want to walk there. It's only 30-40 miles or so from Plainfield outside of which Goddard is. If you look at the map you see that Stowe, one of the skiing-factory towns isn't that far away. But actually, in Orleans County – one of the seven counties making up the 'Northeast Kingdom' – in Barton town, off on the farm named for the man that married the daughter of the old-time family that settled the farm, you are far away. Schumann had moved from academe to Vermont. Or more precisely, to north-eastern Vermont on the Quebec frontier, home of an old-seated poverty, country where from the old time onwards houses were placed on the ground without much excavation or stone under them, put together with no time for an observation of proportions in their thin white shells, poor-soiled country with too much fold of hill and summers too short for paying fields, country where it didn't pay to lug the stones into stone fences. The merchants' village culture of 18th-century N.E. didn't reach up here, nor the 19th-century factory owners' red brick mill-town small-town culture. Big barns are a rarity. And the old-time poverty blends into the new – derelict gas stations, grounded mobile homes, tight little breakfast shacks, slapped-up motels. It is extremely beautiful country. The land itself is still to the fore, not just beauty on a car window, the woods-tinted ovals of the lakes, the froth 'of the stony rivers, the long backs of the hills combine with the weakness or if you wish modesty of the artifacts to give a sense of accommodation between man and place, as well as of the exigency of neighborliness. As settlement, some fifteen years earlier, in the Lower East Side of Manhattan had given Schumann a sense of the urgency and receivability of a strong moral message, so settling into this country made him feel that a hymn in celebration of working man's survival capacity in nature might even in 20th-century America not be altogether idiotic.[3]

---

3. 'We're living in the middle section of the old Dopp farmhouse that hasn't been inhabited for decades, so it's an experiment, to see if it's possible. Before we moved in considerable renovating was done, plumbing, wiring, some new walls and floors, but no insulation, and the cold seeps through the walls. A cement-block fireplace in the living room, a big old kitchen stove, and a stove upstairs are our main sources of heat, so you can imagine that the state of our woodpile is of burning importance. (Peter heats his next-door upstairs workshop with an Ashley stove, so on a cold day when everyone is home, we've got 4 stoves going.) Till late December we were quite comfortable, even when the temperature dropped occasionally to 0°-10°. But lately there have been long spells of −10 to −20 degrees, and the cold seems to accumulate: the windows ice over (what a beautiful gift these frosted-flowered panes are!), the beds are like snowdrifts, and house-plants freeze, the fire in the stove burns yellow and gives out no heat. We pull the table and benches over right beside the stove and huddle around all morning, blowing smoke signals with our frosted breath. Often on the coldest days it is also very clear. By early afternoon the house warms up from

Schumann didn't get to do *Jephthah* again, instead he toured *Stations of the Cross* (April 14-May 5, '75; Vermont, the Cathedral of St. John the Divine, in NYC, Montreal), but he did pay homage to *Ishi* in California. A. L. Kroeber's work on the many Indian cultures of California as reflected in his *Handbook of the Indians of California*, a classic, written like Josiah Royce's, Jack London's and Hubert Howe Bancroft's in the grandly free spirit of that state before the factories in the fields crushed it, is also a hymn to man's material and spiritual survival capacity in nature; Theodora Kroeber's *Ishi* is a memorial to the loss. The Indian had first appeared in Schumann's '71 Cate Farm Circus, then more prominently but as yet only as victim in his '74 circus.

---

the sunlight. And if you go outdoors, the cold keeps you moving so you have to warm up. Besides keeping fires going, there's filling the wood boxes, sawing and splitting the wood, breaking branches for kindling . . .

The winter and isolation bring us together in the evenings when Peter reads aloud. This fall we read Kroeber's *Ishi*, I. I. Wilder's *Long Winter, Huckleberry Finn*, and now are romping through Paris with the *3 Musketeers*, while I knit my dozenth pair of socks or mittens, at which I've gotten really good! Our trips out of Glover have almost stopped since the fall projects have ended: Peter's 2ce weekly workshops and my weekly chorus in Goddard. The Barre-Montpelier area sure looks like a big city now! I still occasionally make it to a Plainfield Word-of-Mouth concert, but the price of gas, bad driving conditions, and the time make these trips not easy. I really miss the singing, though we've started a little round and Sacred Harp group with a neighbor here . . . My parents are still in Connecticut and they visit us quite often, loaded with fancy food and useful presents.

Work and plans: A bunch of typewriter-type projects going, for we have to do things and bring in income, a stark necessity somehow not faced, or just cushioned, or not so sharp within the loose, confused, prosperous life of the big theater. We're trying to find a distributor, publisher or periodical for the little B&P booklets, for one thing. And in the summer we'll open the barn as a puppet museum, with a bread and banner store.

Peter just finished a new paper-mache relief series, single-handedly (with both hands, of course), pasting hundreds of figures in 'The White-Horse Butcher'. It will go up in Lyndon College next week, then Feb. 23-March 8 in Goddard, and then, hopefully, be exhibited in a few other places in Vermont. And now he's started rehearsals on small short pieces, which, again hopefully, we can find dates for in March in Vt. and Canada. (I feel uneasy with all these 'hopefullies' – man proposes, God disposes.) But here goes: we want to sugar in April; in May Peter's invited to the U. of California for a 2 week workshop. There he wants to build a pageant titled: Homage to Ishi; then put on 'Jephte' in NYC in June with a small puppet crew and professional musicians; then create a small afternoon circus here in Glover in July; then maybe go to Europe and tour and visit relatives. How many slips 'twixt cup and lip will there be?' — (Elka, *A Newsletter*, February 7, '75.)

4. The White Horse Butcher.

'During that winter, after all that moving, I made the *White Horse Butcher* things. I remember, during the winter, during the cold months, I did it up here in this room — Mary (Eldridge) and Mark (Dannenhauer) lived in here, in this part of the house, and *we* lived in the *next* part of the house, and the upstairs room was a studio. And I had a little stove in there. (Elka: You did *all* of it yourself. All the paper maché. No help at all.)'

(Schumann, interview, '79.)

The White Horse Butcher imagery came to Schumann in a dream (Schumann, interview, '82), but the dream may have included images he had created previously: the lanced horses of the '74 *Circus* pageant, the drummer in white starting off that pageant (his mask was the prototype of the later 'Butcher' masks), the White Lady on a White Horse that in his '74 Christmas play rescued the Grey Lady. The imagery and its theme dominated his work in its early Dopp Farm phase, last appearing in January '79 at the Brooklyn Academy of Music, joined, as *The Story of Her Horse*, to his play *Joan of Arc*. Ideologically and outwardly, the theme was the death of gentle wild animals, white deer, a white horse, caused by men: their capture and killing of them. It served Schumann as analogue to the fate of the American Indian viewed as natural man, of the effect of American business on American life, of the effect of modern civilization on life. The theme was analogous to the theme of *Hallelujah* ('72), his first ecological statement, and the imagery extended that of the action of Fatso and soldiery in his '60s street work on the saffron Jesus-disciples group or on a file of white Vietnamese Women or Ladies into an ecological context, to nature generally. In his spectacles during this period, the imagery often though not invariably, also comprises a White Lady, mostly Schumann himself, either a suffering woman in white who dies, or a Savior Angel, elevated by stilts, on a white horse, who performs an action resurrecting the dead animals — which may simply take the form of the performers emerging alive from their animal shrouds (Schumann letting slip out that he views performing his puppets as a small death). Some manner of resurrection normally followed the massacre in his spectacles; though not in his graphic treatments of the theme. I suspect that the suffering woman in white — she may also be a lovely virgin — though not the savior angel — was an element of his dream, but I couldn't be sure. The theme of this double figure — sufferer/lover or redeemer — comprises the ideas of suffering woman and of loving woman redeeming by love: the first idea an obvious analogue to the corralled, subjugated and slaughtered animals. The compound theme and imagery — butchery + lady — suggests an idea of nature as feminine and as at the same time victim and savior of man.

290

The *White Horse Butcher* sculpture he made that first winter on Dopp Farm — exhibited at Lyndon College and Goddard in February and March ('75), adorning Schumann's bread dispensary at the '75 *Circus*, under the title *Johnny the Horsebutcher* exhibited in its own tent at the '76 *Circus* — was a series telling the story.[1] The '76 *Johnny the Horsebutcher*, a series of half-relief works in black and white, small paintings, perhaps 12×12, with some of the figures in paper maché, standing out from the carton 2 or 3 inches, was the extended story of frolicking horses, of a black male figure's struggle with a horse (also a playing and love-making with it), of his killing of it. The final picture, by itself, was Pegasus, a winged horse. Pegasus, son of Medusa tamed by Bellerophontes, steed of the Muses, to the Romans a symbol of immortality, was a fighting horse, not the jaded nag spurred by poets that Byron mentions. But whether Schumann's winged horse was Pegasus I don't know. The picture-sculptures did not carry the 'outward and ideological' meaning of the theme in his spectacles. It seemed to express some personal guilty terror. This personal theme — one kills what one loves? the muse of the artist rides on his victims? — and the personal feeling are also conveyed by Schumann's beautiful '77 picture book, *White Horse Butcher* (cf. infra). I sense it still marginally present in the '75 circus pageant, but not in later spectacle versions of *The White Horse Butcher*. Schumann in his spectacles used the imagery to represent national guilt and the guilt of all men. It during this period in his work replaces the image of the crucifixion.

---

1. 'It was a story of horses running through fields and in the meadows and everywhere, and then people come in and start putting fences up around the horses and then finally they take one of the horses, a white horse, and capture him and take him to be butchered . . . And then when the horse is butchered the butcher took the form of the skull, or the skeleton. And then after the horse was killed there was the resurrection . . . No, not then (but in the later shows (SSB)), an angel, or whatever came with the wings and rode the horse, called the horse back to life. (I: But not in this series?) Not in the reliefs . . . Peter did most of them himself and very quickly, very rough. I mean not with taking perfect care to get everything right. And the result was a lot of texture with kind of wrinkles, and that didn't really matter because the main thing was the painting, so the building up of it was the relief for making the shape . . . Yeah, I mean because you looked at it — it was beautiful painting and then, okay, it was a relief and the paper machéing of it wasn't done like a master (laugh) you know, craftsman or whatever.' — (Fernandez, interview, '83.)

BREAD AND PUPPET MUSEUM PRESENTS:

THE WHITE HORSE BUTCHER

OPENING FEB. 23, SUNDAY 7 P.M. TILL MARCH 8
AT THE PRATT CENTRE, GODDARD,
PLAINFIELD, VERMONT

ALSO AT THE PRATT CENTRE ON MARCH 1ST, SAT.
AT 7 PM A BREAD & PUPPET
DOMESTIC RESURRECTION FILM

BYE

5. Schumann goes to California to rehearse his pageant.

May 9th ('75) we find Schumann in California:[1]

'That was a new project that was initiated by a teacher — Davis University. And — I guess what I did there was mainly starting a workshop, a building workshop using whatever I could find there — two weeks? During these two weeks I made all these *Dance of Death* woodcuts. (Elka: Weren't there any *Dance of Death* woodcuts in the '74 *Circus*?) Maybe I started them before, but I know that I did *most* of them there. No, I *started* them there. (Elka: And you made all these puppets.) And then I made the deer — the main production in puppets was the *deer*. (Elka: And you were on stilts in that pageant too.) Yes, there was a parade leading up to it and the end of that — it was in a building site where the large pit was dug, and four walls — four mounds were erected around them. Plus some gigantic building that was not — that never happened. And we performed inside it, and we used the walls. So we put the audience on one wall, on one side of it, and we used the other wall and the entrance. I had given them a list of what I wanted beforehand, but it was one of these gigantic colleges with a big theatre department and a gigantic workshop with a lot of overequipped stuff hanging around that they never used, that they didn't even *know* to use, they didn't know their tools, didn't know what they were good for — *incredible* waste in American colleges — and I just found out what could be gotten when I got there, and I found out how to find white bed sheets for the dresses of the deer that otherwise would have been thrown into the *dump*, materials that were used — we just found out about them when we got there. (Schumann is saying 'we' out of habit. He meant by himself. (SSB)) (Elka: You *had* sent them a pretty elaborate list of material.) Yeah, that's right, but it didn't include this kind of thing. So all the

---

1. 'Early this year, at the invitation of members of the University of California, Davis, the company undertook a two-week project to culminate in an "anti-bicentennial" celebration, centered on the person of the last member of a tribe of Northern California Indians, Ishi.' — (Th. Shank, *The Bread & Puppet's Anti-Bicentennial: A Monument for Ishi. Theatre Quarterly*, V/19, '75.)

'I have quite rethought my original plans, abandoning the idea of bringing a ready-made figured-out show and elaborating on it, and switching instead to a totally original "building and inventing" project.

For two reasons — the proximity of the bicentennial, and the geographical location — I would like to work on an homage to Ishi . . . Indian representatives just rebuffed Washington's offer for an active role in the 1976 festivities. Celebrating Americans would do good to remember the cause of the native Americans, and understand their own jubilee in the light of their forerunners' tragedy.

I am not proposing an historical illustration . . . but a free-form work on the inherent theme: peace of the Indians, war of the whites. 14 days should be enough to get this out-of-door puppet and mask, movement and sound piece, dedicated to Ishi, underway.' — (Schumann, letter of February 4, '75, quoted in Th. Shank's *The Bread and Puppet's Anti-Bicentennial: A Monument for Ishi, Theatre Quarterly*, Vol V, #19, 1975.)

I.e., he had contracted to bring a show, but didn't, and instead of a show about the last Californian stone-ager did the first of his *White Horse Butcher* shows, not a pageant, though he set out to make one, but an approximation to one.

printing and building — the printing of the banners were all done on bedsheets that were about to be thrown into the dump. So we just found out how many bedsheets go into the dump — and we got hold of them. And we printed on them. And we got the deer from them. The *celastic* was *ordered*, yes, and the clay was ordered — it was ordered from the pottery department — it was borrowed, and the cardboard was found — it was ordered. There was a lot of using what they had and improvising at the moment with what was there. That was a strange scene. Nobody knew how to work and what it was to work. Nobody had any discipline whatever. (Elka: But you made so *much*! in that short time.) Well, I started at 6:30 in the morning. And the kids came at 10 o'clock, or something like that, and I had most of the work done when they came. Then they came and I had to run around and show them how to do things. It wasn't exactly fun but it was probably typical for the West Coast kind of scene. (Elka: And you met several people who came here later — Nina and Mark.) Yeah. She was very helpful . . . she was one of the heads of the costume department. Everything was in some department. Took me time to find out how to deal with all that, but she did all the wigs and the dyeing of fabrics — I needed *dark* fabrics and she did that and the rope had to be unravelled, and she found all the girls that would do the unravelling of the rope . . . the witch masks were very important in that pageant. (Elka: You didn't take anything there, did you?) No. Nothing. Maybe my mask.'

(Schumann, interview, '79.)[2]

Shank's account[3] of the making of the *Monument to Ishi* circus uniquely illustrates Schumann's drive and flexibility and his organization and inspirational power:

'Formulating the Conception

He arrived by airplane late afternoon on Friday 9 May, having left his farm in Vermont early in the morning. I showed him several outdoor sites which I thought might serve the needs of the production, including the one he chose. It was an excavation dug for a building which was not built and had become partially covered with weeds. Its dimensions were approximately 97 yards by 58 yards, divided longitudinally at an angle by a mound of earth. There were also mounds of earth on each side of the excavation, and the depth from the top of a mound to the dirt floor was approximately 20 feet.

By the following morning, he had formulated the structure and chief images of the work and had made some notes. It would begin with all participants parading with banners, masks and music through the town and the university campus. The parade would end at the excavation and the pageant would follow immediately. The pageant itself would perhaps begin with the blowing of large horns made of plastic tubing and the waving of flags. There would be many Butchers with tall black hats wearing bearded masks and black coats. There would also be a herd of Deer with masks, antlers of twigs and muslin bodies. The Butchers would drive

---

2. On a 'total budget of $800', he made '136 deer, 21 butchers, 20 hardboard (untempered masonite) printing blocks from which over 50 flags and banners were printed, 16 hunchback witches, and four Gods, ranging in height up to 16 feet, mounted on two carts pulled by dragons.' — (Shank, *The Bread & Puppet's Anti-Bicentennial*.)
3. Copyright Th. Shank 1975.

the Deer across an adjacent field and into the excavation where they would be butchered and their antlers would be broken making cracking sounds. He was considering whether an Indian should also be butchered, but soon decided against it as too literal. Then, after all the Deer had been killed, there must be a resurrection because the particians can only do the killing with conviction if there is a resurrection. Wings made of rags would be given out to all of the people in the dead Deer and they would fly away. There would also be music of some kind and choral sounds.

This conception for the production had been developed overnight after having seen the excavation and surrounding area, and it was considerably different from the tentative ideas he had begun to form before coming to Davis:

"The Ishi idea came first, and I felt that to represent that, it would have to be animals. I would like to have used birds — carrier pigeons which the white man exterminated here; but I tried birds in the Circus last year and I didn't want to do the same thing."

He had mistakenly thought of the university as located in a kind of sandy desert and this suggested to him a herd of buffalo and the image of furniture being moved across a field. It is typical of the way Peter works to quickly adapt his conception to the space and to make major changes in the work if he is not satisfied. He does not persist with a plan when he senses that it is wrong. As *A Monument for Ishi* developed, many changes occurred.

Participants Start Working

On Monday 12 May, Peter met for the first time with those who were interested in working with him. He showed two films of the Bread and Puppet Theater — one of them about their work in New York City slums in 1966 and another about the Bread and Puppet Circus in Vermont during the summer of 1974. Most of those who would work with Peter had not seen his work before and they were especially impressed by the Circus film because of the striking images of giant puppets including a herd of horses and a flock of birds performing in a green meadow. Word spread and the film was shown at least five more times before Peter left Davis.

At this first meeting he also described briefly the proposed Ishi project. He explained that the participants would build in the shop and an adjoining room during the day, and in the evening there would be rehearsals of music or movement. Everyone was encouraged to bring as many friends as possible to the final two rehearsals. The performance would be about sundown on the evening of Friday 23 May. Many of the participants began working immediately on the tasks that Peter had prepared.

In the two days since his arrival he had carved grotesque skeleton figures on several three-foot-square pieces of hardboard to be used for the printing of flags and banners. Several people were put to work inking these printing blocks and printing them on bed sheets. Others constructed top hats for the Butchers from corrugated cardboard. Still others began making masks which at that time were intended for the Butchers. This was done by dipping Celastic in acetone to soften it and then pressing it into the negative plaster moulds which had been made over the clay models sculpted by Peter. By these methods, Peter had nearly complete artistic control of the results.

Each morning Peter arrived at the shop before eight o'clock; how much before is difficult to say because he was always the first one there. Except for perhaps twenty minutes for lunch and an hour for dinner he did not stop working until about 10 p.m. when he was one of the last to leave. From time to time during the day people brought him beer which he drank while continuing to work. In his room at night he would write ideas in a notebook which he carried — notes on a banner or mask design, for example. He would refer to these notes later as he worked on these aspects.

Building the Puppets

Because of his obvious skill and the fact that he worked harder than anyone else, there was no resistance when he demonstrated precisely how various tasks should be performed and was quietly insistent that shortcuts and sloppiness be avoided. He did not become a supervisor who simply checks on others and helps solve problems, instead he continued carving designs for banners, sculpting clay faces for masks, and then began making clay Deer's heads over which others formed Celastic for the Deer masks. Still other activities were added. Some began making beards for the Butchers by unravelling hemp rope and dyeing it black. Others sewed muslin to make bodies for the Deer, and some made wings from diaphanous fabric attached to wire frameworks.

A pair of large iron wheels and a large section of culvert pipe were in the shop and Peter decided they could be made into a cart and a giant drum for the parade. Soon a second cart was added, but only after their function had been altered. On a rubbish heap outside the shop he saw large corrugated cardboard boxes which had contained office filing cabinets. From two of these he made Dragon's heads to pull the carts. Four other boxes with the addition of Celastic noses and ears, became Gods. One ten-foot and one sixteen-foot God was mounted on each cart and provided the large figures Peter considered necessary for the parade. Two days before the performance he asked two puppeteers who had come to Davis to work with him if they would like to be inside the two ten-foot Gods and make a Punch and Judy show in the mouths of the Gods with their own legs becoming the Gods' legs.

Peter had made the clay models for the Butchers' masks without mouths because as bearded Butchers, the mouths would not have been seen. But when the masks were finished they looked like mutes and Peter thought it would be a shame to cover them with beards. So he decided they would be mute Hunchback Witches and carry clubs with bottle caps nailed to them. These "partial" characters would make a rattling sound while the Butchers "killed" the Deer by breaking their antlers. Their black robes, hunched backs and black hemp hair were selected because they looked good with the masks. Then, when the Gods were made, Peter decided that the Hunchback Witches should belong to them, the supporters of the power. They were used only in the parade where they walked on either side of the God carts. Instead of the masks originally intended for them, the Butchers wore large Celastic noses, black beards and black top hats.

Originally, when Peter had sent a list of materials needed, he had included red and burnt umber paint, but as the work progressed, he decided that everything in the show should be white, black or grey except for a little colour on the clowns. In the performance these colours were seen against the green weeds and earth of the excavation.

296

The first two rehearsals focused exclusively on music. Anyone who could play a musical instrument was asked to come. The first evening about a dozen people showed up with saxophones, recorders, harmonicas, a flute and a banjo. It soon became evident, however, that only four were really good enough to play together. Peter amazed everyone by putting on four-foot stilts and dancing to the music. At Peter's suggestion, a group began practicing hymns sung in four-part harmony from the *Sacred Harp* collection of religious songs brought to America by the Pilgrims in the seventeenth century. This group grew until nearly all of the pageant participants knew the three hymns sung at the end of the performance. The hymns were not sung for their religious value, but for their beauty.

On Friday night of the first week enough Deer were finished to rehearse their movement outdoors. Again Peter was on stilts, which again made his work harder than that of anyone else. His emphasis in directing the Deer was to get them to move as a herd and in slow motion. When the Butchers rehearsed, they were shown how to wave the bedsheet size flags in figure eights. In contrast to the Deer, when the Butchers moved, they ran.

At noon on Thursday 22 May, the day of the final rehearsal, Peter did a stilt dance on the central quadrangle of the campus to publicize the rehearsal and performance and to attract participants. The final rehearsal that evening was the first rehearsal at the excavation.

Two days earlier it was decided that the Butchers would not kill the Deer. They would surround them, but then a single mysterious figure with a black plastic sheet over its head and body and a rope tied around its neck would slowly and methodically break the antlers of the Deer after they had lain down. Peter instructed the person playing this role not to be vicious, but to perform the task in an efficient and unhurried manner. Now at the final rehearsal other changes were made. The spectators, standing on the east mound of the excavation, would first see the Deer a quarter of a mile away across a field to the East. The Butchers would run toward the Deer with their flags from a point southwest of the excavation. They would surround the Deer and drive them into the excavation. At the final rehearsal this action was performed once and Peter immediately announced that it should not be done that way. There were too many other things in the landscape, too many differently textured areas of ground, that the Deer and the Butchers would not get enough focus. He decided that all of the action would have to take place in the excavation. After visualizing it one way for nearly two weeks, he was able on only seeing it once to discover the problem and abandon the idea. Several alternatives were tried, all inside the excavation until the best solution was found. Then we had one run-through.

On Friday morning, while other participants worked on finishing up details of construction, Peter ground a bushel of wheat using a hand grinder he had brought with him from Vermont. This wheat was added to a fermented mixture made the previous week when a first bushel had been ground, mixed with water and left to properly sour. Peter formed the dough into loaves and baked them in one of the large university dining hall ovens. In the afternoon, he made aioli, a garlic mayonnaise, which required the beating of four gallons of cooking oil into seven dozen egg yolks. The grinding and beating were arduous and tedious work, but it was a matter of principle that he would not let anyone help him. The making of the bread and the aioli served after the performance was his gift to the participants and spectators.

Creating a Carnival Atmosphere

It was publicized that those who wanted to participate in the parade should assemble at Central Park in the town at 5:00 p.m. for a "talk-through" before the beginning of the parade at 6:00 p.m. University students and townspeople of all ages came to carry banners in the parade or simply to follow the parade in its two-mile route to the excavation. The San Francisco Mime Troupe provided a band for the parade and also were incorporated into the performance.'

(Th. Shank, *The Bread & Puppet's Anti-Bicentennial*.)

The show, May 23rd, consisted of a one-hour parade, and a half-an-hour spectacle. The spectacle translated a 'pageant' into a show in circus format in the 300×180 ft. space of a building excavation and ended with a resurrection stilt dance by Schumann, a resurrection of the animals previously symbolically slain, a miracle, and hymn singing:

'The parade, a quarter of a mile long, was comprised of the following elements:

1) A small truck with a piano and piano player.

2) Peter Schumann on four-foot stilts wearing white and red striped overalls, a badly-worn top hat and a long Celastic nose, accompanied by a small band of four people playing recorders, flute and banjo. From time to time he moved to other sections of the parade.

3) Several clowns (two of whom had worked with Peter in Vermont but were now living in California) with a baby carriage painted with sky and clouds which carried their equipment for the performance.

4) A two-wheeled cart pulled by a Dragon with four people inside. On the cart were two Gods. Inside the shorter God was a member of the Family Bathtub Puppet Theatre who spoke for the God and made his mouth open and close. Sometimes, leaving the mouth open, a Punch hand puppet used the mouth as a stage. The cart was surrounded by eight Hunchback Witches – six shaking clubs with bottle caps and two carrying signs naming the Gods "Stupidity" and "Greed".

5) Twenty-one Butchers in an orderly column of twos each carrying a flag.

6) Another two-wheeled cart similar to the previous one except these Gods' names were "Cruelty" and "Pride". A Judy hand puppet was in the mouth of the shorter God.

7) The San Francisco Mime Troupe Gorilla Band.

8) Approximately thirty banners carried by people who assembled at the park to participate in the parade as well as some regular participants.

9) One Deer and a little girl walking together. The girl carried a sign saying "A Monument for Ishi".

298

When the parade arrived at the performance site, the two carts were placed in the excavation at the North end so the Gods appeared to be observing the performance. The clowns, led by the comically officious Mr. Clack, directed the spectators to the top of the East mound where they stood or sat. An hour had elapsed since the beginning of the parade. The performance began.

"A Monument for Ishi"

The Clowns, including Mr. Clack and Fabian, are spread across the entire length of the excavation facing the spectators, except for Fabian who stands behind Mr. Clack, facing the opposite direction.

CLACK: Ladies and Gentlemen . . .

FABIAN: Ladies and Gentlemen . . .

(Drums and cymbals from the San Francisco Mime Troupe Band.)

CLACK: The Bread and Puppet Theater . . .

FABIAN: The Bread and Puppet Theater . . .

(Drums and cymbals.)

CLACK: . . . presents the nineteen seventy-five . . .

FABIAN: . . . presents the seventeen ninety-five . . .

CLACK: . . . first annual . . .

FABIAN: . . . first annual . . .

CLACK: . . . anti-bicentennial . . .

FABIAN: . . . bye-bye-centennial . . .

CLACK: . . . circus.

FABIAN: . . . circus.

The San Francisco Mime Troupe Band plays as the Clowns do tricks. Mr. Clack juggles as he walks to one of the Gods' carts where he rings a large bell signalling the entrance of the Deer and the Butchers. There are no more words spoken.

The herd of thirty-six deer enters the excavation in slow motion, at the northeast corner. Simultaneously the twenty-one Butchers appear running on top of the mounds to the North, South and West with their flags flying. They stop, evenly distributed on top of the mounds, while the Deer, moving as a herd, take about five minutes to reach the centre of the excavation. The audience has become absolutely silent and attentive, focusing on the Deer in suspense.

When the Deer reach the centre of the excavation a bugle is heard and other bugles answer at various distances. The Butchers run down from the mounds and surround the Deer, continuing to run in a circle around them with flags flying.

The large bell is rung and the Butchers stop. They stand in a circle around the Deer waving their flags in figure eights. Eight people with horns made of plastic pipe and the neck half of a plastic bottle form a circle around the Deer inside the circle of Butchers. The horns make a moaning sound as the herd of Deer mill around their centre pivot in slow motion for perhaps three minutes before they lie down.

The large bell is rung again and the Butchers stop waving their flags and hold them as high as possible as the lone figure in black enters. He moves slowly and deliberately to each of the Deer breaking the wooden antlers as the sound of the horns continues. When all the antlers are broken, which takes about four minutes, the figure walks away and the Butchers lower their flags and rest the poles on the ground.

Fabian, the naive sympathetic Clown, walks to the pile of Deer bodies. He looks at them curiously, tries to arouse one from its sleep, finally realizes they are dead. He runs sobbing loudly and rather comically to Mr. Clack and points to the Deer. Mr. Clack, the epitome of officiousness, blows his whistle and organizes the Clowns into a military formation. He blows again signalling the truck with its piano to move in towards the Deer. The Clowns march to the dead Deer, taking along their baby carriage with their equipment. With gestures Mr. Clack orders Fabian to dig a grave. Fabian begins with a spoon, then after further instructions digs with a shovel throwing dirt on Mr. Clack. When a small hole is dug, Mr. Clack gestures to Fabian to plant the tiny U.S. flag which is among their equipment. It is about five inches long and attached to a rope and pulley system on a pole about six feet tall. The piano plays an arpeggio as the flag is raised. When it reaches the top, one of the Clowns crashes cymbals made from garbage bin lids. The Clowns salute as the "national anthem", represented by a simple Bach piece, is played on the piano.

The large bell is rung and Peter Schumann on four-foot stilts, dressed as Lady Resurrection and wearing a mask, enters from the Southeast corner of the excavation. He dances to the music of the four-piece band of recorders and flute. At the end of the dance Lady Resurrection bows and the Clowns bow in return. Then she signals to the Clowns to distribute wings to the Deer. Fabian puts on a costume painted blue with white clouds that match the baby carriage. The Butchers have disappeared. As Lady Resurrection dances, Mr. Clack knocks on the head of each Deer and the person inside comes out to receive from Fabian a pair of diaphanous wings. The spectators are elated. The winged people form a group, and when all the Deer have been resurrected and Lady Resurrection has exited, they sing three hymns from the *Sacred Harp* book. The performance has taken twenty minutes to the beginning of the hymns. The lyrics of one of them, "Wondrous Love", are:

What wondrous love is this! oh, my soul! my soul!
What wondrous love is this! oh, my soul!
What wondrous love is this
That caused the Lord of bliss
To bear the dreadful curse for my soul, for my soul
To bear the dreadful curse for my soul.

While the hymns are being sung, Peter re-enters without his stilts and prepares to pass out bread and aioli. He gestures to the spectators to come down off the mound to get bread. They do and there is a tremendous spirit of community as they eat and talk until twilight turns to dusk.'

(Theodore Shank, *Theatre Quarterly*, Vol. V, #19, '75.)

300

The gods of greed and cruelty – of business and war – and of stupidity and pride – of suicidally arrogant modern civilization – are watching the slaughter of nature. Then there is a mock resurrection of souls. The message is unclear. Down, then up. Then a bit of that good old Christianity.

The core of the spectacle was the breaking of the deers' antlers – the little dry sound audible in spite of the moaning horns – and their resurrection by a dance. Though the details are Schumann's invention, e.g. that white lady does not to my knowledge occur in known mythologies, this is in the perspective of such as Frazer or Jung old and powerful stuff: in the tradition of fertility rite and of propitiatory offering.

Adam got to name the animals and the Levite priests of Jerusalem faked a contract with Jehovah assigning all living flesh to human exploitation. When, after having gotten down out of the fruit-bearing trees, our ancestors went to carve themselves out a niche in the foodchain of the African savannahs, though what kept them going was their omniverousness, what launched them on the adventure of culture was their carnivorousness, procural by violence of massive doses of protein; and when homo sapiens suddenly escalated that adventure into a quest for world dominance, he did so by establishing us at the end of the food chain, top carnivore, the world's flesh our diet. But the killing of living flesh is not like foraging for plants: the game makes the hunter understand that like himself it does not want to die; and the efficiency of our predation on the great ungulates put life by killing, itself a gamble with one's life, in perpetual jeopardy: whence a double trepidation, which the great hunters assuaged by art: the invocative dance of the shaman masked as the master of animals; images in the interiors of the caves won from the bears – images of the moving game, brought to life by the light of the ceremonial oil lamps: guilty apologies for slaughter and prayer for undiminished supply.[4]

Schumann in unmitigated condemnation had in *Cry of the People for Meat* represented man's subjugation of beasts as origin of man's violent domination of men; but now in the *Monument for Ishi*, who was himself a hunter, though by a delicacy of symbolism rendering its horror with even greater poignancy than it had had in *Cry*'s brutal scene, makes light of it: presents man's carnivore brutality to animals, still, by the watching gods, associated with his brutality to men, as in the course of nature: in effect an apology for all crime. The message that we have got to do it and that nature and we will survive is the same as in that paleolithic propitiatory

---

4. 'The little chirping birds (The Wren, and The Robin) they sing a meane; the Goldfinch, the Nightingall, they joyne in the treble; the Blackebird, the Thrush, they bear the tenour; while the foure footed beasts with their bloating and bellowing they sing a bass . . . Only man as being a wild and fierce creature, hath no certain note or tune . . . his instruments are the guts of dead creatures, a token of his crueltie, and the remainder of his riot.' — (Goodfrey Goodman, *The Fall of Man*, 1616.) – No certain note or tune: art.

magic. The comparison with *Cry* makes Schumann's shift in *White Horse Butcher*, of which *Monument* is the first version, and which dominates Schumann's production during the early Dopp Farm period, evident, but if we disregard it, *WHB* may also be viewed as lightly camouflaged cry of despair over the evil in men.

6. The Museum. An intense appreciation, though grim, of man.

The Bread and Puppet Museum in Glover had an official opening June 14th with 'displays of the theater's internationally renown (sic) giant puppets and special exhibits of masks and paper-maché bas-relief sculpture . . . as well as a variety of puppet-shows at 3 p.m.' (B & P handbill). A play with a title that may possibly have been *'Washerwoman Cantata'* was performed in the backyard to Sacred Harp singing, apparently one of the steps toward the appreciation of Working Woman (alias The Housewife) in Schumann's theatre, an appreciation that, starting with *Emilia* of '70, developing through the conversion of the negative view of job functions in the earliest circuses into a positive one in the *Doors* sequence in the '74 circus, subsequently became central in the '79 *Washerwoman Cantata – Ah!*:

'The Washerwoman here wasn't one of these sort of aproned homely figures. It was a big white and black head, sort of very almost not oriental but a very sort of smooth and simple face with small sweet features and attached to her was a big – I think at first it was a gray burlap bag and then that wore out and it was replaced I think with parachute fabric, so it was just a head and then a bag that was huge. And he wanted that to be like several people inside – one person manipulating the head and one person crouching in front playing the arms and she would be – I think the idea was of her scrubbing something, some fabric and the text that we used was in the local, a small classified ad paper called *The Green Mountain Trading Post* that would – a woman worked on it for quite a while, wrote – it's a bi-weekly, every two weeks – and she had written a very pretty article about how wonderful it is to gather strawberries in the summer and then open the jar in the winter and remember summertime. I think we tried using that and at that time sacred harp music was used in many, many things.'

The heroine of *Emilia* turned into a transvestite clown; the Washerwoman prototype in the '74 circus into a witch; this one, in the '76 travelling circus – Schumann as in '74 incorporating the chores of the living into a birth-life-death sequence – into a furnisher of shrouds (the text of the Museum-opening play being dropped as too insipid). Schumann's homages to Working Woman somehow invited his own negative comments on them.

His semi-retired puppets, grouped by color in the large stalls of the 100-ft.-long room turned it into a savage Musée de l'homme, no cathedral, but a museum of the pains and horrors of the human spirit, the barn became a cool hothouse in which, exotica, the flowers of his imagination bloomed in the barbaric splendor of paste and rags, painted and tinted, willfully alien in the 20th century: visions of a humanity, neither suffering nor aggressive, really, nor saintly, in fact neither moral nor immoral, nor

303

pitied by him, but individuals in the struggle of life growing from the inside out into the weird shapes of survival's glory: to be appreciated. A lack of judgment, and an appreciation not in his plays.

The scarlet and crimson demons and death-god of his *Birdcatcher in Hell* did the honors at the entrance at the top of the ramp. Looming, leaning, the dangling organic knots of vital energy, convoluted by the pain of life, and so caught up in the venture of mortality that each radiates an infinitely cold remoteness from all other beings, crowd out self-contained from the leaning/soaring walls, a heaven and hell of animals caught up in a ferocious struggle with their incipient or precariously established humanity, struggling to get out within them or not to be submerged in them, and powers at the same time, the pawns of time, but epiphanies of force, from tiny to giant, their intense heads and (sometimes) urging hands emerging powerfully from the ethereal tissues of their bodies.

7. The first Dopp Farm *Bread and Puppet Domestic Resurrection Circus.* That the evils of civilization count for little in the regenerative cycle of female nature is the containing effective statement of the event, guirlanding a condemnation of the American experiment. The framing statement, however, has also the aspect of a perhaps or also personal confession of guilt – sin or criminality. Confession and absolution. A revivalist meeting.

The event (Saturday, August 2 and again Sunday, August 3 ('75)) opened at 3 p.m. with a *Hallelujah* on the flattened bottom of Mr. Scott's gravel pit, now a grass carpeted amphitheatre, this opening taking a little less than an hour, continued by sideshows in the rolling meadows around it and within and at the edge of the small pine forest to the west above it – about a dozen and a half side-shows integrated into the event by that opening – and ended with what the program called the *'Circus'*, which was in three parts — (1) *Bi-centennial Spectacular*, (2) *Animals and Acrobats*, (3) *Dance of Death* (or *The White Horse Butcher*). This three-part Circus began at 5 and ended at dark, around 8. Parts (1) and (2) which by their humorousness were quite close to each other and could be said to have been the circus proper were confined within the gravel pit arena. Part (3) a self-contained piece in a different mood, serious, not circus, a dusk-time statement, though in part also within the arena, took in all of the surrounding open landscape. The Museum was opened at 9, and there were additional evening performances, a concert of 'Medieval singing', a 'soliloquy', *She Makes a Speech*, in the barn, by Margo Sherman, an outside shadow play, *The Story of a Thin Man*, there was no major play (other than part (3) of the *Circus*) by Schumann, nor any side-shows by him, though he co-directed two of these, *Little U.S. Dance of Death* (with Sacred Harp singing), and *Dirty Woman's Dream*.

The circus was rehearsed and made in July, beginning at the end of June, and its three parts were performed locally July weekends, e.g. (3) at St. Johnsbury and in Montpelier. About three dozen people worked on it, most of them staying at the farm through July, weekends there would be as many as forty or fifty, by the end of the month and for the August performances there were over a hundred performers, plus about thirty in the chorus (the Word of Mouth Choir) and band.

Perhaps as many as 7-800 people came for each of the two '75 shows, some from New York, the great majority, I would say, from Vermont, especially Goddard students and faculty, perhaps some N.Y. people from their places in Northern New England – many with their children, almost all by appearance hippies, nearly all in their 20s: very few, I would say, ordinary people from the immediate area. Guests and performers had an idealist, cultured, by and large academic aspect: more faculty than student, in spite of the low average age. Though there were not a few Jewish faces, physiognomically cast and crowd were overwhelmingly severely Anglo-Saxon: the incidence of faces not proclaiming, as do those of these two races, the anxious co-rule of intelligence, will and conscience, was slight. One topless girl (with a so-so bosom) was balanced by several clerical collars. It rained hard before and during the Sunday show, but even so about a hundred or two hundred people stayed, huddled into blankets etc. Cars lined the road by the farm. Above it, a field served as parking lot. A bell sounded the hours of the afternoon.

The theatre space was a vast oval grassy bowl, perhaps a third of a mile from the road, somewhat open toward the east, its sides gently rising something like 30-50 feet above the bottom which was perhaps 300, 400 feet across. To the west, a tall but still young pine plantation (sunflecked ground of pine needles between the serried ranks of slender trees) forms a dark straight barrier some 30-70 feet back from the rim of the amphitheatre. In the open – which feels *very* open – the ground is ridged, perhaps from past plowing, perhaps from erosion, small yellow flowers are everywhere among the grass. Violet hill ranges are visible in the further distance. The sky forms a vast pale counter to the bowl below. At the forest-edge of the amphitheatre, white flags with words and pictures of simple things on them wave from a line of 36 very tall, skinned-pine flagpoles. The audience was directed to sit on the incline below them. No buildings were visible from the amphitheatre, nor from anywhere in the ultimately vast performance space.

On the floor of the bowl (leveled during July), beyond a circular arena, bare and sandy, perhaps 120-140 feet across, delimited by a low (2 ft. high?) cloth fence, staked into the ground, stands, on an east-west axis, a huge (perhaps 30 ft.×60) brown, thrice-peaking tent, each peak surmounted by a small white flag saying 'Bread & Puppet Circus', its western exit into the arena covered by a violet draping. This is where the props and costumes are kept, and the backstage from which the performers issue and to which they return. There is sawdust on the ground below it, but you can't see that from the outside. There are green patches on its roof. At an angle to the tent, facing the arena, there is a band and choir stand, perhaps 25-30 ft. long, a trestled structure of planks and plank table-tops, over which a large, peaked and gathered white umbrella, made of something like parachute silk, seems to float. The stand is backed by two large flower screens, one all pink flowers, both abstractions of spring, strangely but not unpleasantly discordant spots in the vast calm cool light green landscape. Two parallel lengths of cloth are stretched upright for a perhaps 6 foot distance from the tent opening to the arena, a path or bridge, distantly

306

evocative of the sunken tunnels leading into bullfight rings. In the middle of the arena there is an octagonal plywood stage, flat on the ground, 15 to 20 feet across.

The concept of the event was not just circus, but panem et circenses. The panem comprised Schumann's rye, dispensed free (Schumann the host

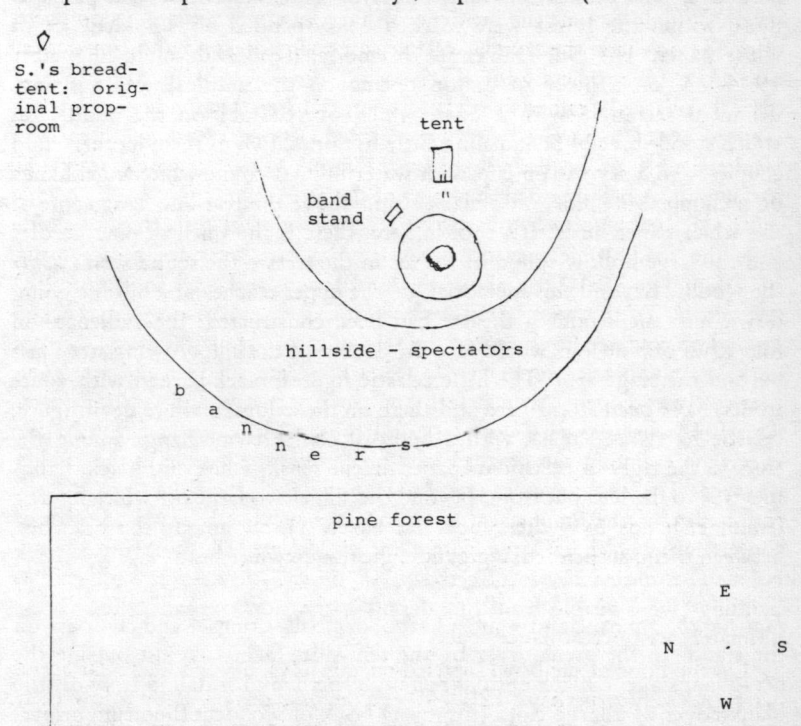

S.'s bread-
tent: orig-
inal prop-
room

tent

band
stand

hillside - spectators

banners

pine forest

E

N   ·   S

W

among the slicers and dispensers) with a choice of butter or aioli from a bread shack decorated with pieces from the spring's *White Horse Butcher* paper maché sculpture show, and food, generally not of the hamburger and hotdogs variety but hippie food, sold off trucks or from improvised stalls by hippie entrepreneurs. Sideshows and food provided the ambiance, and prevented the event from being merely a special kind of performance – out of doors, with the puppets, and taking a whole afternoon, but still: theatre. With the exception of this supplementary food and a memorial show in the pine forest for Bill Dalrymple, for which $10 contributions were suggested, the event was free. Larger-than-life decorated tophats upside down on the ground here and there mutely and in an incidental manner invited contributions, but at nightfall contained only very modest amounts of coin and dollar bills. The event was sedately gay, generous, well-organized and beautiful.[1]

* * *

The theatres at the edge of the woods and inside the woods had been arranged with extreme delicacy and good taste, consisting mostly of a few pine logs, pine branches, strung pieces of material. The several paths to those within the forest were marked by suspended birds folded out of white paper. The Bill Dalrymple Memorial ('Bill Dalrymple Puppeteer 1944-'73' on a piece of carton resting on the needles) was a string-delimited rectangle with a small white-covered table in the middle on which stood three of Schumann's little figurines, two of them mother/child couples, and a styrofoam cup with water in it. A comic white angel hangs on a chopped-off pine, on a black string above the rear-line hang some of the white paper birds. It's cool in here, there is the smell of pine needles and the large hollow sound of the air in the trees – the sound seems *above* the woods. Beyond this memorial, on the upper reaches of a hillside going down into the woods a theatre had been constructed: the audience, on four rows of pine logs would face the decline of the hill, growing steep just beyond the stage area. The little celastic figures, black-backed with white fronts, have been stood here and there on those logs, a white devil figure, celastic hands and mask with a body of coarse twine hangs among the trees to the right, a celastic or paper maché mask, white and black, hangs in a tree to the left, out front, beyond the stage two large off-white figures, feminine, hands over their faces are barely visible among the branches, between them, suspended, a gigantic, grotesque white head.

* * *

Hallelujah, 3 p.m. Band – tuba, kazoo, cymbals, drums – and choir are on the stand. In the arena, over by the tent-side, facing us, just outside the octagonal stage, a black upright rectangle, perhaps 5 ft. tall, 3 ft. wide, the blank cover of a large cloth (flip-over) book of woodcut (linoleum print?) pictures illustrating a text, the titles of the successive actions, hung over a cross piece between two uprights. To the right of it a man in black, tux, tophat, on stilts. The man in black, after a drum roll and a sounded note

---

1. 'Why lavish so much time, work and talent on this free circus in a gravel pit in Glover?

'It is an attempt at a type of community celebration and pageantry that has been lost', Mr. Schumann says. 'The newest feature of civilization is that people don't have that kind of commitment to the things they like to do.'

'Celebrations were once the high point of community life. Weddings in a European village would last at least three days, perhaps a week. There would be fine costumes, quantities of excellent food, music and dancing.'

'With television', Mr. Schumann continues, 'culture, and all that, was classified as a special commercial branch of life – to be taken care of by specialists.'

'There is something old fashioned in what we are doing,' he says, 'But in a way it is also new. This is a time when many people feel like getting out of that bag of being organized by certain powers. They want to do it themselves.' — (Braithwaite, *The Circus Approaches, The Chronicle*, July 24, '75.)

from the choir, each time first proclaiming the text, flips the pages, his reading each time repeated after him, shouted successively by members of the choir in Japanese, French, Italian and Yiddish, and followed by an action relating to the text, which then is confirmed by a hallelujah from the choir, each hallelujah preceded by drumming and fife-playing.

'See the world' – a veiled white-masked, modestly sweet female figure all in white with big white hands has come from the tent, stands to the left of the book, at some distance from it, by herself. 'When you sow seeds in it' – 'And when you pour water on it' – with a flourish he pours water into a shallow container and gives it to the lady. She holds the vessel. 'And when the sun shines on it' – an outcry from the choir. 'It will grow' – going to one of the musicians, the announcer gets a little figure from his tophat, holds it up. 'And the birds will feed on it' – the announcer shows a clay or paper bird at the end of a stick, sound of bird whistles from the choir. 'And the children of the world will eat of it' – he shows a green apple, gives it to one of the cast kids who are standing in front of the chorus, the kid starts eating it. 'And the grandfathers and grandmothers will sing hallelujah' – donning a twine beard, he crosses, stooped over, holding a sign saying 'hallelujah' on it. 'But' – Uncle Fatso, 8 to 10 feet tall, bulky, in black, Uncle Sam stovepipe hat, large and wide, florid, light colored tie, high white collar, his face gigantic, red, sanguine, twisted and lumpy, potato-nosed, one red eye, cigar clamped in one gigantic brown fist, ambles on and stands, off to the right of the octagonal stage (cacophony from band, booing from audience). 'When you put fire to the world' – the announcer, now Uncle Fatso's sidekick, has gotten hold of Uncle Fatso's left hand, to crescendos from the band makes runs at the white world-figure with it, each time making as though to strike her: she drops the water bowl and raises her white-handed arms. 'And when he poisons the world' – 'The world will cry' (tinkle of bells, no other sound, the white figure covers her eyes). 'And the children will die' – she lowers her head, steps forward to the edge of the octagon, kneels, puts her face in the dirt, her back rounded. The choir sounds a note, the drum beats, the announcer puts the big hand away, helps her up, she retreats to the tent. Uncle Sam and the announcer also leave for there. The tuba player steps forward onto the stage to announce the sideshows.

The Circus. 5 p.m. Hurdy-gurdy type music, sun low, people sucking ice cream.

Opening.

Big thin red birds on stilts, 8 feet high or so, one taller than the others (Peter Schumann), perhaps 12 feet, narrow pink long heads, flaming red flaring garments, lifting and flapping their wings (tombant crimson sleeves, cut saw-pattern). More and more. They are suddenly there, actually they emerge from the tent. 6, 8 or 9. Stilts like flamingo legs, one pair is candy-striped, red and white. The move to the music, hurdy-gurdy type music, but old-sounding music – a little awkwardly, lostly, with dignity. Over all air: ceremonial – gravitatious, among them a tow-headed boy on stilts, no costume, a mauve balloon tied to his stilts. A clown in a dark suit, brown hat, light tie, dark brown mask and red putty nose, a morose man, is moving around the perimeter, offering kids bread out of a brown paper bag, squirting them from a squirt-gun, making familiar remarks (Jewish European accent). The birds gradually disappear, stalking off singly. A pause.

A trumpet (Schumann is blowing it) blows from the bandstand area, two or three others answer it from different places on top of the bowl, it answers back – the cast, all in flowing white (pant suits) suddenly appear at a run from up above yelling Indian yells – commotion of a gyrating rising bird flight – carrying tall waving banners (on long tree poles), white, each with a print of a flower, most red, some sun yellow, like poppies, perhaps, come down the hillside at a run, between us, to both sides of us, 5 or 6 kids with shorter flagpoles among them; a team of 10 or so, also at a run, carrying a huge doll, China doll – vast oval pink pretty face over a green neck scarf, protruding blue eyes far below arched delicate eyebrows, a small red smiling mouth, small-nosed, her cheeks rouged, her hair an aura of green grass, grain grasses, Goldenrod, Black-eyed Susans, Queen Anne's Lace, brown-cobbed reeds – perhaps 20-22 feet tall, 4 carrying the pole upright, one each the flares of her dress (white, with the same red and yellow flowers on them), 1 each her arms (which end in leafy, red-berried hands, beautiful sculptures). She is borne to the stage in the center, revolves to a hymn[2] from the band and chorus, clockwise, while

2. *Captain Kidd*, an early American song, its tune an older British or Welsh folk melody (*The Word of Mouth Early American Songbook*, 1975).

310

the banner-carriers still at a run, though a slower one, go counterclockwise around the circumference of the arena, the kids with banners (theirs all have yellow flowers on them) in a smaller circle inside. White in the air under grey sky (Saturday: brilliant blue sky). The stage is being blessed. Evocations of caroussel, maypole, Queen of the May, village greens. The music stops, the doll is lowered, laid to rest, carried off to the tent at a run. Whistles.

* * *

Circus, Part I. *(Bicentennial Spectacular.)*

To music from the band,[3] the crew — they are referred to as the 'garbagemen', all wear green caps which are part of their large though not gigantic male mask-heads, early middle age, lower class stolid faces, their clothes a marvellously varied variety of working men's outfits — suits, overalls, jeans and sweaters — one wears a tight black coat like a checker's or foreman's — fit tight over their stocky (each has a paunch) bodies, they move with deliberation, featherbedding union men — Elka Schumann was one of them (all of Schumann's kids were in the show too). Elka apparently is to be credited with making the crew's stage-hand work an additional, quietly humorous, subtle, subtly and satirically realistic show, accompanying the other, giving it an added dimension[4] — bring out two ordinary black chairs, two men to a chair, one chair has a fleur de lys painted on the back, the other a small golden crown. The master of ceremonies of part I, Mr Kluck (from the '2 penny circus'), in red, white and blue striped pants, short-sleeved black jacket, paper maché nose, tophat, whistle on a chain around his neck, has appeared, with supporting fanfares from the band announces the program with the wont flourish and pretension — 'a first part, the beginning, a second, the middle, a third, the end' — exactly what in this program the three parts are not — 'in the beginning God created King George the Third . . .': 6 garbagemen form an honor guard from the circle to the tent (B & P), flags lowered, raise them as King George, short and stocky, red robe, pantoufles, a tiny crown on his vast pink gourd head

---

3. 'Then comes the silly circus proper, with a circus brass band (tuba, lots of trumpets, flutes, recorder, drums, cymbals, old instruments). Here we played old favorite tunes, *You Are My Sunshine, Billy Boy, Marine Hymn, Yankee Doodle*, etc. Also there was sung by a small good chorus, accompanied by old instruments: *Innsbruck, Ich Muss Dich Lassen.*' — (Elka, letter, '76.)

4. The idea is very simple: workmen do the work. That they are 'garbagemen' probably goes back to Schumann's involvement in the NYC garbage collectors' strike in February '68. They in fact represent the working class, like Uncle Fatso the capitalist class. The *Bicentennial Spectacular* thus discretely presents American history as show put on for the benefit of the capitalist class, with the working class doing the work. What the young Marx called the 'alienation' of the working class is illustrated by the skit *Life, Liberty and the Pursuit of Happiness* — said pursuit in this skit resulting in the overthrow of the capitalist class. He's a cunning one, that Schumann!

311

– small mouth, small protruding red tongue – leading a black toy snake on a string for a poodle, waddles on. Marie-Antoinette is announced, enters in her court dress, short and stocky, her head like the king's, accompanied by a small retinue of little girls in old fashioned dresses. She and the King curtsy to one another, do the rudiments of a little minuet to appropriate music from the band, seat themselves with the stiff awkwardness of puppets, at the tent-side edge of the stage, facing us. The Cardinal Richelieu is announced, enters with a little red devil and a small angel for adjutants, General Marshall, 'winner of the Nobel peace price', is announced, enters (G.I. outfit) accompanied by a band of boy-soldiers[5] in folded tri-cornered newspaper hats, the Cardinal and the General take their positions to the left and right of the royal couple. They have the same pink supercilious pigmeat-heads as king and queen. All this time a small woman all in black, black stocking over her face, black hair, has been slowly leading a donkey (performer under grey blanket, flat cutout brown head on a stick) around the outer inside perimeter of the arena: her circles during the following gradually become smaller, until finally she circles the octagonal stage in the center.[6]

Mr. Kluck announces the great conductor Zubenschmata (my phonetic spelling) who, another 2-penny clown, to ragged music from the bandstand, comes on with his music stand and some ragged music sheets and his four-man orchestra, Orlando di Lasso on the (tiny) cymbals, Josquin des Pres on the triangle, another great on the drum, Fats Waller on the (little) piano. The musicians again have the same big pink heads, but with little hats on them, with great dignity, having been led on (puppets are props) by the garbagemen, take their seats facing the conductor and us in a spread-out line on our side of the arena, on buckets turned upside down, each introduced grandly by the conductor. The court concert – the court is still there – is one note at a time from each of the musicians in turn. The conductor whose music stand keeps falling over, scattering his torn music,

---

5. The cue sheet in the tent refers to them as an 'army of gangsters'.
6. She provides a somber contrast to the effectively boisterous Mr. Kluck (whose performer is neither amateurish nor in his manner kowtows either to the audience or to the event as a whole) and to the hustle and bustle of the court scene and play: but the large calm natural scene holding it all diminishes it all, absorbs the blatancy of tragic black as well as of the announcer's unhesitatingly simple humor, and thus eliminates the shock of the contrast – perhaps also because while diminishing every scenic, theatrical effect, the lovely land also strengthens them, or strengthens whatever in them it has kinship to, such as pointless, childlike gaiety, the tragedy of mortal life: strengthening the opposites in the same respect, viz. as aspects of life, so that it can strengthen them without diminishing their opposition. I imagine the rocky coasts influenced classical Greek drama analogously: whereas the placement and architecture of the Roman outdoor theatres somewhat shielded the drama from the landscape. In indoor theatre, both the innocent-like persiflage of Our Country's history and Margo Sherman's skulking about in black might have seemed just foolish. The 'somber observer' in Schumann's work goes back to his Witch in *Emilia* of early and Sherman's Madwoman in *Grey Lady Cantata III* of late '71.

is greatly and increasingly exasperated by di Lasso who is very slow: it takes him an eternity to decide to lift his hands from his knees. But he clashes his cymbals very delicately. During a moment of inattention from the conductor, the enthusiastically jovial pianist induces the band to a rebellion, they break out into a (relatively) wild concert. The conductor stays them, thanks them, he and they leave, the real band playing a march. The garbagemen deliberately take out their equipment.

Mr. Kluck announces the fight of the century. 2 fighters, the same pink mask-heads, pink body-fitting one-piece suits, small Superman capes, very corpulent in the manner of wrestlers, and their impresario, Greasy McFingers, no mask, huge cigar in his mouth, come on – the garbagemen lead in the fighters, act as their trainers – McFingers, talking through his cigar, introduces them, acts as referee, they fight, i.e. one waddle-stalks over to the other who has his arms in the air he's so frightened, knocks him out flat without touching him, then the other does the same to him, then for a third round they knock one another out, and are carried off on one stretcher.

Kluck announces Christopher Columbus who arrives in a three-cornered hat with a long blue telescope, pinkheaded like the others, kneels before the king – Kluck has to tear him away from his subservience to set him out on his ocean passage: a team of garbagemen behind him, his 'band of hardy men', row him across to a quick march from the band until Mr. Kluck announces 'Land-ho, it's the Statue of Liberty!', but it's Uncle Fatso, huge and ugly, standing there, attended by a big-fisted assistant. Columbus obsequiously gets a tiny Stars and Stripes from him, and in great silence – the audience's laughter was quite subdued, a little strained— to the tinkle from a little spinet that with a flagpole (now held by a garbageman kneeling on one knee) has been brought onto the stage, the flag is slowly run up the pole, everyone saluting. The circles of the black donkey-woman are getting smaller. Mr. Kluck hustles everyone (except Uncle Fatso and his assistant who stand off to the right watching) together for a group photo, himself tall, at the rear, in the middle of the group, king and queen down front, and to cries from Kluck to 'get the flag in there!', an old-fashioned photographer, one of the garbagemen, bending over his tripod camera, his back to us, under a cloth, takes the picture, the click of his camera a clack from the bandstand. But Uncle Fatso, apparently displeased, now has his assistant call (imperiously) on the garbagemen to do something about these good-for-nothing gentry, to cut some heads, and, the garbagemen heavily registering agreement, Kluck after being nonplussed for a moment deliberately removes the king's head, the performer that did the king, a small man with a small head, immediately jumping up from the crown-marked chair and joining enthusiastically in the general rejoicing – a rousing march is being played. Uncle Fatso, his goon and Mr. Kluck do a jig on the stage as all the others (not the woman in black) leave. Fatso takes the throne chair, his assistant the other. There is a shout from above us, a cowboy figure on a gaily bedecked horse (stick with mask head) appears behind us at the rim of the hill, shouting 'the British are coming!' (the band is playing *Yankee Doodle*) wildly gallops down towards the stage: though he is shouting very loudly, Mr. Kluck can't make out what he is saying (Fatso and his assistant sit there immobile), turns to the audience to ask what it is, thinks he is saying 'the Jews are coming', then, as Revere gallops across the stage off into the tent to the rear, understands and is very frightened. After a moment, an animal trainer with three musical bears, one with a fife, one with a drum, one with a Bread and Puppet flag appears from the tent: marching them (more or less) around the stage, the trainer in a military manner tries to keep them abreast and in step behind him, but their formation is extremely straggly, he gets more and more irritated – this happens quickly, they are moving fast – finally loses his hold over them, they start pursuing him, pursue him back to the tent.

Mr. Kluck announces the 'shot heard around the world'. The tall white Vietnamese Girl Angel with white face mask and large white hands comes out and walks onto stage-right, an enormous G.I. figure, in camouflage combat outfit, with small ragged angel's wings on his back, holding a wooden rifle is marched around the stage by 2 garbagemen onto stage-right. To a chorus of low moans from the choir, he proceeds to shoot her. She slowly folds, arms raised, turning full circle as she does so, lies as though asleep, face down. The donkey woman in black gently raises her and she walks out, hands held in front of her. The G.I. Angel marches off.

A young girl in white, with wings also, comes on-stage, puts down some cardboard rectangles, face down. A garbageman lies down in the part of the stage away from us next to something like a shoeshine box. The announcer announces our rights, 'Life, Liberty and the Pursuit of Happiness', and 'The Uncle Fatso Play ending in taps for Uncle Fatso'. Uncle Fatso and his goon are still seated there, the announcer proceeds to pick up the cardboards one by one, the titles of the scenes, announcing them at the same time. Scene 1. 'Sunrise'. The garbageman gets up, stretches. Scene 2. 'Coffee'. He rubs his belly. (The black woman is now seated right behind the stage, by her donkey, also seated. She watches the play, including its watchers, Uncle Fatso cum goon). The young girl in white with the wings flies in (carried overhead by two garbagemen), asks him, 'Would you like some sugar and cream in your coffee?' He thanks her, to a slurping sound from the band, makes the motions of drinking. She is flown off. Scene 3. 'His Job'. A boss in a black suit, with a card around his neck giving his name, 'Bossy', steps onto the stage stage-right, in bird noises ordering the garbagemen around sharply. The garbageman has taken a big wrench out of his box, starts handling it clumsily, tortuously. Scene 4. '5 o'clock'. The workman puts an automobile license plate around his neck. Scene 5. 'He drives home. Remember, God is watching!' He goes through steering motions. Scene 6. 'Home'. He is met by a small beast-figure, with a huge, many-toothed head, his wife. They embrace lovingly, do a dance, sit on the box. Scene 7. 'T.V.' A bunch of kids, perhaps 10, rush up to and onto the stage from both sides, proceed to make like shooting (cops and robbers, Indians and cowboys), killing Fatso and his goon (they get up, turn, fall dead). Taps are sounded. Fatso and goon get up, half-run off, scared, as clowns swarm on. Mr. Kluck has left.

After the clowns carry on for a while (talking to audience, juggling, bumping into each other, etc.), first one, then another, then still another, perhaps five in all, lengthy dragons come on, according to the cue-sheet they were to 'clear everything away'. I don't remember what they did.

*   *   *

Circus, Part II. *(Animals and Acrobats.)*

A new announcer, younger, brisker, handsome, a Frenchified fellow, announces Miss Betsy Ross and her fellow flag twirlers. She comes running out into the menage, blonde, pretty, smiling, bosomy, as they do in the circus, waving a Bread and Puppet flag, followed by a string of girls, waving Bread and Puppet flags. They stop in file, twirl their flags to the music, twice, after drum crescendo, jump over them, a not very difficult feat, run off. The Fabulous Flying Dubeknes are announced. There are two of them, a man and a woman. The keep shouting 'hap hat' like acrobats. He jumps over a snare drum, plays it lying on it, she does a headstand (which during the Sunday performance turned into – unintentionally, I believe – a backstand), plays the trumpet. The clowns are still around. The flag jumpers swarm back in, mingled with kids, all in their white suits. The shout and jump. 'The Grand Egyptian Pyramid and Flying Angel' is announced in an enormous bellow by one of them, little Sara Peattie, and they form a 3-tier pyramid to much excitement and smiling. (A clown is circulating past us with a small doored box bearing the legend 'The first dog in space': he opens it from time to time as though showing dirty postcards on a Paris boulevard: inside it a hot dog dangles from a string.) Sara announces leapfrog, Miss Betsy's team leapfrogs to 'hut hups', a clown whipping them on with a green branch, the little kids finally crawling through the others' legs. (One of the clowns is juggling with 3 balls.) All out. 2 black and red dragons come out on many feet, slowly to a very slow march. It takes a long time. The garbagemen are out with shovels and brooms in case the beasts forget themselves. The dragons are rows of crouching people with a single length of cloth over them, the front man

---

7. The ff. outlines the Sunday performance. It was abbreviated because of the rain. The order of the acts was not as per the cue-sheet. I suppose it was arbitrary anyhow. Everything was done more quickly, jumbled together. This improved the occasion.

manipulating the large mask. A gaily colored dragon dances in, now all left feet, now all right in the air. There are bells on some of the dragons. Some slow music from the tuba. A vast green dragon, at least 15 ft. long, all beautiful, its enormous muzzle mounted on a pushcart, snakes in. One of the dragons is crawling on its belly in the middle. One is lying down, curling up, till only its huge head sticks out from the middle of its coil. Others walk on. The garbagemen are dompting them with their shovels, watchfully. Two dragons engage in a very slow fight in the middle. Perhaps they are courting. A fantastic colorful scene. All off to fanfares. A paunchy old man in shirtsleeves comes on, says he believes square dancing is for fun, you don't have to be an expert, four performers made up as old ladies square dance awkwardly with 4 garbagemen to his very pretty fiddling and calling. A heavily made up girl is leading a giraffe with a vast 4-cornered neck on from the audience. A dragon comes in to watch the square dance. Kids in fool's costumes are tumbling and jumping out front. The giraffe (on stilts) is dancing to the fiddler's tune. 2 young teenage girls in gold costumes, on stilts, join in the dance too. Garbagemen are cleaning up the beasts' excrements still. 'From the further reaches of Upper Pyramania', a fire juggler. 'Fire' song, to drums and fifes, from the choir. He lights 3 flares behind a lowered Bread and Puppet banner, juggles with them, the garbagemen ready with buckets. The clowns form a fire brigade with a cardboard fire engine, pass a bucket to the front, the front man squelches his thirst from it. The Great Rudolfo, Gundolfo and a third — from Lower Slobovia — ride on on ponies gay as Paul Revere's while Elka Schumann, having momentarily removed her garbageman's mask, beautifully sings a soulful Russian song through a bullhorn. To a gradually speeding up Flamenco-type music, they make their horses dance (only one of them manages to convey the impression that the horse, not he, is dancing). The Chicken Lady: the beautiful blonde from before, now barelegged, in black boots, holding a whip and a live chicken: she throws the chicken to another performer. The Cheerleader: a composite person: strong male legs, petite girl's upper body on top, a white skirt covering the juncture. It walks the circle, she twirls a silver baton. As they leave, the skirt falls off, she jumps off him, he chases her in mock anger. All off. Quiet. Bird noises. A black vulture, man-high, large black wings like funeral banners, a small red head, traipses about eerily, enters the octagon, its tailfeathers raised, slowly, with bird steps, approaches a box-like object a garbageman has deposited in the center, stands by it, its head jerking above it in small sideways up and down movements, gets on it, squats on it, brooding, while a large 4-legged (4 performers) purple beast (its head the All-devouring Night of Schumann's Brooklyn small-people show) with brown foxes (?) painted on its coat, vast, round, flat expressionless face, comes on to guitar accompaniment, slowly walks past, not heeding the vulture. Half a dozen weird birds, ostrich-size, in light-colored plumage, one bright yellow, have come on, moving slowly, kneel around the brood-ing vulture. Trumpets. The black bird gets off the box-like object. All swirl off, wings flailing, to trumpets. The purple beast has left. The 2-penny clowns come back out. One of them, Pepperoni, the Great Pepperoni (the sign on the back of his jacket says 'Eat at Pepperoni's') is going to hypno-tize another one, a big yokelish hulk who just knows it can't be done. They are all milling around in the middle. 'Watch, watch', Pepperoni tells the other, pulls out a pocket watch dangling from a chain, 'watch the watch!', dangling it. The other is laughing, making contemptuous hand movements as Pepperoni continues, 'You are getting sleepy, your eyes are closing . . .', but a third clown comes up from behind and clonks him on the head with a toy baseball bat. He now *is* in a deep trance, has slumped back in the chair. They are covering him over with a blanket as though he had seated himself in a barber's chair. Pepperoni picks up a saw, makes as if to give him a haircut ('Shave and hair cut, captain?'), the others stop him ('Just a little humor, folks!'), announces he will levitate him, says the magic words ('Hocus pocus alacazam. You eat salami, I'll take the ham.'), the other levitates horizontally under his blanket. A clown whips off the cover. He's been holding a pair of boots out horizontally from under a blanket. A 'special guest, Beebee Rebozo, all the way from Key Biscayne, Florida!' a bear trainer and 3 bears, he makes them dance in style to different types of music, le tap dance, le dance moderne, an improvisation to the *Rite of Spring*, finalement le jitterbug (a rather good number this). The bears are small, roly-poly.

Schumann (bronzed, bearded) on high stilts to a quick march, in red-striped overalls, bum's slouch hat, dances, half a walk, half the march, not serious, the slight margin of awkwardness a playful style, with tentative grace, skirts the stage teasing us. 10 white horses come on with their trainer, line up between us and him, the trainer makes them bow – a fan-fare from the band – Schumann enters the stage, makes a slight joke of approaching their rears, bending over, looking at their arses. Fife music, the 10 horses – large white clouds – dance. Schumann dances a slow, very graceful dance, nicely, unassumingly, with an edge of humor, a little funny, great control. Stands in clown-stance whenever music stops. The band intunes 'When the Saints Come Marching In.' Horses around and off, Schumann, taller than anything else, stalks off after them, still in rhythm, then the giraffe, then all the garbagemen with B & P flags, then the whole cast in their white costumes: the grand figure behind the horses is at the head of the procession. The last one out is a drummer drumming, a girl carries his drum. 6 garbagemen with Bread and Puppet flags come out again, congregate in the center, the band's conductor, a shy girl, comes forward and announces 'A Dance of Death, or The White Horse Butcher.'

*   *   *

Circus, Part III: *Dance of Death*, or *The White Horse Butcher*.

The chorus, their white robes with black skeletal prints[8] on them sing a verse of a slow chorale,[9] no instruments.

Garbagemen bring in Erik, house, stool etc. They set up house, bird whistle for drinking. House is brought out. (Cue sheet.)[10]

A large, off-white puppet with, ten feet up, a long neck and a wrinkled — worried — lobster-red head, red houses printed on its robe, is brought on by workmen. Standing around a wheelbarrow in a poised ritual of rightful refreshment set to beautiful bird whistles from the band, the singing having ended, they drink cokes from a 6-pack, the large, all in all perhaps sorrowful hulking figure they brought in neglected, despite its height obscured by them, lost among — more or less behind — though over them. Handing their cokes back to the guy holding the container, they fold up the puppet and put it in the wheelbarrow. A small puppet, child-sized, is seated (on an upturned pail) where the House puppet loomed, hands on its knees. It is white, the figure of an ordinary middle-aged man rather like one of the foot-high Johnny puppets Schumann makes. It sits. It is not a puppet, but a performer, with a white face mask, in

---

8. The Dance of Death costumes, the woodcuts for which Schumann had made in California in May.

9. From Larry Gordon's 1975 *Word of Mouth Early American Songbook*.

10. The directions in the left-hand margins in the following are from the cue sheet.

11. Peter Cartwright's *Hebrew Children* (around 1820) (*The Word of Mouth Early American Songbook*, 1975).

white overalls, a black hat on its head, solemnly facing us, not moving. The workmen have left with the puppet he came in. The black woman-in-sorrow appears with her two-dimensional donkey. As the chorus sings another grave verse,[11] she circles the stage, her face turned to the small figure at its center, pointing at him, pointing him out to us.[12] A covey of maenads – black robes, white bird-face masks – rushes out gesticulating, with bird cries, descend on the lone little figure sitting there quietly. Their appearance breaks a stasis, but in this outdoor setting the break is not dramatic. They grab him. He gets up and flees. By the figure's running motion we see it's a kid, a small boy.[13] He runs up the hillside, white – and small – closely pursued by them, he can't run very fast. He and they and their bird cries disappear beyond the top.

Onto the empty stage – the black woman (a mute chorus) has left during this – the workmen come, set up a room – a small, low table on the right, a turned-up bucket next to it   one of them wipes it (an especially funny touch during the rain Sunday) – and, to the left, a door, held by one of them (ruddy-cheeked mask, green jacket). He holds it during the sequel, standing close to it, his burly figure disappearing into it. The door makes it a house. They leave, except for him, and for one other, in a black work coat, standing just outside the floored stage area by the table, facing it. A tall, thin white lady (small head, white face mask) rides in on the small donkey led by the black veiled woman: up to the door.[14] She gets off, opens the door, enters with a stately gait, stooped, her upper body turned sideways, giving an effect of illness and sadness – of suffering. Standing close to the door she closes it slowly – with an effort: not a great effort, but the kind of effort it takes, especially from someone neither young nor well, to shut

---

Song I

Witches enter, dance, exit screaming.

Door, table, etc. enter. White Lady enters. Song II. Deer enter. Song III.

---

12. Margo Sherman who did this as is her wont overdid it: seemed not just to point him out to us, but did it in a way suggesting she was personally involved with him.

13. That whether this victim/hero of the piece is a boy or a man is ambiguous seemed a weakness of the piece to me. I attributed it to Schumann's not adequately directing the boy that did the figure. On reflection, Schumann may have intended this ambiguity, by it telling us: it's the boy-child in a grown-up man; or: it's boy-growing-into-man. The figure replaces the mysterious figure cloaked in a black plastic sheet and with a rope around its neck that symbolically killed the deer in the California show that spring.

14. Peter Schumann on stilts. You can't recognize him.

a door not hung to swing shut by itself. The unemphatic solemnity of the figure's stance and movements gives it a spiritual quality. She advances to the bucket chair, sits. The workman there lays a large sheet of paper on the table, gives her a pen. Stooped over the table, her long legs – the stilts – out sideways, she proceeds to write or to sign.[15] Another tall, though less tall, white, thin, but male figure, skull-mask face, tall white hat with black cabalistic scrawls on its brim, is approaching the house, knocks on the door, bends to it to listen.[16] He is carrying something heavy, in both hands. She slowly gets up, advances to let him in. A large troop of deer have appeared over the top of the hill (in front of us as well as above us to our right), several abreast, large as elk (the performers are walking upright), the backs and long heads of the deer making a straight line, their grey, long-nosed heads are uplifted as though they were following a scent or were searching. They are white. As their procession wends its way down the hillside, the White Lady admits the Skullman (the workman opening the door for him), he enters shuffling, she has retreated to near her table, he advances bent over and puts down a heavy rock in front of her. To eery fife music, she slowly kneels before it, leaning over, bends over it, her head touches the ground on its other side. She is crouched on the ground, now a small figure, figure of a victim, her head toward us.[17] The deer are still approaching. The workman has not shut the door – no need to, any more. The Black Woman, leaving her donkey outside, enters the circle (not using the door:

Skull arrives,
puts rock down.
Lady kneels.
High singing.

---

15. 'She was writing but she was not writing specific words . . . I wanted her to be hungry, to write a letter.' — (Schumann, interview, '83.)

16. This performer's mime-art being slight, he is cramped, what he is doing is in his head only, so that his figure, skull, is less impressive, grand and less well defined than that of the White Lady. These performed puppets are only proximately defined by precision and/or extremity of gesture: ultimately only by the gesture's coincidence with an – however undefinable – integral emotion suffusing it. You saw Skull Man's image but not so it would stay deeply or strongly. The immediate result was that Skull Man and the White Lady were not too strongly differentiated, so the compositions did not quite jell. The tensely august figure of the Black Woman was weak for a different reason: whatever Margo thought she was expressing was a shallow cliché she had acquired at no great cost, so that the – strong – definition she gave her figure entered the compositions as an unpleasant quality fractitiously.

17. Motif from the *Grey Lady Cantata VI*. It reappears in the prologue to the '82 *Diagonal Man*.

she is outside the play), approaches the White Lady, prone, drops a handful of dirt on her back,[18] goes back to her donkey. The deer are still coming on over the green: angular, straight-backed. The full choir is singing a low hymn[19] in several clear voices. Skullman is standing stooped over in the room, hands pressed into his crotch, as though not used to being without the stone. The deer are circling the stage slowly, the details of their heads, they have Black-Eyed Susans in their mouths, their antlers are branches, very clear now. To silence now, they lie down on the ground by us, slowly, outside the stage, a white herd, on their sides: as though, having arrived at the place for it, they die. One has its muzzle on the back of another. Another verse. The four figures are motionless in the center. The Black

---

18. We have seen death as the present of a stone. How many of the audience got this, especially before the dirt was strewn/thrown, is a question. That Schumann needed to explain the stone metaphor by the dirt suggests he was doubtful of its efficacy, and wanted this story element understood. It seems to me the stone episode was sufficiently powerful and 'emotionally significant' to work even if not grasped as story element, precisely. It also seems to me that the use of the dirt wasted a ritual gesture very powerful in itself. But perhaps if Margo had been a better performer, it would have heightened the impact of the White Lady's heart's breaking. Note, finally, that the stone metaphor makes sense: the stone stands for the inanimate, the lady becomes one with it.

19. John Leland's 1835 *Evening Shade* (*The Word of Mouth Early American Songbook*, 1975).

Woman's arms are at her sides, hands a little in front, by her dress. The White Lady slowly sways up to the hymn. She has risen. She dances out slowly, gravely, shifting from side to side. The Black Woman is following her with her eyes as she drifts off to the tent. The door is still held open. The dark grey rock lies there.

Lady exits.
Objects exit.
Drums and
mallets
brought in.
Song IV.

A workman comes in, unhurried and deliberate as always, carrying a snare drum and on its drumsticks, places them near the table, takes off the table with the paper on it. Another comes to get the rock after finickily adjusting the sticks. There is something red over the edge of the drum. Skullman shuffles over, sits on the bucket, bent over the drum, at the right side of the stage, facing the door. The Black Woman's left arm is raised, she is at the southern edge of the circle, facing us, north, perhaps watching Skullman. Her donkey is kneeling beside, a little behind her, just there. There are no workmen around except the one standing there holding the door, now in a shut position. The deer are lying splattered in a heap. A gay tune from the band.[21] The Black Woman approaches the drum, keeping outside of the stage-octagon, stands by Skullman, as a big white horse (2 performers) with a long blond tail dances on led by the small young boy in white, costumed like a small grave man. Little Erik leads the horse to the door, knocks, stands straight holding the horse by the guide-rope. The horse is no longer prancing, occasionally makes a little sidestep to the music. The Woman in Black watching, Skullman shuffles over to open the door (the doorman does the actual turning of the door). Erik with dignity extends his hand, Skull shakes it, welcoming him. Erik enters (the dance music stopping), bringing in the horse, Skullman back by the drum takes a red scarf from it and gives it to him, sits. Erik has the horse kneel on its front legs, blindfolds it with the scarf, the horse making nervous head movements, kneels in front of Skullman, facing him across the drum, back erect. The blindfolded white horse is kneeling behind him. To a stately march-hymn[22] from the full choir, accompanied by bass drum, the white-clad flag runners run on, black picture prints to one word-texts – AIR,

Music as
white horse
butcher enters.
Music stops as
he enters door.

Erik blinds
horse. Flags
enter.
Song I.

---

21. *Road to the Isles.* A traditional contradance. Sopranino recorder, fiddle, toy piano.
22. *Where are the Hebrew Children*, verse 1.

GO, SOUP, BEAST — on their white banners, the lettered and imaged sides facing into the circle. At a slow run, they file around just inside the perimeter of the circle, the choir now on another verse.[23] Music and running end together. Silence. The young people holding the flags are facing outside in a ring, their banners drooping. Silence. Erik pulls on the horse, Skullman starts drumming, the horse gets up, a pulling battle commences between the small person and the large animal, all over the stage and the parts of the arena next to it, the horse stomping, rearing up, trying to get away. Finally the horse collapses on its side, the other side of the herd of deer, between it and the stage. Skullman stops drumming. Erik gets up on his shoulders, Skullman gets up with him, handing him the drumsticks and Skullman holding the drum, they march off across the octagon, past the Black Woman, Erik beating a slow beat on the drum, fading as they get further away, approach the door of the tent. It is dusk. BIRDS come on from a far distance — across the hills to the southeast, large white birds, far off the ground. The flag runners leave with the flags — busying the foreground (and with them, I believe, the puppeteers from inside the dead deer). Workmen take away the pail, help the doorman take away the door.[24] Only the Black Woman and the donkey are there, beyond the dead animals, at the other side of the stage, beyond it. A long heavy wooden ox cart pulled by two white oxen and led by two guides out front is coming slowly down the hill. It is driven by a very tall, narrow white figure. As the cart comes closer you see it's a woman, veiled, all in white, with long blond hair — more emaciated and taller than the White Lady that died.[25] The birds suddenly loom

Drumming and fighting.

Erik exits on Death's back. Flags exit. Objects exit.

Oxcart and stilt angel.

23. *Where are the Hebrew Children*, verse 2:
    'Where are the twelve apostles?
    Where are the twelve apostles?
    Where are the twelve apostles?
    Safe in the promised land.'

24. The departure of these performers oddly enough was not disturbing: the finality of the death of the horse after the — considerable — tension of the fight (more effective image of what the child-butcher's killing act would have to mean to him than any scene of his actually killing the horse would have been) was so great that it didn't matter what happened there — as when a large debacle obscures some small mishap, the mishap even providing relief and in any case not mattering.

25. Peter Schumann again, and on stilts again, but longer ones than previously, and

above us, above the top of the hill, three big birds and one enormous one, even higher up than they: at the end of long poles, their carriers making the noise of gulls. The birds — their incredible lightness up in the air, the cold and lonely gull heads, eyes closed — are so awesome you don't really notice the poles or the carriers. Gull cries in the silence of the dusk — occasional slight tinkling of bells on the oxen — as the birds swoop down into the valley. They leave as the ox cart slowly enters the circle and halts. The Angel climbs off, her long stilt legs first, vastly high, elegant lace wings under her arms, a touch of camp, her white mask remindful of the impassively benign faces on Schumann's Vietnamese Women, but her cheeks faintly rouged, and (the band has struck up an increasingly fast, stately dance tune[26]), after some complicated steps on the grass, arms up (wings flared) dances onto the stage in stomping delicate steps, body slightly inclined. The Black Woman is waiting with her donkey. The Stilt Angel performs a graceful, accelerating dance. The music stops. Schumann still has his arms lifted. He walks over to the dead horse, straddles it. Claps his hands. It rises under him. As the ox cart trundles off toward the tent, Horse and Rider, the rider holding the bridles, do a counter-clockwise lightly triumphant dance together around the ring to the gay fife and bells dance tune. They dance off into the tent, the choir singing 'la la la'.

Applause, the cast comes out, applauds back, jumps up and down.

*   *   *

3-part *Circus+Hallelujah*. Comment.

The three parts of the circus did not relate. The *Bicentennial Spectacle* (Part (I)) though spoof and slapstick was a wry (sour) commentary on the nation's history and fate, astoundingly negative, a series of sketches only formally circus, and even formally only faintly, but rather the components of an arrested pageant — a subversively subverted patriotic pageant — held in place: and really quite rough on the country. I don't think it would have gone down too well with an audience predomnantly of local citizenry, even in this depressed and half-French-Canadian area, though, being

---

aethereally costumed. Yet close enough in appearance to the White Lady in the end marginally to suggest a resurrection of her more definite than the previous one.

26. *Nonesuch*, on the same instruments as *Road to the Isles*, another contradance and fiddle tune.

humorous, and in fact funny, it just might have. *No* positive note was struck — unless we think of its humorous ending, the killing of Uncle Fatso by t.v.-crazy kids, as more than a non-sense-fancy, viz. as expression of hope in youth. The statement was: you slobs just exchanged one blood-sucking ruling class for another and you don't even know it — maybe your kids will do something about it. That a retreatee of genius into this forlorn, left-behind, somewhat frontierish part of the country should have viewed AMERICA as bloated incarnation of murderish, against-nature evil made sense. But that he should have expected such a history of their nation — a worse plutocracy displaces an odious monarchy, the people is a working class portrayed as such in a straightforward Marxist fashion, except a Maoist one, namely as a bunch of slobs — where the patriot might counter-pose the Big Fellers to the Little Ones, Us or the Ordinary man — and then the funny part is where the kids off the rich — to be acceptable to the average native Vermonter with no college education is surprising: he must have thought the funny business would make it go down.

The concept of this first part was in fact quite grandiose: we were seeing a show put on for rulers, the Old World royalty of yore — Schumann using the same elegant malicious '18th century' Bulbhead Family masks for them and for the figures in the shows put on for them, the musicians, the boxers — and the New World plutocracy of the now and here: *their* show: the implication: social life, society, is itself a show put on for (clownish) rulers: looking at history we are looking at a circus. The Woman in Black, circling, closing in — her reappearance in Part III in a *supporting* role supposed to tie Parts I and III together, but this didn't work — puts this circus in tragic perspective. But this concept did not take form. I would say Schumann as director failed to make it work as structure.

Animals and Acrobats expressed his simple sense of what's funny and determination to address a childlike public of the poor whether it exists or not. It was circus without skills. This was by and large the joke. The jug-gler gets up to four balls. Schumann himself, as stilt-walker, was the only one skilled, walking on 6 ft. and dancing (magnificently) — over and over up on just one stilt, kicking up the other — on $3\frac{1}{2}$ ft. stilts. A good clown especially if there are good acrobats around can be funny failing as acro-bat, and good acrobats traditionally include a failure or, better, an ap-parent failure, as gag into their show, but none of the performers was either, they were all rank amateurs doing the kind of thing that's funny: one was entertained because one recognized it as that kind. As it has turned out this absence of talent was no accident nor due to Schumann's failing to get hold of anybody good: while Schumann has gotten better and better on his stilts, and the stilts longer and longer, there has never, in all these years been a good acrobat or clown in any of his circuses, and it took eight years before there was a really good — skilled, daring and talented — stilt walker besides himself, Susan Dennison in '83 as black dancing demon. The two M.C.s of the circus were good, their humor dry and their timing right, and they have remained good throughout: for some reason, Schumann has always gotten good narrators for his shows, i.e.: allowed them to be good, allowed talented fellows to do it: perhaps because he thinks of them as not really in the show, more: his assistants. The absence of skills gave a great lightness to Part II of the *Circus*: a circus of the imagination. The acrobats as fake as the animals. It made Part II unserious even as entertainment, and this may have helped to redeem the radical social criticism and negative view of the American Experiment of Part I by making it also seem just funning.

The distinctive feature of this section — a Zoo of Marvelous Creatures — families of giant colorful dragons, square-necked giraffes, man-high vultures, the purple beast with the painted coat, technicolor ostriches, fairytale ballerina horses — was indistinct: swamped by the 'acrobats'. Potentially, this circus was as splendid as Dr. Lao's (and quite different, a pean to nature and the imagination): but instead of the low grade humor that killed the magic of it required acrobats, jugglers and clowns not only as false (imaginary) but also as marvelous — some puppeteering equivalent of the magic and marvel of good jugglers and acrobats and the pathos of good clowns. Schumann never subsequently either came up with a transposition into puppetry of circus. It seems never to have occurred to him: he merely wanted his show to have the cloak of the pre-existing institution — circus. In fact, whether because of this or because the 'silly circus' just bored him, he soon phased out the marvellous animals also, froze the format to where the event would pass as silly circus.

Part III, *White Horse Butcher*, calculated for the dusk, was a sudden departure, not circus at all.[27] It was a play, its action an interaction of man (the sorrowing woman, the boy) and nature (the deer, the horse, the birds, the oxen), expanding until it became part of nature (of the landscape), and performed as grave ceremony, as though its action were ritual: by its metamorphosis into part of the natural world and its intimation of ritual a pageant in Schumann's sense. And it presented a personal vision, not so much a private and obscure one as rather an amorphous one, brumeux, a soft-focus mystery, rather than — like Part I of *Simple Light* — a hard-edge puzzle. The figures and their functions were hard to distinguish. There was so much *white*; the white was not as clear as in the *Moby Dick* catalogue; the blackness — a spot — Schumann's sorrow and melancholy — was not its opposite. The constellations melted into the landscape. The boy is expulsed; the lady dies freely; the boy returns only to sacrifice his animal

---

27. Identifying Part II as 'the circus proper', Schumann to an interviewer identified Part III as 'the reflective part of it all'. — (Braithwaite, *The Circus Approaches, The Chronicle*, July 24, '75.)

companion; an angel triumphs over death. The meaning seemed: a person dies (as people do die); animals die; the deaths of animals are no different from the deaths of people; a person kills an animal (as people do kill); but life goes on.[28] Yet there seems more to the piece than that: the woman's death seems to reverberate in that of the animals; the boy seems to have been subjected to the force of evil; does not the boy relate to the woman? The boy's killing seems to bring up guilt as theme; and the constellation of deaths seems personal to Schumann: the play seems about personal guilt — more than about death. Its vision is obscure. Perhaps it is *of* something obscure. Perhaps the indefiniteness of human vision in the context of regenerative, indifferent nature was the, or was part of the, point.

Its aspect of personal vision severed the pageant from the preceding parts of the circus, but only marginally conflicted with the whole event's aspect of a community event and celebration because the power of its figures and choreography drew the silenced spectators, on the side of the amphitheatre grouped into a part of the natural setting (by the pageant aggrandized into Nature), into the pageant, made them, I think, feel like part of the ritual, one of its poles, and like a community in nature; and though

---

28. What my father got out of this theme contrasts interestingly with what Schumann here gets out of it:

'O FALLADAH, DIE DU HANGEST!

Ich zog meine Fuhre trotz meiner Schwäche
Ich kam bis zur Frankfurter Allee.
Dort denke ich noch: O je!
Diese Schwäche! Wenn ich mich gehenlasse
Kann's mir passieren, dass ich zusammenbreche.
Zehn Minuten später lagen nur noch meine Knochen auf der Strasse.

Kaum war ich da nämlich zusammengebrochen
(Der Kutscher lief zum Telefon)
Da stürzten sich aus den Häusern schon
Hungrige Menschen, um ein Pfund Fleisch zu erben
Rissen mit Messern mir das Fleisch von den Knochen
Und ich lebte überhaupt noch und war gar nicht fertig mit dem Sterben.

Aber die kannte ich doch von früher, die Leute!
Die brachten mir Säcke gegen die Fliegen doch
Schenkten mir altes Brot und ermahnten noch
Meinen Kutscher, sanft mit mir umzugehen.
Einst mir so freundlich und mir so feindlich heute!
Plötzlich waren sie wie ausgewechselt! Ach, was war mit ihnen geschehen?

Da fragte ich mich: Was für eine Kälte
Muss über die Leute gekommen sein!
Wer schlägt da so auf sie ein
Dass sie jetzt so durch und durch erkaltet?
So helfet ihnen doch! Und tut es in Bälde!
Sonst passiert euch etwas, was ihr nicht für möglich haltet!'

the pageant's vision seemed tragic, its ritual by its ending – and directly by making the relation of man to nature, however criminal, represented by the ritual, seem as inevitable a formal dance as the coming and going of the sun – effectively achieved a transcendence of the tragedy (a catharsis), retrieving the whole event's aspect of celebration.

Though *The White Horse Butcher* was on a different plane from the prefatory *Hallelujah*: a moving image without its specific reference, an abstract vision, an event from inside a personal, long-sustained life of the imagination, it was also a mirror-image and revision of it. For *Hallelujah*, in a cheery mode and starting out upbeat, was without resolution, a somber view of the Human Condition: at the end of it, Uncle Fatso, the evil genius of the present, hardly human, incursion of the principle of evil into the initially shown natural world of nature/labor/children/the aged rules; whereas *White Horse Butcher* moved from resignation, death, killing to a resurrection. The whole was a circle.

The Domestic Resurrection Goddess, heralded by birds and flowers, flowers on the three flares of her dress, her hair straw, reeds and wild flowers, her hands fruiting branches, was effectively the Nature deity of the world praised by the *Hallelujah*. The dance in her honor dedicated the circus to her: the God of the Jews and Christians wasn't around. When in conclusion a male child, that is: an innocent male acting in accordance with his nature, kills the horse not by killing it outright but by dompting – domesticating – it, that world of nature is violated: by the male principle within it. Facit: evil, identified not as self-seeking aggression *(Simple Light)*, but as culture (civilization), is an integral part of the natural world, its complementary male principle. And history (Parts I and II of the circus), a silly show, bears this out. There is in this an acceptance of evil, and this acceptance is reaffirmed by the concluding resurrection: things go on. The world of nature, evil and all, is self-regenerative. Its female principle is insidiously efficacious. This is equally resignation and 'hope'. No function was indicated for the male principle: a conceptual lacuna. This pantheism differs from that represented by the great female deities of the Assyrians, Greeks, Romans, who are ambiguously, by overlays of myths and attributes, both deities of agriculture, i.e. of culture, and of dangerous, disruptive, devouring love and of untamed nature: carriers of both of the opposing principles by Schumann's pantheism distributed to the two genders, and by their duality expressive of an endorsement of culture.

The bicentennial goading (transposition into the social of the ecological tragedy ending the *Hallelujah*, the plutocracy presiding in each case) and the silly non-circus between the *Hallelujah* and the celebration of the deity at the beginning and *White Horse Butcher* at the end were an interlude, and the more so because they shared the texture of silliness, ineptness and 'acts'.

Still and all, the broad satire of the first part of the *Circus*, the innocent

328

gaiety, flecked with fantasy, of the second, and the somber stateliness and elevation of the third added up to a most enjoyable program, the facility of the appeal of which was effectively mitigated by the dignity and remoteness of the manner of its presentation. Though the parts were unrelated — a taking of position, an entertainment, a personal vision of the human condition — they were the recurrent ingredients that Schumann has tried to have and balance in all his shows. We might say, it was a grandiose feast spread by a singularly generous country nobleman for his neighbors, his friends from the city and all the world, a party. If, after the formal welcome, the host mixed some satire of his and his guests' shared condition and past into the feast's gaiety, and before finally, for an adieu, graciously dancing for all his guests, had a brief discordant lapse into his native melancholy, such could be forgiven. Worse occurs at many parties: would all hosts were so benign!

* * *

In New York with all the buildings crowding in, Schuman liked to play in undefined spaces, framelessly, not to bother to define even definable indoors performance spaces. This made the puppets seem to speak for themselves, their macabre rebus free-floated. In the man-made canyons, the big puppets conflicted with the buildings. And when, in a church, Schumann so staged Christ's vicarious passion as to fracture the temple's interior order, the superior rank of man in nature that the Jews thought of as settled by contract was aggrandized. His circuses on Cate Farm Meadow, between barn and river, were organized to assimilate their semi-natural context so that it was no longer, as in the city, contested setting nor incident: nor, however, an outside, containing frame: part of the show, rather. And his indoors shows during that same period did the same thing, they comprised an enclosing box as element, a frame that was part. In the last of them *(Simple Light)*, darkness was used for such an integrated frame. But now, in the '75 circus, though it centered in an old gravel pit, an artifact, but no longer recognizable as such, the show was set into the vastness of a brief summer and Vermont, no mere setting, but real world, and present to the spectator as such, neither subordinated nor integrated: unreduced. The hills did not rise behind the stage, the amphitheatre was open to the south. And the tent did not function in the show as its point of issue or reabsorption: the entrances and exits swamped the entrance-way adumbrated between tent and arena, and the powerful ones among them were over the hills on both sides, into and out of the landscape: the tent was visually insignificant from where the audience sat, did not provide a rear closure defining the stage as world. The show's containment in the landscape, the presence of the year's season, the advent of dusk turned man and human vision formless and insignificant, frittered mankind's dance of death down to a scattering of individual transactions. As heretofore in Schumann's work, the context did not structure the show, the puppets, singly and in their constellations, were self-referent. But the context, Vermont, summer, evening, was co-equally, positively, self-affirmatively there. We could think of the reductive effect of this on the show as a weakness of the show, as a failure of Schumann's as director. In fact, however, it fit in with the nature and meaning of the show, and by its design the show did not fight it, but promoted it, as though by a daring modesty of its designer's, making of his art a sacrifice. The show was meant to be emphatically open to the natural world, as to the community of mankind, and to place man in it.

This relationship of the show to its spatial and temporal environment, though characteristic of the whole circus, became explicit in the pageant, Part III, the *White Horse Butcher*. We might say that Schumann here achieved what his street parades had achieved relative to their Big City environment, though in the opposite way. He used the environment; the show related to it; it, its message and the puppets were realized by it. But in an opposite way: not by protest and domination, but by affirmation and emergence. He did this by making use of the dusk; by the slow motion (which generated some of the kind of anxiety that our slow motion in going about our business in life generates in us, given our awareness of the finitude of our life); by the whiteness of the show (marginally tainted by black like the black of the night that was swallowing it up); by the show's helical combination of repetition and increase of intensity (the woman's death topped by the deers', the woman's and the deers' deaths topped by the killing of the horse), a combination discretely raising it out of the sameness of the nature setting; and above all by the three long and gradual approaches ('entrances') – of the deer, the gulls, the ox cart – and the two long withdrawals ('exits'): the haunted boy's quick, panicked one, the murderous boy's slow, sadly triumphant one. These approaches and withdrawals *made* the play a natural focus of the landscape: a center created out of it – paradigm of ecological care.

* * *

Schumann had at the beginning of June, in time for the opening of the Museum, issued an invitation to the forthcoming *Circus*. We find that at this time, with rehearsals only a few weeks off, not only did it bear the amazingly somber and locally uninviting title *The Big American Dance of Death*, but that that's the show he had in mind, a different one from the one he made, though equally, as he says, a light and bright one. Though his past circuses had given him the recipe – silly circus – for the lightness and brightness, I suspect that the justification for them – viz. the minuteness and dreamlike epiphenomenality and quasi-guaranteed continuance of the human comedy/tragedy when viewed in the perspective of nature –

and the new[29] form of theatre, designed for that perspective, presenting that justification, the pageant, were a discovery he made during those rehearsals only.

'The BIG AMERICAN DANCE OF DEATH is a new Bread and Puppet production, a fusion of dance, circus and puppet-drama, using the experiences and techniques of many years of experiments with puppets and masks, of theatrical performances and social involvement.

The play is composed of several themes that have played an important part in our work for a long time: individual death, war, and prospects of fatality and hope for modern man in general and the American nation in particular.

The historical Dance of Death presented the world defeated. There are many reasons for an up-to-date defeat of the world with a danse macabre. However, the Bread and Puppet interpretation of the old ritual is not dark but light, not gloomy but bright:

See dragons fly to the music of our international garbageman orchestra!

See Death 18 feet tall dump 8-inch politicians!

See Governor Pilate of the corrupt Roman Empire wash his innocent puppet-hands to the hymns of our 'Sacred Harp' chorus!

See the 2 or 4 Horsemen of the Apocalypse ride into Washington!

See: Life and Death of Uncle Fatso
Life and Death of the Housewife
Life and Death of the US Army in Vietnam
The Stations of the Cross
Dance of the End of the World characters
Rites of Spring.'

(Flyer invitation to the 1975 circus, June '75.)

I wrote the following maybe a week after I'd gone up to Glover to see the circus:

Walking by myself through the city, a city, I had lived there at some time, Paris or San Francisco, no traffic, the streets seemed built onto or on the houses, ramps rather than staircases, I looked in a window on what was, at any rate, not a first floor: the young fellow, darkish had just gotten out of bed, stretched, in his pyjamas perhaps, looking down rather, a slow smile broke on his face, someone said 'but she is beautiful, she is beautiful!', the camera slowly turned past him into a darker part of the interior, perhaps by the stove and caught a slight look of her (but before all this I had at an upward angle seen the large studio windows of this apartment) and she was beautiful, small, dark, a big bosom, disproportionately big — to her height, age, beauty — tightly contained within her blouse and bra, a compact stocky figure altogether. Later I came to the top of a street and looked around a corner, winding, curved where it went down again, or

29. His pageants were new not only in being organized around a close-up, quasi-stationary performance, but by being designed not to include nature, e.g. as setting, but to include the spectacle in nature: without theatricalizing or otherwise denaturing the setting, but only generalizing it, a particular landscape, into Nature. I suspect certain non-European pageants, e.g. Hindu ones or the Brazilian Umbande offerings to Iemaja, the ocean goddess or to Cabocla Yara, the river goddess, may be of this sort.

another street, and I knew it all perfectly (Montmartre, Telegraph Hill), the low white 2- or 3-story wooden houses, perhaps, smiling in the bright sun, the car-less wide street: I knew the house the top story of which I was at or by, had perhaps lived there or had known someone in the building: so then I was inside in a long railroad or tunnel apartment, only the woman of the house, a girl, there, by the stove again, perhaps, not un-friendly and not seemingly worried when I made inquiries as to whether M. Etienne Bloch lived in the house (he did not, she said), and she guided me out a door at the other end of the apartment: only at the moment of parting (I was awkwardly saying I would look it up in the Bottin) did she now seem quite unfriendly, I had had no business being in her apartment.

I woke up to think, still in the warm way of sleeping thought, about a movie one could make entirely through a window or windows of some people's private lives, a movie of the seeing camera — I thought of shots outside of the girl, following her from behind or with the camera hidden in one's clothes — perhaps of a couple of working class newlyweds precisely in the morning (all this seems at the edge of sex, but has nothing to do with sex: everything is at the edge of everything, sex or death), getting up, breakfast, he leaving; then she alone, doing housework (problem of shop-ping, breaks the frontier of the glass — or mailman to whom she opens the door: no) perhaps the camera just going up into the sky in between morn-ing and his-coming-back/evening *(Sous les Toits de Paris,* the ending): con-vey the feeling — one movie only, a perfect movie, a masterpiece, perhaps only 20 minutes — convey the feeling of intimacy (not shared), of being outside looking in — the others, they — oneself: in a way intimacy only exists for others: between them there is space, they look at, see one another — of relation, also of life, viz. life passing, life lived (not action), but in a friendly way, showing it as beautiful, showing something beautiful, perfect in its finitude and natural nature.

Like a disjointed dream like which a movie could be, both of them a looking-in, Schumann's *Circus* should probably be thought of as providing a glimpse or shot of something, a huge bird coming over a hillside, a dragon winding slowly in an arena, its skin mullberries and fall leaves of linden ... (Wilson's *Casino/Carnival* had some of this humility of in-stancy). The artist, though laboring at structure, hopes a few moments like this will eventuate, in which infinitude will appear in something finite (this cliché out of the metaphysics of the ages has literal meaning in a way when it is used of say the representation of an animal which is large but appears against the sky, is looked or is to be looked at at that angle: (a) against the sky; (b) appearing and disappearing — infinitudes of sky, time). Perhaps the artist needs structure only to bring about such moments or we need all the incidentiae so the intimate beauty of individual life when seen will not be imposing, boastful, boisterous, nor for us, but withdrawn, within itself, modest, an interiority in outwardness, i.e. appropriate to greatness, great.

What more can one hope for than to bring about a glimpse of the grendeur and misery of life — of mortality — like the couples walking in the park before things define themselves in *Elective Affinities*. I think of this because that work seemed inspired by the hunger of 18th-century (French) science for comprehensiveness and system. Schumann's outdoor circus gives these glimpses of large things lost against/in/within a sum total planar (in spite the hills) landscape, earth and sky and they meeting, them appearing rather briefly and then gone again, beyond the rim of a hill or in the tent as though something glimpsed in the hand of a conjuror or con man, palmed, some colorful little object, a glass pearl like one year in school we all used to play with, some were quite beautiful, slowly rolling in the sand in a shallow indentation.

His *Circus* this way is both the opposite of what I saw him do in Brooklyn and at Papp's place on Lafayette St. in '70 and '71, when he had once before radically resettled, and never described, though they were some of the most beautiful things of the theatre I ever saw, and the same: I am thinking of three pieces, one, the one with Uncle Fatso outside, huge, drinking at a table or reading a newspaper, and a whole world of a city tiny or very small next to or behind him, with houses, tiny people appearing at windows, traffic and traffic accidents in the streets, elevators inside building, (all string-operated), times of day, a Vermont landscape and its times of day and even (in my memory which if I didn't have I could not recall it) seasons, spring and fall (the love-making couple under the cupped green hill, fall foliage), all as though life inside a kaleidoscope or camera oscura, seen through a tiny aperture, Lieuwenhook's glimpse — vision — vision as glimpse; the other, a whole life-day, life/day, in a working class family's life — beer drinking, housework, TV, family — seen through somewhat crinkled waxed paper or a plastic, deliberately, carefully, crinkled, so the vision would be of itself also: as a looking-in — a draft-notice arrives, mailman brings it — and the third piece: a tent with shapes bulging through the walls or emerging up through something like a teepee smoke-hole or from under the edge, or the tent gradually collapsing, coming apart, more monstrous and/or fairy tale figures or shapes in this one, an obscure myth in the minor key of a fairy tale always half-forgotten by who is telling it but remade up, this contributing to the monstrosity, i.e. ambiguity, doubleness, bastardness of the living figures glimpsed (obscurity of memory like obscurity of sight as we pass through the world seeing only part of things, seeing only part of their story, their careers, their lives, and seeing them from the outside). I am sure I 'mis'remember this third piece of his, involving a tent: but what does this 'mis' mean? Art is meant for not just the sight at the moment — glimpse — but for a life, i.e. digesting, revolving memory losing some, retaining other. In the outdoor circus the large things become small against the world-scene of the actual large landscape, and are imperfectly seen appearing briefly, and this is both the opposite and the same as when in those plays indoors we do not as in the *Circus* see things openly, clearly through the thin air of the northern summer, out of doors, in bright sunlight (or even rain), but in a more or less of darkness or through an aperture or through an interfering, distorting (refracting, rather) medium, and when they are small or by their monstrosity ill-defined or/and when the lights are low: each time life is dwarfed, we are outside, what we see is strange to us, strange, and yet grand, very large, partakes of the grandeur (I am embarrassed to use the word 'infinity') of the context, whether that context is obscuring obscurity, darkness, enclosure, closed-off-ness or large land and sky. The poignancy of dream-images seems to go with the disjointedness of dreams. In his Glover circuses, Schumann undertook a representation of mankind in which it would appear as something very small, and yet not seem diminished hereby: absorbed into the largeness of time and nature; and as something in a dream, unreal but significant.

Schumann's hope for an effect on a popular audience may be in terms of this power of art to deliver images that stay and that possibly unbeknownst to oneself alter one's perception, so that exposure to his pageants, for instance, might in subsequent life cause a shift toward revulsion in the feelings attending encounters with even those depredations on the environment by business by the viewers in question consciously accepted as norm. If he could make an *institution* of his circuses for at least some number of ordinary Vermonters, children especially, this power, vested with the authority of an institution would accrue. Since Schumann to a considerable extent placed his hope, what he had of it, in children, this conception of the effect of art would also help to explain his insistence on 'silly circus': not only disarming otherwise surely antagonistic adults, but by its appeal to children facilitating the child spectator's image absorption.

*　　*　　*

The sideshow groups seemed generally to be working with Schumann's masks and outlook, but without his intelligence or gifts, viz. were either sanctimonious and fake-simple, down to basics, or stridently political and righteously simple-minded. He claimed he had provided the 'texts for sideshows, flip-over stories, crankies, songs', but these would not have helped them: his gifts and intelligence get to work in puppet-making and staging. The two he had had a hand in, *Dirty Woman's Dream*, directed by Dupavillon,[30] and *Little U.S. Dance of Death*,[31] were as bad as the rest.

---

30. 'a dream that mom had and that I wrote down after she told it to me and then I made it into a show, with Margo performing the woman and Christian (Dupavillon) the part of the jailkeeper woman, and Steven Light playing some old music for it with his "Fire and Lightning Ensemble".' — (Schumann, interview, '79.)

Dream of the Dirty Woman was published in 1980 by Claire Van Vliet's Janus Press in

But though the sideshows, and they with no exception I know of remained unpleasantly arrogant ego trips during all his circuses, demonstrated a relation between being willing to work for Schumann and being unable to do things on one's own, Schumann had by the time he put on the '75 *Circus* not only reacquired the allegiance of a good many of the people he had just dumped — they provided the core of the performers — but had actually reconstituted a resident group of puppeteers, staying on at

---

Newark in West Burke township, about 30 miles away from Schumann's place. Van Vliet is a graphic artist, printer, and book- and papermaker, and with some assistance designs her fairly numerous publications from scratch. E.g. makes and chooses different kinds of paper for the same or different books — in the case of *Dream*, apparently some of the pictures' colors — it is illustrated by her — are not printed on the page, but are in the paper — the coloring matter was put in the pulp. The book comes in an obscenely opulent box, is a luxury object, and contains a record of the 13th-15th century music that went with the play. Elka feels the English text (there is some French text in between, contributed by Dupavillon who as the play's Jailor Woman invented it), by Schumann, does not quite render her sense of the dream:

'I lived in France at the time of the Revolution. They caught me. They transported me to the Bastille. I screamed and protested terribly as I was prepared for the guillotine.

The Woman attendant who dressed me into the white prisoner's clothes did not much bother about my efforts to escape. She knew that the hallways were long and full of heavily armed guards. She thought, how foolish it was, this protest of mine, in the face of an inevitable fate.

(Dupavillon text, the guardian's mumblings — about how the prisoner has become her friend . . .)

But I did break loose.

I ran and ran, guards behind me.

I jumped into a pile of white snow. I dug through the snow and found a cave underneath the snow.

31. 'A sequence of — there was a long workshop before the final performance, a very unsuccessful workshop, with lots of people from the neighborhood participating and trying to make a show of it but it never came about . . . a skeleton and with various funny, lots of funny . . . (Elka: Each little act ended with a Deathhead, with a skeleton coming out.)' — (Schumann, interview, '79.)

(French text — guardian's ruminations after the escape.)

Then I heard the guards searching for me. So I scraped the mud from the floor of the cave and dirtied my white prisoner's dress.

Then I succeeded to run out, unrecognized, into a big market place with many people, dyed my hair, bought fancy clothes, married a rich man . . .

. . . and only many years later was I recognized.'

Van Vliet's last picture is of a happily married full-bosomed young woman, by herself, arms spread, radiant — Elka, in telling of the dream makes its thrust the lasting feeling of uneasiness that sooner or later she would be found out — and this eventually happening. You can't escape.

The tome qua art work is described in Ruth E. Fine, *The Janus Press 1975-1980*, U. of Vt., 1982, as also two other Janus Press Schumann publications, *White Horse Butcher* ('77), *St. Francis Preaches to the Birds*. Van Vliet has also since '76 designed and printed several posters for Schumann's circuses — 'combin(ing) vigorous masonite cuts by Peter Schumann with the splendid assortment of old wood type that she has acquired over the years.' — (Fine, op. cit.)

Dopp Farm after the *Circus*, selected from among the '74 Cate Farm puppeteers (though only one of them, Barbara Leber, going back to '70/'71, was an old-timer), four or five people that were not only dedicated to him and his work, but in isolation up there rapidly have become professionals, not having anything but the work to occupy their minds; and who became pretty damn good at what they are doing, and have been doing it steadily in and out of season, as a routine. They have been the foundation of his circus and touring output since then and as of this writing ('83) still are, though there are now signs of break-up. When Margo Sherman in '75 came up to work on *Dirty Woman's Dream*, she was surprised by their independence,[32] but this independence has only very occasionally extended to independent productions, and no good ones I know of, though, as I said, they are really good at what they do for Schumann.

---

32. 'Well, I never was under any illusion that it was a collective, that it was a group in which the people and all the group made the decisions. I had seen from the very beginning that it was Peter who ran the theatre and made all the decisions and I fell in with that because of the kind of person I am. What was very, very hard for me was many years later when I discovered that the people who are now in the puppet theatre were more and more skillful at doing things and at making decisions and at their own autonomous creativity, that it was different, that they were deciding things on their own. And my tendency was always, 'Well, we better ask Peter, we better ask Peter.' And I remember one summer in Glover, I was working on a show, a beautiful show based on a dream of Elka's and Trudy was doing the music. And she said, 'Well, what do you think of this music?' And I said, 'I've got to run and ask Peter.' She said, 'I think we can decide ourselves.' This was '75. And that was quite a shock, when I had to start to get used to the maturity of the puppeteers who are now in the company.' — (Sherman, interview, '79.)

8. Failure of an attempt to get an indoors theatre piece out of the Circus, further aggravated by an attempt to substitute Christianity for the pantheism precluded by indoors performance.

He decided to tour the circus, and I know of nothing he did until he went on this tour: with a company of thirty, a third of whom were children, 16 or under, to North Africa and Europe, December '75-March '76. Having, for economic and organizational reasons, though this time, in great contrast to his stance of '73/'74, he put out he didn't mind,[1] to perform in theatres, he had to jettison the pageantry (including the opening dance-around-the-maypole adoration of the Nature deity): abandoning both the spectacle's air of local community festival and its aspect of a (pantheist) religious ceremony.

He reconceived it as a show about America, or, this being now the year of the bicentennial of the Declaration of Independence, about its history.[2]

---

1. Oddly enough, this time around Schumann didn't mind the conventional theatre setting, a total change from his position of '68/'70:

'We got to very good audiences, even though we played in conventional theatres. It's one of the barriers I would like to advise some people to throw overboard – their hostility to conventional theatres as some form of institution. I have more and more respect for these proscenium theatres – they're beautiful spaces. They're the most effective place for theatre which exists, next to Greek amphitheatres. I don't feel at all bad about using theatres like this one. I only feel sorry for our young followers here in Paris who won't come because we are playing in what they regard as a thoroughly bourgeois institution.' — (Schumann, interviewed by Malcolm Hay in Paris, Hay, *Our Domestic Bread & Puppet, Alternate Theater*, May, '76.)

But by '77, his mellow ecumenism of the early Dopp Farm years fading, he was back to his old dislike for traditional theatres:

'El teatro que se hace en las salas tradicionales es un teatro aprisionado. Sus verdades son verdades incompletas, decoradas, artificiosas.' — (*El Pais*, Madrid, May 26, '77.)

2. '(Elka: You thought and talked a lot about the show you wanted to travel, which was – you didn't think of *that* show as a traveling *circus* the way you thought of *this* year's (1979) show, as a traveling version of the circus, but what you wanted of this was like the bicentennial *theme* – it was very *strong* there, and it was going to be divided up into a history of the United States of America. You had a sort of manifesto for the show and I typed it out, and it was going to have – not *Elements of World War II*, but very big historical titles were given the different sections of this piece, but it ended with the *Big American Dance of Death*, I think. And actually, not that many – it didn't seem as though the final show had that much to do with that statement that was sent around to a lot of places that we were going to perform.) It did and it didn't. It was our first really American show in the theatre – it was based on the idea of a presentation of the Bicentennial by Americans, outside of America. That was an important thought to this tour. And I guess eventually we got caught up with the more intricate parts of it and more and more abandoned this over-all political and historical view.' — (Schumann, interview, '79.)

Part I of the summer's circus, the *Bicentennial Spectacular*, thus became the organizing focus (a role for which it was too slight). *Animals and Acrobats* which had been Part II, the silly circus, was thrown out of the body of the show, a logical move since in a show for foreigners it had lost a major part of its function — to make the event a community event. It became a prologue, largely performed by the children, sometimes done in lobbies,[3] not always done. *Hallelujah*, the pantheist invocation gone — it was sometimes performed separately on the tour — the show itself was to start off with a new piece, an untitled 'creation myth' the core of which in the following year's circus turned up as *Red Fire Bird Dance*.[4] The *Bicentennial Spectacle*, as he first planned the toured show, would follow. From it he eliminated its pre-1776 18th-century opening: it started with the attainment of independence, the raising of the flag in the presence of Uncle Fatso, and continued more or less as before through *Life, Liberty and the Pursuit of Happiness*. With its former beginning gone, the bite was gone, the parallel between post-independence plutocracy and pre-independence monarchy by

---

3. 'For twenty minutes before the start of the performance at the Theatre des Champs Elysees, the company take over the foyer and entertain the incoming audience. Seven or eight small acts take place simultaneously, as at a travelling fair: a fireater with a lady assistant beating a drum, a dancing dog, a fiddler accompanying a man sitting on the stairs who balances a plank of wood on which he makes a small wooden puppet-figure dance, a Punch and Judy show, a short play performed by the children of the Company, a small model stage on which tiny figures are moved to enact a scene in which a man catches a bird which flies away, a "cranky" — a toy movie screen on which a roll of paper is cranked to show pictures which resemble in style the images of later Bread and Puppet performance itself. The rich and ornate foyer is transformed for a brief period into an adult playground, a space for informality and enjoyment.' — (M. Hays, *Our Domestic Resurrection Bread & Puppet, Revived, Alternate Theater*, May '76.)

4. 'Die leere Bühne ist dunkel, langsam schiebt sich ein Pflug über die Fläche, gezogen von etwas, das nicht mehr ist als ein vergrösserter Spielzeugesel, noch langsamer, so langsam, dass sich der eigene Pulsschlag zu verändern scheint, kommen die Köpfe weisser Hirsche aus der Kulisse, in einem urweltlichen Rythmus beim Nicken und Schreiten. Vorne simuliert ein hexenhaftes Wesen mit Hilfe von einer ordinären Stablampe, etwas Holz und ein paar roten Lumpen ein Feuer. Irgendwann hat ein nicht zu ortendes, alles erfüllende Zirpen die Luft erfüllt. Eine schattenhaft im Hintergrund wirbelnde Figur wächst sich zum Dämon aus, dann wachsen immer mehr Dämonen aus der Erde, winzig wie Gnomen, riesenhaft auf Stelzenbeinen, mit primitivsten Mitteln wird der hektische Wechsel von Licht und Dunkel des Stroboskops erzeugt, man weiss nicht mehr, wann der Höhepunkt des Stücks erreicht war, wann er anfängt, in sich zusammenzusinken, von einer unsichtbaren, aber gegenwärtigen Sonne vertrieben.' — (Menck, *Unser häusliches Auferstehungsdrama*, Stuttgart newspaper, March 12, '76.)

'. . . something like a beginning-of-the-world part with the red birds and the drums. That big dance. And out of that dance was born the big Godface, and that called in Uncle Fatso, and that initiated the presentation of the history of the Declaration of Independence, with Uncle Fatso present.' — (Schumann, interview, '79.)

'La creation du monde: on creuse le sol pour le preparer. On fait le feu, le feu monte, le soleil se leve . . . La decouverte du feu . . . se deploie dans une danse d'echassiers.' — (program, *Spectacle de Notre Resurrection Americaine*, Algeria, January, '76.)

which he had belittled the American Revolution: *Life, Liberty* etc. retained the criticism of alienation and of the working class. This *Bicentennial Spectacle* would end with a scene, *The Home*, in which the garbagemen as formerly they had done at the opening of the *White Horse Butcher* set up the home of the sad lady in white: now her home is in America, an American home, and instead of writing a letter, she irons, has become a housewife.[5] This made a transition to *The White Horse Butcher* and made of it a comment on American reality rather than a universal statement. Within the confines of a stage, *The White Horse Butcher* was no longer a pageant, the processions making it part of nature were gone, and with them the pantheist religious perspective. Apparently, a garbagemen's dance of death — in the California dance-of-death ponchos, to the music of *Calvary* sung thirteen times — made a further transition from the *Bicentennial Spectacle* to the White Horse Butcher part:

> 'My thoughts that often mount the skies
> Go search the world beneath
> Where nature all in ruins lies,
> And owns her sovereign Death!'
>
> (Daniel Reed, *Calvary*, 1806.)

Having thus converted his religious celebration into a historical anti-American anti-celebration, he got cold feet, however, the show was now too starkly just anti-American, besides which he felt, as he had perhaps already felt about the summer's circus, that without an evocation of the old-time religion, a Christian play, and specifically one bringing up the moral challenge offered the individual by his finite life — which his pantheist pageant didn't deal with — and one set to music — something with the function of the '74 circus *Jephthah* — the show became too one-dimensional, so he at the last minute decided to reintroduce the mollifying higher perspective of religion by somehow making room in the show for *Stations of the Cross*.[6] He had done the same thing when in the spring of

---

5. 'It was a woman who had a life similar to the women that we now call washerwomen, only that — she was a fairy type person with a ghostlike appearance, and not a down-to-earth woman laundering. But her life was dominated by events that are similar to events in the life of the washerwomen.' — (Schumann, interview, '79.)

'(The garbagemen) leave, wisecracking, wishing him (a masked figure standing holding a solitary door) well. Immediately, in an extraordinary surreal image — as from a Bunuel film — a girl in white enters leading a puppet-donkey; on it the graceful figure of a woman. The girl knocks on the door; the masked lady enters and moves quietly over to the table. She leans over it, making slow movements with her arms. With a shock of recognition, one realizes that she is ironing. The fusion of the surreal and the mundane — an eight-foot high puppet, stylized movement, the mime of an everyday task — is always present at every stage of the play's development.' — (Malcolm Hays, *Our Domestic Resurrection Bread and Puppet, Revived, Alternate Theater*, May '76.)

6. (Ephraim: So just *parts* of the show were played in different places. The *Stations of the*

'71 he toured his '70 *Circus* — put in Jesus and the disciples. There was really no room for it, however, it didn't make sense relative to American history — nor did it provide a perspective on individual morality — so he kept shifting it around — originally, apparently, thinking of it as substitute for the *Hallelujah*, having it open the show, but on the tour, e.g. in Algeria in January, in Germany in March, making it a central part, as 'une reflexion sur la civilisation contemporaine occidentale traduite par un chemin de croix' (Algerian program, January, '76, *Spectacle de Notre Resurrection Americaine*), sometimes didn't perform it at all, or performed it separately, and was generally apologetic about it, in his announcements saying it dealt with 'the Christian mythology which (once) was the center of our civilization.'[7] It offended the muslim in North Africa. The play without *Stations*, presented to the more or less recently independent nations of Africa, would have had the clear message 'independence is all very well, but beware lest what happened to us (America) doesn't happen to you, beware of capitalism!', but with *Stations*, not only did the play no longer have any such clear message, but could almost be taken for presumptively Christian propaganda, if only by intimating the paradigmatic excellence of the Christ myth.[8]

Cross would either be played by itself or left out, sort of . . .) (Elka: Well, when was the decision made to include *Stations of the Cross* in it — wasn't that pretty late, or had you conceived of it as including *Stations of the Cross*?) No. That was probably added shortly before we just — departed. To include also *Stations of the Cross* into it. (Elka (laughs): When it was done in Lyndon and in Burlington, it *didn't* include *Stations of the Cross*, but when it was done at Lyndon College, the chorus there did rehearse the music and join in.) The idea certainly was go get an audience involved in the same manner that an audience gets involved into our circuses *here*, that is, not in *one* manner, not in one easy-to-take-care-of piece of entertainment, but in many manners and in many ways.' — (Schumann, interview, '79.)

7. '(Elka: It seems as though, looking back, a lot of what you wanted to take just didn't really work — the prologue, a lot of places.) Yes. We had to tailor it down so often and so much — we had to adapt to *so* many places where what we *wanted* to do *couldn't* be done, including the length of the play, and the requirements for these big differences. There was too much tailoring going on. The whole tour was one big tailoring job . . . (Ephraim: It seemed as though the shows were really worked a lot on during the tour and they weren't finished at all when the tour started — by the time the tour was over a lot of the parts were really different from when it started, so there was a lot of work that was done on parts of the show — it seems as though that is something that is different than a lot of the other tours.)'

8. 'The tour was meant to go to Africa, that was its main goal and we didn't quite succeed to go where we wanted to go. We wanted to go to Senegal and different places in Africa but it just didn't materialize. So we ended up with a European tour that carried us to a *few* new places like Algeria, Tunisia and Greece — and otherwise it was grounds that we knew . . . (Elka: Peter, what do you think of the wisdom or value of the experience of bringing something with a Christian content to a non-Christian country, to Tunisia and Algeria? While we were *there*, people from those countries *commented* about that.) They *complained* about it. (Elka: They were very alienated and said that it had nothing to say to them.) I don't agree with that. That's perfectly okay to — the arguments weren't too good, they said

Being no longer circus, the title of the show was variously *Our Domestic Resurrection, Our Domestic Resurrection Spectacle* or (in Algeria) *Spectacle de Notre Resurrection Americaine*, but Schumann still thought of the show — about $3\frac{1}{2}$ hours long, a little shorter only than in '75 on Dopp Farm the *Hallelujah* plus the *Circus* — as like his Dopp Farm circus:

'The idea was to create a show which would not allow people to have that easy meal which a theatre performance often provides, where they get into the rhythm

that their culture doesn't include Christianity and they know nothing about it and the play's based on the knowledge of the Christian church and they had no interest in it and they had no education that way. Well, that's like telling *me* that I shouldn't go to a performance of an African tribe — where they display *their* religious ceremonies. I am really interested in that. And I wish that they would perform that for me and not a piece of westernized or adapted — piece of culture that they *think* is more understandable to me — so I appreciate, as a member of the audience, when people show to me what they *have* and what they *are*. Often they show to me what they think I should *see*. I find nothing wrong at all to go to Africa with a Catholic show. I am not a Catholic myself, but even so a show has its rights. (Elka: Even to parts of Africa that have a long history of proselytizing and missionary work?) Yes, they also have the proselytizing from western man, from white people, and from white culture *generally* speaking, and from America, so we shouldn't go as Americans and as white people, we should do color over ourselves first and go painted black. We don't do that. (Elka: Well, I felt reservations about going to Africa, and I expressed them at the meeting.) It's true. There are questions about it — where you go and why you go and why you want to go there. (Elka: And what you perform when you get there.) But you yourself understood how *wrong* it was when we at the Polish festival saw Russian groups perform shows, anti-American and slogan shows, telling us about Kennedy's murder and all kinds of secrets that we supposedly are not allowed to speak out about and all this kitsch and schmaltz stuff about *their* opinions and what we ought to *see*. But I feel there is no need to adapt — you speak with this language and with these puppets and this is what we do, a language that is very understandable and that does not rely on learning of a new vocabulary. (Elka: But I felt something about this tour — was that *you* had expressed your desire to go to Africa, you had made that one of the *main* reasons to do this tour, and Christian, with fabulous work and several trips from Paris to Africa and, I guess (laugh) a million dollars worth of long-distance phone calls was able to organize this tour, but it really felt as though — I think in retrospect and also *while* we were in Tunisia and Algeria — it really felt as though we were not especially welcome or desired or wanted. Somebody had obliged Christian or whatever pressure Christian had put, including foreign embassies and so on.) I don't know how interesting this is, what we are talking about now, maybe we should stop right here. Because this is *not* interesting. I *agree* that we overestimated their welcoming our work there, the acceptance there — there was no need for us to go to Algeria and to Tunisia. They didn't want us. It was a French organizer who put us there — it wasn't the Algerians that asked us to come. So probably it is better to wait. We are not pushers. We usually wait. (Elka: Then what about taking the *Stations of the Cross* as a piece which didn't work in a non-Christian country because they weren't especially interested in it, but which was about the most controversial piece we traveled with when we *did* travel in France and Greece, in Italy, everywhere people would — and in Quebec, when we took it to Canada, they would also protest about this being — this is what we've been trying to get away from.) I agree, it's very provoking and I agree with the provocation. It's good. I like that much better than the hand-clapping in the audience. It's very good. It's very good in Quebec when the kids really hate us. It's very good. A very good reaction.' — (Schumann, interview, '79.)

341

9. The Circus of '76: History is insignificant, evil rules, what counts is the moral tenure of the individual.
4th version of *The White Horse Butcher*.

'Art is no longer a decorator for religion. Art is by now what religion used to be. It is the design for the line of thought, the form for the communal event, the shape of the celebrations that we might have with each other.'
(Schumann, interviewed August 17, '76. In F. Falk, *Bread and Puppet Resurrection Circus, Performing Arts Journal* II (1), Spring, '77.)
'Our Domestic Resurrection Circus is the rites of modern humanity – as seen from a papier maché standpoint.'
(Schumann, *River Valley Voice*, September '82.)

There were no new pieces from Schumann from the summer of '75 to the summer of '76. He was preoccupied by the White Lady, by Bob or Johnny or Eric the Butcher, by the capture of beautiful swift wild animals, their subjugation, domestication – which causes them to lose the beauty of their wild unreasonable freedom: killing them is incidental to this though Schumann bore down upon it. There were so many angles to it: is it not the White Lady that captures Bob, Eric and Johnny and domesticates them – to the detriment of their artistic creativity? Or is it men that kill the spirit of their loves once they have captured their hearts? Had he not perhaps killed the wild things of his imagination by his capture of them in art? Had not Yankee capitalism, Calvinist, thus Judaic, killed off the beauty of the wilderness erecting in it the kingdom of Satan? State-capitalism, technology-mad, was destroying nature. And the Indian, the Plains Indian, one with his horse! But then the white railroad layers exterminated the buffalo. Having toured his warmed-over '75 *Circus*, he went straight to the '76 (July 31st, August 1st) *Bread and Puppet Domestic Resurrection Circus*, essentially focused on this multi-faceted theme again.

The first two parts of the '75 *Circus*, the *Bicentennial Spectacular, Animals and Acrobats*, had been fused into one spectacle (2-3:15 p.m.) called *Bicentennial Circus*, but essentially silly circus rather than on America and its history, the subversive sting of '75 reduced to a few good-naturedly satirical allusions. This silly circus was introduced by a Butcher and by the emblem of a Stars and Stripes Peace Band and was preceded

344

neither by *Hallelujah*, nor by a dedicatory dance around a deity, and so had been constituted a self-contained unit, was no longer part of a whole containing the pageant: Schumann had abandoned the formal unity of the event. The message of this circus history may be nasty but is not serious. A Christian mystery play, *Jesu, Meine Freude* had been introduced as second part (6:30-7:15 p.m.). Its thrust was dual: the individual must orient him-(her)self toward the finitude of his(her) life (face your future, it is death!), and: the substance of individual life is moral choice, moral choice is real, a life is the occasion for choice between good and evil: face your present, it is your only chance to do right![1] By it, Schumann achieved what he had failed at trying to put *Stations* into the traveled version of the '75 circus: it worked as disparate unit of the '76 *Circus* and supported the element foregone by the concluding pantheist pageant, the theme of individual morality, in the light of which the message was: though all comes and goes and Evil always again destroys Good, the individual must (should) do good, like Christ going to his Golgotha. *The Domestic Resurrection Pageant*, gathered up into a self-contained unit also (8:10-9:15), introduced by what in '75 had been the dedication of the whole, the dance around the deith, the deity this time around no longer a female nature deity, but a male patriarchal deity combining attributes of stern rule and fecund solarity with Christian allusions, provided a cathartic conclusion. The deity, the deity this time around no longer a female Nature deity, but a part of the pageant's 'story', returns as moon at the end of the pageant – inaugurating its and the circus' concluding 'night piece', a *Red Fire Bird Dance* – to revive the dead animals: there are no white ladies, suffering, loving or resurrecting, in this pageant. It has dropped the private and the story elements of the '75 *Circus* pageant and has taken over the silly circus function of a presentation of American history – as the mimeographed 'circus project' sheet distributed to volunteers has it it is a *Bicentennial Pageant* 'about Indians': but it is history only on a very abstract level, and is no way a political statement. It poetically restates the opposition Business-Man of the Bicentennial Pageant as opposition Business-Nature. What politics there is in this circus has been relegated to the 3-6:30 'side-shows' and concerns the Third World (*The Mountain Man of Chile*, government terrorism in South America, *Lamentation*, famine in Asia.)

*   *   *

No more than any of the others before or since was this circus advertised in New York. A dozen or two of Schumann's old-time followers from there showed up, but overwhelmingly the crowd was locals, Vermonters and some French Canadians, with a predominance of bearded

---

1. Carlene Fernandez after returning from the spring tour to Europe had started working on the *'76 Circus*, but was asked by Elka to leave, and did so.

pseudo-rural hippie transplants and student and faculty academic types, but this time with a good representation of ordinary Vermonters,[2] with small kids, large families, working-class types. The weather was rainy. It had rained for two weeks up there. As it turned out, the weather was reasonably dry Saturday, July the 31st, and the sun actually emerged on Sunday. It is quite a risk Schumann is taking in staging these once-a-year grand outdoor shows. This risk-taking is significant: as gamble per se, as gamble on nature.

A little way from the break in the hedges through which you enter the field from the car-choked dirt road, Maurice Blanc in a little hut sells programs for ten cents, tells you there is no entrance fee. A bucket for contributions is on the ground, not very noticeable. Down nearer the circus playing area, Schumann carves and hands out his rye bread, aioli- or butter-covered – free. He is the host, steadily cutting his bread for the multitude, not looking up. As the previous year, a number of sideshows and food stands line the perimeter.

* * *

Bicentennial Circus.

There is no tent this time. Instead, the two touring buses, one yellow, the other blue on top, green below – sun, sky and grass – are drawn up tail to tail at the eastern edge of the arena, opposite the incline on which the spectators sit. The staging area is to the rear of the buses. Together with a drop that covers the space left for entrances between them – it has a tree and the word 'circus' on it – the buses provide a rearward visual closure. Along the blue and green bus's top is stretched a banner with the pictures of two animals and of a red sun on it, along the top of the yellow one, a semi-abstract grey and white picture of a boiler room. The unrelatedness of styles is the point of this off-hand symbolic contrast. The bandstand area is right in front of the left-hand blue and green bus, and in front of it a big bale of hay with two small U.S. flags. There is a row of six kitchen chairs in front of the right-hand bus, and in front of it a garbage-can cannon on wheels and a tarpaulin. The arena is outlined by a narrow band (a foot to a foot and a half high) of blue and white fabric on short stakes, with doves and flowers on it: open toward the backdrop of the two buses and the cur-

---

2. 'The main thing is, 1976 was the year we made it in Vermont. Until then we had it pretty tough sometimes, disagreeable, often cold acceptance in Vermont, and in '76, in the bicentennial year, when many little villages around here got money for bicentennial parades and celebrations, a lot of them *invited* us. They had heard about – (Elka: I think they made them without getting money – the bicentennial celebrations.) I heard a lot of them having money for their special bicentennial days and they had heard about this stilting Uncle Sam – I guess that was one of the major reasons for inviting us – and about these brass band parades that we did, so we got more invitations than we could take on, and a *great* part of that summer went into parading in the villages and that was one of the major occupations, and it didn't reflect much on the circus, because in the circus all of this is just – well, put *in*, as part of it . . .' — (Schumann, interview, '79.)

tained entrance. In its center a dirty-white plywood octagon, perhaps twenty feet across. It looks very small in the circle.

I missed the Saturday performance. The Sunday performance was postponed to 4:00 p.m. on account of the rain all morning. The line of cars down Route 122 was shorter than on Saturday. It took an hour and a half or less for the circus to be set up. They seemed ready by 3:30. Jugglers and flag twirlers are practicing behind the green and blue bus on the left. The elephant has been carried over from the *Johnny the Horsebutcher* exhibition tent by the bend of the woods, is waiting behind the yellow bus. The black barrel of the ash can cannon is gleaming. The red sun stands out on the banner over the blue/green bus, between the two running animals.

The performers – 90% in white – are busy all over on the sere grass. Schumann, bushy-bearded, is still giving out his bread at the bread hut off in the distance over the rise. The sky is grey with darker grey clouds. The spectators, some one to three thousand, have begun seating themselves from the rim of the bowl on down, a basic blue jeans blue, with specks of other color. The band starts playing a gay smooth march, umpah, umpah. (Just about all march music to this show: gay, merry, nostalgic – not very military.) Generalized afflux to bowl. The band by the green and blue bus on the left is bunched into a ragged crowd – the big gleaming tuba stands out, tarnished silver. A man in striped blue/white/red pants, suspenders, sweeps the hexagonal center.

White runners come down over the bowl's north rim in a motion of enthusiasm, twelve of them, big red and a few green and yellow simplified flower heads on white cloth at the end of long poles, a twirler out front – he throws up his closed flag, it unfurls, has 'Bread and Puppet circus' on it. Four such flags, eight with flowers. Twirling to the march music. The flag carriers having circled on the run, form a double line to the 'gate', flags lowered. An announcer – sharp, dark fellow (same as last year), tophat and tails, red pants – he announces most of the numbers – rough accent, professional slickness – good – in on run: 'The Emperor of the United States of America, His Majesty, Uncle Fatso.' To a heraldic air from the band, flags parting before him, the familiar money bags, grotesque populist image of the robber baron, trust king, enters in black, heavily. Also a crowd of workmen in their little green caps and their miscellaneous working mens' jackets and pants, and a wondrous being in the shape of a polyp, its head sausagey fingers, its body-painting (costume) the design of the American flag, hanging around: Old Glory as an incident. It may be the peace sign incarnate. An announcer (for just this number), also in black, small but bulky shapeless figure of a capitalist/employee/bureaucrat,[3]

---

3. The figure goes back at least to the little seated figures in *Johnny Comes Marching Home*. This announcer is one of the Black Men of the evening pageant. They have a sad, tragic air: of painted duty, permanent decay. The executioners in Kafka's *Der Prozess* may have looked not unlike them. They are Schumann's 'Butchers'.

announces The Raising of Old Glory. Old Glory is raised, i.e. a piece of pipe stuck into the ground. No flag visible. Workmen at attention. National anthem from the band.

The announcer (tophat, red pants . . .), through a bullhorn, back at the bandstand, announces a photo is to be taken, says 'cheese': Uncle, the workmen pose, photo taken.

'Mr. George Washington!'

A little kid in 3-cornered hat, in costume, greets Uncle Fatso, makes a curtsey.

'The famous signing of the American Declaration of Independence!'

The workmen watch George Washington signing it with a long blue quill. It takes a long time (comments from the band). Clapping. Rider with bugle on a one-man horse, i.e. just himself, appears over northern rim, galloping, 'bad news!', 'and now the British are coming!' King George is on stilts with Union Jack, tall — 'The Great American Revolution!' — 'And in this corner, Mr. Max Schumann.' It's Schumann's boy as George Washington: squaring off against big King George. 'The shot heard around the world'. David aims, shoots King Goliath — George III — falls over backwards slowly, is caught by announcer and another. George Washington watches. Workmen carry the King out, to music.

(There is really no point in my describing the bulk of this Bicentennial Circus following its historicising overture. It was a rapid succession of only moderately funny inept numbers, their ineptness ineptly done. I will skip to its end, a sudden emergence of the marvellous.)

Unannounced, a 4-headed white cow, its body a slightness of muslin between the heads — all heads — the heads, joined at the center, are enormous, extend in a circle, enters, rotates to delicate Eastern string-strumming and to bell-tinkling from its white-robed guardian, a silent merry-go-round, a gentle, quietissimo beast, inoffensively grotesque, stunning, touching. Also a gigantic white elephant, perhaps 10 or 12 feet tall, led by a white bear, preceded by 2 oriental fakir guide-attendants, one in black, blowing a recorder, the other in Buddhist orange, holding a Black-eyed Susan in one hand, a long-handled white fly-chaser (with which he fans himself in a steady off-beat to his stately parade walk) in the other. The elephant has a body and 4 tree-size legs of white muslin, a white muslin trunk over wire coils. Its 8 foot (or so) tall face has golden flowers down the middle, petals for eyes, large white muslin ears: utter mildness altogether. On it a silver-guirlanded, roofed litter house, small silver birds at the 4 corners, a white prow-angel ornamentally stuck to its front, in which sits a boy maharaja, diamond in his black turban, and, next to him, a reclining white female — puppets.

The sacred cow is rotating in the center. Almost unnoticed, a purple monster, tie-dyed, low to the ground, like the two others generically bovine, perhaps a hippopotamus, its legs striped (child-carriers inside, presumably), has entered, led by a red hooded figures. Monster and elephant very, very slowly, in little steps, with a Siamese bending of the knees, circulate around the ring. The recorder can be heard only when the elephant guide passes near. A moment – perhaps 4 minutes – of great delicate beauty. The slowly rotating cow, the straight attendants, the mystery beast, the majestic beast. The cow rotates out, the two others follow. (Clapping.)

The announcer announces a gift to be sent to 'outer space', 'to the people's republic of the moon': 'John Glenso'. A busty lady in tight silver gown, blue hair, long turquoise gloves, officiates sexily. John G. in Superman cape, tights, unbuckled black galoshes climbs a ladder after saying goodbye to his mum, also there, climbs down again, climbs into the barrel of the black garbage can cannon ('so long, world!'), the sexy lady pats him down. Drum whirl, count-down stops, it's the President calling – 'Sure, I'll call you President Jerry', he is patted back into the cannon, – 6 – 5 – 4 – 3 – 2 – 1, drumbeat, a small pistol crack, a cymbal clash behind us at the bowl's western rim: an identical figure is landing there! All off.

'The grand finale! Uncle Sam himself and his cavalcade of wars we have known!' To 'My Eyes Have Seen the Glory of the Coming of the Lord', Peter Schumann, incredibly long and slim, Uncle Sam hat, white shirt, bearded face high above the red-striped overall trouser legs endlessly down over stilts perhaps 15 feet long, dances in, the figure's legs (not his) seeming articulate, his arms in a dancer's, not just balancing motions, does a delicate stomping dance on the wood octagon. Continues it during the sequel. The Revolutionary War ('Yankee Doodle Dandy'), the French and Indian War, the War of 1812, the Civil War ('Johnny Comes Marching Home') successively enter rambunctiously: dragons of varying sizes, extremely colorful, all seeming quite small because of the giant figure in the striped overalls. They dance in playfully, collapse around the center. The Mexican War ('La Cucaracha'), the Spanish American War (dragon and bullfighter in red, with cymbals), World War I (multi-colored rag airplane with a beast face; 'U.S. Marine Song'), World War II ('Anchors Aweigh'). The thin figure dances abstractly in the middle, high above. 'And now the war you've all been waiting for, World War III', noise: a 20-person green tarpaulin dragon with a 6-foot crocodile head on a cart snakes in.[4] All the wars, resurrected, and the band parade around: the white band, the green dragon, the many-colored war beasts. 3 or 4 tiny fireworks go off, golden sparks. The band is back at the bandstand

---

4. 'But times have changed. Schumann has radically revamped images of violence. In the total experience of the *Circus* it is even appropriate to laugh at ultimate destruction . . . In this version of the 'World', even World War III has been defused. Its awesome menace is encompassed by a mere dragon.' — (Falk, *The Bread and Puppet Domestic Resurrection Circus*, . . . 1976, *Performing Arts Journal*, Spring, 1977.)

playing 'When the Saints Come Marching In'. Wars out, Schumann with them, dancing. Applause. All back in, jumping, applauding, with two white 'Bread and Puppet Circus' banners, Schumann still on stilts behind them. End of circus.

The circus was purely funny this year. Nary a bit of subversion. An irruption of sheer silliness, good humor. Thus Uncle Sam's wars: glittering worm-beasts, strange and tumultuous, not sinister, mortal themselves, a merry succession. The evening pageant's negativity-overcoming over-view of American history justified the merriment of the circus' bicentennial celebration, rendered a verdict of 'not guilty' over it.

*   *   *

Bach's *Jesu, meine Freude* ('with Bread and Puppet Theatre and Goddard Community Chorus').[5]

You advance by a path outlined by twine with red flannel strips into the checkerboard pine plantation (here and there closer to its edge, some other small cleared performance area, e.g. one of three low rounded huts with erotic sculpture in vivid reds, etc. in half relief on their interior walls) to a small roundish clearing. To trees on both sides of the path[6] are tacked red and blue pictures on carton, the red ones on black, of devils and dragons spitting fire, the blue ones on white, of dancing and of mothers and babies.

---

5. '*(Jesu Meine Freude)* was rehearsed during the same period (as the *Circus*). It wasn't mixed in with any other preparations. It consisted of preparations that *I* did with a *few* puppeteers and I built the puppets for it, rehearsed the ideas with a few puppeteers and had very few rehearsals together with the Community Chorus – it was not available much . . . The skull-masked people with instruments were responsible in the beginning to carry the woman in – out of that house – because this Bach cantata is a dedication to a woman who just died. He wrote it for the occasion of a death of a housewife, I think a Bürger of Nürnberg, I believe. I think it was somebody from far away.' — (Schumann, interview, '79.)

The '75 *Dance of Death* also had taken off from a woman's death – who in the travelling show became a housewife. And Jephthah's daughter welcomes him in the manner of a housewife.

Of Bach's four surviving motets, three are funeral music, one for the wife of a deputy mayor, one for a rector and professor, *Jesu meine Freude* (Motet #227) for 'Frau Oberpostmeisterin Kees':

'Jesu, meine Freude/ Es ist nun nichts, nichts/ Unter deinen Schirmen/ Denn das Gesetz des Geistes, der da lebendig machet/ Denn, denn das Gesetz des Geistes . . . Trotz, Trotz dem alten Drachen . . . Ihr aber seid nicht fleischlich, sondern Geist/ Ihr aber seid nicht fleischlich . . . Weg mit allen Schätzen/ Weg mit allen Schätzen/ Weg, weg, weg, weg mit allen Schätzen . . . So aber Christus in euch ist, so aber Christus in euch ist . . . Gute Nacht, Gute Nacht, o Wesen . . . So nun der Geist dess, der Jesum von den Toten auferwecket hat . . . Weichet, ihr Trauerge ister.' — (J. Franck, 1653.)

6. Tacked onto the first left-hand tree, an advertisement for 'A New England Sacred Harp Singing' on October 2, 1976, at Wesleyan University Chapel in Connecticut, 'Come join with singers from New England, as well as a bus-load of southern folk . . . Free admission with lunch on the grounds!'.

350

The inclined clearing, closely ringed by the woods, is the theatre. Hay bales and rows of split logs provide seating for spectators — though not for as many as the 2,300 that came — at its upper end. The entrance path comes down between the hay and the log sections. Another path goes off into the woods to the right a little below, by a small stockade made of pine sapling trunks held together by twine. It and four more pine constructions — built between and right onto live pine saplings — in a semi-circle ring the small clearing. They have been built for this show, make the clearing its stage. At the lower end of the clearing a pine-branch-roofed log cabin, Humble Abode of the Living Mortals, the bark still on the logs, with door and window openings. To the right of it and a little nearer, a two-story shack, Heaven above and Hell below, essentially a platform six feet or so off the ground, solid wood construction carpentered onto four tall pines, with, on the sides visible from the spectator area, cloth-drops for walls on both stories, blue ones above the platform, red ones on the bottom, a fire-spewing upwardly maw-opening dragon and sinners falling headlong toward it on the ground floor drop, a white sinner and/or Christian, arms uplifted, on the second story, above the satanic beast below, light rays coming out of her fingertips, her breasts the heads of winged angels that issue from her mouth, blowing trumpets out of which fly doves bearing (olive?) twigs in their beaks, stigmatic punctures on her hands and feet. She may be Christ. Invisible from the clearing, a ladder with a handrailing leads up to the second heavenly story in back. To the left of the log cabin, an equally solid tiered stand for the choir (32 singers, among them Elka Schumann), four raw pine planks abutting on the cabin, and, a little nearer to the spectators, a little way out into the clearing, an open platform, about ten feet up, with a homemade raw pine ladder leaning up against it, perch for the angelic director of the soul's judgment.

Saturday I came just before the show started and except for the white-dressed chorus (in front of them in the black of a saturnine school- and ring-master magician, their conductor) and an immobile sculpture on top of the open platform, white trumpet-horn in hand, its large white gauzed face semi-floral (growth and soul the predicates amalgamating the kingdoms of nature in the kingdom of Schumann's imagination, the growth just this side, precariously, of the cancerous), and the spectators perched in the pine needles among the slender trunks all about, the place seemed deserted — no players — and one expected merely a concert, no show.

Sunday, the sunlight came through the pines (they have greenery only at the very top), a wooden chair stood in front of the red drop. Margo Sherman, slight, mounts the ladder to the platform, puts a large (it's maybe $2\frac{1}{2}$-3 feet tall) white mask-head and the trumpet on it, mounts after, untucks the mask's shirt costume from within it, dresses, turns into one of Schumann's elderly monks — the Angel Gabriel? The white angel appears suspended above the choir (an assembly of studious heads, mostly female).

There are grey lines painted on the mask's face, its ears are outlined on it. Its mouth, at the end of a snout-like protuberance, is an open circle, the small eyes are holes. Its expression is one of dead severity. Margo's hands are bare, nothing else of her shows. She stands immobile, an effigy. Elsewhere high above, closer to the two-story structure, a pair of white wings, barely more than a draped sheet, outline of a gull, have been hung from ropes passing between the upper parts of pines, a pull rope going into the upper story of the two-story structure. The sun is behind the trees behind them, a stained glass chapel effect.

A cloaked and hooded figure leans out of the cabin's window with a violin, stroking it. A low hum, barely a tune. A blue-faced woman, her face a chalky blue, silver on her trailing grey headkerchief, purple hues in her milky blue gown, holding a string of crystals, stately, comes out of the hut, sits, eyes closed, under the white angel's perch. A procession of grey-cloaked raggedy figures, their demonic faces grey-fleshed masks of death, silently comes down the path we entered by, carrying silent old-fashioned musical instruments, accompanied by small monster-faced grey beasts, scampering, dog-like, across the clearing, enter, with their hounds, one by one, the stockade. The fiddle stops, the fiddler disappears. The white angel, lifting her horn, turning slightly toward us − its coming to life is startling − in an engaged, emphatic girl's voice announces the first section of the cantata, 'My Heart's Great Joy'.

It is sung. The black bandmaster in his tophat, bearded, is a grotesque touch − l'insolite − in this partly naive, partly sublime mystery. The colored balloons of the many children bob gaily out front. His hands move delicately in precise motion. Two of the grey deaths bring out a crude stretcher with a sheet-draped figure on it, put it down, station themselves at the cadaver's head and feet, another brings out a kitchen chair in which is seated a puppet of an old man, black and white, his face silver, fur-capped, wearing gardening gloves, tie, a white flower in his buttonhole − the attire of a wake? − the widower? The puppet's carrier, bigger than the other deaths, with an especially brutal large face, who has remained standing behind him, lifts up his gloved puppet's hands, holds them over his eyes, holds them there − the sorrowing husband. Two others bring out a used baby carriage, ordinary looking, a dirty pink, with two small paper maché figures in it. The singing ends.

The angel announces 'There is no damnation for those who do not follow the flesh but the spirit.' As the choir starts singing, the blue (heavenly) curtain snaps aside on the tower's upper story, three sun-disk-faced figures in orange-yellow robes, a very tall one (holding the rope going to the suspended white wings) in the middle, stand revealed. One thinks one has seen their like in some medieval print, a frieze of puppets or comedians, looking down from some stage balcony onto a masked crowd in Flanders, the Lowlands or some Swabian town. The two deaths unsheet the body, lift it. It is an ornately dressed woman, her face a white mask, her hair flaxen. She sits on the stretcher, face lowered. The Indian woman tinkles her crystals over her. The Sun King lowers the suspended wings, the deaths fit them to her body. Tinkling. The yellow god pulls on the string, seems to pull the defunct into an upright position, she stands, her arms raised, pearls around her neck, her eyes quick brush strokes. The deaths leave head and foot of the unsheeted, bare stretcher. The blue woman with her crystals remains by it. The singing ends. Silence.

An ornamentation of pot lids hung on a string, honorific emblem of her work in life, protective amulet, is brought out and tied around the Christian woman's neck. She is guided to the tower, seated on the chair in front of it, four scarlet devils throng out from its lower floor, threatening her from the left. She is covered with metal disks, lifts hands to her face — as though frightened?

The angel, 'Even in thunder and lightning I am protected.' Singing. The death behind him raises the husband's arms into the air. The four devils are silently grabbing — in a sea-motion — past him at his dead wife. The blue figure is seated under the angel again. Devils off, baby carriage off, pot lids removed, husband carried out. The three golden figures are still above. Two other sun figures enter, stand by the Christian — protecting her?

The angel, 'The law of the spirit has freed me from the law of death.' Singing. The Sun King's motions (inclinations and arm movements, more blessing than pomp: *all* the sun masks smile) seem to guide the Christian up from her chair, the two new sun figures guide her to the naked stretcher by the Angel's pedestal. The string from her to the sun god is quite clear behind her.

The angel, 'In spite of the old dragon I stand here singing.' Singing. The Sun King claps his hands, a three-headed crimson dragon scoots out from beneath him, from behind the red curtain, muzzle gaping, attacks the Christian. The Christian has been given a pair of old gardening shears, wards off the dragon by snapping them at him snippishly. The dragon draws back, advances again, the four devils with him. The Christian is given (the Sun King hands it down) a pole with a white dove-like bird on it, seems to taunt or tempt the snapping dragon with it, the dragon collapses, is removed. One of the ground-level suns takes the pole.

Angel: 'You are made not of flesh but of spirit.' Singing. The Christian, who has been raised on the litter, is carried, seemingly led by the Sun King's string, preceded by the two suns, the front one of which carries the pole-bird — could it be the Christian's soul? — in procession, the four red devils to the rear making grabbing or spell-casting motions, back to in front of the Sun King (the angel watching), is given the pole-bird, hands it to the Sun King who receives it with benign musical gestures. A small flesh-colored doll is hanging from the Christian's back. Singing ends.

Silence. The Christian is aided off the litter, which is removed by two deaths. Returning, they bring out a covered garbage can, place it in front of her. Three suns on top of the tower, two in front of it. Her back is to them, the garbage can in front of her.

The angel, 'Away with all treasures.' Singing. A death takes the lid off the can, the Christian very slowly takes off her pearls, her bracelets, one by one drops her ornaments delicately into the can. Through the cabin's windows protrude the fleshly fingers of all the devils, wiggling greedily. The singing ends, silence. The garbage can is removed by a death. The Christian stands upright in front of the tower, before the four suns.

The angel, 'But the spirit is life.' Singing, the oriental woman gets up, walks in her sleep-walking gait, her right with the crystals hanging from it, tinkling, out in front of her, up the path past the kennels (where the dogs have been milling about), disappears. The Christian looks after her, raises her arms. She reappears, leading a white horse, its eyes, tail, mane black, with a small sun rider puppet on it, its head a flat disk. The Christian bows down before her, again raises her arms. The singing ends, silence. The blue figure kneels in front of the Christian. The pink baby doll is taken off the Christian's back, given to her. She holds it.

The angel, 'Goodnight o being that has chosen the world. I don't like you. Good night.' (The angel's emphatic tone contrasts with the benign treatment given the baby doll image of the Christian's mortal coil.) She looks fondly at the baby in her hands, hesitates in attachment, perhaps rocks it. The dogs have come out of the manger, crowd between her and the horse. The blue woman is still on her knees in front of her, gently swinging her tinkling crystals like a censer. The Christian is regretfully admiring her corporeal self. Only the tall sun is left at the top of the tower, those flanking him are gone. Two others are below. One of the deaths has put a cradle down in front of the Christian. She slowly places the doll in it. The dark-grey dogs with their beastly masks are all about. The Christian sorrows over her bodily self (this is the first emotion clearly projected by her). It is a long protracted scene.

The sun on the horse is watching. The singing ends, silence. The deaths emerge from the cabin, the dogs crowding near their feet, the devils come out from the bottom of the tower, the two missing suns have reappeared, four suns are bending over the cradle, with the Christian (sorrowing with her?):

Yellow (Suns)

Grey (Deaths)   Red (Devils)
(Dogs)

White
(Christian)

Blue (Oriental woman)

The angel, 'Because the spirit lives in you, your mortal bodies will come back to life.' Singing. The deaths, in a line, have raised their instruments as though playing them, the big-faced one in front bears the cradle, they move off up the hill, along the path they (and we) came, through us, their silent horns strong. The devils have disappeared. The suns, except for the tallest one who still is up on the tower bestowing his blessing, stand behind the Christian, saved, her arms raised. The singing ends, silence.

The angel, 'Away you sad spirits. My heart's great joy is here'. Singing. The blue mystic figure leads the dance-stepping horse with the small sun rider up the hill along the path they came, away from us. The Christian woman, also stepping gaily, and then the four smaller suns, all with arms raised, follow. They disappear. The large sun on the tower makes slow benign movements with his hands. Only he and the angel remain. Is there a tiny puppet in his right hand? The singing ends. Silence. He pulls the blue curtain shut. The angel stands immobile.

Applause.

An intensely gripping sacral performance. The primal colors in the green-roofed brown forest clearing complement the illustrations' neat fit to the text. The metteur-en-scene's hard-headedly naive ingenuity brings off the coup, stunning, of orthodoxy. It's a child's tale, purified in the desperation of hope, upborne, perhaps, not so much by any expectancy of, let alone reliance on, an afterlife, as by the sense of guilt – one hopes one's greeds are extrinsic. The symbolism is extravagant. The brutal naivité of the imagery attests to the power of the emotion. The jumping pictures are carried in a masterly gentle upswing.

*   *   *

Domestic Resurrection Pageant.[7]

8:05 p.m. The spectators have been asked to sit on the amphitheatre's south side, and do. I sit on the west side. Four circumferential plumes of smoke rising.[8] White figures are quietly busy organizing things. Among them, three brown, white-masked figures in what looks like straw or feather robes[9] – they are far away – attended to by them. Crepuscule, a white evening tide. The white attendants are busy around the fires. Now the three straw men are immobile.

---

7. 'CENTRAL EVENT: BICENTENNIAL PAGEANT. (About Indians) early evening. 20 white birds/ 35 deer/ 2 oxen/ 4 sheep/ 1 ram/ 10-20 horses/ 10-15 houses with figures inside (painted)/ 40 flags/ 5-10 giant chiefs on horseback/ 30 stilters in Dance of Death robes. Sound: soft horns and chimes.' — (Circus Projects '76, mimeograph listing what is needed, distributed to performers.)'
8. (Five) fires have been lit. At first we see only the smoke. The growth of fire is one of the elements of this pageant.
9. One of them is Peter Schumann. At the Saturday evening pageant he was on stilts. Regrettably he wasn't Sunday evening (he told George Ashley he hadn't liked the dance he did on them): it made the three less of a ceremonial center to the event. When he was, of course, he was very tall, chief medicine man, lead shaman.

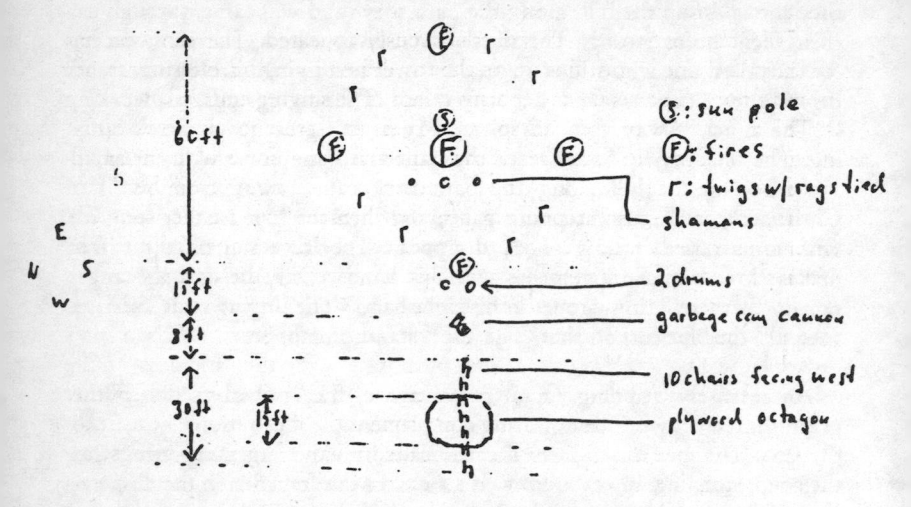

S: sun pole
F: fires
r: twigs w/ rags tied
shamans
2 drums
garbage can cannon
10 chairs facing west
plywood octagon

Ullulations. In the waning light, a vast (30-40 people) white crowd, flanked by a dozen or more carriers of long-poled flags with Indian screams rush down into the bowl over its northern rim. They erect a huge sun-faced figure (its center pole a 20-foot tree, the poles holding up its arms 15 feet long, its berry branch entwined arms 17 feet long, its severe disk-face, ringed by 20 flames, 7 feet across) by the central fire, its arms straight out, a cross.

The sun is the life-giver. Here it has the face of a sky-ruler – the legislator. And it is also a cross. This inverts the symbolic layering of the *Cantata* show in which God the Father was also sun. The five fires form a cross. The yellow of the sun is shared by the American staff of life, maize, and by the ceremonial robe of oriental self-abnegation.

The three shamans in front of it. The smoke, greyer than the evening, whirling over the whole circular field. The white flag-carriers run around the outside, the white crowd of the others walks around inside, the smoke swirls around with them, around them, in it the large red, blue and yellow flowers, strong. The Sun God, dominant giant, but to scale, is turning very slowly, its four white flowered turning streamers a likeness of a mechanism of its revolution over the yellow grass in the meadow. The whole disk, turning slowly at its pivot, fast at the edges. From it rises a hymn, the

356

smell of smoke. Its movement comes to a halt. One of the drummers out front starts a muffled slow beat. The flag bearers exit to the left, the crowd of the Sun God's attendants moves off to the rear, strings out in the distance, disappears.

The sun-image is left. Not incongruously, a yellow quarter moon has risen in the sky to the south-west. Both drums by the fire out front are beating now. The heads and stocky chests of the two drummers, working together, seem close. The three straw men are standing in the distance. Slowly moving. The Sun God stands stiff and very powerful, its arms upheld by two attendants in white. The cannon is facing it, then the run of chairs. Attendants in white are tending fires in the vast space. The shamans move in a very slow dance between the drums and the sun. The drums are slow and low. The straw men are swaying, their arms out. We see a ceremony as a work-process, ceremonial work. At the same time it is the performance of magic. The rigid artifice of a pageant — Schumann's work — merges ambiguously — felicitously — with the strictness of the ritual, imagined, re-enacted, the evocation of the continent's rich culture destroyed, but also, almost, a participation in it.

A white mass has appeared over the hill to the left, sheep/deer, their white heads (the black nostrils and mouths, the large black-pupilled eyes are mere impression) out front, placing their white feet slowly down on

the slippery grass. Smoke rising. The drums beating. The shamans invoking. The gentle animals are attracted, a searching file picking its way, magnetized. (Perhaps a dozen and a half of them.) The clear sky is wide above, in it, at its rim, the treasure of the moon. The drums are very clear, an amplified heartbeat (a beat of 8 with a 4 (5-6) accent?), you hear hands on skin. The sun-image is governing as the sheep or deer approach as in timeless reiteration of rite. The attendants under the arms of the sun straight, men. The fire out front between the two close-together drums is the only bright spot, the other fires as yet only smoke. The row of chairs stands silent over the wooden octagon. The sheep are right behind the Sun God now. Their slow advance is tantalizing. The brown of the grotesque shamans, faces pointing up, contrasts with all the white: darker than the yellow grass. The drums are becoming *louder*.

Way off to the rear, horses come galloping. The sheep are in a double file, paired, gently moving forward past the sun. The horses in the rear are cantering, trotting, gallivanting, frisky, a swiftness in the far meadow, the troop is veering now to one side, now to the other. Their advance is oblique. The shamans are keeping it all going. The drums are faster. To the left, a procession under the very large, room-wall-sized banner image of a

357

white tree (with people figured into it, but you can't see that at these distances) is approaching, distant yet: to a faint sound of horns. The sheep are gradually — comedians — gathering behind the drummers. The horses pace as though aimless in the meadow: in lazy play, at large. White. The shamans are doing their thing. Smoke plumes. Chanting from the procession at the left, which you can now distinguish has the form of a long blue-silvery dragon (a tall (five feet or so) mask followed by a long (thirty foot?) band of cloth). It is led by a backward walking blue and white man and preceded by horn blowers. The horses are still to the rear. The sheep-deer are kneeling, you can discern their spiny twig-antlers. The procession has reached the top of the rise, deploys, as in a military maneuver, along it, sideways: the blue-white cloth body of the dragon is dropped to the grass (an uncovering of guns): a troop of black men, lined up, is revealed. (The tom-toms stop. The dancing stops.) They are relatively small, in black suits, wear very small two-peaked black hats on their white heads, have the stern faces of victims, their little black mouths prim in their very large (bulky and a foot and a half to two feet tall) head masks (at this distance you can't make out their dark grey short horns).

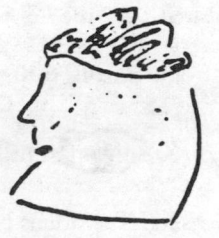

The tree banner is dropped, the white attendants carrying it separate, except for one, leave. The horses are near now, seem confused. The black men with the white heads are standing in a row, arms up queerly. They slowly descend, a deputation, not clearly harmful, seriously, simple men. The horses now are milling in front of them, between them and the chairs and the still drums, the sun, the fires.

A struggle, seeming at first a dance of the clumsily efficient black men with the whinnying white horses, ensues, the horses are put on the ground, one or two last longer than the others, black men who have finished with theirs come over to help their colleagues lay them low. Black and white. The men congratulate one another (decorously hearty conversation as before the start of a board meeting), advance, conversing, to the chairs, sit (morning subway, commuter train), pull out newspapers, read one behind the other. The sheep are in a dense crowd behind them, between them and the sun. Bell sound from the single attendant that remained on the rise. They fold their newspapers, tuck them away. The front black man gets up. He points behind them to the sheep, they look. He gives a sharp military command, a sergeant's bark, they get up, march in a clump, the c.c. off to one side, to behind the cannon, just behind the line of chairs. In the ritual ground, all is quiet. They are grouped around the cannon, pointed toward the ritual ground: the only 'men' there. They are directly in front of the sheep. A salute (?), commands, they charge the gun. They plug their ears — 'Ready — Aim — Fire!' — a gong beat off to the right. Smoke plumes still rising everywhere. The huge sun rotates very slowly, a grandly delicate effect. The black men approach the sheep (deer). Start — it makes a nasty dry noise — doing things to the kneeling sheep. They are breaking off their antlers. The sun-image is still up, very bright in the glowing pre-night air. The sheep fall, are dead. A band marches down the rise on the left — 'Halls of Montezuma'. A ladder is carried out ahead of it. The dark butchers hold up little signs (saying 'NO'). The band's tune is loud in the greater silence of evening, a sound of banal triumph. Silence. The ladder is raised to the Sun God. One of the large-headed black men in a businesslike way climbs up the ladder, stands at the top, deploys a black cloth (garbage bag plastic, unseamed) spreads it over the sun's face, leave it there — sign of victory — a spiderish crumpled black spot — obscene — pausing at the top of the ladder for a moment turning his white face to us, descends. The sun there, with the black on its face. It collapses silently backward. A grand fall. Playing another march, the band makes off with the ladder. The black men, stepping over the horses, leave with the sun. Gone. The dead sheep in the foreground. Dead horses off to the left, fires all blazing. The three shamans are standing quietly, observers. The fire in the middle is very bright. It is the biggest of the five fires. The drum, there's just one left, has moved near it. Smoke rising. Dead horses, dead sheep. Fine white patterns of death on the ground — the heap of sheep, the scattered spots of the horses. White on the brown grass.

The drum starts up again. Another procession, to the tinkling of bells, advances at the very distant rear — at the edge of the forest. The ceremony is quietly conducted in the foreground. It has resumed. The shamans are again moving slowly. Behind them the expanse of the yellowing meadow in the falling night. The drum is beating slowly, its beat gradually becoming more complex.

The procession is bringing a giant pale moon, swaying above its black mass. In the black mass, a glimmer — a live torch. Death has been absorbed, does not matter. There is the light of the dark! It is getting dark. The moon is a half moon. They are chanting harmoniously — an old Protestant hymn? The fires are being tended, the shamans are swaying, the drum is commanding hollowly. The moon is coming head on, broadside, a sail. On it a pale, conventional grimace: it is one of the *old* gods. Its attendants lonely temple servants. Nobody in the ceremonial center pays attention to its approach. The five fires are all bright, the one in the center still the biggest. The moon bearers' simple harmony and tinkling bells contrast with the simpler, strong beat of the drum.

There are perhaps fifteen or twenty of them, all in the yellow of Buddhist monks or of a ripe moon. Among them dancing red men on stilts, costumes flying.[10] As they round the further fire, one sees that the moon is on a long, heavy four-wheeled wagon, pulled, heavily, by two white oxen (performers inside). All the white animals resurrect: a sudden great miracle: fall into a circular procession of torch bearer, oxen attendants, oxen, moon wagon, saffron-robed attendants, file of sheep/deer, horses, white with a touch of yellow, the red of the stilted dancers merging into the darkness, deepening it at the rear of the procession, advancing, chanting to the tinkling of bells, around the fire circle, the ridiculous symbol swaying above them: the oxen very large, bulky, the wagon very real, the horses dance-tripping a little: and moves off and away (leaving only the torch bearer behind) to the left rear, gradually, except for the palely white moon symbol, blending into the dark distance.

The moon off there. The torch bearer moving among the fires. Gull noises from the nearly invisible dark mass where the moon is: five great white birds, their heads outstretched, one of them extra large, come swooping down the meadow to the left toward the bowl's rise, heads bobbing, large-beaked, with shrill cries, wings fluttering, each carried by three runners in black, circle the fire, make off toward the distant artifact moon, through the vast space, seeming more vast because of them, the giant gull last, looking like a spirit.

The fires, their crackle, the torch bearer in white slowly, quietly circulating. Once again it seems the end. (Child's talk and noises in the audience.) (The real moon is real yellow now.)

The artifact moon is stationary in the distance. From where it stands, pale over the dark meadow, a line of light dots – torches held up – approaches to a very slow drum, beaten afar. They come nearer in a quiet resolution, their fires quieter and smoother, rounder, than the live fires on the ground. Behind the stretched-out file of ten nearly invisible torch carriers, a dark mass of attendants in white and a darker rear guard of the red figures on stilts. The torch bearers are slowly circling around the five crackling, now brightly orange, flaming fires, on the outside. The drum is approaching, invisible, a slow, careful rhythm, each eighth beat heavy. The fires. It is *night* now, a mass of people is congregating in the center of the circling lights, around the live flame at the center, the white figures in the middle, the red, almost black, bird-like ones bobbing around them, toward the periphery, tall and raggedy, dipping to the accents of the (increasingly heavy, more 'African') drum, now stationed in the center. Bird calls, only a few at first, isolated, then more, raucous and sustained – cries of jungle birds. Sparks. Drum faster and louder. Cries of 'aaaeeeh' and 'aaahhh' in

10. The red stilt birds whose dance of fire in the toured *Domestic Resurrection Spectacle* of early '76 via the epiphany of God's face brought on America.

alternation, hunting calls. The drum faster and faster. More sparks. Witches' calls. A wild ceremony in the night – 'pagan', 'savage', 'primitive'. Indian whoops. (Parts of the audience are joining in, clapping, some of the children whooping – some small children are crying, frightened, or tired). The fires are very clear. A burning field. It's very dark. The red men are hopping. The artificial moon still stands pale in the distance. The moving dense throng in the night mirrors its opposite, the white shield of humans that at the beginning of the ceremony revolved around with the sun, in the daylight, it contrasts, resolving and compacting them, with the structured scenes and linear processions in between: the spectacle has absorbed destruction within itself. The scene is intense: the steady, heavy, accelerating beat, the slowly orbiting torches, the big fire in the middle, the crowd.

Over the rise approach faintly colored balloons – lit up – lanterns, vast (two or three feet across) and bulky, between roundish and square. They stand, a line down the hill: quietly glowing large *gentle* shapes: candles inside translucent, figured material. The line slowly integrates itself between the torch bearers: both move in a grand-style orbit around the red, tall figures and the dense mass of celebrants[11] around the fire: the two types of light in a very, very slow circulation. The new – gentle – element is transitional: the drum is slowing down and growing fainter as the last lantern joins in the circle. It becomes almost inaudible. The circle is revolving slowly, the big figures are almost immobile.

The fires are very prominent now, their crackling very audible. But they seem quiet. The mass of people down there is no longer moving. From it – the drum has stopped — a low hum (om) rises. It seems to *carry* the slight almost imperceptible rotation of the rim — of the torch and lantern bearers. This lasts a long while. One can smell the fires in the night. There is a slowly rising low warm hum of talk in the audience. Laughter. Some crickets. The hum stops.[22]

Clapping, Indian yells from the audience.

The crowd of performers rotates slowly away to the rear, recedes.[13]

*　　*　　*

---

11. In the Saturday night Pageant, some of the dancers at the center seemed naked.
12. These last two sections stood out much more clearly Sunday than Saturday, seemed to last longer also – as though the positivity of the catharsis provided by the previous, wild, 'Dionysiac', 'orgiastic' section were emphasized more. Also – or – that previous section (the one that develops from the arrival of the torches) seemed to reach only a lesser pitch. These three sections together: a fire that flares, then burns down.
13. 'As I sat on the hillside eating bread, this is how the Pageant looked:
Around me, the hillside is filled with people who huddle on the ground in blankets. On the large playing field at the foot of the hill, what appear to be ceremonial fires are tended by men in white. The fires fill the cool air with a woodsy fragrance.
Suddenly, whooping cries are heard coming from the end of the field; and a group of

---

white-clad figures run out of the forest toward the fires. As they circle, waving banners, a tall golden Sun-figure is erected in the center. This done, the runners disappear over the crest of a hill.

Immediately drums begin. First softly, then gradually louder, establishing an African-like rhythm. Three bushlike figures (puppeteers in cornstalk costumes) begin to sway and dance to the rhythm. Over a hill, a herd of white deer puppets slowly approach the dancing figures: simultaneously appearing at the opposite end of the field, a small herd of white horse puppets prance joyfully in a zig-zag pattern across the width of the field, gradually making their way toward the fires and dancers.

As the deer and horses approach, the drumming stops. A tinkling comes from over the crest of a nearby hill: a large blue banner approaches, then the ridge is filled with a long ark-shaped cloth. A brass band plays a few harsh notes, and the cloth is dropped to reveal a line of businessmen puppets in black suits and bowlers. After a brief pause, the businessmen descend on the white horses, wrestle them to the ground in silence, then walk calmly to a row of chairs, pick up newspapers, sit and read. The leader of the businessmen notices the deer, shouts a few military commands and the deer are also killed. A stepladder is placed in front of the Sun and one of the men climbs up and drapes the idol's face with a black cloth. The Sun dies, falling backwards into the arms of puppeteers. The brass band strikes up a lively marching tune and the Sun is carried off, leaving the area around the fires littered with the 'dead' horses and deer.

In the distance, a tinkling sound, singing, a single torch light and a cart pulled by oxen — puppets appear. As this moves slowly toward the fires, I notice that a large crescent moon is mounted on a tall pole attached to the back of the cart. As the procession approaches, the fires flare up and the deer and horses are resurrected. After they all circle the fires, the procession disappears into the darkness.

Immediately, high shrill bird cries are heard. Out of the darkness emerge enormous white spirit birds (15'×25') suspended above the ground on poles carried by runners. They circle the fires slowly and disappear into the night.

A torch is lit, then another, and another until a torchlight procession is formed: drumming begins again in the distance: the procession moves along the base of the opposite slope toward the fires, drumming as they approach. Swaying gracefully above the torch bearers in the procession are 12-foot stilt-dancers in flowing Red-bird costumes, complete with wings and full bird-masks with long yellow beaks. Smaller red birds dance around their feet.

The ecstasy dance begins. Drums grow louder. The birds shriek and flap their wings in stylized gestures. The dance reaches a frenzied pitch and then the drums ease off and finally cease.

Stillness.

Humming begins.

Over a nearby ridge, appears a procession of colorful glowing lanterns. The lantern carriers circle the fires silently: then, with the torch bearers, form an aisle leading off into the dark.

Slowly, the bird-dancers, musicians, drummers, puppeteers and some audience members begin the mile long recessional down the lighted aisle and back to the Bread & Puppet Farmhouse. — (Ron Argelander, *Bread and Puppet's Domestic Resurrection: The War is Over, The Soho Weekly News*, August 19, '76.)

Argelander felt that 'to-day, the Bread & Puppet is a living monument to yesterday's avant-garde', but his review is favorable — he found 'new and exciting material.'

14. A press release of July 16 dedicated it to 'the original Americans.'

'The idea for this Circus was to have an Indian pageant to telescope, in the midst of

return — a philosophic salute to the life cycle, no jaundiced look at 300 years of White conquest and occupation. The cultural life cycle integrated into the diurnal and seasonal life cycle. The murder of peoples, cultures an analogue to the death of fall/winter: a historicist transposition of the Christian resurrection myth.[15] A message of hope. In *Jesu Meine Freude*, deaths and devils service the redemptive order. And what (who, where) is the New Red Man? Schumann doesn't say. But obviously, the White Man, vide the farm and town houses of New England, the manners of the South, the style of the West, and even the Black Man, listen to the music, have had a good thing going here from time to time these last 300+ years. I don't suppose Schumann has any New Left in mind. The message of hope: let's not take things too seriously. The *Pageant* also reminds us of the pre-industrial adaptation of man to nature, as in Old World pre-chemical agriculture or as in the history of American agriculture, so beautifully reconstructed by MacNeish's archeological investigations in the Teotihuacàn Valley. In this respect it is an admonition. The reminder is ideologically restricted: we are not reminded of the terrors and miseries of this nature-bound existence, especially in its post-tribal, post-'chiefdom' classical stages of kingdoms and epires and of an exploited peasantry — the terrors and miseries glaring at us out of the religious and dynastic sculpture from Chavin and Olmec onward.

A persistent remainder of ambiguity in Schumann's art: the pervasive presence of death. The message is: it is part of life, serves life: don't mind it, accept it. But the emphasis on it intimates perhaps a dread of it.

Schumann's ideology here within and beyond his Buddhistically and Christianly infected pantheism, seems intensely personal Christianism and Buddhism are transcendentalist messages of hope, salvation, redemption: Schumann applies their positiveness to this world. He rejects their rejection of the natural world of man. Nature is good. Its goodness, in the shape of womanhood, suffuses humanity. Yet the individual, and especial-

---

these bicentennial celebrations, what the Indian mind and philosophy is. Their thought and philosophy has been completely neglected by the American people. So the idea was to do a piece of landscape in order to carry that Indian thought — what Schweitzer called Ehrfurcht vor dem Leben — the respect for life. It's a philosophy of equalizing humans with ants and leaves of trees. To make that thought strong and powerful — for us that was the idea of the *Bicentennial Circus*.' — (Schumann, interviewed August 17, '76. In: Falk, *The Bread and Puppet Domestic Resurrection Circus*, 1976, *Performing Arts Journal*, Spring 1977.)

15. Theatrically, Schumann accomplishes this by the devices (1) of giving his synoptic re-enactment of American-history-in-its-essence the form of a ritual, (2) having this ritual by a ceremony of purification by fire, and (3) incorporating the role of the white man into the ritual. We note the man's consistency: the '76 *Pageant* still conforms to the guiding ideas of his '62 programmatic manifestos à propos of his *Totentanz*, and fulfills his ambition of the late '50s of achieving a grand spectacle combining (as Elka in '79 put it) circus and Oberammergau.

*Picture book account of the circus of 1976
by Max Schumann.*

ly the individual male, seems to Schumann to seem tainted with evil: his residual Christianism, antagonism toward the natural, an annihilative urge – a death wish? Set into the entertainment and the edification, there is a dark center, a twist of the sculptor's hand, something awful, perhaps a sense of personal corruption. It gives Schumann's art its substance.

In the end, Schumann's theatre is conservative. But its uneasy humor, childish, rather than childlike, a willed innocence, though by its basic mode sharing the grandeur of his apolitical world view, is still apt to set the teeth of the local Canucks on edge, especially when it approaches in 1976 (no longer reaching) subversion. But even they can't escape seeing the man is a sincere Christian with no political beefs.

His artistry is consummate. Its grandeur lies in its sustained, sure intimacy with space and time. It is sequential, its sequences are musical, precise, overwhelming, as artful as Richard Foreman's and Robert Wilson's. Note e.g. in the staccato of the *Circus* show the inset peace of the oriental number, or the contrast of this staccato with the gentle upswing of the *Bach Cantata* and the wild but controlled sweep of the *Pageant*. He uses space creatively at all moments; the color schemes, mask splotches, routes and symbolizations never obliterate some grand – large or tiny – structuralization of space, the house of God.

His shows are suffused by sweetness and light. Yet, up there in Vermont, he is somewhat removed from the pressing problems of the poor, St. Simon's 'classe la plus souffrante et la plus nombreuse'. The actual misery of the big cities is at some geographical and psychological remove: problems appear larger, the large problems appear small. The poor have never been his special concern: war has. His art has been concerned with the misery imposed by human violence, man's wrongdoing, more than with the misery of the congenitally property-less, a misery contained by the violence that guards property, but structural, not created by it, not due to wrong-doing. There is perhaps not so much callousness in this – though some coldness – as rather something like a blind spot. The lovingness of the shows fails to give them the shape of a concern for the poor. I don't see, myself, that he is subject to censure on this account. Yet there is a certain paradoxality in an expressive humanitarianism silent on the miseries of the modern poor. Schumann's commiseration at this time, as earlier, went to the Third World: but even its misery had become a side-show matter.[16]

---

16. One of the sideshows, *The Story of the Young Man*, surely by him, probably directed by him, could be thought of as about the modern poor. In the traveling variant of the circus (NYC, August, '76), into which it had been incorporated, it went like this: a drop of pictures, suspended from a rod, is lowered, Schumann, stepping over from the bandstand, flipping them over, narrates, the announcer of the preceding and following 'circus' acting as performer – but this only involves singing 'la, la, la' and some walks: 'I am the young man. This is where I live' (picture of an interior, table, chair, flower) 'and this is what I do': one Angel of Death takes him off to work (smoke-belching factory), another off to war

Nobody, seeing all of Schumann's shows, would ever just from them guess that the life of the working majority of the Western countries still, after Bismarck's social legislation, Labor governments in England and Scandinavia, the Front Populaire, the New Deal and the Great Society, is a *hard* one. The working class in his *Life, Liberty and the Pursuit of Happiness*, present in the '75, dropped from the '76 circus, its subject of his friendly pity and contempt, but the skit's criticism of the U.S. is that its — the majority's — life has become a routine: when in the '76 pageant he shows us the class of businessmen, newspaper-reading commuters, whose business happens to be the murder of nature, he shows the life of those 'Butchers' subject to routine also, and to the same routine, that of employment. They don't in this respect differ from those 'Garbagemen'. But in fact, the continuing miseries of wage labor in the late 20th century West are such that only their precarious balance by a qualitatively ever worse but ample and gadgetized soporific consumption staves off, from year to year, the utmost civic violence, fascist or other.

(woman, screaming, leaning out of a burning house), a final one, off to die. A grim, terse story, essentially still *A Man Says Goodbye to His Mother*, with the indication of the man's being working class added, but — cf. the city's smoke in the '70 *Genghis Khan* — as accusation, he is a polluter, as much a killer before as after he gets drafted. The proletarian is an accomplice.

The *Mountain Man of Chile*, dedicated to the Chilean singer Victor Jara, killed in 1973 by the police of General Pinochet, Schumann's first use of cutout puppets: carton (or masonite) figures are spread out, face down, on the ground, one of them, of a flowered hill, raised to the vertical out front. Schumann plays scraps of gypsy chords as it stands there. In the background there is a black figure on the left, a grey one on the right. Schumann speaks the text, 'Once there was a mountain full of flowers; and on the mountain there was a house (carton house put on carton mountain); and in the house there lived a little man (grey and black attendants manipulate a man- and a sun-puppet, the man-puppet carrying a guitar, a performer with a guitar has gone to stand behind the flat man-puppet-carton-cutout, the attendant takes it out, the performer is disclosed), his soul enters the home of the governor (two almost identical red-faced carton figures, in black suit jackets, white shirts, holding cigars in their movable, jointed arms, top halves only, their lower bodies the grey/black smocks of the attendants holding them).' The mountain man is followed and shot by the secret police. The story ends with a repetition of its first line, the flowered hill coming up again, standing there (a more powerful image in the momentary silence than all of the preceding story).

'The *Mountain Man of Chile* was a simple and eloquent parable about the indomitability of the Chilean people under a repressive military regime. Schumann wrote and narrated the story and played 'background' music on the violin. The story relates how the mountain man goes to the city where he is arrested, interrogated, imprisoned, tortured, and finally condemned to death. But another mountain man rises, like a flower, to take his place. 'Oppression' (various manifestations of institutionalized violence) is represented in the form of larger-than-life cardboard figures, each exhibiting a specific *geste* that identifies his (sic) role of domination.' — (F. Falk, *The Bread and Puppet Domestic Resurrection Circus*, ... 1976, *Performance Arts Journal*, Spring '77.)

(Elka: 'Why did you want to make a show about Chile?) Because it was important — it was always our desire to tell people pertinent political news ... I wrote the text down — we tried it with a written text.' — (Schumann, interview, '79.)

LeRoi Jones has been consistently concerned with the bad life of the poor. This effective humaneness expressed itself for a while in a racism directed against Whites and Jews, later took the form of a historicist orthodoxy going back to the Jew Marx, intimately within a Western tradition, and equally full of hatred and violence. Like Marx, he is vituperative in his poetry, in his plays. His art contrasts to Schumann's as darkness does to light. But there he is, in Newark, in the filth, unshielded, in daily contact with many living the life of the poor as industry and capitalism require it to be lived, and the rage of his work is the love of a sociable man, while the lovingness of Schumann's work (who has not sold out either) is the detachment of a loner.

'On the side of the Bread and Puppet barn-museum in Glover hangs a series of eight paintings arranged sequentially to tell a picture story. Farmers, artists, tourists – anyone driving on Route 122 past the Bread and Puppet farmhouse – can interpret the message. The story is simple; it states, partly in words, partly in images: 'While we are eating and drinking and (making love) and (sleeping) Chile is burning.' — (Falk, *The Bread and Puppet Domestic Resurrection Circus*, . . . 1976, *Performance Arts Journal*, Spring, '77.)

'*Lamentation* was a three dimensional construction (approximately $3' \times 3'$) which illustrated the politics of famine in India. It was placed strategically in one area of the meadow situated along the main access path to the "Circus" area.' — (Falk, ibid.)

'*Lamentation*, performed by a single seated figure crushing bits of rock, silently emphasized through hand-painted signs that malnutrition was still a major world-wide problem.' —(R. Argelander, *Bread & Puppet's Domestic Resurrection: The War is Over*, *The Soho Weekly News*, August 19, '76.)

'The one piece that I have seen since 1974, the *Circus* in the summer of 1976, seems more static than in the past. There is a lot of repetition, and the retreat (with the times) from moral and political protest has left it a little churchy. Allegory petrifies fast. Political protest has always been at the center of Schumann's religious vision, and even pieces from the sixties and early seventies had their didactic and propagandistic elements subsumed into a vision of suffering and compassion that was never simply partisan. The image of the Christ as a revolutionary was not the convenient sloganeering young Marxist, but the man of suffering. The taking on of suffering was revolution enough. It is difficult to tell where Schumann will go from this point. While he is hardly in retirement in Glover, it is unclear to me where he will engage next.' — (Goldensohn, '77.)

10. The mysteries of life and love eradicated by business. 5th version of *The White Horse Butcher.*

After the ('76) *Circus,* anxious to retrieve its essence and/or to make use of certain performers before they had scattered; by the circus' *Pageant* inspired to yet another twist to his private myth of the 'white horse butcher', one restating the both more personal and more universal theme appended to it by the White Lady (absent from the '76 circus pageant, sacrificed to a more cohesive statement of its historical theme); desirous to effect the miracle of a transposition of his show in nature to a theatre piece – Schumann took about a dozen performers down to New York City for five showings over an extremely hot weekend, August 20-22, at the old peace church, Washington Square Methodist Church, of *White Horse Butcher, and other pieces from the 5th annual Domestic Resurrection Circus,* a two-hour spectacle in two parts, Part I another more or less unsuccessful attempt to combine silly circus and political-social comment, Schumann's insistence on keeping his silly circus lightly silly defeating the abilities of his by now quite able performers, e.g. Zaloom, Leber, some of the funny numbers from the '76 *Bicentennial Spectacle, the Life, Liberty, and the Pursuit of Happiness (and now: or My Uncle's Life)* from the '75 *Bicentennial Spectacular,* and two of the '76 circus sideshows: *The Story of a Young Man* (one of the *Vermont Landscapes*), and *The Mountain Man of Chile;* and then Part II, a once again completely reworked and altered version of the horse-butcher theme, *White Horse Butcher,* one inspired by the unicorn legend on the Cluny gobelins – 'with the tent and with the lady with the mirror and with the lion' (Schumann, interview, '83) –: political-sociological allegory, but now also an allegory of the violation of lovingness.[1]

* * *

1. This show got Schumann the, to my knowledge, most unfavorable review he ever got:
'Everyone says the counter-culture is dead. That its only possible function in 1976 America is as shoddy nostalgia for aging hippies and their children who don't know better – yet. The Bread and Puppet Theater, which recently bamboozled folks at the Washington Square Church, seems determined to prove all those clichés gilt-edged verities.
The first part of the evening is a 'circus' where the company proves it has no vocal training, cannot move, and does not know how to use the (superb) masks and costumes. Worse yet, all the old-time fun mockeries of 'Uncle Fatso' capitalists and those crass old folks in Washington and out there in the great American Heart(less)land just don't work any more. Calling off the Vietnam Follies and Watergate, some say, put an end to all the fun; Jerry Rubin, growing up, set the seal on the tomb. Like all sealed tombs, opening up the counter-culture crypt brings down curses aplenty. For instance the Bread and Puppet Theater's attempts at agit-prop are weak, without a ground, mere gestures and attitudes of

The audience is seated in the one remaining row of pews, and on benches and pillows on the church floor: also in the balcony. The playing area is between it and the organ wall opposite. It is defined by a suspended black backdrop somewhat away from that wall with two vertical white strip-banners on it, one with a blue, one with a red flower, and by a low, curved, flattenedly semi-circular blue and white cloth-fence (the same kind as used in the Glover circus) delimiting a sanded white floor area, perhaps 10-12 ft. in depth and 24 ft. across, in front of the drop. There are two floor-stand projectors out in front on each side, and more small projectors up on the balconies, and a drum to the left of the enclosure, toward the back. Way to the rear, almost up against the wall to the left of the organ pipes, there is a suspended red cloth – a curtain for Schumann to get on his new aluminium stilts behind for the show's finale. The overall impression is that of a travelling troupe, recreating a minimal but gay setting in different places, come to town.

Part II. *White Horse Butcher.*[2]

Except for in one tableau, the 4th, the acting was not mimetic enough to be called 'mime'. On the other hand, there was too much of it – and the costuming, except for the body of a unicorn, too definitely costuming rather than representation of a puppet's body – for the show to be called a 'puppet show'. The performers' movements – gestural, slow, and deliberate – were choreographed as dance movements, less for accented patterns in time, though, than as images in space. This graphic dance was dominated by the face and head masks and by the simple but not alto-

---

anger from the distant past. When at the end of the circus a stilt-walking Uncle Sam declares the finale will be World War 3, and someone dressed like an airplane (or war dragon?) runs around him a few times and exits, it is all too sad. The many children present were very disappointed.

The second half, *White Horse Butcher*, is a real bummer. In the opening tableaux, white-masked figures aboard a boat (on the Styx?) yearn after a small white bird (which looked like a bat, at first, but was, alas, that old symbolic bird). In the final scene the slain white horse gallops around with an angelic figure on its back. *White Horse Butcher* is a painfully self-conscious piece of 'meaningful' symbolic pretentiousness. The pace is so hideously slow, and the piece such a let-down after the noisy circus portion, that the children present hopefully went to sleep.

Unfortunately, the adults lapped it all up like LSD at a 1967 Pentagon protest reunion. There were bravos aplenty. Restrung love-beads rattled knowingly. Only the budding paunches and receding hairlines let us know it was really just another Elks' Club Amateur Night frolic (circa 1976).

Farewell, counter-culture and Bread and Puppet Theater. We loved you once. It is oh, so very hard to even like you now.' — (Ron Whyte, *Yesterday's Bread, Soho Weekly News*, September 2, '76.)

He showed this spectacle, *White Horse Circus*, in Tuscany in October ('76), e.g. October 11 at the palestra comunale of Pontedra.

2. Except where noted, the following describes the first of the five performances.

370

gether simple achromatic color scheme of the garment shapes. The show was in black and white – and in two greys, a light grey and a sometimes almost purplish dark grey: the light brown, in three of the scenes, of perhaps 6 ft.-long peeled natural-shape staves providing a slight, and the solitary red of a narrow sash and blindfold and, in some performances, of a rosette worn by the chief executioner in the 7th scene a strong contrast. The faces of figures without masks were covered with loosely draped dark grey contrasting with the lighter grey of their cowls, a subtlety.

Two of these hooded performers – Bunraku-style invisibles – spread a white screen, perhaps 10′×8′, on each side tied to a black pole by four white bows, stand on each side of it holding it, the one on the right in a black cowl and grey shirt, the one on the left vice versa. They are altogether covered, even their hands are covered. They are shapeless, somewhat indistinct. They span out the white surface at the end of each scene, remove it at the beginning of the next. The white screen is a handsomely *easy* presence.[3] It is the curtain. Above it looms the top of the taller black back-screen. The performers come from behind the black screen.[4] Above that, the church organ: not part of the scene: the performance space is defined by the two screens, and more particularly by the black back-screen since the front one is not there during the playing. It is not quite black. To each side of the black there is a strip, a foot and a half or so wide, of grey, light grey on the left, dark grey on the right. A performer in a grey cowl and black pants is seated on the floor to the right of and a little to the front of the screen with two small sticks in his hands.

Scene 1   The two floor stands' projector lights are on the screen. They provide an ordinary degree of lighting. They go off. In the dark, a panel of white figures slide out from in back of the white screen. The lights go on. It's six rowers, in white, all white except for the black lacquer of kerchiefs or hair repeated on the back of their heads (extremely slender white heads), rowing very slowly, in time, a dreamlike motion, their nunnish faces silent screams upward at odd and different angles (the performers' heads under theirs, the yellow-white broad cravats tying the puppets' heads to their triangular upper garments), their tall poles, parallel to one another, in visual counterpoint to their upper bodies, crossing down past the hull (a band of grey cloth) of their dream boat. Their large spindly celastic hands rest strangely, weakly on the crooked staves. The seated figure to the right is beating his small sticks together slowly, a little dry sound. At some point there is the sound of poured water. This frieze is very still, a sliding

3. There is no show of precision. The light is not brilliant; when it's dark, it is not too dark; the screen is brought out and removed without stylization, not even the stylization of the workmanlike; when it is held out, most times there are some horizontal folds in it.
4. Except for scene 1, I believe.

panel, the stationary slide of its oblong apparented to the rotation of a wheel.

To a faint shrill twittering whistle, a tiny paper aeroplane suspended from a string at the end of a rod is carried in, fllown about, by a grey Bunraku attendant walking out from behind the right end of the screen. The rowers in diverse rhythms have looked up together at the sound of the whistle. As the bird flutters above them, they drop their oars (or poling poles), sinking to their knees in agitation – the grey cloth hull sinking with them – raise their hands in the air up toward the bird, in gestures of adoration. The lights dim on this second tableau, counterpiece to the initial one of bent backs, straining fragility, silent advance. The lights go out. This little scene, the wanderers surprised, is brief and leads to nothing. It is self-contained and inconclusive, beautifully, before you know it, a prelude.

Lights up. The white screen. Slow bells.

Scene 2 Cloth taken away.[5] A nine-paned window suspended at head height on two straight black wooden poles on the left. There is a frilly curtain on its inside. The curtain is drawn. Behind the curtain a figure in an ornate white gown. We see only the lower part of the figure, framed by the two poles.[6] To the right a minute circular white-slat kennel, effigy of an enclosed garden, containing a huddle of white figures, its center black.[7]

---

5. The following scene had been eliminated from the fifth and last performance. It varied during the first four performances.

6. The window curtain was open from the beginning for the first performance. One saw the lady/girl/angel's pinkish red face framed by flaxen hair, her prettily raised hands: indistinct behind the pane separations.

7. Scenes 1 and 2 develop an image of one of the side shows at the '76 circus, *The*

The bird-carrier, on the far right, to whistles, is bandying the
bird over and behind the window on the left, then, to a low

chorus from behind the tall rectangle of the tall black suspended
backdrop — makes it flutter in the twigs of a dead branch, sticking up out of the kennel/garden from between the huddling
figures. The figures straighten out, the black in the middle of the
garden was the backs of their heads, they are the rowers from before, they look upward, seem apprehensive in their small engir-
dled space, rise. The singing stops. The screen is spread.
Blackout.

(Third performance: The bird-carrier has the bird play in the
tree. The miserable ones there rise up on their knees in delight.
The bird flies to the window. The lady opens her curtain as it
approaches: it visits her through the window. She holds it.
Screen. Blackout.)

Scene 3   Light on screen. Small spaced-out crystal sounds from a kneeling grey figure by the stage-right lights. Screen off. On the left,
the sea visitors are huddled on the floor around the white lady's

Garden Show, put on by Nancy Tyndall, but with puppets and a set by Schumann. Among
the puppets were six White Ladies, rod puppets, who for this NYC *White Horse Butcher*
had had their rods taken out, their heads being mounted on the performers'. They fit badly.
This resulted in puppets effective by their stiff awkwardness. The set:
    'I wanted something that went on inside a white fence and was played in the pine forest.
And I think I painted a backdrop that extended to the floor, so that there was a painted
meadow that extended into a backdrop. And the backdrop had the continuation of the
white fence. So there was a real white fence around it, then a painted meadow, and a
garden scene with trees, or something, on the backdrop. And inside the fence were these
lady puppets and a horse, I think.' — (Schumann, interview, December '82.)
    The puppets were subsequently used in the '78 *In Danger is Help* circus sideshow —
apparently changed back to rod puppets.

window as though abjectly praying to her (last performance: they form a half-circle, facing us, seated, their legs under them, in front of the window — Schumann having in the meantime corrected the players' excessive and graphically weak gestural initiative). To the sound of the police whistle, the grey figure vexes the angel with the bird/plane (my impression at the first performance); the funny little bird visits the maiden in the bower, twittering (my impression, last performance). The supplicators/attendants on the floor rear up, lean back, their anemic faces at all angles backwards, watching her loving commerce with the bird in the window (last performance: delighted by it in their humble way). As the bird flutters toward an effectively mysterious figure, a one-horned horse like a chess knight, standing immobile in a (patched) white gown not unlike the fenestrated female's, facing, inside a low circular picket fence, toward her window, its head a horse mask, grey at the nostrils, the lady is slowly removing a necklace (I assumed it to be a pearl necklace) from around her neck and is bestowing it on one of the visiting women face upturned toward her: in a slow surge, their spindly white hands a frieze above them, they turn, moving in place, on their knees, toward the unicorn, assuming stances of supplication, seemingly addressed to the bird dancing about its horn and adore the bird and/or the unicorn to the sound of a low choir emanating from behind the black screen, but visually attributable to them. The white scene-concluding screen is extended over this tableau. The scene's action seems not so much the dual movement of the bird (from woman to unicorn, left to right) and of the humble crowd (on the floor, up toward the woman, then toward the right, toward bird and unicorn), as rather a two-beat succession of tableaux, from woman on the left and unicorn in garden on the right to one roundly integrating the crowd of adoring supplicants. That is the way one scans paintings. Lights out.

The grey attendants arrange three pairs of grey metal folding chairs, facing to the right, in front of the screen. Another one, seated on the floor out front at the left, commences to saw on a violin. Lights up. A tall, solid capitalist but also monklike — father superior — figure, an Angel of Death with a pair of raggedy fringed long swept-back black wings, a tiny businessman's hat on his enormous white head mask (big-nosed, small-eared, almost without eyes, upward extension of a meaty though deadwhite mushroom-stem neck coming to a focus in a small prim mouth faintly intimating a snout), a column of a man in a vaguely suit-like garment, a grey blouse on top, from which protrudes the skirt of a gown, black on top, grey below, a narrow red sash tied

Scene 4

374

around his chest, its ends hanging down, something like a white and red rosette over the place of his heart, comes out from behind the screen on the right, and assumes positions, conductor-like, in front of the double row of chairs, and commences slowly beating two small sticks together.[8] A murmur rises from behind the screen on the right, Chinesey, voices in conversation, their tone that of agreement in disputation. Gradually, figures like this first one, but not quite as large, emerge, two by two, from behind the screen, on the left, in gravitatious but amiable dispute, or in sociable talk. They come in like a tribunal of judges: to the slow tapping of sticks from their purse-mouthed conductor. Their mouths are slits. Their gestures are marveleously expressive:[9] animate their enormous immobile head masks. They are old, staid men. Their conversations are elaborate, exude good fellowship. They carry something like briefs under their arms. They gradually, politely, assume seats, exchange greetings. They unfold the newspapers they have been carrying under their arms. Sit reading, a textured tableau: the spidery grey of the newspaper print; the white masticated paperheads; the intensely black hats; the soft grey and black costumes. The super-capitalist or angel of death turns his back to the column, makes a train whistle sound, then the chugging noises, 'ts-ts-ts-ts-ts', of a train getting into motion (they make the sounds also, reading), his sticks the engine levers. The police whistle or bird trill calls, the bird-carrier enters with the bird, the train has stopped, the bird flies above it. The six have been made to drop their papers by the whistle, they are looking at the bird, their arms slowly rising in the air (their hands are naked), a gesture that might turn into adoration, but instead turns into consternation, indignation, terror: they have their arms up as though threatened by a gun — not just up, but back: an exquisite composition, a powerful tableau — carrying, half way through the play, the echo, in opposition, of the play's first scene. Screen. Lights out.

---

8. A 'Butcher', chief of the Butchers, important set of figures during this period, representing American business. Mask first used, but without this denotation, for opening drummer in '74 circus; the figures, with the denotation, but with improvised masks, first in '75 *Monument to Ishi*; figures with the masks and the denotation first in '76 Dopp Farm circus. Scene 4 is a close-up, more poetically precise, more painterly version of the corresponding scene in the '76 circus. They are slightly modernized versions of the old-fashioned plutocrat represented by Uncle Fatso, a cross between him and the Gentleman Angel, representative of death in an impersonal cosmos. They don't look like businessmen so much as like capitalists — the east coast Chairmen of the Board, Presidents of the Corporation — they have the late Nelson Rockefeller's brutality. Schumann's later 'Salesmen' are still slightly more modern — corporate employees with a touch of Hitler.
9. Improvised mime, i.e. naturalist mimesis: rare in Schumann's shows.

Scene 5   Violin. Lights up. Screen off. The horse and the angel lady are in the kennel together, the lady is seeking out the mystic beast. They are of equal height, she faces him, both in ruffled white, her long hair not unlike his Isabella-colored mane. She is cutely

playing with the (twittering) bird, her hands cupped, all emotion (stance of her shoulders, arms, bent head). The unicorn is perfectly immobile. Under the window, the white rowers, the wan oriental ladies, have metamorphosed once more: there are three faceless grey and three faceless black beasts there, slowly rolling over on the ground, squirming. The lady releases the bird, it flies all over in a circle – she is regretting his leaving his leaving – she kisses the unicorn, leaning forward, her hands caressing its muzzle: it is a definitely erotic moment, a prolonged one, the unicorn slowly rocks forward minutely, very much a symbol just then, imperceptibly rocks back. The dark beasts are rolling off-stage around the window, lie in a heap at the left-hand edge of the screen, one of the capitalists enters, stepping over them, lifting his feet high, stalking stealthily on tiptoe as though in the performance of an elaborate gag, birdcage in hand, the bird inside, points to the lovers, then points to the caged bird, starts to laugh amply, his body shaking up and down, soundlessly – the sound comes from a tin can off to the right of the screen, filled with loose metal, rattled by a gray attendant, seated there, and behind the first capitalist appear the other capitalists, all shaking with laughter, bulkily, thronging out in various mimicry of robust hilarity, bobbing, while the lady hides her face behind the unicorn's head, sorrowfully holding on to it. The group is there, having its fun, for a long time. One of them once or twice in the middle of his laughter points to the couple: apparently it is not only the capture of the irritating bird, but the carryings-on of the lady that entertain them. Silence. They freeze off the vertical. Screen.

Scene 6   The screen is removed, in the light, off-white against the black surface, stands a giant (the top of its head perhaps 8 or 9 feet up) horse, the unicorn, its body of white cloth, hollow, open at the bottom, its legs the white-trousered, bare-footed legs of two performers, a picture-image, its true grandeur lightened by a frailty, its preposterousness, facing to the right, walking in a stately gait (the performers lifting their knees high, extending their feet far forward, bringing them down in place). On the left, black,

stumpy-muzzled beasts, possibly the same ones as before, but we now see their faces, mouths full of painted-on, square brilliant white teeth, large round white staring eyes, enter, crawling on all fours, nastily, inspect the walking horse off to the right, in front of them — there is some illusion of distance between them — turning their heads, twisting their necks, and in an oozing motion slither, but quite slowly, quasi-statically, off toward — after — it. With them, among them, a capitalist has entered, stands, a white tube, effigy of a telescope, lifted to his eye, pointed in the direction of the horse. To the sound of a wooden rattle, swung by one of the grey attendants off to the right, a harsh sound, the horse has begun to run (moving imperceptibly off toward the right, but virtually in place, remaining in front of the black screen), while the black hounds close in on it, overtake it, the front ones rearing up along its flank, a horrid eddy up its side, pawing it, seeming to hold it back: they bring it down, its rear end gradually subsiding to the floor, its head still up, but not as high, the hounds half covering its body, their master watching. The screen is brought out, covers the scene.

Scene 7   Slow scraping of a violin. The bright lights of the auditorium (small projectors on the circumambient church balcony) go on. The screen is removed. The horse is where it was stopped, half

down. Its two movers lie prone, their white-trousered legs, foot-soles, towards us, crumpled up themselves. Military march order whistles from the rear. The six capitalist commuter judges march in in a straight file, (the rowers') long staves in their hands, at their head their big, black-winged leader, grey-gloved (the others' hands are bare). They stand, stage-right, he steps out of rank, faces them, at his order they execute a face-left, stand at attention, facing the stage, the staves straight up and down, an execution squad. He, with a restrained though rapid step walks over to the horse, standing in front of it undoes his narrow red sash and blindfolds it, steps behind it. A sharp whistle. They march up and scatter around the horse in a circle, surrounding it. Whistle. They very slowly, stepping back a step, raise their lances way up, bending back, the lances point up

377

in the air, and as the rattle (operated by an attendant at the right) sounds, slowly bring them, point-down, down on the animal. The rattle stops. They remove their staves from the animal, stand at attention while it very slowly collapses between them. Whistle. Stomping their staves in unison, they march off. Tableau: the big executioner, vertical, grey, still behind the extended raggedy hull, white, of the animal: very dead-seeming. He quietly removes the white rosette – a pocket handkerchief? – from the left of his chest, opens it, it is crumpled up, takes from it something, strews it over the dead animal – presumably it's dirt – his quiet gestures not pious, but not perfunctory either. He walks off, unhurriedly, not too slowly.

Scene 8   Old black- and grey-dressed men, with white face masks (animal faces, pointy, ferrety), in fact they are still the boatfull of what then seemed women of the first scene, straggle in, bent on their staves (the same that have served as oars and lances), with shaking wagging white heads, shaking all over, mimicking the difficulty of walking, see the dead horse, slowly gather around it, stand, rocking, sorrowing, around it, a low hum (om) from behind the black screen the sound of their wailing. They look like old Jews. Blackout.

Scene 9

The bright lights go on. The horse lying there. A vastly tall figure on white stilts. – Peter Schumann – the white lady, flying, with wings, comes in, rounding the left end of the black screen in two sweeping steps and to stately renaissance dance music – 'Nonesuch' – from an uncostumed group of four on the right, performs a long solitary dance, the flouncy, fancy dress cloudy fleeces, way up, about the foolishly red, smiling face of the flaxen-haired virgin, the rubber-tipped stilts punctuating the sinuous music flowingly and gently, raised in the air, coming down on odd beats: a figure of fantasy *up* there, its softly vivacious gestures firmly rhythmic within the cloud of gar-

mentry: A dance of breath-taking insouciance. He ends the
dance, stalks over to the horse, straddles it, claps his hands brisk-
ly, it rises instantaneously, to another, even more stately tune —
'Road to the Isles' — an old Scottish tune — he rides it out,
grandly standing above it.

*　　*　　*

White Horse Butcher. Comment.
One senses at the circumferences of Schumann's artistic productions a willful retirement into or restraint of himself within (a) a simplicity of mind as
per Jesus, black and white fundamentalism (no accident his black/white
images, the grey assimilating with the black, perhaps also color of the
ordinary man), a firm focus on the simple things of life, (b) irrationalism[10]
as regards his stories and own views, refusal to examine, perhaps twists
given hastily behind his own back, links left out on purpose to make his
position more obscure, and all this re good and evil and life and death,
and/or the role of killing in life. A tight black ideological knot results, an
idea seemingly personal, not only in fact personal. One does not know
what to make of it: in spite of the simplicities. Such a self-inhibition may
be the condition for art: I am of the opposite nature, always wishing to
render explicit. The killing is bad but does not matter; it is horrible, but
also ordinary, the norm, life; the simplicity and the irrationalism conflict.
The utter clarity of the symbols — pearl necklace, bird, rowboat, white
gown, curtained window, waiting, looking out, princess with golden hair,
tree in winter, unicorn, kiss, caress, love, black wings, small black hats,
businessmen, sticks, caged bird, laughter, hounds, hunt, telescope, killing,
blindfold, red, dirt, sorrow for dead — oddly — queerly — compounds into
obscurity: the reverse of simple light from complicated darkness. On their
way into tortured inwardness — correlative to what at times seems an almost hysterically tightly adhered-to or upheld narrative form, that of the
fairy tale:[11] now an extreme artifice — the symbols traverse a zone of ambiguity. During the first performance, I thought of the little white bird as
ambiguously an airplane (naturally a scout plane for bombers), the twittering of the bird to me was the threatening sound of a police whistle (the

---

10. 'Asked if there was a central theme to his work, he confirmed that during the Vietnam
war there was a strong anti-war motif. As for a contemporary theme, he puffed long on a
cigar before he protested, "If that isn't evident . . ." and broke off, exclaiming that the
whole difference between art and journalism was the necessity to use words. "I must be
allowed my unconscious. I cannot be obligated to define because defining it makes it
limited. Basically, the theater is story telling." — (Kunin, *The Bread and Puppet Theater*,
Vermont Life, Spring '77, from an interview of the summer of '76.)
11. 'My favorite writer is Grimm. It is the best writing I know of, together with the Bible.
The stories are very exact and pure. They only say what needs to be said. There's no fooling around.' — (Schumann, ibid.)

379

law in pursuit, someone's being chased, rounded up, surrounded, closed in on), the wonder garden seemed to me a tight kennel and the rowers' and princess' adoration of the bird to me was just terror. The bird/plane seemed ambiguously good and bad, but the reactions in the show to it were as though it was just a death-announcer, threat, the whistling indicating this apperception of it. This particular ambiguity may have been due to insufficient rehearsing for that first performance: perhaps the whistling was a mite too shrill, loud, the gestures of delight not quite exact enough to differ from gestures of terror. And the persistent ambiguity of the show might be cited by defenders of Schumann's art as precisely instance of the setting up of vibrations in the viewer effected by the rationally inarticulated art work, its structure not that of appearances, not of reality, nor of sound argument: desirable reverberation, enriching inner life. So it may be: but it does not seem intended by Schumann – his ambiguities lie elsewhere.

A feeling about life is expressed in a sequential compaction of images, each, though the sequence is a story, starkly an event: the capture of nature's poetry in life (the white paper bird) – a de-poetizing ordering of nature – is followed by ('entails' would be inappropriate as regards such a succession of symbols) the hunting down and killing of life's mystery (the virile, but innocent, elusive unicorn in its gobelin garden). The poetry in life is depicted as that which is free, adventitious, senseless, frivolous, as delicate, not unpretty, but ridiculous rather than lovely, the incursion out of nowhere of a minute gaiety, alleviating the work, confinement and greyness of ordinary life. Life's mystery is depicted as the stately grandeur and calm purity of guiltless sexuality, an unmoved mover, powerful and transporting. This story is topped by a miracle: the hidden feminine principle of loveliness, compassion and love (Schumann in drag) arises to public music and revives the mystery of life – for service to it. Qua story, this wordless mystery play thus clearly celebrates Eros and its conditions, agape and gaily harmless anarchy, mutely indicting, at the same time, their counter-principle, murderous regulatory authority. Qua story, it's a commentary on sex, with political under- and personal overtones.

Yet this is not what we see – are given to experience. The allegorical story is a product of reflection. The verbal identification not only limits the symbols' denotations, deadens them, but by giving their overlappings and the sense of a story eliminates their individual power: the rowers surprised by a bird, the angel in the window, the unicorn in the garden, the corporate herd entrained toward work, the mocking mob of executives, the princess making love to the animal, the magic beast succumbing to the hounds, the capitalist as technological hunter (a spy from afar), the blinding of the beast, the clubbing of the beast, the commiseration of the old, the solitary dancing of the cloud puppet, each stands out in a relief of splendor against its own silence, not sign but symbol. A symbol, a sign

380

fucked up by an artist, differs from a sign because it does not let go of its denotations. Enhancing its presence, they point it up. The sign points to them in a waste of itself: they are the symbol's rays, a solar effect. It is an incorporation of essences, inviting worship. Such retained wealth is easily mistaken for the miserliness of dumbly stark beauty, stunning, taking. But in fact the symbol is open for investment. One cannot pass through it as one can through the virtually immaterial sign. But if by sympathy one takes up temporary residence in it, some of its cognitive radiance may stay with one, once it dissolves. The elicitation of a meaningful story intercepts the symbol's reception.

Definite reference is a sign's virtue. Symbols, luxuriously their own end, feed on a multiplicity of references, but not this is their power, but that each of their references is doubtful, something possible, both as to its very existence (the symbol *is* what it points to), and as to just what it points to (the convention is makeshift, something of a put-on in its very inception, renegotiable). Thus not only do we enjoy in the symbol itself what the symbol stands for, but it restores to us, to some extent, the creative character of distinction, the world's fluidity.

One of the consequences of this, one of which the smashers of icons may not have been unmindful, is a certain moral ambiguity, not attaching to plain language. One may sense one's very submission to the symbol as a morally doubtful disconsideration of reality (to which the sign dutifully points one); and symbolization lacks the neatness toward which its underlying anxiety urges moral distinction: the configurations it presents are incongruent with the dichotomies of moral judgment. This contributes to the disturbing character of symbols, and especially so, because symbols are invariably moralistic. The representatives of Powers and Active Principles, by the imagination cut cleanly according to patterns of Good and Bad, they imperiously demand allegiance and concommitant absolute oppositions: but into the powers and active principles the authoritative rightness of which they proclaim, they import, to the ordinary eye, the chill of indifference, and even some terror of power, and they leave their opposites or negatives not without some humble inevitability or virtue of neededness — as though each symbol's exoteric moralism clad an esoteric epiphany of a world beyond good and evil.

The symbolic action is a rite celebrating not just one but all essence: foreshortened thought by the symbol it dresses in, it abdicates to the way things are — and to incomprehension.[12] In life, right and wrong, good and

12. German reviewers of a version of this NYC show adapted to following *Joan of Arc* as a second part praised it for its impracticality:

'... bleibt ... in einer unverbindlichen Symbolik befangen, die keinen konkreten Weg der Veränderung aufzuzeigen vermag und bei der blossen Hoffnung auf einen letztendlichen Sieg des Guten stehenbleibt ...' — (Kindermann, *Deutsche Volkszeitung*, August 3, '78.)

evil are of life: opportunities for being now; in plain language, they are aggressions on the individual; but in the symbol, they acquire an aspect of perversity.

The submission of the rowers on the stream of life (many other verbations of the symbols are possible) is splendid; ordinariness transcends itself in sadness; but also — by no means less strong for being marginal — there is something terrible in this seried effort, a shivering of despair. Gaiety/ innocent fun/playfulness is surely a good-in-itself. The symbolization of it, an act itself indicative of the adult's and aging mortal's desperate need of it, confers on it some of the astringency of medicine, and, worse, reveals that this therapy cannot be compelled and is the less forthcoming the more it is needed. Charity symbolized is put in doubt, it is so clear that it enriches the giver, and so clear also how the need of those that need it robs it of its essential, its spiritual, value. Conversely, on the Calvinist rationalization of life by capitalist industrialism, a Weberian syndrome, one of evolving humanity's progressive modes of self-discipline, symbolization confers the awesome invulnerability of pure evil, of a negative life force, that can only be opposed and fled, but not harnessed or overcome. Etc.

When Schumann uses words, as in the parables of the mountain man and of the young man, the circus sideshows included in the NYC show, his artistic unwillingness to advance his own understanding or ours — understanding as distinct from wisdom — precipitates him into an alternative of plain sentimentality (*The Young Man*) and crabbed obscurity (*Mountain Man*). Into sentimentality, because the simple verbal signs ('a young man') lack the autonomy and mythic ambiguity (as supra) of his mute 3-dimensional symbols, without attaining to the grandeur of simple universality (which verbal utterance attains to only when refined by a willing deployment of intellect). Into obscurity, because instead of trying for verbal symbols (which, vide the Bible, Shakespeare, Dante, apart from poetic gift itself the elan of thought, require a love of the intellect), he tries for a verbal signification of (non-verbal) symbols ('the soul of the mountain man'), which, though it requires neither intellectual elan nor love of the intellect, requires a semantic care abhorrent to one unwilling to advance understanding. The power of non-symbolic, merely significatory language is only the power of whatever understanding — thought — it expresses; that of symbolic (metaphorical, poetic) language that of the thought which, having gone through it, it transcends: the speech of an enemy of thought is necessarily weak, in fact more or less odious.

The NYC *White Horse Butcher*, fifth version of the theme, was an

---

Schumann told them:

'Wenn wir einen Engel machen können, der das Unmögliche besiegt, kannst auch du einen Engel machen, der das Unmögliche besiegt.' — (ibid.)

extremely beautiful play, elegant transposition of the pageant versions, a chamber play, embroidery translated into dance, a succession of blindingly clear stances.

Schumann, *Story of the White Horse Butcher*, '78.

This is the story of the white-horse butcher. The butcher is strong. He has a telescope to see life in the distance. What does the white-horse butcher see in the distance?
Six fine ladies in a house of snow. Six fine ladies travelling over the water. Six fine ladies and a horse. The horse is as white as snow and as big as life.
The six fine ladies are Wondrous Love. The horse is Life. Love kisses Life. Life is wild and good.
Watch out!
This is the story of the white-horse butcher! The white-horse butcher is not alone! All the butchers together are off to find the white horse! They spare no expense, they travel far. They find the white horse with his love! They look at them, laugh at them, and they fence them good.
But the horse breaks out and runs away, runs away, runs away!
Then the butchers get their dogs, dogs, dogs! And the dogs chase, chase, chase! And they yell, yell, yell! And they bring down the horse.

O, the butchers get their deadly sticks, and they march up to the wounded horse. And they raise their deadly sticks. And they kill the horse with their deadly sticks.
And life is defeated, and the horse is dead. All the wise men know it! All the wise men sob and cry, and the horse is dead!
Hope is an angel. And Hope dance- even when Life is defeated and the horse is dead.
Yes, the angel dances. And after the dance the angel hops on the back of the dead white horse. And the angel shouts: Giddiup!
And the white horse rises, and life is not defeated and the horse is not dead!
Joy rides over the hills and far away!"

11. Fadeout and slaughter of the *White Horse Butcher* theme. The Circus of '77 and its Unicorn Pageant. *The Story of Joan of Arc's Horse* (October '77-January '79). *White Horse Butcher* book, '77.

The circus of the summer of '77 (August 20, 21), led up to by now traditional local showings of parts of it during the two weeks preceding it – Canaan, August 6, Burklyn, August 7, Montgomery, August 7, Bethel, August 7 – and by a scattering of July parades with July 4th motifs – Barton, July 2, Cabot, July 4, East Haven, July 9, Wheelock, July 16, Irasburg, July 20, Lyndonville, July 30 – was attended by 12.000 people: local people from the North-east counties, Canadians, Vermont academicians, the semi-ruralized hippie element.[1]

Besides the usual sideshows from 2 to 4 p.m., among which two, *A Man Says Goodbye*, and a skit entitled *Chile*,[2] by the Pupi e Fresedi, the group of singers with whom Schumann did *Masaniello*, and the frivolities of the *Domestic Resurection Circus* from 4-5 p.m., just silly circus now, without even any vestiges, I think, of political satire, but otherwise pretty much the same acts as the preceding year, frozen,[3] two new pieces of

---

1. 'Many of the people in the crowd are trying to make a go of communal farms tucked away at the end of dirt roads on New England hillsides. For example, Terry McGreevey and Hershey Heyman and their two children share 130 acres of pine forest and meadow with three other families who also migrated north as the sixties wound down. McGreevey is trying to finish building a geodesic dome and cutting seven cords of firewood before the winter. McGreevey and Heyman work in a community cooperative cannery and a trucking cooperative that they helped organize. People on the farm tap their own syrup, cut their own lumber and firewood, and raise animals and vegetables organically. They share work and companionship among themselves and with other communal farms.' — (G. Himes, *The Town Comes to the Circus, Unicorn Times*, Washington, D.C. edition, February, '78.)

2. I don't know how this piece relates to *The Mountain Man of Chile* of the previous year's circus.

'... Victor Jara, a Chilean guitarist who after the overthrow of Salvador Allende in 1973 had his hands chopped off by General Pinochet's police, in a soccer stadium because he continued to strum for the masses of other prisoners assembled there, but who then raised his stumps so everyone could see what had been done to him and sang his song in the hush that fell.' — (Hoagland, '83.)

3. 'At four o'clock, a red jeep and two blue school-buses roar into the valley and the circus begins. Two fifteen foot puppets, introduced as Mother Earth and Uranos, do a bellyrub and have a baby: Schumann's version of the fertility rite as a vaudeville act. The baby is the ringmaster, decked out in tuxedo and a two foot tophat. He introduces a quick succession of acts: A blind knife-thrower, the "Aerial Smooch", "From the deepest jungles of the Bronx, Mrs. Bobo Belinsky and her Good Housekeeping Seals of Approval". A daredevil

Schumann's were part of it, both done between 5:30 and 7:00, a reactionary tragedy, *Masaniello* (cf. infra), behind the circus storage tent, off around a turn of the woods, and, the event's musical Christian play, *Carmina Burana*, with music by the Goddard Community Chorus, in the circus arena, and a third show of Schumann's, *Joan of Arc* (cf. infra), the only new piece he had done since the preceding circus (shown in Canada, Vermont, some Southern states, February to March or April '77), was performed in the pine woods after dark, at 9 p.m. I wasn't there, so I don't know what *Carmina Burana* was like. The particular collection – the *Carmina Burana* – of 12th and/or 13th century 'Goliard' vagrant clerics' – students' – songs from which Orff got his songs seems to consist mostly of drinking and love songs, but some of the songs apparently were satires on the church and on monastic life, and Schumann's piece seems to have been conceived in their spirit.[4]

*　　*　　*

The pageant was a readaptation to the outdoors of the preceding year's NYC *White Horse Butcher*, omitting the figure of the Virgin, and thus getting the story back to the defilement-of-nature, Business vs. Nature theme.[5]

---

driving an electric skateboard through a concrete wall. The Itch Brothers' trained flea act: "The Dive Into Notoriety". Other acts are quite spectacular: five Chinese New Year's dragons chase clowns around the ring. Twenty deep scarlet birdfigures, ranging from three to twelve feet tall, dance amid furious music and incense while a flame-eater swallows two torches. Schumann hops and twirls on 8½ foot stilts as an eighteen foot tall Uncle Sam.' — (G. Himes, *The Town Comes to the Circus, The Unicorn Times*, Washington, D.C. edition, February, '78.)

4. 'It was done with a big bunch of garbagemen that dressed up as ladies.' — (Schumann, interview, '79.)

'*Carmina Burana*, an opera by Carl Orff, is sung by the Goddard Community Chorus and mimed by the Bread and Puppet Garbagemen. Their workingman's enactment reveals the New Testament passages in a manner that is sometimes refreshing and quite accessible. Christ, played by a squat Archie Bunkerish character, chews a large toothpick. "That guy looks like your father", laughs a spectator. The Garbagemen play the Last Supper as a barroom scene; by the end of the chorus they're all under the table. Sometimes, however, the satire becomes as tedious as the opera.' — (Local review.)

5. 'Vers 19 heures, la licorne est apparue dans une clairière. En de longues foulées, elle est arrivée vers nous, tandis que, des extrémités du pré, surgissaient ses partisans, une centaine environ, habillés de blanc, les uns portant des oriflammes, les autres une tête géante qu'ils ont dressée au centre du terrain. Un troupeau de cerfs a débouché de la forêt, des chevaux sauvages sont arrivés au galop. Les animaux couvraient toute la clairière. Dans l'assistance, un hommes s'est levé. Avec son petit feutre noir et son attaché-case, il a déclaré qu'il était maquignon de son métier et que l'abattage était son job.

Une vingtaine de bouchers, tenant des chiens en laisse, ont couru vers lui, escortés par l'orphéon de la corporation et par des hommes de paines bien outillés (masques de mort, canon, boulets, échelle double). La besogne a été vite et bien faite. Les chiens ont été lâchés

Schumann in May-June '77, and again May-June '78 toured Europe (and in June/July '78 took them to Venezuela and Puerto Rico) with *Joan of Arc* and with a version of the *White Horse Butcher* — butchers and dogs pursuing, killing the horse, Schumann as white angel reviving it — adapted to this other play as its second part: about her horse. By the time this com-

---

sur la licorne, le canon a tiré sur les cerfs et sur les chevaux. Le funèbre commando a emporté ce qui restait de la tête, abandonnant sur place les dépouilles des animaux.

Nous avons hué les tortionnaires. A ce moment, au-dessus des pins, nous avons aperçu la lune. Immense lune, érigée sur un char tiré par de gros boeufs, précédée de joueurs de piccolo, d'enfants chantant et dansant.

Au pied de la lune était assise une dame blanche: arrivée à hauteur du carnage, elle s'est levée, a dansé. Elle était très grande. Sa chorégraphie dans le crépuscule paraissait iréelle. Elle s'est approchée, elle a frappé dans ses mains. Par enchantement, l'animal s'est dressé sur ses pattes, et la dame le chevauchait. Autour, les cerfs se relevaient, et déjà les chevaux galopaient. Face à nous a surgi un vol de grands oiseaux blancs. Ils ont plané avec lenteur, puis se sont mêlés, à pied, au cortège des animaux, de la lune, des enfants et de la dame à la licorne. Le spectacle s'est dissipé dans la nuit entre les pins. Nous demeurions assis, sans savoir ce qu'il fallait dire, ce qu'il fallait faire. Plus tard, on en entendait certains pleurer, d'autres chanter.

Ainsi s'est achevée a Glover, le 21 août 1977, la version de cette légende médiévale, *la Dame à la licorne*, le *Pageant*, comme l'a désignée le Bread and Puppet Theatre dans son programme.' — (Christian Dupavillon, *Une licorne géante au-dessus des tracteurs. Le festival du ''Bread and Puppet'' a Glover, Le Monde*, September 29, '77.)

'It's an hour before sunset on a late August day in Glover, Vt. Several thousand dogs, children, and adults from Vermont's communal farm community have gathered on the south slope of a half mile long valley. At the top of the crowd a trumpeter gives a blast to signal the beginning of the pageant, the climactic event of the sixth annual Bread and Puppet Domestic Resurrection Circus. Trumpeters from the other three corners of the valley answer with echoing calls and a white unicorn prances into the valley.

The Unicorn is two dancers from the Bread and Puppet Theater under a white sheet and a large, magnificent unicorn puppet head, sculpted by Peter Schumann.

A shout goes up, and whiteclad bannerwavers come running and shouting over the northwest horizon with woodcuts of wildflowers on their flapping white flags. From the east, another white-robed crowd rushes into the valley. Next to the unicorn they raise an eighteen foot puppet, a beatific madonna with Buddha eyes, a Mona Lisa smile, and lightly rosed cheeks. Her head and out-stretched open palms are moved by eight foot poles. Her body consists of four long white banners, each painted with a bright but simple oriental flower.

Four smoky bonfires are lit north, east, south, and west of the sun mother puppet. A herd of white horse puppets appear on the northeastern hilltop, slowly weaving their way through the smoke. From the south, a huddled group of white reindeer puppets — with polished stump heads, charcoaled eyes, and twig antlers — inch down the slope to join the unicorn and horses at the sun mother's side.

From the northwestern corner, however, a man with a white bulbous head in a business suit waddles onto the scene carrying an attache case. He bleeps his car horn and from over the western rise, the military-industrial complex marching band enters to the tune of "The Caissons Go Rolling". Seven ominous figures swathed in gray and holding the leash to fourteen vicious dogs lead the way. Other gray-cloaked figures carry a cannon and ladder. The white robes and black top hats of the twelve musicians are painted with skeletons.

The effectiveness of the dog masks is attested to by the howls of several dogs in the audience. The effectiveness of the ritual is attested to by the boos and hisses from the

bination reached NYC – the Brooklyn Academy of Music – in January (January 9-19) '79, what was now called *The Story of Her Horse* had turned into slapstick (Murray Levy's term, Levy, interview, '79) tragico-comedy.[6] When in '78 this happened, I don't know, probably at the end

---

audience as Mr. Capital leads in his troops. This is not propaganda theater, because no one in this crowd needs to be convinced that the military-industrial powers that be are opposed to the sun mother, to forest animals, to celebration, to them.

As if they were a baseball crowd, they gasp when the dogs attack and devour the unicorn; they groan when the cannon kills the deer and horses, and they hiss when the army blindfolds the sun mother and carries her off.

The crowd brightens, however, as an ox-drawn cart carrying a Maurice Sendak crescent moon and the moon angel appears in the east. Following the cart is a whiteclad procession ringing bells, waving streamers, and chanting a hymn. By the time the procession reaches the scene of carnage, the real sun is reddening the sky and a real crescent moon is visible overhead.

Schumann as the moon angel is wearing five foot stilts, and when he steps out of the cart, he stands twelve feet tall with translucent wings and four feet of yarn hair. He does a triumphant stilt dance, hopping on one stilt and stamping the ground to the procession's music. He then walks over and straddles the fallen unicorn. The unicorn rises between his legs, and the angel rides off to the horizon.

The other animals come back to life and the procession erupts in pandemonium. Over the northwestern slope come five giant white birds, their conical heads and fluttering fringe wings supported on six poles. The largest bird has a wingspan of twenty feet. They swoop and caw as they circle the joyous valley. The audience is on its feet and cheering.

Myself, I'm astonished. Without any dialogue, the pageant has created an adult fable. I had gotten this sense of a fullsprung mythic world from novelists such as Tolkein and Vonnegut, but never before in a live performance. Moreover, the pageant acknowledges that the struggles in myths between good and evil are essentially political struggles.

The struggle for peace, nature, and justice in Norse legends and Semitic folk tales is essentially the same fight the left carries on today. This struggle can be tied to the specific issues of the day, but it most certainly will outlast them. Schumann ties his fable to current issues, but not so tightly as to prevent its transcendance.' — (G. Himes, *The Town Comes to the Country, Unicorn Times*, Washington, D.C. edition, February, '78.)

6. '*The Story of Her Horse* is introduced by a Chaplinesque puppet-man with a rose in his buttonhole. He enters down the aisle, stopping to tug at a little girl's ponytail and tip his bowler at a surprised-looking greybeard. The horse also enters through the house. And a lovely, two-actor horse it is, with a rope tail, a rag mane and in inclination to dance. Like Joan, the horse is captured and betrayed, lured to his death by a tiny wooden copy of himself, the way ducks are by decoys.' — (Jenner, *Canarsie Digest*, January 22, '79.)

'It, too, is sacrificed, eaten (with salt and pepper) by these great grey/black humanoid puppets, capped with paper maché heads' — (Patterson, *Phoenix*, January 18, '79.)

'The execution of the comical horse, a two-actor puppet – by six pompous white-masked figures who parade around to the tune of the Marine Hymn is intended to symbolize all kinds of obvious oppression.' — (R. Eder, *New York Times*, January 18, '79.)

'a less intense work, far more heavy-handed and diffuse than *Joan of Arc*. There is, however, a single surpassing image, one of the most beautiful I have ever seen: the once-proud horse lies slain on the floor, its carcass eaten away by human teeth.' — (Faber, *Village Voice*, January 22, '79.)

'Our society on a train, pursuing the white horse, getting it, killing it. Cruelty succeeds. Mourners mourn. It takes an angel to resurrect the dead.' — (Schumann, program notes to *The Story of Her Horse*, Brooklyn Academy of Music, '79.)

of the year. Schumann seems to have prepared this version especially for the NYC showing.

Before Schumann killed the image, however, he told the story from the butcher's viewpoint, in the first person singular, in a magnificent book of woodcuts, *Bread and Puppet White Horse Butcher*, published by the Janus Press, Vermont in 1977, and cut by Schumann more or less just in time for the editrice and printer to get out the book, certainly not more than a year before it came out (Schumann, interview, '83). It's the true story, almost revealed in the '75 *Pageant* where the boy 'Eric' turns into the killer — but otherwise well hidden — Schumann killed the horse:

'Ladies and Gentlemen! Have a cup of coffee! (image of a steaming cup of coffee) I am the White Horse Butcher and I escaped from the Devil! (image of a clawed demon straddling a prone man) I sailed over the sea (image of the fleet sailboat) I traveled over the hills (image of the gray goose in angry flight) by night (the black moon over the black land) and day (black trees on a black hill) I stopped here (two houses, smoke from their chimneys), stepped into the house (focus on one of the houses, its door) met the lady (the smiling man is talking to the lady, she has her head turned away), loved her (the lady, face and breasts, embraced by black) Ta-ta-ta-taa! (above a small trumpet, the lady in turmoil, arms, breast, hair: the lady reclining, breasts pendant, belly button, looking: the lady upright, breasts, hand in her hair: the lady smiling, both arms raised, one breast in silhouette: the lady pensive, as though consternated: the lady admonitory, arm up in argument) married her (burst of a flower) Ta-ta-ta-too! (above the small trumpet, the two as one, in tumult: the lady black and solid, down to her crotch) planted a tree (he's putting it in the ground) and saw the Horse! (the horse is white! its head is up, also its tail, and one foreleg — it is cute: the little horse is running, mane flying: the horse is bucking: the white horse is leaping: the white is running: speeding: leaping) I said bye-bye and followed the Horse! (the lady — black, not white, lovely but desolate, head bowed) I caught the Horse (he's black and smiling grimly, his black arm straight into the white steed's muzzle) I fenced it (a black fence on black ground) I sold it (an exchange of money) I rode it (black rider on a white horse) I slaughtered it (the filly on its back, legs in the air) I ate it (plate and knife and fork) and the day after I saw the horse flying through the sky! (sky, and perhaps the image of a horse) Ta-ta-ta-taa! (he's blowing the trumpet).'

There is no guilt expressed by this lovely tale of guilt. It is as upbeat as the *White Horse Butcher* pageants. I see it as identification of personal content, meaning and motivation in Schumann's work of the initial Dopp Farm period. In his pageants representing Man as destroyer of the natural and in his morality plays men as guilty sinners, women as innately moral and carriers of the life principle, he is expressing personal guilt feelings. If this is true, it does not lessen the value of this work, nor does it cast its truth in doubt. Rather it suggests how we should all deal with our guilt.

12. Schumann and the Renaissance. Art is revolution against past art, and art that aims at its own performance is as false and terroristic as a revolution-born society enforcing its own permanence.

In the fall of '76 he hurts his back hauling wood, and is, he says, laid up for a while,[1] but, regardless, we find him in Tuscany in October, cane in hand, he says, and with a belt to keep his back straight, doing street shows and *White Horse Circus*, and again in December, doing a workshop (December 1-16) with 20 students of art at the Florence Istituto d'Arte di Porta Romana:[2] mass producing (polychrome) paper maché figures inspired by the frescoes of Tommaso Guidi, known as The Sloppy – Masaccio. Either the probable origin of this epithet in Guidi's work (it is commonly attributed rather to his habits of dress and deportment, but he was known for working very fast, his contours and articulations are faulty, and his major contribution, the three-dimensionality of his figures, is said achieved chiefly by a somewhat mechanical application of highlights) or that distinctively plastic quality of his figures probably attracted Schumann to him – the former making him identify with Guidi as worker, the latter as sculptor. The work he had his culture-plugged students do made them feel like masaccios.[3]

'Types, in themselves of the manliest, he presents with a sense for the materially significant which makes us realise to the utmost their power and dignity; and the spiritual significance thus gained he uses to give the highest import to the event he

---

1. Taylor Stöhr found him laid up in November.

'In the fall, when I cut wood in the sugarbush – for the sugarbush, and I slept in the woods all by myself, and I had somebody's tractor, and I pulled out the wood for our house down here, and I pulled out – but I did the whole job myself, and at the end of it I twisted my back really badly, and I had to bed down for two months or so.' — (Schumann, interview, '79.)

2. 'A building workshop. I built a lot of clay molds and made plaster casts with the help of some other people and then set up a whole paper maché factory in the art school and made hundreds of copies from that and then mounted them on masonite and painted them.' — (ibid.)

'Die kunststudie in Florence is voor studenten zo drukkend. Hun zenuwachtigheid en slechte verhouding met de kunst van hun stad, dat alles leek mij het onderwerp van een project met hen toe. Voor hen hoorde de klassieke kunst van hun stad bij de toeristen, bij de Amerikanen. Ik wilde Masaccio aan hen teruggeven.' — (Schumann, interviewed by Bardoel and Vastermans, '*Gesprek met Peter Schumann*', *De Groene Amsterdammer*, June 14, '78.)

3. 'Masaccio is an almost oppressive presence in Florence,' said Schumann. 'The great classic in front of which the students are supposed humbly to prostrate themselves. And so,

is portraying; this import, in turn, gives a higher value to the types, and thus, whether we devote our attention to his types or to his action, Masaccio keeps us on a high plane of reality and significance. In later painting we shall easily find greater science, greater craft, and greater perfection of detail, but greater reality, greater significance, I venture to say, never. Dust-bitten and ruined though his Brancacci Chapel frescoes now are, I never see them without the strongest stimulation of my tactile consciousness. I feel that I could touch every figure, that it would yield a definite resistance to my touch, that I should have to expend thus much effort to displace it, that I could walk around it. In short, I scarcely could realise it more, and in real life I should scarcely realise it so well, the attention of each of us being too apt to concentrate itself upon some dynamic quality, before we have at all begun to realise the full material significance of the person before us. Then what strength to his young men, and what gravity and power to his old! How quickly a race like this would possess itself of the earth, and brook no rivals but the forces of nature! Whatever they do – simply because it is they – is impressive and important, and every movement, every gesture, is world-changing. Compared with his figures, those in the same chapel by his precursor, Masolino, are childish, and those by his follower, Filippino, unconvincing and without significance, because without tactile values. Even Michelangelo, where he comes in rivalry, has, for both reality and significance, to take a second place. Compare his 'Expulsion from Paradise' (in the Sistine Chapel) with the one here by Masaccio. Michelangelo's figures are more correct, but far less tangible and less powerful; and while he represents nothing but a man warding off a blow dealt by a sword, and a woman cringing with ignoble fear, Masaccio's Adam and Eve stride away from Eden heart-broken with shame and grief, hearing, perhaps, but not seeing, the angel hovering high overhead who directs their exiled footsteps.

Masaccio, then, like Giotto a century earlier – himself the Giotto of an artistically more propitious world – was, as an artist, a great master of the significant, and, as a painter, endowed to the highest degree with a sense of tactile values, and

---

to have a fresh and useful approach, to do something actively *with* Masaccio seemed a liberating idea for this school.'

The idea came to Schumann when he saw how diligently students would work for a very long time on a single piece of wood or stone.

'I said that in one week we would create something as voluminous as the Brancacci Chapel . . . To do this we had to set up a sort of factory making papier mâché. This is a cheap material which is available in large quantities and we made some 300 pieces this way.'

'The students' concern,' said Schumann, 'was not so much with Masaccio and the themes chosen as with the work process itself. This was the first time they had an occasion to work in cooperation – putting aside their individual artistic goals. All this was new to them and spurred their activity and energy. They were very skeptical at the beginning.'

'After the first day they had a meeting and refused to continue with the workshop. They had expected that the workshop would pamper the individualism of the participants and support the individualistic attitude we are brought up in. But after the second day they were in full swing, and it was impossible to doubt the value of the cooperative, corporative experience once one was in it.' — (Gibson, *Presenting Masaccio in a Humble Medium*, *Herald Tribune*, February 11-12, '78.)

with a skill in rendering them. In a career of but few years he gave to Florentine painting the direction it pursued to the end.
(Bernard Berenson, *The Italian Painters of the Renaissance*, '60.)

Thus in spite of his sloppiness, Guidi ended up securing the art-dealing critic's approval.

The factory's output was put on exposition at the factory *Bread and Puppet/Masaccio. L'Arte della Fragilita e della Cartapesta*, December 17, '76-January 31, '77, in Rome's, Museum of Folklore, June 10-July 3, '77 (the *Herald Tribune* reviewer (*Herald Tribune*, June 21, '77) attributing them to an 'anonymous group of people'), at the Sorbonne chapel, under the sponsorship of Alpha-FNAC, in conjunction with concerts by Italian singers, among them the Pupi e Fresedde, January 31-February 19, '78, where the reviewers thought them the work of the students, and thence traveled via Caen to Genoa.

What Schumann had in mind was a lesson in productive art appreciation:

'LADIES . . .

> Was Du ererbt von Deinen Vätern
> hast, erwirb es, um es zu besitzen.

> Goethe

I did not go to Florence to teach Florentines Masaccio, or to study and analyze his work. I just wanted to dethrone an old master and put him on a kitchen chair, make him useful, take him away from the tourists and art-historians, and give him to my friends who helped me with the papier-mache work.

What could the city of Florence with all its marble statues and churches possibly need more than the art of papier-mache? Marble is heavy and heavy-hearted and sticks with you for thousands of years. Papier-mache is light like wind and exits as fast as wind. And please consider all its unfamous advantages: while you are concerned with the re-rendering of man's expulsion from Paradise, you paste Jimmy Carter's front on Fidel Castro's behind, and thus solve a lot of the world's burning problems in a wink. For 14 days we ran a small factory in the Instituto Statale d'arte Porta Romana, which turned out Adams and Eves and saints and cripples at the speed of the wet paper drying in the plaster molds. Our goal wasn't to be studious, critical, professorial, political.

We started from one quick glance at the work of Masaccio and took our vision from there. The goal was: a production at least the size of the Brancacci Chapel, a grim and joyful, plentiful, big Masaccio, surrounding everybody, pouring down on everybody from 4 sides of the room.

I think that people learn better from participating and doing, than from lectures and analysis.

We did not need to understand the how and why of our Masaccio in order to be involved in and rewarded by the process of production. The insights we gained on the way were not anticipated, they were fresh and true, and we can use them for further work.

... AND ...

> The highest elegance
> producing the least waste.

> James Hayford

Forests are slaughtered every day to produce newspapers which travel straight from our easy-chairs to the garbagecans. Trees are human beings too. We should build our houses and highways from those discarded papers to justify so much killing.

Productions have to justify their means. Not only: how much money, but also: how much time, material and effort produces what. An object of art is supposed to be an elegant and acrobatic example for the solution of such problems. A lot of the garbage of our crazy civilization is more interesting and yields more than all the tired, suffering, expensive hardware available.

... GENTLEMEN! ...

Painters, who are educated in and grow up believing in the power of painting, are lost. They forget the purpose of their production. There are periods when this forgetfulness is excusable, when history seems to provide a purpose. But as a rule, students cannot confide in their teachers and have to define their purpose for themselves. The 20th century more than the 19th century has succeeded to institutionalize painting.

A thoroughly established conspiracy of art-critics, art-schools, collectors, banks and other investors absolve the artist from the task of finding the purpose of painting. With a fantastic esoteric vocabulary they do the defining and evaluating and allow the painter to take his task for granted. Don't believe it! Painting doesn't make sense so easily!

(We didn't start our Masaccio workshop with any credo. Whatever beliefs we gained resulted from doing what we did.)

... SEE ...

Every painting is the result of all paintings before it. Every painting that makes any sense steps out of this chain-reaction and revolutionizes it. What makes it fresh and consumable is its revolutionary content. But, unfortunately, this content wears out. The revolutionary courage fades into history and disappears in the history of thousands of revolutions. The stripped and lesser painting which remains has to defend itself against all other paintings without saving grace.

When you walk through the Museum of Modern Art in New York you dip into 100 revolutions, consisting of paintings that are statements, manifestos, liberations, assumptions of power, paintings which overthrow the government of paintings and establish a military dictatorship over all other paintings. All these paintings together, constitute one full-size painting, one Brancacci Chapel. They don't know this from each other. Even the building which houses them doesn't know

392

this, but here they all are, all together the many aspects of one work, all together adding up to one whole some work, comparable to the Brancacci Chapel.

MASACCIO

In the year 1401 a red angel appeared over the white city of Florence and painted a beautiful blue cloud in the sky. The sun made love to the cloud, and the cloud gave birth to a little pink boy with a golden paintbrush in his hands. When Masaccio was 27 years old, the angel came back and took everything from him: the golden paintbrush, his painting fingers, his eyes and his heart.'

(*Ladies and Gentlemen, see Masaccio!* Schumann, program statement, *Bread and Puppet/Masaccio* exhibition, '77.)

Schumann's point here is not, though there may be some confusion, that he is rightly not concerned whether the collection of the Glover puppet museum will in the 25th century be in as good shape, even, as the Brancacci frescoes are now. His point is only in a subsidiary way that an artist should not be guided either by a concern for the classical or any other kind of concern for securing a place in art history, e.g. as revolutionary. It is rather that an artist should as much as possible keep his inevitable concern for form one for its instrumentality to the conveyance of content, and ipso facto should aim at forms that instead of focussing those exposed to his art on them, divert their attention away from them to content. (He does not make out but presumes the further point, really for him the important one, that the viewer's or listener's aimed-at occupation with content should be beneficial to them, or rather, should promote attitudes beneficial to mankind.) Form that diverts from form has been Schumann's objective throughout: since art is the revolutionary appreciation of what is becoming the past, it behooves the artist to give his art the form of impermanence thus, rather than by his form proclaiming the end of history and revolution, in promotion of future revolution to express by it the sponsorship of its own rejection. This is also a political statement.

'Late in 1428, Masaccio himself died in debt and poor in Rome. He had failed to attract the necessary commissions in Florence. Why this was so must forever be conjecture, because the record is silent. But there is plausibility in the argument that his work was not pretty enough, not elegant enough, not acceptably enough idealized in its treatment of faces and themes. He had all the mastery and craft needed to flatter, to play, to delight the eye with baubles, gold and rich trappings. He performed this way at least once, probably on demand, in parts of the Pisa polyptych (1426), particularly in the *Adoration of the Magi* with its portrait of the donors. But that which Masaccio would not or could not do, others, learning from him, were ready to carry out – Fra Angelico, Fra Filippo Lippi, Mantegna – and their patrons were well pleased with them.

... His *Tribute Money* in the Brancacci chapel, done in a time of acute fiscal distress for Florence, is so austere that it must have been unsettling and may well have driven off prospective patrons: Masaccio was seeing too incisively, too truly. Christ tells Peter to find the tax money in the mouth of a fish in Lake Galilee and commands him to pay it to the Roman tax collector. The fresco is a sermon on paying to the state what is the state's; it may also be suggesting that the Church should make contributions to government to help defend the community. In making such an unusual commission, the patron of the chapel, Felice Brancacci, a respected political figure, was evidently moved by a strong sense of civic feeling, but he balanced the theme of payment to the state with other frescoes in the same chapel, showing the distribution of alms to the poor and St. Peter healing the crippled with his shadow.'

(Lauro Martinez, *Power and Imagination*, 1980.)

Guidi, though (sloppy as he was) his work by its austerity may have displeased a plutocratic clientele moving away from the Republican austerities of their fathers, and though he died poor while young (27 years old), as the groupings of the great oligarchs of Florence with its great painters in his vanished *Procession for the Consecration of the Chapel* suggests, consciously worked for the rich, the Florentine patriciate that in the second quarter of the 15th century by some manner of ambiguous alliance with il populo was struggling for its survival. Of the frescoes with which Guidi (with some help from Masolino and Lippi) 1423-28 decorated the Brancacci family's not long completed chapel at their Carmelite church, eight out of ten deal with the first bishop of Rome: Peter and the Tribute Money, Peter Preaching, Peter Baptizing, Peter Almsgiving and the Death of Ananias, Peter and John Curing the Sick, Peter Restoring to Life the Son of King Theophilius of Antioch, Peter Restoring Tabitha to Life and curing a Cripple.

As Martinez, loc. cit. puts it, the scenes of almsgiving and cripple-curing 'hauntingly suggest (that) Florence had a large number of paupers and unemployed people, known as "the wretched" (miserabili) in the famous Florentine tax census of 1426-1427', and Schumann was inspired by this and by the prominence of money in the frescoes, and in particular perhaps by Christ's suggestion to the bishop that (having been a fisherman once) he find the money for taxes in the mouth of a fish to execute a series of black ink brush sketches, silk screen prints of which were published, loose-leaf format, in Cologne in '77. The series is on the folder, under the image of the expulsion from paradise (the only painting of Guidi's I like), entitled *Bread and Puppet Masaccio*. Inside it has the title that has been given to one of Guidi's frescoes, *La Distribuzione dei Beni et Morte di Anania*. Schumann's series of prints starts off with a rendition of this picture: the bishop, surrounded by some men, is extending his arm over a dead man lying on the ground, apparently Ananias, to hand a poor woman, baby in arm and surrounded by other women and a cripple, the alms. It consists of a pictorial analysis of this picture aided by a few captions: She is Poor, How Much Money Does She Get? The Dead Man, The Poor, Saint Peter and Co., Saint Peter's Halo is a Helmet. The successive prints, done in a sketchy, agitated manner, as though by an eye shocked, isolate details of the picture indicated by these titles. Schumann's analysis (as does, but in quite another sense, namely in support of faithful payment of taxes, probably favored by the Brancaccis, Guidi's picture) relates the good bishop's outlays to his income by evoking that curious event in his career, told of in verses 1-10 of Chapter 5 of St. Luke's history of the apostles, the deaths of Ananias and his wife. Ananias, a member of the bishop's see, had sold his farm, and in contravention of the young church's rules of communism had fraudulently withheld from his shepherd part of the sales price, but fell dead at his feet on telling him this lie: some of the young fellows around taking him outside to bury him. His widow died and was disposed of similarly, but not before the sinister bishop had warned her, 'Look, the feet of those that have buried your man are outside the door, and will carry you out.' The couple's fate, *Acts* tells us, frightened everybody that heard of it. This tale of communism – and not so primitive a communism, note those young fellows ready to dispose of the corpses – explains how the bishop – not out of the mouths of fish – was able not only to fulfill his civic duties as a taxpayer, but on top of that to be charitable. Marx would say it also helps to explain the poverty of his charity cases.

Schumann's attack on the church here, partly perhaps a distancing apology for his use of Christian motifs, fabular, liturgical and musical, beyond this evinces not only his lasting concern for the poor in the sense of the Florentine miserabilis, the needy (not in the sense of the working classes), but by its particular references happens also to be an attack on communism, i.e. on what communism in this century in practice has turned out to be like: a terror regime extracting from the poor, thus kept poor, the same surplus of their labor that the capitalists from Felice Brancacci to the Rockefellers have extracted, returning scant alms.

13. Third morality play, *Joan of Arc*, the glory of the fighter for the people: music as text, puppetry as illustrations. Music in re the transcendental, visuals in re the temporal dimension of morality.

After he got back from the Masaccio workshop, in January '77 or so, Schumann holed up at Dopp Farm, started work on the second of his morality plays to follow *Jephthah, Joan of Arc*: 'all I did was I painted the backdrops and I made the puppets, *alone*. Next door, in the room there, I took all the furniture out and I made it on the floor in that little room' (Schumann, interview, '79): flat masonite cutout puppets like for the *Mountain Man of Chile*, because 'very simply there was no space next door to make things in clay or in — I had no puppeteers' help, so it was the easiest way of building a show' (ibid.). The 'backdrops' were three curtains, to be flipped for each scene, the side ones to be set at obtuse angles to the back one 'so people could see' (Elka, ibid.): a new kind of stage for him. He 'took these items with (him) and set up the stage and rehearsed them, and then did the show' (ibid.) during a 'workshop', February 21-March 1 ('77), at John Abbott College in Montreal, with the students of its Theatre and Creative Arts Department:[1]

'The *Joan of Arc* thing became quite a project, because what I got with the students in Quebec (province) that had performed in Montreal in a few places (e.g. McGill (SSB)) wasn't what I wanted to end up with at all, so I had the puppeteers join in and we went to several universities in Connecticut, and down south (e.g. Chapel Hill, North Carolina, at the end of March (SSB)), and I rehearsed with them more. I performed different versions after an extended stay in

1. 'This year's production is entitled *Jeanne d'Arc*; and in the series of workshops he will conduct as he tours the country, he will piece together the final narrative form of the play. Schumann will arrive at JAC with puppets and sets and, by approaching the puppetry 'as a sculptural process that needs a dancer to invent it', he will explore with the students the plastic possibilities of mask, character and situation. At the end of the weeklong workshop the group will present their work to date.

Students who would like to be puppeteers or band members — and a special need exists for a good percussionist and a fiddle player — must be prepared to work for over a week, i.e. they must rearrange their schedules so they have no other commitments within or outside of the college for the week of February 21 (Monday A.M.) through and including Tuesday, March 1st. If you are seriously interested and willing to commit your time and energy, contact ... The workshop and show, which is open to the public and FREE OF CHARGE, is presented under the auspices of the Creative Arts Festival of the Creative Arts Department to coincide with the Winter Carnival. Schumann and the Abbott students will perform the piece 'Jeanne d'Arc' in the theatre of the Main Building on the Mac-Donald campus of John Abbott College, Sunday evening at 7:00 P.M.' — (Schein, *No Strings Attached*, February '77 issue of the John Abbott student paper.)

each of these colleges. (Elka: Did it really change at all or that much? It seems to me I saw it in Montreal, that first performance (February 27, '77 (SSB)), and then you performed it in Montpelier Christ Church at the end of your very short rehearsal with puppeteers, and that was the show that stayed pretty much the whole time.) Well, to *your* mind things seem not to change, and to me it seems that they are just a lot of work and they seem to change a lot, so that's just a different perception. In my mind the show of *Joan of Arc* changed a hell of a lot from one college to another. They were in very different ways, in each of the places where we went to.'   (ibid.)

He toured it with *White Horse Butcher* (performed with it as Part II or by itself) in Europe (Barcelona, Nancy, Paris) May-June ('77), and, after doing it at the August '77 circus, on a second New England tour (Connecticut College, New London, Providence Theatre, Providence, the Caravan Theatre in the Harvard Epworth Methodist Church, Cambridge, Massachusetts) in October '77, on a second European tour (Germany, Denmark, Holland) May-June '78, in South America in June and July ('78), finally, still with *WHB* performed it in January '79 at the Brooklyn Academy of Music in New York City, where Richard Eder of the *New York Times* (*New York Times*, January 13, '79) liked the death scene, but on the whole felt

'there is something tired and hollow about the work . . . ultimately sterile exercises without much purpose.'

— not strong enough to 'change people's lives', he complained. The *WHB* piece he found positively obnoxious. Are horses necessarily good, ugly people necessarily bad, he asked.

'Bread and Puppet style is that of naive art. The artfulness is evident and admirable. But . . . the naivité has grown languid.'   (Eder, loc. cit.)

The play (October 14, '77, Cambridge, Massachusetts) lasts 55 minutes and is in nine parts, each part consisting of a musical introduction (curtain drawn — the next scene being prepared), followed by a scene on the small, shallow stage (perhaps 8-10 feet deep in the center, from the curtain line back to the center panel, the 'backdrop' part of the three-part screen enclosing the successive scenes). The three screens are large flip-over books, the paintings on them for each scene the setting for that scene.[2] There are

---

2. Dupavillon in Dupavillon and George, *Bread and Puppet*, 1978, describes either the May '77 Nancy Festival or the June '77 Paris production of *Joan of Arc*. I shall in the sequel footnote my descriptions of its scenes by his. Of the stage he says:
   'The set is a box, three sides of which are painted canvas and the fourth is a curtain raised by hand by a person dressed in black. On stage, outside the box stage left, are a large ear and a stepladder with a spotlight attached to it, and stage right are three angel musicians (violin, bass drum and snare drum) wearing white wings. One of the angels, the M.C., opens the show by announcing the name of the play. He also gives the title of each tableau in turn.'

no giant three-dimensional puppets in this play, but — apart from shrouded (their faces covered) performers, more or less like the puppet-operators in Bunraku — it shared this Bunraku style with the August '76 NYC *White Horse Butcher* and, I believe, with the *WHB* toured with it '77-'78 — and from some tiny figures on the floor in the first scene, a foot or two high and operated on horizontal strings — only puppets with giant, over-lifesize flat cardboard heads over bodies suggested by loose flowing fabric. The combined result of the shallow stage, the painted settings and the flat cardboard heads' domination of their bodies is to make each scene an illustration. The heads and puppets detach from the background and as flat sculptures contrast with it, but this complication is not perceived as depth. Each scene is a very brief tableau vivant and mouvant, altogether in blacks, whites and greys.

The music[3] performances between the scenes, roughly of equal duration as they — though the scenes seem a little shorter — are perceived neither as interludes (divertissements), nor as introductions or comments, but as aural scenes not only on a par with the visual scenes, but as statements of the theme of the visual scene following them, stating it in the mode of mood.

This form was prepared by the alternation of chorus and image in the '72 *Hallelujah* and *Stations*, but there was not yet present because the music did not have sufficient complexity and structure, nor, from one interlude to the next, sufficient variety (1) as statement to hold its own against the visual scenes, (2) to make statements as particular as the individual visual scenes: it acted as general comment. And similarly for *Grey Lady Cantatas II* and *III* ('70, '71), also in this alternation form, where the key idea was a variation and development of an extremely simple musical statement that would tie the visual scenes up into the continuum of a figure's story. In *Jephthah* and *Grey Lady Cantata V* (Tallis, then Bach) ('74), the music had finally attained to par with the visual development, but the externals of the form were absent, the music *accompanying* some of the action: music and visual action were correlative wholes. The form of *Joan of Arc* was attained first with the '76 *Jesu meine Freude* ('76), and after *Joan*, was again the form of *Masaniello* and *Ave Maris Stella* (August and December '77), perhaps of *Wolkenstein* in '78, and, for the last time, I believe, of *Washerwoman — Nativity* in '79. It was a form distinctively characteristic of Schumann's 'initial Dopp Farm period', particularly suited for the function of its morality plays: to point up the moral challenges an individual faces during their finite life spans, and their responses to them, the visual scenes focussing us on their temporal, the musical scenes on their transcendental dimension. This was not a concern of Schumann's before or after this period.

---

3. The New Wilderness Foundation put out a tape, 8129A, 'Bread and Puppet Theater', recorded November and December 1980, of six of the *Joan* musical pieces and of some other Bread and Puppet music.

Schumann composed or arranged — Trudi Cohen's term in a letter to me of November 2, '77 is 'invented' — the music for *Joan*, and his fiddle — Cohen, the group's 'musical director', was on a bass drum, Paul Zaloom on snare and tom toms — leads it, playing the tune or repeating a theme con brio — the theme and mood varying considerably from one 'musical scene' to another, but hardly within a given one, Schumann within each varying only speed and pitch. The combination of the music's drive and (within each musical scene) repetitiousness with the length of these scenes gives them the quality of text illustrated by the visual scenes, creates the balance between them. Their excitatory quality balances the likewise intense but quiet, almost subdued feel of the visual scenes. Each provides its own mode of affective experience. The strikingly elaborate musical settings for the slow-seeming little scenes made the scenes seem very distant. And the emotional music is each time an absolute contrast to the gentle scene preceding it: we return to the music, at first don't enter into it, but are then drawn in, come to accept it 'blindly'.

The further effect of the thematic primacy of music over picture was that as theme or content of the play one perceived not a story, the legend of Joan, nor the theme of the repeated rise and fall of innocent redemptive impulse in a history itself the static suppression of suffering man — of the 'people' — by evil powers, but human emotion. The play illustrated the emotional responses of the individual in and to history. Reducing to the occasion of these responses, the play intimated the supra-natural inspiration of those innocent redemptive impulses. It thus at the same time asserted the futility and the absolute value of political action such as Joan's.

*　　*　　*

The audience in the choir of the little church is hippies — youngish, out of uniform, accenting unconventionality, introspective, intensely self-centered mild experimenters with various quack theories and vademecums.

The room is a small rectangle, filled by perhaps 100-150 people (tickets are 3 dollars). There is above us the horseshoe of a balcony, rather prettily curving wood, in front of us a black curtain hanging from a wire perhaps 8 feet up and closing off the room at that end, between it and us a carpeted square perhaps 24 × 24 feet. Something like a double sword, silverish, looking leaden, hangs up overhead this side of the curtain: from a rope passing through a pulley on one of the lighting rods. The rope is tied to something in the area just to the left of and this side of the curtain, the musicians' area. Schumann, in shirt sleeves, old pants, is by 9:08 tuning up the fiddle, the other two, two musicians both in tuxes or tails, with a cap on, both raggedy enough looking — all three of them with raggedy, flimsy white wings — are there by 9:13, 13 minutes late.

*　　*　　*

9:17   Blackout, lights on out front, above the musicians. (This happens at the end of each visual scene. They stay on for the musical scenes.) Peter Schumann quietly says 'Joan of Arc'.

M1   Violin and drums, a dramatic music, the violin scraped, low register, dire rather than ominous, speeds up, increasingly frenetic, 'strong, driving rhythm' — (Cohen, letter.).

9:20 S1   Peter Schumann, his long hair over his face, but lifting it, in an in fact acted but very natural angry tone, 'In the first picture you will see how the people are swept out of their own country'.[4] Musicians' light out. (Curtain opens, stage lit, as in the sequel at the beginning of the visual scenes.) 3 grey figures with identical straw brooms sweeping out (toward the right) tiny ordinary-people figures low on the floor at the right, a gradual, quiet, patient, thorough sweeping. The grey people's faces are hidden behind the covering all around their heads — faceless people (as all performers/figures in the sequel). Mouth harp (from behind stage?) to their sweeping. Before all the little people have been swept out, the 3 start a violent dance with the brooms to the left, the 3 straight broom handles and the spatular broom shapes a sharp repetitive contrast — at different angles — to the softly outlined bending grey figures. A drum and the pounding of the brooms on the floor accompanies this angry violence. Gradual dim-out. Curtain.[5]

9:22 M2   Light on musicians. Slight thumping music on home-made junk-made instruments (coffee cans, etc.) and by plucked violin. 'Pizzicato. Paul — heavy junk metal chimes, Trudi — tin cans with snare drum sticks, Peter — plucked fiddle' — (Cohen, ibid.)

S2   Peter Schumann, 'In the second picture, the people's houses are sad.'

---

4. Schumann is misquoting his own text — it should be 'houses', not 'own country'. The poetry of the first four scenes is that their houses, missing them, stand for the displaced persons (DPs).

5. '1. "In the first tableau, the people are swept out of their houses."

A bell rings. Lights. The curtain rises. The canvas set shows a countryside. Tiny figures (peasants and animals) cut out of wood are pulled toward the wings with strings. Stage right, three people dressed in black and wearing ski masks sweep the stage. A tune is played on a harmonica. When the figures have disappeared, the three people hit the floor with their broomsticks, in rhythm with the drums. The lights go out and the curtain is closed. Music.' — (Dupavillon, loc. cit.)

(All grey and white.) Background of cupped Vermont hills. A figure with a house-face (windows, door, painted onto front of cubic head mask), grey, is kneeling in a posture of sadness behind the cutout (a foot or two high) of a little house, a white hankie in its white-gloved hand. Off to the right behind this person, a figure with a star-shaped sun face (like a bread loaf sun), rather tall and slim, in white, holding a wicker-work basket with natural things in it. I didn't notice how this works, but at some point this sun was without the basket, had brought out a little violin like Peter Schumann's from behind her back and was doing a little slow walk-dance playing it — mimicking playing it: the sound actually came from an organ-pipe played by Peter Schumann like a flute — passage of a day? Sound of thunder (not too loud). The house gets up slowly, its arms rising — gesture of being stunned by grief — drops the handkerchief, sways (to drum). The couple, man and day, an exquisite contrast (both are *very* good performers) — I have noticed before that Schumann has a non-farmer's view of nature as benign.[6]

9:29 (?)   Curtain. (Blackout first?)

M3   Wild music — violin and drums, sort of gipsy. ' "Deedilee, deedilee", Peter imitates that on fiddle, more or less. Paul — snare drum. Trudi — bass drum.' — (Cohen, ibid.)

S3   'In the third picture, a voice from heaven speaks to the kitchen.' Peter Schumann walks out past the stage curtain, with energetic tread. Curtain opens — a kitchen: by the backdrop's images a country kitchen, done in grey. Tin cans are hung in an irregular swarm down into the kitchen space from two poles laid from side to side over the side screens; two vampirish grey-hooded figures agitate them by moving the poles, a tinkling resulting. A feeling of there being "electricity in the air" there — vibrations. A white-clad

---

6. '2. "In the second tableau, the houses are sad."

A bell rings. Lights. The curtain rises on the same set. Stage left, a person is standing dressed in white, wearing a hat shaped like the sun. In the center, a person is sitting down dressed in black, wearing a hat shaped like a house. In front of him are two shoes, and a miniature house and two trees. He rings a little bell which he puts inside one of the shoes, and waves a handkerchief at the shoes as each in turn is pulled toward the wings by a string. As they go by, the person in white throws flower petals at them. Then, accompanying himself on a miniature violin, he dances around the seated person. The latter seems heartbroken, gets up and puts his hands to his hat, as if the house were crying. The lights go out and the curtain is closed. Music.' — (Dupavillon, loc. cit.)

figure, white over its face also, is cleaning the kitchen floor on her knees, image of patience, engagement in duty, honest toil, povery. Zaloom walks gravitatiously into the kitchen, suspends a giant grey-white (plaster?) ear from a wire, the kitchen's ear. Schumann appears on the balcony above us, lowering an enormous (5-6 foot long) homemade Alpenhorn. Zaloom approaches its bell-shaped opening, stands supporting it with his hands, a dark, slightly weird or mysterious figure there in front of the light image of the kitchen, which in spite of the white woman in it seems flat behind him. The woman is cleaning the floor. The cans are tinkling (rather than merely rattling). In between their sound, the horn (twice) begins to emit a large rounded mooing: the woman pauses to listen. Zaloom brings the instrument's head up to the ear: a long message through the horn — extended mooing, the woman motionless on her

9:35   knees. Blackout. Curtain.[7]

M4   The musicians are back in their seats, the lights on them. Fiddle and drum, but Schumann has brought the Alpine horn. Grim, vaguely military music (all the music for this piece is strongly accented, with heavy beats.) Schumann is playing the fiddle, held between his legs and is blowing the horn at the same time. The music takes on the appearance of a kind of jazz reveille, but is still grim, harsh. 'Military rhythm. Paul — snare drum, Trudi — bass drum, Peter — fiddle on his lap, playing open strings; long horn blown like trumpet, playing fanfares.' — (Cohen, ibid.)

9:39   S4   'And now in the next picture, ladies and gentlemen, we are going to show you the famous battle of Orleans.' Curtains up on the light scene. A thronged group of soldiers to the left, soldiers painted on the screen panel there and cartonheaded soldiers (some with George Grosz bared teeth, fero-

---

7. '3. "In the third tableau, a voice from heaven speaks in the kitchen."

A bell rings. The M.C. and a musician go stage left and turn on the spotlight which is trained on the ear. Lights. The curtain rises. The set shows the inside of a kitchen. Utensils and tin cans, hung on strings from crossbars, knock against one another noisily. Joan, dressed in white and wearing a ski mask, is on her hands and knees washing the floor with a cloth she rinses in a tub. On the step-ladder, the M.C. plays the horn. The noises stop. Silence. Joan turns around. The noises begin again. Joan goes back to work. The M.C. again plays the horn, which this time is directed toward the ear. The noises stop. Silence. Joan turns around longer. The M.C. turns off the spotlight. The lights go out and the curtain is closed. Music.' — (Dupavillon, loc. cit.)

402

cious) in an up-and-down huddle on the floor, blending in with the painted ones, all greys, image of destruction in aggression. They are making war on three hooded figures on the right terminating in cubic heads on the fronts of which are faces made up of child's drawings of houses. The white figure emerges, Trudy Cohen lowers the overhead swords of Peter Schumann, he gives them to white figure, she does two-fisted battle with the soldiery, a vigorous combat in dance-type motions, up- and center-stage, between the houses and the military men who are low but octopus-like (they are not separate figures) formidable, terrible dwarfs. She by now is clearly Joan. Schumann, to the left of the stage is equally vigorously, strongly urging her on, two cymbals in his hands, clashing them, shouting. Curtain.[8]

9:42

M5   Mock-soulful, mock-tragic music — the violin, two small ridiculous instruments. 'Peter — fiddle and kazoo, Trudi — kazoo, Paul — maraccas — sarcastic little tune, in thirds, repeated several times.' — (Cohen, ibid.)

S5   '. . . the coronation of the Dauphin.' A tall hooded figure, peak-headed — a trained seal — enters with a ball from the lobby, passing to in front of the middle of the curtain, idiotic. Schumann on a little red velour pillow in a kidding way brings him a paper crown, the curtain opens, behind him an acclaiming crowd, the moron is crowned. Figure off. Curtain.[9]

9:45 (?)

M6   Schumann playing violin and mountain horn together, sort of Indian, oriental chords. Snare drums. A

---

8. '4. "In the fourth tableau, you will see the famous battle of Orleans."

A bell rings. The curtain rises. The canvases to the rear and stage right show the English army. Below them, soldiers cut out of wood are held by unseen puppeteers. Stage left, three people in black, whose hats are shaped like houses, wave their arms to show sadness. Joan is standing center stage. Bright light and percussion. The M.C. rattles metal, the characters freeze and a musician lowers two swords whose handles are hands. The M.C. unties them and puts them on the floor. Joan takes a sword in each hand and, with a jump, faces the soldiers. A strobe light flashes. The soldiers yell, jump around and fall down. The lights go out and the curtain is closed. Music.' — (Dupavillon, loc. cit.)

9. '5. "And now, ladies and gentlemen, you will see the dauphin being crowned."

A seal dressed in pink, wearing a false nose and a mustache, giving loud cries and playing with a ball, hops to center stage. A musician carries in a crown on a cushion, and the M.C. places it on the seal's head. Just then the curtain rises on the actors, minus their ski masks, who jump and shout with joy. The lights go out and the curtain is closed. Music.' — (Dupavillon, loc. cit.)

weird-sounding dirge. 'Peter – long horn with plastic Hollywood tooter for mouthpiece and fiddle bowed in his lap. Trudi and Paul – drum rolls.' — (Cohen, ibid.)

9:48 S6 To the snare drum: '. . . Joan . . . prison . . . 1430.' Curtain opens on a black hooded figure seated, erect, on a stool or chair to the left, a bowl with water at its feet. To the right 3 grey figures are holding and doing things to white Joan, bent over, roped, between them, straining. There is a pitcher there. Whistle from the black figure at the left, the pitcher slides across the floor over to next to the bowl and the 3 elaborately retie Joan in a different way. She is straining, low by the floor now to get over to the black figure and/or the pitcher, the 3 are holding her back. She finally makes it, the black figure vehemently picks up the bowl, throws out
9:50 the water in it. Blackout. Curtain.[10]

9:51 M7 Rhythm music on various homemade instruments – Peter Schumann playing on a little steel instrument something like a tuner held by his mouth, goes oink, oink. Trudy is clapping her hands. (She is in all these musical scenes paying close attention to Schumann's playing, her big impressive pale face from time to time turning toward him. Sometimes she smiles.) Zaloom is drumming lightly on a small square of wood. 'Paul – wood block with snare sticks, Trudi – hand-clapping, Peter – Jew's harp.' — (Cohen, ibid.)

9:54 (?) S7 '. . . court of the Holy Inquisition.' Curtain opens on figures whose head masks are very large light grey noses (2 of them) and ears (5) roughly grouped into an approximation of two faces, Joan in the middle. She does a small tap dance in place, they billow back and forth near her, a grotesque and awful troupe, to her stomping. They dance back. A contest. They finally – by these foot dances – get her down, she is on the floor, her head toward us, in their middle, head

---

10. '6. "In the fifth tableau, you are in a prison in 1430."

A bell rings. Lights. The curtain rises. The set shows snakes intertwined. Stage right, a person in black wearing a top hat is seated on a chair. He holds a string attached to a lunch pail placed center stage. Stage left, Joan is struggling. She is immobilized by ropes held by three people dressed in black. Music. Joan manages to approach the lunch pail. A whistle is blown. The three people in black tie up Joan who again manages to approach the lunch pail. A whistle is blown. The person wearing a top hat gets up and throws out the contents of the lunch pail. The lights go out and the curtain is closed. Music.' — (Dupavillon, loc. cit.)

bowed to the ground. They swell up, growing taller as they stand around her, their organ-heads high up. They traipse out, still in a manner of tap dance. On the screens: straightback chairs, black, all over them. Academic or bureaucratic-managerial cutout carton heads, male, (7 of them) appear through the cracks between the 3 panels, one above the other, on each side of the floored figure. Curtain.[11]

9:55   M8   Violin, Trudi bending forward to sing, wordlessly into the mike. A sad, medieval-seeming sorrowing tune. Snare drum. The violin and snare drum become stronger and stronger, anger increasingly drowning out the sorrow, rise to a fatalistic, though still angry mode, end in cacaphonous sound of strife. 'Peter — fiddle, Trudi — bass drum and singing, Paul — four drums. Based on German Christmas song 'Maria durch ein Dornwald ging.' First quietly with fiddle and vocal harmony then variations building up with strong crescendo and drums, dying down to a slow rhythmic version.' (Cohen, ibid.)

10:01   S8   '... the burning at the stake.' The curtain is closed. A procession of black figures emerges from the lobby door at the left, poles in their left hands (thudding), long, elongated club-like rattles and red watchmen's lights, lit, in their right hands, their big square box heads blank and dark, one by one, 3 of them. Between them dark snouted animals, black pigs, one following them, on all fours. The monks are humming. Curtain opens, the screens closely covered with the black line figures of active skeletons and white flowers. The men and beasts stop in front of the backdrop, turn to us, the fronts of their heads the icons of faces of Greek Orthodox patriarchs, mild, tolerably compassionate faces. Zaloom, a beast and/or death mask over his face, comes out, the rope that the swords were on is lowered to him, he ties to it a dark gray shroud or shrouded figure, having some-

---

11. '7. "In the sixth tableau, you will see the tribunal of the Holy Inquisition."

A bell rings. Lights. The curtain rises. The set shows chairs. Joan is center stage. Stage right and stage left, a judge played by three people dressed in black, the center one holding a nose and the other two ears. There is a dialogue between Joan and her judges, composed of tapping shoes. At the end, Joan collapses. The judges leave, holding high their noses and ears. A door creaks. The faces of four professors cut out of wood, with bald heads and glasses, appear over the backdrop and stare at Joan. The lights go out and the curtain is closed. Music.' — (Dupavillon, loc. cit.)

thing like a head-sized lump of granite for its head and neck, big white hands folded immediately below this head, goes over to rope's other end at the left, slowly raises the figure up into the air: as it comes up off the floor, it grows larger and larger. It is up in the air. The monks rattle their rattles, the white Joan figure — a puppet — falls out of the black shroud onto the floor. The three beasts gather around it, nudging or licking or sniffing at it, and they and the three monks gesturally, the monks raising their arms, express sorrow (Schumann's violin, Cohen's voice). The shroud with its folded hands hangs above the group. The violin and voice stop. The monks take off their head masks of benign sorrow, tearing them up (they seem paper), their heads are black and blank underneath. Blackout. Curtain.[12]

10:05

M9   The shroud with the folded hands is suspended up above and in front of the curtain. Violin, tambourine. 'Peter – fiddle, Paul – dumbek (Turkish hand drum). Single bowed string, very gradually getting higher.' — (Cohen, ibid.)

10:12(?) S9 'Her arrival in paradise.' Curtain opens up on a cloud of angels, their nearly though not quite identical white faces (framed by black hair) carton heads (perhaps 2 dozen of them) emerging out of a single man-high white cloth cloud, their corporate body. To the right of the cloud a prone white figure on the floor. Schumann walks over with an additional cardboard angel's head, as he walks shaking a bunch of short metal staves over it, somewhat in the manner of blessing it: gives it to the prone white figure. She rises, is drawn into the angels' crowd, swaying into it, her head disappearing last, her new face emerging, perhaps — she has dis-

---

12. '8. "In the seventh tableau, you will see Joan at the stake."

A procession of six people arrives from the back of the theatre. Three of them wear pig masks and crawl on all fours. The three others wear, over their ski masks, paper bags with the face of an old man. In one hand they hold a flashlight and a stick; in the other, a "shaker", a piece of wood to which bottle caps have been attached. The procession reaches the stage. A bell rings. Dim lights. The curtain rises. The set shows big flowers. Joan is standing, center stage. At her feet, a mask in the shape of a long face whose neck is a piece of cloth. A musician, holding a string attached to the mask, lifts it slowly. Joan stands inside the mask. The three old men wave their "shakers". As the mask rises higher and higher, Joan tries to hold it back, then lets go and collapses. The pigs sniff the body. The old men put down their sticks, "shakers" and flashlights and, one at a time, they crumple their masks until the paper bags are torn. The lights go out and the curtain is closed. Music.' — (Dupavillon, loc. cit.)

406

appeared among them. Schumann is off to the left, banging cymbals, as from the accreted celestial host there emerges a sustained slightly eerie ullulation (perhaps it actually comes from Cohen), rising to a near-hysterical pitch. They fall

10:15   silent, slowly straighten up.[13]

An exquisite master piece. Dark frames of music around white pictures. Extra-ordinary confidence – precision, incisiveness, economy – of directorial attack: the symbols minimally delineated, perfectly adequate. Peter Schumann's performance as musician/director of the performance equally energetic: almost ferocious. The music-cradled scenes jump like fresh coins out of a mint-press. Excellence as routine. The incisiveness of the imagery allows the expansiveness of its musical expression. The images a scattering of the story, actually rather illustrations of a moral vision, not a story.

---

13. '9. "In the last tableau, you will see her arrival in Paradise."

A bell rings. Lights. The curtain rises. The set is white. Stage left, three rows of women's faces cut out of wood, their bodies hidden by a white cloth, are leaning over. Joan is on the floor, curled up at their feet. Accompanied by the rattle of metal, the M.C. gives Joan a woman's face like the others. A hand helps Joan get up and join the other women. Then, swaying back and forth, the women emit shrill cries which grow louder and louder. A crash of cymbals. Under strong lights, the faces freeze at their highest point. The lights go out and the curtain is closed.' — (Dupavillon, loc. cit.)

14. Fourth morality play, *Masaniello*. A case of a victory of the devil. Hubris of the individual seduced by power. Revolution begets tyranny and terror.

According to George Ashley's publicity release, Schumann met the 6 Florentine (or Florence-based) Italians – one of them John LaBarbera, an American – that provided the set musical pieces and most of the music of *Masaniello*, in Milan in 1976, and asked them – they *then* adopted the name Pupi e Fresedde – to come and put on a show with him at the '77 circus. He paid their fares.[1] The group apparently in Italy had been performing the older Italian music, perhaps mostly 16th and 17th century, largely vocal and perhaps predominantly South Italian folk music (researched and revived by them) that they contributed to *Masaniello*. One of these songs is *O Cunto e Masaniello*, apparently a Neapolitan folk ballad in what seems a revolutionary spirit evoking the somewhat dubious figure and career of Masaniello, the leader of an insurrection in 17th century Naples, dupe or puppet, I have been given to understand, of a faction of the Neapolitan nobility. Schumann heard them do this song, had it and its background explained to him, and was attracted by the topic:

'O CUNTO E MASANIELLO

(THE FOURTEEN DAYS OF MASANIELLO)

In times of poverty Masaniello was a fisherman
He was happy to be a fisherman
Masaniello eats a fish
Immediately came the Prince Regent
This fish is mine and not yours
And if you don't want to pay a tax you will have to sell it
In times of poverty Masaniello was a fisherman

---

1. 'We met (the Pupi e Fresedde) on the Italian tours ... And they were great singers, especially one of them – we liked the music so – we thought that we could work on the piece (*Masaniello* (SSB)) with them. They liked us and called their group Pupi e Fresedde, which means puppets and bread (actually it means puppets and actors (SSB)). And we just had a great time with them in Italy – and we felt that if they were coming here maybe we would help them to remount (?) their group together. And we would enjoy working with them. (Elka: It was a pretty ambitious project, because up to then –) It was. *We* were the hosts and *we* invited *them* and *we* organized the money for it, and *we made* the money for them, and we sent them back home, and all of that – we had no State Department and no organization.' — (Schumann, interview, '79.)

In times of confusion Masaniello dressed like a rascal
A ragged and dirty rascal
Masaniello eats grain
Immediately came the Prince Regent
This grain is mine and not yours
With grain you will get fat
And I will make you pay another tax
In times of confusion Masaniello dressed like a rascal

In times of torments Masaniello dressed like a pious follower
Without a net or a boat
He prays to the Madonna dell'Arco
Comes the Prince Regent
This Madonna is mine, all mine and not yours
This is the tax for the Eternal Father
And if you don't pay you will go straight to Hell
In times of torments Masaniello dressed like a pious follower

In times of despair Masaniello dresses like a lion
A lion with nails and fangs
He has the fame of a beggar
"Enough, Prince Regent, I am tired"
And with the strength of Masaniello
Things could change
In times of despair Masaniello dresses like a lion

In springtime Masaniello dresses like a flag
A flag for which the poor
Return to play the instruments of Revolution
People, beware people,
A cannon has been fired
The Prince Regent has gone mad
Today the price of bread has gone down
But who knows what it will do tomorrow
In springtime Masaniello dresses like a flag

In times of treachery Masaniello is dressed in silver
All in silver
The noble folk see his garment
Immediately the Prince Regent says
We are equal, you and I
Let us be merry for a while
If you accept my invitation I will sew you another garment
In times of treachery Masaniello is dressed in silver

In times of disorder Masaniello is dressed like a lunatic
When he shakes, the garment tears
Even the people spit on him
This garment is fearful
Masaniello goes naked
And the Madonna is indifferent

And if he is killed
He will pay his last tax
In times of disorder Masaniello is dressed like a lunatic

In times of new taxes Masaniello dressed like Punch
He's gone mad, the others laugh behind his back
Then the price of bread and oil go up
And yet more disorders
It is always the people that pay
And never the one who orders these injustices
In times of new taxes Masaniello dressed like Punch

In times of sadness Masaniello is dressed like a corpse
In the coffin a head with bones
Someone has left a red hat
And it is this hat that now awakes the people
When hunger is not sweet
When it is necessary to pay a tax even on the tomb
In times of sadness Masaniello is dressed like a corpse

Masaniello is not dead.'

'they came only a week before the circus, and what we performed in the circus was a *very* rough sketch of the show that we wanted to do. (Elka: But one of the things was that the puppets weren't even built the day before.) Yes, the last puppet was just finished the day before the circus.' (Schumann, interview, '79.)

Masaniello was performed at 5:30 in the afternoon in the meadow around a corner of the pine forest from the circus arena — Schumann's 'positive' morality play was done, as had become the custom, after nightfall in the more initimate setting of a clearing in the forest. Schumann took the week after the circus to restage it, and then sent the company of puppeteers and singers on a tour of the northeast by themselves. They played at the Emmanuel Church in Cambridge, Massachusetts, August 29-September 3, at the Washington Square Methodist Church in NYC September 6-10 and various places in New England for two weeks after this, Schumann joining them for a little more work on the play when they hit New York. Despite the initial enthusiasm, the collaboration with the Italians didn't work out too well: Schumann can't really create *with* other people — his own working procedure is too anxiously intuitive to allow creative inter- action, and his contempt for the lack of artistic integrity of people able to go along with him lurks too near the surface: the Italians just had some- thing he thought he could use. But he reworked the show for them — they of course thought it wasn't Italian enough — for a tour of theirs in Italy. They did it in Florence in November of '78.[2]

---

2. 'We proposed it to them *again* to do it in Italy, to redo the show, because one of their *criticisms* of the show, and they had criticized the show, some of them quite strongly, was that it shouldn't have been an American project, it should have been more Italian. So we

410

The show in 20 scenes, five of them pre-, one post-ludial, freely citing and following the *Cunto e Masaniello*, in slightly more than an hour tells of Masaniello's career.

*   *   *

> By 7:00[3] the Italians and some others were on the church steps, made up, it seemed, like clowns, playing jazz and good-humored brassy circusy music — announcing the show to passers-by and to a crowd of social deviates in good spirits standing in line for tickets and entrance, milling about.
>
> There is about 15 feet of linoleum-covered floor between the audience and a low and shallow (perhaps five feet deep) 2-level platform in front of the huge organ, its bottom level as wide almost as the room, perhaps 30 feet, the top one, maybe as much as three feet above it, about 20 feet across. There are broad steps between them, and on them are stacked a vast assembly — maybe two or three dozen of them — of masks, yellow-grey face masks, lying down, large, maybe two feet long.[4] To each side of the organ the platforms are flanked by tall rectangular banners, a red flower on the one on the left, a blue flower on the one on the right. On the top level there is a piece of plastic the size of a blanket, a stool and a big scuffed white kitchen pot. To the left of the platform, a bunch of pole puppets lie on the floor, to the right stands a card table covered by a white table cloth, 'downstage' from this table another bunch of pole puppets under one of the church windows, even further downstage — the 'stage' comprises platform and floor — near the audience, a snare drum. Downstage on the left, suspended from the back of a small pulpit, from which hangs a small brass bell, a small rectangular scene-calendar, opened to 'The 14 Days of Masaniello.'

eventually proposed that to them and we went to Italy and we got the support of the city of Florence, who invited us to do a project where they would be collaborating with us to make the *Masaniello* and then tour in Italy. And, again, I didn't go on that tour. Just for the rehearsing period. And it didn't work out.' — (Schumann, interview, '79.)

3. The following describes the last two NYC performances.

4. These were the 'People' masks, an important addition to Schumann's iconography: resolving the masses represented by the (frightening) crowd masks of the previous period's *Simple Light* into masses of frightened individuals: the tiny 'people' puppets swept off the stage in *Joan* being the transition link. These masks were also used in a way new in Schumann's theatre: hand held, they were moved in a dance manner up and down and/or from side to side.

Up above, a balcony runs around 3 sides of the ecclesiastic assembly hall, some flood lights affixed. No pews, the audience sits in chairs and, in front of the chairs, on pillows, their backs to the entrance door.

The stage is waiting beyond the marbled, undistinguished linoleum. A good many foreigners in the audience, I hear French and Italian: it reminds me that Schumann is an alien body in this great country. Various puppeteers, performers begin to filter in – the band (six plus a seventh in a pointed hat with cymbals in his hands) is in position in two ranks, the front one seated, downstage to the right, near the audience, at a right angle to it:[5] two guitars, flute, the cymbals, tambourine, trap drum, bass drum, small mandolin-shaped guitars. They are also the singers. Everyone, puppeteers and musicians, is in white with red touches – belts, sashes. Some wear skirts, some pants – not by sex. On the top platform, a woman costumed as lower-class housewife, stuffed for a pregnant belly, a spoon in her hand, a contrast to the more elegant puppeteers and musicians, having helped a man to get under the plastic, a rope tried around his waist (the rope sticks out), picks up the pot there, beats on it with the spoon, 'Ladies and Gentlemen, the Ballad of Masaniello!' Three drum beats and the musicians start playing and singing (I believe that only three of them sang in individual voices, and at most two of these at any one time). They sing vivaciously, with facial expressions, two tenors, one of them in a dress with a lacy hem and a much-tasseled sash. A tall, awkward performer in white with a large white death head mask, dog-faced – a somewhat inexpressive, subdued, conventional mask befitting his role of announcer – and a little black hat stands by the calendar of scenes, stage-right. The housewife has gone to stand near the singers as with some of the hauteur of Flamenco singers, etc., to a firmly accented dance-tune, they sing about Masaniello in the tone of a historical ballad – 'thus it was', one voice, then another joining in for refrain-like repetitions rounded off by shouts. The song ends, the death-head figure jumps into centerstage, it is the announcer, loudly addresses us,

c19:42[6]
c21:27[6]

---

5. At the beginning of the N.Y. run, they had been up in the balcony.
6. One performance I saw was supposed to start at 7:30, the other at 9:30. I give the clock-times for each.

'Ladies and gentlemen, Her Imperial Majesty, the Queen of Spain in all her beauty and glory!' – fanfare and drums as a beautiful, simple and stately, black-and-white puppet – basically white, puffy lace at her wrists with black embroidery on her skirt, a black belt and a black veil coming down from a small truncated-cone silver hat – perhaps 16 feet high, is brought out and erected from stage left – 'And His Excellency, the Grand Duke d'Arco!': fanfare and drum, he's about the same height, his big black white-laced patent leather shoes are off the floor, he wears a formal 3-piece old fashioned black dinner suit, his pants legs dangling to both sides of his central pole carrier[7] – stage-right. Their hands and faces are blue, hers very light, his darker, their expressions, august, cold, distant, sad. They have a dialogue, sung by two girls among her pole-carriers, two men among his: 'Do you know the great city of Naples?' 'Yes, Your Majesty!' 'Do you like the great city of Naples?' 'Yes, Your Majesty!' 'Do you want the great city of Naples?' 'Yes, Your Majesty!' She is making him Viceroy of Naples.

The announcer mock-officiously arranges – 'Bring in the boat, please, Mrs. Masaniello!' 'Okay' – for a toy boat, a raft-like ferry with a small, perhaps a foot high Charon pole-man, and a large paper key, which is suspended from the boat to be brought in, it is put down by the Queen, two crouching puppeteers (announcer: 'Bon voyage, you all!') pull it over to the Duke on the left, one of them pulling the boat slowly, the other pulling so the pole moves up and down – a slow, very beautiful journey, accompanied by delicate music.[8] Announcer: 'There you are!'[9] The Duke's male voices,

---

7. All of Schumann's puppets though impressionistically made have detail not necessarily distinctly perceived in performance – e.g. the Duke's pink boutonière, giant bow tie, black hair, dandy's dashing little tophat. Also, Schumann's giants affect one beyond their humorous detail *and* beyond their approximate specification as hieroglyphs of a mystically metaphysical discourse on Life. E.g. the Duke is not only an adequate representation of post-feudal courtly status-power, neither personal nor bureaucratic, but also hieroglyph for one of the spirit-freezing modalities of mortal man's confrontation with mortal man's companion, Death.

8. A 17th century Puglian cure-song of antidotum tarantulae, composed or recorded by the Jesuit Ludovico Kirchner, priest in Taranto.

9. The brash – common and unintelligent – folksiness of this announcer, totally inadept also in his tones and emphases, was one of the negative aspects of this show. The debasement of Schumann's simplicity into fake naiveté is a hazard of his style, increased by his reliance on adventitious acolytes.

'Thank you, Your Majesty!' The two huge puppets,

21:35

white vs. black, dance to music from the Italians, their crude figures lacey in space[10] – a silent carrousel to the molten flute, and to a song, august, slow, stately, tragic, appropriate to their cold and worrisome faces.[11] The dance ends, the announcer rings his bell, the Queen is retired. The Duke remains.

An Angel of Death, all in black, in a black business suit, sturdy, corpulent, with two smallish black wings neatly on his back, image of a small entrepreneur, perhaps an undertaker, perhaps 12 ft. tall, his face (the

19:47

top third of him is face) sedate, a cornet hanging from his belly region, from the backstage area left rear

21:35

ascends the platform, at the center of which the Housewife has knelt down by the stool and is reading a red book in her hands, presumably a bible, absorbed. The bureaucratic Angel-man hugely watches her. She does not notice him. The announcer is saying, 'Before Masaniello was born in the great city of Naples, an angel came to his mother! . . . and the angel said:', the Angel (his voice sung, in harmony, by two of the Queen's girl-attendants) chimes in with something like 'Believe ye not?' Mrs. M. is still not reacting. He agitates a tiny white paper dove above her head: as she still remains unaware, emits a low whistling sound (the supranatural voice of the Holy Spirit): she finally notices, drops her prayer book in fright. Announcer, 'And the angel said: Behold you shall bear a son and you shall call his name Ma – sa – ni – e – l – lo!' Birth of a savior.

The Angel steps back ('Bye-bye!'), the announcer is ringing his bell, and says 'Now the birth of Masaniello happened in this wise!' and Mrs. M. rises, and to the

---

10. 'The scene consists of each puppet and the five people who manipulate its body. They seem like little figures of common people in old paintings – always looking up at the big figures, but also dancing themselves and part of the total picture.' — (Beverly Brown).

11. The song is an 18th century Neapolitan – Bay of Naples islands – rather than the city – song, the islands songs were quieter than the city songs – called 'Angelare'. They did two verses out of the song's three. The first:

> Nenna mia chi se l'ha pigghiata
> Nenna mia ghiú nun s'é sta'
> Qualche mago, qualche fata
> Se l'avut ripigghia'
>
> Angelare' bam bum.
> Angelare' bum bam.

drum and encouraging shouting from the puppeteers
and musicians to the right, pulls Masaniello, a clownish
unkempt figure like herself, but more distinctively folk-
loric, in red pantaloons and cap (and red and white
sneakers), out from underneath the cloth by the rope – a
cymbal clash, a brassy three-note 'Happy Birthday to You
from the Angel's trumpet, three drum beats. Masaniello
is up now, does a little dance to a quick flute music,
drum-punctuated, and a verse from *Masaniello* – the
Angel, apparently now Masaniello's Guardian Angel,
picking up the rope the other end of which is still
around Masaniello's waist – an umbilical string. The
power of the tableau of the black-winged Guardian
Angel, standing upright and watching mother and son,
twice as tall and twice as big as they, black, they small,
colored and in action, derives from the aesthetic precision of its spacing.

21:38

19:56   The announcer, 'Ladies and gentlemen, you have just
seen how Masaniello was born in the great city of
Naples – and how we will show you (as though announcing the play itself after the foreplay) *the 14 days
of Masaniello!* (turning over the scene-calendar to its
first leaf, '1', with a sketch of a man catching a fish).
On the first day, Masaniello catches a fish!' Bell (prolonged) while Masaniello goes over to the left end of
the platform, casts a string off it, to a drum flourish
jerks it up – no fish – to another verse from *Masaniello*
(brisk, a little sad, the flute, as with most of this music,
leading) tries again: his mother ties the string to the pot
21:40   now under the cover, to another drum rull he pulls it
out, to shouting and clapping. His Guardian Angel
still has him on a string.

Bell, announcer, 'On the second day, Masaniello sells
a fish.' Masaniello, to the bell, bends over his mother
who is kneeling on the platform with her back to the
audience, she gets up, faces us, he has tied a paper with
'fish' on it around her forehead. She stands,[12] to
shouted, semi-oriental intricately polyrhythmic singing

---

12. She is supposed to be selling the fish. Schumann's theatre, though not quite excluding
gestural mimicry, from '68 onward pretty much excluded mime though it crept back in
with Barbara Leber's performances in the '79 *Washerwoman Cantatas*.

21:42   in a sorrowing mode (Neapolitan fronne — improvised
street vendors' cries, w/Arab influences). Drum roll, the
Duke on the right steps forward a bit, claims (male and
female voices) the fish: 'The fish is mine!'. Masaniello
and his mother are flabbergasted. Another drum roll:
'All mine and not yours!' To drumming and triumphant
'ha-ha-ha's' from the pole bearers, the Duke does a
stomping dance of triumph, i.e., his feet are off the
floor, moves up and down and about in place a bit.
Masaniello is holding on to his mother.

19:58   'On the third day, Masaniello — eats a fish!' Bell. (After
each of his scene-announcements, the announcer rings or
is supposed to ring his bell until the performers are
ready.) Masaniello is over to the left on the platform,
on his guardian's rope. The covered table is set out on
the platform to the right, a chair next to it. Banging on
the pot with a spoon, Mrs. Masaniello calls her son to
dinner. The bell tinkling stops. Three drum beats.
Masaniello tries to make it to the table, each time he
tries his guardian prevents him, finally he grabs the
rope, gives it an angry jerk, sits down. The band accompanies the little ballet of frustration by an instrumental bit of the 'Ballad of Masaniello.' Cymbal clash.
Announcer, 'Do you live in the great city of Naples?!'
'Yes!' 'Do you go to work early in the morning, work
all day very hard, come back late at night, knock on the
front door (2 knocks), your mother opens the front
door, lets you into the dining room, sets you down at
the table, so you can eat your dinner with your spoon?!'
'Yes!' 'And — did you pay the spoon tax?!' (I saw this
is addressed to and responded to by Masaniello.) Brief
embarrassed silence, a drum whirl, a cymbal beat: the
spoon, on a string, is whisked away from Masaniello by
a puppeteer stage-left off the platform. A dejected
'ooooohh!' in a descending pitch from the citizenry-
puppeteers, as Masaniello sits there. 'And was that
dinner served on a freshly laundered tablecloth with a
pretty blue border around the edge?!' (Etc. as before,
table cloth jerked away.) 'And underneath that table
cloth, was there a nice long mahoganny table that your
grandfather made for you two birthdays ago last
August?!' (Etc., the puppeteer runs up on the platform,
carries off the table.) 'Now on Tuesday, while you were

416

out at work all day, did you indeed go out to sea, set a few lines, catch a few fish, and then return home?!' 'Yes!' 'And – did you pay the fish tax?!' The Guardian Angel jerks out his chair from underneath him, he falls to the floor. Mrs. Masaniello replaces the 'fish' sign by a 'no fish' sign. Drum whirl, cymbal clash, the Duke does another triumphal dance. A lengthy silence, as though Masaniello, on the floor, were mulling it over. He gets up, and to a sadly resigned minor solo rendition of the ballad of Masaniello on the Guardian Angel's trumpet (which he plays – a miracle! – through a hole in his stomach, a funny but graceful effect, as is the slightness of the trumpet relative to his bulk), Masaniello and his mother do a slow informal dance of commiseration together, their stances as though they were holding each other up. The contrast between the unworldly – symbolic – formal angel figure attending and the two quasi-comic small real people is again moving.

21:47

They stop dancing, the mother stomps her foot, throws her 'no fish' sign on the floor, gets angry after having been depressed. She whispers in Masaniello's ear. Masaniello picks up a spoon, beats on her pot, picks up some more of the scattered table silver (spoons), and jumps down on the floor, tearing himself himself loose from his keeper. He challenges the Duke to a fight, more or less in the manner of a discus thrower or batter, launches a spoon against the Duke, who falls back a little, vacillates: the third throw, hit to the stomach, does it, the Duke is K.O.'d, i.e. is retired, leaned into the up-stage stage left corner in a lifeless way. Each attack is announced by a drum whirl, accompanied by shouting from the 'crowd'[13] the third one followed by admiring 'oooohhhs' and a cymbal clash. The announcer hands the leash back to Masaniello's Angel.[14]

20:05

21:48

21:50   20:06   'On the fourth day – Masaniello – is – a – sinner! – in the great city of Naples!'[15] Some pretty young girl

---

13. Peter Schumann's crowds admire every show of force.
14. This scene like many others in this show is only vaguely humorous. Schumann's child-like manner transmutes into childishness in the performances of his immature followers (the majority), his ease of creation acting as a license for its degeneration into arrogantly shallow self-indulgence. With few exceptions, they lack the tension – a sexual tension effecting a moral tension – required: their innocence is dull.
15. This mysterious, i.e. awkward, announcement apparently is intended to signify that he

puppeteers dress Masaniello up like a donkey, one of them making him bend over with a smart blow to the stomach, covering him with the covering that had lain on the platform, put one of the light grey/dark grey face masks from the platform steps – twice as long or more than his natural face – over his face. His face lodged in the bottom of it, it sticks up backward at a jagged angle over his bent back. At first, to a triumphantly played segment of the 'Ballad of Masaniello' from the band, he is pulling a big wheel in an oval around the stage, followed by a crowd of the puppeteers, clapping – he's going to Golgatha – his Angel marching out front, rope in hand, death, the announcer, guiding the wheel, but then (the band no longer playing) the scene turns into a spectacle of torture, wheel and rope seeming the instruments, Masaniello all tangled up with them as death turns the wheel in the air over him. The black Angel is now watching from the rear, one of the white-clad girl puppeteers, her back to the scene, as though being fortified by him, in front of him. Masaniello collapses down-stage, center-stage, a symbol of 'the oppressed', of 'suffering humanity'. The resolute incoherence of the central image – semi-beastly crouching body, vast, immobilely sorrowful face, no head, bits of clown's clothing, the unsupported wheel, entangling rope – make it powerful. Mask, wheel, donkey skin are removed, he lies there in his previous comic fisherman's outfit. The Angel has left. The crowd of puppeteers is standing behind Masaniello facing us, each with two of the man-masks, hand held before their faces.[16]

20:09   'On the fifth day, Masaniello – addresses the masses!' The Angel has come back, is again holding the rope, Masaniello tears it out of his hand, attacks him,

---

is treated like or feels like one, presumably because of his third day disrespect for authority: or perhaps this scene signifies the revolutionary's typical momentary failure of nerve when the revolutionary situation presents itself, such as has been imputed to Stalin and the majority of the Izvestia's editorial board during the weeks when Lenin had decided on October. What the scene conveys are the inner conflicts of an individual launched on a desperate defiance of authority.

16. Schumann's new use of masks I have mentioned – he in various places in *Masaniello* and in various manners uses them independently of carriers. The incoherent image of the fourth day (there is another in the thirteenth) is similarly daring. His mastery of the medium by now allows Schumann to dispense with some of its elementary illusion-creating modes.

kicks him out, the 'masses' (the puppeteers) cheering him on, the band doing a gay version of the 'Ballad of Masaniello.' His mother is watching from the platform. Jumping about madly, he delivers an incomprehensible harangue of growls etc. to the masses lined up-stage right, who cheer him on.

21:50   'On the sixth day, Masaniello is a lion.'[17] Masaniello is dressed as a lion (actually becomes its rear end), the lion is a loose yellow and orange body of tissues and a big square elaborate delicately fanged Pekingese head, all ornamental curves, not funny but elegant and mysterious. The little Chinese dragon prances with roaring growls, egged on by the masses' roars (to drum and flute.)

'On the seventh day, Masaniello leads 100.000 people through the streets of the great city of Naples to the palace of the viceroy!' Emerged from the lion costume, Masaniello gets a pale red flag – the Duke is

21:56   over to the right – and leads (the Angel going over to stand near the Duke) the shouting and hand-clapping masses (the puppeteers, holding the human-people masks in front of their faces) out through the audience, preceded by the musicians (who with much drum accents are playing and singing verses from the 'Ballad of Masaniello'): they reappear in procession along the left hand balcony above us, reemerge from the left rear onto the platform stage, bringing a cannon barrel and the wheel. Advancing a little way on the platform, they form a revolutionary tableau (1848), the cannon aimed in the direction of the Duke. Raucous firing commands, drum whirl, no bang, a twittering from the Angel's little white bird.

20:14   'On the eighth day, Masaniello accepts an invitation to the palace of the Viceroy of the great city of Naples.'

21:56   The Angel delivers the invitation to him. Surreptitiously

17. During the two performances I saw, the two last ones, the announcer didn't make this announcement till Masaniello was dressed as a lion – he was probably late. The announcer's bell was similarly displaced occasionally. His slackness was deleterious: the loose, serial form of the spectacle required a strict accompanying ritual of narration, clear and incisive gestures, absent also in the accentuation of his pronouncements. His turning of the calendar and his pointing to the successive pages – each time the number of the day and an illustrative sketch – was similarly weak: the calendar might as well not have been there. The narrator's performance in Schumann's theatre requires the energy and incisiveness of a fair or street show barker.

glancing back at his followers, Masaniello goes over to the other end of platform to read it, a chorus of puppeteers quotes it as the Duke advances (vocal trumpet calls) and Masaniello kneels: 'We are equal, you and I, let us be merry, we are equal, you and I, let us be merry for a while!' The crowd dispersing, Masaniello goes back over to the other end of the platform where his mother dresses him up for the party in something like a brocade house coat and hands him a mandolin so he can entertain. The card table, heaped with colorful bits of costuming, has been placed center-stage on the floor, and in a charming scene five of the puppeteers around it dress up (their faces masked or made up in colors, white, green) as gracily grotesque ugly aristos, dancing, at the same time, or trying to, to the proud rather than gay, in fact, like most of this music faintly sad music.[18] The table is set, a small glass of flowers at its center, the five nobility pose for us around it, they are dressed in white with many touches of color, a superbly delicate satirical reproduction of something in the pastoral manner. Masaniello is on the platform to the left, by himself. He attends the party in absentia. His guardian is meeting with the Duke to the right rear. The announcer has fetched a watering can, a basket of twine, a bag with some stuff, he does the waiter. A brief strumming on the mandolin from Masaniello, accompanied by a brief but frenetic rotation in place,[19] opens the banquet. Having announced the course – '... e primo, vino!' in garbled Italian, the announcer serves it to the avid guests from the watering can – drunken 'tralala' singing from the chorus of puppeteers in the background – another bit on the mandolin and another turn by Masaniello, another announcement ('... pasta!') – more drunken shouting: the guests pose in their loosely curved photographer's line behind the table, delightedly united by the tangled mess of twine extended between them. More ominous strumming on the mandolin, announcer ('E finalemente, gelati!'), pieces of

---

18. A traditional Neapolitan folk tune, perhaps 18th century, like most of the others suited for tarantellas, *Rancio e mosca* (The Spider and the Fly), a song on the theme of the larger animal always eating up the smaller, illustrating this in a series of verses.
19. According to Beverly Brown, on the ninth a phrase from *La donna è mobile* on the angel's trumpet opened the meal.

some pale gelatinous plastic which the convivers drape over themselves are served to shouts of joy from the chorus. Mrs. Masaniello, now wearing a sign, 'Lots of fish', is dubiously watching the party from the floor stage-right says, 'I am Masaniello's mother, and I know how much he likes gelati, but I wish he wouldn't eat *that* gelati!'[20] A somewhat drunken trumpet fanfare from the angel accompanied by vocal fanfares announces that the host is about to speak. He expresses himself in a Chinesy gibberish (done by his pole bearers) to the announcer who goes over to him, and who, attending obsequiously, responds to each of the Duke's utterances with a delighted 'aaaoooh!' (meaning: 'I have understood' and/or 'how wonderful'), then translating the Duke's courtly Castilian to Masaniello, who each time responds with the brief rotation in place and strumming on the mandolin: 'Do you live in the great city of Naples?!' – 'Do you like the great city of Naples!' – 'Do you want the great city of Naples?!' – 'I will give you the great city of Naples!' The guests have been taking out the food and the table. The sea voyage of the key to the city to the same nostalgic, carefully pretty, poetic Baroque music (flute, strings) as the last time, is repeated. Masaniello – drum whirl, rhythmic shouting, hacking drum, cymbal – tucks the key in his house coat sash.

'On the ninth day, Masaniello is named Captain General of the great city of Naples.' (The announcer attempting a clipped military tone.) A vocal and instrumental trumpet fanfare, drumming, as Mrs. Masaniello uniforms him in a flowered lady's bonnet. To shouted raucous commands from Masaniello, responding shouts and yes, sirs from the populace, a drum reveille, the populace over to the left raise the (perhaps 12 ft. tall) pole figure of a general – yellow fringed paper epaulets, ribbons and medals, tunic, khaki pants stuffed into black boots, holding in his left a long (5 ft. or so) wooden sword – his large green mustachio'd face – the moustache parallelling his joined eyebrows – that of Stalin. He dances, swaying. The spectre's face is hard and pitiless – though not cruel – and sad, as are the

22:04

20:20
22:05

22:09

---

20. At the beginning of the New York run, she had made a like comment as each dish was served.

other masks' faces. It is as though Schumann making these masks — of rulers, queens, dukes, generals, clerical clerks, as of those ruled[21] (the grey in grey masks), equally masks of human essence — had been looking into man, when thinking up the funny action only looking at him. Masks of empathy, an onlooker's view of the action. Masks thought by his eyes and hands, an action thought by his head.

'On the tenth day, Masaniello — hupp! — cuts off the heads of the noblemen of the great city of Naples.' His mother sleeps throughout this scene at the other end of the platform, behind a small cutout of a house, her head on a pillow. The Angel is off to the right rear behind her. Masaniello is standing to the left, by the General, supporting his sword arm. To Masaniello's raucous commands to the left, and shouts and yes sirs from the crowd, the General, Masaniello moving his arm, successively executes the nobility we have seen partying, each execution announced by a drum whirl, accompanied by a cymbal clash, the victims introduced by the announcer ('Ladies and gentlemen, it is my pleasure at this point to present to you — His Excellency, the Tax Collector General, of the great city of Naples!' — 'Ladies and gentlemen, the tiny but adorable petit Prince Colonel de Baronessa de Baronici of the great city of Naples!' — 'And, lest we forget, the royal philharmonic orchestra of the great city of Naples!'), each dying with (clownish) gestures and (ridiculous) cries of agony appropriate to his or her character, the crowd raucously laughing while they die, a hunchback wiping the blood off the sword (Beverly), Masaniello each time posing afterward with triumphant squeaks, glaring at us belligerently. The death-head announcer shoves the victims back against the huge awkward sword, each time slightly raised, their backs to it, they each die lengthily in convulsions. Military-type music (trumpet, joined by flute, etc.), rhythmic shouts of yes, sir! Silence while the black Angel blesses

---

21. His beast masks (blind and dumb souls), his monster masks (sweetly gay), and in this show the mythic-beast lion mask, fixed in the lineaments of wonderment, his (though grinningly active) Devil — and (threateningly active) death-masks later on, are different: the human masks show awareness, and hopeless acceptance of suffering, the others either unconscious being or awareness as form of destructive agency.

the dead with his little paper dove (and his low whistle), and (Beverly) the hunchback swings a censer over them. Masaniello launches into a satisfied speech, greeted by acclamations, raucous laughter, roughly (it is improvised and not meant to be too clear) to the effect, 'It was a nice day ... we chopped off a lot of heads ... there was a lot of blood ...' Triumphant

20:28 procession with the general, he is retired to the floor upstage stage right. The puppeteers withdraw, the announcer ringing his bell.

22:14 20:29   'On the eleventh day, Masaniello goes — mad.' Masaniello, back in his fisherman's outfit, goes up on the platform to visit his mother, knocks on the door of the house, she at first goes on sleeping, to repeated knocks gets up, but she does not receive him, throws him a bundle of red rags, lies down again. He stares at the bundle, picks it up, it is raggedy devil's clothing, to the prolonged tinkling of the announcer's bell, center-stage, out on the floor, he takes off his clothes and puts on the crimson costume and a red beastly or demonic looking devil's mask — it makes one think of blood and madness, of rage. He is half naked. The puppeteers and musicians, performers in all, have assembled behind him in three ranks, on the platforms, and on the floor below, the waxy everyman masks in front of their faces — two for each — a nightmarish assembly of common humanity, a sea of faces. The tinkling stops, they recite, in unison, from the 'Ballad of Masaniello,' separating the words, 'In times of disorder, Masaniello dresses like a — lunatic! (a shouted 'Hurrah!') When he shakes (an eery 'wheeeee') — when he shakes ('wheee'), the garment — tears!' The masks are moving, assume positions at angles to one another, some are upside down. He is shaking. Chorus, 'Even

20:35 the people spit on him!' Masaniello falls. (In this scene, too, the spacing is superb, the lone flaming figure downstage stage left, the grey chorus of faces on the red-accented white figures up beyond it, more stage right.) They accompany a slow dance of the masks — and down, one alternately up as the other goes down — with a low keening ('whooooaaaah, whooooaaah...', a soughing wind), slowly advancing on the lying figure. The keening grows louder and louder, then briefly dies

22:20 down. They leave. The black Angel stands at the right

rear with his back to the scene. Masaniello remains on the floor. There are some narrow white strips of cloth next to him. The announcer agitates his little bell. Masaniello gets up, picks up the white strips, stands.

'On the twelfth day, Masaniello — shoots — his friends and his followers.' Three drum beats, and to a sadly resolute, militant, flute- and drum-backed verse from the 'Ballad of Masaniello,' Masaniello runs up on the platform, where a chair and the card table with a small typewriter on it have been set up to the left, and three of the white-clad puppeteers stand erect against the rear wall, spaced out at some distance from one another facing us, masks ('people' masks) held over the faces of the two end ones by puppeteers behind them. He blindfolds the two end ones with the white bandages. He sits down at the typewriter (the mother is sleeping behind her house over to the right) starts typing, types with increasing fury (silence except for the staccato of the keys), at the end quite discoordinately, the blindfolded figures collapsing in slow agony to his typing, the puppeteers behind them going down to the platform floor with them. The sound of the typewriter is eerie, mad, obsessive: bureaucratic homicide. A single drum beat follows it. The white victims are extended along the rear wall to both sides, the spared one is standing between them.

'On the thirteenth day, Masaniello — tralala — prays.' (Idiotically, the announcer does this ironically.) Following the announcer's bell and a brief sandpapery scratching of a tambour with a guitar chord, the Italians go into a slow, sorrowful — the words drawn out — initially unaccompanied ecclesiastic song, sung in unison, on the death of Christ.[22] His angelic administrator, from stage right on the platform holding the end of the rope manacling his hands folded in prayer, Masaniello, one of the ordinary-people masks over his face, still in his red flame rags, partly naked, is kneeling in an attitude of prayer on the platform, more or less center-stage, facing to the right: a powerful, again incoherent or chaotic image, the disassembly, as by torture, of a man — the sketch of a symbol. His two white victims are

---

22. *De la cruelle morte de Cristo*, a 13th century Tuscan lauda (prayer) out of the *laudario del Crotona*, a type of song sung in church and at processions, early form of the cantata.

behind him, to both sides of him. The scratching sound on the tambour ends the lauda. Blackout. A puppeteer in the front row of pillows directs a hand-held projector here and there erratically, focusses it on a huge puppet (actually 'only' 10 or 12 feet high) above and behind us on the balcony. It has a gravitatious yellow full moon face, its large yellow hands folded in prayer are raised to its chest.[23] As it appears, the chorus assertively shouts 'the Madonna is mine — all mine and not yours!', perhaps in characterization of Masaniello's attitude of self-righteousness. Syncopated drumming, the scratch on the tambour — to a shouted, guitar-accompanied song (as for fast dances at weddings or other feasts), not gay but celebratory, drums and castanets between the verses,[24] and in the flickering projector light he and his gigantic praying hands separate into two figures and do a dance together, swaying on his part, bopping on theirs, its mode irony and evilly gloating triumph: but when moonface turns, we see that, skillet-headed, he on his back is a red grinning devil in crimson rags like Masaniello's. The overbearing dance in the mind, dually doubled, above us, all around the balcony, repeats a dance of Masaniello's on the stage — a puppeteer holding his substitute human face over his face, he is moving in exultation in place, his upstretched arms red flames (pieces of costuming, that alternatively go with the costuming of the red devil half of the balcony puppet)[25] ending in stumpy red hands, an outstretched finger, destructive rage personified. The music ends with a 'hey', the dancing ends, the lights go back on. Announcer's bell.

22:27

20:45   'On the fourteenth and final day, Masaniello is assassinated in the great city of Naples.' Masaniello's Guardian Angel sits down at the typewriter — the enormous figure perched on the little chair — sparsely, daintily pecks away at the keys (a memo), as Masa-

---

23. You can't make out the printed cloth dollar bills pinned to its yellow and white shirt.

24. *Madonna della grazie*, a processional prayer song from the island of Prodigia near Naples, sung on the feast of Our Lady of Prodigia, August 15th.

25. The *Masaniello* masks were on exhibition at 112 Greene St. during concerts the Italians gave September 22nd to 25th. Here the double — hyprocite and devil — figure had its praying hands on one side, the flame arms on the other. Its yellow folded hands were oddly echoed by the golden hands holding the golden Jesus child of the Madonna appearing at the end of the show.

niello, his arms still lifted, his mask still held, in the course of perhaps a minute collapses, the mask shaking. The two that had been executed are still behind him extended symmetrically to each side of him, they white, he red, his mother is asleep in her house to the right. The Guardian Angel gets up and leaves.

22:29   As the Italians start a melodious, sedately devout song (*Madonna tu mi fai* (You Made Me, Our Lady), a Neapolitan city, not island, prayer song of the villanelle type), two puppeteers from behind us bring in a (16 ft. or so) pole puppet, its white dress, white flowers on its blue hem, billowing, a lady, Our Lady, an elegant diaphanous head scarf (over a blue handkerchief) framing her large impassive dark golden face, draped over the golden baby in her golden hands: she is helped — a white cloud, floating — up on the platform by Mrs. Masaniello, where she gathers in the victims of Masaniello's purge under her dress, Masaniello himself and Mrs. Masaniello, then, in the right hand corner, the other puppeteers, the masses: all procession, her dress distended over them. The chant ends — it was only a verse or so — there is an extended drum roll, and as the Italians to the sharp dry staccato of castanets start a wild but disciplined, faintly oriental song (*Mattacino*, a

22:31 Neapolitan funeral song), Our Lady is joined by a Death Man, as tall as she, but airy, except for his grey skeletal narrow head (black nostrils, big white stumpy teeth), all bones, strung-together pieces of wood, his limb segments peeled branches, his chest crate slats, a barked piece of wood his pelvis. His vertebral pole is carried by one carrier, two others each with two smaller poles moving his limbs — he is a marionette. He is, despite his size, toy-like, and elegant, but neither prevents his being — weakly but definitely — frightening.

22:33 The Madonna and he dance together, a mystery — almost an outrage. Finis.

*   *   *

The spectator probably expects a canonization of a revolutionary hero. In any event here gets a skeptical-pessimistic play à la Genet's *Balcony*: the hero turns into a bloody Stalinesque tyrant, turns insane, is assassinated. This is Schumann's own interpretation of *O Cunto E Masaniello*, which is a revolutionary song in the strong imagery of Neruda presenting him as the ever-lambent spirit of insurgency.

426

Grey Lady Cantata III, Paris, France, 1975.
(Photo: E. George)

Grey Lady Cantata IV, St. Clement's Church, New York City,
May 4, 1974
(Photo: P. Moore)

Grey Lady Cantata VI, Paris, France, 1975.
(Photos: E. George)

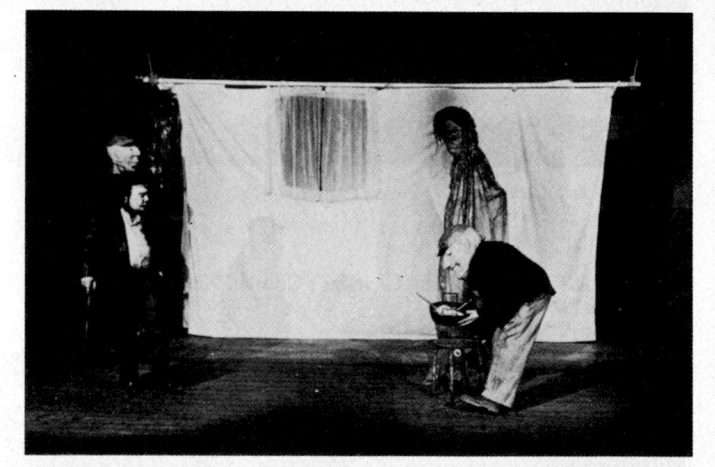

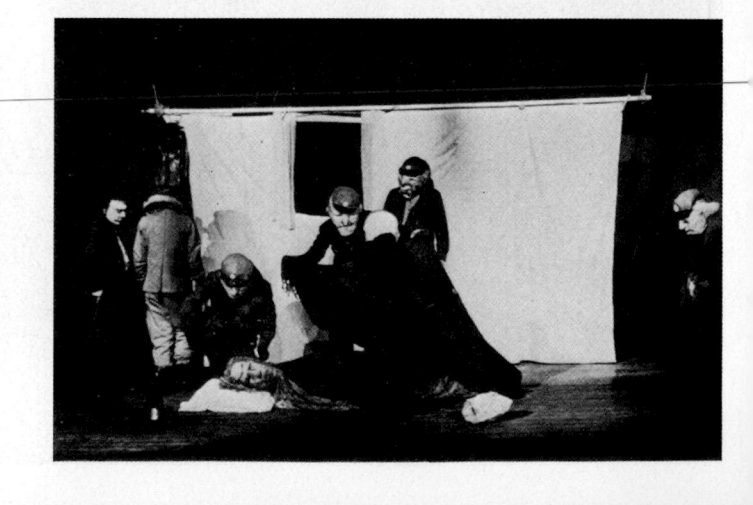

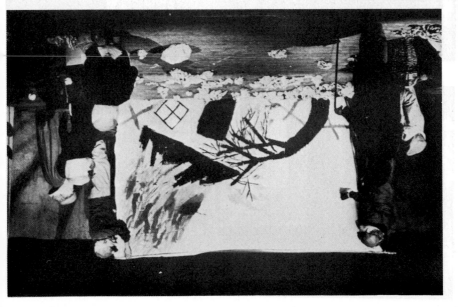

The Birdcatcher in Hell, France, December 1971 – February 1972. (Photos: E. George)

The Birdcatcher in Hell, France, December 1971 – February 1972.
(Photo: E. George)

Simple Light, 1972.
(Photo: E. George)

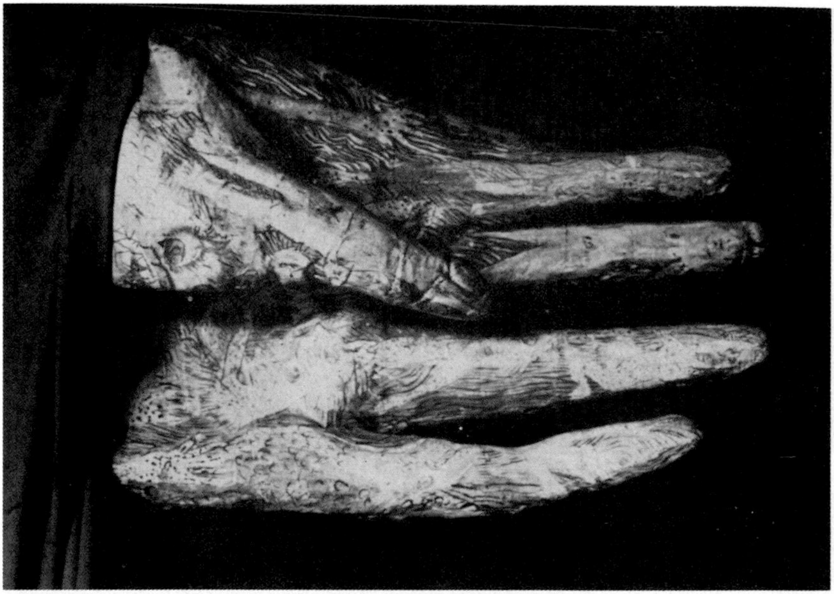

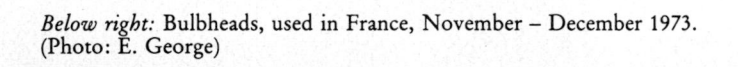

Above and below left: Yama's hand, used in *Birdcatcher*, 1971.
(Photos: B. Brown)

Below right: Bulbheads, used in France, November – December 1973.
(Photo: E. George)

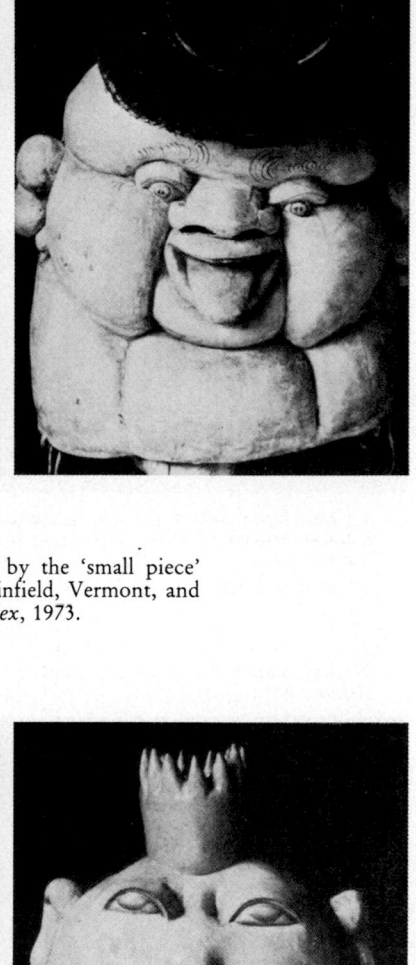

Celastic heads made directly over clay by the 'small piece'
technique. Bulbhead family made in Plainfield, Vermont, and
used in *Tragedy of the Soaring Price Index*, 1973.

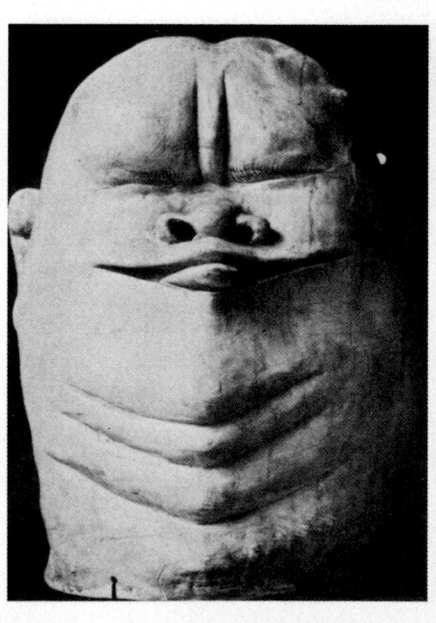

Celastic face masks worn with garbage man costumes, made in
Glover, Vermont, 1971. First used in numbers in Circus of
1975.
(Photo: B. Brown)

Garbagemen in Small Circus, France, 1976.
(Photo: M. Lavoix)

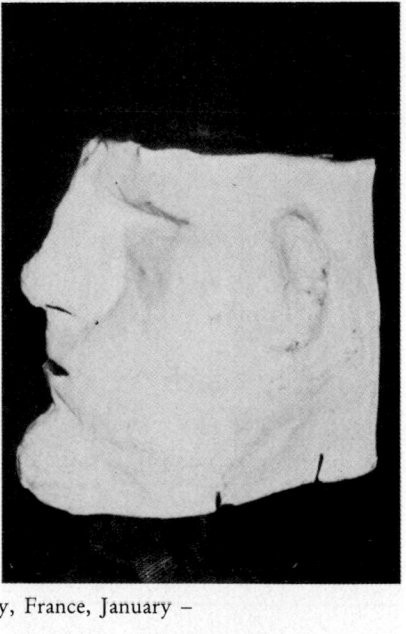

Above left: *Bicentennial Spectacle*, Nancy, France, January –
March 1976.
(Photo: E. George)

Above right: Butcher mask made in Glover, Vermont, 1976.
Butchers first used en masse in Circus of 1976.
(Photo: B. Brown)

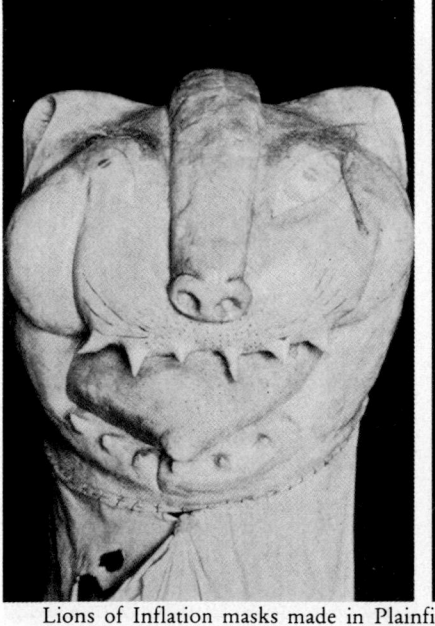

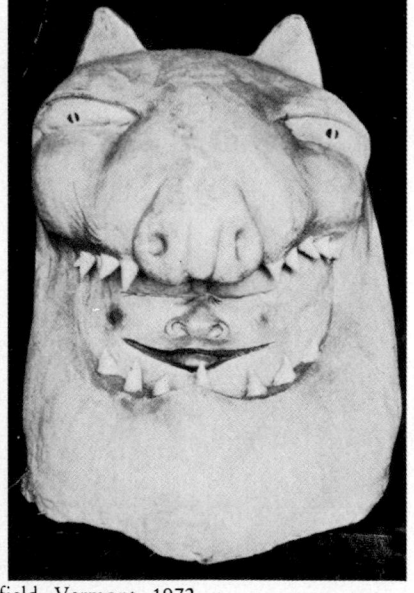

Lions of Inflation masks made in Plainfield, Vermont, 1972.
Mask for a backpack puppet used in *Tragedy of the Price Index
Parade*, 1973. (Photo: B. Brown)

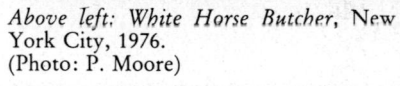

Above left: White Horse Butcher, New York City, 1976.
(Photo: P. Moore)

Above right: White Horse Butcher, Florence, Italy, September – October 1976.
(Photo: M. Berlincioni)

Right: White Horse Circus, Florence, Italy, 1976.
(Photo: A. Sferlazzo)

The pivotal point is the execution of the aristocrats: presented gaily, humorously, as a humorous event, Schumann's point within his context — the whole play — evidently that that's not the way: terror begets terror. Not that he shows it as a revolution's wrong departure, as crucial error: it turns up in the sequence of life (history), so it seems. It's the logical next step from rebellion: so it's not the terror that Schumann in effect condemns, it's the rebellion. Or he notes with a superior sorrow the recurrent cycle from tyranny to tyranny.

At the end the Madonna with the Christ-child — 'ah!' one says — she is joined by a Death all joints and wood, they dance together: What is one to make of this? Death and salvation in one: the totally ambiguous metaphor totally not related to the story's what's-the-use attitude in re revolutionary redemption from earthly misery and from injustice. Though of course one senses (there must be) a relation. Perhaps we all in life face the essential choice between love and sterility (a choice that in the morality plays of this period Schumann has women naturally make one way, men having difficulty choosing (*Wolkenstein*), or making the wrong choice (*Masaniello*)).

That view of history seems correct. Repression follows revolution. So if the play's after-play counterposes to the terrorizing self-righteousness of those that make history (Masaniello's thirteenth day) a withdrawal into faith-hope-and-charity in the private shadow of death, though personally I have neither hope for nor faith in faith or hope, that choice is okay with me. But nothing seems to me to justify in this hungry world, an anti-revolutionary attitude.[26]

---

26. *The Boston Ledger* reviewer noting that there was 'still a hint of protest in *Masaniello*, but it doesn't dominate the stage,' added that 'if the story could be labeled protest, it would have to be in an anti-revolutionary motif.' (September 2). Tish Dace in the *Soho Weekly News* (September 15) considered that if Masaniello's 'revolutionary spirit is to redeem us, it is appropriate that the political ceremony conclude . . . with a secular mass — the distribution of bread'. Michael Feingold welcomed the piece as proof that the Bread and Puppet Theatre, which 'retreated as the Vietnam War waned into a period of mysticism and rural communality, has reemerged from its withdrawal as a great tragic theatre, content neither to promote simple solutions to the problems we face, nor to hide from them in dream visions, but to celebrate the depth and intensity of those problems and leave us, shaken, to find our own way out of them.' — (*Village Voice*, September 19, '77.)

'Mr. Schumann scowls at the notion of any didactic intent in *"Masaniello"*. "This is not a message piece at all," the 42-year-old puppeteer, who has a beard and dark shaggy hair, asserted: "it glorifies the hero who opposes the taxes, and people can take from that what they want to take, but it is not based on a principal (sic) political position beforehand". It is not saying "hooray for tax evasion." Moreover, Mr. Schumann does not consider the loosely formed company to be true political theater. "Our political involvement has never been based on a preconceived philosophy about what is good and what isn't," he said . . . "it has been a spontaneous reaction to what we did not like — not out of a moralistic or puritanical kind of attitude, but from a sense of what our lives are about." ' — (Blau, *A Bread and Puppet Visit, New York Times*, September 9, '77.)

Masaniello is the political manifesto of Schumann's third period, not representing necessarily his political thought throughout it — the message of the silly-circus *Life, Liberty and Pursuit of Happiness* skit, ending with the kids' killing of Uncle Fatso is ambiguous — but the facit of it, what it came down to. It stands in a line with *Cry* of '69 and *Simple Light* of '72: he went from Resist! to Drop Out! to Revolution begets Tyranny and Terror! Well, we need mercy: we get death: same as mercy. A mercy, death. However, I would say Schumann enjoys life. I see him with a beer, a little paunchy. Always with a beer — other times not paunchy. Plenty of pretty girls, his wife stoutly backing him up. Always making these incredibly beautiful masks — surrounding himself with his own universe of faces, hieroglyphs, a private pantheon — pandemonium. Telling these gay little tales, and putting the faces in them. Withholding nothing. A very moral man: no foundation money. A good conscience. And a performer! There's something a little wrong with his back. He is *too* busy, *too* productive. To the ordinary mortal that might evince malaise, flight. But it's just the common malady of the gifted — they are, pain and all, enjoying themselves. So where does he get those faces? From people's faces? In the street? How could death appear a mercy to *him*?

Perhaps it only seems to him a mercy to others. Beyond the bloom of youth, the prolonged adolescences, a taut skin stretched over a chaos of miseries, those faces are ubiquitous, the subways are galleries of those grey-in-grey faces, the teachers have them, the politicians in the newspapers — the lips withdrawn into the mouths, the inverted eyes, the crumpled foreheads: natural signs not of internal Hiroshimas, but of daily anxious care. Except for a higher incidence of fatty tissue, physiognomically the industrial (or industrial-bureaucratic) individual's life seems as hellish as was that of the peasant: the shifts — facial and existential — from muscle to nerve and from moral-religious to pragmatic self-discipline seem incidental. Schumann's masks might thus be essentialist studies from life — registering that the quality of life has not appreciably improved from Uruk to New York. In this case he would not be looking into a private, but into a common hell.

*   *   *

This particular show, *Masaniello*, isn't too good. It's a little slapdash; the country fair thing is not quite working. In fact, it *is* phony. Nobody quite knows what, stylistically, he is alluding to. Perhaps my father still saw some such theatre in some meadow on the outskirts of Augsburg. The form derives from that of the come-on show outside the tent, before the performance, and from circus shows, the riding master announcing the trapeze act. Apart from that, we are back in the Middle Ages, burghers and yokels entertained by the sacred mysteries. Schumann's audience enjoys this form in a sophisticated way — the way kids don't mind Dylan's fake country accents, accept them *as* facsimile. Nevertheless, there is a lack of authenticity here, something false.

Masaniello didn't quite work. On the one hand, the puppets didn't dominate it: the Queen was extraneous, the Duke not *the* antagonist, in fact not worked out into *an* antagonist hardly even, and the other puppets, including the Guardian Angel in black who was so ambiguous he was undefined and whose part in the play was more an unrealized idea (of the lethal guardian angels we all have) than a part, seemed symbols extraneously introduced. On the other, the performers were too sloppy to carry an epic meta-chronical's defining episodes demanding not just clowning but precision (even just to be funny). The band's mugging further tore the thing apart: and would have, even if Schumann had integrated them into the play by substituting their numbers from the 'Ballad of Masaniello' (they would have had to be sung in English) for the announcer's scene announcements. They are not street musicians (e.g., even though this saint is patron of Naples, they didn't want to take their chance on playing at the Mulberry Street St. Gennaro festival): they are university students. The play of and the music to *Masaniello* did not quite cohere: the expressiveness or professional enthusiasm of the musicians seemed an alien inset into the balladesque story told by the play, their contributions intermezzi preventing it from creating its (visual) rhythm, one's focus was divided, their performance seemed or was too demanding, their sound insufficiently universal. So what we had were glimpses of Schumann's superb intelligence, i.e. sensitivity to the reality of things, beautiful instances of his artistry in scene arrangement, and, above all, some splendid moments of puppet theatre, the Guardian Angel playing the triumpet, or perched over a miniature typewriter, instrument of death, the dances of the giant puppets. I.e. a lot, but not adding up to *a* work of art.

Schumann in his work insists on consciousness, the work is to provide consciousness, he in, by it strives for consciousness, it recommends – urges – consciousness – of the human condition: an effectively-evaluatory cognition, not separated from or accompanied by emotion and morality, but at one with them: and contradictory: whereby Schumann joins or finds himself in the irrationalist camp, e.g. with Kierkegaard (Chestov, Schelling, Dostovievsky, Tolstoy). Masaniello's fourteenth day is a fine example of this latter characteristic, i.e. of Schumann's trying to incorporate contradictions systematically in his presentations, as form and technique; the post-ludial scene (Madonna and Death) a fine or simple example of the whole thing.

Formally, *Masaniello* is significant for some traits characteristic of the following period – the free use of the hand-held masks, the 'chaotic' or 'incoherent' images of internal states of conflict – ambition vs. fear or defiance of vs. respect for authority in Day 4, criminal urges vs. fear of God in Day 13 – and some features relating to the period in Schumann's work it belongs to, some assimilating it to the silly circus or circus proper, some relating it to the other morality plays of the period. Without a backdrop and flanked only by banners it on its platforms had an open-air sprawling quality somewhat remindful of the circus, and the frame provided its loose succession of scenes by the consistently brassy, circusy narrator's announcements and the music also made it similar to the circus — as well as its colorfulness. The play presented the interplay of Hero/Individual, without mask, uniformly masked Masses, and the Great (General, Queen, Duke) represented by giant puppets. The hero's mother, his guardian angel, the two-faced figure symbolizing both the hero's hypocritical piety and the Church, and the Madonna-Death couple, symbolizing the forces vying for him and for anyone provided an extension of the hero's situation into the private and interior sphere. Acting and staging used this essentially three-fold configuration of acting forces to focus us on the hero as individual, and in moral terms, rather than as embodiment of principle (as the similar division focusses us on the Holy Family in Schumann's Christmas plays) or on him as character engaged in the adventure of life. This focus was appropriate to the morality play form.

15. *Ave Maris Stella* at the '78 Circus: the positive morality play turns into a mass in celebration of woman, Christian in form, pantheist in substance.

Larry Gordon having in the summer or fall of '77 suggested to Schumann that the Bread and Puppet Theatre join his Word of Mouth Chorus — 'a group of singers and instrumentalists dedicated to performing a wide variety of medieval and renaissance and traditional music ... one of the first groups to revive American shape-note singing in the North ... founded in 1972' (Program, *Ave Maris Stella*) in a production of Josquin des Pres' late 15th century mass *Ave Maris Stella, Hail to Thee, Star of the Seas*, Schumann decided to make a play to go with this music that would have the liturgical structure of the ordinary Roman Catholic mass, and that would as a whole, and to some extent in its sections, have what he considered, beyond doctrine, its essential meaning. A real mass. He consulted a priest. Roman Catholic spectators averred there was indeed a correspondence. The pole star to which the mass is addressed is, I believe, the Holy Virgin: so Schumann understood it; decided to make his play about her; and did: turning out another variant of the *Christmas Story*, a mariolatric one; felt uneasy about it; so in his printed programs instructed the audience he was just a gentleman paying homage to the fair sex:

'Mary is Miriam, The Bitter One, Venus, Star of Hope, Lady of the Sea, Isis, Helping Power, Mother of God, Mother of us all, our Mother, every Mother.'

— though above all to mom. The little bastard baby had never had a good part in his Christmas plays, Schumann had always resisted the temptation to put a creche on stage, but this time he cut Him out of the script, so that in fact the play was not about mothers but about women: Eve. He eliminated the husband also, no Joseph, the woman pulled her donkey herself. The only man in the play, a new character, was God, but his part was a small one: he watched and wept. The fulcrum turning point of the play was not birth but conception: conceived as the work of a woman. Schumann explained this in the program:

'In the beginning was the Word. The world was created and rotted fast. But the Word was in it and stayed pure and strong. A woman listened to the Word so well and understood it so perfectly that she grew pregnant from it and gave birth to a son. And the Word was flesh.'

The 'flesh' he was referring to was woman. And the 'Word' was not any woman-born man's, but the 'pure and strong' essence of the (rotting) world: anterior to mankind; an essence of which women partake; and

431

they only; and by partaking of which they conceive. I.e., the logos is life, a creative lovingness at the heart of the cosmos present among us as the female of the species.

Committing the outrage of a mass, he reached the acme of his Christian fakery: a purely pantheist – and gynolatric – service in a theist form of the utmost innocent naiveté (cutout puppets, a Christmas tree.)

He made the masks and backdrops in October/November ('77), worked out the staging using students at the Montpelier Vermont College, put it on there December 3 and 4, took it on a small tour of N.E. (Vermont, Rhode Island), under aegis of the Chelsea Theatre showed it at the Brooklyn Academy of Music January 25-29, had a few more scattered showings in the East, decided not to take it on his May to June ('78) tour in Europe, but did it at his August circus, where in the intimacy of the nighttime pine woods clearing, under the shining stars it as his last feminist positive morality play complemented the afternoon meadow performance of *Wolkenstein*, his last male-contemplating negative morality play, as the year previous *Joan* had *Masaniello*. The group without him then took it on a tour of the West Coast.[1]

Part I, with narration[2] and with instrumental interludes by the Word of Mouth Chorus dressed in red as devils, following God's relegation to

---

1. 'It was made in a workshop, with community college students, in Montepelier. I made the puppets beforehand here, on my own, here on the farm, just like *Joan of Arc*, flat puppets, colored puppets. I painted the backdrops and then some of the puppeteers helped me to stage manage and to set up and rehearse together with those community college people and eventually we got the Word of Mouth Chorus – Larry Gordon's Word of Mouth Chorus – to sing in it, and we performed together. (Elka: – it wasn't that Larry Gordon – that you got the Word of Mouth Chorus to *sing*, but *they* had that piece of music and they asked you to use it in a show.) No. I knew that they wanted to do this mass. Right. That's right. It wasn't that *I* thought of doing that Josquin piece. (Elka: And you listened to it a *lot*. You had the tape for most of the fall, and what you created somehow came out of that music.) Yes. Well. The theme – the thought – *was* to find a way of how to do a Catholic mass and this really was one. The *Stations of the Cross* are not a mass. They are just a mess. Sort of fooling around with the Catholic mass. But this Josquin music is an orthodox mass in all its purity, and to reinterpret that and to understand it, and I went to the priest and I read up on it – and I *did* understand the mass, and what we did was reinterpretation mostly. Garlic being carried around instead of incense – at the crucial moment. (Elka: The tour also left and went by itself.) Right, there was *another* attempt at setting up a tour. (Elka: But it had been organized maybe much better with much more –) Oh yeah. Much better than *Masaniello*. (Elka: Everybody worked on it very hard and very vigorously.) It was done with people I knew much better than the Italians and who I could trust much better. Quite a few puppeteers who had really worked with me for a long time. (Elka: That was a three month tour to the West Coast.) That must have been the time I went to Australia.' — (Schumann, interview, '79.)

2. 'Leading the proceedings is a top-hatted master of ceremonies carrying two outsized hands with which he applauds, points or smacks together for attention. The latter usually is addressed to the orchestra, which is made up of red-suited satanical figures.' — (Mike Steele, *Bread and Puppets now 'yes'-oriented, Minneapolis Tribune*, March 13, '78.)

432

heaven[3] presents the 'bad part' of the story by three 'calamities' (fall, expulsion — which takes the form of Eve-Mary's flight (Eve and Mary are the same figure) to Bethlehem, a demonstration of female fortitude and the flood). The advent, through the audience, of a Christmas-tree-lights-embellished Ark carrying the eight Word of Mouth people, now dressed in acolyte white, back in, singing,[4] makes the transition to part II, the 'good part' of the story, essentially the Conception[5] and des Pres' mass. The service ends with communion, the sharing of bread and garlic, the crew of garbagemen munching.

There were, as usual, some lovely inventions of exquisite simplicity. God sustains Mary: a pair of naked arms stretch down from the bridge, their naked hands hold the woman's lifted hands moving her gently to and fro. The conception: the woman has received a green box, she opens it, turns on a little light over it, inside is a stage with herself on it and with the same backdrop of table and chair that is behind her, but then a bright light goes on over the stage and she looks enormously different. Divine compassion: the woman has strings coming out of her very crude — vague, undifferentiated — face mask's eyes, her tears: after she has conceived the God face comes down from above, hangs suspended, the tear-strings are pulled through its eyes, joining woman and God, the strings are cut, they now pend also from God's eyes. Woman's fortitude: when at the end of her thrice-repeated cross-stage wanderings (each time entering stage-left)

---

3. 'The piece begins with Paradise. There's a procession with a woman in blue (who is Eve, later Mary) leading her donkey. God also joins the procession before ascending into Heaven via a ladder held by two ambiguous but definitely working-class men — both with marvelously weathered pug-puppet faces.' — (Mike Steele, ibid.)

4. '. . . there's the flood and after seeing the flood . . . You were aware behind you of these voices singing the Mass. And you turned around and you saw a ship sailing up the aisle with Christmas tree lights. I mean that to me, it is childlike almost but it evokes that in me I turn around and I cry. It's just unbelievably lovely. There's suddenly a ship sailing up the aisle and after the flood you're seeing, again it's a statement of strong religious belief, of course. You're seeing all of the oppressive violence of the human race, then you're hearing the beginning of des Pres' Mass and you're seeing it as a ship riding the crest of the flood as something that will survive, that will come through it. It still brought tears to my eyes. It was incredibly lovely and very, very strong and compassionate. It was a ship with a string of Christmas tree lights, so that you were looking at sort of a child's vision of a lovely magical ship lit up and sailing down the aisle. You know that sort of touched me, those little things that do involve a childlike view of magic, is another constant theme of Peter's work that's just you know, I don't know anybody who's anywhere near that. (Omar Shapli, interview, '79.)

5. 'The impregnation of the Virgin was such a marvelous moment. I remember she had a large box hanging in front of her and the box was open and the Holy Ghost was thrown in and then everybody fell on their knees, suddenly like that. It was both extremely funny and very moving. I mean a lovely moment of a kind of Schumannesque originality. There's nobody who does it like that. There's nobody who believes in that sufficiently to be able to be that light with it.' — (Omar Shapli, ibid.)

she is finally utterly exhausted, her guardian angel[6] pulls her in by a double rope around one of her ankles in an elaborate pulling operation: the whole scene that pulling and the female figure's placing her feet foward, pulled.

But I found the goody-goodiness a little cloying, and the willful naiveté of the humor on the verge of being disgusting.

The program notes among the representatives of womanhood, alongside of Venus (by Schumann carefully identified as the lovely star, but in the context clearly representative of carnal love) mention Miriam the Bitter, the prophetess sister or step sister of Moses jealous of his Negress wife, known for her bout of leprosy and her song in celebration of Jehovah's assassination of the pursuing Egyptians:

> 'Let us sing to the Lord
> For He has done a marvelous thing.
> Into the ocean He threw
> horse and man.'

Though what made Schumann think of her was probably the parallel of her staunchness on the journey to the promised land to Mary's on the trip to Bethlehem, his reference to this tough cookie like that to Venus Aphrodite surprisingly amplifies the usually more narrow appreciation of women in his work, essentially: as housewives.

---

6. 'Her herald angel is a figure familiar from other Bread and Puppet presentations: militaristic, with silver foil wings sprouting from his air corps greatcoat, wearing a large helmeted puppet head and blowing through his trumpet with a small soprano voice. — (Jan Carr, *Wonder marks 'Ave Maris Stella', The Detroit News*, March 27, '78.)

16. *Wolkenstein* at the '78 Circus.
Second and last negative morality play,
an autobiography.

The splendid plaints of Oswald von Wolkenstein, '1377-1445, Knight, Poet, Singer, Thief, Composer, World-traveller, Prisoner, Diplomat, Crook, Cook, Oarsman, Merchant' (Schumann, NYC program of *The Life and Death of Oswald von Wolkenstein*) had been in the repertory of Music for a While,[1] but as Schumann remembers it he approached them with the idea of them working on a production of it together.[2] They took the idea of cooperation more seriously than he usually did when work with musicians was concerned and spent the summer months preceding the circus of '78 at Dopp Farm working it out with him.[3]

He did *Wolkenstein* August 19, 20 at the '78 circus and centered that

---

1. 'Since 1970, Music For A While has been presenting concerts of Medieval and Renaissance music to audiences all over the United States and Canada. Three long-time members of the New York Pro Musica form the core of this ensemble, which has become widely recognized as "among the most distinguished purveyors of the repertory." — (*New York Times*.)

   In addition to performing and recording, they are Artists-in-Residence at Sarah Lawrence College, where they serve as faculty for a Graduate Program in Performance of Early Music. They are also on the faculty of the State University of New York at Purchase.' — (Music for a While, press release, NYC Program, *Wolkenstein*.)

2. '. . . the '78 *Circus* was the circus with the idea of Wolkenstein – his work and life. (I: Did you think of Wolkenstein first and then approach the Music for a While people about it, or did they tell you they wanted to work with you and then you together found this?) Well, I think that was my proposition. We had discussed with different people I wanted in my show, and I think I proposed Wolkenstein to them, and they had performed Wolkenstein. They knew his music. They were *good* at it. They knew a lot of his work. They liked the idea of the production so both sides agreed. — (Schumann, interview, '79.)

   Unlike the other musical groups Schumann had worked with, these were a group of high-powered, slick professionals.

3. (Ephraim: So the *Wolkenstein*, just working with the Music for a While on the *Wolkenstein* show but also on the circus, was I guess the third time in three years you worked on a show with a different group from the outside.) It wasn't just the *third* time. I did that with Marc Estrin years in my life. And I did it with the Judson Chamber Ensemble before. So I kind of had a long row of experiences of working with this classical music . . . But with them the difference was that they were here all summer and that they were in the process of making the show much more than Marc Estrin with his Community Chorus or than the Judson Chamber Ensemble or anybody like that. (Elka: Did it really make a difference that they were here all summer? Do you think that really changed –?) It only pointed out that that was not necessary. To do it that way. But the fact was that the music was given much more time. Much more than with any of the other productions. (Elka: And they also provided the music for the *Pageant*. With the final song and something else?) Yeah, they came in with the oxcart, and they did the stardance music. (Elka: Did we ever see them again after that?) I see them sometimes. At performances of music.' — (Schumann, interview, '79.)

circus around it (eighteen out of thirty four sideshows were on him), and then did two productions of it in which he finally seems to have succeeded in two different settings to reproduce the civic-feast form of theatre he had developed for his Glover circuses, one the weekend of September 15th – 'a magnificent medieval spectacle within the great space of the largest cathedral in the world' – at the Cathedral of St. John the Divine in NYC,[4] the other, billed as 'pageant performance', in Bushnell Park in Hartford, Ct., September 21st.

As in the case of *Masaniello*, he based the play on a biographic ballad, the story of a movemented life, this time, because of the hero's peripaties, a close analogy of a man's 'way through the world', life as journey, and an autobiography, Wolkenstein's marvellous *Es fügt sich* :

'Es fügte sich, als ich zehn Jahre alt war,
da wollte ich die Welt kennenlernen.
In Not und Armut, in manchem heissen, manchem kalten Winkel
habe ich seither gehaust, bei Christen, Orthodoxen, Heiden.
Drei Pfennige und ein Stücklein Brot im Beutel
waren meine Wegzehrung von daheim, als ich ins Elend lief.
Im Streit mit Fremden und Freunden habe ich seitdem
manchen Tropfen Blut gelassen, dass ich schon zu sterben glaubte.
Ich lief zu Fuss wie ein Büsser, vierzehn Jahre lang,
bis mein Vater starb, und nie kriegte ich ein Pferd.
nur eines, einen Falben : halb raubte, halb stahl ich ihn,
und auf die gleiche Weise wurde ich ihn wieder mit Schaden los.
Ich war Laufbote, Koch, wahrhaftig, und Pferdemeister,
auch am Ruder zog ich, das war schwer,
bis nach Kreta und sonstwohin und wieder zurück.
Oft war ein einfacher Kittel mein bestes Kleid.

Nach Preussen, Litauen, in die Tararei, in die Türkei und übers Meer
zog ich mit eigenen Mittein, getrieben von der Minne; in die Lombardei,
nach Frankreich und nach Spanien mit den heeren zweier Könige,
Ruprecht und Sigmund, beide mit dem Adlerwappen.
Französisch, Maurisch, Katalanisch, Kastilisch,
Deutch, Lateinisch, Windisch, Lombardisch, Russisch und Rumänisch,
diese zehn Sprachen habe ich gesprochen wenn mich die Not ankam.
Auch konnte ich fiedeln, trommeln, pauken, pfeifen.
Ich bin um Inseln Halbinseln und um manches Land gefahren

---

4. 'There are religious processions (a blend of Christian and Buddhist), political symbols (Uncle Sam on stilts), and revivalist-type parades merging and parting on stage, building into a lively spectactle that lifts *Wolkenstein* suddenly out of its medieval setting and places it Everywhere, at Any Time. Life-size puppets move up and down the aisles. The focus of the action moves on and off stage. Eventually it envelopes the entire theater; it moves out of its confines and blossoms among the audience. The illusory barriers between the stage and house wither and fade.' — (D. R. Wilson, *Puppets and Pageanty, Soho Weekly News*, September 21, '78.)

auf grossen Schiffen, die mich vor den Fesseln des Sturms retteten,
und so bin ich über alle Teile des Meeres gerast, hinauf und hinab.
Das Schwarze Meer lehrte mich, ein Fass zu umklammern,
als zu meinem Unglück mein Schiff zerbrach
(ein Kaufmann war ich damals), doch blieb ich heil und kam davon,
ich und ein Russe; in diesem Gefecht fuhr Kapital samt Gewinn
zum Meeresgrund, und ich schwamm an das Ufer.

Eine Königin von Aragonien, schön und zart war sie,
vor der kniete ich und reichte ihr ergeben meinen Bart hin;
mit weissen Händlein band sie ein feines Ringlein hinein,
freundlich, und sprach "non maiplus disligaides".
Von ihrer Hand wurden mir auch die Ohren
mit einer kleinen Messingnadel durchstochen,
und sie schloss mir, wie es dort Sitte ist, zwei Ringe hinein;
die habe ich lange getragen; sie werden racaides genannt.
Alsbald suchte ich König Sigmund auf, wo er gerade war.
Er riss den Mund auf und bekreuzigte sich, als er mich erkannte;
er rief mir gleich zu: 'Was zeigst du mir da für Tand?'
und fragte mich freundlich: 'Tun dir die Ringe nicht weh?'
Die ganze Gesellschaft betrachtete mich da lachend;
da waren neun Persönlichkeiten von königlichem Rang,
dort zu Perpignan, und ihr Papst namens Petrus von Luna,
der Römische König war der zehnte, dazu noch die Frau von Prades.

Mein törichtes Leben wollte ich ändern, das ist wahr,
und so wurde ich für zwei ganze Jahre ein halber Begharde.
Der Anfang war ehrlich und gewiss voller Frömmigkeit,
wenn mir nur die Liebe nicht das Ende gestört hätte.
Ich war geritten und hatte Ritterwesen gesucht
und hatte einer Dame ergeben gedient, wovon ich schweige;
doch die wollte mir keine Nusschale voll Gunst erweisen,
ehe eine Kutte mich zum Narren machte.
Da ging dann manches gar leicht,
als mich der Kapuzenmantel mit den Zipfeln kleidete.
So etwas Gutes hat mir gewiss kein anderes Mädchen jemals auferlegt,
das die freundlichen Worte anhörte, die ich zu ihr sprach.
Schnurstracks fuhr meine Andacht durch das Dachfenster
in den Nebel hinaus, als ich die Kutte abschüttelte.
Seither habe ich um Liebesglück manchen Kampf erlitten,
und meine Freude ist fast erfroren.

Es wäre zu lang, wollte ich all meine Not erzählen.
Doch vor allem bedrängt mich ein edler roter Mund,
von dem ist mein Herz auf den bittern Tod verwundet.
Wenn ich vor ihr stand, ist mir oft der Schweiss ausgebrochen;
oft ist mein Gesicht erst rot, dann bleich geworden,
wenn ich in die Gegenwart des zarten Mädchens kam,
vor Zittern und Seufzen habe ich oft meinen eigenen Leib
nicht mehr gespürt, als wäre ich ausgebrannt.

437

Oft bin ich mit grossem Entsetzen von ihr fortgerannt
zweihundert Meilen weit, und niemals schöpfte ich Hoffnung.
Frost, Regen, Schnee konnten mich nie so schmerzen mit jagender Kälte,
dass ich nicht gebrannt hätte von der Sonne der Geliebten.
Wenn ich bei ihr bin, so ist mein ganzes Wesen bedrückt.
So muss ich wegen meiner Geliebten auf fremden Wegen ziehen,
wo Hilfe fern ist, bis Gnade von ihrem Hass lässt.
Hülfe sie mir, mein Leid würde zu Wonne.

Vierhundert Frauen oder mehr ohne irgendeinen Mann
habe ich zu los gesehen (die wohnten auf dieser kleinen Insel);
kein Mensch hat je in einem Saal ein schöneres Kunstwerk erblickt,
und doch konnte keine von ihnen sich mit dieser Frau messen.
Sie, von der ich eine schwere Last auf meinem Rücken trage,
ach Gott, wüsste sie nur um die Hälfte meiner Leidesbürde,
so wäre mir oft schon viel leichter, wie weh mir auch wäre,
und ich könnte hoffen, dass sie sich erbarmte.
Denn fern von ihr muss ich oft meine Hände ringen,
unter grossem Schmerz entbehre ich ihren Gruss,
ruhelos bin ich und kann nicht spät noch früh sanft schlafen,
das klage ich ihren zarten weissen Armen.
Ihr Burschen und Mädchen, die ihr Liebe kennt, bedenkt mein Leid,
bedenkt, wie mir zumute war, als mir die Zarte den Abschiedssegen gab.
Bei meiner Ehre, wusste ich, dass ich sie nie wiedersähe,
mein Auge müsste oft von Tränen heiss werden.

Ich habe nun an die vierzig Jahre gelebt – nur zwei fehlen noch –
mit Wahnsinn und Rasen, mit mancherlei Dichten und Singen.
Es wäre wohl Zeit, dass ich das Geschrei
meines eigenen ehelichen Kindes in einer Wiege gellen hörte.
Doch nie und nimmer kann ich die vergessen,
die mir in diesem Leben das Gemüt erweckt und erhoben hat.
In aller Welt konnte ich nicht ihresgleichen finden.
Auch fürchte ich sehr das Bellen von Ehefrauen.
Mancher weise Mann hat mich zu Urteil und Rat herangezogen,
dem ich durch lockere Lieder gefallen hatte.
Ich, Wolkenstein, lebe wahrlich sehr wenig weise,
dass ich so lange mit der Welt zusammenstimme.
Und ich sehe wohl, dass ich nicht weiss, wann ich sterben muss,
und dass mir dann kein anderer Glanz folgt als die Frucht meiner Werke.
Hätte ich dann Gott nach seinem Gebot gedient,
so fürchtete ich nicht das Wallen heisser Flammen dort.'

'Es fuegt sich, do ich was von zehen jaren alt,
ich wolt besehen, wie die weit wär gestalt.
mit ellend, armuet mangen winkel haiss und kalt
hab ich gepaut pei cristen, kriechen, haiden.
Drei pfenning in dem pautel und ain stücklin prot
das was von haim mein zerung, do ich loff in not.

438

von fremden, freunden so hab ich manchen tropfen rot
gelassen seider, dass ich want verschaiden.
Ich loff ze fuess mit swärer puess, pis das mir starb
mein vater zwar, wol vierzen jar, nie ross erwarb,
wann ains raubt, stal ich halbs zumal mit valber varb
und des geleich schied ich davon mit laide.
Zwar renner, koch so was ich doch und marstallär,
auch an dem rue- der zoch ich zue mir, das was swär,
in Kandia und anderswa auch wider här.
vil mancher kitel was mein pestes klaide.

Gen Preussen, Littwan, Tartarei, Turkei über mer,
gen Lampart, Frankreich, Ispanien mit zwaien küngesher
traib mich die minn auff meines aigen geldes wer,
Rueprecht, Sigmund, paid mit des adlers streiffen.
Franzoisch, mörisch, katlonisch und kastilian,
teutsch, latein, windisch, lampertisch, reuschisch und roman,
die zehen sprach hab ich gepraucht, wann mir zeran;
auch kund ich vidlen, trummen, pauken, pfeiffen.
Ich hab umbvarn insel und arn, manig lant
auff scheffen gross, der ich genoss von sturmes pant,
des hoch und nider meres gelider vast berant;
die Swarze Se lert mich ain vass befreiffen,
Do mir zersprach mit ungemach mein wargatin.
ain kauffman was ich, doch genas ich und kam hin,
ich und ain Reuss; in dem gestreuss haubtguet, gewin
das suecht den grund und swam ich zue dem reiffen.

Ain künigin von Arragun was schön und zart,
darür ich kniet zu willen raicht ich ir den part,
mit hendlein weiss pand si darin ain ringlin zart
lieplich und sprach: "non maiplus disligaides."
Von iren handen ward ich in die oren mein
gestochen durch mit ainem messin nädelein,
nach ir gewonhait sloss si mir zwen ring darein,
die trueg ich lang, und nent man si racaides.
Ich suecht ze stunt künig Sigmunt, wo ich in vant.
de mund er spreutzt und macht ain kreutz, do er mich kant;
der rueft mir schier: "du zaigest mir hie disen tant?"
freundtlich mich fragt: "tuen dir die ring nicht laides?"
Weib und auch man mich schauten an mit lachen so;
neun personier künklicher zier die waren do
ze Pärpian, ir pabst von Lun genant Petro,
der römisch künig der zehent, und die von Praides.

Mein tummes leben wolt ich verkeren, das ist war,
und ward ain halber beghart wol zwai ganze jar,
mit andacht was der anvank sicherlichen zwar,
het mir die minn das ende nicht erstöret.
Die weil ich rait und suechet ritterliche spil

und dient zu willen ainer frauen, des ich hil,
die wolt mein nic gcnadcn aincr nussen vil,
pis das ain kutten mainen leib betöret.
Vil manig ding mir do gar ring in handen gieng,
do mich die kappen mit dem lappen umbevieng,
zwar vor und seit nie kain meit so wol verhieng,
die meine wort freuntlich gen ir gehöret.
Mit kurzer snuer die andacht fuer zum gibel auss,
do ich die kutt von mir do schutt in nebel rauss,
seit hat mein leib mit laidvertreib vil mangen strauss
geliten und ist halb main freud erfröret.

Es wär zu lang, solt ich erzelen all mein not.
ja zwinget mich erst ain ausserweltes mündlin rot,
davon mein herz ist wund pis in den pittern tot.
vor ir mein leib hat mangen swaiss berunnen;
Dick rot und plaich hat sich verkert mein angesicht,
wann ich der zarten dieren hab genumen pflicht,
vor zittern, seufzen hab ich oft empfunden nicht
des leibes mein, als ob ich wär verprunnen.
Mit grossem schrick so pin ich dick zwai hundert meil
von ir gerost und nie getrost zu kainer weil;
kelt, regen, sne tet nie so we mit frostes eil,
ich prunne, wenn mich hitzt der lieben sunne.
Won ich ir pei, so ist unfrei mein mitt und mass.
von meiner frauen so muess ich pauen ellende strass
in wilden rat, pis das genad lat iren hass,
und hulff mir die, mein trauren käm zu wunne.

Vier hundert weib und mer an aller manne zal
vand ich ze Nyo, die wonten in der insel smal;
kain schöner pild besachnie mensch in ainem sal:
noch mocht ir kaine disem weib geharmen.
Von der ich trag auff meinem ruck ain swäre hurt,
ach got, west si doch halbe meines laides purt,
mir wär vil dester ringer oft, wie we mir wurt,
und het geding, wie es ir müest erparmen.
Wenn ich in ellend dick mein hend oft winden muess,
mit grossem leiden tuen ich meiden iren gruess,
spat und auch frue mit kainer rue so slaff ich suess,
das klag ich iren zarten, weissen armen.
Ir knaben, mait, bedenkt das lait, die minne pflegen
wie wol mir wart, do mir die zart pot iren segen.
zwar auff mein er, west ich nicht mer ir wider gegen,
des müest mein aug in zähern dick erwarmen.

Ich han gelebt wol vierzig jar leicht minner zwai
mit toben, wüeten, tichten, singen mangerlai;
es wär wol zeit, das ich meins aigen kinds geschrai
elichen hört in ainer wiegen gellen.

So kan ich der vergessen nimmer ewikleich,
die mir hat geben muet auff disem ertereich;
in all der welt kund ich nicht vinden iren gleich.
auch fürcht ich ser elicher weibe pellen.
In urtail, rat vil weiser hat geschätzet mich,
dem ich gevallen han mit schallen liederlich.
ich Wolkenstain leb sicher klain vernünftiklich,
das ich der welt also lang beginn zu hellen.
Und wol bekenn, ich waiss nicht, wenn ich sterben sol,
das mir nicht scheiner volgt wann meiner werche zol.
het ich dann got zu seim gepot gedienet wol,
so vorcht ich klain dort haisser flammen wellen.'

The spectacle, set between heaven and hell, its set[5] that of the *Jesu meine Freude* of '76, but over an area several times larger, wide and open, and flamboyant rather than lyrically contained, the world still delimited by heaven and hell, but a large world, followed the ballad about as closely as did *Masaniello*, deriving its images from it, but selectively.[6] But Schumann

---

5. 'If you missed the Bread and Puppet Theatre's free public performance of *Wolkenstein* in Hartford's Bushnell Park in late September, you missed a rare treat . . .
   At performance time the two booth shaped structures making up the set had been completely assembled. The one to stage right, with a series of beatific heads about two and one-half feet tall, painted white and blue with straight white banners leading from the heads to the bottom of the booth some 15 feet below, represented Heaven; and the other, made with bright red banners, a painted falling figure and some rather unthreatening birds, represented Hell. The set had a direct, handmade and childish look about it.' — (Stearns, *Sharing with Bread and Puppet, Hartford Advocate*, October 11, '78.)
   'Last week, he presented *The Life and Death of Oswald von Wolkenstein* at St. John the Divine, a great space which creates great expectations. The ceiling is so high it almost vanishes into the dark, there is a comically ecumenical jumble of icons . . .
   One walks into medieval excess and splendor: everywhere there are small stages with scenes from the life of the poet Wolkenstein . . .
   On the audience's right is Hell, neatly marked with a crew of red gargoyles playing raucous kazoos and drums. On the left side is Heaven, whose angels take two forms. Below they are comical big-headed, big-assed, bosomy peasant washerwomen with doll babies hanging at their belts. And above is the celestial Word of Mouth chorus (several are from the original Pro Musica, and all are marvelous) who set the emotional tone as much as the puppets do.' — (Munk, *Ciulei's Inspector General and . . . , Village Voice*, October 2, '78.)
6. 'We follow Wolkenstein through his birth (an unlikely and amusing affair complete with announcements from angels who make deals and buzz off with the sound of sirens), his childhood during which he loses his eye in a deal with another angel to get a pair of hands that are small enough to play musical instruments (he is born with huge hands), and on through extensive travels . . . One of the extraordinary moments of the play, pivotal in terms of tone and mood, occurs about two thirds of the way into the action. Having traveled through the world, Wolkenstein encounters the plague, represented by a dancer in a skeleton suit holding a crudely made wooden airplane painted silver. At the side of the stage, the eerie masked figure of fate with a spindle and Wolkenstein's life thread which she spins throughout the play moves in and out of the gathering dusk shadows. A series

left it to the set and the ending to reproduce the ballad's motif, the violent and desperate conflict within the hero between (sexual, not a Minnesinger's fabled pure) love and piety. And set and ending censured this conflict into the vague one of worldliness with redeeming charity, the imaged fable of the spectacle rather one of travels and of the artist's sacrifices for his work.

For Wolkenstein's focal image of the 'out-of-this-world little red mouth that hath wounded my heart unto bitter death' Schumann substituted an image of the plague. In fact, what he had had, starting out work on the play, in mind,[7] was to make rather a different image of Woman a central

---

of donkey puppets pull crude wooden plows guided by farmer puppets with skull like masks, homespun costumes and wearing latticework breast and back plates made of woven bark. They move very slowly in lines across the large space in front of the audience until they surround the figure spinning and the skeleton with the airplane.

As the music that accompanies this number stops, each donkey and farmer lie down slowly and silently until we are left with a field of dead creatures. This hauntingly elegant moment of the play recalls so many earlier Bread and Puppet shows protesting the war: tonight the scene brings the action to a halt, forces a brief look at why we are watching the play, and allows us a moment for thought. Then the bells ring as the heavenly cleanup squad helps the donkeys and farmers into heaven. Wolkenstein, who like so many of us, has passed his life doing whatever he wanted with no regard for the needs of his society, may now find himself without food, because the farmers are all dead.

But, in true puppet show style, he survives into a crotchety old age, is struck by his wife for complaining about his noisy children, and eventually dies. Hedging all bets, Schumann has two Wolkensteins at this point. One soul is bundled up by the heavenly washerwomen in a white cloth and carried off to heaven, while the other soul is placed on a red cloth and taken away to hell by the demons. A giant god/motherearth figure rises in back of the stage and, as it rotates in a dance and benediction, a group of star puppets revolve around it.

Demons and heavenly washerwomen parade off to the rear of the park, and as the audience leaves the park, a huge ship (of fools?) puppet, 40 feet long, and 20 feet tall, with three masts complete with sails, moves slowly along intercepting the crowd and moving out to the park exit. The crowd has suddenly become a part of the action, as huge birds controlled with rods by three operators fly rapidly over our heads.' — (Stearns, *Sharing with Bread and Puppet, Hartford Advocate*, October 11, '78.)

'How his mother damned him with huge awkward hands to prevent his destiny as a lutist; how he bartered one eye for usable hands; how he ran away from home with a penny in his pocket; how he stole his sister-in-law's jewels and the heart of his enemy's daughter. Puppet figures listen wearily to a preacher in a wheelchair rant of pain and retribution (in German), a woman swathed in white stands in a cage with a raven above her.' — (Munk, *Ciulei's Inspector General and . . . , Village Voice*, October 2, '78.)

7. 'I don't think there was much really new in (*Wolkenstein*). The idea was to have a longer line. When I started I wanted the whole thing to take place between heaven and hell, with the final idea being that the man gets divided into both a heavenly and hellish man, and so going off in both directions but the longer line I thought of as being the Washerwoman job, as being the omnipresent feature throughout the performance and then I had to scrap that. It didn't work. So it ended up being only in the prologue to the piece in the very beginning. Then the thing was on one side heaven and another side this little demon stage and in the middle a table — I don't remember if the table was there all the time. I guess it must have been. No, it must have been brought on, or was it there all the time — a giant

element of the play, one relating more closely to Wolkenstein's contrite ideal:

'I've lived now almost forty years, have only two to go,
Have spent them rioting and raging, on poetry, on song.
It's time I heard a child of mine, in wedlock born,
ascreaming in its cradle but . . .

. . .

and also fear a married woman's bark.'

The central image was to be that of his Washerwoman puppets, the image of a robust, cheery and presumably though independent good-hearted (but by no means charming) working woman, the kind – though Schumann did not have this in mind – a poet can use to keep the kids in line and see to it there is a clean shirt in the drawer and supper on the table at supper time. But the simultaneous presence on stage of this figure and of the kind of girl that really shook up the poet would have been disharmonious and lent itself to misinterpretation. In any event, he was not about to be side-tracked by the image of woman as temptress, the eternal Eve, garden of earthly delights, at a time when he was with difficulty changing her image from passive, dutiful sufferer (*Jesu meine Freude, Jephthah, Ave Maris Stella*) to active, tough fighter (*Joan, Washerwoman Ah*). To the extent he concretized Wolkenstein's sinfulness it was by the image of his feasting with the Great while the poor were dying in plague and war: rather as in *Masaniello*, though now in *Wolkenstein* this was only a pecadillo.

Though from within the play radiated an absolute despair which for our benefit the jovial showmaster, Schumann, or for that matter, Wolkenstein himself transmutes into a surface of human foibles, actually – were it not for the kindly and humorous gesture with which they are shown – contemptible weaknesses the play's image of the sinful musician poet was positive, the play was definitely a comedy. And what finally came across as the major point was: the man was an artist: from out of a life of inner and outward miseries, ending in miserable ordinariness, squeezed a jeweled tear of music. A gift of alchemy has been placed in the world so that out of the world's clashes and depravity something like an equivalent of the light that is up above and beyond can be manufactured – a resemblance, a faint hint. Is there redemption in art?

---

table at which Wolkenstein ended up sitting and eating and drinking with the nobles and on which also the battles took place. When these tiny little junk puppets – I wouldn't call any of them very new. The only thing that was *new* was the recital of Wolkenstein's poetry, sort of the weaving of that poetry into the story the way it was – I don't think I had done that before. That was interesting to me, to use poetry like that.' — (Schumann, interview, '83.)

'Well, the doctor told me, Carl,
you don't need no pill,
eeeh, the doctor told me, boy,
you don't need no pill,
just a handful of nickels and a jukebox
will cure your ill.'

(Carl Perkins, *Boppin' the Blues*.)

Heaven in this play is a white place of music, but while the angels are peasant women doing their laundry of Finnegan's winding sheets with big masks of tough cunning above their stocky bodies, the (red) devils with the flaming beaks of carrion-eaters are, of course, he-devils and the hero is the weak man Wolkenstein, the artist. His good fortunes – his share of such – are visualized, an arabesque about the likewise visually presented story at this point, as their – the tough women's – adulation in his perambulations. On the other half of the stage he, the same figure, is being whipped along by the devils. If the making of art is a substitute for salvation (and so it appears to many of us), the consolations of the mothering cunt substitute for the joys of heaven (as many of us also feel). This casuistry is a strong sub-dominant. In the end, Wolkenstein is carried off to hell by the devils, bundled away heavenward by the angels, a grasping conniver, who is, however, proficient on a variety of musical instruments.

Schumann had made a portrait mask for him, with the exception, perhaps, of ones of Nixon and of our quondam secretary of 'defense', MacNamara, the only one he has ever made, though in *Masaniello* there is a likeness of Stalin. The mask, on its underside fashioned into scarcely visible demon heads, signals that the play is about an individual. I would say Schumann saw himself in Wolkenstein and that the play is about himself, an artist torn by inner conflict (and not least the one he censured out of the ballad), perhaps redeemed by his art. The music of that age in those northern latitudes was still popular, the tunes of simple instruments, the speech of the peasant's profligate son raised up slightly into song: the kind of art Schumann has aimed at.[8] An orison funebre for sinful Man, this last of his negative morality plays is also an apologia pro vita suum.

---

8. 'To consider Schumann on the basis of his famous Vietnam works (*Fire, Meat*), with large puppets in the street, is to miss out on the spectrum of his entire repertoire. Bread and Puppet each summer offers a twilight medieval pageant along the hillside of Schumann's Vermont farm. And it is to this sweeping panormaic spectacle, contrasted to the Brechtian political pieces, contrasted to his circus, contrasted to his smaller oriental pieces, that we must look to grasp the scope of his genius.

Schumann is a National Treasure. And ongoing. His last works, *Masaniello* and *Wolkenstein*, focus on popular heroes in a dark vein: Masaniello sells out; Wolkenstein watches the famine and weeps. he has in effect sold out, too. And in the middle of the spectacle is Schumann himself, on a hobbyhorse, smoking a cigar. The work may contain an autobiographical dimension, a development that will have more relevance as time goes on.' — (David Sears, *Big Time Dolls, Other Stages*, March 8, '79.)

17. The Circus of '78.
Christ redivivus.
No other hope.

He has retained the elements of his late summer festival, the sideshows, the circus, a chosen spectacle, the pageant as main event, evening entertainments, with the aioli-buttered bread dispensed all day: a feast and surfeit, nothing charged, his party. A vast crowd arrives, perambulates, sits, gaily red and blue in the green. It is now a local crowd, the New York intellectuals, the out-of-state students, the Vermont students even, in a minority, a crowd of Vermont and Canadian families, with much of the soft, light Canadian French heard. The circus is totally innocuous, a gay succession of humorous ineptnesses: Schumann's dance on high stilts at the end its climax – he is in Uncle Sam overalls, the figure's red-striped legs gigantic. He and the show get a standing ovation at the end. This figure is the only political touch, its humorous patriotism apparently sincere and accepted. The Vietnam war is far in the past. Uncle Fatso makes the rounds with the bearded lady and the upside-down man as one of the circus' 'incredible phenomena' – waving his cigar at the kids. The politics has gone out of this show: the religion is strong. And the religion is not pantheism: it is Christianity.

Ave Maris Stella and *Wolkenstein*, Schumann's two plays for the year, as *Joan of Arc* and *Masaniello* were for the year gone, are his two special offerings at the circus, as those were for his '77 circus. Whereas in *Joan* a political figure, female, to strident sound died for her principles and love of the people, her assumption into the corporate mass of the heavenly host seeming merely a manner of endorsement of such stances taken in life, in *Ave Maris Stella*, the polished voices of an angelic choir rise toward the stars in the Dorian mode, a rule of the angels inexplicably follows, without struggle, ex machina, the anarchic regime of the demons, a woman communes with God, and the mystery of the ingress of some Divine love into Woman unfolds in the pious images of the classes that prepare for first communion. Whereas in *Masaniello* the same figure as in *Joan*, also a political figure, also a fighter for the people, had been shown corrupt in principle and heart, and had been, though with compassion, condemned for it, in *Wolkenstein*, between the battlements of heaven and hell a world stretches, the battlefield of war and errancy on which a man, though his voice is transfigured by art, stumbles in discomfort and pain toward his end. Though the change is not absolute (Wolkenstein sups with the nobles and watches wars as though they were games), it is clear: society as correlate and proving ground for the individual has faded out of the picture, we

445

are directed toward the personal realm, and there to an attendancy on miracles of transcendental grace.

The message seemed the same in Schumann's two minor pieces at this circus, the new *St. Francis Preaches to the Birds* and the old *Dead Man Rises*.

St. Francis was done various places locally just before the circus, e.g. at Burklyn Manor, West Burke,[1] as sideshow again at the '79 and '82 circuses. Eight performances of it, March-April '79 by a Bread and Puppet off-shoot on East 9th Street in New York City were sloppily directed with self indulgent whimsy by Amy Trompetter with Margo Sherman as the sentimental narrator ('who is made into a character, who delivers the text independently from the acting that occurs' — (Schumann, interview, '79)). It takes place in Apt. # . . . in New York City, the sink and other furniture of which, including the refrigerator, are painted on the stage drops. The apartment is successively occupied (scene 1) by an old woman suffering from the cold, the devilish landlord coming and taking away her heat, by (scene 2) an old blind man, whose light he has taken away, and then (scene 3) by a poetic middle-aged couple whose younger member's life Death comes and takes; whereupon (scene 4) the saint of the

---

1. 'The steps and sloping lawn of stately old Burklyn Inn provided seating for the audience, some two or three hundred folk, about half of them children . . .

St. Francis Preaches to the Birds, was performed in a nearby barn. It contains four tiny scenelets set in New York City apartments: A poor elderly woman is deprived of her heat; a lonely old man has his light taken away; an affluent young couple is parted by death; and St. Francis goes through his morning regimen — thanking his teeth as he brushes them, his coffee as he drinks it, his window as he looks through it. The four apartments are ingeniously depicted on recessed backdrops with the scenery or, in one case, a verbal description of the apartment's contents, painted on. St. Francis, who narrates all four scenes, is played by Margo Lee Sherman as an old Hasidic rabbi. The effect is strangely cross-cultural: A male character from Christian legend presented as a male Hasid, played by a woman crowned with medieval-Christian-style halo, and placed in contemporary New York.

St. Francis has a distinct message about affirming and finding joy even in the midst of urban misery, but like much of the Bread and Puppet's work, it is richer as a succession of resonant images than as a moral illustration. When they are analyzed back to their message, the forms seem reduced.

The best of the images are beautiful, expressive, and witty: The fluid poses of the black-and white-dressed couple; the designer-chic air of their apartment, done in black lettering on white walls; the tight, concentered lines and features of the old woman's mask, combining the dignity of African sculpture, a ratlike sneer, and the vulnerability of a lonely old lady; the perfect ease with which the old woman and man sit down on a chair that is painted on the backdrop.

Other elements of the play seem insufficiently worked out — stereotypical heavy labeled 'The Boss', who has a wonderful mask but crudely dull words and gestures, an uninteresting portrayal of the old man's dog by a masked actor on all fours, overlong chanting by the St. Francis character between the scenes.' — (E. Blumenthal, *Affirmations in the Hills, Village Voice*, September 4, '78.)

446

poor wakes up, and after washing his brethren toes and brushing his teeth with his sister the toothbrush spends his day looking out the window, no great help to the old, blind and ill: the birds in color descending from strings come and sing for him till the sun, a paper disk, sets. A sentimental piece of crap, the playlet twisted the pantheist glorification of nature of the preceding three circuses into a recommendation of individual unity with nature by pious contemplation – and identified this piety as variant of Christian God adoration.

Dead Man Rises which I had some ten years earlier seen as a statement about love, identifying it in a not negative but still reductive manner with death, this time struck me, as much by its ascetic form as by the minimalism of its figures' tentatives, as a straight rendition, cleanly – a little tired now, or slightly faded, yellowed – in black and white of Schumann's approach to a personal vision of a minimal personal existence in which purity may be – at least nearly – attained, the purity of conduct dictated directly and exclusively by an emotional life of the soul in harmony with and in response to the elemental exigencies of life – death and cooperation – and with the purity of such a soul. Schumann's own existence is far from – is far above – this minimum: if only by the business of his art. In this play, the lid is on: no transcendentalism – Schumann is doing without the apparatus of the Christian lie. There is no beyond, all resources are immanent. And the requirements of the good life are severe: it is lived at the edge of not being – for instance, without humor. The ideal, however, is not unChristian: that of the early monastic orders: of a life in silent labor, and chaste and poor (die Armut ist ein grosser Glanz von innen): and though the play showed a social act, its ceremony seemed to say that, like for Calvinism, business, social acts are to be performed for the sake of the soul's purity and ipso facto without involvement.

Wolkenstein exuded a strong intimation of a transcendental reality in the nature of a personalized principle of love, compassion and concern, holding implications of this-wordly ideals of peace, humility, devout labor, ideals in absolute conflict with the reality of life in this world, reality of misery, greed, brutality, murder, strife: a combination ironically arranged for bad conscience, guilt and guilt feeling, crass imperfection, duality of conflicting urges, for a life ill-compounded of half-lives – man at his best half angel and half brute. It was a baroque vision of this world as hell not least because of its opening into heaven – an open skylight admitting the light setting off the darknesses of agitating matter, convulsions of death-dealing flesh, defining our evil indubitably, almost: constituting it. Its humor – which was befitting: no one is condemned, all being hopeless – was a cowering, a reduction of the acts of men to small neat colored gestures, so to salvage a bearable view by separating them from their evil, cutting off the extending shades, closing them out. *Dead Man Rises*, without transcendental intimations expressing the same most unhappy state of

447

mind, seemed to tell us that this world's reflection of the other – this world so abominable, really, humor almost seems displaced, in spite of its simplicity almost a mask – is such that the other world's principle – or force? – of love in this one is reflected as promise of the peace of death: wordly compassion a garnering in of the living into this peace, a work in the dark; and so seemed a supplement to *Wolkenstein*'s Christian statement.

The pageant[2] was, roughly speaking, a double feature. Its second half was more or less according to the by now traditional formula of Schumann's: a meeting of the sun goddess, revolving slowly in raiments of white, arrived on a blue and white dragon ship, with a slender half moon pulled from afar by four oxen, their meeting celebrated in the oncoming dusk by a flight of huge white birds, caw-cawing, brought on by runners. Its first half was unrelated: a dream of the adventure of knights. They arrive, stiff and white, square-chested on their spindly stilt legs, each standing for a word that is somewhat arbitrary, twelve of them, led by a squat sergeant major, arranged by his sharp commands into the military formation of a line; their twelve red horses are brought on by their foot boys (who hold small banners undoubtedly corresponding to their masters' wimpled lances) and arrayed into a linear formation opposite their riders:

---

2. 'From far down the field trumpets announce the procession. The fading light picks out the white against the green forest. A troupe of 12 foot tall red soldiers follow the band, and following them 12 horses emerge from the forest, prancing to the beating drums.

From beyond the hill, across the amphitheatre, mad howling precedes the appearance of a line of racing white bodies, who hold high, long banners that whip around them; they race around the stationed soldiers on the field, who mount the white horses.

From the pine forest a trumpet heralds the advent of lurid red suns, led by a crazed demon, dancing on long, long legs; the soldiers about face and maneuver on the field, while the red suns watch from the lip of the amphitheatre. The demon descends, and whirling about a wooden shrine, commands its burning.

While the flames leap, the soldiers leave, the demon disappears. A sudden drum beat signals a procession of skeletons; the first in the line has a luminous bluish white face, held aloft on a long pole, while its bony arms jounce and threaten with the insistent thud of the drum.

Darkness throws the white faces into relief, and the flickering flames give them animation while they descend into the amphitheatre. Then they too disappear, and the field is empty.

From the far end of the field, a white cart drawn by four huge oxen emerges, carrying the medieval singers toward the field. At the crest of the hill opposite, a huge blue and white ship is sailing; the ship touches land and is abandoned by a crowd of white bodies, who swarm down into the field and raise high into the air a huge female face, calm and beautiful; she has two huge hands open, and her arms, long swathes of cloth, are held high above the field, spread open.

The white bodies form two circles around her; they carry white suns that bob with their dance to the woman's silver voice from the ox cart, a glowing white pavilion against the shadows.' — (Nancy English, *Figures on a Landscape. Bread and Puppet Amazes Again*, *Vermont Vanguard Press*, August 29, '78.)

as in a battle, riders and horses confront one another; and when the boys in two outcurving lines lead the horses between their masters' legs, the battle is consummated in the mounting; but at the edge of the now quite dark forest at the top of the bowl, there emerge crimson red musical fantasmagoria, their faces blunt musical horns, overlooking the mounted troop below and a village of reed houses that their leader has set afire beyond the troop of knights, and as the fire flares and consumes itself, the red creatures to the sounds (seeming to issue from their faces) of braying trumpets over the light whisp and tap call of a drum rhythm advance along the upper edge of the bowl and the white knights – there is no encounter[3] – troop off; upon which the procession of arsonist musicians leaves. There is a pause, and then the unrelated marriage of sun and moon takes place.

Abandoning the *White Horse Butcher* theme and imagery, reverting to the image of opposing armies of '74, but now shorn of the battle, no contest, the '78 pageant, an adumbration of the pageants of '79 ff., abandoned not only the resistance of good to evil (absent '75-'77 also), but death and with death resurrection; and substituting the burning of a village for the killing of an animal, abandoned the focus on man's relation to nature peculiar to the *White Horse Butcher* theme. Thus when in the concluding imagery of the pageant the Resurrection Deity arrives – not as in earlier pageants as the initially presented patron-Deity of the event, but as issue of it – and is celebrated – the Christian accents of the Word of Mouth singers (substituted for the earlier pageants' white Angel of Resurrection) tempering her heretofore purely pagan adoration – this celebration seems not of any divine essence of nature, but of a transcendent spiritual principal, an otherworldly goodness relating equally to nature and man: and not evoked as an overriding reality presiding over death and resurrection in nature and in man, but invoked as a hope: pretty much as the merciful mother of god might be. The landscape stretches under the contesting armies merely as an enduring battlefield.

In spite of all the Christian airs and doings, the circus did not to me convey a Christian faith so much as rather a weakening of Schumann's

---

3. 'Instead of a battle there is a two-times approach and the battle is shortened to one lance stroke; that's what it was ... There are other preparations for battle and it looks like them, and all it is is there's a lot of preparation. What it ends up doing is that they kill each other with one stroke of a lance ... These knights kill each other. But since they don't fall, since they're on stilts and they haven't learned yet how to fall from stilts, they are not killed. I guess they are set to flight. That's what it was. And the horses run wild ... There's a demon who does a demon dance ... I think I did that. And some kind of cymbal player with me and that was made into a dance ending up with putting fire to the village. (I: So then the sequence is this very stately preparation for battle?) A battle array, right. (I: A kind of symbolic achievement of it?) And then the result separately afterwards is something that's initiated by a demon and then happens. (I: And in that village, there are no people there?) No.' — (Schumann, interview, '83.)

initial pantheist serenity attendant on settlement on Dopp Farm. Feeling himself, four years later, less securely upborne by nature's promise, perhaps become more accutely aware of the city's — industry's, commerce's — inroads on the countryside and its inhabitants, he no longer had quite the heart for The *White Horse Butcher*'s coupling of just this process of destruction with a 'Nevertheless' in the image of a resurrection affirming the overriding power of natural life. But finding himself equally incapable of a hope-denying circus — resolute negativity being incompatible with the nature of the event — and of in fact abandoning the relative ease of hope, for vestment of a gesture of hope fell back on his old duds, the tatters of the Christian faith, ill-fitting though they might even to himself seem here and there to have become. The circus during this period had been his attempt to substitute a meaningful religious festival for the Christian ones no longer meaningful to men. This presupposed a post-Christian faith. If by '78 he was in process of losing this faith, a reapproach to Christian forms perhaps seemed in order.

That momentarily his circus had lost its meaning for him is suggested also by his attempt to give it a 'theme', that of Wolkenstein, spread through the sideshows; and by the vacuity of this theme. The bicentennial of independence had in '75 and '76 been a valid theme in the sense that he was still pursuing his original idea of selling his critique of the U.S.A. to the masses in the gaudy wrapper of circus, i.e. the American past and present was in fact, the newer, positive message of his pageants aside, what his circus was about: but Wolkenstein the artist stood for nothing that it was crucial to tell people about or that related intrinsically to circus. Similarly, he may have betrayed an unease with puppetry, perhaps a feeling that by his mastery of it it had become too pat, so well-defined in its conventions that it invited a disregard of substance,[4] when he put on his first regular play, i.e. with pre-existing text (by another), with actors and dialogue and without masks.

---

4. Prince Bernard of the Netherlands, one of the Lockheed aircraft company's numbered-Swiss-bank-account agents, in '78 — June 3rd — at the Royal Palace rewarded the Bread and Puppet Theatre's 'contributions to European culture' by a fourth of that year's Erasmus Prize (the other 3/4ths going to the Tandarica puppet theatre (Roumania), the Fratelli Napoli Catania's La Marionettistica Theatre (Sicily) and Yves Joly's Paper Theatre), and only four days later his status was further secured by that year's Obie 'for life-time achievement in the theater' from the *Village Voice*.

'The latter accolade Schumann sees as "slightly ridiculous", because — back in the early 1960s, when Bread and Puppet was a struggling New York City phenomenon — the Voice "gave us such a hard time." Accordingly, perhaps, the gold plaque is resting in the arms of a large, green, slightly stupified-looking puppet in the ranks of the animatedly inanimate occupants of the Puppet Museum.' — (S. Green, *The Free Press*, week of August 12-19, '78.)

Uncle Mel at the *Times* the next year called him a 'National Treasure' and on March 21, '80, the government of Vermont awarded Schumann the gubernatorial Award for Excellence in the Arts.

For, as an incidental offering, its carcass displayed at the Glover Town Hall, Shakespeare's *Othello* was butchered with Margo Sherman as Desdemona still in pursuit of her ambition to make it as an actress,[5] her nervous face altogether chalked, red circles on her cheeks for the bride's coquetry, the quick movements of her small searching eyes clashing with this pseudo-mask, Schumann's, the officiating butcher's, contributions consisting in her makeup and that of the other two principals (Othello in NYC had snakes painted on his face), in the slashes administered to the text, and in the instruction to keep emotion out of its 'delivery'.[7] For Schumann who has no interest in motivation, but only contempt for it, as of no mitigating account in life and as of no interest for attribution or analysis, and in speech sees virtue only in simplicity of true reference, to stage the great playwright glorious above all by his expansion of concentrated motive into vast fortunes of metaphor, luxuriant gardens of grace above those dark roots, and to do so off-handedly and without recourse to his own peculiar power of masking had no meaning other than that of a gesture of contempt.[7] It was a disaster, and one that Schumann, amazing-

---

5. The following summer she was Masha in a production of *The Three Sisters*:

'. . . she allows all the pretentions of her style full rein, and the director seems never to have tried bringing her up short. Her voice sinks with hollow ominousness on random syllables, a strange basso glissando that makes me feel like I've been dropped into a well. She shows erotic interest by staring, letting her mouth fall open, and then blinking furiously. This Masha doesn't care for anyone except herself. When Vershinin says his final good-bye she gives a scream so calculated it is embarrassing to listen to, as if an acquaintance unintentionally revealed a false feeling and the only possible response was to pretend one hadn't noticed.

Chekhov was nothing if not honest. Fakery does him no service; and fakery in this setting is not merely an annoyance, like a mediocre production in a theatre. It is an affront, all the more troubling because cheerfully well-intentioned, compounded of good vibes and bad thinking.' — (Erika Munk, *Far From Moscow, Village Voice*, viii/3/79.)

6. 'But then we have *Othello*, which *is* done with actors, where the actors *do* deliver the text. (Elka: Where there are no puppets or masks at all, it's just actors.) Right. Well – there *are* masks that Margo got on her face, a painted mask that was a face that was painted to the point where it *became* a mask.' — (Schumann, interview, '79.)

'I just wanted to tackle this Shakespeare to see if – I didn't reach out for any special effect or point of view to bring across other than – to see what was so much mass of text, how one could deal with cutting it into – and I just had a great – I felt I could do Shakespeare and anything — I wanted to start a Shakespeare society, a royal Shakespeare society. I didn't think of one (laughing), I thought of five pieces. We do one this week, another next week.' — (Schumann, interview, '83.)

7. 'I've never really seen Shakespeare performed the way I feel it should be performed and I've always walked out very disappointed. The only performance I ever liked was a British high school troupe that came to my high school in Germany and did *The Taming of the Shrew*. Just a bunch of boys that had got together to do this thing. They threw on wigs and played it beautifully.

The stylish modern versions of Shakespeare I've seen over the years or those tries at making Shakespearean Shakespeare, making all kinds of equipment that looks Elizabethan

ly, seeing himself only, as with regard to another classic, *Masaccio*, two years earlier, a St. George fighting the beast of authority, was unaware of. But while it is true that the ways the respective national classics were staged and performed during the 19th and much of the 20th century in England, France or Germany were integral to the respective power systems' self-maintenance, and to a Kultur inimical to art, the only effective utilization of this 'cultural heritage' (a concept guiding communist ministries of culture and Texan oil millionaires) — a heritage in the West comprising also e.g. the Greek classics, whose sideshow productions at his circuses by his children and their friends during the early '80s Schumann has been fond of — is by subversive appropriation, as e.g. in Goya's versions of Velasquez, in Jarry's *Le Roi Ubu*, in Pound's adaptation of *The Women of Troy*, in Richard Foreman's production of *Don Juan*, i.e. by a revivifying expropriation.

Schumann's *Woyzeck* ('81) and *Diagonal Man* ('82) suggest that Schumann's male morality play series at least in part ended with the *Wolkenstein* of '78 in part because though his interest shifted away from individual morality, his interest in individual choice and — especially — lack

---

— I usually walk out. I just don't have the taste for it.

I saw a horrible *Othello* in Germany directed by Peter Zadek. And just the hatred for that work and suggestions from others made me choose to do the play. I love *Othello*. It's a vastly beautiful, incredibly powerful story. Even though it's a tragedy, the whole thing is like a burst of joy — the strength of the characters, the strength of the constant great ideas they have and how they say things. It's so lively, so energetic, so overwhelming.

If we find a way to do Shakespeare, then we will do a lot of plays I think. As we learn more, it will be necessary to do another and then another. With this production, the whole idea of making it in a tiny box with no big space movements — concentrating on the words — that's a real solution to a lot of the problems. The style we are working with is to my mind necessary to present the play in an understandable manner. Fred Neuman will wear a little bit of makeup, but it should be obvious that it isn't a black man, but an actor with something black on his face. I think the only makeup job I'd like to do is on Margo Sherman — white face and Japanese makeup.

If the Royal New York Shakespeare Society instigates a more regular New York performance schedule, I would be very much for it. I would like to have a little permanent company here; it would be good for us (Bread and Puppet) to have a second home, to do more here. We don't want to come with a piece of an hour and a half entertainment and then say bye to our audience. We would rather bring a whole day with as much contrast as possible — tragedies and comedies, pageantry and little Punch-and-Judy things, all included and made into one piece. That more our style and what we can give to people.' — 'William Harris, *OffandOn, Soho Weekly News*, January 18, '79.)

He put on his *Othello* in NYC, January 23-February 4, '79, with two excellent actors, Fred Neumann of the Mabou Mines as Othello and George Bartenieff as Iago at Crystal Field's Theater for the New City. It was no better. The next year he did *Lear* as sideshow in the circus, in the pine forest:

'It was my idea but it was a total farce. It just was these cardboard figures that move an arm (jointed cutouts, a new type of puppet (SSB)). It was called *Shakespeare in the Pasture* and was done on a tiny little stage and was a big run through of the plot. There's very few lines left in it.' — (Schumann, interview, '83.)

of choice – remained intense. His attempt to stage *Othello* may have been neither just manifestation of an imperial ambition to invade legitimate theater, nor an onslaught on bourgeois Kultur, but signal of a new interest in portraying individuals – expecially male individuals: as social creatures moved by character, imprisoned in character, not just as moral agents – and not free; but that at first he did not see how he could do it with masks and puppets. Finding the moral viewpoint on individuals – e.g. Wolkenstein, or: himself – deficient, he turned, as if to show its deficiency, to the 'character is fate' viewpoint (as regards man: as regards women, cf. the *Washerwoman Cantatas*, rather to the viewpoint of 'biology is fate'). He could have found nobody better than Shakespeare to try to make this apology with.

Part VII.
1979-83. The later Dopp Farm period,
or The Age of Murder.

Working with a highly skilled team of corporate employees. Production for a community festival that has become an institution. Stuck with an institution, a constituency and a production routine no longer in accord with the state of his mind, viz. horror and desperation. Ostensible form of communication: leading a congregation's prayer (that the worst may be avoided), voicing its hope (for deliverance from evil by spiritual regeneration). Actual form of communication: the prophet's warning to the people (that evil reigns and the end is near).

> 'Aber weh! es wandelt in Nacht, es wohnt, wie im Orkus,
> Ohne Göttliches unser Geschlecht. Ans eigene Treiben
> Sind sie geschmiedet allein, und sich in der tosenden Werkstatt
> Höret jeglicher nur, und viel arbeiten die Wilden
> Mit gewaltigem Arm, rastlos, doch immer und immer
> Unfruchtbar, wie die Furien, bleibt die Mühe der Armen.'

(F. Hölderlin, Der Archipelagus.)

Contents: Part VII

Part VII. 1979-'83. The later Dopp Farm period, or The Age of Murder.

1. The nature of his work during this period.

I would say that Schumann in – by – '78 incurred a loss of faith: that his perception of civilization and human nature shifted in such a way that its theatrical representation could no longer adequately or to his satisfaction be given the forms he had evolved since '78, the forms of the circus pageant, of the circus morality plays, and of the circus as a unitary whole ('silly circus' had already lost its meaning for him earlier, when he purged it of its social criticism to accomodate it to the circus as a whole). This shift was not to aspects of civilization and human nature that he had not attributed to them before, but a shift of focus and emphasis and in his estimation of capacities. Basically it was perhaps due to a weakening of the will to believe, to a growth of worry. But it amounted to a loss of faith: a loss of faith in men's capacity for being to any extent that would make much of a difference and regardless of inspiration provided them guided by morality; and a loss of faith in the regenerative power of living nature to withstand or make up for the destructive effects of civilization, and of modern civilization in particular, imposing the alienation of man from man and of man from nature and the technological, commercial and bureaucratic dynamism of the Big City on the world and on all of life. I have no direct evidence for this hypothesis. I advance it to account for the change in his work discernible in spite of the inertially persisting masking effects due to the demands of institutionalized production and performance set-ups) from the 'Initial Dopp Farm Period' to his later time at Dopp Farm. I don't, for instance, know of any important political or personal events that could have occasioned the change. We can correlate the two changes of perception and losses of faith, though I don't know how pertinent to what actually went on inside him the correlation is. In terms of morality: men are too base (weak willed, appetitive, fearful) when in subordinate positions to oppose the destructive tendencies of their civilization (or to follow the inspiration of leaders encouraging resistance), or when in dominant positions not to reenforce them. In terms of 'civilization': the modeling force of culture on the individual is too great to expect much resistance to its destructive tendencies from men. In a sense this was a return to the pessimism of his youth, but with the terms elaborated.

In some way, the change in his outlook must have related to his children's growing up. The youngest, in '78, were approaching the end of high school, the oldest had, I believe, started college, some (on scholarships) were away at prep school and spent summers away from the house. The family, and it very much as reproductive unit, had been the anchor of his existence. Time was pushing him and Elka out of the 'regenerative cycle of living nature'. The children were starting their own lives and were with

459

their friends defining themselves: presenting him with worry about their lives in the larger world and with their emergent independent worries, concerns and perceptions. The prospect of an empty house (with, to be sure, a wont companion, Elka, and with summer visits from these new people, his children) was presenting itself. All five (cf. infra) of his new theatrical concerns seem to relate directly to this change in his life: at least two of them, the atom bomb and terror, were directly presented to him by his children, and a third, the individual as person, was forced on him by their new powers and by his new relationship to them. I would say that this change in his life on a personal level had the influence on his work that at the beginning of his Goddard period his irruption into a love life, and at the inception of his 'Initial Dopp Farm Period' the death of his father had had on him.

Schumann's chief new subject matters during this recent period have been the atom bomb (the threat of nuclear warfare: which he views as threat of an extinction of man and may even view as threat of an extinction of life) (*Washerwoman – Ah, The Story of One, Insurrection Oratorio*), the world food crisis (which he views as due to an imposition of American 'progressive' agricultural technology and of American economic interests on the 'underdeveloped' countries, and as a threat to ways of life essential to mankind's spiritual regeneration) (*Cambodia, Histoire du Pain*), terror (terrifiedness, whether due to terrorism or an intensification of the fears natural to powerlessness, as e.g. that of children, as well as the exercise of terror, terrorism, whether the political terror exercised by governments or the terror exercised by nations against one another, notably: by the threat of nuclear war) (*Cambodia, Goya, Venus, Washerwoman Nativity*), children (their capacity for being terrified, their capacity for coping with terror, their resistance to socialization and to the evil aspects of modern civilization) (*Washerwoman Ah, The Story of One, Thunderstorm*),[1] and the individual (no longer in the perspective of the opposition of a good female to a bad male principle, nor in the moralistic perspective of the preceding period, but as person, and in particular as a person exposed to society's pressure for assuming a culture-defined role, and as apt to either give in to that pressure or break under it) (*Woyzeck, Diagonal Man, Othello*). The nexus between these concerns seems to me the one I have indicated: they are the probes of one whose attention has shifted from the regenerative powers of nature to the destructive powers of civilization and who has pretty much come to feel that men are too weak (base) to resist these, or

---

1. While from the mid-'60s onward, up to and including *Ave Maris Stella* ('77), the victims of violence in his art had been women, though often women with children (i.e. women as childbearers); the children, like as not, if they were male, future killers; he now, as of both of the two *Washerwoman Cantatas* of '79, came to think of the victims as children – the continuance of the race's life cycle seemed in danger.

not to promote them when it is in their power and interest to do so: regardless of the horror — and even finality — of the consequences.

The attitude conveyed by the theatrical presentations of these concerns is one of worry — unease and apprehension. Their common theme is danger: their topic threat and fear. With few exceptions (*Washerwoman Ah, Diagonal Man*) they are explicitly horror shows, and in the two exceptions the 'something horrible' presented — the world of terror haunting the child in *Ah*, the imposition in the 'hell' of the city of a rigid social mask on the individual in *Diagonal Man* — is prevented from becoming the topic and focus of the play only by the application of a mechanical upbeat formula.

He has retained the format of his pageants, his morality plays and of the circus as a whole. He had too much invested in them to do otherwise, and besides one always needs time to work through new positions and/or to find new forms appropriate for their communication. It had taken him four years to attain affirmative conceptualizations going beyond denial of the '60s and/or to find a form of communication adequate to them. It is easy for a critic and intellectual to talk about changes of viewpoint. But an artist's ideas are fused with his medium and his work, and time and work are needed to arrive not only at new forms but at a mode of presence of new ideas within himself in which they can generate new forms. So for a while the changed viewpoint expresses itself merely by sophistications and corrosions of form, by the mechanical application of formulae, and by vacuity and ambiguity: characteristics of his work during this period.

Having lost faith in the healing powers of nature, he ruined his pageants by unbalancing and disrupting their delicate balance and flow between a near, fixed and artificially shaped and demarcated arena and the indefinitely extending sinuous lines of the landscape. He no longer brought nature *into* the show. He progressively increased the heaviness of the static foreground scene in which you saw man acting on man (notably males on women, murdering them and children) rather than interacting with nature, specifically: in which you saw businessmen and salesmen selling country people on television and the atom bomb and doing away with them and with themselves. A mechanical application of formula provided for concluding resurrections now unrelating to what you had seen. Interestingly, having (in 1980) unwillingly, for money's sake, to do an indoors i.e. pageant-less circus abroad instead of the old thing on the farm, and having to do it under extremely unpleasant circumstances at that, he came up with a show ('*Histoire du Pain*') and with puppets (representing individual people) that stimulated and served him for the next several years, and that probably were, at least in some ways of the form that the new content (in this case the world food crisis) called for.

Having with *Wolkenstein* and *Ave Maris Stella* in '78 done with the moralistic and male principle/female principle approach to the individual,

461

he used the formats of the 'positive' and 'negative' morality plays of the preceding period – adapted, respectively, to two different nature frames: an enveloping forest in a clearing open to the stars, a daytime meadow at the dark forest's edge – for presentations of his new concerns and outlook. But whereas previously the warmth of the containing forest and the openness above had corresponded to and reenforced the 'small' circus plays' picture of woman – small parcel of infinite love – and the forest-limned openness of the meadow had corresponded to and reenforced the 'big' ones' sprawling and peripatetic image of the male – torn and enterprising, confronted by choice between right and wrong – and both the openness and the containment had come across as, in their mutual complementations, something positive and cheering, good for the principle-embodying moral agents the plays were about, in the staging of the horror shows of his last period, the tight containment of 'small' shows (*Washerwoman Ah, Venus, Goya, Thunderstorm, The Story of One*) have given them a claustrophobic quality, and the unlimitedness of larger shows (*Washerwoman Nativity, Histoire du Pain* (?)) a feeling of agoraphobia: limit and space from being opportunities have turned into dangers. And when these later shows were done in the nature settings of the circus, that it was nature that enclosed or opened up was quite irrelevant to their effect, for the universe they were about was no longer structured by the opposition of inward moral choice to the wide world of action, but by that of individual and society. They were essentially placed not in our shared natural world, but in the limbo of alienation, unique to each individual.

The framework of 'circus' has been alien to these plays and they have exploded it. The definition given the circuses by their pageants has been changed from that of a congregational hallelujah to that of a congregational prayer in distress. Those more recent plays, indications of danger and expressions of fear, would, it might be thought, fit into supplications for succour. But the 'prayer in distress' formula though the one indicated by the recent pageants, does not work for the circus as a whole: the circus constituency, the congregation, is not ready for it, the prayer is not theirs and they will not join in it; the 'silly circus' conflicts with it; and Schumann, even in pageants, is not ready – or is afraid – to go all the way with it: he can't abandon his uplift formula. The plays are the outcries of the prophet not listened to, and even if he were listened to – the Jerusalemites rushing to the temple to wail with the prophet – the circus would have to be radically other. So what actually seems to have happened is that Schumann has become disinterested in circus and has turned to a formal development of his medium in directions away from circus.

This development has taken three forms: development of a sophisticated mode of puppetry on the one hand adapted to his new concerns and outlook, on the other (cf. infra my discussion of *Goya* and *Venus*) tending to disrupt form, diminish impact; approaches to traditional theatre (actors, dialogue, individual heroes, interaction of individuals) (*Othello, Woyzeck, Diagonal Man*); emergence of operatic form (music – by Schumann – as primary element) (*Insurrection Oratorio, The End Falls Before the Beginning*). I have here presented these trends as adaptations to changed concerns and a changed outlook. But they may also be seen as expression of a disinterest, because of that outlook, in communication. What use?

Schumann produced a number of extraordinary – splendid – shows during this period, notably *Goya, Woyzeck, Cambodia, Washerwoman Nativity*. They further developed – and demonstrated the theatrical potentials of – the theatrical medium he has invented, the power of his puppets to represent man's social condition.

2. Recrudescence of political agitation in '79 or '80.

I know of no shows of Schumann's '74-'78 that could in any narrow sense be construed as 'political agitation'. In a lax sense, the political satire of his '75 and '76 'silly circuses' could be construed as such, but it disappeared '77, '78. Only in a very very wide sense could his pageants during this period be construed as political agitation: deploring the war of modern civilization on nature.

There is a reference in the Bread and Puppet files to a Washington D.C. Bread and Puppet 'peace parade' in October '76, and in '77 they had put on (cf. supra) an indoors 'Vietnam pageant' celebrating the admission of Vietnam to the U.N. But it is my impression that after not much political street agitation by the Bread and Puppet Theatre, whether in the small towns of northern Vermont or elsewhere '74-'77, there was a resumption '79 or '80. The only instance I have come across for '78 had the '78 circus' apolitical and religious flavor. Schumann with a flock of white birds on bamboo poles (Vecsey, *U.N. Rally by 2000 Backs Disarmament. After March from Church, Clergy and Laymen of Many Faiths Call for Slowdown of Arms Race, New York Times*, May 27, '78.) on May 26 led a march across Manhattan on 42nd Street, from the church of St. Paul the Apostle, where an Islamic call to prayer and blessings from a Dakota Indian had been followed by readings by a rabbi and a swami, to the U.N. The demonstration, sponsored by Mobilization for Survival, was attended by two jetloads of Japanese carrying seventeen million signatures against nuclear weapons.

'Today, at 1 p.m., the group will continue its religious-oriented program outside the U.N. For the remainder of the body's session it will hold secular programs at the Ploughshare Coffeehouse at 777 U.N. Plaza.'   (Vecsey, loc. cit.)

His return to political agitation was signalled by his inclusion of Grace Paley's anti-nuclear war statement in *Washerwoman – Ah!* in '79 (cf. infra), but political agitation seems to have become a major component of his output only in '80, the year his play *This Is* on the Cuban missile crisis of '62 was published and in various reduced adaptations performed (cf. infra). It apparently, in '80 and following, only exceptionally took the form of street agitation, open air marches or shows in public places, typically rather that of skits on specific political topics, notably the threat posed by nuclear armament, though a variety of other specific issues as well, performed indoors – perhaps mostly at colleges, but I wouldn't be sure about that.

At the beginning of February 1980, while doing a show for relief to Cambodia, he appeared in an anti-draft demonstration in the vicinity of

464

Columbia University, where he was rehearsing the NYU students in that show's cast, 'with Uncle Fatso and some signs. It was invented for the moment because that demonstration went on and they wanted...' (Schumann, interview, '83.) Sometime in '80 also, apparently (Schumann, interview, December '82), he did a political clown skit, *Vermont Powerline Show*, in various localities in Vermont – 'there's a big, giant power line that's supposed to come down from Canada through Vermont, and we did a show about that when that came up in the newspaper.' (Schumann, interview, December '82.)

The annual Bread and Puppet accounts submitted to Bread and Puppet board of directors meetings as 'Political demonstrations' among the productions of 1981 list a New London Trident Demonstration, a NYC El Salvador parade, a NYC *Chile*, and three to four repeats of the *Vermont Powerline Show*.

In the spring of '81, they put on a show about the El Salvador civil war, called *Goya*:

'based on the story of a guerilla fighter who called himself Goya after his family was killed. He used to be a government soldier, then after all his family was killed by government troops – and tortured to death, and stuff like that – he changed his name, and one doesn't know what his real name is but he called himself Goya. And he became a guerilla leader – one of the most important ones in El Salvador. It was made when that article appeared in *The New York Times* about it ... and performed locally on various occasions. Also performed on tour sometimes as a side show or prologue.' (Schumann, interview, December '82.)

And sometime in '81 also,

'... a French skit, *Deux Villages*, that we worked out in a workshop last year. I went and did a workshop with various pieces with them, with these people, and at the University of Quebec. Two workshops at that workshop we worked a few sketches with white clowns and one of them was successful. It was called *Deux Villages*. It was very nice. In this case we had two white clowns with detachable arms. Their own arms were hidden inside the blouse and then we had built two stuffed arms that acted as their real arms. And in the process of the skit they had to pay for their equipment that they got with their arms. So they lost their arms.' (Schumann, interview, December '82.)

In addition (cf. my account of the '81 circus) there were in '81 two antinuclear armament shows: *The Ploughshare Eight, Seven Obsessions with the End of the World*.

In '82, there was another political clown skit, 'about what was it called, this kind of emergency shelter operation of the earth? Relocation. About relocation.' (Schumann, interview, December '82.)

'The original impetus behind the formation of Performing Artists for Nuclear Disarmament (PAND) was the vision of a performance caravan bringing the antinuclear message into communities, using theater to educate and enlighten. This

465

spring, that vision becomes a reality as PAND's Performance Caravan for Nuclear Disarmament tours New York State, Vermont and Massachusetts from April 20 to May 15.

The 63 performers who will be touring include: Mabou Mines, performing its acclaimed *Dead End Kids*; The Talking Band in *Soft Targets*; Bread & Puppet Theater, offering parades as well as performances of *The Story of One Who Set Out to Study Fear*; the cast of Emily Mann's Obie-winning *Still Life*; the Caravan Dancers, with a repertory of eight works, all having political themes; Paul Zaloom and Rebecca Wells, each of whom will present solo pieces which deal cleverly and thoughtfully with timely political issues.

The caravan is the result of a cooperative effort between PAND and a wide range of community groups in each of the host cities. Producer Charles Tarzian cites the sympathetic and enthusiastic response he encountered on visits to upstate New York (Albany, Syracuse, Ithaca, Rochester and Schenectady are among the more than 20 places where the Caravan groups will appear). He brought together activist groups, arts councils, and presenting organizations; and observed the galvanizing effect which the cooperative effort had on the communities. Many performances will take place in theaters on college campuses, but Tarzian has also arranged for *Still Life* to be performed in state prisons in Attica and Elmira, and Bread & Puppet will go to two Indian reservations.

In addition to performing in theaters, the Caravan will also bring puppet shows, films, lectures, workshops and discussions on disarmament and related issues into communities. "We're doing this because we feel it's important to capture people's imagination," Tarzian remarks. He expresses PAND's hope that this novel form of 'portable festival' will serve as a prototype for other activist groups around the country.

On Tuesday, April 12th, just before the Caravan sets off on tour, New York City will get a chance to preview highlights of the venture at Martin Luther King, Jr. High School, 65th Street and Amsterdam Avenue, at 7:30 p.m. Ossie Davis, Ruby Dee, and Grace Paley will host the evening – which is a joint benefit for PAND and the War Resisters League. For information, call 431-7921.' (*Other Stages*, IV/7/83.)

'. . . The Bread and Puppet stages parades and performed their great outdoor circus everywere they went.

The Caravan toured 20 cities and small towns, playing to public schools, universities, churches, prisons, and even the Onondaga Nation. Wherever they went, they made not only theater news but "real" news, with front page stories, welcoming editorials in major papers, and coverage by all three local network affiliates in each city. Audiences were overwhelmingly favorable.'
(Elinor Fuchs, *Playing with Fire, Village Voice*, June 7, '83.)

3. A new style of puppetry, emerging in '77, established in '80, '81: artistic alienation of the means and of the work-process of puppetry. Sophistication. Decadence?

Starting in '77, Schumann got into two new forms of puppetry, the general character of both of which can perhaps be indicated by 'artistic alienation' and 'play with the medium'.

By 'artistic alienation', I mean an in the end not de-illusioning exposure of artistic means of work, one in which they appear as artistic elements and are as such integrated into the work of art. Alienation as aesthetic rather than as didactic device.

In general, when an artist or a school of art starts using perfected devices in ways that show them up as devices, but do so in a manner creating special artistic effects, not just content to let technique show, as a master sometimes might, but getting special values from this, reintegrating the exposure of how it's done into the medium, in the manner of a kidding magician letting the audience in on a trick but not divulging others so that the audience with a shock belatedly realizes there is still a residual impossibility, the magician thus, after all, maintaining the illusion in a partial or seeming destruction of it — when this becomes form, we are apt to think of decadence. Thus the conspicuousness of the highlights in the work of certain masters of painting created a magic of light illuminating a candle or betraying an invisible source of light, and the late masters of polyphony drew affect from exposures of the mathematics of thematic variation.

The first way he did this was by an exposure of the means of puppetry, masks and puppet half-shells[1] He put them into evidence not as the faces or bodies of operators behind or inside them, but they were placed or moved so that they appeared on their own: as masks or puppet shells rather than as faces or bodies. But they were held or moved in some formal manner, so that in spite of their detachment they made some artistic and, generally, semantic contribution to the show. We might, with slight exaggeration, speak of this as a 'dance of objects'.

The second way involved an exposure of the work of puppetry.

---

1. Half-shell puppets: a new type of puppet made during this period: concave, one-piece celastic shells representing the front of the head, trunk and upper legs of a figure, with, sometimes, hands and arms worked into face or trunk. They were generally hand-held in front of them by the performers.

'... for big bodies. They're just easy to build, you know. You put the clay down, you model it, you pick it up, you take off the dry form, and you make the next one, right away, on it. So it's a very fast way of making big things.' — (Schumann, interview, December '82.)

Puppets were held, handled or moved in a way focusing attention on this activity, but the so exposed work process had been so designed that it appeared not as such but as artistic and, again, typically, also semantic, element of the show. The operations and operators and the operated-on had been fashioned to appear as components of artistic (and, typically, semantic) compositions. The work process appeared as constituent of such compositions. We might term this a 'pictorial integration' (and, typically, a 'semantic integration') of the work process.

The first of these forms may be thought of as having for its antecedent Schumann's use, throughout the years, of giant puppets as effigies, put on display more as statues than as puppets, their operators reduced to carriers or stationers. And he on occasion had used masks as independent objects also, e.g. the Godhead mask, hung on the back of a parader, or positioned somewhere by itself and covered and uncovered. But he now began to move them; in movements that could not be seen as the movements of a face or body; dances of masks or puppets qua objects.

The second of these forms, artistic work-process alienation, had non-artistic-de-illusioning-work-process alienation for an antecedent in his work.

From way back, Schumann not only had not minded the puppeteers and their mask- and puppet-handling or operating activities being visible and in evidence, but appreciated this – e.g. the outside operators of his giant puppets – and deliberately included work process as such as theatrical (though not as semantic) element. But what he got into now was different. He began to use as artistic and semantic element holding, handling and moving of masks and puppets that was not work-process at all: not even artistically or semantically considered and fashioned work-process; or else that in addition to being plain puppeteering, i.e. holding or moving a puppet and making it do things, clearly had been chosen or fashioned also for formal or pictorial aspects, or for meaning it added to the show.

The technical devices for this transcendence of the medium have included: hand-held masks, hand-held puppet shells, the manipulation of dummies, dummies tied onto performers, the untying on-stage of dummies tied to performers, either by themselves or by unmasked (and not role-performing) other puppeteers, the handling of dummies, of other puppets or of masked performers by hooded puppeteers of a Bunraku type, but with roles (e.g. war demons, torturers), such handling either direct manipulation or operation of a string or rope, masks over masks and their removal, puppets whose inside operators are masked and intermittently step away from the puppet, assuming a role, the use of cutouts or pictures as though they were masks or puppet shells. Dummies are central to this: their operation in such a way that the operator has if not a semantic (role) then at least an artistic-pictorial-function – as when a crawling unmasked operator by hand moves a partly string-operated dummy's feet in a walk, or – duplication of an image – guides the gestures of a dummy tied to his or her front, occasionally perhaps substituting gestures of his or her own for the dummy's.

The theatrical effect of these techniques may arise from a focus of the spectator's on the mask, puppet shell, dummy, cutout or picture used or from a focus on its user, the operator. But it will in either case depend on the spectator's awareness of both as distinct from one another. The point of the technique is not fissure of illusion, however (as it was when puppeteering activity as work-process was made part of the image), but a theatrical use of mask or puppets, or of a holding, handling or moving of them, or of both: independent of illusion. The theatrical effect generally is a complication of the image: the dance or pictorial effects are on the verge of self-destruction.

The movement of detached masks (up to '83) generally was used to create the effect of fear (terror) and to intimate the disappearance of the individual in fearful crowds in societies subject to terror. The manipulation of figures by others tended (though it did not invariably, cf. *Venus*) to convey the terrible intimacy between terrorizers and victims.

He started to develop this kind of puppetry in '77, with the fifth tableau (scene 6, 'You are in prison in 1430') of *Joan*, Joan in ropes struggling against three grey hooded figures holding here, and a black hooded figure, seated, withdrawing from her a pitcher it holds on a string, and with, in *Masaniello*, Masaniello's 4th Day ('Masaniello is a sinner'), Masaniello on his guardian angel's rope, with Death's wheel turning over him, working his way across the stage, with the dance of the People masks on his 11th Day (Masaniello mad), with that angel's in much of the play having the hero on a rope and the hero's actions relative to this, and with Mary's, in *Ave Maris Stella*, exhausted on her flight to Egypt being dragged by her angel by a rope around her ankle.

At this point, in '77, there is hardly as yet reason to speak of a new kind of puppetry. Though the image of Masaniello's walk to Golgatha on his 4th day derived its power from a mad disconcatenation of its pictorial elements that had its like in no previous production of Schumann's I know of, the manipulation of roped figures hardly goes beyond the dragging of manacled prisoners in his parades of the '60s and in his early circuses except by its theatrical elaboration, and the chorus movement of People masks in *Masaniello* appears as an isolated invention only.

But when the devices reappear (I don't recall them in the '78 *Wolkenstein*) in *Washerwoman Nativity* in '79 – Schumann as the Spirit of the Time of Herod intimidating the People in one scene, arranging the mothers in attitudes of grief when he slaughters the Innocents in another – one gets the impression that Schumann now consciously employs them as form. And in '80, though the manipulation of the Famished in the 12th scene of *Cambodia* goes beyond any previous use of cutouts of his by the deliberate use of the physical quality of cutouts to create a theatrical effect, that of feebleness and abandonment, when taken in isolation would not merit the appellation of 'new form', the '80 *Venus*, dominated by the intimate manipulation of the birth-giving and rising Venus in the first and of the descending Venus in the final scene, is altogether in the new form, not just because of the visible operator on the upper stage level and the animating interventions (e.g. in the 3rd scene) of a curtain-operating frame figure, but because the handling of the puppets throughout is such a dramatic part of the action. Its effect is that of an interaction: the operators seem lovingly concerned with the figure represented by the puppet. (Compare this with the 'construction of Jesus' in the '69 *Cry*: the performers there acted personally concerned, but we still saw only the work-process as such.) And similarly for the manipulation of jointed cutouts in *Cambodia* ('80) – apparently preceded by similar use – I didn't see this show – of such cutouts in *Shakespeare in the Pasture* (*King Lear*) at the '79 circus. The impression of a new form is even stronger in the '81 *Goya* and *Woyzeck*. The handling of the eight victims by their torturer/executioners in *Goya*, images of involvement, make up the show, it is *the* action. The play is technically dominated by dummy-manipulation at which the group by this time has become skilled. The dummies are emphatically dummies, yet also convincing figures in the play, their handlers manifestly dummy-handlers yet like them have roles in the play – both come to life 'on the level of' the play, and the handling is the major part of the play. And similarly in *Woyzeck*, though here the operators, notably Leber operating the heroine, are not parties with other roles than those of the dummies they handle, but their dummies' alter egos, and are unmasked, rather than, as in *Goya*, hooded. In the '81 circus pageant, *The Fight Against the End of the World*, and again in the Prologue (*The Tragedy of Ineffectual Man*) to the '82 *Diagonal Man*, Schumann uses the half-shell puppets, 'masking puppets', we might call them, in *Fight* fashioned after the Condemned in Michelangelo's *Last Judgment*, in *Tragedy* pregnant women with clinging babies built onto them. The 'Condemned' shells are defecated by a Hell Monster – thrown out of the rear door of a bus – and reappear, held by two three-tier (kneeling, crouching, standing) male and female choruses, moved from side to side (the women), up and down (the men) to the singing. The Pregnant Woman shells were moved up and down and tilted by a group of massed operators, and finally bobbed out held horizontally. Above and behind them a puppet made of two of these shells was suspended from a string. This double woman is lowered when the others leave and, two unmasked operators untying her two halves, gives birth to a dummy beast, dropping out of her, which is held and then operated by the two operators. (The ensuing scene of this beast, and then of a male dummy puppet that in the course of a struggle of the beast with its operators emerges from it, with the two closely attentive operators is also of the new sort. The operators

470

relate to these puppets as Robert Anton does to his. This was a complete novum in Schumann's theatre, first appearing in the opening scene of *Venus*. The operators' attention to the beast and man, as though they were not puppets but real, restores to these puppets the illusionistic roles in the play that their ostentatious treatment as dummies has endangered. The tableau offered us comprises (1) dummy operators, (2) a dummy, (3) a figure represented by the dummy, present to us even though the dummy qua dummy is also, (4) figures represented by the dummy operators relating to this figure. The half-shell puppets like the People masks show Schumann adapting his puppet making to the new performance style, as do, in *Diagonal Man*, the Demon dancers — dance of two large hand-held masks.

The hand-held Individuals-in-the-Big-City masks (made in '80) used in the telephone directory scene of *Diagonal Man*, like the mad Masaniello's People mask in *Masaniello* tilted at various odd angles, inclinations that a human head could never assume, the investment of job-applicants, in a later scene of this play, with head masks appropriate to their jobs, the masks before their entrance brought in and suspended in the fly-space, then lowered onto their heads, and in still another scene, the death of a Salesman, for which a dummy Salesman of identical appearance is dexterously substituted for a masked performer that up to then has been playing him, his death taking the form of his operator forcing the dummy down on the floor in a struggle, are still other examples of the new style. We see the puppeteers *playing* with masks and puppets.

Apart from the dummies and semi-marionettes and the hand-held masks and puppet shells used in his latter day sophisticated puppetry, the salient feature of his more recent mask and puppet making has been the emergence of masks and costumes, generally colorful and satiric (but not grossly caricatural), representing Individual Persons, not as embodiments or emblems of moral principles and forces, good and evil, nor as typifications of sexual or social types of agents of Good and Evil, Man, Woman, The People, but as particular people or as sexual or social types of agents in the struggle between the individual and society, the individual's struggle for individuation. The mask for Emilia in the '71 *Emilia* may have been his first approach to such a mask, but the more direct taking-off point for this line — because the Garbagemen masks of the '70s represented a type more than individuals and the Washerwoman mask of '78 and following was an idealizing abstraction — was, I suspect, the portrait mask for Wolkenstein of '78. He turned out a slew of these individual-person masks for his *Histoire Du Pain* ('80) and used them in his *Woyzeck* asnd *Diagonal Man* ('81, '82). The Salesman, that in his '81 pageant as commercial/bureaucratic agents of Civilization, replaced the capitalists ('Butcher') of his earlier pageants, also represent a move in this direction: like Doctor, Killer and Cop in *Diagonal Man* they appear more as de-individuated agents in

471

the society-individual than, as the Butchers, as non-individual agents in the good-evil struggle.

The first 'Washerwoman' face masks and costumes were made for the '78 *Wolkenstein*. Additional ones were made in the fall of '78 and the spring of '79 for the *Washerwoman Cantatas* of the summer of '79, as well as four giant centerpole 'Washerwomen':

'Then a group of four giant puppets were built with patchwork fabric, but otherwise pretty much like the other puppets ... for a Washerwoman. Only that the heads were built a little smarter, in that the *backs* of the heads are a wired network construction that can be taken off the face, so that the *packing* is easier of these big things. They fit into boxes. There is nothing much new about those puppets.'

(Schumann, interview, '79.)

The Washerwomen were of a new type physiognomically: they smile! and though like the Garbagemen, whose female counterparts they are, they are 'ordinary people' types, realistically reproduced, they at the same time unlike the Garbagemen, represent an ideal, the tough, free, cheery and goodhearted working class woman, active, not a sufferer. Neither their faces nor the whole puppets are interesting, however. They have no charm. They are stylistically quite different from the 'Garbagemen': brightly colored, positively jolly figures, pretty, one could almost say 'cute'. Having, like Elka, but also like many people where Schumann comes from, a Slavic cast of countenance, they are not individuated facially, but are insipidly anodyne idealizations. The many modestly gay colors of their aprons and crazy-quilt dresses, and the brighter and simpler colors of the faces themselves – inspired (Schumann, interview, '79) by the illustrations of colored Normandy sculptures in a book he came across – don't work on stage. The big – 18 ft. tall – Washerwoman puppets in fact are dull. I attribute this to Schumann's inability to arrive at any conception of the type where it would embody an essence or dimension of life that he was interested in. The giant colorful and elaborately costumed Queen and Duke and General puppets in *Masaniello* worked fine.

('Elka: You were looking a lot at this book of French sculpture from Normandy at the time that you were working on these heads.) Stone sculpture – it was beautiful. Big masses of stone – groups. (Elka: And that style is noticeable in these puppets, isn't it? Simple – harmonious.) The Normandy stone faces, rustic and thoughtful – some look older – what I was really looking for was very *bright* colors, pinks and reds and blues, and –'

(Schumann, interview, '79.)

Ephraim (Schumann, interview, '79), with Elka and Schumann agreeing, points out that:

'... the puppets in *Ah* were a little bit different from the puppets that you made in the shows before that. They were simpler and some of the puppets like the Pointer were like the old, a little bit – like the old Disciple puppets.'

'The only thing that is different and that doesn't work is that I tried *hard* throughout *most* of that to paint elaborate costumes for them, to tailor and paint *colorful*, varied and sort of wild costumes, and I found out that that kind of thing is not interesting on a puppet, so I had to – that's probably the reason why we ended up using the puppets so little – (Elka: The big puppets.) – and the show becoming so much a washerwoman story. It was originally meant to be a puppet show with big puppets, but the puppet work in these elaborate costumes is not interesting. What you usually have, these monochrome *figures*, are there for a good reason, I found out. It needs to be as simple as that in order to get *movement* from these things. Once they become dressed up in dresses and elaborate kind of con-structions, they have to move in imitating the movements of costumes, and that is not good for them.'   (Schumann, interview, '79.)

Conceptually, the Washerwoman figure goes back to a puppet with a big white head and a huge grey burlap bag fixed to the head's rim for a body, with three operators inside, one for the head and one for each arm who in the '70 and/or the '71 circus operated the transition from the birth/life to the death or dance of death parts of the circus. She changed the per-formers' masks, and then herself changed, turned into a drumming demon (Schumann, interview, '79). She may at that circus already have done laundry or sewed or ironed, but at Glover, at any rate, Schumann 'did a lot of experiments with that, using different texts to that figure washing, washing and wringing the laundry and hanging up the wash' (Elka, ibid.) (the chief homemaking activities also of Emilia in the '71 *Emilia*), except now with the one (?) operator's real hands sticking out, and at this stage the puppet was referred to as 'The Washerwoman':[2]

'That was a puppet that existed for several years in a row, and was tried out for various jobs, with different kinds of music. There was a show here, done in the back-yard for the opening of the museum, quite a few years ago (June 14, '75 (SSB)), that was called *Washerwoman*, maybe even *The Washerwoman Cantata* – Sacred Harp singing was used and a text from the local paper here.'
                                                                              (Schumann, interview, '79.)

Washerwoman Ah!, the second of the '79 *Washerwoman Cantatas* was a family play and its figures – the red devil on his monster, sword and shield raised, the one-armed 'good' parents, patriarchally bearded grandpa and the serving lady who is like one of the little Russian peasant toy box-within-box toy figures, all now in the museum, are fairy tale figures, stylistically the closest to traditional wooden-headed hand puppetry figures of any puppets by Schumann I know, figures for a children's pup-

---

2. Schumann's Washerwoman does not in the least resemble Picasso's presumably absinthe drinking proletarian ironing woman, a bony-shouldered wreck equally marked by labor and dissipation, but

'Many years ago he (Schumann (SSB)) said to me something about an ironing woman. So, I was looking at paintings of Picasso's of women ironing. And it was an idea that we had and then, years after that image we created – several times, actually – scenes in which I would be a person ironing.' — (Sherman, interview, '82.)

pet theatre. They share the innocuousness of the 'Washerwomen', their lack of reverberation. A play with hand puppets by Elka, *Solomon Grundy*, and a strobe light enactment of poses derived from Goya's *Disasters of War* by the Schumann children, with, I don't know what costumes or masks, were 'fleshed into' the earliest version of this play. As counterfoil to the sweetness and light of his Washerwomen, Schumann in the other *Washerwoman Cantata, Washerwoman Nativity*, assembled an iconography of death, vastly amplified from what it had ever been before in his work. The giant skeletal Death Man from *Masaniello* rode on the giant skeletal Death Horse made for the circus of '78, preceded by six Death Flag carriers, and accompanied by a horse of Skeleton Men. The Death Flags were substantially like those he had made in California in the spring of '75. The Skeleton Men replaced the similar ones of the circus pageant of '78 that had fallen apart. And there was a new King Herod, spindly and black, ludicrous, grinning, his face livid welts, carried overhead by half a dozen puppeteers in the *Masaniello* 'People' masks. He is in the caricatural tradition of Uncle Fatso, an image of horrible power, the horror of it greatly strengthened, however.

Presiding, iconographically, over the figures of life (the 'Washer-women') and death in this play, were the first giant kite-type stick puppets since the 'White Birds' of '74, two angels with cutout heads, one, Mary Elect, a little over man-sized, in loose white, angelic garments, with the face of an early renaissance adoring angel, large, beautiful, its blue hair smoothly painted on, wingless, so perhaps not an angel at all, the other an Annunciatory Angel, Gabriel, and at the end of the play an Angel of Peace, very, very large, its wingspan possibly as much as fifty feet, blond hemp tresses at the back of the coldly serene white quatrocento face some twelve feet above the ground, with, like Mary Elect, a voluminous, white, draped fabric figure, not a body but the picture of a body: 'a big angel . . . the body built like the body of the big white birds and the head a cutout, rather a chic face with a *big* wig from unravelled bailing twine.' (Schumann, interview, '79.) The Angel of Peace was built for this play. Their power and lightness (the lightness enhanced by their flat, forward-pointing cutout heads) makes these giant kite-type stick puppets sui generis among Schumann's puppets. Their manipulation reached an apex in *Josephine the Singer* (1984).

The use of pictures painted on masonite, carried and moved like masks and puppets — a jonquil, cows, birds, a house, clouds, a heart, a large Holy Ghost dove, agitated people — was distinctive of this show. We may, if we wish, view them as masks or puppets. There were elephants, frogs, bears, a bull, cows in the circus of '79. The bull and the cows were, I think, new. The cows expanded the repertory of animal groups idealizing nature begun by the deer puppets of '75. The cows have a swinging move-ment in the direction of their walk: the '81 pageant rehearsal indications

474

to their carriers were that the double sawhorse skeleton suspended over their shoulders by crisscrossed straps was to rise and dip – was not to be held at a rigid horizontal. They were to have an ambling walk, there were to be head movements of curiosity – they were to buck when led off by the Salesmen of Civilization that steal them from Adam of the Onion Farmer and Eve his Wife. In the Context of their role in the pageant's drama, the cows seemed to look fearful, upset – thick mouths open, ears erect, nostrils flaring, the black-centered white eyes staring, their heads at a slight angle of apprehension or rigidly straining forward. In the great anti-nuclear parade of that year, as part of the parade's cheer they looked vulnerable – their bodies bulky, downward-tending; but at peace.

In *Cambodia* ('80) I note the five-six foot tall, manipulated, long, vaguely feline cutout puppets, The Famished, white with their ribs showing in black lines, in prone postures, operated in prone positions from above, their cutout arms raised by strings. The first cutouts with movable parts (arms also) had been used in the '79 *King Lear*, done entirely with them. The device sophisticated the use of cutout figures started by the '76 *Mountain Man of Chile*.

Schumann built a great many new puppets during a six week workshop at Villeurbanne, near Lyons, France, in the summer of '80, most or all of them used in the show that resulted, *Histoire du Pain*, and again in later shows, notably *Swords and Ploughshares* ('81) and *Diagonal Man* ('82).[3]

---

3. 'So then the building projects, the first part of it, naturally, there had to be building done. I wanted it to be the history of bread. That was the overall idea before even the musicians and the piece of music were found. So what I built for it was some large puppets for bright colors; some large puppets for dull colors; some set of flat puppets, cutout puppets that could move their limbs . . . the 'Famished People'. Then, well, masks, all kinds of masks. Some masks of a French farmer and a farmer woman and beasts, a group of beasts, of these riding type(?) masks and costumes. I think that was in general what was built there (I: The 'bright ones' would be like the 'telephone directory' people later on in *Diagonal Man*?) Right, a big group of many colors of masks which we wanted to use as a population – we had available to us the costume rooms of the Theatre (National) Populaire, so we could go there and pick out all the stuff, so we had all kinds of crazy costumes and this was just right for those masks. That's how the thing started. So the rehearsals were sort of what to do with the population, how they moved, what they did. Then the city, a cutout town, was built. Then demon figures were built with open mouths. They were later on used in *Woyzeck* with tongues sticking out. (I: The 'laughing guys') Yeah. They were originally eaters. Their tongues came out and they ate the town. Then some kind of rattle machine and the *Story of Bread*, which was a flip-over story that was turned over and told and was sort of the outside structure to the thing. "This is the story that we tell you" and – the big god figure was the Stomach who was painted . . . and was hanging full of forks and knives and was talking in French proverbs about food.' — (Schumann, interview, '83.)

The 'Famished' had already been made – used in the New York City *Cambodia*, The cutout town was used again in *Diagonal Man*. The TNP costume room costumes also served for a *Cid* put on by Romanyshyn, and, if I am not mistaken, now dress puppets Schumann made for this show in the Dopp Farm museum – a bonus on the Villeurbanne workshops.

475

Among them were two hunchback 'Prophets', kite-like puppets; a 'special Washerwoman created as the chief character for '*Histoire*, the woman of that thing' (ibid.), 'a pretty faced woman who otherwise was in the style of the Washerwoman, but a young and pretty Washerwoman' (Schumann, interview '83), actually a 'farmer woman' (Schumann, interview, December '82), wife of a 'moustached French farmer man' (Schumann, interview, '83), later, but then as a dummy, 'Marie' in *Woyzeck* ('81); and two masks of Demon Eaters, with cutout tongues — 'they had the job of eating up the town. Their tongues came out and they swallowed up and they ate it up' (Schumann, interview, December '82). They were then used in *Woyzeck* as lap puppet dummies, partly string operated, and were laughers, the 'Laughing Guys'. The Big Stomach puppet of *Histoire*, perhaps 20 ft. tall (four ft. of that for its deep red wine bibber's head) is now in the Glover museum. He has small, blue, ferociously joyous eyes, wears a ridiculous little black hat over his round red face, his pink hands are large, a fork is tied to his left hand, the thumb of which is *out*, curved, while the other 4 fingers are bent back to the palm. The pink index finger of his right hand is raised: he is explaining something to his drinking buddies. He wears a small, shiny — plastic — black waiter's jacket cut out in a curve in front, showing the black-buttoned white shirt he wears underneath — it goes down to the floor.

The most important of the puppets made in Villeurbanne were the 'population' of the 'town', i.e. the bread-consuming but not-producing urbanites, serving the Stomach God and devoured by his and their demons, important because of their ridiculous — sympathetically but also satirically viewed — individuation, an individuation despite the caricature going beyond that of the 'Garbagemen' and of the big puppets for *Masaniello*, and new in Schumann's work. Emilia's mask ('71) is a distant predecessor of their masks, but whereas Emilia's designates a particular of 'this' individual, theirs designates 'an' or 'some' individual. Their bright colorfulness continues the 'Washerwoman' line. Stylistically they are in the Kasperl hand puppet tradition — not sculpturally oriented abstractions. Their masks hand held, they were used in *Diagonal Man* as telephone-directory-individualized (urban) Individualities.

Possibly also in '80, though probably a little earlier he made 'twenty to thirty' 'White Clown masks — 'in a row, probably done in a few days.' (Schumann, interview, December '82.)

'They were white, with white clown costumes, sort of big pants, big blousey kind of a white shirt, a hood on the mask. The whole thing was an idea to create a circus clown of a certain style — like a white French clown — like a traditional white French clown. And it didn't work out. We did it for many circuses in a row — maybe three, four circuses in a row we tried skits ... This year, in the circus we had a white clown skit, or a couple of white clown skits, a tight rope walking skit with two white clowns and then a political skit ... They are masks I would very much like to work more with, but they are hard to work with. (I: What makes them hard to work with?) I think I'm obsessed with a certain style I have in mind and I can't find it – in the players who play with them. I found, a couple of times, people who could do it. (In) a French skit, *Deux Villages* . . . at the University of Quebec, we had two white clowns with detachable arms. Their own arms were hidden inside the blouse and then we had built two stuffed arms that acted as their real stuffed arms – what they could do with that, made more sense for the whole mask. It was the first time it was fun to work with these . . . Very light shading on the faces; strong noses; most of them, strong chins; they are all big – like Basel-style carnival masks. Basel has a special style of carnival mask that they sell in the stores. And they usually sell them without any makeup on the face, it's just a sculpture. And the people put their own paints on them. They're quite ugly, quite horrible, but simplified shapes – but it's a style. This is a bit in that style.'

(Schumann, interview, December '82.)

I shall abstain from a review of the many new puppets in *Venus* ('80), *Goya* ('81) and *Woyzeck* ('81), the three plays developing the technique of ostentatious dummy-manipulation, but do want to say a word about the puppets in the pageant of the '81 circus. Salesmen costumed performers with Salesman face masks) had replaced the Butchers. They were Hitler-wise mustachioed despoiling agents of commercial (secretly militaristic) Civilization. Barbara Leber, as head Salesman, quite elegantly mimes him as a wise guy. To performers, Schumann defines the Salesmen as those who 'bring the objects of civilization to the world – they bring the atom bomb'. The puppeteer instructing volunteers performing them, tells them to act as a team, and to move 'with good sharp movements, kind of precise, they know what they are doing.' One of the hunchback Prophet kite-type stick puppets of 1980 heralds an Atomic Missile Launching Tower Monster, a mechanical golem. Humanity appears in the guise of turdlike Michelangelesque Lost Souls, the Condemned of the final judgment: brown, legless, their legs cut off at the knees, one hand welded onto either eye or an ear in a 'Weh ist mir' gesture (head masks into which a hand had been integrated were a feature also of *Goya* and *Venus*). They were puppet half shells, a new type of puppet, held in front of them by those appearing in them by a string across their concave interior, sometimes moved in unison by a chorus of the Condemned as were the People masks in *Masaniello* and in *Washerwoman Nativity*. Little red demons clean up after the Last Judgment – clear the t.v. sets and cardboard houses. They are done by children, by black kids when such are available (casting going back to the '66 *Crucifixion*), the kids' slim, upright shapes obscured by loose layers of coverings in different reds cut into finger length strips that flutter like hair or feathers of flames as the kids rush about, jibber-jabbering. The masks are of different animals, traits of different genera or orders mixing in the same mask – as since time immemorial, the counter-natural hybrid, equated with the bad, has been the customary graphic representation of evil. But because of their sharply

477

articulate, angled and split noses and thin lacquered shell, they evoke the crustacean. Hell itself, Schumann's biggest-ever puppet, follows them, the Bread and Puppet touring bus, masticating and to firecracker farts posteriorily ejecting the Condemned: covered in red with giant in-gathering red fabric arms ending in giant bloodied fists, its frontally affixed head a dragon's, ridden by a second generation red Yama (King of Hell) puppet.

4. The crisis of '79-'81. Separation of family and puppeteers. The corporation acquires tangible assets, its employees gain salary increases, increased medical coverage and prospects of individual recognition.

Elka had revolted in '73, in '79, after the August circus, she revolted again. Deciding that the circuses were just too much for her,[1] she recalled

---

1. '. . . that the circus, having it here just – I couldn't stand it – and actually, ever since we moved to the country the circuses that happened in '70, I think I – I don't know. I feel that I have some kind of nervous breakdown every summer because it would just get really hard; the people, and the pressure, and the – I guess – I mean I didn't solve how to participate in the theatre in a really thankful, creative way. I felt most of the time I was left cleaning the toilets and washing the dishes or having to pick up children, or whatever it was so that my participation – I don't know, even now also I find it very hard to define what I'm, doing and at that point I did the bookkeeping and I did keeping track of things, and letters, but it all felt like very insubstantial things. I didn't feel I was doing that much, plus feeling all the – so every summer I'd be very – there would (laugh) be a crisis – it just felt like it wasn't going to stop and it was just going to be terrible like that. And it seems every – especially after we moved here we would try to make our family, Peter and I and together with the puppeteers who became, you know, really close and then the theatre tried to figure out a way to make our family situation more manageable during this time. And people did cooperate and did try and – but I think it was just built into this – I mean, given the kind of person I am and then that situation, there wouldn't be – the more efficient we got the more, you know, better organized we got it got better organized but it didn't really change the situation of being in the middle of this big event, huge event which culminated in 3,000 people kind of not walking through your house but in a way just taking over your life. And maybe I'm super – and I would think I was some freak kind of person who couldn't cope with something that any sensible person could. And then at times I think enough people have told me they don't see how that could be lived with, so that I think it wasn't so abnormal on my part not – to have such a hard time with it. And after the '79 circus I suddenly (laughing) – and I thought, it's a very simple solution. I'm just going to say there's not going to be another circus next summer. And I hadn't thought of the new house or anything. I just thought I'm not going to go through another summer like it. I don't have to and I'm not going to. So I had suggested let's do the circus on the Barton Fair Grounds, or let's skip it – I don't know. It wasn't like I was saying we'll never do it again but I just said that it was not going to happen and I didn't ask. I just said it. And I could say it because this farm was mine. I don't like saying that, but – and I think most of the people who worked in the theatre and around the theatre assumed it was the theatre's property. But in a way, I mean in some way I feel my parents have really subsidized and supported the theatre. And I don't think that has been (enough appreciated(?)).

My father signed it over shortly before he died, to me . . . I asked him if he really wanted to give it to me or to the Bread and Puppet Theatre or to Peter, maybe. So he said, "You are our daughter so we want to take care of you." (Laugh) And I think that's – you know, and it seemed almost uncannily thinking of the solution to our life. It was such a smart and insightful and compassionate thing that he did because maybe now I would be

479

that the farm was hers, given by her father, and that she was in a position to do something about it. She declared there would be no more circuses.[2]

I think the reason the circuses – the hundreds of volunteers, the thousands of spectators – got to be too much for her was that she was hardly, at most minutely, involved in their creative aspects, as all these years, influence of her reactions apart, she had been involved in her husband's work hardly at all, but that at the same time she shouldered the burden of much of the onerous incidental work, not so much the administrative work, but the physical work, her housewife's chores of cooking, cleaning and gardening – chores along the lines of those of the figure honored by that circus of '79, and modeled on her, the Washerwoman – which may

---

more careful and more aware of things like documents or deeds and whatever it was, but at that point the whole living in the country was just – was a lucky thing that – we'd gotten this invitation to Goddard and we didn't – I mean the idea of having a claim to a piece of property I don't think made any difference to me and my father really kept sort of nagging on this, harping on this thing, that he wanted to make it legal. I didn't see really what the hurry was or why do it at all and wasn't it good enough now. But as it turned out it really made *my* life so much more good. It made solutions possible for things that were really hard for me.' — (Elka Schumann, interview, '83.)

2. 'I want to say that the Circus was good this year, and that it should not take place here again next year.

The Pageant was just beautiful . . . The Circus proper was good too.

. . . The practical work and organizational aspects of the Circus went well too, smoother than other years, with more people sharing in the hum-drum housekeeping jobs. Sara was a dependable cook, cheerfully and punctually producing meals to feed ever-increasing numbers; Barbara handled all the money, and we almost made it on the $9,000 budget we'd allotted for these 6 weeks. More than half this sum came back to us on the 2 Circus days, through contributions and sales of posters, books and banners, twice as much as last year! Annie Romanyshyn took care of all the phone calls and questions and details that mount up and take ever so much time. Of course, I'm mentioning only a very few of the many whose dedication and efforts made the whole thing possible.

But still, and yet, not that much was really any different from the Circuses of other years. It was bigger; it was run somewhat better. It is still a rather shattering experience, to have all that intense and frantic work going on here for 6 straight weeks (the 'day off' is a fiction), and then some 15,000-20,000 people trooping around and by and through the quiet home in the country.

During this time, everything takes second place to the work on the Circus. It has to, for that's the only way this gigantic task becomes possible. So normal home and summer life ceases to exist for our family. The garden was a fair disaster. I never finished planting, and from late June on no further work was done in it. It supplied the company abundantly with salads and peas, some onions, carrots and cabbages, but now there is neither corn, beans nor squash, and scarcely enough of anything else for the winter – except garlic!

The fields are another area of neglect. The farmer was told to start mowing late, closer to Circus-time, and by the time mowing was started, the grass was not worth much. Then the machine broke on rocks which were hauled under people's cars to get them out of the mud during last year's Circus-parking. After spending a week and couple of hundred dollars repairing the mower, and finding the grass worth even less, the farmer gave up in disgust, and even offers of money did not entice him to come back and finish the job. We

have gotten her goat too – spilling over into work for the puppeteers and the circus volunteers and visitors. The family and the Bread and Puppet core group had shared the farm house since '75, and since she was cooking for her family anyhow, somehow she often enough ended up cooking for everybody: she was cooking for these young people who *were* involved in her husband's work. Her children were getting to the age where they no longer required or wanted so much of her services or attention as earlier; she had never been able to get into a line of work of her own; and due to the shared quarters and her husband's work-relationship with the young people they were shared with, she didn't even have much of a family or conjugal[3] life – no privacy!

She thought of an arrangement, however,[4] and a compromise was ar-

---

have to buy hay – with nearly 50 acres of available fields! And pay someone, if I can find anyone willing to mow the fields. (Note: no one was willing as of Oct. 3.)

Even though we rented 2 cabins and full-time puppeteers live in a house 2 miles away, the place here is always an open and public space. It has to be, of course, since everything – the tools, materials, puppets and working spaces – is here. I understand these things, and I myself start thinking and acting the same way: Theater Needs First and Foremost! But it is hard to live like this, constantly, in one's own home, especially when much of the year, except when the company is on tour, is a smaller, more subdued version of Circus-time.

This summer I realized that this place is, first of all, our home, that I can do something about a situation hard for me to bear, so I said that the Circus will not be in Glover next year. Whether we skp a year, or have the Circus somewhere else – that is not yet decided. We plan to meet later this fall to talk the matter over and settle it.

I understand that this decision does not solve or eliminate the difficulties inherent in the situation. But after 5 years of Circus summers it will give this place and me a much-needed respite, when other matters pertaining to the farm and our life here can get some much-needed attention.

I thank you for you attention. Comments and responses are not expected, but welcome, if you feel like writing.' — (Elka, *This Year's Circus*, letter to puppeteers, September, 1979.)

3. Elka (letter, September 10, 1984) protests: 'Well, if you asked me about that, I'd have to say, I can't complain.' But I'm not referring to anything more intimate here than simply quiet times spent alone together by husband and wife over a cup of coffee.

4. 'Before the current tour started, there was a meeting with a small group of the puppeteers, and I said that there will not be a Circus next year in Glover. Perhaps you heard this, or heard about it, but I would like to write down my thoughts and try to explain, clarify, justify this decision. It is hard to put these thoughts and feelings into words, and into clear and concise ones. Also, I think: And who's interested in your 'reasons'? Main thing is: What to do now?

So much about the Circus is beautiful and splendid. The effort going into its production every year is gargantuan. The results are, usually, mostly, important and worthwhile.

This year the organizational and practical aspects of the Circus went well, better than ever before, with more people sharing and taking responsibility for more jobs. I like what I did in the Circus, and feel proud to be a part of it all.

But, can you also understand, over the years it has become too much, it has simply become too much. All of it: the final frantic days with the thousands of people and cars, the weeks before, and in the context of the whole year – the years – everything has become too much.

481

rived at. The Bread & Puppet Theatre Company, Inc. was going to have a house of her own built for her up the hill from the old farm house, and in

---

This year, again, it became too much for me, and if it had not been for Peter's mother coming, and Scott and Helen, I would have gone away. It was then I realized that I could do something about it, that the Circus was not a force of Nature (it is, sort of, but it can happen somewhere else, or wait a year), and that I am in a decisive position, about whether it happens in Glover or not. This realization made staying possible for me, and now I am acting upon it by saying: no Circus here next year. Now what? What then? Amy is right: the Theater needs stability and continuity, and should know, as soon as possible, if the Circus can take place here the year after, and years after that. At the time that she said this, I felt completely unable to see that far ahead. But now I have an idea.

First, though, I want to try to define the situation, and that is hard because it is all so connected, so intertwined, so unclear and undefined: family, Peter, Theater, puppeteers, farm, me; what we-he-it-they-it-I want(s) and need(s) – I can't even get and keep the pronouns straight! (Yes, I do often feel the Theater is We, but for clarity's sake I will separate the two.) All I know is that "communal" living, the undefined "us", has always been hard for me, and it hasn't gotten any easier. I have not "adjusted" to, nor learned to cope with, these constantly recurring situations, where things are not defined, neither time nor space nor property; what is the Theater's and what is separate; where the Theater and its needs and demands spill over and affect everything in my life. For somebody more gregarious, motherly, kind and/or photogenic, such a wife-of-the-director role might be enviable, a challenge, a triumph! It isn't for me.

As the Theater gets older, bigger and more complex, its needs and demands grow too. I have countered them by trying to arrange things to achieve and protect our privacy, but these efforts haven't done much good. For example, housing is rented at a distance from the farm for puppeteers who are in the Theater because they want to work in the Theater and need its resources to do so. And I, longing for privacy, live in the midst of an expanding center of all the stuff the Theater is made of, that everyone else needs to use and be close to. It is a sad and perverse situation, that Linda has to ask me whether I mind if she comes and works in the costume room during the week off. How could I say, yes, I mind? I think it admirable that she feels this attachment and responsibility, and wants to do this in her free time. And yet this place *is* my and my family's home, and such comings, however discreet and well-intentioned can't help but feel like intrusions. We moved to this farm in order to be a family, distinct from the Theater, and I have become very attached to, and possessive about this place, the whole place. An exception to this is the Museum; it is truly the one place that feels public.

(A note for those unfamiliar with the background of this farm: my parents bought it from the Dopps in 1970; B&P rented it for a small group of puppeteers in 1973 and 1974; in 1974 our family moved here and rented part of the house to 2 puppeteers for a year; in 1976, shortly before my father died, my parents divided the farm and transferred this half to me.)

Through conversations with Daisy Dopp I feel a link to this farm's past. And I have come to think of it as a place I'd like to live in all my life, and grow old in, too (these 2 things aren't automatically thought of together, you know). Yes, it is very big, too big for just one family. But, as long as it is all one place, it's our home. This feeling is hard to reconcile with the Theater's presence.

Over the years I find myself opposing, more and more, the Natural growth of the Theater. I don't want it to get bigger, become more public, well-known, attract more people and publicity, because all this growth becomes an invasion of the private sphere. But it's a losing battle, and how stupid it feels, too: Let's all work hard to get fewer people to come to the Circus!!!

exchange she would give it the farm house, the Museum-cum-workshop barn and the storage shed across the road (her own proposal had been that she lease them to the corporation), and a 15-year lease on the circus

---

We have tried to find solutions, and I feel that many of the puppeteers, close and more distant, have been genuinely concerned that this place be liveable for me and my family. I deeply appreciate this. But as long as our family remains here, in the midst of all the things that are, should be, public and accessible to those interested in the work of the Theater, it feels like an irresolvable problem.

And now, here's a big, radical, new idea:

I propose that Bread and Puppet Theater lease, on a long-term basis, all the existing buildings, the Circus Field and the Pine Forest, and in exchange, build for our family a house, elsewhere on the property. This agreement should be put into a legally binding document.

Here are the arguments:

The Theater needs space, lots of it, and long-term security about the space. B&P has never had an agreement for longer than a year about staying anywhere, and has been evicted from the Delancey St.loft, the Public Theater, the 2nd Ave. Courthouse, and the Bank in Brooklyn. It was our decision to leave Cate Farm at Goddard College, but we had no assurance, while we were there, how long they would let us stay. When we moved to Glover, nothing was further from our thoughts than a lease (who with? what about?). Then there seemed to be no need for anything so explicit and formal; now I think there is. Nobody could have any idea what directions the work of Theater would take, or how much the Circus would grow (didn't it seem HUGE in Cate Farm?). But the time has come, I think, when a long-term assurance about staying and developing somewhere (whether in Glover or elsewhere) would be very advantageous for the work of the Theater and the people in it.

This farm seems perfect for the needs of the Theater, providing housing, indoor rehearsal, work and meeting spaces, and storage room for tools, materials, boxes, puppets. (If our animals move out of the barn, lots of additional space would become available.) Already a lot of B&P money and work has gone into improving and creating these facilities. Then there is the Circus field, with the amphitheater, and the Pine Forest. It is a big place, and land and buildings need more care and attention than one individual can provide. More and more often I feel overwhelmed by all the things that need to be done here, and I realize that this part of the farm, as well as the Theater, needs a group of people to maintain it and work it. Since Bread and Puppet has had nearly unlimited use of the place for the last 5 years, it seems right that it should contribute more to the upkeep here.

A long-term lease would give the Theater security and stability, not subject to the whims of city burocrats, college presidents, or property owners, on the place where it has already invested so much time-effort and money.

Our family and I need a home, separate and distinct from the Theater, where we can carry on what we are now doing. Wanting a home apart from the Theater does not mean that I want nothing to do with it; I very much want to continue to work in it and with the children growing up and leaving home, we no longer need such a big house; and as we get older, it will be an advantage to have a smaller place to keep up.

This property is large enough to provide for the needs of both our family and the Theater, and the lease would clearly define appropriate boundaries and responsibilities for both parties.

I know that building a house is a very expensive proposition. Here it would have to include a road, electricity, woodshed and small barn. But look at the money the Theater and individual puppeteers have paid out in rents and transportation to and from Montpelier, Barton, Wheelock, Daniel's Pond, and Dexter Hill! These rents will only increase with the

meadow and the pine forest.[5] The house was finished in September '80 and the Schumann family moved in, ending a ten-year relationship (inter-

---

passing years. I think that in the long run the cost of such a house would not be exorbitant or unreasonable. It would be a good economy.

Of course, there are many things left to figure out, to discuss and define, before this proposal can be decided upon; and all the money to raise, before it can be acted on.

But I think it is *is* a good idea, beneficial to both sides, to all of us, and with some willingness, organization and hard work it is possible to realize it.

Please forgive the repetitions and the ramblings, and give this proposal your consideration. I would like to hear your comments, questions and alternatives.' — (Elka Schumann, *Long and long-range letter* (to the resident puppeteers), September 17, '79.)

5. 'Dear Friends,

Our 1979 Domestic Resurrection Circus was the biggest yet (over 15,000 came both days) and one of the best. However, we have decided not to have a Circus in 1980. The pressures on the Schumann farm and family of preparing an event of this magnitude have been overwhelming. After 5 Circus summers in Glover, we have decided to take a much-needed break.

But a long-term solution must be found which will make it possible for the Circus and our work to have the security needed for continuation and development.

We all agree that this farm is ideal for the needs of the Circus, with 24 acres of rolling meadow, the natural amphitheater, the pine forest, the museum-barn, and the buildings, which provide housing, work, meeting and storage space. We very much want to stay here and develop all these features.

Purchase of the existing structures and the long-term lease of the part of the property used for the Circus would endure the continuity of our work. A separate house would give the Schumanns the privacy they need. They have agreed to sell the buildings and lease the Circus field and pine forest to Bread and Puppet, and with the money they will build themselves a house elsewhere on the property.

At our recent annual meeting attended by 25 puppeteers and trustees, everyone present supported this proposal (actually, we only talked of a lease at that time; the sale is new, simplifying and a better plan), and felt that it provided fairly for the needs of both sides.

In order to put this plan into effect, Bread and Puppet must raise all the money — about $60,000 — by next fall. Plans are being made for extensive touring in the coming months, to Montreal, New York City, France, and wherever we can get good invitations. We are also asking help from friends and supporters of our work. We welcome contributions of any size, and they are tax-deductible.

Milly and Jack Cohen have generously offered to handle this project, so you can send your contributions to them:

Milly and Jack Cohen
60 Crescent Street
New Haven, Connecticut 06511

Thank you for your support, and greetings from the Bread and Puppet in Glover.

P.S. Checks should be made out to Bread and Puppet Theater Fund.

The Bread and Puppet Theater is exempt from Federal Income Tax as an organization described in section 501 (c) (3) of the Internal Revenue Code, and contributions made are deductible by donors as provided in section 170 of the Code, as amended by the Tax Reform Act of 1969. Bequests, legacies, devices, transfers or gifts are deductible for Federal estate and gift tax purposes under the provisions of section 2055, 2106 and 2522 of the Code.

rupted for less than a year, in '74/'75) of quasi-communal living.[6] The
house, small, that she had had built for herself, was up the hill from the big

---

P.S.S. If you know of anyone else who might be interested in receiving this letter, we'd
appreciate getting their addresses so that we can include them in the mailing.' — (Letter of
solicitation from the Bread and Puppet Theater, dated November/December 1979.)
6. 'Meanwhile, back at the farm, a crew of five builders (1 Schumann (Ephraim (SSB)), 1
puppeteer and three local professionals) built a new house and small barn for the
Schumanns, who moved in on schedule September 15 and are happily settling into the
luxury of fresh lumber, brand new window, 6″ and 12″ insulation, etc.' — (B&P Newsletter, October '80.)

'We had a Board of Directors and general meeting – combined Board of Directors and
general meeting . . . what has transpired since you saw them last was that last season they
made a lot of money deliberately to build a house. And now, the Schumanns have a house
up out of sight beyond where the old house was. (I: The old house was so lovely.) Well,
that has become the puppeteers' house. They have their own old house. Because in building
a house obviously Elka couldn't make anything except an old house. It is fit – she built this
house 50 years ago, 80 years ago. But she does have the most elegant bathtub – a wooden
bathtub with copper around it – it's beautiful. She has the prettiest bathtub in all of
Vermont, I am sure. The house looks – nothing modern has happened, the house is rude
and crude and was built by local laborers and the joy of our life now, Ephraim. Ephraim
has become – has solidified as a human being in opposition to his father. He is really very –
he has established his own personality, no longer competing with his father, he is a
different person, is secure – I was very happy to see that . . . . There were two or three
really professional house builders, but he (Ephraim) was added on to the crew and they
paid him . . . The meeting had to do with the fact that the theatre had for the very first
time in their career really gone out after money to find the money to pay for this house
where the Schumanns could live, separately from circus and public activities. Obviously,
what was never mentioned was where does Peter sleep? . . . It is called Elka's house. Elka
wants a house. And in those early negotiations – Elka also owns the land. Elka leased what
used to be the Schumann house, and the land, to the Bread and Puppet theatre for a 15
year period, I think. 15 or 12. For which the theatre has to pay money. But it is a definite
separate situation. Which never was that way before until she demanded that they respect
her right to privacy, and they said no. Drop dead. She said wait a minute, let's think this
over again. This is mine, you will remember what is mine and we will now discuss what is
mine and thine and – she really did. It was (inaud.) Wait a minute, don't talk to me this
way. This whole place is mine. She has her house. Together, they built the house very
cheap, under 40 thousand dollars. (I: What was Schumann's attitude during that discussion?) He agreed that she could do whatever she wanted. (I: The disagreement came just
from the fact of certain ideals?) The ideals didn't come up at all. He agreed completely that
she had the right to.' — (Ashley, interview, '81.)

'After months on the road, John, Trudi, Barbara and Michael are finishing weeks of
sanding, plastering, painting and much-needed renovations and repairs on the big old farm
house, which is now their home . . . We are all pleased with the progress we have made in
improving the physical conditions of our lives in the theater. Hopefully a lot of unnecessary
strain and uncertainty will now be eliminated and the way cleared for more and better
work in the future. Now we must learn to live with the changes that have been made.' —
(B&P Newsletter, October '80.)

'. . . my father had died. The more we live here the more we appreciate this place. And
because this property was mine I could make this exchange. It was possible then for us to
buy the house – I mean to get the money to build this house and in exchange for securing
for the theatre the permanence, more or less, of the circus as long as we can find people

485

house and barn where the puppeteers lived and worked. Schumann moved up there too – whether that had been the idea or not. The little house is heated by a single stove downstairs and is altogether unluxurious. It is, at least in summer – in winter, after a while, the road can no longer be

who can stand that kind of – who thrive on or can live with that kind of insecurity. (I: Has it been easier now, being up in the house last year?) Oh yeah. Yes, yes. (I: It really puts you out of the thing.) It does. It makes it possible for me to go away and shut a door, you know . . . maybe it would be possible after several years to look at this and sort of look at it as a cause and say it's all right, it's really hard, or whatever, but – I mean not to have your privacy. I know how I would treasure every – the worst thing was when strangers came in to breakfast. It would always make me want to throw up not to be able to sort of have that little bit of time just where family – and then Peter and I – I think after a while Peter began to really appreciate having time by ourselves and we would have little cups of coffee (laughing) at times just to get away and be able to just, you know, the two of us at the table with just – with our children – I don't know, maybe it sounds terribly spoiled to think that.' — (Elka Schumann, interview, '83.)

plowed and provisions have to be pulled up by sled — a fairy tale house. On the way up, there is the little vegetable garden, densely planted, and the pig pen — the black pig is fed on slops only. There are geese, a ram, two ewes, a dog with one eye, a variety of cats, stray and Siamese. The small house has many rooms in it. In the kitchen hangs a smoked ham, stands a basket with giant goose eggs. From each window there is a different beautiful view — the hills in different distances' blues, a full tree, a leaning meadow. The children come and go — in the fall of '82, the last two were leaving — Maria, the youngest for Exeter: all or almost on scholarships. There is Beethoven from the piano or Bach from the ancient record player. Schumann severely sends Elka out to gather the choke cherries that otherwise will soon be lost to the birds. The jam is good, he likes the choke cherry wine. He likes the Vermont sky — its variety.

The house was financed partly by a fund-raising drive, partly by a second European tour in '79, in December, and a workshop in Lyons and another European tour in the summer of '80, making a total of seven months of touring that year.[7] The starkly commercial purpose of the summer of '80 tour in particular, and its integration into the European tourist business disturbed Schumann and the puppeteers.[8] There were minor resi-

---

7. 'Bread & Puppet has had a heavy schedule of performances, including these major tours: four months with *Stations of the Cross*, starting in the U.S. in April, ending in Italy in June (via England and France), a collaboration with Word-of-Mouth Chorus singing Sacred Harp hymns for the show; a six week workshop in Lyons, France during which a new Circus was built in an abandoned factory with students, workers and street kids and in spite of uncooperative administrators; a week at the exceptionally successful and jolly Puppeteers of America Festival in Washington, D.C.; a six week tour with a new show from Lyons, *The Story of Bread*, through France and Yugoslavia at the height of the tourist season ... The response to Jack & Milly Cohen's fund raising was generous and over $5000 was received. This, in addition to the money made from extensive touring, has made last year's plans a reality. We thank everyone who contributed...' (B & P Newsletters, October '80.)

The Villeurbanne/Lyons workshop yielded $34,978.56, and the tour of *Histoire du Pain* yielded $41,395.58.

8. We travelled this summer with a crew of 15 for about 6 weeks with 'The History of Bread' through France and Yugoslavia. We rehearsed 20 local people into the show and several times they travelled with us. We performed in many exquisite sites, beautiful landscapes, grand old cities. We travelled because we are puppeteer-travellers, puppeteer-missionaries, missionaries of what? Nonsense, beauty, political and social truths — and because we make our living this way; also and specifically because we are buying the Schumann's house and barn and they build a house with that money.

Quite a few years now we have spent our summers pretty much at home, puppet-building, circus-making, parading in local towns. Those home-summers have been described as high-strung and hectic, heavy working periods, too much for some people.

Well, this summer we experienced the hectic ways of tourist culturism or cultural tourism in these stuffed-up medieval towns to which people flock from all over the world to enjoy peace and harmony or something like that. But medieval cities have been visited before; museums, castles and all the riches of a 1000 years of European spirit have become a bore; new, tickling attractions have to be added to make the money-spending of these peace-and-harmony seekers more worthwhile. And so God invented puppet-shows. And Maria Rankov and other theater agents learned about them and bought a suitable product from us: a 1½ hour entertainment for tired people, bored by too many cathedrals.

That's excactly what I felt we were doing there – and I know the rest of our gang felt pretty much the same way.

I am sure there is much to say for the humane liberties which bless modern men and women with journeys to France and Yugoslavia. Some secret enrichment which I can't figure out must take place during this nibbling of foreign foods and cultures.

The Yugoslavs very readily charge and overcharge their guests, and even offer their bed-and living-rooms in exchange for good money. But they also make it plain that they despise your presence, that they reserve their respect and friendliness for their own kind. After you pay, their gestures suggest: Get out of here. They make their living from this obscure traffic, and they hate it thoroughly.

It's like this: the world is old and rich with relics of its past. To study the sculpture of Dubrovnik is an overwhelming experience when you pursue it with intelligence and heart. But these quick stops and glances, these non-commital gapes and stares at foreign edifices, are nothing but a bother to the mind. They have no results inside you, they make you lazy and slack instead of productive and sharp. They wash out your natural originality and flatten out everything and make it the same.

When we travel, we always say: Thank God we are not travellers but producers, we have work to do, we bring our job and our joy with us, we answer the strange things we encounter with activity. We are not tourists but doers, puppeteers, story-tellers. To correspond actively with the impressions one receives, to make use of these impressions, to make them fertile, make them grow, seems to be one way to make sense of them.

The civilization we belong to, our Western, international mish-mash culture, suffers from this needless, constant over-eating: a little bit of everything, no passion for any particular drive and strife of its own.

O.K., let's look at ourselves in this context. We are part of this culture, we cater to it, if we accept carelessly these commercial consumer-commodity offers.

Remember, we had this thought once before, on the 'Simple Light' tour in the '73-74, and as a result of that thought we decided to undo our group, to stop and start anew.

I think there is nothing wrong with making a living of our puppetry. It's terrific that we can, that we (or at least a few of us, and there are a lot more of 'us' for whom this is not true) don't have to do some lousy slaving job just for the stupid daily money.

But the tendency of the theater- and entertainment-market is to eat you up, to make you serve its true function, namely to support this rich society, to glorify it, to make more wealth for the wealthy.

Puppetry in Europe and elsewhere, before it ever achieved any status as an acceptable art form, was the tool of bums, outsiders, reformers and revolutionaries. Puppets were used to say things that actors and orators would go to jail for. Punch is the greatest anti-establishment character in the world.

Puppeteers shouldn't strive to enter this acceptable art-form-business! Who needs it? Those who want it have already too much.

Having said all this, I should come up with a neat little manifesto about what to do. Unfortunately, I can't, manifesto-time is over for me. I still want to make giant pageants for 500 pink flying dragons and I still want to make slow-motion grey-and-white or blue-and-green box stage shows that don't tell anybody anything unless they can find it.

Ideas for new puppet shows don't profit much from the reflection on how we sell our products. And the Blues from this last tour are not over with. We just have to risk more, work with friends instead of agents, with possibilities instead of contracts. More street theater and not just nice little circuses. More political parades and shows.

Maria Rankov, our agent for 3 tours, is not our enemy. She has done a good job for us,

dual problems and conflicts concerning the rights of the company under the lease.[9] Elka's hard-won life-of-her-own with Schumann in the house on

and if we can't manage with what we want to perform, we may ask her help again. But, more important: whenever possible, let's do our own bookings, let's scrutinize the places we go to better, let's do more performing at home, as much cheap and free theater as possible.

The world looks beautiful when you look out the window here in Vermont. And the world looks crazy and senseless when you think of Mr. Carter's proposals for limited nuclear war. We have to scream and yell and we have to help other people scream and yell against this madness.

What are we?

What are we doing?

We are taught that the arts prosper with prosperity, that they are a pleasant addition to tough life, a sweet decoration to our sour span of life. In other words: it takes a complacement, self-satisfied bourgeoisie to bring forth something as superfluous as art-products. Open the N.Y. Times or any other important paper and look at their list of priorities: politics, merchandise, movie-stars, sports, and, finally, housekeeping, flowerpots, front-lawn-improvement plus the arts, the pleasantries and luxuries of our serious lives. It fits the size of their mind and they deserve exactly those arts, the arts of home-improvement. By the same token they print pictures of starving Cambodians together with the latest styles in underwear. Both items sell, and because they make money, are serious.

If puppeteers ever want to say anything to those popes and shitheads of culture, it's just that: keep that culture for yourselves, you can have it, you service your own selves and nobody else. Let's stay away from this educated nonsense without fun, art-appreciation they call it. We don't need it, nobody needs it. Puppetry and all the arts are for the Gods, are wild, are raw materials, are bread and sourdough. They are for life and death, births, weddings, funerals, exaltation and sorrow, not for professionals and specialists of culture.

U.S. prosperity costs many lives in many parts of the world. Our liberal culture is extremely oppressive to unappreciative pagans. We export military hardware and liberal culture on the same ships.

No, puppeteers, we don't belong into this bag of official capitalist culture. Let's stay away from these clubs, these foundations, newspapers, television crews, all these functionaries of a rotten system. Let's stay outside of it – outside means fresh air!

Thank you.

Sincerely,

Peter Schumann — (*Blues of a Summer Tour*, September 30, '80.)

'As a result of these financially lucrative tours, we puppeteers have serious doubts about selling shows to commercial enterprises and being used as part of the tourist and entertainment businesses. — (B & P Newsletter, October '80.)

9. 'Thank you for sharing thoughts and concerns with me, and thank you now, for your last letter, written just before the start of this European tour. I'd like to respond to some things in it, although again, the immediacy has passed.

You wrote about the pine-woods meeting, and though it was miserable for me – and not much fun for anybody else, I'm sure! – I welcome the chance to recall it and try to bring something to a resolution, at least in my head.

Yes, I felt really bad during, after, and about what transpired, but it was also a useful lesson for me, and high time I learned some things.

Disagreeing isn't pleasant, and not resolving anything is frustrating, but the worst thing for me, was that I felt terribly misunderstood, right from the beginning, and that is obviously my fault, for not being clearer, not being able to defend my point of view more convincingly. I felt as though everything I said was interpreted in the worst possible light,

489

and that it was impossible for me to explain, protest or reason, because that only made everything worse, made my position look weaker and nastier and greedier. And for such misunderstanding, the issue of those heaps of logs certainly wasn't worth it! It was stupid to let myself be bothered by those heaps of logs in that way . . . but, and here the unsaid arguments, justifications, protestations, and what I *really* meant, spring anew to mind. But they really should be smothered in the interests of greater harmony, so let them lie.

That Peter vetoed the proposed solution was almost a relief. It saved me from further embarrassment and being still more misunderstood: I had decided, some days before, that I would return any proposed (by me or others) compensation to the theater, to show that it is not the money but the *recognition* that the trees have value, have intrinsic worth and preciousness, that is important to me. But at the meeting that seemed totally irrelevant. Also, it is healthy to see that there can be a real disagreement about something, and still the world doesn't fall apart. I feel I deserved Peter's veto, he had said very strongly earlier, that he was against any such transactions between our family and Bread & Puppet. Although he'd also said, this is your affair, I want nothing to do with it. So it should be fairly simple to stay away from them basta! to give freely what seems right and good, and not do business with the rest.

So, in the case of the pine-woods-tree- and cedar- and poplar-pole cutting, 1981, let's say that's over with and done.

Anything in the future is just as unresolved as ever, and I agree with Michael and the lease-stipulations that say: decisions concerning woods, cuttings, building, etc. (whatever that clause says – I'm too lazy to fish it out and quote verbatim), whether one-shot or long-range deals should be written down and agreed to by the 2 parties signing. We were smart to specify as much as we did in those lawyer-papers, and see, the trouble comes from those areas not written out.

So, that is a kind of resolution, only I felt too dumb and depressed at the meeting to even agree with him, when Michael brought it up.' — (Elka, letter to Trudi Cohen, December 22, '81.)

10. 'And it also bring difficulties that I hadn't envisioned because then I do feel more out of it and when we were down there, automatically everything that happened I knew about and I was in on, not everything but certainly on – now Peter, and I more than he, because he works with the puppeteers more, feel more and more on the outside edge of things. It's the puppeteers who are at the center of it and the museum is there, the telephone and the mail all go through there. So it's like getting – but that's – you know, you can't have it both ways. And I'm pretty happy that this is possible because I think the other way wouldn't have – It seems silly to talk so much about – And so far, when I've asked the puppeteers who live down there how it's for them during the circus, and I think of it as the same thing for me, that if anybody asked me specifically how has it been for you, how was the summer, you would think your immediate reaction would be that people are trying to be considerate and things are better organized and the other kitchen is being used more and all that, but I think it's a cumulative effect where – and I think I hear sounds of it among the puppeteers where they say "You can't get away from these things," and you can't – (I: No, but, hell, it's their work and it wasn't yours. Isn't that a major difference? It's their work and it only is a month, that's all.) Yeah, except then they spend – It's two months and then –' — (Elka Schumann, interview, '83.)

'Dear Friends, John, Trudi, Barbara and Michael, I would like to request from the Bread and Puppet Theater a Sabbatical – a leave of absence with pay for one year, starting very soon.

I am on the brink of a very new situation in my life when Maria leaves for boarding school this fall. She will be home for vacations and some weekends, of course, and she still needs us in many ways, and, of course, the other children still visit and sometimes stay here and I'd like to give them the time and support they need. But a 21-year period in my life of child-care and family-centeredness is coming to an end, and it feels like a good time to re-examine options, to look around, see what other directions there are, evaluate what I can do, what new things I want to learn.

Besides the family, including Peter, my life, ever since the Delancey Street days (1963-), has been dominated by Peter's work, the Bread and Puppet Theater, and not always in comfortable or pleasant ways (understatement). The main occupation for almost half my life has been providing support for Peter, the children and the Theater, mostly in a series of unending, amorphous, undefined, repetitious tasks, and, more, in a state of mind which excludes specific, creative, goal-directed projects (something more permanent and satisfying than cooking a great meal, balancing the books, or posting 27 letters into the mailbox). Yes, motherhood has lots of ecstatically happy moments; yes, I created and worked on my own children's theater and a few times felt we did well; and, yes, the idea and building of the new house is a definite achievement.

But for me to think in a serious, long-range way about what I *choose* to do, what I want to do, that is very unfamiliar territory and I feel pretty lost.

At first I though of the obvious, the thing-at-hand: to plunge full-steam and full-time into the work of the Theater, especially after this extended period, since the last Circus, of withdrawing from active and direct participation. (Though there are a lot of passive and indirect, but also time-consuming, ways of participating, too!)

I've always felt keenly my separateness from the Theater, an uneasy, difficult, strained and strenuous relationship. Sometimes the separateness was chosen deliberately (and wisely, I think) when the children (and Peter) needed the stability of a settled family life more than I needed "to be in a show"; sometimes the separateness stemmed from inalienable differences between Peter and me – still unresolved and making working together still pretty damn hard or well-nigh impossible; sometimes the separateness was by default, by not being there at the needed time, not being talented or skillful or quick enough for the job, being afraid of and insecure about the super-duper commitment that work on a show entails. And sometimes the separateness was urged, advised, thrust on me by P. Sch. Anyway (I'll use this word a lot!) I thought: now, with house built and moved into) for at least the BIG part of B&P-Schumann existence figured out (for the Schumanns)), with children grown and gone, and growing and going, there would be only the sheep-cat-house-and-garden baby-sitting to solve – and then I'd be free to join in on intensive experiment-rehearsal projects, free to join prolonged world-tours, starting, after the Circus, with Cuba, then Germany-Poland, etc. I would get really involved, do it full-time, and see how much I was capable of contributing and how this life suited the 46-7 year-old me. I've never done this for longer than 3 months at a time, and all the while juggling a full-time, many-membered household.

But I've also thought of other things I want to do, try out, get started in, develop more of, which I have not been able to. I've wondered what I can do, what skill do I have, how can I support myself when I'm old or if I'm alone. I've done so little outside the home and the Theater all these many years. And, though I've also loved and appreciated the good things of these two institutions, I've also felt trapped and suffocated by them.

Another consideration, crass but of great weight, especially when you have children, is money. That has always been a problem, and now is worse, I'm surprised to discover, even with the children gone so much. As much as I can figure out, it's inflation, it's the move to the new house, and the bigger demands of the growing children. I've thought: can I develop a skill, a business, to earn more money to get by and support our children in their education? What we have gotten from B&P, salaries and benefits combined, improved as it is over the early and middle years, is barely adequate for a single person, as you all know; it's insufficient for a family with a car, animals, appliances that need repair, dental bills, eyeglass-frames replacements, 7 birthdays, an occasional graduation present or round-trip

491

busfare from NYC or Boston, etc. etc., not to mention tuition for boarding school or college. So, I've worried a lot about that lately, feeling on more than one occasion, that I should leave the Theater and get a job (any, old) just to make ends meet.

The pain of giving up these old, deeply-rooted connections, of giving up "my turf" (the same things that I do, do well, am in charge of, you know that), is very strong, very wrenching. (Pure possessiveness and pride in MY paltry portion of the puppet pie.)

Anyway, thanks to a fight between Peter and me, 2 days ago, I suddenly faced, very clearly, a question: Would I be doing this if I had no personal relationship with Peter? The answer is, clearly: No. I have neither the special skills nor that kind of driving ambition for performing and theater-work which would pull me to this sphere. (But, hey, please give me credit, that, when I've been in the shows, I do as well as most, and maybe my greatest achievement in the Theater has been to keep out of the way as much as I have.)

So, I would like a year to work on some projects. Some are connected to or could become part of, the Theater's activities; others, not at all. Some are very hazy and ill-defined, others quite specific.

1) I would like to:

learn a new instrument, or get my flute fixed and relearn that;

find, collect and do research on Daisy Dopp's articles;

apprentice with a printer for at least a little while to learn something about presses;

research and develop some agricultural possibilities that might be developed more here (more sheep (cries of dismay?!), berries, bees, exotic plants, woodlot-management, sugaring, etc.);

learn book-binding;

2) I would like to be free of the duties connected with: B&P business (checks, bills, bookkeeping, yearly summary, etc.)

B&P letters (except see below)*

the Circus work this year (except see below)*

B&P meetings, except where they concern the use of this land as specified in the lease (tree-cutting, building, and fences); portentous decisions reaching out over the years; public summing-up/evaluation meetings; the yearly Board meeting;

B&P tours (except with Goya, see below)*

3) I *do* want to continue these projects which I have initiated and/or developed over the years:

the book-and-booklet mail-order business;

the scrap-book collections of reviews, press-releases, flyers, programs and publications;

the photo archives;

the public pageant rehearsals and parades;

the Goya production this summer and Peter's workshop in Berlin, because that's the only way I could get to visit Peter's mother;

I am willing to sell posters during the Circus, since I've done it over the years (later: be generally in charge of the poster-room and selection and printing of posters);

I would like to be a friend and good-neighbor, and help out where needed with: watering plants when you're on tour, pushing cars out of snowbanks, taking and relaying phone messages, forwarding mail, and, when you're on tour, doing any emergency business, banking, correspondence, museum-tours or exhibit-work.

492

At the end of '80, at the annual meeting of the Board of Directors and Members of the Theatre, December 14, dissatisfactions of the puppeteers with their lack of recognition, especially since the theatre was known and advertised as Schumann's, surfaced.[11] The listing (alphabetically) of perfor-

---

If this is acceptable to you, I need about a week to wrap up loose ends (the books, bank-statement-balancing, letters and (ugh) phone-calls).

(What have I overlooked? The importance of the farm?
What have I bludgeoned into the ground?)

Later, July 8: Had a meeting with us six on July 1; John, Trudi, Barbara, Michael were very understanding and accepted this proposal. Yesterday we met so that I could hand over the check-book (beautifully balanced!!), letters, folders, papers, etc. Still a few letters to write, lots of office and house-cleaning to do, calls and letters to get my projects started.

Note; I am very grateful to the "Theater" and the people in it for making this possible for me. I feel very privileged and fortunate, for I feel that my situation is very common, universal (?) for people, women, of my age and of other ages, and so few can do anything to try things out, to try to change or find themselves (perhaps right where they were (left)). — (Elka Schumann, letter (to resident puppeteers), June 30, '81.)
"I feel in a funny position now, vis-a-vis the theater, and maybe that contributed to the bad meeting. It's great to have the sabbatical, and I'm consciously happy to be in this position, to have all this time. I'm trying to stay out of my previous activities, to give this change a chance to be really different. But given lots of givens, which I wouldn't want to change, it's hard to make it *that* different. I miss some things a lot, like, well, working for my living, contributing to the enterprise which puts food on the table. I miss the feeling of connection to something that's been such a big part of my life for so long. But time passes, and things change, and maybe that something has become something else over the years, to which I don't have such a connection any more.

Living with Peter has been easier and evener and less full of strain lately, as my involvement with B&P has lessened so have our disagreements; I don't have my own (often opposing his) opinion about meetings, rehearsals I don't attend, facts I don't know, so clashes between us are fewer; I am more supportive, and that makes living together easier, so perhaps I should stay clear of those areas permanently; I'm trying to be correct, for now, to be removed and give this a try — but how can I not care?! And some things I care specifically and deeply about, and want to continue caring, but as I become disengaged in the other areas, my connections to everything and people, weaken, loosen.' — (Elka Schumann, letter to Trudi Cohen, December 22, '81.)
11. 'Discussion of following topics:
critique of theater-business-at-large,
policies towards the media,
unscheduled time,
recognition of work in B&P,
salaries, etc.

Recognition

Barbara — worth talking about for different people on different levels. I've worked in the theater for many years. I don't think many people know how the theater works. People call and ask for Peter when it's not even him they need to deal with. The name Peter Schumann becomes Bread and Puppet Theater. People don't get the chance to realize how many people contribute to it. It starts to feel after all these years that my contribution isn't recognized. At the Pentagon there was another problem because it was called B and P puppets — that how the public understands it.

493

John B. – an element of rightful confusion. B and P puppets go everywhere. 9th St. is and isn't. Partly related to our relationship to the media. We don't present ourselves to the press.

Linda – Often an interviewer asks how do you work.

John B. – Peter is responsible for the theater, it is his theater and shows and art. Press wants to have a figure to ascribe things to. Easier for them.

Elka – Most theaters give credits for everything.

Peter – We could give credits and over the years people would get used to seeing names. Becomes more complicated with big volunteer crews. It must be ungratifying to you puppeteers that you're always lost in big companies. I object to listing people's names, also to using my name. But I make no effort to prevent them from using my name, either.

Barbara – That's probably not the answer. I wish more was called B and P instead of Peter Schumann.

Paul – Should put something in the contract not to bill show as Peter Schumann's Bread and Puppet Theater. I have one that says I'm not B and P in my contract. At BAM 2 years ago we had a discussion and I was the only one for credits. Peter said we traditionally don't do this and in the current glorification of the individual it was better not to stress names.

Elka – We could invent words to describe our group.

Peter – In the late 60's everything had to be "collaboration" and we were called a collaborative and I hated that because it wasn't true. It's not democratic and there's no point to pretend it is. But that doesn't help now. I don't like Peter Schumann's Bread and Puppet either and maybe we should get used to credits. I would prefer it was anonymous but we can't do that anymore so let's have a credit sheet.

Peter – But this isn't solved with crediting alone. It's real recognition more than seeing your name.

Amy – Sometimes we get the opposite of credit. "Much help and little inspiration from the puppeteers" was written by Stefan Brecht.

George – You can always identify yourselves as long-term members of the company.

Paul – I put my work with B and P in my press release. I try not to exploit that connection. It does bother me when somebody says they've worked with Bread and Puppet and I never heard of them.

Amy – Do you get upset when things get called Bread and Puppet which aren't?

Peter – Yes, sometimes. We're big enough, though, that B and P can absorb some bad shows." — (Trudi Cohen, Minutes of the annual meeting of the Board of Directors and the members of the Bread & Puppet Theatre, December 14, '80, at Paul Zaloom's loft in NYC.)

"So one of the things that was brought up by the puppeteers, some of whom have now been with Bread and Puppet for 10 years, are credits – recognition. They don't get any. Rarely is there a program. Never is there a credit by name. (I: There never was.) Right, there never was. But then on the other hand, never was a kind of itinerant in-and-out of people. You would advertise, get some people and they would perform and that was the end of it. (I: Also, it was never Peter Schumann's and Bread and Puppet Theatre.) But, the point that was raised, was that now people know it is Bread and Puppet. And they know it because up in Vermont people call there and ask for Peter Schumann. It is that – Barbara Leber does most of the business with Elke, but people don't call up and ask for Elka, or

mers (and non-performing members) in programs was, along with pay raises and increases of medical insurance coverage,[12] decided on, though

---

Barbara Leber, they ask for Peter Schumann, and they have to say, well, what can we do for you? And they say, we want to talk about booking you into Berlin or Copenhagen, or whatever, and they say, well we can take care of that. Peter doesn't answer the fucking phone. Why should he? It has become known as Peter Schumann's Bread and Puppet Theatre. now, the people who are working at the theatre are not jealous of that fact. They would like somebody to say – Oh, you are a puppeteer, and for Peter that is an accolade. These are puppeteers – he never called me a puppeteer. He didn't call Maurice a puppeteer. Puppeteer is an accolade that he gives to professional skilled accomplished people. Maurice was an actor, not a puppeteer. So these people who are finally now puppeteers would like a little recognition. If there is to be a program, could their names be in it? If there is to be a poster, could their names be on it. Is there some way of recognizing their existence as humans and performers? And that was very hard. I mean, we tried to talk about it diffidently, but insistently . . . Leber was definitely the leader. And of course I was supportive. I think people ought to be recognized. People should be thanked. Bob Wilson used to put in like 97 names of people, thanking them – some had nothing to do with the production, so what – say thank you. There is nothing wrong with saying thank you. I don't – somehow my ego does not need to be massaged by this kind of thing. I don't care about it. And I say that, and then I will tell you a separate story, that when the postcard came out for the Gertrude Stein reading for New year's Eve and my name wasn't on it, I was furious. And I didn't know about it. Why is my participation important? It is not, except that I arrive with stones from Gertrude's grave, postcard made a tribute to Gertrude, two of them, in fact. I always recruit a dozen people to read, and I was just feeling my involvement with the annual Gertrude Stein reading was something that was important. To be left off, I was absolutely furious . . . Because – Peter did say – well, of course. Program credit, print whatever you want, I won't stand in your way. now, let's have the birthday cake for Paul Zaloom, and we will go on." — (George Ashley, interview, '81.)

"Dear Editor,

Thank you to the Chronicle for your friendly coverage of Bread and Puppet Theater's work, but there is one important fact that any description of us should contain, namely, that the theater in its present form would not be possible without 4 people whose contributions and talents rarely get public acknowledgement: John Bell, Trudi Cohen, Barbara Leber and Michael Romanyshyn. They joined the company between the years 1971-75; they all make their home here in Glover; and their work most consistently contributes to Bread and Puppet productions both at home and on tour.

Besides this core group there is a second one of people who do not live in Glover but who have worked with us most summers since the first Glover Circus in 1975 and who have taken part in many of the tours. This includes Ron Kelley, Linda Elbow, Joanne Schulz, Ralph Denzer, Richard Norcross and Genevieve Yieullaz. Margo Lee Sherman, Sara Peattie and Amy Trompetter have participated intermitantly in B&P since the mid-sixties; Paul Zaloom and Mark Dannenhauer since the early '70's. Many others have become involved during the last few years, and this summer saw a big increase in the participation of people directly from this area. I wish I could mention everyone's name, but the list would cover the page and still leave some out, I'm afraid. All contribute in unique and invaluable ways.

Peter Schumann founded the Bread and Puppet Theater; he authors the shows and bakes the bread. But it is inaccurate and uncalled for to label the Bread and Puppet Theater as "the Schumanns' ". Thank you.' (Elka Schumann, letters to the editor of *The Chronicle*, September 7, '82.)

12. 'They had decided they had certain responsibility in the theatre to the people who were

no indications of who performed what were to be given. Both the voicing of those dissatisfactions,[13] and the agreement[14] engendered further disharmonies during the following year.

---

working there regularly. And they have been paying eyeglasses, John Bell constantly breaks his glasses and needs to have new glasses, dentistry, eyeglasses and minor health things, the theatre has been paying for. Then they decided they would set aside one percent of their income in a special bank account for serious medical things. 1% of 186 thousand does not pay for three days in a hospital. And I was able to make this telling point because Charley Adams has died. Charley Adams, went into a brain tumor and he was in a hospital and I am sure he was on every kind of special tube, what have you, and undoubtedly in three days he ran up 6 thousand dollars worth of medical bills, and I tried to point this out that they had to buy Blue Cross and Blue Shield Insurance for catastrophic injuries and every other kind that they could not buy out of 1% of their annual income, that was a total waste of their time. 1% takes care of broken eyeglasses, that is about all. My first proposal then, was that they investigate and become members of a group ... Then, I also pointed out, that – they haven't had a raise – they are earning 60 dollars a week. And that has been going on for a long time. It is time to give them more money. Why? Holy poverty. Holy poverty. The idea of being able to buy a hat or a pair of gloves – or whatever. Sixty dollars just doesn't – especially up in Vermont where long underwear, just washing clothes, you know, it is all – (I: 60 dollars a week is pretty low.) Yes, and then they point out, they are also getting housing, and they are getting heat – for their – they have a house, they have food, and they get 60 dollars a week. And I say – well, in the old days when I smoked, I was smoking 12 dollars worth of cigarettes or more, I was drinking at least 12 dollars worth of Bourbon. I can't live with you – that is crazy. So I also voted that there be a raise in salaries. For all the puppeteers. (I: Capitalistifying it –) Absolutely – I am truly ruining it. And everybody knows. I talked to the – the puppeteers are coming here to do the Theater for a New City – they need a place to live.' — (George Ashley, interview, '81.)

13. 'I want to make a few things clear that have suffered from ambiguity and need not be ambiguous at all.

What does the Theater have to offer its members, and what not? What kind of membership is its membership and what organization is there for it?

As of 1980 the Theater offers 6 members a very small salary and adequate housing plus some medical support in return for work that extends from garbage-removal to puppet-manipulation, from celastic-crafting to concerteering, from bookkeeping to circus-planning, and creative participation in performances which range from slapstick to puppet-poetry, from fun and nonsense to groping with major human issues. The work-load is big, the responsibilities are many, the variety of tasks – plentiful. Now, for the first time in the Theater's history, there is a small, richly-talented group that has been consistent for a whole row of years and is able to tackle the multiple problems of Bread and Puppetry in the US and abroad.

I am glad that it is like this, it's much easier to work like this, and I know it's due to the personalities of the people involved. I am grateful to them and hope that they continue.

We are trying to run this company by democratic methods, by concensus on all major issues, with common sense and friendship. We used to say that we have a communist organization, because we got reimbursed according to need and not according to contribution, and that is still true.

The form of our organization is not rigid. We have produced a few hundred puppet-shows with the help of this organization, without much bother, without analyzing and scrutinizing our productive process.

The work and the chores that it requires do not guarantee gratification; the appreciation

496

that one has of this work is bound to change. Personal desires change. Personal input and enthusiasm change.

Judging from recent meetings, the stage of naiveté of our company and the satisfaction deriving from that stage of naiveté have come to an end. Our organization now needs to be analyzed. What does it, how is it doing what it does, how come and in what way? The organization can change, can adapt to growth, to wider perspective, to greater justice. We are now talking about changes, we apply them, we try them out.

But there is one thing that will not change, and since there seems to be some confusion about it now, as there has been on and off, let me express it for you in all clarity:

Yes, my name is Bread and Puppet, I conceive the shows, I author them, I create, design and direct them. Or, in other words, however necessary democracy is as a just method for the functioning of our company, it cannot apply to the production itself. Inspiration is a relationship to God and not to colleagues and friends.

By saying this, I don't think I deprive you of your personal merits. Your improvisations and inventions, your costumes and stages, your musical instruments and performances are important for what they are, they are the flesh of the production.

But the apparent arbitrariness of choices made from so much material at hand and the chaos of the many try-out sessions on the road towards the next puppetshow should not deceive you into assuming that these shows come together haphazardly. I do try to explain as much of the inside of what is going on as I can with my limited vocabulary, but the best part of it, unfortunately, is not explicable, at least not from the maker's standpoint. (The viewer who is confronted with the (not so) finished product is in a different position.)

Yes, I rely on your gifts, your work, your commitment to ideas and compositions that often must seem unreasonable and weird to you. We are better off with each other if you realize the nature of our relationship as it really is and not for what it is not.

These puppetshows don't spring from experiments. They are visionary junk that gets put into the frying pan to be made palatable — or rather, not palatable but hopefully edible.

But they rely on visions, and these visions are exclusive, private dreams and are soloistic by nature.

There is no justification why this is as it is. I just want to tell you that changes in organization will not change this basic characteristic of our company, because that happens to be its limitation and its strength.

No, friends, our puppetry is not communally-invented, Schumann-directed theater. If you think that you only fool yourselves.

I don't particularly enjoy spelling this out. And until now it was ok to not say this. But now that we have started penetrating this theme I feel obliged to these definitions. I can only do that much. Your personal searches for identity and happiness in work and life can only be pursued by yourselves. Let me remind you though, that what you are participating in is not an ordinary job, and there is absolutely nothing degrading in this form of participation. If you understand it right, the rewards are obvious.

I hope you understand that I am not talking about credits. We have discussed credits, and, yes, if we are now beyond the state of grace and anonymity and you feel that printed credits do more justice to you, then this will be done in whatever form we decide together. Let's not worry too much about the credits though. You can call me Peter Schmalz or Joe Misfit or anything you like. This presentation to the outside world we can make up in any fashion whatsoever. But as far as we ourselves are concerned, let's be clear.

I can definitely say that I am doing what I am doing for the matter-of-fact of it, for what it is objectively, for whatever it's worth doing this kind of stuff for, and for nothing else.' — (Peter Schumann, *Letter to Now and Former Hardcore Puppeteers*, January 8, '81.)

'Dear John, Trudi, Barbara, Michael and Peter, This letter concerns the discussion we had last week about credits and recognition. I was upset by the final form of the decision and it has taken me a while to sort some of the reasons out for myself. I'd like to share these thoughts with you.

The issue of "recognition for work done in Bread and Puppet Theater" is valid and important, but after saying that, it gets very complicated to figure it all out. Recognition, fine, but in what form? Outward/inward? Who? How? Printing credits on programs and posters, etc., is one way, and certainly seems worth trying out, to see how it looks and feels and does it do the job it's supposed to? So, I did support the decision to make a printed credit sheet for the NYC run in February-March. However, the specific working of those credits, as written by Peter for the flyer, I find increasingly disturbing and unsatisfactory, and I'll try to explain why.

The main specific and immediate reason is, that the credits say, by omission, that I am not a member of Bread and Puppet Theater and that others, who have worked in the Theater only sporadically, are members, and that is not right and not fair. I guess we should define what constitutes a member (or find other words): is it one who participates in performances or tours? In that case, if we had had the same system this summer for the Puppeteers of America Festival show, the credits would have stated that Vance was a member and, by omission, that John and Trudi were not. Or, for the Stations of the Cross tour, neither Barbara, Michael, nor Peter would be members. So, what happens to those who work long and hard in Bread and Puppet, who then do not participate in a tour? You all have been in that situation, so how would you feel if the statement presented by the Theater of who is and is not a member, whose work is or is not valued and recognized, left out your name and included others with much less involvement. What would you think would be a better solution? (And that sometimes there might be arbitrary mention of your name in the (usually mis- or un-informed) news media, is, to my mind, a completely different matter from the deliberate statement by the Theater about who works in it, and doesn't "make up" for being left out at all.)

I disagree with Peter, when he says it does not matter what we say to the outside world. I think it matters a lot, because we are stating it for a fact to everyone, the outside world and our friends and ourselves, too. It doesn't really matter what outsiders say about the Theater, though it can be annoying or infuriating (". . . on stilts 20 feet high . . ." or "of course anyone can join the company . . .", etc.).

So, it is simple not to give credits and let the audiences and reviewers choose to think whatever they want. It is very difficult to credit correctly and fairly. How to be fair and include everyone in the right way? One possibility would be, to call the participants in a performance "The Bread and Puppet Performing Company", and then it is correct that those not performing are not in the performing company. But it is still not fair to the hard-core members (and I am not questioning that I and you five are the hardcore members) who happen not to be in that particular performance or tour. It also puts everyone in the performing company on the same level: here are the people who got together for this tour. (If Peter is not on that tour, is his name then not included, and is that right?)

Or what about two lists on a credit sheet: Bread and Puppet Theater Resident Company and Bread and Puppet Theater Performing Company, and have some names appear on both lists?

The first proposal sounds incomplete and inaccurate, and the second is cumbersome and awkward. And as we pursue a greater accuracy and completion, so will the awkwardness increase, and will justice and fairness be any closer? (And the more breakdown in the jobs and design credits, the more often Peter's name would appear, and is that not what you want to avoid?)

Also, if credits are given, I'd like to speak up for the director being named as the director, and again, if applicable, as a performer. I think that a director stands in such a different relationship to a show (especially if he also conceives the "story" and designs the masks, backdrops, etc.) from the rest of the company, that that kind of information warrants being put in an accurate credits sheet. The show would simply not come into being, not exist, without its creator, but it could and can exist, and has existed, with other people doing the jobs that you and I do: the staging, lights, costumes, letters, music, performance, bookkeeping, etc. (And that should not take away from the feeling of accomplishment for the decent, dogged, consistent, good, splendid and marvellous jobs we do at our various jobs, either!) If the credits are to include important information about the work that went into the shows, then naming the director is that kind of information.

If we do that, then perhaps we should add the assisted-bys, the lighting-costumes-stagemanaged-bys, and why not? But now, for me, it has all become too complicated and stupid, so blown out of all proportion, that I begin to see a lot of virtue and wisdom in skipping it all and returning to simple "Bread and Puppet Theater", and let whoever read into that whatever they want, and who cares?

What has done before without thought and deliberation and because of tradition, could, after thinking through the ramifications and consequences of crediting, now be done deliberately and with full appreciation for its brevity, cleverness and (yes, compared to the morass of accurate yet unsatisfactory and unsatisfying detail) clarity.

But, let's try it out this way, and or, perhaps one of you has another, better solution' . . .
— (Elka Schumann, letter to Schumann and to the resident puppeteers, January 12, '81.)
14. 'I saw a copy of the program for the Goya/Venus shows with the lists of credits on the back page, and I want to state my objection to the use of my name in this way. I was neither consulted nor informed about having my name included and being called "administrator".

As you recall, we had a meeting in Glover before you left for NYC and discussed crediting then. Peter had made a list of everyone in the NYC performance and then repeated his name after "directed by". The rest of you objected strongly to this singling out of one of the names with its special job. I think it was John who said that if noone else had their special jobs mentioned, then Peter shouldn't, either, and the rest of you agreed. George Ashley, at the December board meeting, had proposed listing the names in alphabetical order, with no distinction to that too. After a decision is made in a group that way, I don't think that it should be lightly changed, without another group decision, especially when it affects a particular person.

I would not have agreed to being singled out and would not have agreed to being called "administrator". I would not have objected to being included in a list, because it feels so bad to be left out. If anyone were to be singled out, I still strongly believe that it should be Peter, as director, and I think that it is stupid and misleading not have him named the director, as though these 8 individuals had equally created these pieces.

That the particular job to be singled out is "administrator" I find puzzling, petty and silly. What is an administrator? (To administer, dictionary definition: to supply, furnish or provide with; to apply, inflict, mete or measure out, to have the charge or direction of; to regulate . . .) Who does the administrating in B&P? I do some, Barbara does some, other puppeteers do it on other occasions. Peter is certainly the only one who has charge and direction of. Does B&P have AN ADMINISTRATOR, a janitor, costume-maker, star-puppeteer, solo-singer? I think not, and I thought we prided ourselves, that, unlike other companies, most of us did most of these things. Is my notioin outdated, mistaken?

And that I am picked out to be called the "administrator", just doesn't feel right. It is so limiting, so demeaning, and untrue. I do some of that kind of work, and so do other people. But I don't want to be called that, and am not that. Maybe it is a way to make me feel even more excluded and set apart. Maybe it is someone's idea of a joke. Most probably it was well-meant, so that I wouldn't feel so bad about not having my name listed on the program, but it feels belittling and condescending. At least the choice of label could have been more true or poetic: wife-who-stays-at-home-and-writes-letters, sugar-maple-tapper, Black-Hills-sunset-observer, etc. etc. You just can't win!' — (Elka Schumann, *Letter to Whom It May Concern* (to Schumann and to the puppeteers), March 12, '81.)

Elka's dissatisfaction with being distinguished from the puppeteers as 'administration' resulted in a new formula from sometime in '81 onward: listing of the actual performers on stage in a given piece. This excluded her. It also excluded the director, Schumann, when he

This compound and apparently minor crisis, '79-'81, has not as of now (October '83) had any results visible to an outsider such as myself, other than that there was no Glover circus in '80 – the group put on one in Villeurbanne, by Lyons, instead. It was an indication of strains, further indicated by rumors, in '83, that two of the resident puppeteers were intending to leave the group.

On reading the minutes of the meetings, the letters exchanged: the high-mindedness of everyone involved is remarkable: no egoisms, refined or crass, are pushing to the fore, it's just a matter of people, ordinary people, not geniuses, having over a long time of steady great pressure been pushed into very restricted positions, or: maintained there while time was passing and their lives with it, and now bethinking themselves of their modest needs and wishes and timidly and with trepidation making them known. The pressure has been exerted, the load put on them not really by Schumann – who *is* a genius and practically the sole asset of the Bread and Puppet Corporation whose salaried employees he and all the others involved in this crisis are, they as of '79 – but by his work: he is easily as high-minded as the rest, and if, as I believe, part of his private guilt is a need for power during his life in practice fulfilled not only by power over audiences, but also by his leadership of his group, he has never, I would say, consciously pursued the satisfaction of this need in his relations to his group, but has in whatever manoeuvering he has engaged in aimed only at creating and maintaining propitious work conditions for himself, for the sake, not of himself, but of humanity's welfare, and keeping in mind at all times the benefits of the individuals he was dealing with accruing to them from their assistance in that work. The four periods of his creativity are separated by crises both in his personal and work circumstances and in his ability to arrive at conceptualizations serviceable in his work.

'60/'61: inability to embody his life-death dialectic in a dance work; '69: inability to accomodate the benign God of the Christians in a biblical representation of history; '73: inability to identify theatrically serviceable reasons for hope for humanity, given man's predatory and competitive character; '78: inability in pageants to accomodate the destructive efficiency of civilization in an anthropocentric pantheism.

---

was not a performer, as was not frequently the case. There were no credits in the circus programs '81 ff.

5. *Washerwoman ah!* ('79). The emergence of new themes: the terrors of childhood and the conquest of them; terrorism; and nuclear war, the different war of the future.

Schumann had since '71 had 'garbagemen' in his shows, representatives of the working classes, and thus generally working — e.g. as visible stage crew. A married garbageman appeared in '76, his wife an amiable small Beast. In '78, as complement to the male sinner Wolkenstein, he created the female equivalent of the garbageman, the 'washerwoman', representative of the woman of the people (Frau aus dem Volk, femme du peuple), a stout little female, vaguely Slavic in dress and mien, modeled exteriorily on Elka, and, starting out to make a play in which she would be more important that in *Wolkenstein*, ended up[1] making of her the central figure and heroine of a play, cheerful incarnation of good sense and fortitude, down-to-earth version of the heroines of his 'positive morality plays' of the Initial Dopp Farm Period, expression of a development and partial revision of the view of woman as passive sufferer suggested by the Grey Lady of his Goddard period. This play, the first of three such, turned out to be *Washerwoman Cantata I – Ah!* It was Elka's play:

'But the First Washerwoman Cantata, Peter created that show for our family to take on tour. We just decided we would do it. We had been together on the '76 tour and this very big group and then somehow three years later we thought it would be nice to do a smaller tour with all our family. Maybe it was shortly before Tamara went to finish high school. I guess we thought if we didn't do it then our family would really be — it would be hard to work together in any project, although Peter suggested it last year for doing this Christmas. But again it's already very difficult now, you know, people's schedules to get together. But that one we did with four other people so there were 11 on the tour. Suzy Francis Dennison was on that tour so more than half the company was below — was 16 or younger. It was a really, you know, very young . . . And I don't know, the way Peter had described the show I thought it was going to be very different, like

---

1. 'Well, the Washerwomen were already in existence (when puppets from the '78 *Circus* and its *Wolkenstein* were made (SSB)), at least some of them were, as complementaries to the garbagemen for the *Wolkenstein* production, and they ended up being the angels, the heavenly lot, on the other side of the devils of that stage. Then it was felt that that didn't do them justice, that there needed to be a *Washerwoman Cantata* – a washerwoman show. That was the next show that was made, even though really when I started making a new show that fall (fall of '78 (SSB)), with Ruth and Linda helping me out, I didn't *mean* to give the washerwoman this *prominence*. I only thought of *one* washerwoman that would be in that show and I built a whole set of new puppets. Most of them were not used in this upcoming show then'. — (Schumann, interview.)

in memories of childhood, and instead it became to me very sort of rooted in this one Washerwoman character and sort of her trials and tribulations. But I felt an affinity with her and played her and it was nice to be that character . . . I feel that I sort of invented her (the figure of the Washerwoman (SSB)) . . . I felt that was something that I could do convincingly (laugh) and I was heavy and slow and not . . . but that I could do these simple things . . . It had a chorus of Washerwomen with one main one and I played her and when it was taken on tour later Trudi played her and that Washerwoman sang the Russian song at different points.

(Elka Schumann, interview, '83.)

The play was taken on a small tour locally (February 22 and 23 ('79) at the Alumni Hall of Vermont College in Montpelier, February 24 at the North Country Union High School in Newport, February 25 at Trinity College in Burlington), then went to Europe on that family tour (Holland, England and Scotland in March, France in May), was shown, one time only, in the pine wood late at night, at the '79 circus, and in the fall it and *Washerwoman Cantata #2* were taken on a tour of the eastern seaboard that Schumann had orginally intended[2] to take the circus on — starting Labor Day weekend, September 1-3 in NYC as part of the street fair part

---

2. 'Dear Theater Sponsor:

The Bread and Puppet Theater will be touring the eastern United States during the fall of this year and we are looking for performance engagements. We will be presenting our travelling Domestic Resurrection Circus, a festival, staged and performed by 25 puppeteers and musicians together with 50 to 100 local participants.

The enclosed materials provide some added background for those of you unfamiliar with the kind of work we do. For a while now we have been feeling a growing need to expand on the limitations imposed by a strict theater setting and theater-going audience. Each summer for the past eight years we have done a large two-day festival here in Vermont, including a wide range of large and small puppet productions, exhibits, pageantry, circus and music. This year we would like to take as much of that as possible to other communities, involving local people as well.

The performances include a one-hour outdoor paper-mache circus with live brass band, a large outdoor pageant with giant puppets and masks to be performed at dusk, several fairy tale and Punch and Judy-type shows for the entire family also meant for outdoor performance during the afternoon, at least one major inside production for night time, and assorted parades through town. The company will prepare this festival in the community for several days, rehearsing and training the volunteer participants and setting up outdoor booths and stages, banners and flags, indoor theater sets and exhibits of paintings and colored woodcuts. The festival would then be performed for a day or more, either in one fixed location or travelling it to neighboring communities. We can also consider doing any combination of the performances we will bring (for example, simply an afternoon parade and evening indoor production), although we much prefer to offer the entire event.

For a full week's production we are asking $5000 plus room and board for the large travelling company. Our usual fee for a single indoor performance is $1200. As we are interested in performing in a wide variety of places with resources equally varied, we are willing to negotiate prices on the basis of what you want us to do, whether other performances can be arranged in the nearby vicinity, and your ability to pay. We hope to leave Vermont Sept. 1 and finish the tour mid-October.

For further information, please contact me at the above address. I look foward to hearing from you as soon as possible.' — (Trudi Cohen, letter of solicitation, April 10, '79.)

502

of the Bread and Roses project of District 1199 of the National Union of Hospital and Health Care Employees, 'the largest program to bring culture to the rank and file in the history of the labor movement' (Doug Ireland, *Soho Weekly News*, September 6, '79), and continuing on to Atlanta, Ga., Catonsville, Md., and Philadelphia. It was again shown in NYC at the Brooklyn Academy of Music, January 15 to February 3, '80.

The play, in three parts – (I) Joys and Plights of the Members of the International Union of Washerwomen, (II) Life of a Washerwoman as a Child, (III) Life of a Washerwoman as a Woman – as usual underwent various modifications, notably the eliminations of a *Disasters of War* scene derived from Goya,[3] and the inclusion of an anti-nuclear armament statement[4] by the writer Grace Paley, 'which she was not permitted to give in

---

3. 'And in our version (spring '79 (SSB)) we had a series called The Disasters of War, which the kids did mainly, Ephraim, Tamara, Solveig, Michael, I think, where they – they looked at the prints of *The Disasters of War* and picked a few poses and then acted them out to a strobe light, violent war things, kind of done in the flickering light where you couldn't see too much of the detail but it just felt like some horrible – But later those parts were eliminated.' — (Elka Schumann, interview, '83.)

4. 'The reason I'm here is I live next door to a school. Every morning the kids go in kind of solemnly and at 3 they come flying out. You know how nice and lively they look. But I and my friends really and truly believe they will never grow up. Certainly they'll never get to be 56 which I happen to be this very day.

So – while the great important powers of the world are piling up arms, nuclear armaments – all the noise and terror of coming war – we did a small quiet kind of simple thing. We stepped out onto the grass of our own President's public home and our friends unfurled a banner in the public place of Russian power and we said listen! Stop!

Whatever you decide about us – guilty or not guilty – we hope you hear what we're saying. Otherwise you'll be taking risks much greater than we've taken and the grass of the whole world will be dangerous to all the children. In fact there won't be any grass and there won't be any children.' — (Grace Paley, statement, '79 (?), program, *Washerwoman Ah!*.)

'(I: When you started work on it did you have in mind coupling it with Grace Paley's statement?) No. (I: Was it "inspired" by that statement?) No . . . I imagine that the first performances didn't have the statement, that then I learned to know about the statement, or read it, and that was just put in as an epilogue to what was seen. Yes, I remember that during the – but where, that I don't remember. And then it was worked into the show slowly in different ways.' — (Peter Schumann, interview, '83.)

Paley is a long-time admirer of Schumann's work:

'ADMIRATION

Oh! Ah! The gorgeousness the solemn size the humorous disparities

HAPPINESS

Sheer happiness just plain happiness

RESTFULNESS

In some of the long slow pieces often of holy intention – rest – the spirit – also the body rests inside the event the work-with room and permission for absence. The gathering of knowledge at the "five senses' entry to the soul" – so with rest comes thought – time – room for thinking *during* the work not only after it.

503

court', but though it never, except by Schumann's or the local washerwoman's recitation of Paley's statement, to any notable extent[5] developed a focus on nuclear war, as fable it seems to have remained pretty much the same: an allegorical fairy tale about a princess (the Washerwoman's fantasy of herself as a child) threatened by a devil and/or dragon representing

---

ARTISTIC INSPIRATION

Why not speak the truth directly? Just speak out! Speak to! Why not?

POLITICAL INSPIRATION

Why not speak the truth directly? Just speak out! Speak up! Speak to! Why not?

CORROBORATION

Yes! That's just what's happening.

ENVY

Because the work is so useful the courage of its usefulness in a long period when usefulness was mocked Envy as an artist for the beauty and usefulness of the huge puppet figures, like legends out of history, the grey women of suffering, the ridiculous evil Uncle Fatso, the lovely oxen turning round and round in the dance of silent beasts, the white deer on the hill under the red ball of the sun, the high birds bravely carried that have flown before and after us on our demonstrations and have waited fluttering in the wind outside the jails of New York Vermont Washington.

To have been useful As An Artist to the important movements of our times: to have spoken out as artists for the poor, the oppressed and humiliated in Europe Africa and at home AND BEEN HEARD

AND FINALLY LOVE AND GRATITUDE

for Peter Schuman and Elka Schuman and that solid core of puppeteers – also for those who came, worked with Peter for a couple of years and then went off to Maine California France Italy Germany Ninth Street New York, Brooklyn Gratitude for their gifts to us of labor and beauty from the earliest unknown days on Delancy Street when we were sometimes fewer than they – to these wonderful summer circus days in Vermont where we, their comrades and friends meet one another in the thousands, AND GRATITUDE also for the opportunity generously given to be one of them, an ox, a deer, a stilt walker, a horse, a maintenance man, a washerwoman.

> And thanks
> Peter for the
> tens of thousands
> of Loaves of Bread

and the music

and for the woodcuts and drawings in this book which are all the work of Peter Schuman' — (Grace Paley, *Feelings in the presence of The sight and sound of the Bread and Puppet Theater*, The 1981 peace Calendar.

5. 'I had not seen Bread and Puppet since the war in Vietnam ended. Even though it was billed as a play about the "fear of annihilation through nuclear war," *Ah!* seems to make only the slimmest of connections between the International Union of Washer Women, the life of a washer woman, and the fear of nuclear holocaust. For most of the play, masked figures enact in stylized, sculptural movements the actions of mundane work and portray in

The Boss (part I), devoured by the dragon (part II) and retrieved from its interior by a militant army of washerwomen at which point the beast may represent The Bosses qua military-industrial complex (part III).

'The work is in three parts. The first is the story of the washerwomen and their plight, which led to the forming of the International Union of Washerwomen (I.U.W.W.); the second part is the story of the Washerwoman as a child; and the third the triumph of the Washerwoman. In the first section we see little cardboard figures pulled across the stage, the ominous huge hands of the bosses, an innocent and joyful princess who, because the actress wears no mask, becomes a dream symbol and a puppet herself, while the masked performers take on the reality of people. A dragon and a devil figure appear in four manifestations – all of which symbolize the voraciousness of the bosses, who are the unnecessary but human extensions of pain and death. The second section shows how the Washerwoman recalls summer and winter, the death of her grandfather from an apparent heart attack, and the sorrow of her parents whom she remembers as a king and a queen. The princess is devoured by a dragon. The last section finds the Washerwoman opening a Christmas present which contains a man – her true love! – covered with Christmas lights. A comical stork reminiscent of Sesame Street's big bird brings them a child who grows up and goes into the world. Peter Schumann then delivers a speech which Grace Paley wasn't allowed to say in court when she was tried for staging a disarmament demonstration on the White House Lawn. Though simple, Paley's speech lacks poetic penetration, and it falls through the play like the proverbial lead balloon. Since Paley is far from a Washerwoman, Schumann seems to be trying to tell his upper middle class BAM audience that there are still dragons left to slay. The passage, however, didn't work.

A big noise disturbs the Washerwoman. She disappears into the wings and returns with an army, leading them with sword in hand. She slays the dragon, and the princess, like Jonah, is released from his innards. The audience is exhilarated. With the exception of the Paley put-off, this is another triumph for Schumann, who continues to invent, as he says, his same message over and over.'

(Stanley Crouch, *Reinventing the Message, Village Voice*, January 28, '80.)

'But in the first part the Washerwoman is shown in a group doing – what did they do? They shuffled across the stage carrying shopping bags and they come out and pick up scraps of paper, sort of clean up jobs. But they're threatened by a devil. He also looks like Peter (laugh). He's in the lower part of the barn. There's a whole little scene from the Washerwoman stage with the King and a Queen and this Devil riding a little Monster. So this figure is there and there is the sort of threat of some kind of destruction and darkness and with a lot of chairs

---

similar movements the common emotions of the individual life ("When I was a child, my father was a king and my mother was a queen.") Near the end, the washer woman decides to fight the symbolic dragon and, by killing it, free the world. At the end of the play, Schumann reads a statement which the American author, Grace Paley, (who along with others was arrested on the lawn of the White House about a year ago for protesting the arms race) was not allowed to give in her courtroom defense. We are left to make the connection between that statement and everything that comes before.' — (Walter DuPre, *Bread and Puppet Here, Marquee*, Atlanta, Ga., September 14, '79.)

that were thrown over. But it's a kind of an alternating maybe of ordinary tasks: cleanup, and sewing and things and then this sort of lurking threat. And then the second part of it Susie Dennison, who was at that time very small and quite young, plays like the Washerwoman remembers her childhood and she comes out in a very pretty gown and these big puppets, which are kind of like the Disciple puppets, very simple, big heads held inside on a pole with one moving arm. They are her, sort of very big and colorful and kind of stolid, her mother and father and she was with them in a happy way and then she's forced to flee and then there's a whole refugee series of — where the stage went black and all of us went across the stage in different rags — a picture of fleeing, people fleeing from some disaster . . . and then it ended with this little hand puppet show of Solomon Grundy . . . Solomon Grundy, born on Monday, christened on Tuesday, married on Wednesday, took ill on Thursday, worse on Friday, died on Saturday, buried on Sunday. And with my dancing Hard Scrabble Mountain puppets we had made — that was one of the nice things we did, a little maybe seven or eight minute enactment of this rhyme which just begs, is just right for little hand puppets going through very quick, simple, you know, scenes with all these images of a life. So that was fleshed into it. Oh, then the Garbageman comes. That was a whole little series. It was all like snatches of a biography of a washerwoman with flashbacks to her childhood with her king and queen parents, and then her marriage to a garbageman who's presented to her as a giant Christmas package and is all wrapped in Christmas lights that are blinking on and off and she takes off the paper and then they have a baby who's a little pink pig and take care of the baby but then there is a threat again and the Washerwoman comes out and makes the statement that Grace Paley made about feeling the threat of — to children and then a Dragon comes out and he has a fight of the Washerwoman against the Dragon . . . The others are sort of cheering in a circle and then she runs and that was the end.'

(Elka Schumann, interview, '83.)

'In het eerste deel: zien we hoe de wasvrouwen zich verheugen over de komst van de was-machine en meeneuriën en meevan bij het gezoem en geklots van het wasgoed achter het ronde raampje van de machine. We zien ze in regenjas, pantoffels en plastic tassen boodschappen doen, waarna vervolgens een stroom van lelijke maar nuttige bookschappentassen over het toneel schuift. We zien hoe de wasvrouwen een uitje hebben, uit de bus stappen en met nette hoedjes, damestasjes en hoge stemmen het landschap bewonderen: "Ah . . ." In een volgende scene trekt een grote kale figuur met opgeheven vinger de kleinste van de wasvrouwen naar zich toe — het is de dood. De wasvrouwen deppen hun ogen met een punt van hun schort en binden takkebossen om het gestorven meisje.

We zien hoe de wasvrouwen gezellig op een rijtje zitten met naaiwerk op hun schoot; in het midden zit een grote strenge figuur die het tempo aangeeft: de goddelijke vrouw die de draad van het leven vasthoudt. We zien hoe na geweld en vernietiging de wasvrouwen hun kinderen in hun armen wiegen. Een van de vrouwen, die telkens als musicienne optreedt, speelt op haar kartonnen viool en zingt met hoge stem een lied.

Kerstboomkaarsjes

Na dit deel over de vreugen en plichten van vrouwen wordt in het tweede deel "De jeugd van de wasvrouwen" getoond. Op het toneel een prinsesje met blote voeten in (illegible) ze door haar vader de koning aan een monsterachtige draak ten geschenke gegeven, die oorlog in het land dreigt te brengen. Het geweld van de oorlog gaat over in de ijzigheid van de winter, maar deze naargeestige periode eindigt in een winters feest met een dansende sneeuwpop en opgewekte was-vrouwen die met lepels en vorken op hun pannen en wasteilen rammelen. Na hun onbekommerde jeugd en de harde aanpasing aan de maatschappij zijn de vrouwen volwassen geworden.

Het derde deel "Het leven van een wasvrouw als vrouw" speelt zich af in een keuken met kachel, schilderijtjes, stoelen, een strijkplank. Midden in die keuken staat een wasvrouw met een groot pak waaromheen een rood lint gebonden is. Ze pakt het uit en er komt een man uit te voorschijn, behangen met elektrische kerst-boomkaarsjes en voorzien van militaristische kledij en pet. De wasvrouw is nu in de fase dat ze een getrouwde vrouw is, die haar man bedient en verzorgt. Vervol-gens verschijnen de koning en de koningin, een koe en een ezel ten tonele en weer-klinkt er een kerstliedje – in deze bijbelse sfeer wordt een kind geboren. In een volgende scene is het kind een klein rose varkentje geworden, dat tenslotte tegen-spartelend door autoritaire mannen – die de harde maatschappij symboliseren – wordt weggehaald en verkocht. De man en di vrouw blijven alleen in de kauken achter, maar de wasvrouw is nog niet aan het eind van haar krachten.

Zondagsschilders

Ze blijft zich verzetten tegen geweld en onrecht. In de laatste scene (illegible) het prinsesje te voorschijn komt.'

(De Groene Amsterdammer, 14 March '79.)

Initially, thus, the play turned out a family piece, both the way it was put on – the family did it – and as regards its subject matter, and though its inceptional focus on a certain type of woman new in Schumann's theatre then, as Schumann developed its first version, shifted to a focus on a child, and specifically on the anxieties of childhood and the child's overcoming of them, a key subject matter of Schumann's from '79 onward, it was very much dedicated to Elka who as its heroine sings her Russian song (which, though she didn't mention it in speaking of the play, I suspect she brought to it) and whose children's hand puppet play, *Solomon Grundy*, more or less concluded this first version. In this form it was an inti-mate play and as such was at the ('79) circus done in the intimate setting of the pine woods clearing, continuing, in mood the series of 'positive morality plays' about women staged there since '76. The statement about nuclear war may for this performance already have been grafted onto it, but in any event was for the showing of the play in the U.S. hereafter, a graft of politics like that of the Nixon/Calley material onto the '71 *Birdcatcher*, shifting the focus to the coming Armaggedon: a second major preoccupation of Schumann's work since '79. The evocations of terror of the *Disasters of War* scene in the first part, contributed by Schumann's children, who, together with their friends, from '79 onward seem to have had a certain influence on Schumann's preoccupations, was sacrificed to this focus, not, I would say, as inappropriate to the fear of nuclear war, which it is somewhat but not altogether, nor because terror was not a major concern of Schumann's '79 ff. – it became a third major preoccupation of his – but because in terms of the structural dynamics of theatre it would have lessened the impact of the terminal evocation of nuclear war. With it eliminated, Part I's evocation of war was limited to what surely is an evocation of Schumann's own experiences as a nine- and ten-year-old in Silesia: the flight from the Russians. The reference of the allegory thus in this second version was shifted or altered slightly: from the maturation of a girl child into valiant womanhood toward the growing up of children in a world threatened by something like mankind's extinction. Elka was a little disappointed:

'So it was a very pretty – I don't know. I felt a sort of lack or disappointment in some of the more recent shows of Peter's because I felt when he would describe to me what he wanted to do, or the first versions of it what I see, I would envision something very, I don't know, dreamlike and mysterious and then when he would actually do them they would become very – the outlines would be drawn very clearly and the show would be divided up into these very clear chapters and everything would be sort of simplified and the mystery would disappear into something beyond – a feeling of way more beyond what we're seeing. It was very pretty, very nice, but without depth . . . that's what I felt that our show really became smaller then, the boundaries were too clearly kept.'

(Elka Schumann, interview, '83.)

Elka is probably right: Schumann sacrificed some of the quality of the play to didactic function. But the unconscious shift from woman to girl child was as important in Schumann's development as the deliberate shift from the Bosses and from war generally to the nuclear threat.

Formally, a distinctive aspect of the play, not particularly aimed at child audiences, was the naiveté of the fable. Schumann had always had dragons – mythologically resonant animals – in his plays, but with the miraculous rescue of a princess from one, he reverted all the way back to the level of naiveté of *King Story*'s fable.

Max Schumann's pen and ink version of *Washerwoman-Ah!*, Part I.

508

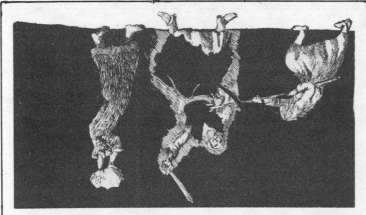

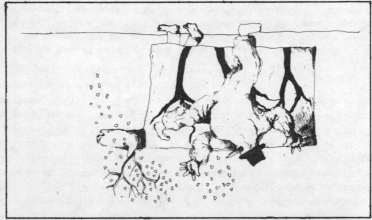

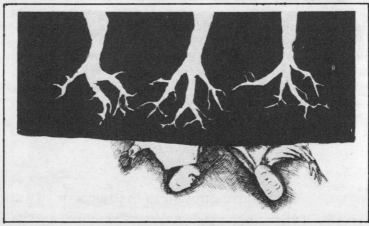

6. *Washerwoman Nativity*, '79. The birth of Jesus as the travail of all women to bring forth babies to be slaughtered.

He made his second washerwoman play and probably the giant washerwoman puppets for it – a big sewing job – the first giant puppets to represent something like People rather than Powers (Uncle Fatso) or Principles (the giant Indian Chiefs of his '74 circus, Mother Earth), somewhat grotesque representations of a somewhat idealized type, colorful and unmysterious – in the early summer of '79. He may have worked on the giant heads earlier. The play and the puppets were made for that summer's circus, at which, as an afternoon show out in the open, in the forest-edge meadow where *Masaniello* and *Wolkenstein*, pieces colorful and expansive like it, had been performed, this play, *Second Washerwoman Cantata – Nativity*, was first performed, then, as I have mentioned, in September, going on an Atlantic seaboard tour starting with street show presentations of a truncated 'circus' type version of it in New York City. It was toured in Europe that December, was given 5 performances in NYC at the Cathedral Church of St. John Divine December 9-13, '80, and a dozen in France in January-February '81, and had another run in NYC in December (Dec. 20-23) '82. I suspect it was done elsewhere 1980 82. It had become Schumann's Christmas show.

The Labor Day weekend ('79) performances in NYC:

'Tuesday, in front of the old Custom House: Clerks and Secretaries from Wall Street – some executives too in their designer suits from Syms – find new tenants in the sunny square where they bring their lunches. An old schoolbus, not predictably yellow but awash with a meadow of colors, has pulled up to discharge its strange membership. There are about 15 of them, wearing basic baggy white but with plenty of leeway for extra adornment, rushing to arrange a jumble of masks, papier-mache figures and other props. Occasionally some of them will stop what they are doing to become part of a loud, irresistible ragtime band – "Come on and hear, come on and hear . . ." The side of the bus says Bread and Puppet Circus, Glover, Vt.

Wednesday, St. Marks Church on the Lower East Side: The same bus follows a parade of giant figures – some of them tall stick creatures arrayed in tatters colored like fire – and the same rollicking band. Ahead of them all, towering on stilts too high to believe, a bearded man does an astounding dance – grinding, hopping, twirling, plunging ahead. The march funnels the raffish energy of the rest of the street. A cabbie, in love with the anarchy, offers the stiltwalker a ride with elaborate courtliness – "Gonna meecha in a taxi honey." The march ends with another circus, deep in the barrio.

Thursday, Tompkins Square Park, still lower in the East Side: the band again

512

and a crowd expecting a play. Children jockey for places down front or dart up to check behind a large banner, painted with the same profusion as the bus, set up in the middle of the playing area. It announces *Washerwoman Nativity*. Youth lounge about, peering suspiciously from beneath their tough cool. A wino, his pants at an anxiously low ebb, entertains everyone with a stately reel. The play begins around dusk. The bearded man who danced on the stilts narrates a simple story of a washerwoman. Some find it worthy of their attention, some not. But suddenly a great, white angel soars from behind the spectators on a swift, silent course to announce that the washerwoman is with child. The majestic passage of the figure, only a giant cardboard head with a vague body of sheets supported on poles, galvanizes the air. Something is happening here; everyone leans forward with attention.

Friday, 9th Street east of Second Avenue: Three fair booths line the street blocked to traffic. "Shakespeare in The Pasture" compresses *King Lear* into an offhandedly comic folk tale with rod puppets. *Carmen* is played like Punch and Judy moderated by Mephisto. Two washerwomen swat flies and cheat each other at cards in a little domestic spinoff from the last night's nativity play. Children skateboard among the spectators, a young woman passes out No Nuke leaflets, people return home from work and grin with surprise at their discovery at the end of the day — all move casually from show to show, sampling each until everyone gathers for a circus finale.

Two weeks ago in these pages, my colleague Elinor Fuchs marveled at the *Washerwoman Nativity*, presented as part of the Domestic Resurrection Circus at the Bread and Puppet's permanent home in Vermont. She wondered how this spectacle, which seemed to harness the very drama of nature for its special effects, could be transferred to New York, even in condensed form. What space here could possibly correspond to the great green amphitheater of the Vermont hills? The answer is indicative of the genius and commitment of Peter Schumann, the founder and director of the theater (and the world's greatest stilt dancer): Carve up the Resurrection Circus and perform parts of it in variously lively places in the city, especially in that cauldron of impatient energy, the Lower East Side. Let the rough pavement-passion of these ideas flow through and transform what was brought from serene, verdant Vermont. Elinor and I both saw the *Washerwoman Nativity*, but we each saw very different plays.

The Bread and Puppet is the most political of theaters, but in a totally extraordinary way. Even at the peak of its tremendous contribution to the anti-war movement, its greatest strength was not to call for programmed action, but to focus on the passion of the victims of war and other social cruelty. So many of the puppet masks from that period, unforgettable to anyone who ever saw a procession of them, were almost blank with pain and endurance. They worked like conduits for our own outraged emotions and gave us the respite of elegiac meditation.

In the '70s, with the war no longer there to make the fight between good and evil concrete, Schumann and his theater have relied more explicitly on folk material, particularly on a direct, utterly undogmatic Christianity. (This element was always in the work, but submerged by the press of current events.) The *Washerwoman Nativity*, part of a larger piece as yet unfinished, is a retelling of the Christmas story that brings it back to its popular roots. Herod is there — a kind of Every-Oppressor — threatening a population of terrified masks, expropriating the

Washerwoman's house and sending her to inhospitable Bethlehem. The Three Wise Men are there with other salutary spirits (the same tall figures we saw in the parade), dancing at the end of the play in celebration of the birth. But the most powerful image of all is the least assertive one: the Washerwoman herself, a mask as eloquently blank as those from the peace marches, but now glowing with good humor instead of wrapped in sorrow. She reflects and transmits a new energy from those who watch her, something outgoing and popular.

The Bread and Puppet itself seems to close a circuit of power running from contemplative Vermont to raucous New York, from the natural, lush oneness of the country to the multifarious life of the Lower East Side. I understand that the Washerwoman piece performed in Glover was explicit in its alignment with the anti-nuclear movement, but here there was only the quiet, efficient passing out of leaflets. Perhaps the theater tried to activate a different kind of force in the city. But, of course, the two energies are really one.'

(James Leverett, *Dancing in the Streets, Soho Weekly News*, September 13, '79.)

I thought the transposition from meadow to street less successful than did Leverett. Whether from a seat among the Afroamericans and the curbside welter of trash on West 42nd or standing to the rear of the equally appreciative and almost equally black-and-brown audience in the Lower East Side park, though the spectaculars — the stilt dancing stars, Schumann stilt dancing, the coming of the Angel of Annunciation, a giant bird light as a kite, sliding-fluttering-flying-gliding in from behind the audience — a moment of grace because power, in silence appreciated by the audience (a fact indicating that their appreciation before and after had an aspect of courtesy, the appreciativeness of the poor for who comes to them) — were still spectacular — and some of the performances preserved some of their effectiveness — the little evilly shivering Blackbird demon, Herod's servant, the Mary-Washerwoman's graceful movements slipping into or out of her recumbent giant effigy to give birth (Barbara Leber) — whatever was cute, such as for instance the giant Washerwoman, who in the traditional dance of Mother Earth with Uranos replaced that ferocious ogre, and the washerwoman figure generally, or the show of cutouts — daisies, cows, blue sky — by ballet lines of rushing-out performers — here was insultingly cute: its phony naiveté a gesture of condescension to this audience. The powerful, non-naive masks, i.e. those other than the Washerwoman ones contrasted revealingly with the silly scenes, and the same contrast (likewise revealing the willfulness of Schumann's plain-manness) held between the predominant naively bright primary colors and the high fine taste and striking rightness of the colors, exotic, rich and stirring, of the four thin giant stars. Not tightly integrated either into visually framed tableaux or into well-defined acts' well-timed devolution, the disparate formal elements failed to balance, and the disparate stylistic borrowings failed to fuse and to take on the color of the whole, and perceived in isolation, some of them seemed cynically naive.

514

But done, where I saw it again, at Judson Memorial Church in December '82, in a full version, substantially unchanged from the December '80 one, the play turned out a highly organized, splendid piece of theatre, each of its five acts a well rounded symbol. Its masked performers beautifully complemented its giant puppets. Its unmasked performers, scads of lovely young girls recruited locally, were effectively used in choruses and, with the giant kite puppet, in a concluding ballet-tableau. Cutouts gracefully met head on with puppets and performers. The instrumental music provided some splendid driving rhythms; several chorales and a hymn or two complemented the visual as commentary; and one preludic musical interlude gave an example of a successful independent contribution of music to visual theatre.

At the end of the large floor space in front of the audience a perhaps 20 ft. long, shallow (6 ft. or so?) platform shelf, perhaps as much as four ft. off the ground. Behind it in a niche a line of 6 bare fir trees – part of the season's decor, but good background, it turned out, for the platform tableaux that came. To each side of the platform, slightly in front of it, on the floor at an angle to it, a hugely tall four-paneled screen, each with one long-stemmed flower painted on it, one blue, one red. To this side of the left hand screen, along the side wall, the band area with a number of instruments, 6 musicians, including Schumann, Trudy Cohen (the maestro), Michael Romanyshyn, and John Bell (who doubles as announcer – the announcements are sparse, though: just the act titles). Here and there along both walls, small bundles of identical masks, the grey-brown tortured People masks, face down.

Blackout. Murray Levy, returned for the occasion, a fat ghost, is from the choir loft above the audience doing the lights. A drum roll. Brass fanfares. Lights. A big colorful curtain, held up, covers the platform. On it are pictures, words, 'Nativity'. Tall, lanky John Bell stentoriously announces 'The Washerwoman Nativity. Part I.' Curtain carried off at a run. Revealing 18 talking little Washerwomen – big masks making them seem extra petite, in aprons, wide skirts, kerchiefs. The steady good humor of the but slightly varied woman-face masks a little unnerving. But a charming picture. A little like wildflowers. They are excited. There is something wrong. Ah! The soap had been missing. Another washerwoman brings a jumbo size carton. One washerwoman launders something in a small center stage plastic tub, hands it to another; the other wrings it, hands it to a third (a Negress, this one), who pins it – it's a small striped skirt – on the stage-right line, falls on one knee, with one arm, hand open, outstretched toward it, in a gesture commanding universal acclaim of their performance, the work – they are now all in that position.

A giant bronze Madonna in a white, blue-flowers-hemmed dress is brought in from behind the right hand screen, her bronze babe in her bronze hands held far from her face and presumptive tits, in a gesture of

515

exhibition or offering. There are six people under her skirts, moving her, the bottoms of their white-clad legs visible. She does a waltz, high up and stately, to accordion.[1] The washerwomen have come down off the platform, folklorically, in their many pale colors, in a wide circle surround her turning figure on the floor. She stops, a moment passes, to drumwhirls they all rush onto her, grab hold of her dress hem, lift her dress, one more washerwoman jumps out from underneath it, the triangle of a kerchief dangling from her left hand, her costume's colors mostly pale blue. She's no different from the others, but she seems special: they recede into a wide circle and she does a dance by herself, using the kerchief for effect, a dance of no great art. (This is Amy Trompetter instead of Barbara Leber who usually does the part. Amy in life has no charm either – an ingrown toenail in person. She overdoes the cute just a little in this part, sort of spoils it. No clear gestures. Too much. This dance is supposed to be artless, but as she does it, it lacks charm.) The tall Madonna has been taken off. The idea seems to be: This particular washerwoman – woman blessed among all women, Mary, it turns out – is born of the Madonna, ergo (poetic logic) *is* the Madonna. Washerwomen off, goodbying her, but on the whole discretely. Their retreat a little lacking in grace. (But Schumann has had only since Monday – and this is Thursday – to rehearse this piece with the 2 or 3 dozen local volunteers and to whip it into shape.) Mary is down in the wide floor space. On the platform up behind her a black haired girl in a black gym outfit dances in carrying a flower-in-the field, a painting on a board, dances it in, the flower mostly hiding most of her body, all of her face, she is holding the picture in front of her – a little ballet number, quite nice, the evocation of ballet formality contrasting prettily with the cut-and-dried naiveté of the flower. A picture playfully used as a mask. She comes to rest stage left, plants the jonquil there, is off.

A herd of cows enters on the floor below the platform, pink udders, pink muzzles, Jerseys. They are pictures of cows on boards, square except in one corner, where the board's outline follows the cow's, pictures on the way to cutouts, three columns of three, from the right, the pictures held up by the white-clad 'puppeteers' walking sideways, half masking them. Mary is retreating before the herd, leftward, in tiny tripping steps (cute mimicry or rudimentary approach to dance-type-motion?) but lets herself be pushed only so far, stops, shooes the cows back out. She is still on the floor below the platform. There was mooing from the horns to this, and when the cows came in there was a yellow sun – board on a stick – behind them: when they leave, turned, it's red. To beautiful whistling from the band, in no way like any wild goose cries in the fall I've ever heard, red-

<hr>

1. 'The song I play on the accordion for dances of the Madonna, the little washerwoman's birth, the flower, and the giant washerwoman is (I think) a Welsh waltz called "Jeltin Lonin".' — (Trudi Cohen, letter March '83.)

beaked geese fly in from the left upstage – on the platform above and behind Mary, cutouts on sticks. They fly in 2 flocks of three, a longer follows – Schumann insists on these minute touches of sentimental humor – on being corny: it is to him, I would say, part of the craft of entertainment. Mary has ostentatiously, hand to ear, heard them come – that whistling. They fly across and out behind her. Only the flower is still up there – and Mary. The pictures of a house – of the outside of a house – enters from the right. The boy carrying it, holding it in front of him again – this can again be considered a form of masking, and the picture-carrier as a marginal kind of puppet, a house puppet – advances sideways, hopping up close to Mary on the left, she – gesturally – tries to make him stop in place, but the house teases her, hops away to the right, etc., she finally gets it (carrier and picture) settled behind the flower. (This entrance is to a very melodious plucking of bass (and cello) strings, over the bass drum. Each object-dance has its own kind of music.) The pictures are all cute: children's book illustrations for – or by – 3-5-year olds. It's an animated children's book. Mary is standing by the house behind the flower. (There is no Joseph in this play at all. It's all about Mary.) A group of white clouds (pictures) in, stand in two rows near Mary, sound of rain, she mimicks, verifying it's raining, knocks on the house, it turns, the interior of it is on the other side – she has gotten in out of the rain. Girls come on in rapid succession to gay bass (and cello) strings, bring Mary a book (black) – the Good Book, presumably – a large cutout heart, red, and a metal folding chair on which she sits down by the house, holding up the book in one hand, the heart in the other. Intellect and feeling, the scholastics and the mystics.

Fanfare. 'We are happy to announce the annunciation' (John). A relatively small, perhaps a little over man-size angel with a cutout profile face, simplification of an early renaissance Adoring Angel, its hair a smooth area of blue paint, in loose white angelic garments, wingless, perhaps Mary yet over again, Mary Elect, emerges smoothly from the right, kneeling down (in front of – or over? – Mary and the house), facing left, a hand with the black book emerges in front of him/her, he/she now appears to be reading, his/her large beautiful face slightly bent over the book, a beautiful picture. Wild, raw fanfares ('dissonant horn blasts' (Cohen, letter, March '83)), an announcement of power, a very large cutout headed blond angel – a woman's head of wool, hemp or whatever blond hair in long, loose strings at the back of its coldly serene large profiled face, limning it – is run in on the platform from the left. Its body like a giant white cruciform kite, extended backward, its head up, it hovers over Mary (the blue-haired Angel has disappeared, Mary is again seated there with book and heart) with most of the length of the platform between them. A ladder and a rope or some string are brought in – immediately, this is done rapidly – and while two or three performers hold the 12 ft.-

or-so ladder going up to the annunciatory angel's face, another climbs it, and the string is extended from the angel's face to Mary, perhaps to the heart. A tall (7-8 ft.) red – red-headed, its tubular body red – puppet has emerged on the floor from behind the screen at the right, its one red-sleeved arm raised, its hand pointing to what is happening up on the platform: a small white sign with black lettering, 'Fear not', is sliding down the rope to Mary (who has been registering awed agitation, arms upheld, leaning backward). The flaming pointer puppet is immediately gone again, to wild fanfares the very big annunciatory angel is run out of view (with the ladder). A girl performer in white – no mask – now holds the left-hand end of the string at that side of the platform, a large, white delicate dove, i.e. large for a dove: 2-3 feet long (another cutout?) – has appeared there, flutters up and down. The Holy Ghost, I suppose, engaged in transcendantal coitus with the Mother of God. It is a come-down to a more contrived, finicky sort of representation than the preceding, but the succession works: a story told with many means. (The succession of the dances of the picture book illustration images and of the two angelic creatures with the renaissance allusion was similary discontinuous – another defiance of the usual desideratum of unity of style.) Dove out. The giant Washerwoman puppet reenters from behind the right-hand panel screen, to accordion does a sedate country dance. (She has only one pole-bearer, three operators in all: this makes her seem very light, but she in fact isn't.) She has stopped, is standing,[2] her sturdy bland face high above her ginghams and crazy quilts, and Mary, the small washerwoman, gets in under her skirts, settles down in there, looking out at us through a square window-hole cut near her skirt hem – which is uncovered because the big washerwoman is raising her checkered apron. The apron is tied by one corner to her right hand, that one of her two ancillary pole operators, one for each arm, is holding up, resting his pole on the ground. The little washerwoman no longer has book or heart, but through the open window, index finger raised, directs the large – 20 or 30 people – whiteclad chorus that has assembled at the left through several verses, in several voices, of a chorale, Schumann holding up a prompt sheet for them to see, and Trudy Cohen directing them.[3] The stately music complements the stately puppet. The small head and hand set into her dress achieve a surrealist pictorial effect – Bosch, or Breughel. Three unmasked performers are in a spaced circular procession around her holding up the book, the heart, and the house – a consecration of the hostie. When the hymn ends, they are standing in front of her holding up the three objects, again a pictorial conceit of the late Middle Ages or early renaissance. All out. Blackout.

2. 'Peter plays a tiny clay ocarina for the 2 moments when the washerwoman is left alone and for the flying of the little blue bird.' — (Cohen, letter, March '83.)
3. A 'Sacred Harp' song, *Milford*, by John Stephenson, about 1802, in the key of A Major:

Drum roll, fanfare, diffuse light on the band corner, John: 'Part II. This is the time of King Herod.'[4]

The hall is dark. In the small oval spot of a spot-light on the floor, in the middle of it, lies a sword, a patently theatre wooden sword with a big lumpy white plastic glove-handle for a hand to fit in, its blade pointed straight out at us. Sound of the plucked bass, low humming. A crawling white figure emerges from the rear left. As it comes nearer the light, you can see it's a man (Schumann: recognizable by his bald spot), its weakly

4. '... Also mit Tropfen
Stillt er das Seufzen des Lichts, das durstigem Wild
War ähnlich in den Tagen, als um Syrien
Jammert der getöteten Kindlein heimatliche
Anmut im Sterben, und das Haupt
Des Täufers, gepflückt, war unverwelklicher Schrift gleich
Sichtbar auf weilender Schüssel.'

(F. Hölderlin, *Patmos*, third version.)

glittering face a featureless silver mask (wadded staniol paper or alumi-nium foil). It is crawling like a man-animal, loup garoux, werewolf or other. Its obsessive, slightly erratic, concentrated movements suggest madness, a cunning and aggressive paranoia. The spirit of the times of King Herod. The movement, like the sword and the mask, is 'cheap' drama, drama of crude means and effective clichées, focussed toward in-tensive effect. He reaches the light – its oval has grown – covertly – this is a danger spot – approaches the sword, puts his hand in the handle, crouches over it, behind it, rises on his knees, his front leg half straighten-ed, raising it, swings it in a circle, holds it in front of him, looking at it, as though it were the antagonist, a dangerous one, goes down into a crouch again, his mask looking at us, then way down, head low over the sword in his right, his left on the floor, fingers spread, next to it, the blade again pointing toward us. He is not quite still. There is another crawling figure now in the semi-darkness beyond the large oval, a girl, one of the large, somber People masks hand-held before her face, approaching the mad silver-faced armed animal in a careful, hesitant but drawn-by-curiosity manner, intrigued and surreptitious. It approaches up to the edge of the light, hesitates, enters, jumps back – there are other like figures in the rear now, circuitously approaching. The large masks are so detached from their holders – we again and again see the sides and backs of their heads, even their faces now and then, they are holding the masks at some distance from their faces, and some are more careful than others about keeping their faces hidden – that attention flickers back and forth between the crouch-ing animal images and the masked-as-crouching-animal or fearfully-sly-man images: almost as though the mask by itself provided a separate illu-sion. (Schumann at this point in his work is *playing* with the mask's power. By no means bent on always utilizing it for maximum illusion. But the awkwardness of the recruited performers is also for something in this.) The crowd – a dozen and a half – of fascinated people-animals is insectlike. The central predator is quietly heaving: a distinctly more human, but bad animal. Throughout all of this there is a heavy bass drone, a sawing 'danger' music, the bass, some violin, occasional hollow thumps from the drum.[5] The scene lasts a long time – 5 minutes? The People have gathered in a dense formation to the rear at the left, the bass saws faster, they are heaving-bobbing up and down in rhythm with it, i.e. moving their masks up and down, the ones in front crouching, at this remove and in the half-light and crowded together, again human: convincingly a mass of semi-animalic, scared, grotesque humans. The predator man-animal slowly rises from its crouch, not looking at them, slowly half turns, standing now, his sword pointing toward them, a wild whistle, he lunges, lifting the sword,

5. '. . . a long slow crescendo of amplified fiddle, cello, bass fiddle and sun drones, together with entrance and development of drums.' — (Cohen, letter, March '83.)

strikes, they all scatter all over, collapse, the floor is flecked with the white bodies and the yellowish gray masks. He stands there in a *dejected* attitude, shoulders forward, head lowered, the sword half-down, pointing at the floor, a portrait of sickness and of only half-slack tension. They gradually get up, gradually, moving backward, to speeding-up music, reassemble, at the right rear this time, their masks moving forward and back in front of their faces now, toward us and back to their faces, a weird, abstract effect of agitation, of crowd fear. He is straightening out, turning around toward them, the sword rises, he goes berserk again, to the drum's quick beat strikes at them jumping toward them, two or three times – wild rolling of the drum, wild movement of the masks, he strikes again, they scatter, but are still up, all around him, almost a little aggressive now, he whirls, sword out, at sword point gathers them in, chases them out through the audience. Blackout.[6] The scene has been exciting. Schumann's performance had been excellent, but not great. A touch more energy – intensity, concentration – might have made it great. But he would then, by perfection of the illusion, have been in another kind of theatre, expressionist melodrama. And also his performance would have clashed with the kind of performance his volunteers (given their lack of training, the lack of rehearsal time, and the fact that there was no selection for acting ability) would have been capable of, whereas as it was they blended, in the area of a sort-of-make-belief theatre, *half*-serious drama.

Lights up on the platform. Drone from the bass. A small black demon, face a surrealist jumble of features, including a long black beak, tasseled body, comes out, up on the platform, from the right, dragging behind it, on a rope, little Washerwoman Mary's house, held by Mary. They stand, the string taught between them. To loud shouts 3 performers run in from the left, standing behind Mary rapidly raise and lower pictures of shouting people with agitatedly upraised arms, run back out. Demon, rope, Mary, house again add up to one of Schumann's good compositions. The tableau

---

6. The dance develops the individual-vs.-crowd motif Schumann had brought to America from Munich and first – Death as the ruler of the crowd, their opposition to one another and to Janus – staged in *Totentanz* in '62 and then, in various forms – the crowd stones and/or absorbs the individual, the crowd is attracted to and recedes from the individual, the individual establishes himself as leader of the crowd – in Part I of the '72 *Simple Light*. In *Totentanz* there had been no value judgment, in *Simple Light* the individual, whether leader of the crowd or its opponent, seemed favored, but when the motif reemerges with the *White Horse Butcher* story – first, but only formally, in the '75 *Monument to Ishi*: the black-hooded delegate of the Butchers breaking the antlers of the deer – the leader (the Head Butcher) is definitely a negative figure, and in the '77 *Masaniello*, the leader (Masaniello) in his opposition to the crowd (the People) also figures as negative, and the crowd now as positive: as in *Washerwoman Nativity*. But there are also good leaders – Joan in the '77 *Joan of Arc*, the head washerwoman in the '79 *Washerwoman Ah!* In fact, Schumann, ever the German, doesn't get around to choreographing in an evaluatively positive way, a leaderless crowd until 1980 (*Cambodia*).

is held, as from behind us (down the stairs from the choir loft) a large dense crowd (perhaps a dozen and a half performers) of the People, to a steady, overbearing broken drumbeat (a 'slow military drum beat' (Cohen, letter, '83.)) marches in holding overhead — seeming to sit on them — the grotesque figure of a king with a yellow paper maché fudged crown on his nasty head — a black, ludicrous smiling figure of horror, his grinning face livid welt. They raise and lower his spindly black figure to the broken beat. His big feet are naked. They carry him around in a circle, stop when he faces us, he makes a mad gibbering speech, still raised and lowered to the barbaric drumbeat by his immediate carriers, the others in the crowd having scattered and fallen on the floor as though in terror of his proclaimed intents. Speech finished, he is carried over by the platform, leans over it in some mock intimacy, the demon ties Mary's house to his head, he straightens out with an evily triumphant 'ha ha ha' (from John in the band, I suppose) and is marched out in a continuation of his triumphal procession. The demon follows, having taken the house from Mary, carries it. The scene has beautifully inverted Mary's flight.

Lights out except for a spot on Mary on the stage (the platform) who, arms upraised, goes into an extended pantomime of despair: to sad, melodic bird whistles from Schumann in the band. She ends up crouching on the floor, head down. The spot dims out. Blackout. John: 'Ten minutes intermission.' Lights.

End of Intermission. Blackout. Drum roll. Fanfare. 'Part III. The Three Kings from the East.' Cymbal clash. (Irene Leherrissier, like Murray Levy, a remnant from the B&P past, is on the cymbals.) Oriental-type chimes. From behind the screen on the left a huge tent-like structure emerges, orange and white parachute silk in triangular vertical strips, the moving puppet of the 3 Kings, whose relatively altogether tiny upper bodies emerge at the top, half compacted, the three tiny heads close together, with one prettily tasseled telescope between them to spy out the lay of the land.[7] We could conceive of them also as riding on an elephant or on the traditional three camels: the tent-like structure translates these half-remembered popular image-shapes into a visually effective equivalent. The Three Kings are followed in — drums joining the chimes[8] — by a splendid red star stilt puppet, all red, flatheaded (you don't even think of where the operator's head might be), its head more or less a cookie star, sun or planet, burning in a lion's mane of crooked flames, its smile enigmatic,

---

7. '. . . a very tall stilt figure (with a) 3-heads-in-one mask, carrying a cardboard mailing tube telescope decorated with a gold tassel. It is wearing a vulgar looking dress made from a white and orange parachute.' — (Ashley, notes to his outline of *Washerwoman Nativity*, December '79.)

8. 'The 3 Kings stilt scene is a development of various kinds of chimes and bells and junk played rhythmically with (usually) a conga drum. It starts very sparse, and builds up to a strong jazzy beat.' — (Cohen, letter, March '83.)

doing a dance, i.e. coming in dancing; followed by an all yellow one, followed by a purple one, each dancing in its own manner, ending up dancing around the orange and white Three Kings like planets: an exuberating spectacle of exotic splendor *not* gaudy: thus one envisioned the splendors of the East. Light, gay, odd. Irene, still pretty, her little tits bouncing, pretty because good-hearted and freely sexy, runs out with her cymbals, energetically chases the high born stars and the bulky royal monster off to one side, making room for a white comet exuberantly cake-walking in to jazz, the post-funereal 'O Didn't He Ramble!', doing a Charlestony number – it's Schumann – leading the desert parade of stars and kings (under the kings' collective skirts we faintly see the white operators distending the skirts) out.

Cymbal clash. The scene portrays the anticipation of Christmas. A true masque – the kind of spectacle, briefly, that once in formal allegory shored up failing royal power. Blackout.

Lights on band, fanfare, John: 'Part IV, Christmas!' Accordion, lights on stage platform. Washerwoman Mary is extended asleep out front on the platform, a suitcase next to her. Down on her luck. 7 performers dance in with pictures adding up, once they stand side by side, to a stretching-out Green Mountains landscape – but Schumann has avoided making the lines of the hills in the several pictures meet. The seven pairs of hands holding the pictures are part of the picture.[9] A white door, held by an eighth, has joined them at the right end, the music is off, Mary wakes up, gets up, with suitcase in hand (and a handbag over her arm) walks over to the left, as she starts walking (too daintily) back past the 7, toward the door, they one by one lay down the pictures before her feet, she walks over the prone landscape, thanking each for his/her homage, each bowing in return. Trompetter's prissy-cute preciousness spoils this pretty homage to Vermont. She knocks on the door. The landscapers, buckling their masonite boards, produce the rolling sound of theatre thunder. She is waiting for a response, there is none, she knocks again, again no response, thunder, she bethinks herself (mime), gets a compact out of her bag, makes up elaborately, gives her bra and corset some energetic tugs, an old-fashioned gesture that no longer works – one of Schumann's slightly musty German memories[10] – knocks again, again no response, with elaborate stealthiness

9. Schumann could have made them hold the pictures top and bottom, but didn't. Perhaps this was sloppiness, but I don't think so: the hand-accents in the horizontal line of naive pictures are Schumannian in essence: helping to keep us seeing not just products of performing-activity, but that activity as show; conveying an appreciation of the human hand (transformer of landscapes, link to them); and, in fact, pretty.

10. 'There was a white door and the washerwoman – and there was nothing for a long time. And the wait was painful. Barbara (Leber) makes that mask come to life. She is a consummate actress. I don't know whether you like her or not, but I think she is superb. The

tiptoes up to the door, bends down to look through the keyhole, straightens up. Landscapes and door off. She starts walking again — flute bird whistles — alone — sits down center-stage, legs off platform, puts her head on the suitcase, sleeps. The cowherd enters mooing from the left, the big washerwoman is brought in on the right, laid down on her side, her arms towards us, their two operators by their poles, seated on the floor in front of her, her center pole sticking out of the open circle of her skirts. John, in red-banded tophat, black jacket, walks over, ceremoniously wakes up Mary, in dumb-show introduces her to the cows (exchange of greetings) — distant echo of the bible story's stable — then to the prone giant washerwoman: Mary dives into her open dress, disappears. (John back to band.) The cows are watching. To a sax and other horns,[11] slowly at first, the big washerwoman goes into labor pains, heaving, her arms moving, faster and faster — it's an extended scene — the instruments going up in pitch: the little washerwoman (her dress now roughly but only roughly the same as the big one's) jumps out! holding up a small flag of triumph (with the pictures of a washerwoman on it), cradling a small white fabric-wrapped parcel in her left arm. The parcel's baby image is weak, there has been no effort even to shape it as a baby, a discretion of Schumann's that actually spoils the effect of this scene.[12] The big washerwoman has been erected behind her, holding a washerwoman flag as well, though no baby, and a full chorus has assembled to the left of them. Hymn (*Milford*), male voices vs. female, then in unison, off, the choir disbands to Indian cries, re-emerges as flag carriers (flower flags), on the run, to jubilant shouts from the band circle the two washerwoman, run out. Blackout.

In the almost-dark an enormous piece of dark plastic covering nearly the whole floor is spread out. Faint light on the band. Schumann and Romanyshyn emote on two violons — a little like slow gypsy music. The bass joins in. A concert — 3-5 minutes perhaps. The straight white musicians make an effective contrast to the dark square of plastic. (This musical interlude is one of the relatively few examples in his work of one of the things Schumann wants to achieve — music as an independent but inte-

---

mask is always alive. She knocked the second time. There was no answer. Then she stepped away, thinking she had come to the wrong address or something. Then she thought — whatever. And he has done this before, maybe she is not appealing — she should look in her purse and put on some lipstick and pull up her bra and straighten herself out — this has been done before — it is very vulgar. But she did it. And she went back and knocked again, and again — no answer. And that was the first omen that something was happening.' — (Ashley, interview, '81.)

11. '. . . horns playing long pulsating notes. It usually was saxophone, clarinet, trumpet and trombone and 2 copper pipes blown like a trumpet.' — (Cohen, letter, March '83.)

12. Though in the following Act V, it is effective: the universality-neutrality of Mary's little baby there aptly differentiates it from the mere baby-like doll babies of the other washerwomen. As Jesus is different from the common herd of the sons of mothers.

524

grated contributing element.) The music gets more and more strident and agitated, repetitious, just a few notes repeated, Schoenbergian. Then slower again, sad rather than wild. Music off.[13]

Just half-light on band still, John: 'Part V. Slaughter of the Innocents.' Lights up over the floor, but only slightly, a dim, eery light, two runners, one on each side, running from one end of the plastic to the other, after ten or twenty seconds to low moans from the horns, are roiling it, dark brown, faintly glittering, over and under, toward and away from us, finally producing giant horrid waves, a sea of muck, suddenly the crowd of the People are there, at the back of it, lined up at the end of the water as though it were their collective body or as though abandoned in it, drowning, the large, sad, unpleasant faces bobbing up and down — the plastic now agitated by performers that have gotten in under it, the runners are off. The horns are moaning, the flotsam crowd approaches and recedes. Increasing agitation. Drum roll. People and plastic out very fast. This scene is quite as abstract and symbolic as was the sword dance. We are far from Christmas and from the Christmas story.

The lights are still very dim out front, but there is a spot on the platform. Mary proceeds to march across up there, baby in her arm, leading an elegant grey and brown one-operator cutout donkey, its forelegs a single stick making a comic thumping. The six firs behind her make an effective background to this Joseph-less flight to Bethlehem. She stops center-stage, lies down with her baby to sleep. A small, blond handpuppet angel appears above the donkey's neck to urge her on, its first exhortation a faint bell tinkling, its second the sound of a toy trumpet. Mary is heeding her, on her knees, her arms uplifted, gets up, walks on, her donkey graceful as before. Off. Blackout.

Dim lights back on over floor, first one, then another — eight in all — the Washerwomen are in a circle at intervals of perhaps ten feet, in silence except for the rapid jiggling strumming of a loose-stringed bass (mandolin?), you hear the shuffling feet: they are walking in tiny steps, not lifting their feet, each carrying a baby (real dolls these, not a little white package like the Mary Washerwoman's had been). Their compact bodies (the costumes are stuffed) look delicate because of their relatively big heads (face masks, head kerchiefs). They have come to rest, stand in a large circle facing us, cradling the babies in small rocking motions to low mooing raw horn sounds.[14] An extended moment. Broken by howling screams from behind us, a driver's screams, 'Giddy up', 'Whoa there, Yah!', sharp and

13. 'The music is (similar to the first grey mask scene) a long slow crescendo of rather undefined sounds: trombone, cello, bass fiddle, rumble on bass drum, copper pipe horns.) — (Cohen, letter, March '83.)
14. 'Peter played the 2 copper pipe horns together at the same time for the washerwomen to rock their babies. When the washerwomen shuffle in with their babies, the cello and fiddle (amplified) pluck very fast, making a drone effect.) — (Cohen, letter, March '83.)

mean, accompanied by a rattling ratcheting: three black-grey demons — hooded — run in a large black polesled, one of them the screaming driver, the two others his beasts of traction, the floor-dragging ends of each of the sled's two black poles a large grey bony hand. They stop at one of the women, the demanding hands surrounding her feet. There is a spotlight on her. Schumann, with his mad swordsman's silver mask on again, in a deliberately easy, rolling workman's gait, walks over to her, briefly rattles a gaudily red toy rattle over her shoulder, puts his arms around her from behind, grasping her hands, with a show of strength rather than force twisting her upper body slightly backward, separates her arms, shaking her baby off into the black carrion-sled, raises her arms above her head, brings her hands down over her eyes — arranges her in a gesture of horror — and briefly shakes the rattle over her again. The demons, screaming, run their sled over to the next woman and the action is repeated. It is repeated, with slight, but only minute, variations — e.g. one (only one) of the women puts up resistance, it is easily overcome without breaking the pattern — for each of the women. The spotlight follows him. Carrion sled out (screams). Schumann back to band.[15]

The women go through slow body motions of sorrowing, ending up on their knees, heads by the floor, in slow motions up and down, their hands still where they were put. The six members of the band, upright in a line, intone a stark, harsh hymn (*Milford* again, actually), it and their white figures a good contrast to the moving, softer sculptures of the eight sorrowing women. The long chorale ends. Women with their heads down.

Six flag carriers, death motifs in black on their white flags, enter quickly on the platform, line up and swing their flags to a beginning heavy death march rhythm from the alligator drums[16] as from behind the screen out

---

15. 'So it (Schumann's mask (SSB)) was not a life mask, it was a kind of off mask with slit eyes, and wearing that he went from woman to woman and they were there, and he simply reached out and took their children from them. They didn't resist, but he definitely took them from them, and he threw them in this charnel cart, these babies, and then he went over to the women and took their arms, and bent them, twisted them like wire sculptures into attitudes of sorrow and left them standing — there were 12 of them he did this to. These babies were thrown — it was like a concentration camp — a slaughter. And it went on. Twelve of them took a long time. And he moved around tearing these babies up with his arms and throwing them without any mercy. If one, one would have been devastated — but all of them. Terrible. Why?? Unbelievable. Then when he had this great, huge skeleton come in and the skeleton horse come in — they were monstrous events happening in this cathedral.' — (Ashley, interview, '81.)

'This is the first time in Peter Schumann's theology in which the Angel of the Lord does not come to prevent the Massacre of the Innocents.' — (Ashley, comments on his outline of the '79 *Washerwoman Nativity*.)

16. 'The Dance of Death drumming is more hollow and solemn (than for the marching of King Herod) — we call it *Al*-li-ga-tor, a strong slow 4/4 beat, with heavy emphasis on the first beat. The beat changed to very fast and crazy for the final dance and exit of the skeleton horseman.' — (Cohen, letter, March '83.)

front to the left, a giant wooden skeleton Death with a large white death head riding on a wooden skeleton horse rides out, surrounded by his operator-attendants, and from behind us, down from the choir loft, a procession of Schumann's skeleton men, flat-bodied, their bodies black pictures with words ('Old', 'Today', 'Home', 'Darkness'), their bony hands dangling, their loose heads jiggling, march onto the floor, and, to the heavy drum rolls, in a kind of devil worship march in a circle around Deathrider and his horse.

March out. (Flag-swingers off too.) The terms 'dreadful confusion' describe this scene — all cheap stuff, rags, paper maché, crude sculptures, cratewood, the images of death over and over, in black and white. It is very effective — superb. Representation of the inner truth of a militarized stage: disintegration. The giant horse rears up with a whinny and it and its rider prance around on the empty floor, death all that's left, in a triumphal parade, round and round to the rapid jagged rhythm of the drums, Death's gaunt face spotlit. Off. Blackout. A heavy silence.

A huge white shape, half as big as the floor area, but not overly high, moves in in the dark, gradually discernible as the Angel of Peace (the Annunciatory Angel of earlier on).[17] A bell is sounded. The Angel is extended on the floor. It starts heaving in the half-darkness, a slow ascent — up, down, up a little further — of the vast white light shape — its tail stays down, but its wings rise — to the sound of breath or air only, the several dozen young white puppeteers, girls mostly, under it, going up and down with it, bending down, rising up on their knees, stretching up their arms, eyes shut, bending backward, till suddenly, on a cymbal clash from Schumann, the Angel rears all the way up above them — they are there as though in ecstasy in the silence — its pure flat masonite head high in the air, protecting them. The end.

The performance lasted perhaps a little above an hour and a half.

The play is distinguished formally, both relative to Schumann's prior

---

17. 'All right, turned out the lights, and the next thing we know, when they turn the lights back on, is this huge angel, it's at an angle in front of us and it is throbbing. And there is a strong guy underneath and he is lifting it rhythmically. And we discover that underneath there are people that are crouching, and they are going up and down — and then there is another row back here further where they are bent over and they are going up and down. So we have this whole group of people going up and down rhythmically with this huge angel — I think they made it larger. But gradually, this great thing kept going — and finally the people underneath were all standing with their hands up. That is the message. It didn't used to be quite Schumann's message. Everyone has to be part of something . . . He did not just arrive at this. I mean, nothing happens in this theatre by accident — it is all being developed from somewhere within. And this is what he was saying in 1981 . . . I think he has finally almost abandoned hope that the world will be saved. (I: Why do you put in the "almost".) I put the "almost" in because he keeps switching. When do you stop working and you go to the top of the mountain? And say it is going to happen now. Finally, some people do that — he doesn't.' — (Ashley, interview, '81.)

work and relative to other theatre stuff, by its sophistication and theatricality, and as regards content by its absolutely negative outlook.

Its sophistication consisted in the juxtaposition, within tableaux but especially sequentially, of (numerous) disparate naive styles, by their juxtaposition given the value of artistic means – so that revulsion due to an impression that naiveté is pretended is overcome, and the objection of phoniness cannot validly be raised any more than that of bad taste (vulgarity) or that of camp (delectation by a displayed hypocrisy of naiveté).[18] The spectator, naive or sophisticated, is aware of exposition to established genres normally for appreciation requiring stupidity, a will to be deceived, an inability or unwillingness to expend effort on either intellectual or perceptual analysis, and a hunger for the satisfactions that the deception, i.e. the irrealism of the abstractions provided, can procure, and of a calculation on this disposition on the part of the producer. The naiveté of the show is obvious, and is enhanced by simplification and by that juxtaposition of disparate genres of naiveté. And the spectator, though not fooled, moreover goes along with the game: appreciates. But in addition, going further, takes in the style elements as established language, and from their deployment – simplified and offered in artistic doses – in juxtaposition derives aesthetic satisfaction of a non-naive, sophisticated sort. It is a dangerous game both for the artist and the spectator, but if, as e.g. in this play, done

---

18. 'And Peter Schumann was there with a ratchet and wearing an incredible strange unlike-him mask with sequins, white, close-fitting mask with no character. Full of sequins. But it was unlike . . . a mask bought from a dime store – cut straight across, down around. There is no character whatsoever. Covered with sequins . . . The end of the piece was even more disturbing, because for the first time, for the very first time I faulted Peter Schumann. He did something which I think was – it goes back to the '20s maybe, in Germany. The resurrection if that is what you call it, was prepared for by blackout. I have now reached the point in my life where I don't want to ever see another blackout. It is a foul, weak little way of dealing with a situation . . . First of all it is dumb, second of all, I have done too many shows where I have to sneak out in blackouts – I don't think – there is no magic to it. Nobody is fooled by it. He keeps working . . . There was another thing – the three kinds, had a parachute mask, orange and white nylon parachute thing, dress. And they were holding up there – you know how those three kings' mask was solid – the three heads in one mask. He had that from the very beginning. Three kings' heads in a row – worked by one person, and he had a mailing tube glass to look for the new king – in this case it had a gold tassle from it which was a – disaster. It kept bounding about. But, it was on stilts with this orange and white vulgar parachute dress. Totally ugly vulgar thing. And I would have thought he would have said no, we don't want this. I mean, somebody showed it to him, they sewed it, they hung it, they displayed it, and he said yes. Well, orange is a very vulgar color anyway, for me – maybe not for other people.' — (Ashley, interview, '81.)

Ashley saw these vulgarities as lapses into vulgarity, not as artistic devices. He thought they were due to the 'loss of hope' evinced by Schumann's in this play actually going through with the slaughter of the innocents (rather than as in his earlier Christmas plays, having the Angel intervene at the last moment). I thought they functioned (successfully) as artistic devices. But the sophistication I saw them as evincing may have been expression of a 'loss of hope'.

528

with the restraint and judgment carrying the artisan into art, may be artistically successful, and even, as e.g. in this play, provide a medium for an emotionally strong and in its abstractions, realistic statement. It does, however, indicate a certain detachment of the artist from his work: the playful attitude of a master perhaps afraid of boredom.

The theatricality – overt disposition of strong means towards emotional effect – is like the sophistication, a novum in Schumann's theatre: he had heretofore aimed at and obtained strong emotional effects by restraint, and in the '71 *Birdcatcher*, a case of use of strong means for strong effects, the effect was aesthetic, not emotional. The play uses theatricality to convey terror – in the Spirit of the Times of King Herod dance in Part II, in the Slaughter of the Innocents and in Herod's Victory parade in Part V – and in one place, the postludial establishment of a place of peace, to convey the special peace of escape from terror.

That a new urgency of communication has prompted the recourse to theatricality becomes clear, I think, if we compare these dramatic scenes to his previous portrayals of a regime of terror, the torture scene in *Joan*, the terror and madness scenes in *Masaniello* (both '77): evoking fear rather than terror by relatively discrete and abstract means. The focus there was on the individual, and Joan was not terrified, Masaniello exercised the terror.

Schumann adopted the form of theatricality to convey a new perception, that of terrorization as means to achieve terror: in which deployment terrorization itself theatrical, a theatrical use of power. The theatrical terror scenes or sequences alternate with pretty, even cute, pastorally idyllic scenes and sequences on the one and only topic of child bearing (and correspondingly the acme of the terror parts is on child murder, the Slaughter of the Innocents): Annunciation, Conception, Pregnancy (Part I, Nativity) and Birth (the interludial Part III, The Three Kings, i.e. the birthday party, and part IV, Christmas, the birth itself). The birth scene is the first in Schumann's nativities. The alternation, since both the theatrical terror and the pictorial pastorally idyllic scenes employ naive styles, is itself an instance of the play's peculiar mode of sophistication. The play is the first of Schumann's many nativity plays in which the innocents are slaughtered, and goes beyond this by Herod's powerful cortege of victory, the formal triumph of power directed toward stopping procreation. Like Paley's statement in *Washerwoman Ah!*, it proceeds from parental feelings and appeals to them – powerful affects normally underlying virulent patriotism in association with the equally powerful, and often even more viciously deployed 'We've got to protect our women' idea – the women, as often as not, I would say being precisely the daughters: not the wives. This is a turnabout for Schumann who had heretofore celebrated mothers. He is at this point 45 years old and his children are in their late teens.

The play does not overtly invoke the atom bomb, and Schumann went on to deal with terrorism more focally than in this play. But the atom bomb, an artifact installed for 'mutual deterrence', in our age like up to now the plague, scourge of primitive urbanization, and famine, result of the combination of a feeble agriculture with urbanization, but unlike them precisely in being, qua deterrent, an instrument for terrorizing is our age's salient exemplum of terror — and is, specifically, a genetic threat. This Nativity play, therefore, presented the essential *general* features of the age of the atom bomb.

There have been few plays of Schumann's since *Cry* of '69 — where a terminal 'resurrection' was quasi-forced on him by a coalition of hippies and revolutionaries in his group — and *Difficult Life* of '70, without a terminal tableau in some manner indicating or urging a positive outlook, some hope, however marginal for humanity, often some indication of 'resurrection': from the Grey Lady's dance at the end of the *Grey Lady Cantata #2* and the Ark-for-All procession at the end of the first circus, both of '70, to the arrival of the Christmas-gift Ark and the signing of a mass at the end of *Ave Maris Stella*, and the problematic saving/condemnation of Wolkenstein at the end of *Wolkenstein*, both of '78. In '78 these endings had become a little dubious. The assumption of Joan into the heavenly host at the end of *Joan of Arc* ('77) had still been more clearly in the main line of happy endings of '70-'78. *Washerwoman Nativity* (like *Washerwoman Ah!*) has such an ending. But what distinguishes it from the earlier ones is its clear separation from and simple opposition to the totally downbeat body of the play. It is not a terminal resurge of the play's line of intermittent positive accents, the idyllic birth-relating stretches of it. It does not relate to them. Rather than a positive complement of its negativity or even just a subjective positive supplement to its negative report, it reenforces its negativity: pointing up the value of what all is lost. We may alternatively interpret it as reenforcing the play itself conceived as warning, but to the extent the play functioned in the communicational model of warning, it reenforced the warning: rather than diminishing the probability of extinction that the play warned of, it underlined that extinction was in question — a total endangerment. It seemed to pertain less to the probability of what was in store than to its nature.

Before the destruction of the temple and the removal to Babylon, the prophets used intermittently to couple their statements to the people that their God would certainly destroy them for their sins and for the sins of their forefathers with indications that Jahwe's day, the day of destruction, would or might be followed by salvation, at least for a remainder of the people, surviving the destruction. The efforts of commentators to construe this as a consistent doctrine seem to have failed. Though we are here dealing with images, such inconsistency seems the case of this play.

7. The '79 Circus. Dedicated to the working woman.

The circus of '79, *Our Domestic Resurrection Circus*, August 11 and 12, maintained the established form and spirit. It comprised the *Bread and Puppet Circus* (4-5 p.m.), this year started off by a walk by the King of the Northeast Kingdom (promoted from his viceregal status in *Masaniello*) with the Queen of Spain and ending with Uncle Sam Schumann on 20 ft. stilts dancing with the entire cast to the *Stars and Stripes Forever*. Its big play was *Washerwoman Nativity* (5:30-6:30 p.m.), and on its first day there was a nighttime showing of *Washerwoman Ah!*, a *Resurrection Pageant* (7:30 p.m. ff.). There were as always a number of sideshows, including one on the circus' motif, Washerwoman, *Lives of Washerwomen I & II*[1] and miscellaneous evening activities, e.g. music by the Bread and Puppet Band for an open dance, and Isaac's *Missa Carminum* by the Word of Mouth Chorus. Scott and Helen Nearing lectured on the good life, Bob Nichols, Grace Paley and others read poetry. The puppet *King Lear*[2] was done in the pine forest. Like the previous year's *Othello*, it was redone, but only once, in New York. There was also an abbreviated *Carmen*, with rod puppets.

The pageant continued the '78 pageant's development of the motif of marching armies of the '74 pageant: this time the destroyed village was inhabited:

'Dancing around a gargantuan God, the ten "human" washerwomen celebrate symbolically the routine of their lives — washing their garments, hanging them up to dry, waiting through the rain, believing in the sunshine.'

(N. Clemmons, *The Tampa Times*, September 11, '79.)

'As the red of the setting sun turned the day's persistent rain clouds to flocked fire, in just that moment, the Bread and Puppet Theater's great white flying angel appeared against the sky, held high by a dozen running puppeteers. She streaked

---

1. 'The earlier sideshows were dominated by the theme of the washerwoman, with little vignettes set up in 3-sided cottages, the walls painted with the backdrops of their lives: kitchens, living rooms, bedrooms.' — (Elka, *This Year's Circus*, letter to puppeteers, September '79.)

'. . . displays and skits about washerwomen . . . women wearing oversize masks and in peasant outfits portrayed washerwomen tending sick husbands, being persecuted by police and doing their age-old chores.' — (Abbey, *Jugglers and Poets Delight Thousands, The Burlington Free Press*, August 12, '79.)

2. '. . . a show only with cutouts, operated from either the top or from the sides — a little stage like a marionette stage but instead of movable marionettes the figures were unmovable masonite cutouts and the whole show consisted of that with a hidden operator.' — (Elka, in Schumann, interview, '79.)

out of the west across the northern rim of the vast natural amphitheater ... and swooped down its steep slope to rescue the 10 little washerwomen whose circle of dollhouse farms lay in ruins, put to the torch of war ... Minutes earlier, the mild washerwomen (the Washerwoman ... provided a theme that ran through the entire Circus) had stood by their little white houses and their grazing cows and showed us, in broad pantomime gestures below their smiling masks how they washed their clothes and how the clothes dried in the warmth of the sun. As they raised their 10 yellow cardboard suns, in just *that* moment, the circle of dark hills in the distance suddenly shone brilliant green as the sun broke through.'

(E. Fuchs, *Village Voice*, August 30, '79.)

The '78 shift of focus from man's inhumanity to nature to man's inhumanity to man was thus continued: and was maintained henceforth. The pantheist theme was gone for good.

8. *Cambodia* Terrorism vs. food production.

The day after his January 15-February 3, '80 showing of *Ah!* at the Brooklyn Academy of Music, the Bread and Puppet Theatre 'in collaboration with NYU Experimental Theatre Wing' did a benefit for two outfits organizing relief for Cambodia, Oxfam and some 'Concerned Clergy and Laiety for . . .', the place a 2nd floor loft on lower Broadway near Canal.[1] The show, *Cambodia*, apparently done again that summer in France, but not otherwise that I know of, was preceded by a slide lecture on Cambodia's recent history, summed up in one of Schumann's little $4\frac{1}{2} \times 6$-inch newspapers: 1969-73: 'the greatest saturation bombing in history'; 1973-75: the puppet government of Lon Nol; 1975-79: the 'regime of horror' of Pol Pot (leader of the Khmer Rouge, the communist organisation that overthrew Lon Nol and tried to impose deurbanization); 1979: 'Heng Samrin with Vietnam support defeats Pol Pot'; 1980: 'Oxfam, Unicef, Russian and Vietnamese Food and Medical Supplies get to Cambodia. Cambodia needs our support.'[2] The show's 15 scenes roughly

---

1. '. . . a benefit for Cambodian relief staged by Bread & Puppet at NYU's Experimental Theatre Wing. Here Bread & Puppet held a workshop at the same time as its BAM run, rehearsing *Cambodia* in the day, performing *Ah!* in the evening . . . Bread & Puppet took part in an antidraft demonstration at Columbia, much reminiscent of the Sixties.

Argelander asserts that "the era of theatre for theatre's sake is over. Conceptual avant garde visual theatre has exhausted itself. We are seeing a rebirth of humanism; students are investigating emotions rather than the actor-as-machine." Political consciousness raising in the manner of Bread & Puppet is important, he believes, because among young people "you can't take for granted a knowledge of Vietnam or the civil rights struggle as you could up to a few years ago."

The NYU workshop was educational in more ways than one. Peter Schumann wanted to do a piece on Cambodia; Ron Argelander, Program Director at the Experimental Theater agreed; but the politics of the piece were uncertain. A research effort was undertaken, seminars were held in which various relief organizations, visitors to Cambodia, and the different sides in the Civil War, were represented. This investigation convinced Bread & Puppet and the NYU students that Oxfam was the most effective relief organization, and a benefit performance was the result. The workshop was in place before Carter announced draft registration, but was easily adaptable.' — (J. Leverett, *Other Stages*, February '80.)

2. Who feeds what starving? The Cambodian constellation of contenders for domination of the Pacific Basin in 1985 was still the same as it had been in 1980: the Russians via their Vietnamese clients propping up the Cambodian government, the Chinese backing the 'Pol Pot' insurgents, the Americans backing guerila forces claiming divergent derivations from the Sihanouk monarchy. Humanitarian gestures are instrumental to such historical struggles. I don't think this is a sufficient reason for abstaining from them. But one should know what one is doing. In the Cambodian case in the 1980s this for a supporter of U.S. power would, for instance, have been:

'The memory of Vietnam has prevented America from responding to the rape of Cam-

follow this history: 2-6 deal with the U.S. bombing, 7-9 with the Khmer Rouge terrorism; 10 can be construed as (peaceful) entrance of the good guys, the Vietnamese; 11-12 portray the famine resulting from the years of U.S. and Khmer Rouge terrorism, 13-14 the reestablishment of a beautiful agricultural society, portrayed in scene 1, but now without the U.S. threat, 15 the promise of relief.[3]

Schumann sat in the audience. A clamp lamp clamped to a chair between us and the performance illuminated the show.

(1) A group of peasants robed in two or three shades of grey, one or two of them in off-setting black, their faces white oriental face masks, with very slow gestures[4] plant rice: individual grains. A

---

bodia. But national security and human rights concerns suggest that it should provide military and economic aid to the non-Communist Cambodian forces fighting Vietnamese colonialism.

America must provide economic and military aid to the beleaguered resistance movements of SonSann and Sihanouk. Only these forces represent nontotalitarian, nationalist values. That they survived against 180,000 heavily armed Vietnamese while receiving minuscule external aid testifies to their grassroots support. If food, medicine and light weapons were provided, the non-Communists could expand their manpower and effectiveness dramatically. The Vietnamese military, occupying Laos as well as Cambodia, and pinned down by an angry China to the north, cannot escalate much further. The Soviet Union, burdened by its aid to the Polish, Cuban and Vietnamese economic fiascos, and unable to deal with its own Afghanistan quagmire, is in no position for large-scale intervention in Cambodia. Thus, American aid to the Nationalists would impede Hanoi's imperial drive. — (S J. Morris, *Aiding Cambodia, New York Times*, December 15, '82.)

3. 'Political theatre was the flop of the Seventies. Abandoned by a mass audience after the draft's demise, it had a rough time, in both theory and practice, adjusting to changing circumstances. Hard questions arose. What happens to the avant-garde when no one is shocked anymore? Does government support affect artistic independence? Why do exradicals have trouble resisting the caress of corporate foundations? If potent issues from the Sixties — Vietnam and racism — are now condemned by the establishment, has political theatre become obsolete? Is theatre without audience futile? . . . Bread and Puppet, which has never been afraid to attack political problems, owes much of its popularity to Peter Schumann's remarkable imagination; his is a theatre of Resurrection, rooted in Eastern European folk theatre as much as any Sixties traditions . . . The humans in *Cambodia* are clad in black skirts and white masks. In the first of three movements, life is reduced to a heap of bodies: bombs are dropped by a dragon-like plane. Gunfire is expressed by the clanging of empty cans. Bodies are stripped of shoes. In the second movement, black and white skeletons — the black/white opposition of life to death — crawl across the stage. In the final movement, village life resumes in a ritual procession — oxen, humans, puppets.' — (J. Antici. *Flop of the Seventies: Political Theatre, Other Stages*, March 6, '80.)

4. This, I believe, is the first serious presentation of work in Schumann's theatre: though it is preceded by the Uses of Hands shows in the early circuses, and by both the comic stagehand activities of his Garbagemen and the more comedic laundering of his Washerwomen in the later circuses. The work gestures, however, are not functional but ritualistic, i.e. indicative of the significance (sacred nature?) of the activity.

shark-headed grey airplane is suspended above them near the ceiling.

(2)   A line of four maskless performers, in the 'ordinary-but-festive' white quasi-uniform of 'puppeteers' seeming slimmer and taller, more linear, than the kneeling figures, make a slow, circular tour around these, who are now unmoving: a girl with a mallet moving backwards, hitting the bells festooning the cross bars of a wooden musical tree carried by the man following her, and two more in line behind him by means of a string rotating the plane above the planters.[5] They had been standing at the edge of the cleared space around the group in the center, to the left: near a dark, conical shape there.

(3)   The kneeling figures do a slight collective dance in place, each rising slowly, with slow arm movements, subsiding again.

(4)   Another rotation of the plane.

(5)   The group in the center contracts into a tight, mounting huddle, do a heaving movement perhaps suggestive of fear.

(6)   Rapid alternate descents and rises of the shaking shark plane gradually descending till it covers the huddle, hides it. Three musicians in white at the right play shaking instruments.

(7)   Seven or eight musicians. The puppeteers have left, reenter, and line up at the left with grey mechanical-looking soldier puppets, more or less their own size, almost faceless, their arms broad-barreled pipes pistoning toward the mass covered by the plane. The puppets are stick puppets, they are raised and brought down to produce a stomping noise. Their machine gun terrorism alternates with a crawling of the huddlers from under the plane toward the right: a sweeping out.[6] Musicians and plane off. The huddlers a rim of corpses by the right hand wall.

(8)   The conical black shape at the left, as we now see a monster puppet (with a performer inside), bulky, its lower legs encased in silver, a mass of empty tin cans hanging in a dense fringe around the lower

---

5. That this is an image for the hovering of a helicopter is obscured by its integration into the planting ritual by means of the tree-bearing procession. This integration is analogous to that of hunting and butchering into the ritual of his *Resurrection Pageants*: death as part of life.

6. Enforced exodus into the countryside: Khmer Rouge reagrarianization. Scenes 2-6 cover the four years of U.S. saturation bombing, scenes 7-9 the four years of Khmer Rouge terrorism. The play effectively focusses on this latter.

edge of its covering, clankingly advances on the corpses, stomping its feet: a powerful and sinister image.[7]

(9) Musicians back in with horn instruments. Lugubrious tones. The peasants along the wall slowly arise, their arms going up, are lined up along the wall, their backs to us, hands above them. The black monster does a devil dance behind them. They collapse as though under a fusillade. The dead this time do not look like the mass dead in a concentration camp photo (as previously), but more like the victims of a mass execution, e.g. of guerillas caught.[8] The monster approaches the cadavers, works his way down the row away from us, bending down to remove a shoe here or there, throwing it behind him into the center of the floor, a baby shoe among them.[9] The monster stalks out.

(10) Entrance, from around both ends of the large black backdrop, of two puppets (performers inside) in light grey, with huge white benevolent male 'ancient sage' faces (face masks), two others following, all carrying tall pastoral staves. They advance slowly (almost a sliding motion) toward us through the scattered shoes, seem to study the shoes, pick up individual ones and turn them over in their hands, studying them. The three-member white band is standing at the left. The dark grey (isolated blacks) dead peasants along the wall at the right. The four tall, bulky figures in the center. These retreat: their capes at the back are beautifully patterned in white and grey, ceremonial.

(11) A small tinkling bell is sounded by the girl seated by the chair with

---

7. It made me think of the huge Marlon Brando doing Mr. Kurtz in the necropolitan temple city to which Coppola's crap art had transposed him. This and the helicopter of Scene 2 suggest Schumann had seen *Apocalypse Now*.

8. Schumann is exploring the visual potentials of homicidal terrorism. One associates terrorism – i.e. institutionalized intimidation by an actively deployed armed force – more with civil war in its open and cryptic forms – e.g. collectivization in the Soviet Union in the early '30s, working class intimidation by the Nazis in Germany just a little later – than with war, but it is not only associated with war in the forms e.g. of colonial terrorism and of the terrorism waged by occupying forces, it is the essence of war: a continuation of politics with other means, designed to break the enemy's will. Schumann's theatre had always focussed on war, but he was now dealing with a new dimension of it: the institution of fear. I am not aware of any good film art on terrorism other than in certain Japanese movies. A comparison of the mediocre treatment of Khmer Rouge terrorism by Roland Joffé and Chris Menges in *Killing Fields* with scenes 7-9 (or with Schumann's *Goya*, cf. infra) suggests the peculiar (though not necessarily superior) powers of theatre to portray such large scale social phenomena by focus on essence.

9. This echoes one of the slides: a picture of the peasant garments bundled together in storage in a depository allegedly of clothing taken from peasants executed by the Khmer Rouge. It also reminds one of the contents of concentration camp warehouses.

the clamp light in front of us (its seat a spot of red in the picture), the 'corpses rise, stand by the wall, their backs to us, swaying, to moaning horn sounds from the musicians (one of the horns a long, curved, open piece of piping). Above the peasants (we may only now notice) two large, slender, long-fingered white hands hand from some pipes by the ceiling.

(12) Five chairs are placed on the floor at distances from one another in no particular pattern by the white-dressed musician/attendants. Five large — perhaps 5-6 ft. long — flat white carton figures with black streaks, vaguely animalic (feline), vaguely human, are brought out, made to lean, lying on their sides, against the chairs, hiding them. Five performers in grey (like the peasants) get up on the chairs behind them, strings extending from their hands down to the carton puppets. Tinkling sounds as the two white hands are slowly lowered (by other strings extending in two lines diagonally across the stage, handled by two additional performers at the left) over a group — four — of the grey peasants, seated on the floor in two couples, down-stage at the right, each couple with a concrete building block flat on the floor between them: one in each couple slowly does a gesture of releasing a handful of grain taken from a bowl in front of them onto the cement block, the other proceeds to grind the grain with a piece of firewood: the sound oddly that of corn being ground. Then, to string music — all the music is vaguely oriental — the grey puppeteers on the chairs, leaning over the feline carton forms on the floor in the center, cause these to raise their arms in begging gestures up and down: famine victims, their bones showing through their skin, begging for food: the curve of the operators contrasting beautifully with the softly extended shapes below them. More grinding of corn. Gesture of the famished. The plaster hands are slowly re-raised to the ceiling. The five grey puppeteers come down off the chairs, lift the carton figures up in their arms, slowly move them to and fro in a cradling motion, then deposit them, one after the other, dead, in a flat heap out front, each ending his/her deposition with a grieving gesture of hands to eyes, and leaving, hands to eyes.

The girl by the light chair angles the light downward, this way dimming it.[10] Hands, everything, is removed.

---

10. She handled the lighting throughout the show, but this gesture of hers was noticeable. George Ashley regretted it as being the show's only evocation of theatre. I thought the economy of it beautiful. Nor did the fortuitous dime-store red of the chair's seat bother me. To me it did not, as it did to Ashley, clash with the show's array of greys, pointed up by blacks, and framed by white, but as a clearly outside element on the contrary tied them together.

(13) Two puppeteers with a large landscape painting – of a vast grey hill with streaks of black trees, etc., not clearly figurated – perhaps 7 feet high and 10 or more across – stretched between hand-held poles between them, enter in the dark. Lights up. To thin string music, a dense crowd of the peasants in grey enters around the curtain at the left rear, dancing in a crowd, the individuals turning and the crowd as a whole turning as it advances. It rotates to a position below the hill, kneels down in front of it, their backs to it, facing us, raise their hands to face height, palms out, do a swaying dance in place to the sound of a flute. They rise and leave as they came in, in a snake curve, this time, to a wordless oriental song, the picture remaining, a stark hill.

(14) A single masked figure with a musical instrument, a strikingly red pole, first touch of color within the play, at the top end of which can lids are suspended, enters, sounding the canlid-pole in the air in the manner of a herald, standing in front of the landscape. Leaves. Another dense crowd of the grey Cambodians enters from the right rear, in a squared off rectangular formation, embedded between two white oxen, whose large low-hanging curly-horned faces head the procession and define it as plow team with a yoked pair of plowing oxen. The oxen advance to the accentedly rhythmic tinkling of instruments within the group. The group is powerful by its compactness.[11] They make a tour toward us, turn toward the left, leave.

(15) Two white puppeteers enter on the run with a large gull, it sweeps in in intimations of air currents, to gull cries, light and airy, going round and round. Out. Blackout.

The gull is a signoff, a signature at the bottom of a scroll.

The suffering and resilience of a people.

---

11. Schumann in this piece consistently uses a *mass* of people as dance unit: a group of people close together doing the same thing at the same time so that the group moves as one. These mass dances (3,5,13,14) contrasted as distinctively dance with the generally stylized gestures making up the piece. These dances of the masses (unlike e.g. the movements of the crowd in *Simple Light*) pictured the masses positively. The crowd dances harmonized with the unison of the planting and the unison and complementation of the grinding movements. The opposition and dialectic of crowd and individual somehow for Schumann, it seems, does not apply to the peasantry of Southeast Asia. Like Bob Nichols, he has held on to an ideal image of these populations (China is too big, there are too many Chinese). Not an anarchist ideal, not exactly a conservative one. A biological view of humanity as colonial mass, productive of grace. The American people, in his '79 and '81 *Pageants*, his '79 *Washerwoman Cantatas*, his '81 *Story of One Who Set Out to Study Fear*, represented by his Garbagemen and Washerwomen, the Onion Farmer and his Nurse's School instructress wife, has not come off so well. Even though he, during these years, is trying to represent them in a positive light, they are nothing but grotesque.

The successive tableaux coming from behind the black curtain were like the fruit tumbling out of a cornucopia.

* * *

Cambodia, a truly lovely, ritualistic dance piece, counterposed inoffensive food production, harmoniously integrated into nature, to terrorism, that is, to an aggressive violence that like most aggressive violence is designed not only to do away with physical capacity to resist but to do away with the will to resist by creating the fear of further violence: terrifying violence. The opposition, conceptually and as staged, closely parallels that between giving birth and terrorism in *Washerwoman Nativity*. Since the play's subject is famine, it focuses us not on war or on war's victims' as such, but on the victims being agriculturalists. *Washerwoman Nativity* and *Cambodia* show power cutting away at the two roots of survival, food production and procreation.

But the tragedy of bread, i.e. of mankind's tying its life to that of certain grass seeds manipulated by it, labor assuming the form of that dependent manipulation, is that terror is intrinsic to it: the reason being not greed but that there is never enough of it. Labor sensu strictu, it has come to be seen, cf. e.g. R.B. Lee, *The !Kung San*, makes its appearance with agriculture only. The strolls of the women out to gather seeds, fruit, nuts, roots and the men's hunting expeditions are merely modes of living, but not, like the millenial labors of the peasantry, abstentions from life for the sake of it. Agriculture, Cain's business, is a violation of nature, it is married to penury, and their off-spring is the state — terror: men forcing men to give up of their harvest more than they can afford to, though not more than they must give up for the intertwined cycles of human and cereal life to continue. Preferring to ignore our history, we forget that famine has been the perennial ancillary of agriculture, and not liking to confront our true predicaments, we prefer to ignore both that the state is terror, and that without terror, agriculture would not work. Of this terror, war is a merely incidental form, a by-product.[12]

---

12. 'Agriculture was the great leap backward. It returned the majority of us to the restrictive food-getting state of our primate past: we spent most of the day in food-getting activity, each day and every day, year in and year out. It condemned us to live and depend on small areas of land, and robbed all but the rich of the pleasures and drama of the chase. It let us continue to wheel and deal and make alliances through our females (the peasant raised all this to a fine if petty art), but it did not connect all this to the macro-structures of economic power. It left us, as individuals, no longer contributing to the destiny of the larger group but insecure and at the mercy of those who were able to maintain the predatory life. Finally it created slaves and serfs who were robbed even of restricted territory and autonomy. And it did this in a breathtakingly brief period, a mere ten thousand years. It did it to an animal that had carefully and beautifully prepared itself through millions of years of natural selection to range and gamble, lounge and play, feast and forage — all in pursuit of four-footed protein over wide and varied areas of the world.' — (Lionel Tiger, *The Imperial Animal*, 1971.)

When Stalin, killing some 10 or 15 million peasants in the process, instituted collective agriculture in Kolhozes and Sovhozes, the modern equivalents of the communal village agriculture that Marx thought the essence of the 'Asiatic mode of production' and the basis of 'Oriental despotism', he did so in the service of industrialization, but when the Khmer Rouge forced the Cambodians out of their cities, they were trying to achieve the ideal society that the Scott Nearings and the communard hippies of the '70s and late '60s and Schumann himself, sapping the maples on his wife's farm, were trying to achieve for themselves. I don't think Schumann even came near to facing this. Yet: that the Cambodian spectacle upset Schumann's facile opposition between peaceful, beautiful, beneficent agriculture and nasty war may be suggested by his shift from the 1980 *Cambodia*, in which he presents this opposition, to the 1981 *Goya*, in which war – or more generally terror, terrorization in war or in civil war – appears as intrinsic to the human condition, not as mere aberration interfering with peaceful pursuits (of which the essential is cultivation).

9. *Histoire du Pain.* 2nd famine play. The city is guilty. But the city is seeded by the grain —?

Schumann got up the money for Elka's house by inducing Roger Planchon, director of the Theatre Nationale Populaire, to commission him to do a six-week summer workshop in Villeurbanne, the suburban extension of Lyons where Planchon had commenced his rise to power, at a factory there, the Amtec factory.[1] As has been his wont, though he may have felt pretty adaptive doing a show on food in France and in the world's best-eating city, Lyons, at that — the show had in it 'quite a few painted stories on French proverbs about bread, or eating and not eating' (Schumann, interview, '83) — he did what he had intended to do anyhow, viz. a summer 'circus', more or less like his Glover circuses, and a show on bread, the subject, with childhood, fear, terrorism, newly preoccupying him, a show, rather, on how modern international captalism 'or sump'n' threatened the world's food supply. The 'sump'n' might be 'modern civilization'.

His thought seems to be that traditional forms of agriculture (plus fishing, foraging, etc.) or intelligent adaptive improvements on them could do the job of feeding the world's population, but that the operation of Western economic power in the world market is causing monocultures producing raw materials for the West and/or industry-dependent — West-dependent — and land- and community-destroying forms of food production to replace them, and that this process not only has famines as transient by-products, but raises the probability of greater famines to come.[2] More-

---

1. 'The reason was that Elka didn't want a circus on the farm — she wanted to build a house, and we needed to make the money for that and so I offered it to Planchon because he had said for a long time, do a workshop here — so I said, we need so much money — and then he did it.' — (Schumann, interview, '83.)

2. '(I: In other words, your concern here related to what usually is thought of in terms of overpopulation?) Well, it seems to me that talking about food as a resident of the United States could only mean that, that one considers that position of being a resident of a country that does not only produce food in abundance but stores food in abundance, controls market prices all around the globe by its over food production and non-distribution policy or political policy of food distribution, so we are in this precarious position of being not allowed a general global philosophy on food but having to consider that we are here in the United States and we are dealing with politics that manipulate food at will and to their advantage at all times. So food in the world probably isn't just — definitely isn't just a problem of production, of overpopulation, of scarcity of topsoil or waters that produce fish but more or less a political problem of not only distribution but the fighting and manipulating of this power that food constitutes for these giant states. (I: What about this other area, like American agriculture. For instance, what we see globally is that Russian agriculture is not very good and the Chinese are weak and even the Indians. And so the one system that

541

over, he seems to perceive a nexus of this process to terrorism, a nexus I perceive, but only dimly and the nature of which in Schumann's mind is unclear to me.

Histoire du Pain was, with considerable friction not only with the local TNP bureaucracy but also with the workshop participants, dissatisfied, apparently, both by the lack of formal instruction and by Schumann's sovereign determination of what was going to be done,[3] gotten together

---

works for the masses of humanity seems to be an agriculture based on exploitation of the soil and on chemical means to keep things going and on the use of a great deal of machinery to do the whole thing.) Well this is not true. That is not the – globally, you say, that's the only way that works. This would only be true if we take globally as what has the greatest influence in the world. But if you really look globally into smaller food systems, into smaller cultures, then as far as I know there are many places who are very able to produce their own food, who – that get discouraged of doing so, who get disadvantaged by this superpower food production to do so for the advantage of the superpowers. I mean, that's – again and again many, many little societies where food production was not really a problem. (I: It became one.) And does become one as soon as the – I went once, I did work up in Martinique, a very rich country in all kinds of produce and of fish and what have you. The fish that I ate there was imported from France and it was outrageous. They were not allowed anymore therefore – and all that was grown was bananas and sugar for rum, nothing else, no food, no nothing. It was imported. Vegetables came from France in a country that was much richer in topsoil and in natural growth than in France and any place. So it's like that. There are many places in the world like that.' — (Schumann, interview, '83.)

3. 'It was terrible. The people were absolutely terrible – disgusting – who we had to work with. Not the people who worked with us so much as the administrators, the TNP people, not Planchon himself, but everybody else. The people he works with are full of shit. Terrible, terrible people. (I: Bureaucratic, or what?) Not only this, they – the first instance when I came and told them what I wanted to do, they hated it and they, from then on, countered every move we did. (I: Ah – the French, with delicate meticulousness.) Yes, right. With great politeness and great smiles. And they worked against us as hard as they could, on every level. When we ordered fabric, they got us the wrong stuff. But meticulously. With every move we did. The tools wouldn't be there when we needed them – everything was wrong – every time we did a move, they countered it. Our technical director was like that – the administrator was like that – the whole thing was a fight – a crazy fight for a one-time performance. It was ridiculous. But for a lot of money – we built a house with it. So I shouldn't complain. (I: Why did that happen? What was the –) The reason was that Elka didn't want a circus on the farm – she wanted to build a house, and we needed to make the money for that and so I offered it to Planchon, because he had said for a long time, do a workshop here – so I said, we need so much money – and then he did it – he did it – he said yes, but the people were – (I: But was there something specific they disliked about what your proposed to do there?) Yes. That I ran the show. That it was not a – they had already lined up painters and sculptors and art students, organizations, and friends of their own from their theatre, who would come and make and design these masks. They thought of it as a kind of a school where all these – and I came in and I designed everything. And I told people what to do. And they hated that attitude and instead of helping me to persuade the people to accept that for this short period of time, and to work with me, learning all kinds of techniques and what have you while doing that, they made a revolution against us, continuously, and sort of intrigued little groups of students and of professors against us who then dropped out or even persuaded other people to drop out. So

542

and — to music not by Rameau or some other older French composer, which Schumann would have preferred, but to Schubert's *Miriam's Gesang*, a piece his workshop collaborators had in hand — performed at the Villeurbanne factory, with a prologue about the Cuban missile crisis based on Schumann's *This Is*.[4] *Histoire du Pain* was the centerpiece and only substantial component of a circus[5] comprising, due to the locale, I suppose, no pageant, but a parade and some other shows as well, e.g. a

---

there was a constant fight — to have people in it that would do the work and have them — right materials and everything — it was terrible — absolutely terrible — but lots of things were made, nevertheless.' — (Schumann, interview, December '82.)

'Peter (Schumann) — described the Villeurbanne workshop and pains involved. The main bulk of puppets built this year came from there. They worked on a Moliere production at the same time as the B & P festival which cost 10 times as much. Their complaints about the money we spent were crazy in relation to what they're used to . . .

Raised question of difficulties of working with people to do big shows. Trudi: Two things for us, wanting to work with people and offer them something, and also needing them for the shows to happen. Elka: Different at the circus, when the theatre doesn't make money. Annie (Romanyshyn): Here in New York people don't think that you're making huge money from it. In Europe there's a different feeling. Elka: People's positions vary. Students do consider it part of their education. But it's different if you're somebody struggling to do similar things on your own.' — (*Minutes*, Meeting, December 14, '80, B & P members & Board of Directors.)

4. *This Is*, a play in eleven scenes, tells the story of the 'Cuban Missile Crisis' of '62. It was inspired by R. F. Kennedy's *13 days* and John Sommerville's play *The Crisis: The True Story About How The World Almost Ended*, and was with illustrations by Schumann and a subsidy from the Literature Program of the National Endowment for the Arts published by *Janus Press*, Newark, Vt. in '80. I don't know of any performances of it in its entirety, though such may be in question in the reference in a list of B & P productions in '81 appended to the minutes of the December '81 B & P board meeting to performances of '*The Cuban Missile Crisis*', but an abbreviated version of it, with cutout puppets, apparently based on its last scene, and with a chorus listing 'all the things that would have been destroyed if that crisis had gone to its terrible end' (Elka, interview, *NYT*, April 25, '80), was done as prologue to performances, April 24-7, '80 of *Stations*, put on by Larry Gordon of the Word of Mouth Chorus, and this was probably more or less what the Villeurbanne prologue was like, as was the sideshow at the '81 circus, *The Cuban Missile Crisis*.

As prologue to *Stations* and *Histoire du Pain*, the evocation of the 'end of the world' by atom bomb was as extrinsic to the main spectacle as it had been in the '79 *Ah!* — an incidental reminder, a tone awkwardly struck by the play's opening statement: 'At this moment in history, let us remember the Cuban Missile Crisis of 1962'. Schumann only with the circus of '81 came to deal centrally with the nuclear Armageddon.

5. 'We wanted to work on an all-around program similar to our circus here. That is, we wanted to develop one major piece of indoor theatre independent of rain and shine and do it in that large, big factory that was available to us. In that piece — for that piece I wanted to use as many people as possible but as much original material for it and find what the most interesting piece of music that was going on in that area and try to get them to participate. That was one program. The other programs were the normal ones, to develop a circus from scratch, from having people invent circus ideas, jobs, etc., build them and do the performing invention after it, and then bring all of that together, choreograph it into a little circus. And the third idea was to do political ideas, make them into theatre, one of which

version of *Cambodia*, and one of *Venus* (cf. infra) and a *Cid*, gotten together by Michael Romanyshyn, and after its Lyons showing was, over a
six week period, in a reduced version, toured in France and performed at
the Dubrovnik Summer Festival and perhaps elsewhere in Yugoslavia. It
wasn't done again, but yielded puppets for subsequent B & P shows, and
puppets and story elements for *Inneffective Man-Dream Woman* and its
derivative, the prologue of *Diagonal Man* (both '82.)

'So then the building projects, the first part of it, naturally, there had to be building done. I wanted it to be the history of bread. That was the overall idea before
even the musicians and the piece of music were found. So what I built for it was
some large puppets for bright colors;[6] some large puppets for dull colors; some
sets of flat puppets, cutout puppets that could move their limbs – The Famished
People. Then, well, masks, all kinds of masks. Some masks of a French farmer and
a farmer woman and beasts, a group of beasts, of these riding type masks and
costumes. I think that was in general what was built there. And a big group of
many colors of masks which we wanted to use as a population with – we had
available to us the costume rooms of the Théâtre Populaire so we could go there
and pick out all the stuff so we had all kinds of crazy costumes and this was just
right for those masks. That's how the thing started. So the rehearsals were sort of
what to do with the population, how they moved, what they did. Then the city, a
cutout town, was built. Then demon figures were built with open mouths. They
were later on used in *Woyzeck* with tongues sticking out of – (I: Laughing guys.)
Yeah, those guys. They were originally eaters. Their tongues came out and they
ate the town. Then some kind of rattle machine and *The Story of Bread*, which
was a flip over story that was turned over and told and was sort of the outside
structure to the thing. This is the story that we tell you and then – The big god
figure was the stomach who was painted – and was hanging full of forks and
knives and was talking in French proverbs about food. It started with, again, a
beginning of the world food story. There was a giant hand mounted above the
performing area and on it a little bag of grain was mounted. Then the music of
Schubert was a theme of – was utilized and when the woman and the man pulled
at the string attached to that bag and the grain fell down on the ground, that's
what started the play. And then – what happened then? What grew out of that
grain? A city, brought in by black cutout faces. One house after another was born.
Then the population for the city. There was all these pink, yellow, blue, green

---

would be the *Cambodia* show, and others would be newly invented things and things that
would come out of this workshop, out of discussing with people. The fourth idea was to
parade a lot of side shows, especially for the kids in the neighborhood, with them and
some for them with adults, but also those that would be done by the kids themselves. And
the other idea was the painting of the walls of the factory inside and out and hanging
exhibits into that building. So these are the projects. (I: No pageant in Villeurbanne?) No,
instead of – the pageant would be that big inside piece (*Story of Bread* (SSB)). So the
music that I found – I tried to push for a French composer, Rameau because Rameau is
from that area. But the musicians who we met, who I made contact with had no interest in
Rameau. They had been working on Schubert and they were enthusiasts of Schubert, so
what I used was – (Schumann, interview, '83.)
6. The 'Individual People' masks used in shows '81 and ff.

faces. And then — I don't know the then, then, then anymore so well but things went wrong. The stomach god appeared and things were taken from what had grown out of the grain and the grain, after it grew, in addition to being a city, having grown into a city, it also had grown into a field of grain. It was harvested by the man in the moon and their likes. It was taken from them. The grain became the story. The woman was made into the grain. She represented the grain for the second half of the play and then was — her husband was taken from her. She was stripped of what there was, was imprisoned and was tortured and killed. It was the grain that became personalized in the story of — when the story of the grain was told. (I: How does it end? That's the end, her death?) No. There were again so many different versions I have to concentrate now because we had one version in Lyon and then later on we traveled the piece so it became very different. I can't think of that. What was the end of it? I know that there was that piece of music for all these hungry skeletons that came in. That was — I think that was the end of it. (Schumann, interview, '83.)

The Washerwoman, finally making it, becoming the individual heroine of a play, though, as Schumann points out,[7] having become pretty, a pretty Frenchwoman — I suppose she had to to make it with Schumann — who had already in '79, in *Washerwoman Nativity* assumed the aspects of a cowgirl, has now turned into a Farmer's Wife, an occupational category henceforth hers. It is as though simultaneously with losing his faith in nature as Sure Provider he had at the turn of the decade woken up to the fact that nature is not only a landscape but place of work — humanity's basic work place. Grain seeds the City, and the City, whose god is The Stomach, devours it: Famine stalks the land.[8]

---

7. 'It was a pretty-face woman who otherwise was in the style of the Washerwoman, but a young and pretty washerwoman. The man was sort of a moustached French farmerman.' — (Schumann, interview, '83.)

8. Misled by the prologue, a peripatetic N.Y. reviewer misinterpreted the ending as preview of the world after World War III.

'The Bread and Puppet's *The Story of Bread*, premiering in Europe this summer prior to a New York appearance in the fall, suffered from the apparent difficulty of transporting all the necessary props — minimalist B & P is like Rothko in black and white — but even more from a kind of dilettantish pessimism. With simplistic irony, little humor, less mystic fervor — and with only occasional hints of the hyperbolic architechtonic inventiveness that so often characterizes its work — the piece begins with an embarrassingly agitprop version of the Cuban missile crisis, then flashes back to deal with the entire course of human civilization (B & P is nothing if not ambitious — one of its more modest projects, a few years back, was a version of the Bible). God gave humans seeds, seeds gave us wheat, wheat gave us bread — but then the story of bread becomes one of exploitation, famine, warfare, and eventual nuclear self-destruction. Perhaps the work was being shown in a truncated version — in any case, despite a few vivid images, the final scene of the extinction of life on the planet seemed only a little more horrific than a Halloween skeleton.

The politics of the past year, admittedly enough to drive one to despair, seems to have led the group into a kind of placid defeatism. What was missing was not only any real feeling of rage, but any sense of a countervailing redemptive force — what was lacking, in

short, was the naive but transfiguring love behind their anger, the simplistic but transcendent optimism beneath their pessimism — for the essence of B & P politics has always
seemed to me their conviction that the apocalypse can still go either way, that what we do
matters.' — (R. Wetzsteon, *A Sense of Loss in Dubrovnik, Village Voice*, September 3-9,
'80.)

10. *Venus Rising From the Water*. About the lovely light that signals the onset of terrible darkness. The play itself participant in that darkness.

Venus Rising From the Water was done again, on a double bill with a new play, *Goya*, in New York City, February 25-March 8, '81, in the chilly basement of Crystal Field's and George Bartenieff's Theater for the New City for the usual crowd of scruffy homebodies that go there, with, very probably for the first time in Bread and Puppet history, something like a disclosure of the performers right in the program — a list of 'puppeteers', including besides the 7 performers — the salaried core group plus Joanne Schultz, Ron Kelley and Richard Norcross — also Schumann who was assisting as musician, but not Elka, who was separately listed under 'Administration'.

A curtain, plastic but opaque, stretches across maybe 15-20 of the approximate 25 ft. width of the platform stage, 3 or 4 feet back from its edge, narrow, also plastic curtains, probably shower curtains, to each side of it closing off the rest of the space. Above the 7 ft. or so of curtain, a black space. The stage platform is low — maybe two feet up. Out in front of the curtain, stage-left, there is a curtained board on a pole, its curtain red and a red strip of cloth running from it to the mouth of a pink Venus, big-breasted, emerging on a suspended piece of fabric further stage-left from blue waves (turning red around her head) her hair. Next to the pole, on the platform with it, a chair. Stage-right a second chair, a piece of red fabric on the floor, a violin case, violins. By the gallery at our right, where it extends beyond the balcony that above it runs the length of the wall there, but down on the floor with us — the gallery is two or three steps up — a reading stand and a clamp-on lamp fixed to the bannister next to it. Obscurely somewhere on the floor in this area a metal pitcher and a white mug.[1] The whole place has a cramped feeling, but the Schumannites have distributed their stuff, from curtains to mug and violins, with a kind of carelessness suggesting *they* weren't cramped, and giving them *enough* space: their own theatre, sort of — an impermanent one.

Schumann: white open shirt, bulky pants, beard and hair joined in a dark frieze around his brown face. Picks up a violin bow, resins it. A sea-captain figure is coming down the aisle, doubled over, blue-eyed face mask, cap, cane, boutonnière, greeting the audience, his shirt stuffed for a stocky, gouty figure (Barbara Leber). Clearly to be taken humorously.

Up on the platform, he bangs his cane on the floor. Lights out. A dimly

---

1. A sloppiness not uncharacteristic of this production: they are props for the evening's other play, *Goya*.

perceived kneeling white-clad assistant up above the drop curtain – there must be a second level there, its floor near the curtain's top – extends a light on a pole over it, over to above the covered board on the pole. The sea captain gets up on the chair there, laboriously, parts the curtains over the board, the title – 'Venus Rising from the Waters' – is on the board, he indicates it with a formal gesture, comes down, bows. Light out above the title board.

(1) The sea captain undoes a rope to the left of the curtain that's apparently holding up the main curtain in the center, in the dark slowly lowers it to the ground. (He curtains/uncurtains the scenes throughout the show.) We see curtains that were behind it, transparent gauze, meeting in the middle. Behind them on the dark stage, an indistinct light near the ground. Gentle humming from there, in several voices. Movements. Something is being unveiled behind the gauze curtains which stay closed: it is the source of the light, which grows stronger as it is uncovered. All in all, straining, it perhaps looks most of all like a flower, with aspects of a crystal. Intimations of a seashell? Hint at a vulva? Or the very star?[2] We can now discern, behind the veil-curtain, and suspended above the light now clearly visible on the ground in front of it, a large-faced figure – puppet – its face, lit from below, an oval, somewhat insipid, pretty-girl face surrounded by bridal veils whose white goes down to around the light source on the floor: four unmasked assistants crowding around the luminous object have been gradually uncovering it by lifting the puppet's bridal dress skirts off it. An obscure birth of something bright.

As the obscure white object emerges and lights up its immediate surroundings, e.g. the four witchety midwives (one of them a young man) – due to the strong shadows a passably though by no means stunningly handsome grouping – we notice two giant hands floating around it, vaguely cradling it,[3] vaguely – they may be the bridal figure's, don't particularly seem hers, they just seem hands – for a moment seeming to lift it up to her. One may have the impression she is discovering it – imputations of maternal delight? She – face and dress – is slowly rising behind the gauze curtain. As she rises, the dark drop curtain slowly rises also. The Old Salt is raising it. It gradually covers the (ground level) space in which we had glimpsed the delivery of the bride, but as it continues to rise, uncovers it again. The people and the object are still there. She is rising just a little faster than the curtain which now covers the upper (bridge) level and the bridge operator. The curtain keeps ascending, disappears above the bridge level. When it uncovers the bridge level, the white figure is gone. With something like veneration, the midwives are slowly putting the bright white object into a large tin can – the large hands dangling to each side of

---

2. It is in fact a roundedly conical wire structure, perhaps 18-24 inches long, its base c. 8 inches in diameter, with small pieces of muslin or the like sewn or otherwise attached to the wires in a raggedy fashion, and with a bare bulb inside it.
3. They are in part manipulated on strings by the upper level (bridge) operator in white whom, if we pay attention, we can see bending out over the floor, in part, for close work, by strings attached to the forearms of two of the mid-wives down there.

it – which is placed on a low stool, center stage, where to flute sounds from Schumann out front to the left, with the two floating hands in a silent dance around it, the fire of the flower slowly fades and dies. Curtain down. Dark.

(2) The sea captain lights the light by the reading stand outfront. (He does this for each of these scene changes.) Up above, on the uncovered bridge level, the white clad assistant is taking away and arranging things, this work process – careful, but simple, unaffected movements – a not strongly but still vaguely interesting action. The sea captain meanwhile with a slight, sly humor – 'of the simplest', like the scenery and props – seated in his chair acts as conductor of the 'concert' Schumann is giving – fiddling. It is not clear to me why the M.C. suggests an Old Salt. Concert over. The Old Salt pulls up the curtain.

(3) Behind the transparent curtain, on the ground or performance floor, a seated grey figure on the left, a huge, standing grey-blue or greenish puppet figure on the right. The captain opens the transparent curtain. To the left, in dim light, in a grey gown, the seated figure has a broad, beautiful, mature female face, a baby in her left arm, part of her, welded into the arm and of a piece also with her head (mask). The greenish figure opposite her on the right has a face (mask) that is long and narrow, its forehead very tall, the nose large and hooked: to me he has a perverse look. Its small, girlish hand is visible outside its monkish gown. To the right of it, a ladder. Between the ladder and the black side-covering of the stage, a glimpse of some mysterious object, a box or alcove, golden, its gold perhaps a covering of floral embossments.[4] No enclosing wall behind the two figures – just blackness, a hole. The captain walks between the immobile figures, laboriously bends over, picks up an arrow-shaped cardboard sign, very slowly rasies it, it has 'rising' written on it, it does not seem to fly, it is lifted: the top-level assistant (invisible) picks it up. The captain touches each of the immobile figures in turn with his cane. Each starts moving slowly after he 'brings it to life': in a dance of sorrow. The mother-with-child slowly rotates her upper body. The hook nosed green male repeatedly bends over, bows. A projector light is turned on, stage left. Invisible assistants hold up a red backdrop behind the tall male and the now illuminated ladder. The captain gently nudges him, he ascends the ladder slowly. While he does, mother and child are again motionless, perhaps watching. Curtain down.[5]

(4) On the upper level we see the huge male ghoulish puppet lit by a flashlight held by the whiteclad assistant up there, to the left, to drums doing a dance, willowy, very long necked now, its small bare girlish hand (the operator's), index finger extended, close to its swaying body, pointing to

---

4. Sloppiness. It's the golden sun not used until Scene 6 and is not supposed to be standing around there at this point. Alien details have a major (negative) effect in symbol-reliant and compositional theatre of this sort.

5. One spectator thought of him as spirit of the darkness in the waters, another as male rising principle. I had no associations. It may have been supposed to be the moon.

the suspended arrow that says 'rising' — hanging from the ceiling, center-stage.

(5) Whiteclad assistant busy on Level 2, ghoul gone, Schumann is fiddling on two violins simultaneously, scraping dry sounds. The captain sits, belly out, studying the Venus picture — to suggest to us we are watching the pink Venus rising out of the blue waves? Lights out. Schumann gets up stage right, picks up the piece of red fabric on the floor there, starts agitating it at the edge of the side curtain there.

(6) The side curtain is pulled up. A white female figure dressed in many veils, all white, slowly emerges from a gauzetent (like that of a Jewish bride). As she steps out, a blue-light projector on a clamp-on lamp on the floor in front of her, lighting her up, is slowly receding to the right, as though pulled by a spring. She stops right in front of the tent, under a second — overhead — projector: her many veils are lifted off her (by the invisible assistant above), one by one, thrown at her feet, over the floor projector, a luminous spray, then foam. A beautiful moment. Uncovered, she is revealed as an oddly clumsy, sportive, stocky female figure in a costume of (felt?) scales, grey work-glove-mittened hands, her face bandaged as though in a fencer's mask. As she kneels down in place, the Old Salt picks up a sign stage center, holds it up for us to see, it says 'from the water'. She starts swimming motions in place, rising to her knees each time her arms do a breaststroke movement. The Old Salt knocks his cane on the stage floor and overhead lights go on in back — slightly behind him and her, only, revealing three gauze veils, bluish, a pale Indian blue (in the light), extending behind one another across the stage, rising and falling in wave motion as she swims, the calm huge waves of not particularly agitated open water. To lugubrious sound from a mouth instrument (Schumann), a large, square golden metal disk, corners up and down, with a sun embossed on its center, and something like leaves or possibly elaborate fat rays around it, slowly descends, glittering (an assistant is holding an amazingly inobtrusive light at the end of a pole, pointed toward it in front of it) stage left toward the waves. The naiad is swimming sturdily. The waves reach and cover the lower corner of the sun, arrested in its decline. To a tinkling bell, the sun shakes in place, glittering. The lights slowly dim. (The shaking, a poetic allusion, perhaps, to the sun's evening descent into the ocean.) Curtain down.[6]

---

6. How I first saw this scene:
   Seated figure, female, stage left, thickly swathed, mask of bandages like a protective mask, whitish colors, leaning forward and back with arm motions of a swimmer, gauze bands agitated like large, pale, ocean waves in the open sea in background, no storm (though Peter Schumann, in front of stage, at extreme left is agitating a red cloth, its color not prominent, producing sounds representative of rather than imitative of wind sounds), but impression of the general dangerousness of the open sea. A laborious rise upward through the waters of Venus, At end of scene, after a seemingly long while of rising, a large rhomboidal (?) plate — more or less a square, really, but held points up and down — copperish in color, glinting in the light of a light held at end of a pole between it and us (so we don't see the light itself), its surface embossed abstractly, but around a traditional solar

(7)   Upper level scene-change activities. (A second assistant has joined the first.) The Old Salt conducts Schumann's scraped (2 violins and a kazoo) musical accompaniment, while laboriously extracting a small pipe from his pocket, then lighting and smoking it (through his mask), which interferes in a weakly comical way with his activities as conductor. A knocking from the rear announces to the Old Salt the scene is ready. He rises to turn out the light and to raise the curtain.

(8)   The light on the stage is dim, bluish. Behind the transparent curtain, at the rear, to the left, something like a sea bird flops its wings – the motions of a sea bird beneath the surface of the water: it is something at the end of an agitated hand held pole. Under it, on the stage floor, a dark, recumbent, odd, very large, unidentifiable shape or figure, its two extended sides raised, flapper- or wing-like, upward. After perhaps a minute the distant bird disappears. The shape on the floor slowly rises, and we recognize the male ghoulish thin giant figure from before, but now provided with huge, dark, shiny plastic wings (seeming part of its gown, attached to it, but held and moved by strings from the upper level). It flaps its wings awkwardly, more awkwardly than the smaller (by implication perhaps distant) bird before – perhaps it, come nearer? An agitated clumsy motion as the large shape – an albatross? or a ray? – slowly, swaying, rises: motions of flight or of trying to fly? I had an impression of fear. Its movements are increasingly agitated: a drum beat: he – it – collapses (Dimly, through the gauze, we see the performer inside the fish-bird-man get out, leave with the costume.)

        Over its collapsed body a short tangle of jerking rope appears, dangling from above, illuminated from above, and more or less as the fish-bird-man performer hurries off, there is a commotion in the messy rear of the stage, white and red lights, and crude shouting ('Hey! Hey!' etc.), and a crowd of assistants half obscured by a red piece of cloth – or something of this sort – slowly but agitatedly throng forward in the deep background, behind a huge hollow open red dragon head, the Chinese New Year accompaniment of a dragon that is wheezing onto the stage and that – appropriately for a dragon – is mostly or all head: I did not notice its tail. Maw opens, the head is a sort of impressionistic filigree of a head in the not too well lit stage air.[7] The dragon is down-stage, close to the ground, a mouth: snapping with upward jerks, abortive leaps at the dangling rope – to isolated double tom-tom beats from Schumann out front. (During the March 1 performance, the Old Salt was instead agitatedly banging his stick on the

---

pattern in the middle – slides out from stage left, above the waves, a mythical sun, appearing somewhat perhaps like the diamond shaped glints of sun on the surface of moving water: The swimmer is emerging. After a moment the sun sets in the waves: momentarily its surface pattern to me suggested in the dominant glints reflected from it, the face of a woman. Apparently Venus emerged in the evening. The heaviness of the figure swimming up, a turgid figure like a tight feeling in one's throat, suggests that more than delight is involved: desire as force.

7. The staging of this – like the bird-man-performer's getting out of his costume and off stage – seems deliberately crude, juvenile, silly.

floor out front to the right.) An image of danger and aggression, but of impotent aggression, a not serious danger – relating to what? Silence, darkness except for the red light in the collapsed monster's muzzle on the floor, center-stage.

Peaceful humming as at the beginning. The 'white flower' is handed in from the wings, down-stage, stage left, illuminated, is carried, held high (as though object of worship or veneration), by 4 whiteclad performers illuminated by it, across the stage to above the collapsed beast, here seems to rise to the large enfolding floating hands as the Venus puppet – large pink face – slowly descends from above, down onto the dragon, descending again with her then held under her face, the large hands holding it seeming the puppet's. Venus is seated in her white bridal veils on the pacified beast with the bright white thing. All this behind the transparent curtain. She begins to rotate backward and forward, the beast rocking with her: somewhat as though she were riding somewhere – perhaps towards us. The humming is still continuing. As the (not very bright) lights go off, the curtains are briefly parted a little and the white bright thing held – thrust – out toward us: very much a bouquet at this moment. Lights off, dark, humming stops. 8:35 or 8:40, the piece has taken a little above half an hour.

One got away with the idea that the idea of the piece had been an equation of the Deity – i.e., as usual, not the lady of the Circus Maximus and the wine harvest festivals, residing over orderly planting, but the oriental woman of dubious repute that made it onto Olympus: sea-principle of all the disorderly fertility of nature, whom in Hesiod's painful catalogue we encounter as the sea-sprung – with the great shining double star, great star of the evening, arising out of the dusk, great star of the morning, swimming ahead of the light: and that perhaps all the world-ocean of air had been equated with the dark sea full of monsters, from which that light lady may be thought forever again emerging: the lovely light, therefore, the native ruler of the ferocious and fearful dark, neither of them alien to the other, just as gentle love emerges from the ferocious twisting of limbs in the dark as pure essence of the sweaty war of cock with cunt. Clearly, however close to or remote from these highly unchristian conceptions Schumann's piece may have been, there was the intention of presenting some intuited concatenation of the ideas of sea/darkness/danger, loveliness/light/serenity, and of birth and death naively.

But not only naively: also without formal finish. I.e. crudely. But not in the sense of rough work and simple oppositions, normal in Schumann's pieces, but in the sense of the raw or half-baked, and of lack of outline. *Venus* had been carelessly and sloppily done and so much so that it announced there had been no other intention. As though, perhaps, to intimate either: these are just glancing thoughts, things glimpsed around a corner, I don't know *what* it was I saw, or: these are hypotheses to which I am not committed. Either way: I wouldn't wanna be quoted on it. Or

552

else: I had something in mind but it didn't seem worthwhile to work it out – either in my head or on stage. What was conveyed was an obscurity in the maker's mind, not in the object represented.

Venus was crude, not just be what might pass for 'devices', but in its simple workmanship, e.g. the Waterwoman's dangling hands that didn't seem to belong to her, but above all: the plastic curtain + blueish lighting did not get the idea of water across! In fact, being rather dumb, i.e. direct in my appreciations, just looking, I did not get this idea except by reflecting on the title of the piece subsequently. It seems to me this was simply a technical failure of Schumann's explicable only by an extraordinary distraction, in turn hard to explain: the year '80 was busy for him, but he can't have spent much time improving *Venus* for the NYC presentation in '81 either. Nor was it clear that the piece was about what the title said it was about, the rising of a heavenly body and the concomitant descent of another. That the *evening* star was in question, was not implied by the title, and so the sun's descent baffled whoever was more familiar with the morning star – early risers like myself. To have the mythological figure holding the planetary body was a lovely idea, suitable for an observatory architrave, but also confusing: for why bridal? Why maternal? As for the obscurity of the secondary figures in the piece – the Waterwoman's ghoulish 'husband' (?), the bat ray monster, the Chinatown dragon – it was like the obscurity of the figures of darkness and crowd life in the darkness part of *Simple Light* ('72), but not quite, for though one could not identify (as one can in fairy tales, as one had been able to in Schumann's work of the '60s) those '72 figures in terms of the coin of the imagination, one accepted them as the unpleasant – and ill-defined: obscure – complications of individuality in the dark world of the crowd, whereas in *Venus* Schumann seemed simply to have failed well to imagine monsters of the deep: as though himself drowning and gasping for air while working on the water piece.[8]

In his previous period of discouragement, at Goddard, Schumann had represented obscure things, objective confusions and things hiding from view: the privacy and the motivational and emotional involutions of

8. '... fanciful ... a mythological abstraction, an underwater ballet of images ... occasional signposts ... but not enough to make this piece entirely accessible ... has a gentle, lulling effect, floating its creatures – mermaids and goddesses – on a wave of tranquility, until interrupted by a fiery red dragon wearing a yellow hat and followed by a processional.' — (Gussow, *New York Times*, March 4, '81.)

'... an odd departure for the company: mostly form with little content. We see various permutations of blue-lit gauze and muted, draped lights, with a few mannequins suggesting not-quite-coherent images of a goddess rising from the sea, a family group, and the goddess returning to the sea ... The between-episode interludes are rather fun: Schumann, unkempt and wacky, plays a kazoo and two violins at once, while a grey-masked nightwatchman stage manager snoozes. But basically, *Venus* is, for Bread and Puppet, slight.' — (Blumenthal, *Village Voice*, March 4-10, '81.)

family life (*Emilia*), the deceiving hypocrisies and the messy incompletions and involutions of a social life malarranged by the compactions and aggressions of crowds and individuals (*Simple light*) – intrinsically obscure objects. But the obscurity of *Venus*, though it conveyed the otherness of the dangerous sea (as otherness, perhaps, of a world indifferent to and possibly ultimately inimical to man) and blank night's dimmed-out puzzle of lurking threats (as perhaps the state of a world, though this would not have occurred to a spectator, dominated by the terror of opposing arsenals of nuclear missiles, and from which the very basis of human existence, the practices of a renewable use of the soil, was fading), went beyond this to indicate the working artist's obscurity of mind, viz. his not having worked things out, neither what the figures were he wanted to present, nor how to present – stage – them: an obscurity of the mind indicative of a slackening of the will: a state of discouragement. *Venus* seemed to say: the world has become so terrible that art is frivolous, the expression of its terribleness pointless. Its ragged form and uncompromised obscurities conveyed a revulsion from play-making going beyond the gesture of disdain for the pretensions of art to self-worth that is conveyed by the crudeness of most of Schumann's shows, beyond his disdain for the Kultur of the bourgeoisie.

The titular Venus it turned out was not Botticelli's, not Phosphorus, harbinger of day, but Hesperus, the evening star, announcer of night. The rising light that the play proposed for our appreciation was not the glimmer of female goodness in the darkness of social life offered by *Simple Light*, nor the radiance of the reliably reenergizing sun erected as divinity at Schumann's pageants, nor the gentle moon's reassuring reflection of this divinity when it is gone, presented at his pageants' conclusion, but a distant light in cold serenity proclaiming darkness. The play was about the coming of night. If, by habitual response, one viewed the light as representing hope, it represented hope specified as contrary to the certainty of deepening darkness, and represented it in that aspect. Still feeling somehow impelled to signal the arrival of night – and perversely to present it as appearance of the most lovely of the stars – the signaler thought it appropriate to give this signal a form indicating how he at this point felt about signaling, or at least not to bother to hide it: that there wasn't much point to it.

Venus shares with Schumann's next piece, *Goya*, the use of a certain mode of puppetry that first appeared in *Masaniello*, the new form of mask-and puppet-handling distinctive of Schumann's work during this period: the use as theatrical element of interaction between handler (puppeteer, operator) and handled (mask, puppet). E.g. the manipulation of the *Venus* puppet and of her hands. Unlike the sloppiness of *Venus* represented by its figures' and actions' lack of definition, this is not a corrosion of form but a sophistication of form (characteristic also, in quite a different way, of

Washerwoman Nativity, cf. supra): but it equally indicates the maker's detachment from his activity.

The ancient Mayas' sign for Venus during its eight-day passage through the world's ocean from its last annual appearance in the evening to its first in the morning was the wasp. This indicated its dangerous infestation by Night. Viewing it for the first five nights of its reappearance mornings as last great self-assertion of the night and as night's confident assertion that after brief day it would return, they covered their eastern doors and windows to shield themselves from its night-bearing light. Neither sun nor moon but the stars will properly shine on this earth from the last death onward, and among them, among them but not of them, Venus will proclaim the rule of the law of passage.

11. *Goya*. The age of murder.
The act of execution.

Goya, instigated by Schumann's children's contribution to *Ah!* of impressions of Goya y Lucientes' *Disasters of War*, apart from various agitprop pieces at the circus later that year, was Schumann's only new puppet show of '81. I know of no performances of it other than as second part of a two-hour program with *Venus*, February 25-March 8, '81 at the Theatre for the New City. It explicated one of the dimensions of the darkness announced by *Venus*.

The stage is open, there is no curtain. The crew is fixing up the scenery. The stage has an industrial chaotic look, image of desolation, of times of disruption. The area to the back of the stage, a kind of tunnel, is partly covered by a hung backdrop, a painting, perhaps twelve feet wide and 8 feet high, grey: a rural black and white landscape, a flight of black birds above it, in a grey sky. The strings by which it is suspended are fuzzy — the cheap kind. Two figures are suspended from close to — the ceiling over the stage: at the right a very small grey-locked, grey-faced (the face mostly nose) old man in black clothes with a black tophat, a seated dummy, bowed over, in a chair, and a black, scarecrowish male figure, just the slack clothes and head, with a red scarf, a little to the left of the center of the stage, above the center-stage end of the white (its paint scuffed) bit of picket-fence there. Between the two figures, up against the ceiling also, a small drum. Behind the picket fence, by the black-covered left side of the stage, stage-right, a small hut at an angle to the stage, tent-like because of its open triangular front, now covered by a thick plastic curtain divided in the center, its roof quilted of square rags. In front of the fence, a very small make belief lawn mower, its machine part a raw piece of two-by-four with tin cans and such tied to it, and behind the fence a chair. Stage left, downstage, another chair. Center-stage, down-stage, a black stool, an upended crate.

To our right, at the forward end of the bannister separating a narrow corridor along the right side of the audience space from the audience, a pulpit-like arrangement, a sawhorse thrust, with its top ledge toward us, into the bannister, with a huge book open across the V of its top-side pair of legs. Three musicians, one of them Peter Schumann — two violins, one bass — will shortly assume positions there. Behind the pulpit, on the elevated floor, a white donkey head mask, more or less life-size; on the open book a large pair of white hands. Next to it, closer to the stage, a floor-stand pole with a clamp-on lamp clamped to it.

Peter Schumann in a black monk's cowled shirt and grey skirt puts a metal water pitcher near the pulpit light pole. Lights down. In the half-

556

dark we see a figure – its movements those of a young woman – sitting down on the stage left chair. A tall rectangle, perhaps 10 feet high, is carried on, held by the carrier behind it, its lower edge resting on the center-stage stool. The stage is quite dark. Music from the violins and bass.

(1)   Overhead lights slowly go on and illuminate the plywood or pressed-fiber board, gradually we can make out the text on it (the seated figure next to it, in a loose grey cloth robe, its head mask huge, a hand built into its face as though in a perennial gesture of woe, a small bare hand on its knee, nice contrast to the puppet hand in its old man's head, is in a slow pendulum motion rocking to and fro sideways): 'When Goya is an old man he draws the horrors of war. Life sits in a house. Women flee. There is a family . . . many children . . . the husbandman . . . The army arrives, he is cut from his family. The army takes him. His wife runs off to find him. She loses her children. War moves through the country. The people die many deaths. The sword rages. Those who don't die by the sword get hanged by the executioner. Nothing is learned.[1] Women flee. The last woman pleads for her life. She is tortured and killed. Why? Is there no remedy? This is Goya the old man, who draws the horrors of war.'

The music, as it gets stronger, to the nodding of the head, is Phillip Glass, but this is mitigated by an old, soothing, sad melody from the lead violin. Dark, no music. Open stage. Board, stool, seated figure out.

(2)   In the dark, a figure in a black jacket over a long grey skirt, perhaps the bottom part of a robe, faceless, grey cloth over its face, its skull black cloth, settles on one knee, out front to the left, turned as watcher toward the stage. 4 not very bright overhead projectors go on. He quietly watches a large, longish beast, deer-faced, bovine-bodied, just an old cowhide loosely over a blackclad performer and an animal head mask, its eyes red, a red tongue protruding or red blood coming from its muzzle, slowly, agonizing, emerge from the stage-left rear, behind the landscape, belly to the ground, tossing its long head in slow writhings, in an extended progress making it to the hut's covered opening. We can see two held-up small signs behind the covering. 'Why', 'Nobody knows'. The faceless figure from out front and another like it go to the hut, open the curtains covering its opening, tie them to the sides of the opening. The house is filled by a tall – 8 ft.?, 10 ft.? – grey clay-colored figure – loosely robed – with a large, grey, lumpy expressionless patient or suffering head. In its right, the 'Why', in its left the 'Nobody knows'. The two faceless demons of war kneel before the old man, one of them placing a bucket in front of him. They set fire to the signs, the signs burn quickly in silence, only the wire that held them onto the old man's large white-grey hands (a 'ring', glued-on silver paper, on his right) remaining. They place the ashes in the bucket, take it away. A drum – a small steel drum – starts beating, and as the vast, grey, dumb figure in the tent sways to it slowly, the animal with its bloody muzzle crawls up to it and in a gesture initially seeming that of an over affectionate dog, slowly crawls up him to an increasingly agitated beat, until the huge

---

1. 'Nothing is learned': echo of *Mother Courage?*

puppet collapses under it. Dark. In the dark, the war demon – it had resumed its position at the left end of the stage – closes the hut curtain.

(3)   Rapid, hard breathing in the dark. Some light. A middle aged man with a bourgeois look – not ragged – dark overcoat, hat, white shirt, a grey bonhomme mask-head, shapeless in the manner of a potato – emerges on the run but slow, at the end of his force, from behind the landscape stage-left, mimicking someone pursued or believing himself pursued. The breathing is not his, it comes from behind the black curtain closing the stage at the right. He falls, stumbling in terror, just before he makes it, around the stage right end of the picket fence, to the illusory safety of his home, losing his hat.[2] The war demon picks it up, reaches it to him. He stands, catching his breath, in front of the house, slowly shuffles to the chair behind the fence stage right, sits, hands on thighs, gets up, leans over the fence, listening. (A good performance, not overdone.) He goes to get the small lawn-mower, starts it, making appropriate motor-catching noises, with a jerk to the line, promenades the machine up and down in front of the fence a few times.[3] He puts away the mower, pulls back the plastic sheets covering the house front. Inside the house – which has windows and the patched roof of which we on the inside see as ceiling – there is revealed a dense statuary group of immobile people, chiefly his wife, a grey-faced, sturdy woman, clearly person, not puppet, in a fitting face mask, voluminous off-white skirt, brown net-shawl, bare arms, more picturesquely attired than he, as though Schumann had recoiled in horror from a social identification of Mother/Woman, i.e. pretty much Mother-Courage-ragged, but entwined with her children (dolls), at least three. There are other figures in the hut as well, grey and faceless these (one with a flute): as though the hut had been invaded by fear. A brief dialogue between man and wife breaks the mute-ness of the play. He asks her questions, – 'Is the cellar door closed?', 'Has the mailman come?', 'Is the water on?', 'Does the telephone work?' – she answers, repeating the words, affirmatively or negatively, the dialogue conveying a state of siege of the home, a breakdown of the functioning of society, but discretely, the answers are not all in this direction. They shake or join hands, he is still outside, to the right, she inside to the left: stand with extended arms, hands joined.

The war demon from out front gets up, goes over, wraps the woman's head in newspaper (powerful gesture of negation, incidentally a comment on the press). They stand immobile. A loud commotion at the door to the auditorium up front to the right, the door is opened to a tall black and white Goyaesque figure, cloak, triangular hat – he has a silver hand – comic and sinister, somewhat like a Guardia Civil, S.S. man of another

---

2. March 3rd, not March 1st: it was probably not planned.
3. This tentative *return* to normalcy is a beautiful touch of Schumann's: when the play opened in New York, the citizen was not in terror, but *quite* at ease – painted his fence. That was weaker. In this kind of theatre, the question of what acting details – the charac-ter's initial terror – and actions – his painting the fence – to leave out is delicate: you want to leave out the indications of 'mere psychology', but not thoese that by indicating a mental stage or habits of conduct also indicate the larger lineaments of social situation.

age, who enters angularly to the harsh electrical sound of a power tool or the like, and stars raucously bleating, cackling, uttering loud derisive gibberish, on a note of terrifying false humor and true delight in the fear of the others: his mad babbling apparently an indictment: as he comes to a rest behind the back of the Husband/Father, his screams seem to say 'You, you,' and his silver hand is pointing at the man. From out of him, out of his back — we are surprised to find that this figure, police chief, spy, informer, was only a puppet — emerges, all in black, a Bunraku-handler with a touch of the Inquisition, one of the faceless war demons, leaving him standing there. Another war demon lowers to this one the black, red-faced puppet that has been hanging overhead, center-stage, its extended arms are tied, spread-eagling it, to a suspended short horizontal bar, a rope is tied to its red scarf, and the scarf, now like a tongue, roots and all, is pulled out of, it seems, its face; the black war demon taking it, still tied to the rope, and tying it around the couple's joined hands. A momentary tableau (the woman's newspapered head, the flame of blood around the matrimonial juncture), then the husband's hands are jerked from his wife's (the rope to the rag around his hand being pulled). The black war demon again inside the Policeman puppet, this latter with another burst of screamed gibberish leads the Husband, crowding, pushing and pulling him — he does not resist — to down-stage stage left, from where, the red rag remaining on the floor, he is taken out.

The wife, one arm remaining extended after her husband, takes the newspaper off and, a doll child (given her by one of the grey faceless puppets in the tent?) in her arms, is made to walk, the out-front war demon agilely on the floor at her feet moving her heavily shoed feet, to the red rag remaining of her husband. As she is walked over, the two raggedy grey-cowled faceless figures still in the tent tie two other children (dolls they had been holding near her) to the picket fence in broken-boned postures. One of them leaves. She kneels on the red rag, child in her arms, under the tiny, aged, capitalistoid suspended under the ceiling. To the sound of a flute played by the last Grey One in the hut, the mother plays with her doll-infant in a dancelike manner, making it move in front of her, lifting it high. She holds it there. Three war demons enter with a ladder, place it center-stage under the drum by the ceiling, one of them mounting the ladder, the other two lowering the old-man-in-the-chair mannequin to just behind the mother and tying the raised child to the arms of the old man. To harsh, flat drum beats on the overhead drum, the child is pulled from its mother's arms (the suspended old man in the chair being pulled back up with it). She remains, up on her knees, with her arms raised after her dangling child. Executioners off. The flute player is still in the tent.

A gracefully moving young woman — with a face mask? — grey-brown above, black skirt, brings in, from the rear — no music — a rudimentary, small, relatively large-headed figure, consisting of a large grey face mask open in back (it has a smaller mask inside it, perhaps to fit it onto a face), and of a short black robe dangling from it. The mother rises and her arms are put into the sleeves of the puppet's dress, and the three of them, the puppet held up by its carrier, to flute from the tent-hut, in a quasi-dance, ceremoniously walk in a circle center-stage, and over to the end of the picket fence over which the mother's other two children are hanging. They stand there. One of the executioners comes in to sit on the floor stage left by the red rag (puddle of blood?), with padded drumsticks beats – a soft putty sound – irregularly on the floor, while, behind the standing three – adding to the murkiness of the composition – three faceless figures, one black, two grey, on their backs or bellies wiggle out from under the hanging landscape (the idea perhaps: the country is just crawling with these demons – what Jünger under the Nazis referred to as 'Lemuren') and, still to the scattered thuds, approach the group by the fence, rise about the Mother, the grey ones putting the two children dangling on the picket fence in her arms and, holding them there, surround her and them closely from the sides and in front, the black one behind her, his black arms around her and them by the two figures in the tight group that have been holding them, and a second mask is fastened over the mother's face mask (turned away from us)[4] – she turns her remasked face toward us – the new face is beautiful, round – and one of the executioners tapes small back flaps over its (her) eyes. She and the two children are draped over the fence, she as though being impaled. The out-front executioner holds up the mug, deliberately empties it onto the floor (strong gesture). All the executioners walk out. The dead mother and children remain on the fence. Blackout.

(4) Lights on. A scarecrow object, skeletal, of rope, string, branches, wire, a primitive machine gun on striding legs or a medieval torture instrument, with a fair-sized grey head close to a death head, nested in its nasty structure is standing at the right. At the left the tent-hut is open to a small round grandmotherly puppet inside in the older Spanish (or in Catholic peasant) women's black, with a small white apron, a white handkerchief dangling dainty from her skeletally bone-fingered hands and to a pretty-pretty, red-cheeked slip of a puppet daughter, white faced and very thin, wan. A ten-foot high crude-faced Guardsman, stiff and pompous, with a nicely gauged mix of arrogance and formal semi-courtesy – stalking over to them from the background landscape – takes her from her grandmother (who seems, her arms out, a grey figure behind her holding her, perhaps only tradition-ally unwilling to part from her) – and only as he takes her does it become clear that she is only a puppet with nothing inside her pretty white dress – and commences, his shoes creaking, to promenade up and down in front of the landscape with her (something that was by a critic interpreted as travel, figured by simultaneous movements of the hanging landscape in the opposite directions to their walk, but that I saw as traditional though un-duena'd promenade on the ramblas) first step in a seduction, in this case not really far from rape. The light by the donkey preacher is turned on again, he preaches, a message issuing from him is carried over to the little black-clad woman: 'This is worse'. An executioner connects the grandma/mother by a rope around her neck to the horrible stick puppet at the right. The puppet starts jumping crazily to the sudden inhuman whir of a motor

---

4. I don't remember where this second mask come from. Possibly it is the mask inside the one of the puppet into whose sleeves the Mother's arms had been thrust.

(power tool?), seeming to tug at the rope, the grey figure behind grandma holds her for the brutal — this is very brutal — garroting, releases her, she falls, lies behind the fence — she is just a puppet. The Grenadier and his (now) whore stand still at the edge of the landscape while she is murdered.

Two figures, their faces covered by flaps, in the tent. A black executioner tears the pretty young girl from the guardsman (the figures in the tent accompany this and the following with song: 'la la la'), gets her on the floor in a tight embrace, the guardsman remaining calmly, very upright, hand on his belt buckle by the rear landscape, as he wrestles her over to the end of the fence near the corpse of her grandmother, killing or torturing her — the puppet shivers in his grip, she and her bourreau a terribly intimate couple. She rises to her knees still in his grip (he raises her), stretches her thin arms beseechingly out toward her quondam lover, begging for mercy (rather than for secours), he turns his back on her. She jumps on him in terror,[5] he turns, taking her in his arms, holds her up (she is half his size), shakes her, breaks her neck shaking her, advances with her all-white corpse draped over his extended arms, stands, his huge, military, bureaucratically dumb face high up center-stage. A huge black puppet, funnel-shaped, perhaps 12 feet tall — I don't recall its face: both this play and *Venus* lack the powerful *symbolically* individuated suffering or horrible (mask) faces of Schumann's earlier plays — enters from the right and crosses to the left of the Guardsman, stands, vaguely clerical in appearance, and also like nighttime. From it emerges a lady, a sinisterly grey-faced lady in an elegant black velvet dress and sensible shoes, a vampire, and to the sound of a flute (played by an executioner, up on the ladder, half visible in the rear — the multitude of figures and of modes of symbolization in these scenes is visually disorienting) takes the dead girl from her lover's arms and proceeds to dance with her slowly (it looks like the adumbration of a waltz), finally gently lowers her to the floor out front, decently crossing her hands over her chest (actually over her belly, the performers are not *perfect*), and leaves her there, retiring inside the huge black puppet, which proceeds slowly to walk — its sensible lady's shoes now noticeable and a queer contrast to its size and august mien — over to in front of the picket fence, where it stands, a mute presence, facing us: at which there is a sudden, odd, violent interlude, a crazy incursion into the 'story': one of the executioners runs out brandishing still another child puppet high in the air, perhaps triumphantly runs about the stage, while another runs about also, thumping two wooden staves on the floor in a rapid, urgent clatter. (I think they exit again almost immediately.)

An ox-headed beast emerges, low to the floor, timidly guided by a fussy little flustered man, roundheaded, all jittery feet, a little afraid of the beast, the two of them a comic touch, followed by a priest (bible in hand), a

5. She is a dummy: it is her rapist-manipulator that makes her seem to jump onto the other puppeteer's back. The handling of her was — throughout — technically superb puppeteering, and the puppeteering in *Goya* was generally on a technically very high level. The proficiency Schumann's people have attained by this time and that his staging counts on, contrasts not only with the low levels of skill his earlier productions generally required, but with the careless staging and puppeteering in the *Venus*.

humble though sufficiently pompous village priest, who directs him to pick up the girl's corpse, which, while the priest stands by her head reading in the bible, to confused bird whistles from backstage, the little man agitatedly does, loading her across the ox's head, and then trying the mother's corpse lengthwise to its back. He takes the loaded ox out, the priest following. Blackout. Grenadier and tall figure with lady inside out in the dark.

(5)   Candles shine through the backdrop. One of the executioners or demons of war, black jacket and grey skirt, grey face covering, black cowl, emerges around it, backwards, a candle in each hand held high to each side of him. There is a slow beat on a tomtom or metal drum. He is walking in a dance motion, his upper body dipping, placing his feet in time. In the light of the fat white candles we see Goya in place again downstage. The dancer with the candles is acting as guide for two huge, thick white animalic wraiths with small elegant white heads who dance in, dipping and bending sinuously, around the landscape backdrop. Their guide kneels down in front of the seated Goya, candles in hand; they dance willowly, worm-like behind the old man, apparitions to his imagination perhaps, bending over him, close to him: the monsters that the dream of reason produces?[6] Their guide rises, facing them as moving backward he guides them toward us and over to the right, up onto the musicians' gallery. Their movements suggest mock shame, they shyly press against the wall, joining and parting, they seem to seek a mock comfort in intimacy. Their bendings are hesitational, yet threatening. It is as though they had a dirty secret. They are signs of horror, perhaps, but really not definable: they suggest an autonomy of a spiritual realm governing the horrors of war unreachable by, ununderstandable to us. But at the same time they are nasty. The conception – or perception – is not Christian (e.g. not the one urged on Job) but whether it is or not, it is very dark. They dance out along the white wall to our right, but separated by the railing of the gallery from us, to the gradually quickening drum beat (metal drum and tomtom), an exciting, great dance, an entirely successful finale. The candle bearer entices them out the entrance behind us. Lights go up briefly on the Goya who slowly wags his head two or three times, on the otherwise empty stage. Finis.

The ending leaves the suggestion that the powers of darkness (cruelty, brutality) are great and perennial, in their greatness and lastingness fully the equals of artistic perception and compassion.

The performers (Schumann and 7 others) come out and take their bow. Time: 21:50. Playing time: close to an hour.

As Goya's series of etchings on the late war of liberation of the people against their liberators and its aftermath had not been about that moment in history nor about the lust celebrated by de Sade, but, preparing the vision of a world ruled by unreason that he subsequently painted on the

---

6. The usual translation of Goya's caption was 'sleep' rather than 'dream', but I take his meaning to be not that when his reason sleeps man becomes monstrous, but that man's rational ideals turn out monstrous in execution.

walls of his house and sketched as *Disparates*, about *senseless* cruelty, so
Schumann's puppetry memorial to him was not about cruelty, feature of
the KZ, but not of the gulag, but about murder: in the age announced by
Rimbaud. We see a family eradicated. The eradication of a family, in more
sensible times the object of a blood feud, today appropriately represents an
aggregate of activities of global scope that can be summarized as war
against mankind.

As Clausewitz, another modern, noted, that Iberian war was in fact a
civil war, and this, the state of peace in the age of assassin, is what we see
in Schumann's show: a neck of the woods in which, how strange! The
business of the authorities is murder. I.e. Schumann had infiltrated Kafka
into Goya: for in the *Disasters*, Goya makes no great distinction between
the French and the people, shows senseless cruelty as generic disposition of
combattants; whereas in *Goya* the victimizers were the minions of power,
securely in charge, the people were the victims.

The faceless agents of death are incorporated into the figural compositions of *Goya*, destroying the simple outlines of these scenes of murder by a
monstrous complication of the victims' stances. The resulting compositions
are frozen dance. The spectator is bereft of the pleasure of contemplating
elegancies. This is an aesthetic loss[7] that Schumann may have felt appropriate to the subject matter. He achieved it not just by borrowing the disappearing puppeteers of Bunraku, and then exposing them in a manner
emphasizing the *work-process*, by first integrating the puppeteers into the
action by giving them the roles of torturers, and then rendering this integration incomplete by using them also as shapers of their victims' stances
(as he, as Spirit of the Age of Herod in *Washerwoman Nativity* had shaped
the women's stances of sorrow or the handlers of Venus hers), *and* as abstractly symbolic aquatint components of the images, thronging about
their victims, an aesthetic use of puppet-operating going beyond exposure
of it. This resulted in images rent by (monstrous) intimacies, the aesthetic
debit of whose visual confusion not only was outbalanced by a conceptual
gain: reference to the social intimacy, in interrogation rooms and outside
of them, of victimizers and victims, e.g. the working men casting their
votes for the corporations' candidate; but also by an aesthetic gain: the
loss of simplicity and elegance was compensated for by a gain of pictorial
dynamics.

---

7. '. . . there is something soft about the work. The artful rawness of Goya's etchings give
them a sense of urgency and drama; the Bread & Puppet's work, though rough, is often
too obviously constructed. Actors draped in grey or beige, their faces covered, manipulate
the mannequins and dolls like Bunraku handlers; the setting-up between scenes, in blue
half-light, is careful and unhurried. This craft adds up to a kind of charm that undercuts
the horror. Finally, though, the work is passionate and expressive – and these days,
especially, we need all the reminders we can get that war is not just a national
hard-on.' — (Blumenthal, *Village Voice*, March 4-10, '81.)

Though *Goya* shared some of the raggedness of *Venus*, there was less of it, and what distinguished the piece and made it one of Schumann's masterpieces was on the one hand the level of excellence the performers had reached — delicate mime, bravura puppet handling, good timing throughout — on the other the sophistication of its mode of puppetry, notably in the use of dummies — utlization of their lifelessness, dummy-puppets not initially evident as such at the right time revealed as such — but also e.g. in the use of puppets inside puppets, the emergence of masked figures from puppets and their reentry into them: double puppets. These devices, like that conversion of puppet-operating into role-performance and aesthetic element noted supra, are among the characteristic devices of Schumann's work during this period, and in this play to the portrayal of the age of murder added features also noted by Goya: false intimacy, duplicity, role-performance.

12. *Woyzeck*. Legitimate theatre. Drama of the individual in society. The conscientious job-performer's destructive explosion. Inference: better, like Wolkenstein, to play a sly game, fuck off a little: even at the expense of morality.

The *Woyzeck* that followed *Goya* and *Venus* almost immediately – March 18-29 ('81) – at the Theatre for the New City was with some glee – they are impatient with Schumann's genius, can't wait for the end of the output – then he will be like them – and he dared do THEATRE! – clobbered by the local critics,[1] but this and the miserableness of his preceding regular

---

1. 'If over the next few weeks you happen to run into drama critics with large clumps of their coiffures missing, the chances are they have been seeing the Bread and Puppet Theater's *Woyzeck*, which certainly made me feel like tearing my hair. I doubt that any theatre artist in history can ever have combined the utter brilliance and the devastating stupidity that are the poles of Peter Schumann's approach to Buechner's play. The things Schumann does right virtually rank him next to Gordon Craig as a master designer, conceiver and visionary of the stage; the things he does wrong would be humiliating in the work of a freshman at a junior college in Iowa.

I don't know if the dreadful aspect of Schumann comes from ignorance, schizophrenia, some obscure minimalist theory, or plain self-indulgence and wilfulness, but its attachment to his genius is a major tragedy: You mustn't miss the production, because, once seen, its images will last you forever, but be forewarned that while it is going on, its hour and 15 minutes will seem like a decade.

Part of Schumann's problem certainly lies in his theory of the play: He would like Woyzeck, barber and wife-murderer, to be what the Captain calls him, 'a good man,' a phrase which is written all over the set and chanted by the offstage chorus Buechner's Woyzeck, however, is not a well-meaning lower-class victim; he is a dangerously deranged man whose derangement intersects the larger derangement of society, with fatal results – a worst-case version of the common man, to be pitied, not pardoned, for his lunacy.

Schumann's chief problem, however, appears to be a total immunity to dramatic literature. There is no question of his skill at presenting narrative or action, which he has demonstrated a thousand times, and there is no way the creator of *Masaniello*, to cite just one example, could be blind to the twists and turns of Buechner's dramatic irony. But he seems to think that a succession of images from *Woyzeck* is the equivalent of the play itself, and in leaving out most of the dialogue and many of the key events, he has left out what makes Buechner fascinating and vivid. This may stem from his view of Woyzeck as a totally passive victim; in any case it's a conception grossly at odds with the reality of Buechner's play. (It also gives the character of Marie an unpleasant tinge, since her infidelity no longer has the additional motive of stress over Woyzeck's instability.)

When Schumann does condescend to show us the action of *Woyzeck*, the results are stunning: The lovemaking of Marie and the Drum Major, with alternating choruses of male and female voices chanting in the distance; Woyzeck, after the murder, dragging the huge, potato-headed Marie puppet, now inert, across the stage; the entrance of the Doctor, a ferocious, red-faced marionette. Though any number of significant characters have been left out, all the remaining ones are superbly designed, the best being the giant, puffy, triple-chinned head of the Captain, twice as large as the others. But when they speak, these

theatre piece, *Othello*, notwithstanding, *Woyzeck* in fact turned out to be a splendid though wrongheaded theatre piece, i.e. not just a puppet show, but a miniature rendition of the play. (Though done in the larger, ground level space of Crystal's cut-rate art emporium – the Bartenieffs refuse to charge much admission – the stage, perhaps 10 feet deep and 15 feet across, looked tiny.) To the extent that its unfinished state and our ignorance of what sequence of the scenes Büchner intended allows us to speak of 'Büchner's play', it was Büchner's play,[2] conform to Büchner's spirit and the play's, and producing the kinds of interest and attention (in the Old Man's hypnotizing formula: pity and terror) characteristic of performances by people impersonating (even in my father's theatre) people rather than, as in Schumann's puppet shows proper, i.e. in all else he had done up

---

magical creatures talk a word-for-word translationese that is equally insensitive to English and German.

Even this word salad carries power in the mouth of George Bartenieff, who as Woyzeck is the one non-puppet figure of the evening. If I seem particularly irate at Schumann's failure, it's because he has allowed Bartenieff to create something between a third and a half of a magnificent performance, and then actively kept him from fulfilling it.' — (Feingold, *Songs Without Words, Village Voice*, March 18-24, '81.)

'*Woyzeck* would appear to be the perfect vehicle for Peter Schumann and the Bread and Puppet Theater. What other group has so consistently managed to compress deep human concern, particularly for the downtrodden, into images of such poetic power? Indeed, Schumann and his cohorts have tried to condense the already perfectly distilled stuff of this play (it is only 30 pages) still more, bringing it as close as possible to an experience of pure sight and sound. Some of the pictures are quite elegant, as are the chorales fashioned from Buechner's terse, repetitive language. However, what has been taken away is *Woyzeck*'s actability, and with it much color and substance.

The Bread and Puppet has never been a theater for actors. The performers, accomplished as they are, must ultimately hide themselves behind the figures which they manipulate. Schumann always prefers a tableau to be unfolded instead of an action to be accomplished. Hence, this is a *Woyzeck* minus many of its richest parts – without, for example, the scene in which the main character becomes a guinea pig for a riduculous professor's mock-scientific investigations. The dialogue is, for the most part, read by a group of rather weak voices . . .' — 'Leverett, *The Maddening Chatter of a Faithless World, Soho Weekly News*, March 18, '81.)

'This production virtually dispenses with the psychopathological and metaphysical aspects of the play, but this is less a problem than the way in which it is turned into an anti-militaristic tract. The reorganization is not expecially coherent and is not complete.' — (Th. Ryan, '*Woyzeck*': *Buechner's Towering Work Corrupted, The Villager*, March 19, '81.)

2. 'They began by closely following the sequence of the playwright's scenes, influenced somewhat by Schumann's study of the text in the original German. Short scenes followed by blackouts were played in rapid succession, reflecting the fragmented form and feeling of the text. Soon the shape of the piece began to change to suit the needs and discoveries of the company. Segments alternated between controlled and flexible structure with some, particularly those involving the Barker, allowing room for a great deal of improvisation. Additional scenes were added by Schumann; some – like those of Woyzeck eating, working and performing military drills – served to develop the relationship of the man to his world.' — (Sobiesky, *The Bread and Puppet Theatre's Woyzeck, The Drama Review*, #90.)

to then, representing essences or essential types. I.e., his use in this piece of huge face masks (not infrequently suspended by strings or held from above) and of carried or held life- or super-life-size dummy puppets, and the transfer of the voices of the characters (other than the hero's) to an off-stage speaker (the excellent John Bell) and a stage-side voicer (the disgusting Margo Sherman — at the makeshift stage-side dimmerboard) notwithstanding, Schumann in this piece showed us individuals. For his abortive attempt to portray the patrician republic's loyal and eo ipso insecure and passion-wracked servant, he had abandoned his art, puppetry, but for this portrayal of a 'good man' who unfortunately 'thinks too much', i.e. another insecure and passion-wracked servant of the authorities, Woyzeck, he resolutely *used* his puppetry, and that he had so used it was evident in that there was a story about people, conflict, and a residue of the characters' dialogues and (in the case of the hero) monologues: dramatic art.

His ability at this point in his medium to do drama was due to two circumstances: his command of a crew that had worked with him from six to ten years, half of them steadily and in isolation, and his development of his medium into a sophisticated form using the distinction between the puppeteers and their masks and puppets theatrically.

Also, he had for secondary characters available the face masks he had made for the city of consumers in *Histoire du Pain*.

In addition he had George Bartenieff, like Fred Neumann, his Othello, an excellent actor, but unlike Neumann, who is one of the Mabou Mines, not an intuitionally working, primarily timing-skilled and personality-projecting comedian, but an actor capable of working from the part inward, using his appearance as tool and oriented toward developing a part in terms of a character's social situation. Schumann used him, as hero, maskless — but with a (multiple) puppet alter ego — and due to his minimal and exquisitely precise acting we saw him shifting back and forth between the identities of George Bartenieff the performer and Woyzeck, an alienating effect enhancing Woyzeck's pathos by making us see him at a distance as a social figure (everyone's ineluctable piteous and tragic status), and also preserving his consonance with the other — masked and puppet-like or puppet-manipulating — figures.

Leber — her long yellow hair red-tinged, her faintly Jewish face gentle, piquant, strong, slim and small-breasted, strong-legged and full-thighed, smiling easily, with small lovely teeth — a delicate, economic performer, consistently maintained a presence beside the large-headed woman puppet representing Woyzeck's wife Marie, held by her, and handled it so finely, with such purity of gesture and rendering its — largely its head's — gestures so expressive, that in spite of the humane serenity of her features as she does this and her apparently habitual expression of childlike anticipation of good things to come, she seemed — effect not just of puppeteering, but of acting — to be interacting with the unfortunate orderly that George

Bartenieff acted out in a series of stunning tableaux, with a minimum of tightly controlled movements of his small blue eyes, of head and torso, his control of his acting merging with the character's strenuous, pressure-building self control, conveying in fine gradations the deterioration of an individual interiorizing a number of authority-stresses on him into an unparanoid[3] schizophrenia.

The essence of the puppeteering in *Woyzeck* – as in *Goya* – was that the handling of the puppets had become part of the stage act, Schumann was not just putting it there alongside of the puppets and *their* movements and appearance, but was figuring it in to begin with, was making something out of it. But whereas in *Goya* the characters handled by the puppeteers were mostly other characters than themselves – they the bourreaux, them the victims – and on the few occasions on which they were the same, the handling of masks and puppets was restricted to making the abstract distinction between a person – a person whatever – and their social role (representative of authority), in *Woyzeck*, the operator of the heroine-puppet had no other role in the play, so that she and the puppet appeared as the two manifestations of the same character, Marie, and the bunch of puppet ghosts into which (like Joan of Arc at the end of *Joan* into the heavenly host or like the small washerwoman into the large in *Washer-woman Nativity*) the hero recurrently is absorbed in the play represented his alter ego. The appearing performer is integrated into the play in a manner enriching her puppet, the actor is related to puppets in a manner enriching his acting. In both cases the enrichment is in the direction of individuation and personalization. The mime skills of the puppeteers pro-viding the secondary characters and John Bell's skillful provision of realistic accents to the dialogue bits he delivered for them, in conjunction with the new individual-person masks from *Histoire du Pain* that they wore, gave to these secondary characters also an individual dimension.

The combination of the group's performance skills in combination with the deployment of these skills for individuation justified the listing in the program of the performers and of their parts, the first such credits in the history of the Bread and Puppet Theatre.[4]

---

3. Making a point of Woyzeck's paranoia amounts to saying he, i.e. not society nor his superiors, is at fault. Bartenieff's denying himself the pleasure of acting out Woyzeck's paranoia was a self denial of a kind actors find difficult: giving up bits of characterization that not only are effective and fun to do, but that make the acting job easier, i.e. that are facile. Of course: Schumann's having provided him with live puppets – masked, puppet-like performers – enacting the multiple alter ego in Woyzeck's head enabled him to concen-trate his acting task on the social aspects of the character, essentially: the interiorization of stress. Like all human beings Woyzeck's psyche is of course a little pathological. We are all potential psychopaths – depend on luck to make it sanely to death through an insane society. Schumann's puppet-exteriorization of madness made it properly epiphenomenal. According to Sobieski, *The Bread and Puppet Theatre's Woyzeck*, *The Drama Review*, Summer '81, 'Bartenieff apparently developed the character of Woyzeck independently.'
4. 'Woyzeck: George Bartenieff/ Marie: Barbara Leber/ Voice of Marie: Margo Lee

Woyzeck, a 'good man' — that he is that is constantly reiterated: unfortunately the epithet when spoken with the stress on the adjective, as in this production it was, rather than with equal stress on the two words, does not have the emphasis on reliability rather than on moral goodness that 'guter Mann' tends to have in German, since in German you would say 'guter Mensch' to affirm goodness — ends up destroying his anchor in the world, his woman: he is so poor he can't help impoverishing himself absolutely, so imposed upon, his movement is restricted to the negative: a common condition. The play's topic, like that of *Othello*, is jealousy: its subject matter, however, is the destructive effect on the individual of authority, or, bearing in mind that we can deal with authority, or, bearing in mind that we can deal with authority as did Schwejk, need not in the manner of Woyzeck absorb its charges, the destructive effect on the individual of compliance with authority; and its conflict is that between a poor, i.e. weak man's, attempt to sort out his world (which constantly overwhelms him like the big waves near the shore the swimmer too poor a swimmer to dive through them) into an order inclusive of and tolerable to him, and a strong woman's strong hunger for joy. There isn't much Woyzeck can do for her on a diet of peas.

Thanks to the intensive individuations of the focal characters by Bartenieff's acting and by Leber's puppetry and projection of personality, and to the intensity of their relation achieved by this, and to the skill and grace of a sophisticated puppetry that allows us a view of the puppets as persons, we perceive these Universals of the play not as abstractions but in res, individuated.

I said it was splendid theatre, but wrongheaded. It was wrongheaded because of the language. Schumann did the German lines into an English echoing the strength of Büchner's sculptured peasant language, an emotionally intense language of strongly graphic turns of speech,[5] apparently simply not caring how the English sounded (wrong), or else thinking an evocation of the play's being German was permissible, that the accent of the syntax would blend in with the productions's fair-style (a Jahrmarksbudendarbietung) and the crudity of the puppets. But it jarred,

---

Sherman and Joanne Schultz/ Captain: Joanne Schultz/ Captain's voice: Michael Romanyshyn and Richard Norcross/ Doctor's Head and Arse: Ron Kelley/ Doctor's Feet: Barbara Leber/ Doctor's voice: John Bell/ Drum Major: Richard Norcross/ Barker: Michael Romanyshyn/ Barker's voice: John Bell/ Grandmother: Trudi Cohen/ Grandma's voice: Margo Lee Sherman/ 2 Journeymen: John Bell and Michael Romanyshyn/ Horse's Head: Joanne Schultz/ Horse's Rear end: Richard Norcross/ Accordion: Trudi Cohen/ ... Administration: Elka Schumann and Barbara Leber/ ... Distortions of original text and Directing: Peter Schumann.'

5. Büchner's language — in the tradition of Luther — is not only splendid: he is one of the few German dramatists before Wedekind — Lenz and Grabbe being two others — whose characters (though in *Danton* he is sometimes seduced into rhetoric) speak real German and the German of the people.

and particularly so because this was a theatrical production rather than a puppet show. The accents don't bother us in the circus. Also, Schumann tends to use — and here used — language as though phrases were images: the single phrase being supposed oddly to wrap up the emotional burden of its point. But this calls for a lapidary style, and may be impossible in American English, and, in any event, does not happen when the phrase by its awkwardness presents itself as translation, as mere reminder, and neither hits, nor having hit, twists in.

The fact is that Schumann has a tin ear for language, loves it, but has no sense of it, even in German mistakes the falsely for the truly simple. Oddly, words and pictures — but not sculpture — to him seem to seem innocent if only they are simple, as though plainness guaranteed elementality. He seems to forget that the power of language depends on the gesture imbedded in it, and that the individual can not arbitrarily create verbal gesture by linear addition of simple words, but can only, all words and all their combinations and permutations being loaded with the gesture of a hundred generations, with humility and sensitivity ease his/her gesture into the dance of death. Aware of the loss of substance in translations substituting for the strong idioms of German the most nearly equivalent working phrases of American English, he allowed himself the illusion that something approaching literal or word-for-word translation would retain at least some of the slicing power of our wild mother tongue and that the American ear would forgive such translation's infraction of the social contract carried by American speech, its air of egalitarian assertion tempered by democratic modesty, an air associated with the use of stock phrases and circumlocutions peculiar to American English and distinguishing it from British English. But the American ear is most jealous, this being a country of immigrants and thus less than many one of emigrants. Englishmen had substituted for the Germans' faith in their words' direct relations to objects referred to and command over the objects they name a proud confidence in an Englishman's ability by his individual handling of vocabulary and art of syntax to contribute to intercourse his version of whatever is spoken of: but in the 17th century commonwealths of New England (whence comes 20th century American) such faith and use began to appear presumptuous and were abandoned — read Jonathan Edwards.

The Germanicism of the play's language thus did not work as the sovereign artist's gesture, but was simply offensive. It made one feel one did not know what was going on, that one was being forced to deal with unwarranted strangeness, irrelevancies. Margo Sherman's sweetly humorous and/or sentimental cuteness of delivery made this worse. John Bell's incisive and strongly American-accented (Southern, Midwestern, in any event Country) rapid and masterly intoned delivery of texts either not by Büchner, or — when he speaks for the mincing-voiced Doctor that uses Woyzeck as lab animal for his diet experiments — heavily distorted, worked fine. But many of Bartenieff's Büchner lines — e.g. he addresses the doctor as 'Mister Doctor'! — were embarrassing in spite of his optimal sounding of them. He later had the same trouble in *Diagonal Man*.

The production made 'splendid' theatre in that Schumann had tellingly summed up the play — with Lenz' *Hofmeister* among the few revolutionary German plays — there are none by my father — in a few visual vignettes whose trajectory amply carried the play's theme, topic, conflict and pathos. The recurrent invasions of the play by a heaving clump of vast, ghostly puppets (four performers only, I believe, each carrying three large, sorrowful masks), besieging the hero, gobbling him up (he sometimes enters or leaves with them, becomes one of them) were not redundant but gave that trajectory rhythm — one supposes Woyzeck as of at least half a mind to think of them as his real self, and to think of his own corporeal and social self, the one he knows his woman and the others deal with and take for him as a perhaps clever disguise of his: so that these demons would to him be frightful and yet reassuring — a coquetry of madness that in a mild way Schumann may not be unacquainted with. One or two funny scenes — e.g. the Doctor as exhibitor of the astonishing counting horse Hans — added a congenial spice of stark humor.

The production was toured along the Rhine at the end of '81, opening November 12 in Cologne, and put on in Rome also (*The Villager*, November 19, '81.)

The play starts to accordion (Trudi Cohen). The front curtain (greyly depressing, with the heads of Woyzeck's ghosts on it in white scribble, and what is said of Woyzeck, 'a good man', twice over) rises. The stage is dark. The single bulb in the small ordinary conical light in the room's ceiling goes on. The room is empty, against its green back-drop an orange kitchen chair, centered. A moment. The light goes out. When almost immediately it turns back on, a small male figure, booted, in close-fitting olive drab shirt and pants, is seated on the chair, hands extended on his knees, a (perhaps 2 feet long) grey mask, expressionless but in its configuration expressive of anguish, one of the Ghost masks, over his face — held by someone standing behind his chair and visible behind him only in outline. We have this vision for a moment. The mask is lifted. Bartenieff/ Woyzeck sits, rigid, the tension on his small pale face is frightening: the mask hadn't been. His hair is very short, flat on his head, neatly combed, his head almost looks shaved. Out in front, to the right, a small stocky comical figure, headmask and costume,[6] the performer

6. He is dressed in a three-piece suit, the vest only partly buttoned over the belly. His pants are pantaloons, they are sloppily untied around the calves — his boots are laced only half way up. His ears are big and pink and red, they jut out on his big head which is a lighter pink. Way up on it is perched a tiny mountaineer's hat. Big moustache, curving up at the ends. Standup collar. Large, inexpressive brown eyes. He is sloppy. But respectable.

Romanyshyn) inside — he later turns out announcer. Though the program calls him barker, this figure is silent throughout, his voice done off-stage, to the left, by John Bell: a caricature Bavarian, his pants too short, not jolly, but a jolly type, the jolly type that's not jolly. Lights out.[7]

Light back on almost immediately. George-Franz Woyzeck is sitting on the chair, sewing on a dark jacket, busy, preoccupied — at work. Twice an off-stage voice commands him to 'Take it easy, Woyzeck!' He jumps up, snaps to attention each time, body tense, face drawn, responding with a crisp 'Yes, sir!' Lights out. Back on. He is squatting, kneeling on one knee, next to his chair, lightly, rapidly polishing two boots. Command. He snaps to attention. The boots move out. (Pulled by strings.) Lights out.

Lights back on. He is sitting behind a table, eating peas with a plastic fork off a paper plate, a large paper cup from which he occasionally — washing the food down — takes a swig, next to it. He is eating in a concentrated manner, perhaps a little too fast, as though forcing himself, in every respect of course disregarding us, but occasionally looking up, not really quite pausing in his eating, as though thinking or trying to think of something, or about something — just a faint sign of disturbance, if any at

---

7. 'The audience in the Theatre for the New City sits in rows of chairs that are raked up to the lighting booth at the back of the theatre, or on pillows arranged very close to the playing area. The action of *Woyzeck* takes place on a simple, one-unit set. Black flats are positioned at angles on the sides of the stage and above it, framing the space and concealing puppeteers at work. Key lines from the play ("What's the matter, Woyzeck?", "Watch out, Woyzeck") along with recurrent visual images are painted in primary colors on the black overhead borders. The pre-show setup consists of a single chair in the middle of the stage and four two-dimensional pig-like figures that are pulled into the wings as the performance begins. A music stand and a small lighting board are placed almost out of sight in the front left corner of the space.

Shortly after eight o'clock, the performers begin to assemble in the playing area. The street band — consisting of an accordion, a fiddle, a bugle, a trombone and a bass — files in from the lobby where it has been entertaining the audience members as they gather for the show. When all are in place, there is a blackout and silence. A single light comes on above the music stand, revealing an actress named Margo dressed in a long, blue skirt and white blouse; she is to serve as the voice for several characters, including Marie and the Grandmother.

At the sound of a bell, lights all go out again except for an overhead lamp that hangs directly over the chair. For several minutes, the audience's attention is focused on the chair while accordion "volksmusik" plays offstage. After a third blackout, George Bartenieff as Woyzeck appears in army fatigues, his face concealed by a long, gray mask suspended from above the stage. The mask is lifted as a voice offstage introduces him to the audience: "Ladies and gentlemen, let me introduce to you Johann Friedrich Franz Woyzeck, a good man."

The following sequence of scenes depicts Woyzeck, the man, engaged in the activities that best characterize his life. The scenes are short, accompanied by the accordion, and concluded by abrupt blackouts. During all of the scenes, the Barker (whose voice initially introduced Woyzeck) stands to one side. He is portrayed by an actor in a shabby black suit, red tie and full head mask.' — (Sobiesky, *The Bread and Puppet Theatre's Woyzeck*.)

all — settled into a tense but unexcited preoccupation with his eating, but his mind wandering between mouthfuls a little. Throughout this, two choral groups, a large one with an accordion on the left, a two-person one with a scraped violin on the right, are singing the words 'a good man' in several voices: the canon gradually speeds up to a frenzy.[8] The plate is almost empty. The jolly announcer briefly conducts the chorale, conducts it to a finish. Goes to the drum in front of, at the right of the stage, beats a low roll on it with the curved handle of his walking stick — a nice action: the lights are dimming. George or Franz is finishing off his plate — stuffing his mouth a little now. Tall ghosts sway in, in a dense, heaving clump: large, pale, sorrowful but expressionless faces (2 foot high masks), peaceful, almost benign, but beyond life, perhaps a dozen of them, behind them the hardly discernible dark-clad bodies of those wearing and carrying them (only four or so people), linear, mostly just legs, merging into a dark mass, ooze around him, he is gobbled up by them, has disappeared into their mass as they slide out. The table, the paper plate, the paper cup — a large refuse can that has been there throughout this scene, near the table. The jolly announcer advances on the table, one by one picks up plate, fork, cup, his voice, from off-stage, inventorying them precisely as though recording unremarkable but pertinent and unalterable facts of Woyzeck's life as he picks up each and drops it in the trash can. This is quite humorous.

He (his off-stage voice) a little hesitantly calls for George and Bill. They enter after a moment, garbagemen-stage hands, the elderly working men that are nightwatchmen, janitors, street cleaners, thick of body and head (headmasks), the one small and a shade ingratiating, the other large and truculent,[9] both moving very slowly. They stand about. He proposes (with the deference due union members) they do something about the table and chair. With some considerable effort they carry them out. Return. He calls their attention to the garbage can. They move to it, the tall one keeping him in eye in a routinely male threatening or self-assertive manner, and shaking his head at the excessive and ridiculous demands made. They heft the can between threm, move off in opposite directions, stand arms extended with it between them, unable to move any further.[10] He clears his throat, in a manager's manner, solicits they exchange places, each grasps the handle the other had held. They do so not very willingly, move off as though the thing were possible this way, the right way, though it had posed insuperable technical obstacles the other. Brains and brawn.

---

8. 'I worked them (the tunes (SSB)) out with proposals from the singers. They will sing something. I will change the beat or change the pitches and then we establish them. But it didn't get written down or anything.' — (Peter Schumann, interview, '83.)

9. The program identifies them as John Bell and Michael Romanyshyn. But since the 'barker', also identified as Michael Romanyshyn, is onstage with them, and the barker's voice, identified as John Bell's, speaks while they are onstage, I don't see how this could be. Whoever they are, they are both quite good.

10. This comic number was dropped from the last NY performance.

Announced by the announcer's gentle drumming with his walking stick on the on-stage drum, the ghosts enter, to heavy eery breathing, releasing George/Franz from among them into a pose of apprehensive listening, legs positioned for immediate flight, head perched all spying ear, slide out swaying, leaving him there solitary in a hostile universe. During the following we see them — see the heads only — watching him from both sides: they have turned into his watchers, he is not one of them. He straightens out, stands, stares, speaks — disjointed sentences: the ground is hollow, the horizon is afire, the fire is closing in, there is a noise above, it is coming down. Silence. He is still fearfully listening.[11] Finally relaxes ever so slightly, says 'It's so quiet!'[12] The light on stage is (a weak, ethereal light from way above, not the kitchen light bulb's) in the stage ceiling. Blackout.

Entrances in the dark to trumpet sounds. Lights on: the sturdy, not outside but — with its tall feather-bushed hat — tall figure of a decorative military male of other times, in parade ground finery, a colorfully banderoled thick staff, easily ten erect penises long, in his hand: a puppet strapped onto a man. Backed up by a regimental trumpeter and drummer, he stands, as though at the head of a regiment just arrived in town. To the right a white four-paned window hangs suspended. Behind it, the vast oval of a pretty — insipidly pretty, its mouth tiny and dark red — face (face mask), a possibly faintly regional country maiden's costume (long pale blue skirt, voluminous black apron, dainty white blouse over pigeon breast, lacy gloves) beneath it, and the body and face of its more than pretty live handler, Barbara Leber, visible counterpointally behind this life-size but not life-like doll, a confusion of white-gloved hands, hers and the doll's, with, in one of them somewhere, a lace handkerchief. The young lady is watching the soldier. He stands. More fanfares. Drill gymnastics with his staff. At ease. He slowly leans forward to stare into the window, an off-stage trombone mocking his gallantry. He slowly lifts the staff at his side: taps on the window. She waves at him, a tiny hand, lifted, a whisp of lace. She is holding a baby. It is a rag doll kind of doll, strapped to her front. He leaves to fanfares, followed by his men. We hear her voice, 'Like a tree! Like a lion!' A knock. She calls out to enter. Franz enters, a humble figure indeed. It's his home. She's his wife or woman — Marie. He stands, raves

---

11. During the last performance this poised stance of anxious apprehension was extended effectively. It seemed to last minutes.

12. During the performance of March 20th, one through the silence heard, faint, a radio announcer's voice from somewhere. I mistakenly thought this was intended, a nicely ironic comment along the line of 'a person would have to be insance, now-a-days, not to be paranoid', and that Woyzeck's ensuing comment 'it's so quiet!' was a psychologically just lie to himself, denying The Voices. During the performance of the 31st, there was unfortunately a squealing baby in the audience, so that Woyzeck's comment this time was greeted with titters.

about the coming conflagration. He is in a rush. 'I have to go.' He leaves. A flutist and a young man with a lidded paper cup, neither of them costumed or masked, enter, the flutist, a girl, stands to Marie's left, he kneels, facing Marie, at her other side (faint echo in this configuration of an Annunciation, a medieval triptych). Flute play as Marie behind the window, petting Marie's baby with Marie's lacily gloved hand in her plain-gloved one, muses. It gets dark. As it gets dark – no more flute – the cup bearer raises the cup, shakes it, it rattles drily, a kind of warning. She is uneasy.[13] Blackout. Curtain down in dark.

Lights up. The front curtain with the ghost faces on it covers the stage. Fastened to it, almost covering it, a diagram, as in a child's book, lines in bright colors on white carton, an anatomic chart, extremely simplified, of a horse, the horse and its insides. The jolly figure of the announcer in front of it with a pointing stick. He, in cheaply pompous fairground tones, announces (in the following scene one pleasurably registers the coordination of his separate off-stage vulgar lecturing voice with the small, realistic, occasionally faintly apologetic, monstrating gestures, his mask-face as is normally the case with masks, though of course immobile, seeming to change expression with the situation) a lecture on the subject of The Horse, edifying as well as educational. In fact, the lecture following concerns the animal's digestive system. Placing his curved hand by the picture's muzzle: if for instance we feed it some grain, the food moves up the head, moves round and round (the stick follows the yellow spiral) to the heart (the stick pokes at the big red picture of the heart), goes down to the stomach. With delicate phrasing ('You know what I'm talking about'), the lecturer traces it through to reemergence in part through the kidney and the little tube between the horse's rear legs, but mostly – the picture is simplified – out through the tail and onto the road, 'and then we have a problem'. (The simple humor has no great effect on the audience.) The lecture is followed by a bonus, the presentation of the amazing white counting horse. It troops in to accordion music, very big, stands in front of the chart: long white mane, long, plaited straw tail, sackcloth body, the white pantalooned legs of two puppeteers for legs. The lecturer vaunts its mathematical powers (and other accomplishments: it has recently lectured on English literature at several universities), for instance: it can, by stomping its right front hoof, tell us how many hours there are in a day. The horse gets to 5 in its count, pisses on the lecturer's boot. The lecturer gets mad, chases it out.

Curtain up. Franz seated stiffly, facing out, center-stage. A doll-puppet, a string from its cherry red balloon head (side burns, the eyes looking down its nose) upward, strings going up from its gesticulating arms and

---

13. Flutist and cup-bearer here function for an exteriorization of mental state as do, with respect to Woyzeck, the ghost puppets.

from the white gloved hand permanently fastened, palm out, in the small of its back,[14] enters, Barbara Leber uncostumed, in white, unmasked, slender, on her knees on the floor behind it, it is male, a small grotesque figure in formal professional attire, dark jacket, striped pants, giant polka dotted bow-tie, her hands on his ankle boots or large shoes, she is moving his feet, he is walking. He immediately, in a snivelling, driving voice, high pitched, almost incomprehensibly – you can make out a sentence here or there – drivelling, starts to hector, harangue, chide, but not in an unkindly way, the seated Franz (the voice is off-stage, Bell's). George's little blue eyes are shifting uneasily. Franz is unable to furnish a urine sample. But it seems he has been seen pissing on the street. Franz has no manners. The doctor is jumping up and down excitedly. Franz excuses himself in a strained voice – 'the call of nature'. The doc invokes Schopenhauer and Goethe and Jung and Freud: man is free – not dominated by nature. He, the doctor, is *not* angry, *not* excited (he is acting crazy). He wants to know if Franz has been eating his peas, performing his duties – Franz has done all his duties, gives his money to his wife. He announces a two-Pfennig raise in Franz' salary. Briefly sits down, listening to Franz tell of his visions of a 'Second Nature' seated on Leber who is on all fours behind him – her rear toward us, the image is faintly obscene, the puppetry involved probably of a fairly high order. Hearing of the vision, he jumps up in the air for joy ('a true aberratio!') – Leber has his feet way up in the air. He ends up taking Woyzeck's pulse: Leber places his hand on Woyzeck's raised wrist with her left, raises her right, looks at her wrist watch – a charming moment. The doc jumps out. Lights out.[15]

Trumpets. Lights up. Woyzeck, erect, is standing, centrally, to the rear, the ghost mask over his face, a black-sleeved arm down from above him, holding it. A momentary, stunning image. He is standing at attention, a slightly bulging, narrow, contained figure, grey-brown, masked in his interior identity, over-life-sized. Arm-hand-mask-man. The mask is lifted. Bellowed off-stage commands: drill, crawling, pushups, runs. 'At ease!' Woyzeck stands at attention. George is almost bald. The drill is terrifying. We see here a man pushed beyond his limits by the everyday forces to the suffering of which most men insanely accomodate themselves. Blackout.

Lights up. A tiny (2 foot) military figure, an officer with a vast head (4 feet, perhaps), shining with military unintelligence, flushed with good living, multichinned, the rills of his chins complementing the wrinkles at the top of his head – on which is a tiny cap. By no means evil. Standing.

---

14. A marionette operated from a bridge.

15. Whether this scene suffices to make clear to an audience that does not know Büchner's play that Woyzeck is subjecting himself to dietary experiments in order to make a little extra money on the side so he can support his family is doubtful. Schumann may simply have forgotten that he had to make this clear. Or he may have thought that it didn't matter. If this is what he thought, he may or may not have been wrong.

(A puppeteer is holding him. His arms — empty sleeves — are manipulated from above by strings.) Next to him, seated, Woyzeck: again being lectured. The captain is benign. He is having a discussion with his orderly. Woyzeck thinks too much. That's unhealthy — very unhealthy. His speech is in a multiple, reverberating voice (several speakers at once off-stage: the overly sensitive Woyzeck hears the powers-that-be, his superiors, in a distorted manner, his schizophrenia is worsening). Woyzeck is a good man, but the captain discerns in him a lack of morality, virtue — of virtues. Woyzeck admits it, without apparent irony excuses himself by his poverty — if he had a frock coat, a pocket watch, a . . . , maybe he would have virtues too. (The B. Brechtian simplicity of the revolutionary Büchner's irony grates on the modern, especially the modern American ear: poor and rich have been taboo categories here since World War II terminated the Great Depression, the American poor, the population's vast majority, a class calling itself 'middle', too frightened by their condition and by the ease with which, they know, it could get even worse to admit it.) The major terminates the discussion. It has fatigued him.

Another drill scene. (Both drill scenes are illuminated brightly, harshly: from two sets of three lights clamped on two poles set in little concrete rings out front.)

The colorful drum major, a shiny boy's Christmas feast Pfeffernuss figure, and Woyzeck's woman, he to the left she to the right, are having a tryst. Marie's speaker, Margo, out front, says the one word 'money'.[16] Marie, hip out a little, pertly raises her long apron a little — shows a black-stockinged ankle, stands, arms akimbo, hand on waist. He boasts, she flirts by an affection of slight derision, doing, very gracefully, a little dance movement to her repeated 'go on!', but we hear her thought, she is admiring his physique, Leber, visible to Marie's right, beautifully manipulating Marie to the effect of coyness and expectancy, he moves to the attack, she pertly pushes him off — a stand-off, she slowly turns her head a *little* toward him, he moves toward her again ('Does the devil look out of your eyes?'), she yields ('Why not?'), her — the puppet's — arms steal about his neck. She has a few, a very few long black locks to each side of her flat face. The two of them stand, sway, embracing: to tragic, flute-accompanied song (lalalas). Music over. The handsome young kid working him detaches himself from him, Leber ditto from her (they undo sashes about their waists: though Leber has a tiny moment's trouble untying the bow behind her back, both of them move with an admirable ease, with no hurry apparent, once separated from the embracing figures), Leber leaves, he is supporting the two figures at the right. An assistant enters to help him arrange the figures' final tableau: they are lowered, at the left, into a

---

16. This comment had been dropped by the last NYC performance. It had, indeed, been a mistake, vulgar.

near-horizontal position, their lower bodies on the floor, their upper bodies oddly off it at a slight angle, held there by the kid kneeling behind them, part of the tableau, Marie, slender, on top, embracing, their heads apart. To a slow bass violin, echoing the sad song of before and the lights dimming, their large heads slowly meet. One feels one has witnessed their love making. It is a moving, lovely scene, holding no adverse comment on the lovers, the music expresses pity for them. Blackout. Curtain.

The curtain is down. On it a vast, childish chart of 17 numbered pictures: military jacket, boots, shirt, the captain's regulation-size head from behind, with a fringe of hair, a mirror, a comb, a chamber pot, 'The 17 morning duties and responsibilities of the private and orderly Franz Woyzeck'. The announcer out front enumerates, briefly describes them, he's being practical, realistic, it's Woyzeck's job, everybody has a job, a man does what he must do. At the right, a slight, red-blond girl, a puppeteer, vaguely folk costumed, Eliza Doolittle, with a crankie music box, on which she accompanies intermittent verses in a ballad tune concerning Woyzeck, his birth, his parents' hopes, his age. The ballad is of everyone, puts Woyzeck's humdrum and degrading duties in perspective. The audience is dead serious, listening to it. There is clapping at the end. Does the scene have a tragic effect? It probably represents what Woyzeck is doing while his woman is off fucking another man.

Curtain up on the empty stage. Drumming. The hanging window is back, in front of it the orange chair, a tiny bed (doll's pillow, small blanket) to the left of the chair, chair and bed in line. Marie's room.[17] Empty for a long time under the harsh light of the one bulb. Behind the drumbeat, stage thunder. The beat is becoming more intense. The light is shaking. The room's occupant is absent: the image is an image of her adultery. Drumming ceases. She slowly enters with her baby, sits in the chair, an assistant enters, detaches the baby from her, places it in the toy bed, its legs stick out. She puts a glittery trinket, perhaps a bracelet, in Marie's extended hand – the doll-woman's delicate white-gloved hand held out by Leber. Marie holds the hand out, palm up, slightly toward us, her head turning to look down on it. She is admiring the drum major's gift. (Echo of Faustus' Gretchen.) Leaning over it, she talks to her baby, tells it to shut its eyes, tightly. Woyzeck enters, advances to her rapidly, wants to know what has she got there. Nothing. She has closed her hand. He insists. She says (her voice from out front to the left), 'What am I – a

---

17. The window identifies it as the same room from which Marie earlier on first saw the drum major. But we are now inside. Schumann employs such 'relativity devices' with great delicacy. Representing someone's entering a house by turning a picture upstage from them on one side of which the outside of it, on the other side the inside is painted (*Washerwoman Nativity*) is a device of this sort also, as is the moving of landscape screens (in some of the *Grey Lady Cantatas*) to represent motion.

whore?' He steps back, stands there, looks at her, a long silence, Leber has turned Marie's large face away from him, finally he says, 'It's alright, Marie.' He says, 'I have to go', bends down to touch the baby's head, leaves. He has left. She says, 'I could stab[18] myself!' She lets the jewelry slip off her hand. Keening from off-stage. She has raised her arms – Leber Marie's arms, one at a time, so they extend upward to both sides of her face, a stunning gesture of grief. Blackout.

The curtain is down. Woyzeck just in front of it, at the right, facing us. The paper cup is rattled near his head.[19] Marie in from the right. Solicitous. 'What's the matter, Franz?' 'You are out of your mind Franz.' – repeatedly, in several shaky women's voices, overlapping echoingly with one another. She wipes his face. He has turned to her, screams 'Was he standing here like this?' They are standing closely together, her upper body pulled away from him a little. She is almost off-stage. She sways, not answering: twists her upper body, writhes, as he watches her (i.e., of course, Leber is making the doll do all this): to a sad and beautiful song in several women's voices. End of song. He, 'I saw him.' She is hard: 'Anybody can see anything, if they have eyes they can see,' etc. Hand on her hip. Her voice's coming from off-stage contrasts appropriately with Bartenieff speaking his own, Woyzeck's, lines: she is lying. He (anguished, harsh voice), 'With my own eyes.' She (pertly), 'So what?' She leaves. Bartenieff crosses to the left, stands by the small dimmer board, up on a small stool, facing us, very straight, his hands pressed over his eyes.

Curtain up. Woyzeck/George, an anguished figure, still there, up on the stool, his back to the brightly lit stage, on which, otherwise empty, at its rear, are two puppets, small, with silly similar heads, brightly clad, in the laps of invisible puppeteers behind them, but seeming seated, rocking on their coccyx on the bare floor (strings from above to their arms and perhaps their legs), large red tongues flopping out of their florid faces, laughing. They laugh and laugh and laugh (women's chorus: 'Dancing, dancing . . .'), a huge laughter, rocking to and fro, from side to side, raising their legs from the floor, hugging themselves. Woyzeck, the cuckold, has, it seems – seems to him, at least – become a figure of fun. He takes his hand off his eyes, 'it's so hot in here!' A polka (accordion). The drum major and Marie enter, gaily dance. The two clowns are up, behind them, also dancing, jerkily. We hear Bartenieff speaking what is going through Woyzeck's mind: 'They are doing it in public, fornicating in public like

---

18. Example of Schumann's lousy English. 'Kill' would work, 'stab' doesn't. But he wanted to pre-echo Woyzeck's stabbing of Marie.

19. Schumann's home-made symbol, in this play, for fracture and agitation of the spirit, used earlier on when Marie was getting ready for adultery. We may compare it with Schumann's use of a stone in *White Horse Butcher* to indicate death. But it is essentially a musical device.

flies.' There is an Old Testament moralistic end-of-the-world tone to his jealousy talk. The dance ends, the couple leaves. The cup is rattled next to his head. He closes his eyes again. The two clowns are sitting on the floor, screaming with laughter.

He crosses the stage in the dark, dimly visible. Lights up. Woyzeck is on a bed, on top of it, it is neatly made, under him the covering blanket is tight. He is rigidly extended under the bulb's harsh glare, arms along his sides, muttering 'Stab her, stab her', he suddenly sits up, calls out 'On and on and on'. The chorus sings 'On and on and on' as he writhes, sitting up on the cot: the singing gets quite wild, disconsonant – it's a powerful melody. He is covering his ears, upright, squirming on the bed. Chorus off, he shouts into the wings, 'Andreas!', falls back on the cot. Two black-clad arms come into view, extended from off-stage, stage-right into the stage space. Woyzeck sits up, gets up, takes a black jacket from the bed, goes to the arms, puts it across them (a violin player has entered, stands behind Woyzeck, playing), starts taking things out of its pockets, muttering: a ring, it used to belong to his sister. He is leaving it to his son Andreas. He takes out a little book, opens it, reads from it, it is his passport, his identification. He reads out his name, his birth date – a drum whirl: he stops, comes down-stage, facing us announces his exact age: 40 years and so and so many months and days. Blackout. (George has taken up position out front to the left again, hands over eyes. The cup is rattled by his head. He is there when the lights go up again.)

Lights up. Marie is seated (Leber invisible), apparently relaxed, on the ground, leaning against the wall on the left – a tree? her baby in its crib further up on the stage, behind the baby, watching over it, the seated figure of a grey granny (Trudi Cohen), a very small figure, dressed in grey, its hair thick strains of grey corded wool, its face (headmask) the magnificent Noh image of an old demon woman ghost, formalized by parallel wrinkles, frightening, telling the baby boy a frightening story (spoken by Margo Sherman, unfortunately, in her usual maudlin style, not as story told a child, but as eery augury) of a little boy left all alone. At the end of the story, Marie suddenly (we are surprised to find Leber was be-hind the immobile – listening? dreaming? – puppet) gets up. (Strident violin playing.) George – Woyzeck – has been standing on the little stool out front to the left, his back toward them, his hands over his ears: he moves quickly to her, pulls her out. Silence. Granny finishes, 'And there he is still – and is still alone.' Her head is shaking. Dimout.

Lights up. Dim lighting. Heavy breathing. The light is from way over-head – eery. A 'night time' light. The troop of ghosts, Woyzeck's personal demons or himself, dances in, manyheaded, their pale, flat faces slightly various, swaying, pausing, then withdrawing again, comes in more fully (on stalking black legs), is wafted across the rear of the little space, smoothly reappears retracing its dance back to the left, after them, her white arm, extended, coming into view first, pulled by them, the figure of the adulterous woman, her face still smiling, leaning back. George/Franz delves out from among the receding group, it's he who's pulling her. They stand. He is muttering. He kneels down in front of her, at the right end of the stage again, makes her kneel down. The demons are watching, their masks (only) leaning in at the left side of the stage, seeming to hang suspended there, breathing heavily. She strokes his cheek as he mutters. He fumbles in his hip pocket, pulls out a knife: as retreating she recedes into invisibility off-stage, he stabs and stabs. The demons come in, with dog noises, obscenely excited whimpers, as he kills her, surround him, drag him out. Blackout.

Lights up, very dim. Effect of fog or mist. Two figures appear, entering from the right, capes and caps or hats, we see their backs – the silhouettes. They stand in listening postures. Words about did the other hear it? Hear something? They seem to strain into the fog. The words suggest a woods, the nearness of water. Silence surrounds them. They make to move off. Stop to listen again: as though another sound – a cry? – had reached them. Blackout.

Lights up. Less dim, but still dim. George/Franz in on a run – on the run. Stops to listen, is anybody there? In a low voice calls out to Marie. Goes over to where he has killed her, pulls her (the puppet) in by the skirt, she is hauled into view, flat on the ground. He kneels by her, bends over her. Strokes her. Sees the blood on her chest, mutters about the blood, he must wash her. Margo Sherman, her voice, walks over with a bowl, puts it by the cadaver. He takes a rag, she is extended over his knees now, in a dead curve dips it into the water, squeezes – sound of water splashing lightly on the floor – wipes at her, his head goes up listening, he rises hastily, flees.[20]

Granny on, squats, head bowed, tiny hands on ground, the corpse very flat on the ground next to her. A puppeteer enters with a square of gauze, slowly lowers it over the corpse, raises it. Ground fog. Owl hoots. Granny in an old-age shiver, we see her clearly – Cohen's acting is very good – is groping on the ground, a voice tells us groping among the sticks of dead wood, the voice is telling her mind: the sticks are sticky, there is blood on them – the little grey figures is seated only a few feet from the cadaver's feet – blood is welling up out of the ground. The ground-mist person walks over to her, lowers the transparent grey veil over her, she rises under it, is guided out, bowed, grey under grey. The little bell tinkles again.

Light up, brightly, all lights, the corpse on the right. The jolly announcer enters matter of factly, standing by the corpse calls for George, George, the smaller, compact handyman, little cap on his round head,

20. Sherman had stayed on stage, kneeling center-stage. She gets up and takes the bowl off. Rings a small bell as at the beginning of the play. Says 'ground mist . . . grandmother kneeling . . .' Intermittent owl noises – ooo, ooo – during the sequence.

overalls, enters, the announcer, here seeming in the role of a minor village or small town official, turns to the left, bows as the doctor with the tomato red globular head enters,[21] with pompously fussy officiousness, surrounded by their deference, traipses up to the corpse, the points of his feet on the ground (Leber there, guiding them: the sight of her, alive, the corpse of her previous persona on the other side of the same stage, is a little strange), in harrumphing chirps – talking, talking – directs George to uncover its face, bends over it, scrutinizing it from a distance, straightens up, indicating to George he may cover it up again, with fluttery gestures of his free small hand pronounces her dead – undoubtedly – from asphyxiation due to the passing of a k-nife (he pronounces the 'k') through her aorta. Drumbeat, George dragging corpse, announcer off.

The drumming continuing, Margo places a stool center-stage, the looped, dangling end of a solid rope immediately falling into view (downstage, center-stage) from the fly space, directly above the stool, and (to trumpets?) a procession entering at the rear: a ranking military figure, officer or non-com, who positions himself on the right, hand in his uniform jacket, in the Napoleonic manner, a soldier or guard, marine medals on his chest, leading Woyzeck, prisoner, and, last, a cassocked priest in a black tophat, bible in hand, who stations himself in the background, to the left. They are all, except Woyzeck, in head masks.[22] At the commands ('Hey op!')of the c.o. or sergeant at the right, the guard leads Woyzeck to the stool, makes him kneel on it, places the loop around his horizontally extended neck – it is loose around the neck – ties the end of another rope – a short piece of rope – to one of the legs of the stool, steps back toward the right, holding the slack rope in his hand, and stands thus as the priest advances, opens his bible and silently reads in it (it is interesting that neither for the execution in *Goya* nor for this one does Schumann provide the officiating servant of the lord with a text from the good book: as though the cleric reads for himself, not for the victim), closes it (an awful gesture, actually), puts in under his arm, looks at the condemned man without any particular expression, e.g. of compassion or solacing, of face or body, and withdraws to his observer's post in the background, the soldier, at his superior's command (and to a drum whirl) by a smart, athletic and military step backward, tautening and straining the rope on the stool leg. Curtain. Dim-out. (The economy and indirection – poetic, almost metaphoric character – of this execution lends considerable power to it, as did similar characteristics e.g. to the love scene.)

---

21. His 'All right, Doc. It's all yours' contrasts with his portly bow – John Bell's American text vs. Peter Schumann's Germanic conception: not a bad contrast here, actually.

22. Very generally we may perhaps say that head masks though not necessarily setting a comedy tone, set a lower tone than face masks, whether fitting or not: face masks tending to set a tone of tragedy – in terms of Aristotle's distinction, elevate figures to the superhuman, whereas head masks tend to lower them to the sub-human.

13. The '81 Circus. The danger of extinction. The totality of the threat blocks Schumann's imagination and upsets his artistic judgment.

The overriding datum of the age, the atom bomb, had in spite of his pre-occupation by war surfaced in Schumann's work only in '79, with Paley's statement and then in 1980, with *This Is*. It came to the fore in '81, the year Burlington, Vt. elected a socialist without necktie, Bernard Sanders from Brooklyn, mayor, as theme of that summer's (August 15, 16) Dopp Farm circus. He seemed to view the threat as not just one of a major disaster, a vastly more hurtful war than previous ones, but as threat of the end, and though he indicated the parties he thought responsible for it, businessmen with a touch of the military about them, suggestive of the 'complex' referred to by Eisenhower, he seemed to feel that if the threat materialized, moral guilt would, as in the revelations of John of Patmos, attach to more or less the totality of mankind. As the ultimate cause of this probable terminus of history he seemed to identify the technological proclivity that has advanced the human species beyond a more or less rudimentary agriculture, though he probably had in mind as more basic causes certain other traits stimulating the exercise of this proclivity such as desire for comfort, distaste for work, greed. His attempt to deal with the topic head on had up to this point not been artistically successful, though his treatment of a topic probably for him closely allied with it, that of terror, both in the sense of terrorism and in the sense of terrifiedness, had.

The *Our Domestic Resurrection Circus* of '81, apart from an *Antigone* done by children, and *Goya*, performed after nightfall as the circus' 'small play' in the pine forest, and the usual silly circus and array of no-account amateurish sideshows, featured an afternoon performance of *The Story of One Who Set Out to Study Fear*, the circus' 'big play', an information booth on How to Fight Against the End of the World, a talk by Dave Dellinger on Living in the World We Live In, afternoon showings of *The Story of the Plowshare Eight*, of *The Seven Obsessions With the End of the World*, and of *The Cuban Missile Crisis*, a Hiroshima Memorial,[1] a sideshow on *The MX Missile* and one entitled *First Strike*, and nightime readings to candle-light from the *Book of Revelations* at a newly installed *Chapel of the Condemned*: all on the topic of nuclear war: which was also the theme of the *Resurrection Pageant*.

---

1. '. . . a Zen garden-like mausoleum of grey papier maché corpses' (Bauer, *When Church Picnics Make Sense, Village Voice*, August 23, '83.) It was retained for the '82 and '83 circuses.

The Story of the Plowshare Eight was probably developed from or had been a part of the *Swords and Plowshares* program 'of appropriate puppet shows, dances and music, poetry and speeches presented simultaneously in three theatres with Daniel Berrigan (hopefully), Robert Nichols, Grace Paley and others in support of the Plowshare 8 who on September 9, 1980 put into action the words of the prophet Jeremiah by trying to beat two General Electric nuclear warheads into plowshares', presented March 28 and 29 ('81) at the Theater for a New City, this TNC program apparently comprising the *Seven Obsessions*[2], readings from and choral singing of texts from the *Book of Jeremiah*, and a mask or puppet show.[3]

The Story of One Who Set Out to Study Fear (its title a gruesome translation/adaptation of the Grimms' *'Wie der kleine Hans das Gruseln*

---

2. 'That's a play that we did several times maybe. Barbara Leber took it to – several occasions – and Amy Trompetter – they took it to a women's demonstration in Washington. What was that called again – that women's demonstration? And they rehearsed it with women there and then performed it for the women who participated in the demonstration and it was performed here at the circus ... The play was invented right after we came back in the fall of the year when we went to Lyons, to Villeurbanne, because I painted the things in Villeurbanne. So that was '80 ... and in the fall of that year the story was made ... It's two picture sequences. One is a flipover story of a life of a woman, how things are taken from her, right. (Elka: What she *does*.) What she does. (Elka: She cooks, she gardens, she ...) Aha, and I go there then and finally I go to New Jersey and then I go – (Elka: And then she sits and thinks.) – and I think, right. And then after she thinks she gets up and she packs up and she goes to Washington to tell them, "I have seven obsessions with the end of the world and these are the seven obsessions." And then that is seven more pictures of the same size as the flipover story that are actually dancing around and then come forward and then get identified by the woman – what they are – and a stilted demon dragon dances with that picture(?) as she yells out what each obsession is ... The first is the power of the Pentagon over my garden ... the power of the Pentagon over my house – power of the Pentagon over my this and that. (I: I see. And in each case the same stilted demon dances?) Yeah, and a different picture dances on it. (I: That is carried on?) It's carried on on a stick and then all of them dance together finally. (I: All the pictures?) Yeah. (I: And with the demon?) Yes. And that's sort of it. It stops right there.' — (Schumann, interview, '83.)

3. This program was advertised during the run of *Woyzeck* at the TNC by a dozen or so paintings by Schumann in black on masonite, hung in the lobby: with his *White Horse Butcher* book, his Attica Negro head paintings, and his Dance-of-Death poncho-prints among the best graphic work of his I have seen. Fleeting, flowing figures – heads – in a rush of air, mostly just their outlines, Jeremiah, etc. – the end of the world – a kind of shorthand notation painting of man in a hurry – time fleeting, running out. Hardly warnings, just signs in the wind like the involuntary facial expression of an obscure observer: without the aggressiveness of address of the street corner religious nuts; deeply felt, but detached from those addressed, as somewhat were the Hebrew prophets by their arrogance. We are in fact facing a likely terrible destruction. The arts seem largely unaware of it. These paintings were, I think, perhaps, paintings of disaster: rather than, say, of a vision of disaster, of a vision (as for instance the *Woyzeck* curtain with similar haunted male faces seemed rather to tell us of a vision). They were without the willful naiveté of Schumann's springtime-in-flower painted cloths. They made a flat statement.

Lernte')[4] starts out in the raggedy manner of a make belief carnival representation of an eviscerated version of the fairy tale. The onion farmer and his wife, avatar of the Washerwoman, advanced from farmer's wife (*Histoire du Pain*) to nursery school teacher, have this kid, redfaced and ugly, born at age 14-25. His father, despairing of his ever amounting to anything, sends him off into the wide world. The kid, riding his flat donkey, unlike the kleine Hans is not out to learn how to be afraid, he is a student of fear. By the relativity of motion, his travel observations take the form of his stopping, down-stage, stage left, to watch, held by his handler, he's a dummy, what the successive occupants of a small up-stage, center stage tent, opened and closed by a small teacherish Jewish lady, gotten up to look just like that, are doing and what's happening to them. The people in the little house are to begin with more 'ordinary people', the common man and woman, Schumann's Vermont neighbors, but get progresively weirder, till they are fantastic beings, dream images to the presentation of which Schumann had probably been inspired by the liberating influence of Goya, and who seem to represent not so much people as such, but whatever is odd, personal, anarchic, beautiful — individuating — about individuals and about the life they manage to arrange for themselves, emblems of individuality escaping homogenization. Each time, what happens to them is something bad. Threatening figures, 2-5, depending, in ties and jackets, etc., tallish, vaguely bureaucratic and/or policeish or military (Schumann's 'Salesmen') come in from stage left in a threatening manner — the first few times brandishing crows' wings, black, at the end of sticks, later these are abandoned — and do something horrible to them: wilt them, arrest the man of the house, kill them, etc.[5] Once or twice some angelic, really tall, yellowish figure, female, attended by sun emblems on poles supervenes, but it never makes much difference really, the evil happens. Individuality, the individuals are squashed by the state. (As also in *Goya* and, essentially, in *Woyzeck*.) Little John the Watcher looks stupid — his red face immobile, screwed up, squinty — but his heart is in the right place and he's plucky. He interferes, but most of the time — not always: he beats a nasty King Kong sadistic murderous monster in a boxing-wrestling match, tries to save an Average-Joe couple from him — ineffectually. Though this part of the show is, withal, in Schumann's primitive fashion,

---

4. Repeated the following year ('82) in NYC, January 26-February 7 at the Theater for the New City, June 15-20 in the P.S. 41 auditorium, corner of 11th Street and 6th Avenue.

5. 'To the affluent, fear comes as a bat — two scraps of black vinyl on the end of a bamboo pole, that flap ominously up and down, with a gentle hooting noise. To the poor, fear comes as a death's-head, wrapped in black cloth, that shrieks and gibbers. To the honest working man, it comes as a gorilla, which pummels him in his own home. And to all of us, of course, it comes simply as "It," the giant thing that will destroy us all. — (Michael Feingold, *Unclear War, Village Voice*, February 3-9, '82.)

humorous — there are laughs — it's more a horror show and evil is regularly the winner: times are bad. But worse is to come. The kid returns to the parental manse. We have been shown certain developments that have taken place there. Soon after he left, the Evil Ones had arrived there too, selling his parents on retirement, planting them (in a mime of glee killing themselves laughing at their stupidity) down-stage, stage right, in front of a TV set, glueing their eyes to it with white tape: they steal the overhead sun that as the play began shone upon their good labors and substitute for it something in a black garbage bag, hauled up in replacement: leaving the couple there, immobile under the black garbage sun. The kid having come back, they return. They now wear white death-head masks, but otherwise still look quite civil. They uncover the contents of the bag: a large, quizzically leering silver mechanical-toy monster head, Mars himself perhaps, or the Golem, the kind of head one sees in toy and head shops on robots — there is some red in it someplace, perhaps under the white of the eyes or in the mouth — and their leader proceeds to lecture the family and the assembled populace on the need for this monster machine: nonsense game-theory talk about defense and deterrence with allusions to Them who are threatening Us, the Them representing the 'dark side of our civilization'. The kid asks whether they are going to use it, the answer is unclear, they do. A puppeteer behind it leans out with a lit match, and a piece of carton saying 'this is it' descends from the monster's mouth. Everybody falls down dead. An epilogue follows: to a hymn, the text of which repeats the 'let him who has an ear hear' of the Book of Revelations, a beautiful song, large carton ears are put on the corpses, who after a while get up and join in, covering their (now maskless) faces with the ears, then, depositing the ears on the ground, joining the choir stage right and picking up various primitive musical instruments there, play on them, ever more stridently and loudly. This epilogue is a beautiful scene.

The play was an artistic failure. Its focal image, that of the atomic missile, was ludicrously inadequate to the threat represented by it and to the anxiety or even terror under which we quasi-universally though in a quiet way labor under this threat: a sad come-down from the powerful image of the black sun (adequate representation of our misfunctioning industrial civilization) and curiously weaker than the images of terrorism given by the mechanical puppets of *Cambodia* and *Goya*. Its piteousness may have been a deliberate expression of contempt for industrial technology, but not only is this contempt wrong, both from a humanist and from an aesthetic viewpoint (the soaring missiles as awesomely beautiful as the old fashioned open-hearth steel foundries and steam lococotives, as our great suspension bridges, silos, skyscraper skylines), it is out of place in the context, a petty distraction. Except by the television image (equally inadequate to the horrors of *this* machine: anaesthetizing humanity by a sinister misrepresentation of it theatrically consistent from ads to talk shows and newscasts via soap operas), the play did not lead up to and was not consistent with this final Luddism: its thrust up to this climax was anarchist (destruction of the individual) and populist (the state as agency of the individual's destruction), and so lacked the underlying consistency of Schumann's viewpoint. The lack of conceptual relation between the play's initial images of terrorism as repression of individuality and its final image of the total terror that the combination of outmoded nation states with nuclear technology has gotten us into was reflected by the discontinuity of form between its earlier mobile section and its terminal static climax. And the weakness of the play's fable, namely that no progression from lesser to greater terrors was shown, nor, in fact, any *fear* — nobody is frightened — so that the hero neither learns to be afraid, nor learns anything from his 'studies', was consistent with these conceptual and aesthetic weaknesses: like them indicating that Schumann hadn't thought things through, nor had made the play out of an inner emotional focus on its topic.[6]

Schumann built his '81 *Resurrection Pageant* around the climactic scenes of *The Story of One*:

'Arena is empty. From the southeast corner, originally hidden by the slope of the amphitheatre, about 50-100 people dressed in white carrying small yellow flags, waving them, yelling and cheering as they run to the center — bringing with them the earth puppet figure. Also three large women, one with a black face, one red, one white/yellow.[7] From the northwest, at the same time, over the crest of the hill, 20-30 figures also in white and also carrying flags — their flags are much larger (5 feet long) and are all decorated with a flower. They run in single file over the edge of the arena, down into it and around in a circle. Their running in carrying the flags is fantastically beautiful. The two groups converge and split into a large circle around the puppet figure. The figure is turned one way. They walk the other. The outside circle is tightly knit, their flags are down, they walk slowly and very close together and sing a hymn of at least six stanzas about the earth.

After the hymn, the flag carriers run away up the slopes (the north and northeast slopes) leaving Schumann, the Earth puppet and three lumpy shapes.

At the edge of the audience are 5 people, in white. They repeat whatever Schumann says in a round-like way. He says the whole phrase, the next one be-

---

6. 'When it was done here at the circus in the rain I felt that there was such a promise to all this — the potential of what it was showing. There was something very poetic and undefined and beautiful and when it was done into a show it became very — became like a mechanical sort of putting together of that part plus those salesmen and the nuclear threat and the biblical thing and it was sort of artificially grafted together ... It's one of the puppeteers' favorite shows because people do a lot of interesting things in it.' — (Elka Schumann, interview, '83.)

7. These 'large women' — 20 ft. tall, perhaps — each have many children under their skirts who, once each of the giant dolls is positioned, (ultimately they stand in a line opposite us, not for long) scatter from underneath her skirts and lay out a little toy village, one for each doll — subsequently destroyed — and scurry back under her dress. When these big mothers walk off, we see the many small legs moving.

gins, after two or three words the next begins, then the next (in French), then the next, finally the last. The middle people never speak alone.[8]

The lumpy shapes are three puppets – Schumann introduces the puppets.

First, a Schumann work figure in black: "This is Adam. He is an onion farmer. He needs a fiddle to make his onions grow." Schumann gives Adam a fiddle.

Then one of his washerwoman ladies: "This is Eve. She's Adam's wife. She needs a mop to polish her front lawn." He hands her a mop and she vigorously starts mopping the grass.

"This is their donkey. He's a donkey by profession. His specialty is plowing."

Adam hooks Eve and the donkey up to the plow. Very slowly they walk around the puppet withershins, Adam walking backward and playing the fiddle, Eve pushing the plow, the donkey pulling. Schumann plays the fiddle too.

Beyond the area, in the north meadow, a herd of cows comes into view – they move slowly across the meadow, a shepherdess on stilts is herding them.

Their progress around the puppet is very slow and beautiful. The sound of the fiddles is very high and thin. It is a great contrast to the sound of military drumming that begins to be heard as they are almost all the way around the circle.

From the northeast corner come two military groups. One in black, one in white, with black words painted on them. The white ones are playing a stirring military tune. The tune is a variation of "When Johnny Comes Marching Home Again, Hurrah."

The donkey and Eve and Adam stop to watch the two groups coming. The black clothed group is pulling an enormous figure swathed in black plastic. It is as high as the figure already there. They march up and stand to the east of the Earth puppet and the farmers. Then the capitalists walk around to the other side, leaving their black plastic figure there. They are all in black and grey with white shirts and little black bowler type hats. The top capitalist speaks to the farmer in a jovial nice-place-you've-got-here tone, a kind of condescending tone with a threat behind it:

> "Is this your farm? Yes, it's my farm.
> Is this your wife? Yes, it's my wife.
> Is this your donkey? Yes, it's my donkey.
> Are these your clouds? Oh, no, no, no, no, no.
> (Laughter)
> What do you fear? Nothing.
> One can see that you have lived a good life."

Up come two capitalists with a little rug, two chairs and a folding card table and set them up. The capitalist tells the farmer that this will be a nice little retirement home for him.

Then the capitalists starts to take away the donkey. Adam protests (all this conversation is done in the same way, with Schumann talking first and the chorus repeating.)

> "We have something better for you."

And up comes a little television. (Boos and hisses from some of the audience.)

---

8. *Hallelujah.*

The capitalists sit Adam and Eve down and plug them in, Eve first. They stay sitting there, plugged in through all the rest of the action. They stay till it is *too late* – even then they never voluntarily unplug themselves. One of the capitalists cuts the wires, keeps them from anesthetizing themselves until the very end. Just the way all the descendants of Adam and Eve, who have had a good life are sitting plugged in and will stay that will till it's too late.

Then the capitalists pull the black figure forward. The military band has gone and sat at the edge of the audience and they play music from there for the rest of the piece.

The head capitalists pull the black figure forward.

> "What is a bird?
> Is it something that sits on a tree
> in the orchard and says tweedle dee?"

He asks more questions about birds and talks about them in a disparaging way:

> "What use are they?"

Then he begins to lovingly describe another kind of bird which does not sit in a tree and say tweedle dee, it does not sing, but it flies and sends lightening and bolts of thunder from it.

Around this time, the cows begin to act disturbed and pawing the ground, they try and back up the hill; the capitalists come and rope them and drag them closer to the black figure.

After the capitalist has described this new, better, and more useful kind of bird, the black figure is unveiled. The black plastic is slowly pulled off and a grotesque and stark silver structure is revealed. A scaffold type figure with no body, nothing to make it graceful, no smooth or rounded lines in it. A face reminiscent of an uncaring and omnipotent Egyptian kind – the whole a dull silver color.

One of the capitalists cuts the wires that attach Adam and Eve to their electronic placenta. "Now we are afraid" they say. They have their arms around each other.

Out of the southeast corner (from where only the good come) the peace protestors come running. They carry signs that say: "NO", "STOP", "NO MORE". They wear white. They run in and hold the signs up to the capitalists who ignore them. The peace people somehow feel threatened and they run away, taking the Earth puppet with them.

The capitalists then line up for some military drill. They engage in the senseless stomping to the left, right, back and center which is supposed to instill discipline into soldiers. Then they fall to the ground and do pushups. The capitalist-general clearly enjoys this part. He jumps up and down and yells at them to make them go faster.

Then Adam talks to the capitalist. He asks him who controls the bomb.[9] The capitalist answers in a self-deprecating way, "Well, I sort of do – *but* it is too much for any human mind to bear the burden, so luckily we have this box which is programmed for logic, to make the decision."

---

9. In here, the shepherdess comes over and does a dance. She lifts her legs (on stilts) in a crazy and vaguely erotic dance. One thinks of local girls whoring with the occupying soldiers – she drinks with them.

"Are you going to use it?", asks Adam. "oh, no, no, no, no" answers the capitalist.

"But why do you need it?" or "When would you use it?" The capitalist gives a very convoluted answer in which the words "if" and "then" and "when" are repeated so many times as to render it incomprehensible. The point is well made. This sentence was so complex that the chorus had to read it from little cue cards they held in their hands. The real answer could be "anytime!"

In fact, suddenly a bell rings, then more bells — the capitalist holds up the box, the logical programming has made the decision. (This is in fact true. Any bomb decision would be the result of information obtained from radar and such computers, programmed by logic).

It is time for the bomb to go off — a man has climbed the scaffolding — he is holding a sign (couldn't read it) at the top of a wire which slopes to the ground. "Ten!" he shouts. The band is playing, drums are pounding. A long pause until "Nine! — Eight!" It's a long countdown.

At "One!" he lets the sign go. It slides down the wire and arrives at the bottom. Nothing happens. Everyone raises their arms and stands stock still. It seems that the bomb has had no effect.

Then, slowly, everyone falls to the ground. A slow and quiet dying. One thinks of acid rains and slow poisoning. The cows die too. One last cow is still alive, shaking his head in horror, but then she falls on her side and dies too.

The cows dying have more pathos than the people.

The bomb kills *everyone*, including those who championed it and set it.

Toward the latter part of this scene, from the northeast corner (from where the bad come) a noisy, clanking procession comes into view and make their way slowly across the arena. It's getting dark at this point, and hard to see them. The dragon is red, with a big green dragon's head. Accompanying it are red-fringed skinny monsters on stilts, reminiscent of devils. They are banging cymbals and dancing gleefully. The dragon circles around the devastation of dead bodies. The dragon is vomiting dead bodies out of its back — vomiting is not the right word, defecating is — a man is throwing them out in a circle, increasing the number of corpses. There is fire, too. And a continual clanking.

With the dragon and devils have arrived a small phalanx of knights (four of them) 20-30 ft. tall, on horses — they are puppets. They are white and red — they stand to the edge of the bomb-face and the cadavers as the dragon makes a full circle around them, clockwise.

The knights come into the center, the cadavers have gotten up. The cows get out of their cow costumes and the costumes are carried away. All of the people, all now in white, pick up one of the corpses dropped by the dragon and arrange themselves on either side of the clump of knights in two large and tight groups. With the body-masks held up in front of them, they are like stark groups of naked survivors.

On the side of the hill, behind one group of survivors (the west side) a dark figure crouching behind a body-mask, like a savage behind a shield, is watching and moving down the slope.

Someone comes with a torch. It's quite dark now. He holds the torch to the knights. It doesn't seem possible that he's going to set them on fire, but he does. Other torches light up the other knights, and all at once there is an incredible fire

— not just enormous flames, but a huge number of sparks and tiny burning things flowing up into the air and a tremendous crackling.

The burning goes on for a long time. The audience is quiet watching it. It is impressive and shocking. The fire lights up the elaborate and ornate faces of the knights before it burns them. The dragon has been driven away.

The two groups of cadaver-survivors have begun a low chant, an early Christian type, slow and low-toned sung repetition of the words: "We will have that here."[10]

The burning scene is very long. The fires burn down slowly and change the look of it as they burn up different parts of the knight structures. The two groups have formed into one and are backing slowly up the west slope. They continue their chant, sometimes there is a harmony and a solo voice, mostly just the solid chant which changes to: "He who has that here, let him fear; We who have that here, let him fear."[10] They probably repeat their chant 100 times as the fires burn down and they back away.

The black savage figure has come down and is dancing among the burning wreckage. He emerges briefly twice.

The burning scenes goes on so long that it seems to end the pageant. The knights have almost completely burned when some gulls come swooping down, also from the northeast, over the crest of the arena. They are enormous and feathery and they droop down although they are very high. They circle around the fire, getting quite close. There are about 6 gulls and they circle around with their plaintive and lonely bird cries. Then a boat — hard to see the boat — but the sails were painted light blue with a white tree (like the Shaker tree of life) painted on the blue.

The birds circle the fire more than once. (Does the boat? I didn't see.) Then, still calling their sad cry, the birds fly off into the darkness, across the field.

(Cherida Lally, *description of '81 Dopp Farm circus pageant.*)

The distant approaches were more or less as wondrous as ever, but what was striking was that the spectacle enacted in its focal area, the circus arena right in front of us, viz. the atom bomb skit, had no intrinsic relation to the large approaches through the landscape: a comet severed from its tail. The relation between this focal area and the landscape, the coming together and coming to a head of the spectacle in this circle (by extension: where we were), its impulses through space and conversely the reverberations of the focal acts before us through a wider space, had in earlier pageants defined (and contributed the value of) this art form. There was no visual reason why the atomic salesmen should have come from a distance, nor did we see any extension of the catastrophe through the hills. This reduced the processions to mere embellishments and made them trivial — vain. The close-in, contained sketch, in addition, had no magic or mystery, there was nothing archtypal to it making it the equal of and consubstantial with the landscape and the dusk. It lacked the awesomeness of the *White Horse Butcher* theme, which, because of the ideas of Horse

---

10. 'Let him who has an ear, hear.' — Cherida misheard.

and Hunt and Capture – of the wild animal and its subjugation – *had* related to space, to landscape, and to movement through the landscape and to the coming to a tragic focus of them in a small place. And the atom bomb skit was rendered static and was detached from the pageantry by its comedy and its dialogue: which jarried in mood with the processions and with the landscape.

This destruction of the pageant form in '81 had been preceded by a hollowing-out of it '78, '79: when the focal scene of destruction (and resurrection) in the arena before us had ceased to be – as with the *White Horse Butcher* story it had been '75-'77 – the destruction of something natural, and had become the destruction of a village, something human (albeit in Schumann's mind standing for humanity in a natural state). This shift – signaling the shift of Schumann's focus from the regenerative and consoling power of living nature to the destructive power of man – had already weakened the (conceptual but therefore also aesthetic) nexus between the pageant's focal scene and its processions' inclusion into it of the natural landscape. But though weakened, the nexus had still been there, namely to the extent one, with Schumann, saw the village settlement as image of a natural (good) humanity in its place in nature, at one with it; and seeing it that way was quite possible because the village and its destruction did not, like the atomic bomb scene of '81, scene of an essentially urban and technological civilization, outweigh and overpower the landscape and the processions through it.

This *End of the World* pageant was another one of Schumann's recurrent overviews of human history. It stretched from the origin of humanity (divine) or at least the beginnings of agriculture – village, plow, donkey, cow – to the last judgment. Its central idea seemed to be that 'civilization', apparently defined by commerce and by a technology that goes beyond the arts of agriculture, or more abstractly defined as life in abstraction from – in disregard of, without interaction with – nature, and thus in and of itself apparently in Schumann's eyes suspect if not definitely evil, has for its concommitants war, progress in the art of war, and alienation, that is, a depoliticizing manipulation of populations bereaving them of the capacity to resist war (Schumann is no longer speaking of participation in war . . .) and to control their own fate generally, and, a corollary, that before the progress of war is apt to terminate humanity; with the further point: the alienation produced by civilization is no excuse: who does not resist war stands morally condemned, and humanity if it commits atomic suicide stands condemned as homicidal. (1) Civilization = denaturation = desocialization; (2) Pacifism is a moral duty, and abstinence from active opposition to war (and to preparation of war, notably by nuclear armament) is a moral delict. Since Schumann presents theses (2) in terms of the religious fictions of a Last Judgment and a Hell, the Pageant had religious overtones: the obligation to fight the Bomb is sacred, excusing oneself

592

from this fight is sinful. It thus showed us not only Adam and Eve conned by the Salesman of Civilization into bartering their cow (natural life) against a TV set (denaturation/desocialization: alienation), but, following a final click of the TV button, the natural result of this trade, atomic extinction followed by (not the Last Judgment itself but) the disposal of the Damned. Turned into the excrement that they have proven themselves to be, noxious reject, shit, they bewail their former blindness and deafness.

As Ms. Lally's preceding account shows, Schumann failed to make the *Pageant* clearly carry this lesson. The scene carrying it, at dusk, did not communicate. The condemned had been, with firecracker farts, rectally ejected from the Bread and Puppet touring bus, which, by a red covering, attached red reaching fabric arms with huge bloodied fists, a frontal Devouring Satan (formerly a Dragon) mask working its jaws to a masticatory clatter, and the figure of Yama, King of Hell (not the original one from *Birdcatcher* but a successor to it built in '78 or so) astride it, had been converted into a Hell-on-Wheels puppet. They now, arrayed by gender in two tiered groups, and dressed in allusively fecal puppet half-shells.[11] derived from the Condemned in Michelangelo's Sistine Chapel frescoes, chant a chorale on the theme of 'Let him (her) who has eyes, see, let him (her) who has ears hear'. The Condemned puppets are brown, legless trunks plus heads, with one hand molded over and covering either an eye or an ear, and as those wearing them chant, they rock in choreographed motions of despair, the men forward and backward, the women from side to side, while by drumming with their hands on the puppet shells producing a sound that could be interpreted as the chattering of teeth. it is a powerful scene and there is nothing like it in Schumann's previous production, but the staging of the pageant threw it away: not just because of its timing (at dusk), nor just because of its distance from the audience, but because, unlike the scenes of his earlier pageants, but like other scenes in this one, notably the atomic detonation scene, it had a static quality not in the least bad in itself, but, I would say, unsuitable for the pageant from of theatre.

*   *   *

A space above the dressing-, working- and common room of the puppeteers had for this circus been accomodated in Schumann's fabulous barn for nighttime readings from the *Book of Revelations* into a penitential chapel,[12] the *Chapel of the Condemned*, that was a work of art. It was a long, low, better than narrow, amply wide hall, its ceiling curved in the angles of a

---

11. 'Half-shells' of the Condemned puppets: they have no backs. The wearer simply holds them up in front of him- or herself by a string across their concave interior.

12. It existed for only a week: '. . . it seemed then unreasonable. Work had to be done up there.' (Schumann, interview, '83.) Michelangelo is said to have painted the now on papal orders decently clad figures in the Sistine Chapel in the nude.

roof designed to shed the weight of snow and yet to maximize the space underneath, warmed, not by chance without any odor of sanctity, by rows of alternately lit low, fat candles, walls and ceiling like the erotic exterior of a Hindu temple covered with repetitious groups – different in different areas – of brown-painted large figures, half-shell puppets of The Condemned like those in the pageant's Last Judgment: one wall entirely fat-pricked males without legs below their knees, hands in anguish and in violent regret about their distorted meaty faces, wellnigh all other figures, some painted, most sculptured, the figures of naked women: one small row eating their children, one long row, above the men, voluptuous, curving: men and women falling in space together in an anguish of regret – for the occasions they had missed, it seemed to me, in their fleshiness, for a meeting in the spirit. For a gesture of kindness? The chapel, a devotion of utter humility, self-disgust elevated into self-condemnation without hope of redemption, was a true temple. It was about sex, I would say, sexual guilt.

*   *   *

The barn museum had been extended by an additional floor. On the antique upper floor, the puppets had been congregated in the wide stalls into harmonious groups of one color, but on the lowest floor, now in a throng of chambers, enclosures and narrow passages, with the ancient confusion of dimness and hay and the business of harvest time hanging on,[13] Schumann had arrayed tableaux of figures – no actors turned willy-

13. 'From the outside the building looks like a typical old New England barn, a large uncomplicated structure half hidden behind a hedgerow of burdock and chokecherry bushes bordering Route 122, a small tarred road. Its vertical board siding is darkened and eroded with age, the west gable towers over a small field, the east end runs into a wood-shed which connects with the roomy, rambling farmhouse and the garage-workshop. A neat, newly repaired cupola gracefully caps the roof-ridge, and worn basement doors swing in the wind . . .

The first floor once housed the 50 or so head of dairy cattle of Jim and Daisy Dopp, who farmed here for half a century until the mid-sixties, when age forced them to retire, albeit reluctantly. The wooden stanchions are mostly gone, but the stalls remain and make perfect little stages on which some of the shows are recreated. The ceiling is low, criss-crossed with hefty beams, and the floor is uneven, a jumble of rough boards of various thicknesses and widths. In the entrance, a large pink face smiles a mild welcome, and arms gesture the visitor to enter and explore further.

The three aisles running the length of the 100-foot-long barn are lined with puppets and dummies, grouped together by show, color or age. A cluster of hand-puppets peer out of a frame and one finds characters from Punch and Judy among the odd assortment. Some figures are familiar from the world of conventional drama, but they are presented in startlingly new ways and in unexpected surroundings. A cutout painted King Lear addresses his daughters by way of a comic strip balloon, and a herd of masonite cows surrounds them. The sign informs you that this is "Shakespeare in the Pasture". Farther on, boldly painted rod-puppets from Carmen flaunt their wire arms in a Spanish dance. In the far aisle a group of life-size marionettes recreate a scene from "Le Cid". And in another aisle the Christmas

594

nilly into puppeteers! – objects, materials flatly on both sides of the plank walls, side by side in utter contrast: tableaux-mortes, each a perfectly coming-together spectacle of dramatic intensity, a moment of theatre congealed into a relation of figures exposed to view, the masks mutely speaking – statement is the essence of human life, who does not come up with one, doesn't make it – for him: by and large horror shows of muted terror, but with the shocks and pressures – of war, famine – retreated into the cell walls, the many cries of anguish (for actual pain) and gasps of fear (of what mostly then does transpire, properly anticipated) transmuted into a single clarinet note of almost only sadness. The pictures are well organized; with tumultuous force; almost in only the planes of the walls of the huge barn, a kind of half-relief; each complete in itself; neither theatre, nor sculpture. In the light of the superb artistry of their arrangement, the invalidity of the masks as sculptures emerges clearly. The statement they carry has not by their form become their substance. Instead it subsists as event: as action conveyed by shapes in relation – frozen theatre. In the old part of the puppet museum, on the second floor, the art of the arrangement had made mortuary chapels of the hay bays, places of timeless communion. This new section was secular, a review, in story-telling form, of Schumann's work. It shared the retrospective form of the *Chapel of the Condemned*.

Story is retold with a three-headed mask representing the Three Kings and a grotesque Herod with helmeted baby soldiers in his lap. Most of the figures are strange, unrelated to traditional theater but uncannily recognizable from dream and nightmare: a faceless warrior in a spiked vest straddles a dark ungainly beast, part steer, part hippopotamus; a sorrowful black woman leans over a hand-chiseled pine trough, patiently kneading invisible dough; a group of rod puppets seem to pause in the midst of a ghostly procession. Crudely made figures robed in shreds of black plastic torture one another and struggle to break loose, recreating scenes from Goya's "Disasters of War". One of the most popular sections on this floor is a corner where four life-size dummies busy themselves with housework – wiping dishes, ironing, sewing. Their weary, good-humored faces relate them to someone everybody knows: mother, granny, cleaning woman, washerwoman. And not only figures are on display – almost every inch of wall surface is covered with painted backdrops, bright papier-mache reliefs and paintings large and small. They tell stories, too, either independent of their surroundings, or else echoing the themes of the nearby puppets and masks. The aisles are narrow, the puppets lean over you, crowd around you, invite you into their space.

Upstairs the sight is completely different, the cozy, cramped intimacy is gone – the ceiling soars, the walls expand. This used to be the haymow, and a team of workhorses once pulled wagons piled high with fragrant hay up a stone ramp (now replaced by a smaller wooden one) and down the single 10-foot-wide center aisle. The hay was pitched into the windowless bays in mounds 18-20 feet high, and above them a platform held sheaves of flax and tangles of dried beans. The slender rafters slant up to the ridgepole, disappearing into the gloom in medieval cathedral style. Hand-hewn 12-by-12 inch beams tie the structure together in a post-and-beam fashion, the joints fastened with wooden pegs.

The puppets here are giants, superhuman effigies towering 12, 18 and more feet into the air.' — (Elka Schumann, in Elka and Max Schumann, *Bread and Puppet Museum, Bread and Puppet Printing Press*, Glover, Vt., '83.)

14. The Circus of '82. Tolerant acceptance of past and present — mechanical, de-individuating, antagonistic — society; or condemnation of it as — by those features — preparation for the horrible end?

The '82 *Our Domestic Resurrection Circus*, August 28 and 29, in addition to the 4 o'clock *Bread and Puppet Circus*[1] and the 7 p.m. *Domestic Resurrection Pageant*, Schumann's *The Thunderstorm of the Youngest Child* at 8:30 on the pine forest stage and his *Ineffective Man — Dream Woman*[2] in the barn basement after that, featured Byrd motets by the Plainfield Chorus at 9:30, and (on Saturday only) an *Apocalypso Concert* in the 'ballroom',

---

1. 'The Circus goes on a four P.M. with a homemade prayer for peace in eight languages, from Russian and Persian to Schweizerdeutsch. Then nine gorillas vault into the arena – tall, strong men maneuvering on five-or six-foot stilts and evocatively got up in raggedy, black-dyed cotton costumes that project the illusion of wild fur better than fur would. Besides, they have hooked additional stilts to their arms, and by this furry motive power swiftly swing themselves along the way apes do. The stilts brilliantly lift them out of the human realm, and after romping through an animal kingdom of stunts, they raise their lengthy arms in a haunting, mute, emotional salute to the crowd across the milennia from long before Adam and Eve.

There was a Horse Ballet in the 1982 show. Annie Oakley put on a Wild West act, and Sultan Ottoman Sofa, with harem and entourage, decapitated a flunky who had misbehaved. Noah paraded with paired frogs, elephants, turtles, skunks, cockroaches and giraffes to the Ark. And eight gigantic Garbagemen and Washerwomen twenty feet high (each manipulated by four individuals underneath) floated out and did a square dance for a finale, whereupon – as the music changed from fiddle-and-accordion to slaloming brass – Schumann joined them dressed as Yankee Doodle, boogieing on stilts as tall as any used on earth to the Dixieland jazz that, in all his circuses, resurrects the world: "When the Saints Go Marchin' In."

The Circus seems to be of secondary interest to him, however; he leaves a lot of it to the puppeteers to develop, in contrast to the Pageant, which is always about life and death, evil and good, way beyond even the momentary influence or control of single human beings, and which he oversees to the last detail.' — (Hoagland, *Let 'em.*)

2. 'And in the basement of the barn, a number of the other puppeteers were gearing up for Peter's post-pageant offering. *The Tragedy of the Ineffective Man and the Dream Woman.*

More people had lined up to see this bonus playlet than could be fitted on the benches. It was about Michelangelo, and in miniature was a précis of much of the Schumann method. That is, it contained a clichéd idea – that all women are "dream women" to their men – wedded to an outlandish interpretation – that Michelangelo was an "ineffective" man – and sketchy research – that he was mainly heterosexual, not homosexual, and phlegmatic, not mercurial by temperament, and that his periods of production work constituted only a brief portion of his life. As applied to Michelangelo, in other words, it was a nonsense tale, despite a reading of discouraged poems from his last years. Nevertheless, if one paid no attention to the conceit that this was Michelangelo's life story, the puppetry was stunning.' — (Hoagland, *Let 'em.*)

poetry readings, an *Agamemnon* and a play called *The Fountain of Youth*, both by the Jr. Bread and Puppet Drama Club, and the usual sideshows, most of them on the circus' theme, St. Francis,[3] among them two by Schumann, one, [3]The Two Villages[3], a clown sketch, on the cost to the small farmer of government aid in modernizing – it costs an arm and a leg, i.e. the farmer puppet must give up its two legs in exchange – and the '78 one, *St. Francis Preaches to the Birds*.

The St. Francis theme was carried into the pageant by a dozen or so big though not giant – perhaps ten ft. tall – St. Francis puppets, looking like oriental sages, perhaps as penates doubling the lares of the little village communities they were stood up next to. Their introduction was an aesthetic misjudgment. They unharmoniously doubled the household deities and cluttered up the scene, as though an afterthought.

*   *   *

I went to see *The Thunderstorm*, etc.[4] neither at the circus nor when it had played in NYC (February 9-14, '82, at the TNC), its crabbed title put me off. The comic book program comprised a characterization of the world of the 'youngest child' – that's the Benjamin of which nothing much is expected, the gay little one – and a profession of a hope put in that child. The two do not seem compatible. That child's world is characterized by the strength of its parents ('I am the man and I am strong. I am the woman and I am strong. We eat and we drink. We go about our business. We are not afraid. We rest. We get up. We eat. We eat again. We are strong. And that's life.') and by the terrors to which it is exposed: Schumann's illustrations suggest the youngest child is to an extreme beset by fears. This is a realization that strikes a parent at some point. The little book starts out with the hope:

'We are in a mess. As a result of our most glorious achievements this whole earth trembles from fear. The youngest child is the youngest child of our civilization. It grows up among the condemned of the apocalypse. It is blown around by great

---

3. 'The theme of our Domestic Resurrection Circus is our domestic resurrection. Because we recognize that we are drowning in a domestic mudpuddle of gigantic proportions we propose and exercise the rites of domestic resurrection in this year's rites. St. Francis is the leitmotiv for 2 reasons: 1) 1982 is his 800th birthday. 2) He is a bright and clear man who sets the human record straight. He preaches to pigeons as well as to popes. He tells us that the sun is our brother and the toothbrush our sister. He calls things by their names and puts us into our proper place concerning our relationship to the world.

The arrogance of our humanizing and civilizing history has jeopardized that simple relationship. We need St. Francis to correct that situation.' — (Schumann, program, '82 circus.)

4. *Thunderstorm* grew out of one of the five skits, *Serious Window*, constituting *La Necessité*, a show Schumann put together with two French Canadian groups, the Théâtre de Rue, and a group of students of the Mattrise du Module de Théatre de l'Uguam, in the winter of '80/'81.

winds until it becomes a great wind itself. We are condemned like the condemned bodies of the apocalypse unless the youngest child stops our civilization. A strong wind starts. This wind is from all human beings blowing hard, all blowing together until they make a thunderstorm. And that is the thunderstorm of the youngest child.'

(Schumann, program, Thunderstorm, NYC, February '82.)

This makes the play sound like an abdication of parental responsibility in response to the statement of Grace Paley that inspired *Washerwoman Ah*! But the hope that a generation of fearful children might turn into a generation of world-reforming adults seems as ill founded as the hope of Marx and Engels in the 1840s that the misery and alienation of the Industrial Revolution's factory workers would enable them to institute and manage a communist world. Partly Schumann is expressing an American parent's hope his kids will do better than he did (and make up for his guilt for spending his life enjoying himself making good art, but not, as he had hoped when he was young and foolish, affecting the multitudes), partly he is harking back to the '60s' hopes for a youth rebellion, is surreptitiously voicing an appreciation of the hippies that he then did not at all feel.

'It's definitely about childhood dreams very much. It's dreams that I remembered quite clearly, not just in childhood but from childhood on and that's – especially two different types of dreams. One is flying for fear, flying under a low ceiling and not being able to escape, a sort of really ultimate of these kind of trying-to-escape dreams where you can't escape because it's all too slow and so you can't get anywhere, and then another type of dream that is almost the opposite of that one. It's kind of being in an outside place and – quite clearly these dreams – so I think that these oppressive and liberating flying dreams – that they are very strong in this play – are in it. But what's *meant* with the thunderstorm is, well, another one – is really the one that – the rebel – the rebel-rousing – the, the getting on its feet of the child, blowing everything over that is in the way and – getting rid of obstacles in a quick, tremendous way. That's what the theme of the thing is more than the relation to those dreams. (I: But you see children doing that?) Yes. (I: Those radical gestures?) Yes, I feel that that is very much in kids. I just talked in Germany, I talked with some kids, some high school kids about these elections coming up and they're so bad, these elections, and the kids feel so bad about it because they don't believe in any of these parties, not even the Greens, the Green, and they want something very, very strong. But naturally, they are kids and they are not in the power or in the organization, and that would spoil it also if they would be. So all it is is a – an inside rebel action, an inside individual rebel rousing, but if the right words and pictures could be found for these kids then it would be more than that. And in the sixties that's exactly what happened, pictures and words and instigations were found that did bring forth these desires and made them go together. So I think the thunderstorm tries to be that instigator. (I: And what does thunder have to do with it particularly?) Only that, that it's a big clearing noise. (I: Konnoff mentioned some young people that he thought might have influenced you lately.) ... these kids are Max and Solveig and the Rabins' kids and Dennison's kids ... They started an organization: The

Children's Protest Movement,[5] a campaign . . . these kids did sort of make you think of – (I: . . . that kind of force?) Yeah. (Elka: I think, it seemed to me when the children started their campaign it was – it had a built in turn off mechanism because they are going to – if they work at it long enough top get really good at it they're going to grow out of it and if they just come in it for the few years that they're young and enthusiastic they'll never get the expertise in the – and the contacts and all this business that you need to get to be a real power.) (I: . . . children rebel against their elders and against their parents to begin with, and it's a very specific thing and it almost seems timed in the animal, in the human animal to get started at a certain time, to go on, grow and then to disappear.) That is true, but this thunderstorm is something else than that. It is not that private rebellion that's built into any growing up but it is the rebellion against a civilization that is self-glorifying and that believes in itself basically and that doesn't admit that it itself, this civilization itself grows these forces of self destruction by the very guts that it puts into its progressiveness. That's the point. I mean, that's what latently and unconsciously is there in the rebels, in the rebel mind of our time and which isn't expressed or isn't put into clear cut terms, or doesn't lend itself to the political movement, or organized structure movement but is the mind of the thing. There is no way of protesting against civilization that one is part of but that exactly has to be said and that has to be – it has to be recognized that it's in that – in this progressiveness, in this unchecked jolly go-ahead that's in our – in the tendencies of our western civilization. (I: The first part of the *Thunderstorm of the Youngest Child* has this puppet being mistreated, generally speaking, manhandled?) Not only. It's also its instruction, its family partaking – it is sometimes even ecstatic, joyful, ecstatic and then the forces take over in a vague way, not in a way of trying to portray real forces of the present, of nowadays like unemployment, or the difficulty of finding a job after you study so-and-so long, or the worthlessness of those studies, or any of that. None of that. It's all done assuming that people are able to make such connections themselves, so I don't know how valuable that is to say that. You know many people told me no, it is not, because unless you tell us what it is then leave us along with the thought also. (I: And how does fear appear in the play, if at all?) It does. It's a tiger . . . My tiger idea – to make use of the tiger in the show really was this "Tiger, tiger burning bright", Blake poem. I love that thing. I thought of that very strongly with that tiger scene.'

(Schumann, interview, '83.)

I.e., the play was to express a hope that a teenagers' rebellion against our civilization and its (destructive) progressive tendencies might come about 'if the right words and pictures could be found for these kids', a qualification analogous to the Marxist one that the proletariat needs leadership and organization from outside of itself to realize communism. I doubt that Schumann thought that with this play he had found those 'right words and pictures'. In fact, I don't know if he was even looking for them.

---

5. CCND (Children's Campaign for Nuclear Disarmament). Maxie Schumann was active in this movement '81/'82. January 18-February 7, '82 he and his father had a show in support of it, '*Exclamation mark – Paintings*, a Bread and Puppet Production', at Gallery 345 on 345 Lafayette Street in New York City.

'They were doing *The One Who Set Out To Study Fear* and working on *Thunder Storm* and the whole time he said, "Oh, it's so hard. It's coming to such difficulty. I'm having such a hard time." And it was only performed, I think, four or five times and he said, "Don't bother coming. It's terrible. It just doesn't work and I don't know, we've got to do it because we've got to do something, but it's not really — it's no good." And I had been thinking should I go down to see this new show or not. And so I decided, partly because of that and partly because it was winter and the trip was so long, I didn't. And then when he came back he described it to me and it sounded just wonderful because — I don't know words to describe this tiger leaping out. It just sounded so terrific. But I didn't see until — I saw it here but I came late to the performance and was way in the back. That was frustrating. Then I tried to see it as many times as it played around here and it's such a — it's really — oh, I feel that in some of Peter's pieces that he just makes it for himself and there's a real attitude in the show that says "I don't give a damn if you like it, if you don't like it, if you understand, if you don't, if you can see anything." Because, like when I was watching it a lot of times, I'd say, "My, they forgot to put on the lights." And then Peter would say, "I don't care — you know the lights were right." You couldn't see. And he would say, "It doesn't matter. You saw as much as you should see." But then there'd be long stretches where it was too dark to really make out what was happening or the puppet wears a poncho that has a whole text written on it and I don't have good eyes and I couldn't read the text and I feel that was so arrogant, you know, to say, that "I don't care" attitude toward the audience, I don't care if you can read it. And it was all redeemed by the ending with the tiger. There's this little blue puppet, a doll really, a rag doll who gets carried around, very cleverly manipulated but she also gets sort of strung up on strings over a flying — sort of tormented, and she gets taken to school and all these things. But in the end she — the condemned bodies, these Michelangelo bodies, have appeared on and off and at the end they fall down and she appears over them. She comes in as if in triumph and she marches with the puppeteers, you know, marching over the bodies and up a ladder and she picks up a flag and then she raises the flag in big swoops and kind of drives the bodies out and that's a wonderful, beautifully done, strong, very exhilarating feeling of this power and this sweeping them out. And then just as there is this triumph, a huge tiger jumps out and she's petrified and trembles and tries — it's like a nightmare when they do it well. It's really like a terrible nightmare where you see her grappling, trying to escape this huge animal and it kind of pounces on her and just misses and then she tries to clamber up the curtain and falls, and suddenly she just jumps on its back and then they have this triumphant march around the ring. I don't know if it sounds the way — when Peter described it to me it just sounded so wonderful, and it is wonderful, but the whole — all the events leading up to it I thought — it was so murky. A lot of symbolism, like there's somebody who's supposed to be a teacher and somebody who's a school — but I guess it doesn't matter who was what. It wasn't done right. And there's some rattling contraption that falls out of the sky and gets rattled around, and I hated that. It was like such a — and there were very clever and well done small pieces within the show, something with pictures, with these pictures of hungry people eating and not eating . . . they're paintings, very simply painted. They're kind of presented there and changed very quickly and in a very quick, smart way.

That was a very striking episode. And there was a part with the band and all the chorus together saying a text, sort of like parents of the child, sending her off in the morning to school and – all saying it with very precise drumming and trumpets and it's very well done, but it seemed to me so overdone somehow in the context. So I had a lot of reservations about it. And now in Europe, apparently, Peter says it was changed a lot. It was expanded a lot because we had a huge stage to play.'

(Elka Schumann, interview, '83.)

I.e., in fact, regardless of what Schumann though about it, *Thunderstorm* was not about child politics, youth rebellions, the atom bomb, etc., but about childhood fears and children's coping with them, fears such as those still besetting Schumann, in his dreams taking the forms of trying to escape by flying, but not being able to fly high or fast enough, and of the fearfulness of open places.

*　　*　　*

The pageant of '82:

'At sunset they massed again in the bowl of the gravel pit and heard a homemade prayer sung by perhaps a hundred people moving in reverse directions but concentric circles around the Godface, down on the floor. Then Andrea Mugnai's white-clad, sword-wielding army battled John Bell's red-tunicked, short-stilted battalion up along the rim where they could be seen, while, close by, there in the pit, a ritual of spring planting was under way. The distant soldiers had drums and trumpets, but a dozen cupid-sized winged angels and their female mentor were dancing slowly to the poignant, penetrating sound of a tiny-dime-store piano. As though in a kindergarten commencement ceremony, they stopped once in a while to "plant," but the strange, stunning notes of the Woolworth piano somehow made it all right.

After the Trojan War, the U.S. Civil War, and the Second World War had been disposed of, and the little angels had left as well, Barbara Leber led a herd of cows down into the amphitheater with her milkmaid's magic dance on stilts of medium height. Garbagemen and Washerwomen in family couples transporting eight patchwork huts also arrived; and Marvin, with a decorated forest accompanying him, to give Nature a stake in whatever was going to happen to them. Eight St. Francises materialized; and the symphony orchestra, with its marimbas, fiddles, wind machines, Coke bottles, brass doorknobs, lengths of pipe, sat front and center, with Schumann as director.

Now, at the eight established households, chickens crowed, cows mooed and were milked, newspapers were perused, people went to sleep at nightfall, woke up again when the roosters crowed, and drank coffee ("At night I dream/Of you and cream . . ."). Then the milking, and newspapers. Babies were born, and married, in good time, to an accordion jig.

Peter stood up and rang an altar bell and in his loud, melodic voice introduced the Household Gods, which were gigantic Garbagemen and Washerwomen floating forth as lightly as balloons to "When the Saints" and other strains of Dixieland. They were respectively the Goddess of Good Humor and the God of Bad Moods, the God of Cleanliness, the Goddess of Messiness, the God of Clarity, the Goddess of Wishywashiness, the Goddess of Brightness and the God of Boring Stupidity, and stood behind the homey life-sized households.

All of the St. Francises moved out to chant to the audience (with John Bell and a chorus) part of St Francis's "Canticle of the Creatures":

> Most high and most holy, most powerful Lord . . .
> To Thee and Thy creatures we proffer our praise:
> To our brother the sun in the heavens ashine,
> Who brings us the beauty and joy of our days,
> Thine emblem and sign.
>
> We praise Thee, O Lord, for our sister the moon,
> For the stars of the night shining sweetly together,
> For our brother the wind, for the bright of the noon,
> For all of Thy weather.
>
> For our sister the water, so humble and chaste,
> For beautiful fire, with his perilous powers,
> For our mother the earth, who holds us embraced,
> Who delights us with flowers . . .

These St. Francises and giants were imposing. Moreover, the music of the theological Coke bottles and wind machines, banjos, spoons, and strings of nails denoting time passing was gradually joined by a tattoo of drums which became menacing, and brass and saxes and violins wailing. This broke off. A sweet, soft, six-note refrain, begun by the accordion, was picked up by a cello, then the trumpets, then the voice chorus and all the rest of the ensemble. In its compelling gravity, its inevitability, it soon stopped sounding merely sweet. With repetition it became a clear, relentless, and yet still gentle, dirge of death.

Beyond the householders and their new-fledged children, beyond the Godface and the big modest Household Gods, a plume of smoke was rising. Though it was almost dusk by this point, at the far edge of the field, the audience now saw indistinctly four huge Horses wheeling toward the amphitheater, with a retinue of attendants walking beside them. The snare drums slid into a kind of playful syncopation, and a brawling cacophony from the brass instruments broke the sweet nostalgia of the insistent refrain. On the four great Horses drawing closer, the audience now spotted individual demon riders gesticulating. A jawed, enormous Dragon appeared behind them, five times as long as each of the Horses, and streaming the slow tower of prophetic smoke.

As when a person, dying, remembers being in love, and playing with his children when they were young, the music was regretful more than fearful, the six repeated notes still sweet with memories. But the drums' syncopation became not simply high-spirited and disruptive, but evil and vindictive. The trumpets' incoherence began metastasizing to the other instruments, passing like a cancer through the orchestra. Like mahouts on an elephant, three energetic demons were seen to be leaping about on top of the Dragon, which was bus-sized, spewing firecrackers, and equipped with fifteen-foot arms that swung and pointed into sections of the crowd.

Yet, as in the course of a disease, the drums and trumpets had moments of remission, when they played in peaceable and even confident-sounding harmonics,

602

before lapsing helplessly into incoherence again. Strings of firecrackers kept going off. The eerie rubber hoses with clarinet mouthpieces were blown. When the Four Horses arrived, the Four Horsemen in trumpet-mouthed, horned masks leapt down and ran with wide long flags among the householders and their homey world – flags they swung and swung and swung, flattening all the people, all the animals, all the gods.

There was silence.

Suddenly, then, the horned demon-horsemen blew fierce whistles and clashed cruel cymbals, dashing about. All the dead people who had been flattened started up from their deathly positions and slunk and snuck away. Marvin, the Godface, and the Household Gods were also removed, and the Dragon, its mission accomplished, backed out of the way. The Horsemen next wheeled their Horses alongside the forest of decorated trees that had surrounded Marvin – Horses that could be seen to have been painted with bogeys, banshees, fiends, imps, genies, ghouls, incubuses, succubuses, Satans, serpents, ogres, Lucifers, snarks, sirens, yetis, trolls, werewolves and vampires – and set them all on fire. The trees, made of mill ends and cedar bark, crackled quickly; and the Horses, sporting large saddles of hay in which more firecrackers had been seeded, went up in a great brutal blaze, before subsiding to a bonfire.

From above the opposite slope, after an interval, we heard the liturgical tones of the Coke bottles, as well as gull and raven calls and low trombones. In a little while, white Birds of Salvation swept down into the hippodrome and crossed and recrossed it with their raw vigor and ocean cries – not, as in previous years, as though intending to repopulate it, but scouring it for signs of life and to rescue any dead souls that the demons had missed. They flew off to join the three-masted blue Ark that appeared majestically on the high ground, escorted by a swan and other birds. Every human being was enclosed inside, slowly sailing away to a better world to the same lovely, nostalgic but ominous refrain, their voices added to the instruments now.

When they were gone, Peter stepped out to the fire, standing with his chief of the demons, Michael Romanyshyn, to beat out flying sparks and consolidate the fire but prevent it from burning up too fast. Leaning on long-handled shovels, they stared at the flames and coals, warming their exhaustion, murmuring to each other, reassuming the mantle of everyday civility.'   (Hoagland, *Let 'em*, '83.)

The ending of the pageant: within the green circular landscape under the shallow grey cloud cover of the sky a modal village or small town, paradigmatic of community, consisting of small tent houses within itself linear and repetitive, is erected on the run, each home with dad, mom, cow and, neatly to the left of the house, a small day-announcing rooster, the household demon: a ruler to measure by laid out in the cold August weather for the packed audience of one or more thousands, ruddy-faced in red and brown equivalents of homespun, bathed in children. Repetitively, again, the day's chores, the same in each ideal household, are gone through, a humorous effect, punctuated by brief melodious choirs, the cows give milk etc. A procession of Household Gods and Goddesses, lares, approaches in male-female couples. Schumann, in his broad German accent, his deep voice, identifies them: the God of Cleanliness, the Goddess of Messiness, the God of Bad Humor, the Goddess of Goodhumoredness, the God of Brightness, the Goddess of Wishywashiness (some in the audience thought his theology sexist). The masks of the fair-sized puppets seem to bear out the identifications physiognomically, but I suppose he named them after he made them. They are gently, humorously antagonist couples, the opposing male-female principles of Family/Household, always the same, essences. They align in a shallow arc around the community, totem poles of stable, not ideal, but good (it's all we have . . .) family life. In a procession announced by tinkling musical noise, along the curving path up around the backup hill elevation bordering the amphitheatre, a second assembly now approaches: a red and yellow Devil, actually a large red vehicle, in fact the Bread and Puppet touring bus, decked out in masks and red, gigantic and ambiguous, with a sinister but not outrightly horrible or terrible head, accompanied by red demon-warriors, servants of the ambiguously deadly and jocular bus, not too many, a half dozen maybe, and by white-clad carriers of large banners with absolutely neutral words — 'air', 'lady', 'gentleman', 'wind', 'house', again 'air'. The Satanic Hell on Wheels and its red minions stop. They wait. From a middle distance, not far off, they are watching the little toy community. But the white spirits of the air insinuate themselves, without drama, into the little village. We don't know what's happening. They look like good guys. In position within it, by their presence breaking its rigid geometry (sign of achievement, stability, of the humanly possible, of order), they wave their banners — and this brings down the large solid deities of Household and Family. They are — were — we did not see this coming — spirits of destruction. The red servants of the immobile Hell off to the rear now ride in on their horses, set up camp within the circle of the faded-out community. All — all of the village, of ordered life — is carried off (a stream of white up the hill taking it all away beautifully). Only some vestigial structures and the invaders in red — Visigoths, Huns — and their horses are left. A small fireworks display erupts the while from the supervising, attendant Spirit of Evil or omnibus of hell, evincing its pleasure or signaling. The red destroyers — they carry torches, I don't remember if they brought them flaring or only now light them — set fire to the solitary central camp: to the black and white horses. The encampment burns in the deserted plain. Dusk has come, darkness. They have set the animals and the slender vestiges of the village afire. We watch them consumed in a bonfire, the sound of burning a pleasant one, light and dry. A long pause ensues while the fire burns down; the God of War — the demon bus — and his attendants have left; a flock of gulls swoops down over the hillside, swoop around the burnt-down fire once, leave — ghosts, the spirit of what has been, of absence, of the past's lack of vestige; we see a truly vast-looking army in white, ranked and serried, massed, off in the background in the gathering dark,

604

spearheaded by large white and light blue banners (perhaps with pictures of trees). This army — angels? resurrectors? — not saviors, not rescuers — stands. The show is over.

Simple or complex? Clear or obscure? The theme is one carried forward in Schumann's productions from the beginning of his New York period, theme of *Elements* ('63), *Apocalypse* ('63)/'64, *War Demonstration* ('65), *Flower Mountain* ('65): reemerging in his first real pageant in '74, and then, after displacement by the White Horse Butcher theme, theme of his pageants from '78 onward: the destruction of the small community, serial compact of householding families, by the catastrophic interference of a destructive outside agency, identifiable as war, putting an end to the serial recurrence of its daily activities — Evil conquering Good, good not resisting. But there is a complicating factor now. The invasion and the destruction are this time preceded by something like an insinuative corruption or not really corruption but enfeeblement or the like. This nuance was absent as yet in '78 and '79; but by '81 it was there: salesmen moved in and sold the farmer and his wife on the latest achievements of civilization: this year, '82, the destruction of the family is the critical event preceding annihilation. And the enfeeblers — those 'spirits of the air' — look like Schumann's good guys of yore — hippies.

The Good — family, nurturing utilization of the bounty of Mother Nature, community — is here not by Schumann presented as Pure Good, nor yet, however, as infected by outright Evil, but as in itself good-and-bad, cf. the Household Gods supra. Schumann takes a humorous, wrily sceptical, gentle look at 'Life', does not behold, lo! it is Good, but rather, well it's pretty good — it's all we have. Somehow not even the insidious disease of high-technology industrialization or of profit-oriented work in his view seem quite able to negate that pretty-goodness of all-that-we-have. There is a Bad distinct from Evil in the scheme that somehow he upholds and maintains and it is paired with the Good. But he won't let the ultimate dichotomy break down, nor will he see Good and Evil as interdependent and growing out of one another. There is in this something of the willful blindness of the conservative, insisting that the essence of the present is still that of an idealized past, and also something of the willful hopefulness of the liberal, unwilling to let go of the present, discerning in it 'much that is good and valuable', seeing in it some of the hoped-for future, persisting in viewing it as capable of self-reform: but none of the radical's stand, in rage, against the present, viewed as in essence wrong and to be done away with.

Before the pageant end that I described — the Village, the Fire, the Gulls, the Waiting Armies of the White — there was really only one other part, it seemed, namely a picture of war: three battles between Whites and Reds (having nothing to do with the whites and reds afterward involved in the destruction of the village). The Whites are no longer as in the pageants of the mid-'70s the Injuns. Who they — in terms of his use of colors up to now, the good party — are, seems to depend on the war — on Schumann's judgment of the war. Thus in the first battle, that of York, we may presume them to be the Americans (with the British as the Reds), in the second, that of Ypres, the British and the French, with the Germans the Reds, in the third, that of Normandy, the British, with the Germans the Reds again. Each time, the armies, brilliant in the distance, way off on the ascending incline beyond the circus arena, the Reds in formation, smartly marching to the barked orders of their leaders, the Whites on horseback, in loose formations, yelling when they attack — the details suggest that the paradigms for all the battles are the battles of the British Hessians with the American colonials in the American Revolution or War of Independence — clear as on an old battle print, maneuvered, marching in simple yet sufficiently complicated patterns, angular zigzags, across the hill contours toward and away from one another, the three battles successively closer to us, but never quite near. The first march, one of the Reds from the far distance into the further distance — the ditches, the fences, the stones very clear — was a beautiful beginning: astonishing us, it established the distance as the field of battle. Each battle, after a seeming victory of the Reds, ended with the death of all, white and red: strewn across the meadowland. These were, it was clear, wars of yore: in which combattants killed combattants.[6] And also, it seemed, wars of perhaps arguable merit, but certainly not all bad.[7]

In this part of the pageant, Schumann in fact seems to be abandoning, if only implicitly, the unconditional pacifism of his earlier work. Its point or at least a point it makes seems to be that just as in the last part of the pageant the family is not all good, but only relatively so, so war has in the past been not all bad, but only relatively so. As though to put into perspective the absolute evil of the coming world war, Schumann in this pageant for the first time seems to find some good in war — in some past wars — and some bad in the family: telling us, it seems, that that some wars deserved to be fought no more justifies the war threatening us now than that that family life is not an unalloyed pleasure justifies destroying the institution. This makes good sense. But there is a blurring here of the ethic that

<hr>

6. An idea of 'classical war' in Schumann's theatre first emerging in *Simple Light*.

7. 'Andrea Mugnai, a Florentine mime, covered his chest with pawnshop medals for the Pageant and led his Foot-Soldier Army against John Bell's Stilted Army in extended identical tableaux of the battles of Troy, Gettysburg and Normandy to demonstrate the futility of war. Typically, however, Peter, in staging this event, made no distinction between a war fought to avenge Menelaus's chagrin over being abandoned by Helen of Troy and a war whose purpose was too overthrow Adolf Hitler — just as in an ingenuous sideshow called *1,000 Eyes for an Eye* a committee of his puppeteers managed to compare the actions of Israel in Lebanon to those of the Nazis in Europe, while in the next breath they said that the Palestinians who had been displaced from Israel proper were merely a "wild people." ' — (Hoagland, '83.)

had up to this point sustained Schumann's art: by its rigid simplicity had given it power. And in fact the qualifications – the forgivingness and the accomodation – that by '82 had entered his judgment weakened the structure and sweep of his art.

And seen under the aspect of this two-part structure, the point of the pageant's end or 'second' part seemed that modern war is different: invading the city and the home, it strikes at everyone and destroys the community itself. The battle is no longer in the distance.

One could, however, also have attributed a 3-part structure to the pageant, taking into account its traditional opening, the celebration of the young and pretty female deity of the circus, goddess of spring, earth, cereal and the little scene enacted for her. The 20-ft. effigy was brought in on a run, laid down in the grass, erected, her arms spread so that she would also be a cross, made to rotate slowly, circled about by youths in the direction contrary to hers, then held flatly and quite immobile, facing us: while those armies marched to and fro in the distance; the deity silent in the foreground to the distant yells and commands, alone at first, but then joined by a small group – twelve children and a grownup lady all dressed in poetic gauze, the children gauze-winged, 'little angels' – who proceeded to enact a minor ritual against the background of war: after traipsing, hand in hand, in a circle between her and us, assembling in another circle, kneeling down, dipping their joined cupped hands in the grass, then as though drinking from their hands, ring-walk-dancing again, etc. Their delicate, almost transparent (but a little cute) configurations imaging Peace as a sacred communion, in spirit and by hand, with nature, counterposing Innocence to War, contrasted with the immobile giant puppet over and behind them, as both together stood in contrast to the distant pattern and din of formalized warfare. It was only after this ceremony that the paradigmatic community was erected: a *contrasting* pattern of order and repetition in sameness: to be infiltrated by the spirits of the air; and to be destroyed: as though by cancer, leaving left only the waiting armies of the righteous, a chimera in the mind's night.

The reason I described the Pageant in this backward manner, retrieving it in reverse from memory, is that in fact that last two-phase development, from peaceful though mechanical and monotonous order to destruction in the viewer's mind displaced what went before, so that one came away with an ideal picture of that order, and regretting its destruction, and with only as afterthought a memory of that brilliant linear warfare in the hills: recalling the initial image of a state of innocence of humanity at one with nature only by a second afterthought, as mere preface: not even an introduction. Yet, once one considers the three-part whole of the pageant, retrieving its dreamlike unrollment by an effort that has to work against the effect the Schumann by his timing of it and by the weight of his images had the pageant achieve (and I think the capture of the pageant's whole would have required such an effort from any of the spectators), it seems evident that the image of an abstractly geometric and repetitiously cellular order, mechanically compacted of the lives of like families and like communities, the pageant's *second* part, represented not the ideal nor even the 'reasonably-close-to-the-ideal', but a state of fall from grace, a fall from the grace depicted in the pageant's opening part, tainted, and tainted not just by, as I initially said, tolerable and subsidiary badness, sharply distinct from evil, but by a badness the germ of evil, the badness of a reglementation ruling out individuality, and of a separation into units — families, communities — unrelating but not individuated, and perhaps even the badness of a subversion of love into bitter monogamy; and that what the pageant suggested was that given such mechanical civilization (comprising, moreover, warfare of a like sort: geometric, mechanical and kept apart from other pursuits), the rest would follow as depicted: such an order would be vulnerable to, would perhaps even invite the operation of agencies invidiously, not alien to it, invading and in its essence destroying it even before a more horrible war now attacked it: the physical empire of death would succeed the spiritual empire of death over mechanical civilization.

Assuming that this was the meaning of Schumann's '82 pageant, why did he sabotage its delivery? I may be over-interpreting. But it seems to me that some hesitation to be forthright, some wish not to affront the clients of his art, may from his remove to Glover onward have caused his pageants to complexify: merely so his meaning would be hidden, the crucial details being lodged in some cranny of the event. I think art is in essence dissimulation and the artist most accomodative, wishing to give what is wanted. To prevent this creature, the artist, for sale and eager to be bought, from displaying to every passerby, if he can, the thighs of their choice and from merely being the mirror of our stuntedness, comforting echo of our addicted fantasy's idiot reiterations, and thus of not much use to us, some thoughtlessness fatal to its self-prostitution is required. So that the truth will out. But since absentmindedness is fatal to art, it must be thoughtlessness due to an obsession of the intellect. The creature's marketing strategy must be crippled. But not just by inadvertence, but by an egoist delirium of self-preoccupation. If the desire to refashion the world by incorporating into it one's own peculiarity weakens beyond a certain point, namely the point at which it only just balances the urge for self-prostitution (equally essential), the art begins to fall apart.

The figure of St. Francis, loveable fellow, was not exactly extraneous to the '82 pageant. But it was a facile borrowing from the public domain. Schumann himself in no way experiences that sweet fellowship with all things natural by the expression of which this other man became famous. So his statues stood out in the pageant like sore thumbs: there being no coincidence of intellect with feeling, Schumann's sense of placement failed him.

The same was true of the cute little ritual of child angels traipsing in the green. It was humorlessly saccharin: where Schumann elsewhere had approached the cute, as with his little blond pop-up hand puppet guardian angel, he had been careful to keep it at least in intention funny. The scene looked to me as though he had accepted somebody else's idea and had let them direct. The shallowness of this presentation of peace and innocence vitiated all that followed. And here again I am sure that Schumann himself has a tougher conception of innocence and a more virile one of peace — represented for instance by the figures of Simple Light and Joan of Arc, by the puppets of white wild animals, of the unicorn, of the Angel of Peace, or perhaps by the image of Venus giving birth to the Evening Star.

These were absolute failures. We may compare them with the relative failure — weakness — of the pageant's Household Deities or of the Washerwoman puppets in recent plays and pageants. The Household Deities turned out trivial. The Washerwomen are corny. But in both cases, Schumann tried to tell us about something essential to him, the flawed nature of a supreme good, marriage, the imperious necessity of coping with it positively, the grandeur of the working woman. He picked the wrong image, somehow right ones, e.g. one of the Afro-American mother, were not accessible to him, but the failure is only a relative one.

St. Francis and the child angels were absolute failures, but minor ones. I have mentioned one of two major flaws of the pageant: the flaw that skewed the syntax of its statement: its effectively third part on the self destruction of mechanized culture obliterated its first two parts, on the true Franciscan ideal of oneness with nature, on the complementarity of classical war and mechanized culture, and this second part the first such obfuscation of meaning is not incidental. It vitiates the aesthetic. And it is due to embarrassment, a feeling of insecurity as to one's meaning, a fear that it may not be acceptable.

The pageant's other major flaw related to space rather than time. It was the same as the preceding year's pageant's and '79's. The foreground scenes — the fakely pious little ritual, the village order — were held so long and were in their detail so solidly established in our view that the final long distance trajectories and arrivals seemed discontinuous with them, in a theatrically unrelated mode. The contrast of the intimate foreground with the distant battle movements worked fine: because the point was their unrelatedness. But when the two spaces had to be connected by making the dangerous and formerly distant invade the near and dear, the divergent modes of the distant — in the modes of unreality of legendary/ historical pastness and dangerous apocalyptic futurity — and of the near — in the modes of reality of (in the '82 pageant) a sentimental picture without transcendental reverberations and (in the '82 pageant's following part, but also already in the pageants of '79 and '81) of a representation of Our reality, a mechanical society — clashed. The middle distance became pertinent, but it was neither real nor unreal. Its unestablished mode was theatrically disturbing. The fault lay not with the unreality of the distant, but with the reality of the near. Up to '77 and even '78, the ontological mode of the near (the circus arena) had been a mode of unreality, namely first the transcendental and mythological unreality of the giant God Father or female Nature Deity figure, of a ritual with effective transcendental reference, then the poetic unreality of the White Lady and the White Horse of the White Horse Butcher dream. All the space of the show was homogenous. No clash resulted from the action unifying it. But once he lost that dream, a clash of quasi-realism and cliché with myth began to fissure Schumann's pageant.

15. The Circus of '83. Schumann has lost interest. Takes up music.

The theme of the August 13 and 14, '83 circus was 'the dangerous kitchen': as developed in the pageant actually, the fairy tale idea of an ordinary soup pot in a farmer's kitchen turning into a witches' cauldron from which come evil things, a a variant of the universal folk tale of the three wishes whose fulfillment turns against the wisher, with the fact that the evil that comes was wished for suppressed but the show's subjacent point. This subjacent point or implication was the point also of the discrete indictment of complicity returned against the common folk by the insidious invasion of the white spirits into the village settlement preparing it for destruction in the '82 pageant and of the retiring farmer's sell-out to the salesmen in the '81 pageant that sets up the atomic finale, and in more general form it was the the point already made by the emergence of the evil city from the farmer's grain in the '80 *Histoire du Pain*.[1] The thundering pre-exile prophets of Israel inveighed against the people's breaking of the covenant, but that, since '74, is not Schumann's way. He is addressing himself to the perpetrators as victims, softly.

After the usual beginning with the presentation of a nature deity — large- and crude-faced, the face of an actress, a theatrical face, half-smiling — the pageant started with a foreground scene that in fact, thus converting the whole pageant into a play, subsumed the larger action in the landscape under itself: a procession brought in what turned out giant furniture, a huge bed, carried by 20 or more people in which lay a Washerwoman and a Farmer (developed form of the Garbageman, with a tougher, leaner face), a huge table with a huge pot, a huge chair: i.e. Home, or the home, was brought in as though constituted by sacred objects, and some scene developed with the Farmer being served by his wife, etc. A tiny Washerwoman, played by a child, who climbed up on the table, did the coffee pouring — she later turns into a child cradled by the huge Washerwoman. A furious dance by a black demon in a costume of streamers or fringes — Susan Dennison on stilts, a splendid performance, the high point of the show — an outside force, not out of the soup pot — puts the jinx on things.

---

1. Schumann's idea for the '83 pageant developed out of plans he had for the '81 one, in turn inspired by the '80 *Histoire du Pain*: 'I thought of bread and hunger as theme for next year's circus, coming partly from work in Villeurbanne, but not the "Histoire du Pain" show . . . One idea that I have is to write a dialogue acted by giant puppets with giant equipment. Food and no food, bread and hunger, expanded to neonationalism that disregards world situation.' — (Schumann at December 14, '80 Bread and Puppet Board Meeting, in re '81 circus: as reported in Trudi Cohen's *Minutes* of that meeting.)

It brings on the adversities of life – a milk inspection, drought, a heart attack – all of which the farmer manages to cope with – but then a greater evil arrives in the form of a metallic contraption making ugly engine noises, essentially an airplane, and it wellnigh has him beat. It infects the soup with Badness[2] and the pot now produces 'an awful army of airplanes' (Banes) that 'marches over the landscape, destroying cows, flowers, birds, chairs, and finally, a city' (Banes). This is the landscape or pageantry part of the pageant: in the distance. The farmer and his wife sit and weep. But the dead arise, 'and, forming a great ship with chanting, playing drums and cymbals, waving banners and huge blue hands marked with red hearts' (Banes) they sail to the kitchen, and 'the wife takes fire from her hearth, ignities the enemy plane, and joins the ship' (Banes). Banes has those inspiring saviors be urban insurrectionaries (inhabitants of the city who 'rise'), but I think she misinterpreted that.

The small pine forest clearing play at nighttime and the big meadow afternoon play that Schumann had since '78 regularly been producing for his circuses in '83 took musical form, an opera, *The End Falls Before the Beginning* in the afternoon, the *Insurrection Oratorio* at night, musical pieces conducted by Schumann, with librettos, music and the (rhyming) text of the opera by Schumann, the text of the oratorio mostly, I believe, newspaper quotations illustrating the irrationality of the nuclear arms race. Schumann had been working on these pieces, though especially perhaps the oratorio – he put on a performance at the Plainfield, Vt. Community Center of a four-movement *Insurrection Symphony! No. 1* on January 23, '83[3] – with people outside of the theatre during the winter. The opera was

---

2. I am here following the account by Sally Banes, *When Church Picnics Make Sense, Village Voice*, August 23, '83 – I missed the crucial details.

3. 'In January the Bread and Puppet Theatre will offer The First Insurrection Symphony, a workshop led by Peter Schumann. It will be free and open to everyone. All vocal and instrumental sounds available will be tried, added on to each other and turned upside-down until they fit. All kinds of instruments are welcome: classical, toy, home-built and found objects. All voices too: opera singers, showerbath singers, bird imitators old and young.

Sometimes sections will be rehearsed in homogeneous groups, just brass or percussion or string or voice, and sometimes all forces will be combined for the chaotic fun of it. We will fish for all possible and unheard-of sounds and organize them into some shape, and that shape will be The First Insurrection Symphony, to be performed for the general public at the end of the rehearsal period.

Rehearsals take place in the Plainfield Community Center during January 1983, on Thursdays and Fridays at 7 p.m. and Sundays at 2 p.m. That's January 2,6,7,9,13,14,16,20 and 21. You have to attend at least two rehearsals per week to participate.

The performance will be on Sunday, January 23, at 4 p.m.' — (*The Chronicle*, December 22, 1982.)

My impression at the broadcast performance of the *Insurrection Oratorio* at Judson Memorial Church on December 16 ('83) was that most or all of the 15 or so people in the choir had been thoroughly rehearsed and/or had done the thing often, and anticipated and

in puppetry form, i.e. accompanied by mute puppetry (some of it closer to dance than in any other Schumann piece I have seen), but in both pieces the musical element was (for the first time in Schumann's work) the primary element: they were performances of music with text or with text and puppetry.[4] The primary constitutive and organizing element of the music — except for some sections of the opera dominated by rhythm (to my ear an aberration and error in the composer's part) — was tonal quality, the quality of raw sound, unconfined by scale or pitch, produced by home made or conventional instruments or voices. The music was an episodic succession of aural events in which materials moved or struck showed aurally. I suspect that an awareness of contemporary work in music condemns Schumann to an unrewarding primitivism in this area. He doesn't know what has been done. But you never know what a man of genius will come up with.

The circus as a whole — respectively watched by a large audience, over 10.000 Saturday, thousands also on Sunday — French Canadians and Vermonters — though more of a hippie middle class than of a working class or farmer sort — to me had the deadness of an institution. The sideshows, emitting their usual aesthetic and/or liberal whine gave it a foretaste like the aftertaste of vomit, the 'silly circus', though there was one good gorilla family number, had been invaded by French Canadian skits like the side shows, and seemed to me not only as deficient in humor and imagination as its predecessors, but had replaced their energy by a willingness to do what was expected, and the pageant, though the hugeness of its props was an ingenious solution to the problem of making its stationary foreground focal part adequate to what was now merely its setting, the

---

were familiar with Schumann's rather elaborate conductor's hand vocabulary, and that the effect — not too dissimilar to my tin ear to that of traditional Western highculture music — Mahler, Schönberg — depended on his tight control by rehearsals and conducting, not only the sudden cessations and beginnings, but the smooth augmentations and diminutions, the effect that, on the whole, of a politely controlled anxiety. The intelligible text consisted of quotations of newspaper statements on toy sales — increasing sales, recently, of military type toys, though at or toward the end the whole group, I think, recited some text, presumably of Schumann's, anent, I believe, houses, towns, perhaps seasons — some evocation of an imputation of value to life.

4. Speaking of *Diagonal Man* (first showings, November '82), Schumann (interview, December '82) finally avowed that his puppetry really doesn't have much to do with puppetry, that it is a new art form the potentials of which keep him busy, almost overwhelm him, the only thing to compare to which might be opera, and came up with the formula that it is music and noisemaking plus sculpture and painting, all used so as to independently develop their power. *Diagonal Man* was in no way opera (its prologue made a very sculptural use of certain puppets, however): Schumann actually had in mind his work just then on the *Insurrection Symphony* and the status of music in what became *The End Falls*. These works resume, as regards music, the line of development through *Grey Lady Cantatas II* and *III* and *Washerwoman Nativity*, but go further by having music not just as independent and developed element, but as the dominant one.

landscape, was no longer a pageant, and the nature of its address to the audience had, both as regards the particular point made (indistinct because the cauldron metaphor, giving it no structure, made no point), and as regards form (neither warning nor reproval, nor plea nor communion, and certainly no celebration) become indistinct. In the middle of it all was Schumann, his back turned, making music, his own music – taking up something that he had all these years wanted to get around to, something else.[5]

5. The Bread and Puppet Junior Drama Club put on the *Agamemnon* they had first done in the region December '82/January '83:

'The ten young members of this newly-formed group are all friends and neighbors of the Bread and Puppet Theater of Glover. Starting some years ago with rigorous apprenticeships in Paul Zaloom's kids' shows, they eventually proceeded to select and produce their own adaptations of plays, including a Pushkin tale in verse and Sophocles' Antigone. They have successfully performed at the annual Domestic Resurrection Circuses and are now preparing to tour their latest effort during winter vacation ... This shortened version is directed by Tamar Schumann of Glover, who is a senior at Bryn Mawr College. King Agamemnon is played by seventeen-year-old Suzy Dennison of Temple, Maine; his wife, Clytemnestra, by fifteen-year-old Maria Schumann of Glover. Thirteen-year-old Torin Porter, also of Glover, portrays Prince Aegisthus, and Plainfield's Nessa Rabin is the prophetess, Cassandra. The other five members of the company, all in their teens, fill the remaining roles of herald, watchman and Greek chorus.

The schedule for the performances of Agamemnon is:

Wednesday, December 29, at 7:30 at the Bread and Puppet Farm, Glover;

Thursday, December 30, at 7:30 in Plainfield's Community Center; Sunday, January 2, at 4 p.m. in the Wood Art Gallery in Montpelier.

The company will also perform in several high schools, including Cabot, Twinfield, Lyndon Institute and Lake Region, on January 3, 4 and 5. Then the members will return to their respective schools and studies.' — (*The Chronicle*, December 22, 1982.)

16. *Diagonal Man*, '82. People at best are only half alive. Job holders are dead.
The half alive ones are misfits.
An autobiographical play about 'The Individual'.

Diagonal Man (Theory and Practice) was done November 19, '82 at Whitcomb High School, Bethel, Vt., November 21 in the Municipal Building in Orleans, Vt., November 23 at the Haybarn Theater at Goddard College in Plainfield, Vt., and then in New York City, November 30 to December 19 at the Theatre for the New City. In New York, at any rate, it was done with a prologue, *The Tragedy of Ineffectual Man*, more or less the same playlet as the *Ineffective Man — Dream Woman* which had been done as sideshow during the August circus, and which in term came from *Histoire du Pain*.

Prologue. Tragedy of Ineffectual Man.

The front of the stage starts out as a red surface: a red curtain in a red frame. Curtain and frame are dirty and scuffed: this has not the effect of not mattering, but of an affectation or stylistic device. Yet one might say that to deliver the wealth of puppetry Schumann delivers, he has to skimp on work of upkeep devoted to neatness.

A hand held notice comes out in the rift between the curtains: 'The Tragedy of Ineffectual Man. Prologue.' The lights go out. The musicians are off to our right, under a balcony. The curtain rises, it's almost dark on the stage, there is a humming (it continues through this part), pale figures seem to be bobbing up and down up there, the lights grow, they are truncated — i.e. the legs from the knees down are missing — half-shell puppets of women, big-breasted, their bellies like third breasts, pregnant, with many different, different also stylistically, faces, some pretty, some earthy, held up by the performers behind them, moved up and down, tilted sideways: a dense crowd of them, it seems, on the little stage: their surround, sides and back of the stage, a series of tall paintings of females like them. Puppets and the women in the paintings all have babies at their breasts, are nursing, and another baby by their thigh and belly, clinging to them: and toward the back, a little sinisterly, two of the half-shell woman figures have been joined in an appropriate fit, tied together, a hanging two-fronted woman, the two women not altogether exactly a fit, but pretty much so, twisting a little, hanging from a wire or whatever. There is some music/sound to this. Then the women, pretty much held horizontally, are slowly bobbed out, the performers bending over behind them so that their upper bodies remain more or less invisible, though their legs are showing. Right and left on the stage there are two or three angled screens that they glide out between. These remain for the play. The hanging two-faced woman is slowly lowered, she comes down twisting so you see both halves alternately, and at each side of the stage when she then hangs there near the floor, the pair of hands of a performer emerge in an ecce homo gesture, palms up, apart, fingers slightly curved. This is a separate held moment. Then from each side an everyday-clad 'operator' emerges, from the left George Bartenieff who will play the conferencier and the Diagonal Man and John Bell, who will do the speaking from the right, and with some slight ceremony of gesture the two woman halves are partly untied at the bottom. Something drops out of her, is born, and the double mother jolts back up to the ceiling. Woman is the Origin. The baby is a greenheaded, toothed beast, i.e. a small limp dummy with that beast maskhead. As the creature drops it is held, brought out and down on the floor by the two operators in a manner making it look pretty life-like standing there on all fours, with its tail dragging, breathing heavily facing us, the heavy breathing being supplied by the two operators. They crouch next to the beast, advance it toward us, the one on the right manipulating its head by a hand on the scruff of its neck and also advancing its left paw, the other holding up its lower body and advancing its right paw: the trio of them is the image as the beast advances in a ferocious but weak or weak but ferocious manner: something really quite nasty and dangerous. Down-stage it seems to struggle to escape them — an untroubling confusion of the idea or image — at any rate it gets excited, suddenly it flips over backward, comes back down forward without its former head, but now with the head of a man, a grey-brown also sinister pained male head of a middle aged man, the beast is a male man, man is a beast. The man is upright, by his position half-beast, looking at us gravely, threateningly, really. (Music. A Chorale.) He studies his hands, each is brought up to him for inspection in turn. A small podium, i.e. the front of one, with a landscape painted on it, a shelf that comes out below the landscape, and a small round emblem, part dark blue, part a yellow quarter moon, suspended over the landscape's sky, is moved onto the stage, an operator crouching behind it, holding it center-stage, the Man is brought behind it, emerges above it, positions himself (so to speak), almost in the manner of a lecturer, his two handlers still to each side of him, kneeling on the floor, manipulating him, he is looking down the front of his lectern. A slight pause, then he sows: his right hand is repeatedly brought down behind the lectern to grasp something, and then up above it, releasing something sounding like sand across the landscape's sky and onto the shelf and floor, each time to bird twittering, and each time the performer behind the lectern, putting out one hand at a time, positions something on the shelf, small dark cutouts in various shapes, a star on each. A big cutout Eye enters from the right, brought in by a puppeteer of whom only the black-clad legs, not the Eye's, are visible. It regards the

616

man's work, leaves. The operator crouching behind the lectern turns the small moon-carrying emblem around, it is white on the other side – flower-like. The moon has turned into a sun. His hand turns all the star-bearing cutouts on the shelf around so they stand colored, lively side out: a tree, apples in the tree, a little costumed peasant woman, a cute little house, a black and white cow with pink udders. The idea of this little ensemble's, culture, being the fruit of (male) Man's nighttime seeding, fruit of dream-seed, is conveyed. The man's face, unaltered of course, now almost seems to be smiling. To evil cranking sounds from the musicians, a stone-like grey object – small, the size of a grapefruit – is lowered a little way from the ceiling to above and a little in front of the man and his operators, held there, above the landscape, way above it. The operators' eyes have been fixed on him throughout intensely, now their eyes travel to the object as his head gradually lifts (is lifted by one of them) to look at it. He looks down, his hands are lowered behind the lectern, bring out, one after the other, the hands of the operator crouching there, joins them in a protective gesture over the house and landscape. (Inversion of relation between puppet and operator!) He starts swaying from side to side as though in the grip of emotion – with an air of agitation, distress – his arms held up in the air. He collapses on the floor next to the lectern. He is lifted (a third operator entering to assist in this) up in the air and made to fly, head held high, in gentle swoops, he flies around the stage (the Eye is in the background watching), up to the suspended stone, cradling it in both hands, it slowly recommences coming down, in his hands, as though he were bringing it down, gradually his arms shift above him, and the stone, in his hands, comes down upon him, on his head, weighing down on him: his dummy figure crumbles, crouches inertly, all surrounded and covered by the variously but all similarly crouching three operators (another puppet-operator ensemble tableau) on the floor, his head presumably squashed by what he fetched from the sky – or was unable to prevent from falling out of it. The hands are no longer protecting the house at this point. The chorale is sung again, more dirge-like this time. The woman paintings in the background are watching. (My companion thought it was all a kind of parable: justly proud of his creative activities, translation of his nighttime dreams into daytime reality, he had let his pride wax excessive, fostering excessive ambition, and his too high-soaring project had brought him down.)[1] Dimout. Gong. All out. The crushed man is left behind. Two operators strip the woman paintings off the side and rear panels: under

---

1. '. . . the stone that hangs above him and his world there (is) a power that he can't stop but he tries to and he sees it's a calamity that will follow and it falls and he tries to stop it but he can't.' — (Schumann, interview, '80.)

But this is not how it looks. It looks like a metaphor of the hubris that produced the atomic missile.

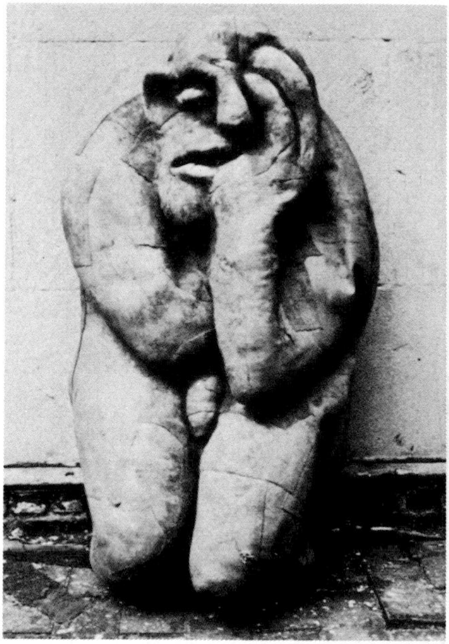

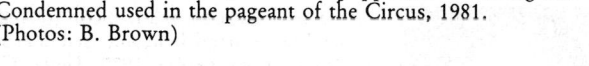

Above: Celastic half-shell, hand-held puppets, from among The Condemned used in the pageant of the Circus, 1981. (Photos: B. Brown)

Below: Skeleton heads made of scrap wood for stick puppets, 7 or 8 feet tall, used in *Washerwoman Nativity,* 1979.

Paper mache Demon mask, about 4 feet tall,
used in *Diagonal Man*, 1982.
(Photo: B. Brown)

Circus, 1979.
(Photo: P. Moore)

Washerwoman Nativity, 1979.
(Photo: G. Lange)

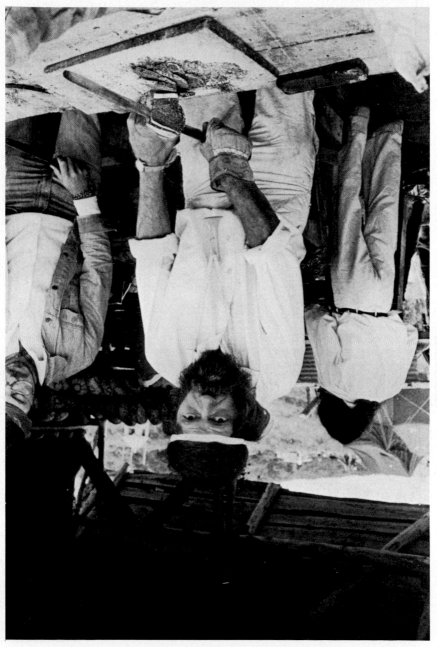

Circus, 1979.
(Photo: P. Moore)

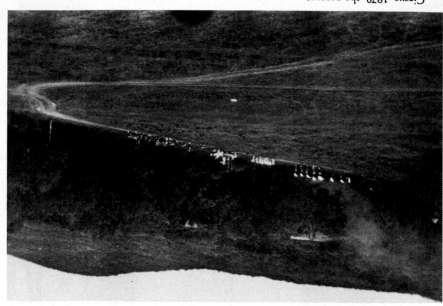

Circus, 1979, the pageant.
(Photo: P. Moore)

Circus, 1979, the pageant.
(Photo: G. Lange)

Circus, 1981, the pageant.
(Photo: G. Lange)

Circus, 1979, the pageant.
(Photo: P. Moore)

Woyzeck, New York City, 1981.
(Photos: G. Lange)

Woyzeck, New York City, 1981.
(Photo: G. Lange)

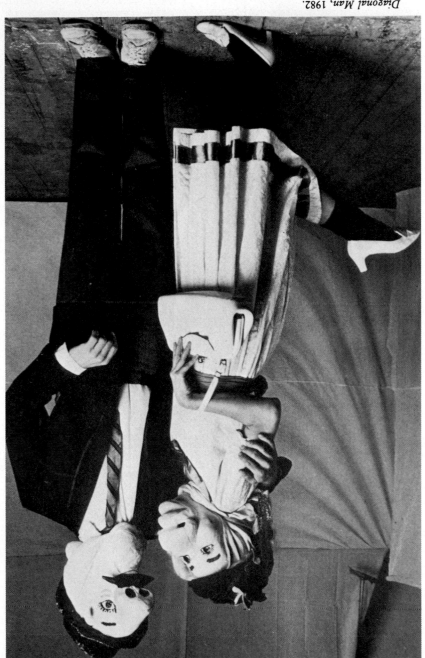

Diagonal Man, 1982.
(Photo: G. Lange)

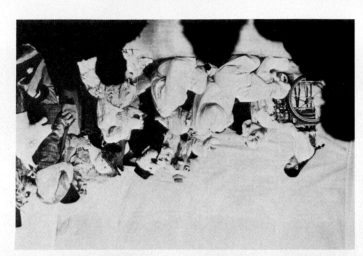

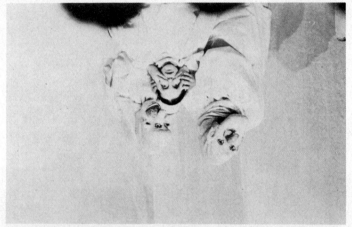

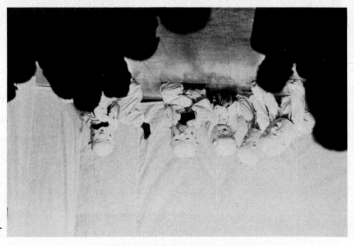

Josephine, 1984.
(Photos: P. Moore.)

Nuclear Freeze Demonstration, New York City, June 12, 1982.
(Photo: Keith Myers, New York Times Pictures)

Death on his horse, Nuclear Freeze Demonstration,
New York City, June 12, 1982.
(Photo: B. Brown)

pets seated on papier maché chairs, are carried in smoothly, held high in the air, they surround the prone figure, hold still, in turn recite the concluding admonitory lines of the text – 'Wake up' etc. Evidently his good spirits, and the bad ones – hell and heaven, fear and aspiration. He stays down. The flamboyantly hellish backdrop paintings are peeled off, below them in black and white and grey, the Big City, groups and clumps of tall houses, tenements, scenery for the remainder of the play: the hell the hero is born into. The refuse dropped by the Demons, I presume their turds, is picked up. Turned over, they turn out to be cutouts of houses like the painted ones on the backdrop, small cutouts, foot-high. They are positioned city-wise about the stage. Our cities are Satan's excrement.

George, George Bartenieff, the Diagonal Man, lies crumpled up between the painted buildings and the cutout ones (a perspectival effect this, too). The large eye carried by the black legs enters again, slidingly, leans over him. Two players, one from each side, enter, each with two red large ears in their hands, and in formation to both sides of George, lean over him and the small make-shift muslin wings on his back. He is gotten up by the city's attention. 'Wakes up', gets up. Stands blinking. Over-tight jacket and pants, no mask, his overly plastic actor's face effective and pale. An operator in civies, from the left, kneels next to him. Supported by him, George slowly goes into an off-the-vertical position, pronounces the play's title (I have no idea what the title's parenthetical 'Theory & Practice' refers to), rattles the little tinlid rattle he is carrying, 'flies' over to the left, agitating his wings minimally with an almost perfunctory but accomodating gesture. Mouthharp (John) and rattle to a dance of the Ears in the cutout slum. Listening city. Mouthharp mutes.

George is down-stage at the left with one of the flip-over story boards traditional with Schumann, and having uncovered its first page, pointing to it with his rattle, he commences in a balladeering prose – no song quality – to recite the first part of the program text.[3] A viciously barking puppet dog, grey, led in from the rear on a leash, is chasing the red ears out.

Act 2 (*The inhabitants of the city are introduced*). Appropriately, succeeding the dance of the ears, the inhabitants of the city appear out of the telephone directory: entrance and diagonal traverse upstage of a succession of players with masks, (the 'individual people' masks from *Histoire du Pain*) human faces, about two or three times the length of human faces, but not

---

3. The words and pictures in the flip-over book that he points to relate only in a jumbled and fragmentary manner to the recited text: as though to give a non-syntactical impression of life's and the hero's confusions and vagaries. George spoke the text meaningfully and with emotion, but its obscurity and its not being a poem defeated him: its awkwardness seeming precious, he could get not pathos or 'large meaning' out of it, and he didn't want to come across as conferencier, e.g. by acting out being puzzled by it, because (unwisely) he was afraid it would break the continuity with his character in the play.

much wider than one, caricatures, but pleasant ones, and quite handsome as pieces of sculpture, the faces mostly of middle-aged people, mostly hand held, often at slightly odd angles. But the resulting figures are surprisingly believable. Their entrances and exists are separated by some briefly held characteristic (comic) pose. At our right, in the meantime, John Bell is at the mike, reading a succession of names, one for each, with an address and a telephone number, identifying the individuals as entries in a telephone directory. The idea of the skit is the trite idea that a city is people, but it is given quality by the tension between the rejective grotesqueries of the mask faces (well supplemented by the performers' walks and stances – they are good) and the intimations of the loneliness and desperation of so many people; and because, of course, their reduction to isolated telephone subscribers modifies – adversely – the individuation normally implicit in 'people'. They come in in profile, make a turn toward us there and advance full face, leave, some in profile, some turning their faces back toward us, still seen en face, not all too careful to keep their heads behind the masks as they enter and leave, but the shallowness of the masks in any case puts them in evidence as masks when seen from the side: they suddenly become plausible faces when seen head on. The names do not necessarily apply, e.g. a studious no longer so young female has a male name, a man a female one. Curtain. The cutout houses remain in view on the floor in front of the curtain.

Another 'verse' of the text from Bartenieff. John comes out, his head loosely swathed in black, he and George kneel by one of the houses, George from another black cloth unwraps, behind the cutout tenement, a love-making cutout couple, holds them above the house against the night black of the cloth hanging down from his hand slowly moves them in a see-saw pattern, the couple is as big as the tenement, not young people, corpulent people, welded together. John is playing his kazoo to this, inside the black cowl – the music of the night. John off.

Curtain opens. (Act 3. *The Coffee Dialogue*.) Behind a table to the rear a small costumed performer, suited, shirt stuffed for roundness, with a big red maskhead, jolly-expressioned. He (i.e. John at the mike does his voice, but he does the gestures) tells us with gravitatious but inoffensive bonhommie – Schumann is not down on this petty-bourgeois – it may be his father – 'This is my house, this (pointing to a painted backdrop scene) country is my country – this is a normal tree, these are normal people' – all with much satisfaction. 'And now let me introduce my son, Diagonal Man, to you' – George comes over, they evidently love one another, he is commiserating with George over something – the dialogue is such that clearly the father is concerned and clearly doesn't hear what George is saying. The daughter (with the smiling, slightly consumptive, pinched, tight and sweetly pretty face mask of Marie in *Woyzeck*) comes in, serves her coffee, to the father's immense satisfaction, an angel popping out of the

620

can to take the orders (one regular, one . . .), she goes to get a copy of the Times for him, a big pink foot suspended up above to strokes on a bass guitar walks a little, father and son speak of life some more, the father rotundly but not meaning it admitting 'it's bad, there is nothing else to call it.' George leaves, dad remains, tomato-red head in his hands – the older generation. Curtain.

Bartenieff with gumption delivers another passage from the text. John brings a toy truck tied to a plastic cord stage right in front of the curtain. It is pulled across through the cutout houses (this whole play is about life in the city), John doing its raucous noises – half words – talking to itself as it makes it through the city.

Curtain opens. (Act 4 *The Job*.) An office. A secretary – the mask a slightly nasty small-animal snouty face, in the cute genre without being cute, with a minor mess of blond-white-silver indeterminate hair – behind the table facing toward us, her boss – he has on a 'Salesman' mask, the face of a mind identifying with a function and therefore, though full of small gears and small cunning, almost empty, on a chair to her right, alongside of the table. They are processing people: who have been assigned jobs, conceived here not as something done at a given time, but as what persons do in life, settle for. The salesman is selling social identities. But it's more bureaucratic than that, no selling job. He has a set speech, which is exceptionally good: I suspect somebody else than Schumann wrote it. It's to the effect that people do this and that wrong, or things go wrong, etc., 'we' – fate, society, the salesman bureaucrat – make arrangements, our – a job-holder-downer's – job is to get rid of the resulting mess, problem, trouble, etc., that's all, 'it's a job like any other' – the refrain. People are miscreants. The speech is cackled off by the office boss to the same brief burst of jazz each time. There are three job-needers, then the Diagonal Man as fourth, they are made cop, doctor, mugger, he a garbage man. Before each comes in, a head (-mask) is brought in, hooked on a string, raised into the fly-space, invisible. The applicant, face covered so it's no face – that of a willing seeker of a place within the society's pre-set division-of-labor cum repressive system – enters, sits, responds affirmatively on being asked has the job been described to him, does he want it, has the job-head lowered on him, the secretary/office bunny on a red pillow like for a medal, brings him his 'equipment' (the doctor's a bit of bandaid, the cop's a club, the mugger's a gun, George's a garbage can), he is asked is he 'happy', he responds affirmatively (enthusiastically), leaves, an assembly line routine for turning out socialized individuals, except that it becomes just a little sticky when the Diagonal Man comes in, he doesn't seem happy with the job, instead of saying he wants it, he says, with evident difficulty, 'I will do it', then 'I am not afraid', then he doesn't get up, the job dispenser has to repeat part of his speech, get rid of George + equipment. George leaves with the garbage can. Each time an applicant is processed, the processor brings in a 'Men Working' sign, presumably stolen by some Bread and Puppeter from some construction site. George having left, a brief flirtation of boss and secretary commences — very nice — as they are about to kiss, three others, like the boss, also with moustache, cane, identical little black hats, same mask, enter, sit here and there, surprising the couple but saying nothing, staring briefly at them: all are chased out (funny end to scene) by the angry little dog. The person doing the processor/office boss is an excellent mime — fine timing.

Another interlude for scene change, this time with the lights on over the audience. George does his text, then goes about his job, the garbage can with him, knocks on one of the cutouts, female voice responds, John comes out from the wings with a cutout of a dog, the dog (i.e. John) spills a mess (plastic cutlery), George disposes of it. It's a shit job.

Curtain opens. (Act 5. *Death in the Family*.) Schumann probably decided he was going to give a little structure to the play by relating the Jobs of act 4 with what happens: in this scene the Doctor is utilized. The father is in a bed, red head and blue quilt, the daughter seated in back, the pink foot suspended above (a moment of time standing still?). Heavy breathing (John at mike), daughter wipes father's forehead. George seated at bed. Coughing fit. Daughter feeds father medicine. Knocking, doctor in, carrying lozenge-shaped speaking signs (as in some older comic strip cartoons), holds them up to his mouth — 'That be', 'Wounds', 'Fear' — they are dropped into George's garbage can (Schumann apparently esteeming physicians' medicine no more highly than did Moliere) — doc bends over bed, a person with four of the big ears enters, holds them over the bed also. Doctor. 'He's dead.' Scream of anguish from daughter (i.e. from John), her four lacy-blouse arms (her own, her puppet's) upraised. She bends over dead dad, George by her, curved around her really, comforting her: one of the puppet/man compositions in this play, developing the *Goya*-line. George knocks at the door of the church in the backdrop landscape picture, it opens (with some help from him) the coffee-can angel leans out, says, 'That's it. You can go now.' He leaves. Sister is kneeling sorrowingly by father. Curtain.

Bartenieff does another verse to music, goes center-stage, a small wooden arm chair has been put out — suspended — over the top of the curtain, John grandly announces we will now see a chair fall from heaven, George has opened his garbage can, the chair drops into it. It's a nonsense scene obscurely relating to a father's death — pathos converted into comedy.

Curtain up. (Act 6. *Love and Murder*.) Half-dimmed lights. To tinkling from a tympano, George rearranges the houses into two groups apart from one another. Different parts of the city. Man with a large, benign head (-mask) enters at rear, stands in one of them. Whispered words (as though in his mind), 'Grief in my head, joy in my feet'. A brown leaf drops lightly over the backdrop. Diagonal Man's orphaned sister in, stands in the other-part-of-the-city – a whispered 'high up in the air, halfway down in the ground': her state of mind. Then more whispered text, dialogue in the mind between strangers that have not met. George redistributes the houses into a large circle around the sister, the stranger enters it, speaks to her 'What a night.' (Another leaf drops.) Poetic dialogue – he is picking her up. The dialogue is accompanied by violin. He kneels before her: she dances in place to the music. The masks seem very large in the half-dimmed light. The two spots are on the masks. They do a tender stately little dance together to the violin. They go off to see the old trees on the other side of the park. George rearranges the houses (perhaps they are now around the park.)

There is a whispering of dollar amount figures, the amounts starting low and going up, as though in someone's speculative or, more likely, day-dream fantasies of enrichment, debate with himself. The Job Distributor of Act 4 slowly enters, stooped over, spinning out his financial projects/prospects/desires, looking very middle-aged now, more pitiful than odious. There are two strings from him to up above somewhere, seeming to pull him, hold him. He stands, the dollar amounts increasing, in his mind he is getting rich, his left hand in small calculative gestures seems attached to one of the strings, the other seems to go to his head (a pseudo-marionette). He has snowballed his investments up to a million, the figure is whispered weightily (all we hear are the figures). The Mugger with his big squarish grey-brown brutish head (-mask) and gun enters from the opposite side to a count placing his enormous (2-3 foot long) shoes down, clump, clump, the count (by John) fate's countercount to the speculator's hopeful arithmetic. On the shoes there are (glued, I presume) other shoes, ordinary size, real ones, presumably those of the victims he has stalked, emblem of his profession, the pursuit of others. The Mugger shoots. The Salesman's coat flies off, up, hangs up there, the strings had been attached to it, he has lost his protective covering, stands with arms raised, out, straight, at an angle. The Mugger backs back out to a negative count. The Salesman clasping his belly staggers about the stage in death agony (very well done), to tortured gasps staggers off the stage on the opposite side, reappears, but it is now an identical dummy, wrestled onto the stage by an operator (Mike) holding him clasped in front of him, he is wrestled down, Mike Romanyshyn leaves. George has been watching from left rear where his can is, walks over to him, stands by him, puts on his cotton work gloves, with effort drags him over to the garbage can, commences to stuff him in. The city-scape looks convincing in the half-light. Vicious barking, leashed dog in (George frantically stuffing), attacks George, Cop appears behind the dog, holding the leash, George down on the ground, trying to ward off dog. Cop and dog off. The overhead coat comes down flapping, attacks George. Fight of George and coat. Coat wins. George lies there. Slow, spaced tom-tom. The city's population, the figures from the telephone directory, enter one by one, stand about grieving to the tom-tom — gestures of desolation, the elongated faces rotating to the horizontal and beyond (hand manipulation, but I don't know how they do it, in between the masks are attached to the performers' heads). Tom-tom stops.They are still there. John onto stage, takes off the recumbent George's wings and coat. George gets up. John gives him another coat, a shillelagh, a bottle, a cosmetic stick. George blackens his face stubbly, takes a swig — John off — stands, looks around, the grievers recede from him in a movement of recoil. Mouthharp. George does a drunken dance, leaning on his shillelagh. Band out onto the stage, stands in a line behind George, playing the music. No uniforms, miscellany of civies. George recites the entire text with music in between, the band members mildly reacting to it, he does it boisterously, all stops out, sort of as a bum. The music stops as he comes to the last lines. He recites them looking at us grimly ('You better!'), 'Wake up and eat. Go on and stop. Wake up and stop and go on and eat.' A challenge.

*　　　*　　　*

The play was Schumann's breakthrough into 'theatre' (individuals, characters, interactions, if not motivation then the problem of motivation, a story, dramatic incidents); as though with *Woyzeck* he had proved to himself he could do it, and now did it: with *Woyzeck* as puppeteer invading theatre, in *Diagonal Man* recreating it in his own medium. His two pitiful Shakespeare productions had in a negative way led up to it; the breakdown of the morality approach to the individual in *Joan* and *Wolkenstein* lay in the background; and the play itself, an hommage to Chaplin, developed his '60s mime skits about the Young Man in the City. The conceptions, some of them, were grandiose, and the staging ideas, some of them, beautiful — Schumann making good use of what I have called this last period's 'sophisticated' approach to puppetry; and getting splendid work from his puppeteers:

Prologue (Act 1): A life is determined by the conflict of aspiration with fear.

Act 2: The modern — urban — condition is one of isolation (reduction to a name, an address and a telephone number that others may or may not utilize): which stimulates (and renders futile and comic) heroic attempts at self-individuation.

Act 3: Family affords no sustainment: the old time self-satisfying security of the burgher is gone.

Act 4: Society's demand is ineluctable; it is: get a job; which means: define yourself by a social function; and social function = contribution to social order by contribution to cleaning up the messes people invariably make.

Act 5: The deaths of fathers leave men on their own: only now do they face themselves; only now do choices take on horrid reality.

Act 6: You can't afford messing up on your job; society will drop you; and: the only alternative to zerofication by social identity is to become a bum. This may be preferable.

But the play — almost, not quite, a wreck — didn't realize the conceptions. Schumann lacked the shamelessness and the bad taste to bear down on them. He wanted to keep things light and oblique.

The play was rendered ineffective above all by the unresolved ambiguity in the figure of the hero: were we to take his difference from other men as a dramatic device to highlight the nature — or situation — of all men, or was the point that he was different? Was Schumann aristocratically saying: some men are better (by their weakness, conflict, inadaptability) (thus also more to be pitied) than other men (than the generality of adaptables), or was he saying: this is how everybody is inwardly or when focused on and closely regarded: mixed up, self-conflicted, unable to strike out on their own, but able to conform ('deny themselves') only at great expense of anguish, self-mutilation and unhappiness? The prologue, except for its confusing contrast of Man and Woman, alien to the play, went in the direction of the Everyman idea, and so did the use of the recited text as interior monologue of two of the characters other than the hero. But the hero's contrast not only with the 'inhabitants of the city' but also with his more immediate relations, his dad, his sister, his sister's suitor, went in the other, the aristocratic direction. The play's disorienting confusion in this regard reflected, I would say, Schumann's own ambivalence between the European elitism of his youth — most people are base, a few are noble — and a more American 'respect for the individual'.

Schumann's notion of puppeterring by calling for naive, poetic and playful representations might seem to preclude the resolution of such ambiguities. But as, in this sense, puppetry, the play failed (1) by not being funny enough, (2) by having the hero acted, rather than mimed and clowned. It wasn't funny enough in the sense that its humor was delicate, rather than of the slapstick sort or in the area of the grotesque. This provided some beautiful scenes, with humor ranging from the tender irony of the visit to dad through the stark comedy of the office routine to the pathetic clownery of the hero's attempt, in line with his job, to dispose of the victim of crime (the fight with the coat). But at this elevated level of humor, the clumsiness of ideas withal perceived to be very much in question becomes an artistic minus. Having an actor rather than a clown and mime hero precluded the distance from him at which we could see him as, in all his particularity, everyman: but though Bartenieff did very well with the part, Schumann had not by the 'script' or by directing — he left him pretty much to his own devices — given him enough to work with to portray the hero as an exceptional individual either, e.g. as schlemiel.

The recited text that framed the play was as awful as most of Schumann's writing. Schumann does not select words, he uses what pops into his head – 'chiefs', 'grief/joy', 'bread not death', 'desire' – and what pops into his head tends to be a little odd, but to no purpose and tritely odd, cute and awkward. The recited text calls for rhyme, and that it doesn't rhyme is made even worse by the one rhyme in it, early on. I imagine he shirked the work involved in rhyming, and for Schumann to shirk work is so out of character, it would in this case measure his resistance to language, his need to express contempt for it. He probably feels it rivalizes with his puppets, feels it shouldn't be needed, his puppets should be enough, and treats it contemptuously to keep it in its place. But above all, language carefully used tends to define one's meaning, and Schumann neither wants to commit himself to one meaning nor give away his hand – baldly convey his one meaning or his alternative meanings. The evasiveness of the text – as exemplified notably by the feebleness of its central image of diagonality – a state between the uprightness of both the truly alive and the truly individual and the horizontality of the dead and of those prone to do what is demanded – precluded the play from having power. What were we to make of 'Wake up and eat/go on and stop/wake up and stop/and go on and eat'? One sensed a sense, but the words didn't carry it. But the speech impediment was not verbal incompetence. It was Schumann's unwillingness to recommend to individuals any one attitude to take in life: not that he doesn't know perfectly well what he thinks individuals should act like: but he doesn't want to commit himself. His true recommendation would be brutality: energetic and authentic self-realization. But then what of morality?

The play itself, *Diagonal Man*, text apart, is about The Big City, and thence about a world that has assumed the big city's social form, a form the play defines incidentally by bureaucracy and commercialism, not so incidentally by people's not knowing one another, as non-community, Gesellschaft rather than Gemeinschaft, by unrelatedness and loneliness, but primarily by a division of labor so demanding it comports a loss of selfhood or individuality in the assumption of a role (notably of a role associated with a job – an occupation – one is committed to). This characterization accords with the image of what I termed 'mechanical civilization' in Schumann's '82 pageant.

The play is also the story of its hero. The man finds it difficult to fit in, to assume a role. He tries hard to do so, but then is so tense he fucks up. Insofar as it is his story, the play seems merely to make the point that such people exist, and that compassion is due them. He is a little like Woyzeck, really, and the play's theme seems very close to what we might consider *Woyzeck*'s theme. To its tragic hero, outsider and misfit, introspective – Romantic – it juxtaposes job-carrying morons, dumb-bunnies and beasts: with his actually very nice though not particularly bright family on the

626

side-lines: Schumann goes easy on them: kinda old-fashioned people. With heart. Then, in Act 2, a whole bunch of additional people is introduced: the many O.K. people in the outer boroughs, slightly or more than slightly grotesque, it is true, but not on the make, trying for a little personal style – under their circumstances it will have to do in lieu of personality – and (end of Act 6) with a feeling for their fellow man, at least as long as he keeps up appearances. In all, we get something like a typology of the contemporary citizen, a reckoning of the humanist potentials of urbanized industrial bureaucratic society, quite a way beyond the simplicities of Schumann's earlier treatments of The People. Part of the reason for this mellowness, I would say, is that the Diagonal Man is himself[4] – when the Diagonal Man finds himself – or his role? – by leaving the Sanitation Department for a corner on the Bowery, 'there, but for the grace of God, go I!' To some extent focussing on himself in this play, and not just qua artist, nor, as in *Wolkenstein*, in a moral perspective, Schumann could not help but allow some humanity to the Others.

But then again, the play so points up the contrast of the hero to people integrating successfully, assuming one of the identities offered by society, and on the whole – e.g. simply by their masks – characterizes these people so negatively – *as* mask-wearers – that it seems not about an individual, but about role-identification, and in this regard makes a point something like: socializing requires socialization, socialization (in some societies? in contemporary society especially? in all societies?) amounts to being stereotyped, that's bad, but the alternative is to drop out, become (like the Diagonal Man at the end of the play) a drunken bum, and that's as bad or worse, and you probably don't, then, really get to socialize. Even as commiseration with misfits, the play could be seen as plea for a looser, more tentative, perhaps more playful division of labor, and for a set of good, non-demanding, neither foolish nor mean social roles. Both ways, the play seems to advance the communist ideal of a society in which 'each person giving according to his (her) ability and receiving according to his (her) need, the society serv(ing) the individual as much as the individual the society.'

The play was not moving, one didn't care what happened to the hero. It was not terrifying. By and large its effect was humorous, but it was not very funny. It jibed neither with its framing text nor with its prologue, and it had no structure. It marked new directions in Schumann's work: an

---

4. 'To me that, the main character was Peter, you know, and that sort of reveals to me a lot of his biography. I knew his father. I mean, the man to me was his father. And being in hell in the first part. That to me is a lot maybe the war and Peter's demons in his later life. That made things very exciting – and then – (as) we were saying about the drinking of beer the man later he loosens up and at the end of the story he dances and drinks a little bit. Peter is awfully shy about things like singing.' — (Fernandez, interview, '83.)

adaptation of his medium to the traditional direct referent of theatre, the individual, and an interest in this entity. If he had made up his mind what he had to say about this entity, and resolved to say it, it would have been his latest period's big statement of position (corresponding to *Cry, Simple Light*), and might have been a great play.

17. *Josephine the Singer*, February 1984.
A splendid artistic success. On Man's
dangerous but invaluable consolation by
art and on the artist's negligibility.

Josephine the Singer (after Franz Kafka), February 28-March 11, 1984,
Judson Memorial Church, prologue and 2 acts, was a hymn, not without
equivoque, to art and to music in particular, showing music — art — as unifying and consoling social force, the attention to it freeing man from his
numbing immersion in work and from the exercise of his characteristic,
practical cunning, and valuable in these regards not as showing forth of
special gifts, but also presenting it as a danger to man, distracting man
from the dangers man poses to man; and as in no way indicative of any
corresponding grandeur of the artist's — in this play a megalomaniac preoccupied by esteem, and unconcerned with those dangers, indifferent to
the noxiously distracting seductiveness of what he/she is doing, of her art.
The examples of art given, the play itself apart, were a scratchy record of
Kathleen Ferrier's singing of the first of Brahms' four *Serious Songs*, a
high-art Kunstlied, at the beginning of the play, vocalizing by Lyn Spottswood (as 'Josephine'), a young woman with crippled legs, doing her part
— very well — from her wheeled, metallic chair, and by singing by a gifted
trained singer, Remi Boseau, to violin by Schumann, of music of
Schumann's, a very good, modern piece of music. Spottswood's vocalizing
was artfully sustained — with acting out of effort — in a mode in which it is
pleasing enough not to become irritating but was in no way art or beautiful song. The play ends with her doing this lengthily (10 minutes?), while
her suffering-humanity audience ('Grey Lady' puppets) are laid out (killed)
by a minimally enacted air attack (three men on stilts crossing repeatedly
holding small planes overhead, their legs tied to the short stilts outside
their trousers) and their bodies devoured by lions and tigers.

The play, essentially in a musical genre, was beautifully unitary, held together, the off-stage citations from Kafka well subdued, its spectaculars
and divertissements well integrated. Among the divertissements: the
arrival of a popular audience of highly diverse individuals à la *Star Wars*,
animals and men, for a concert chantant by Josephine that turns into a
scene of blackmail, Josephine trying to push through her demand that she
be exempted from the tribe's work requirements — the audience puts on
more of a performance than does Josephine — and some excellent, beautifully mimed clown and baby scenes. Among the spectaculars there was
notably the flight of an angel representing the spirit of music, a stunning
dance in the air. A high point artistically in the history of B&P puppetry,
this number stood out in that history on two further counts: it was tech-

nically sophisticated, something Schumann had, up to the theatre's work with dummies, 1981 onward, which was equally sophisticated technically, consistently and deliberately avoided, and it was created by others than Schumann — 'rigged' by Michael Romanyshyn, 'engineered' by Howard Cantor. The angel swoops down over the stage, hovering protectively, at one point its tail up above its head, over a toy city and its toy city population, its spiritual ministration causing the houses to withdraw in a miracle of rehumanization, leaving only the people, small paper machè 'Johnny puppet' dolls, who are replaced by live unmasked girl actors in white whom it enfolds protectively in its wings and raises up from the ground when under life's burdens they collapse. It swoops — actually breathtakingly — out from the play's framed stage-within-the-stage to hover above us for a great moment, again withdraws into the timbered confines of that stage (a bravura piece of puppeteering technique) has a dance there, dancing from side to side, hovers vertically (at which point Ms. Spottswood in her chair is entered in under its dress from the rear), and rises (disclosing Ms. Spottswood, 'Josephine', looking at us, unconcerned), and for the remainder of the play floats suspended high above the stage and above Josephine the Singer.

The distracting seductiveness of the unitary play's artistry and its relative unconcern — its main focus on the social and personal function of art — with the dangers man poses to man exemplify its thesis on art and on the artist. The Great Angel envelops the kids walking the streets with their big transistor radios blaring or their inaudible Walkman tape cassette players, plugs their ears.

18. The last parade. June 12, '82. A 'No' to fight.
A prayer for spiritual regeneration.

The march and the Central Park rally in New York City on June, '82, originally, since the beginning of the year, promoted by an organization called 'Mobilization for Survival', formally in support of the efforts of the United Nations Parliament on the East River, then in its second Special Session on Disarmament, specifically in support of the movement for a 'nuclear freeze', but in terms of the sentiments expressed by the participants in support of nuclear disarmament, and taken by the media as demonstration of this support, were in terms of the wide range of their sponsors and endorsers,[1] and being, pretty nearly, opposed and suspected of 'communist' inspiration only by the conservative wing of the Republican party and by the people it represents just about as non-partisan and universally representative a demonstration as could be. They not only, though I suppose leftists of one sort or another were among their most active organizers and participants, had nothing 'left' about them, but had no aspects of protest either.[2] The demonstration was not against armament or the arms race or those pushing these, but for disarmament, a distinction that's not a quibble, but a crucial characterization of the demonstration. The grotesque discrepancy between what is needed and its objective, the freeze, perfected its innocuousness. However, it was a gesture pointing to the Great Threat, and its positive (non-protest) character gave it purity, and the multitudes[3] that turned out for it turned out to have beauty.

---

1. 'The rally and march yesterday were planned by a steering committee of 13 organizations, ranging from such religions groups as the Ministerial Interfaith Association and the Riverside Church Disarmament Program to newly formed coalitions of minority groups. Established groups of peace activists such as Mobilization for Survival and SANE were also on the steering committee.

Plans for the rally, which was scheduled to coincide with the Second United Nations Special Session on Disarmament, began about six months ago, with Mobilization for Survival laying much of the groundwork. A benefit sponsored by Performing Artists for Nuclear Disarmament and two concerts by the rock singers James Taylor, Linda Ronstadt and Jackson Browne helped defray the costs of the demonstration.

The June 12 Rally Committee brought together 26 organizations backed by more than 100 national sponsors. Religious groups had a particularly strong representation among the sponsors and on the Rally Committee itself, including, among others, the American Friends Service Committee; the Fellowship of Reconciliation; Pax Christi USA; Progressive National Baptist Convention; PUSH, and the Southern Christian Leadership Conference. The Nuclear Weapons Freeze Campaign-National Conference was also on the rally committee. — (*New York Times*, June 13, '82.)

2. Cf. Appendix XXI.

3. Police estimates of attendance at the rally varied from five to seven hundred thousand. There were not far from half a million in the parade – it was three miles long.

631

Schumann came into town at the end of May to participate in the parade and to do a few other things: put on *Goya* before, *The Story of One* after the parade, do a few outdoor circus shows (in Tompkins Square Park, by the New York Public Library, at Lincoln Center, at the Judson Church) and run workshops to teach people how to do street shows on their own (he was ready to lend masks, costumes and ideas), redo the preceding summer's circus pageant in Prospect Park in Brooklyn the day after the parade and at some point put on a puppet show in Central Park to go with Beethoven's *9th Symphony* as performed by the United Nations Symphony Orchestra. The last two things he didn't get to do, the pageant was rained out, the U.N. Symphony was unwilling. He brought truckloads of puppets (enough for 250 performers, including flag runners, musicians, etc., in the pageant, for 800 marchers in the parade), but only eight or nine puppeteers – the ones he needed for the two theatre shows. He figured on the arrival (by chartered buses) of around a hundred volunteers from Vermont the day before the parade. He needed a few – say 700 – more locally. There had been no advertising. About thirty or forty people showed up on June 2nd at Charas (a Latino community-racket center in the Lower East Side) for the organizational meeting for the pageant, maybe twice that many, but partly the same, for the parade organizational meeting June 7th. He was going to have a run-through dress rehearsal (dress was white – anything – but white) of the pageant June 10th, another at noon the 13th. The New York volunteers were to learn puppet operating (and stilt walking) for pageant and parade (and speeches and a song for the pageant) June 3-11 at Charas. In short, pageant and parade were (but this has been normal for Schumann's work, especially when volunteers were required) high-risk enterprises, and needed to be prepared in an open-ended way allowing for considerable variation in the number of performers eventually available and with an anarchist mixture of permissiveness and discipline. Schumann's appearance was distinctly rakish, his greying thatch composing nicely with his grey beard around his tanned, taut skinned face, crinkled eyes, his shirt, white with blue stripes but faded down to nearly white, clean and soft with wear, over his pants, its tails tied over his belly, its small white buttons open over his tanned youthful chest, his blue wool socks slipping down into his blue and white track shoes, and the strands of some soft material in warm colors that replaced his wristwatch band tied with a minute flourish into a bow.

The assembly area for the march, closed off to traffic, were the blocks between 56th and 47th Streets between 1st and 3rd Avenues, and it was to start at 10 a.m., moving south on 2nd to the U.N., turning west on 42nd, and splitting at 5th Avenue, one contingent moving up 5th, the other up 7th and then up the west side of the park. The Bread and Puppet parade went up 5th.

Endorsed by a wide range of figures, meeting with the tourist's appro-

632

bation of the old people in their Floridian clothes on the sidewalks, animated by, though in no part expressing, wonder of the spirit! the horror of the permanent possibility of death within the next twenty minutes, but rather, beautifully, the rage for expression of those of the living accorded just the little plus of energy for that expression, the parade flowed up the Saturday's anyhow empty 5th Avenue seeming, nevertheless, momentarily to cleanse it of the heavy burden of the traffic's weekday cares: a river of people as people, substituted for crowd, persons for the gasoline-born individuals on their demeaning pursuit of a living. Those thus strolling up the avenue could be said to have been the younger and poorer of the population pool from which they had so selected themselves, but above all, to an encouraging extent, the demonstrators were freaks having sucked out of the vast uneducatedness which is this mercantile system's first rampart against its abolition, forced on the population by its guardians, some choice ideological idiosyncrasy, their very own, and silently or with worn indifference proposing it, some ethical gesture of concern, some sign of this animal's rationality, to the slavish majority. In this manner, the parade was a show of spirit, simply.

The structured parade of Schumann's puppets was integrated into the New York demonstration, which, except for a group of children[4] that preceded it, it lead, as ornament: jewelled pendant of this necklace of the city's. It lent to the vast movement's inchoate welter of home-made ideologies a touch of delicate gaiety – refinement.

He had given his parade the title 'Fight Against the End of the World'. Swelled by the last minute arrival, a tremendous tribute to his evangelical activity up there, of about ten times the number of whiteclad Vermonters he had counted on – more than by any considerable recruitment of New Yorkers – to what I estimated as between 1200 and 1500 participants, it nevertheless had structure. Offering no advice or analysis, no freakish niceties of intellect, it offered images, three in number: the image of a gently loved pre-industrial agricultural world, supposed natural, image of country life and labor (The World: first or white segment of the moving show), the image of destruction, death and sin (crimson and black: the

---

4. Organized by the Children's Campaign for Nuclear Disarmament, the organization Maxie Schumann had been active in. But there were few children – more kids in their late teens, and more grownups, presumably protective parents, than children. Also a quotation from Lenin in re the bourgeoisie.

'. . . and he would like to be in front of the parade. Well, I was listening to WBAI the other night and there were two or three black people talking to two or three brown people and they all intend to be at the head of this parade. They're tired of being left at the back of the parade, they want to be at the front. Why does Peter want to be at head of the parade? Because he wants to be able to load his stuff on people, have his trucks zip up ahead and be able to load back into the trucks, because storage is impossible and theft is ever present, whereas it wasn't in Iran. We put down the rod puppets for King Story and nobody would touch them.' — (George Ashley, interview, '82.)

End of the World, second part), the image of gentle spirituality, of serenity of inwardness and — yes — of detachment (its third part, colorful, ending in white: Fight Against the End of the World). Its front section sub-
liminally, the pretty puppets being admired, may have in many evoked a
feeling for a paradise lost, not so much a Garden of Eden to be attained as
rather the honest world of their forefathers and some imagined gentleness
in a blade of grass. The central stunning part, inferno to the preceding
limbo, playfully alluded to our adolescent visions of hell, to some rampant
Evil in the world, by its withal humorous and fanciful air so cunningly
softening the impact as to cause beholders to see and accept the image as
one of just retribution for their own sins in allowing that gentle world of
nature to be defiled into the cess pool now their place of work (there the
sin) and their abode, modern plastic industrial commerce-obsessed
America. The tail end of the artistic defilé then in the classic manner of
therapy offered these sinners no action — for all remedial action would partake of their corruption — but coollly offered them only the exorbitant demand of their own purification, cleanse yourselves of desire, it said, be
innocent, and said it so as not to be heard — for this would have been
aggression — and yet understood from what had been seen: afterward,
over the night, in the long run. The paraded pageant thus advanced from a
non-existing past through the inward hell of the present to an impossible
future. All this, of course, in very colorful images, the pure whiteness of its
very last part in the glittering greyness of the city's windows and supporting structures the most colorful of all, thus primordially a gay show of
gaiety exuding a gay air, in stark relief from the, in contrast, nearly brutish
spiritual turmoil presented by the march in general (mirror image of the interior of the passive onlookers, a confrontative effect ultimately terribly
and endearingly human). The artifacts displayed seemed precious as well
as ingenious, their variety astounded, their size made an impression of
opulence.

The peculiar aspect of a parade show is that though it is a line, a
moving one, a fact you are conscious of both because it keeps coming at
you and unlike a movie keeps leaving you behind — offered to you in its
successive arrivals but, self-subsistent, withdrawing itself from you in its
continual departure — it is taken in very much in fragments, reaching you
(jostled, your perception already fractured by the street scene's physicality)
as what it is right then and there, happening upon you as a series of discrete visual explosions at best tenuously ordered in the back of your mind.
Schumann's parade, at 10 a.m., before it started moving, was two blocks
long. After only an hour or so (it took four hours), distended by stops for
traffic lights and by an influx of late Vermonters as well as by the lags
natural to any interrupted sequential movement of people, it stretched over
some ten to twleve blocks and its passage then past a given point or observer may have taken as much as 45 minutes. Nevertheless, so strong was

Schumann's shaping of it (and his success in imposing a uniform white and in suppressing independent contributions, be it of signs or puppets),[5] that the statement it made as a whole, even unto its syntax, remained reasonably clear. It made a statement, and a syntactically complex one. Its statement may be rendered:

'O Lord how wondrous beautiful is not this living earth! (First or white segment of the moving show.) And yet how full of black corruption and crimson seed of self destruction! (Second or crimson and black segment.) May childlike mirth and calm serenity preserve its worth! (Third or colorful segment, ending on white.)'

It was a statement in the mode of a prayer, and a complex one – A, but B, so C – and the fragmentation of its syntax was the more undesirable as the isolated intake of its parts would have had undesirable effects: reverentially contented delight (Part I), grimness and the exhilaration of despair (Part II), gaiety, boisterous or mute but myopic (Part III). But, I believe, thanks to his artistic power and discipline, the statement pretty much tended to come across as a whole. I.e. most watchers got a meaning out of his parade and their understandings of it varied somewhere in the region of the one I have indicated. Schumann's communicational amibition went even further, however. Each of the three parts of the parade, as I have tried to indicate in my verse, was itself compound. 'Wondrous beauty' and 'life' were distinctly indicated in its first part, 'corruption' and 'destruction' in its second; and the spiritual state that its third part indicated constitutes the potential for an effective fight against the End of the World – or, more probably, nothing in the parade indicating a fight ac-

---

5. 'Well, it's interesting that his record is a little bit lost in the confusion, because the first meeting we went to which was at The Theater For The New City, while he was closing down the last show and going away – whatever that last show was – *Fear* – the place was packed with people who all wanted to be involved in Peter Schumann's parade. Nevertheless, regardless of age – there were a lot of people who were around in the '60s who were sculptors and painters, who wanted to paint dragons and make puppets and make masks, who had no understanding that he was designing the parade. That it was his puppets, his idea – the color is red, now, red is going to be the – they all wanted to bring a puppet dragon or a mask or a banner and he had a very difficult time trying to explain to them, please keep your banners. Walk at the end of the parade or some other place. Stay out of my ... Now we have these people who didn't seem to learn much – who were totally insensitive. And there were grade school teachers who said, now, I've got my 4th grade class and we'll all make a small sign for the children to carry in the parade. And Peter said, I don't like to exploit children for political causes, you know, don't bring them. Especially, don't bring them with little American flags or United Nations flags. I'd rather they would not come. But he was having a great deal of difficulty in dissuading people from joining his parade with a lot of crap, because he really wants to have an artistic structure to it.' — (George Ashley, interview, '82.)

The Bread and Puppet contingent's white served as background and part of a meaningful color scheme. It, to an extent was a self-preserving feature in that it discouraged people not in white and not in some way supporting the effect of his puppets, possibly carrying extraneous signs, from joining his part of the march.

tually, the attaining to which constitutes that fight itself — was also complex: something like 'childlike mirth' and 'calm serenity' tempering one another. And there were transitions, nuances and qualifications, though these were less clear and less surely attributable to Schumann's intent: Part I on wondrous beauty and life ended on a warning note (warning signs, a prophet), a connective to Part II; the appearance of Uncle Sam with a merry entourage of capitalists, but with a cop puppet balanced by a blue, white and red Peace Hand puppet at the end of the End of the World section, suggesting that as a nation America was on the negative side, but not irrevocably nor unambiguously so, made a transition to the Fight Against the End of the World section;[6] and the imagery of Section III that evoked the hopefulness of spiritual simplicity ('childlike mirth', 'calm serenity') also evoked, in succession, the cheery sturdiness of a natural life and supernatural grace, and so carried the suggestion that man's spiritual potentials might not guarantee salvation, but required extraterrestrial guidance or even interference, an ambiguity or ambivalence probably in Schumann's mind also: but not making that final section less a statement, nor the whole parade less a prayer.

Schumann for his grand reappearance in the streets of New York had successfully compacted his Vermont pageantry into a street demonstration. There were two big differences from the old days, however: he wasn't challenging his audience (they weren't meddling in Vietnam, they were threatened by the atom bomb, he addressed them as potential victims, not as perpetrators), and he really wasn't asking them to fight. He was leading them in a prayer that he presumed (if not actually, then by the form of his parade) had in this age of plenty and atom bombs as their daily prayer replaced the Lord's Prayer anyhow, a prayer for spiritual regeneration.

*　　*　　*

The parade.

'The World' announced by ghostly white-faced announcers. Loud, clear voices. Clown costumes.

An ox-drawn cart with a dense band of small, deeply colored paper maché figures on it, seated together, small, bulky women, Elkas. Many small Elkas. Lovely. Above them hangs The Glove, an opaque Japanese lantern.[7]

---

6. The originally announced 'procession' order — 'very much subject to change' — had Uncle Sam and his entourage near the head of Section II (End of the World), preceded only by red devils on foot, cymbals, stilted dragons and horn demons, a still earlier intention of having him preceded also by hell (the 'Yama bus') having been abandoned (the bus was to conclude the section). By June 8, he was still to be up there near the head, but the original position of hell ahead of him had been restored. His eventual position June 12, following the 'Yama bus' at the end of the section apparently was due to the late start of the bus.

7. By the time the parade got up around 65th Street, each of its lovely little vertebrae was

636

White stars carried on sticks.

White stars walking on stilts.

A three-headed white cow. It pulls a half moon on a bamboo pole on a small platform with two wheels. The slender moon has two slender veils floating from it.

Black and white horses, each with two bridle attendants. One-man puppets.

White deer inching forward. They walk with small bended steps, their knees springy with native caution.

White masked oriental women guiding plows. The plows are pulled by donkeys with carton donkey heads and burlap bodies.

Twirlers of gauze banners and white stilt ponies, the ponies' rectangular box bodies fret-patterned in black like archaic Greek vases, a dozen of them, all light and gay, in rows, five and five, bowing in unison, circus menage fashion, little merry-go-round ponies with fairy tale book illustration heads. Long, tongue-narrow silk twirls of the banners.

A flock of large gulls, seven slender delicate birds on 15-ft. poles, one for the body, one for each wing. Gulls' cries.

(The cops. Grave expressions over instrumental clothes. They are finding refuge in their job.)

(The puppet parade sweeps the street with Sunday. But the march in toto, peopling the street, reminds people of their concern for people. The buildings become insignificant. The march is exerting no action on the buildings; there is no contest; they are just not there, not even backdrop.)

Conch blowing, a barely eery soughing, the voice of ghosts. Signs of warnings: 'Hold it', 'Stop', 'Watch out', 'No'. Their carriers cry the words. They act out warning in their voices. They surround a giant stick animal, the one called 'The Prophet', black and white, with a corrugated brow, its spinal mane a mass of rags strident in the sun.[8]

An old fashioned soldier in tight black carrying a sign *End of the World* surrounded by skeleton puppets in small black hats, their big white heads over their dangling, jerking jointed limbs jigging ten ft. up, three-toed, clad in sheets with black words and pictures of death on them. As they advance, they are dancing to a military drum beat, up for three beats, down on a beat, down for three beats, up again.[9]

---

surrounded by a throng of figures in white, often – since Schumann had managed to distribute music throughout his parade – more or less dancing, at any rate moving gaily. E.g. the world cart by about two dozen, the moon following it by another two dozen, the horses, deer and plowing Vietnamese women by perhaps four dozen, etc. The clown heralds had bells, the world cart chime ringers, the stars again bells along with them.

8. By 65th Street, four dozen or more warners accompanied the Prophet. There were not that many signs.

9. They are lifted up, the center pole held at its bottom and above, their legs and arms dangling. Held up, the tops of the small black hats are 10-11 feet above the ground. They

Death on a horse, both skeletons of wooden bones, gigantic, released by the strangled lamb's undoing of the fourth seal.[10]

(The Bread and Puppet procession is working as theatre at this point – there is something like a story. It is paralleled by a march of 'ordinary people', i.e. freaks, next to it, on the left side of the street – the 'real' demonstration. But there is no confusion visually.)

Large death flags, 3 ft. by 4 ft., on 6 ft. poles, twirled. Same as the garb of the skeletal dancing men. Cortege of the triumphal rider.

A halloween mass of butchers, somber faced retailers, black and white, welfare administrators. With compact grey beasts, leashed, straining, dark sniffing beasts.

(These are all puppets for fun. The fright is inside of them. In the Book

---

are raised and lowered to the drum beat: abruptly raised and lowered, on a beat, held at either level for two or three beats (not that easy to do!). The sudden interruptions of the steady positions have an exciting, upsetting effect. The somber, not really skeletal or skull (but blackly pitted for eyes, mouth, ears) heads shake up there, high, i.e. dangle foolishly back and forth even as they bob with the rising and falling poles. Black prints of skeleton men on the two sheets, sewn together, cover their fronts and backs, with words such as 'Byby', 'Darkness', 'Yes', 'Field', 'Home', 'Night', 'Office', 'Car' illustrated by the pictures, e.g. 'Yes' goes with a descent into a grave or a prone position in a white rectangle in the black underground. These black and white prints on the white dresses of the jointed stick-men with the small black hats are some of the best graphic work Schumann has done, e.g. 'Evening', with death pulling the curtain away from darkness, perhaps grinning. Or 'Home', where seated death with hands lifted seems to welcome a very old bearded man with a crooked cane, perhaps is just keeping him company.

10. Cf. Dürer's *Apocalypse* series, the *Four Horsemen*. Schumann's Death is of a royal size (three times a man's), and has a mount to match. Death as fate, not as oppositional force. He is not mean looking. His mouth is grim, his hollow eyes look upward, but his expression is unconcerned – like the butchers following him he has a job to do, is in the scheme of things: like them he almost looks imposed upon. He is not merely privative. The traditional appreciation. In this parade, however, he represents something else in addition: he comes riding along as a threat and danger, and we see him as an opposant also, capable of spreading his empire within the realm of life, the smell of plastic in a car, the shoddy cooling system around the core of an atom plant, the dumbness of an ill-taught ghetto child. This non-traditional reference of the death figures would have been syntactically more evident if they had, as had originally been planned, followed, rather than preceded the figures of evil: death as havoc wreaked by evil. Death has a single black and (dirty) white ribbon from each shoulder – abstraction of a cape. The horse's rib cage – a construct of 1×4s – dangles from its long high backbone, its wooden mane mounts drily to its neck, which is the upper part of the vertical pole that carries its head. It could be said to be blind. It has spittle hanging from its mouth. Death's pelvic bone is the only handsome piece of wood that he and his horse have between them: penis, barbed. Death has three carriers, the horse four. To make the horse move right, its carriers should do a 'real kick dance' – lifting their knees as high as they can. The motion of horse and rider, a parade grand strut, to the heavy drums (threatening as when someone is executed) is powerful: the majesty of great power, as in the spread of an epidemic. For the Brooklyn pageant, Death was to mount the horse, the horse was to rear up, then trot off, whinnying as it sets out (the whinnies from the band).

of Revelation, this whole section is the 'Hell that follows the rider called Death'.)

Salesmen in businessmen's black and white, scurvy-looking creatures with little moustaches, briefcases: engaging in salesmanship, gesticulating.

Stilted fox demons, two tiny ones, five taller, real vertical ones. Green-snouted, jackal-faced dragons on stilts.

An ominous physician and an angel of death (George Bartenieff, Crystal Field.)

Red screaming wolf birds, their wings multicolored, two of them in cock fights, fifteen feet up in the air.

(By way of the salesmen, dealers in death and defrauders, we have advanced from the realm of death into the realm of evil. The fox demons look depraved, the wolf birds real nasty.)

Big, ulcerous, convoluted black and red megaphone mouths, faces all mouth. They trumpet rawly overhead. Garden hoses go from the mouths of their carriers up to them. Calypso music and scampering small red demons, dwarf spirits of maliciousness – kids.

(The puppets in this section in all their silliness disclose, sugar-coated in their beauty, remote in their form of child-age legend, some of contemporary life's true horror. Not club-wise, but stiletto-wise.)

Red headed saurian monsters, their carriers snake dancing with their tails to the Trinidad beat. Birds. A small green dragon.

A big red bus made up as hell, clanking and clattering along, its arms and pole-held bloody fists outstretched, grasping, dragon-headed, quite unbelievable. A picture, though, of the real thing.[11]

Uncle Sam Schumann on the extra long stilts, the mast-heights of his overalls' legs extrapolated by their stars-and-stripes, bare chested, his muscled chest tanned, his beard dim under his Uncle Sam tomfoolery stovepipe hat, stalking, surrounded by smiling capitalists, in a dancy step. The capitalists, ugly buggers, amiable grotesques, are asphalt-bound beneath this soaring figure, its clients more than its patrons, paunchy. In his entourage there is also a club-carrying Keystone cop and a child-size all-fingers Peace Sign Hand puppet, red, white and blue.

A brass band. It plays Dixieland Jass. Schumann, up ahead, is its leader and dances to it. Infectious, no way funky.

Signs, 'Fight Against the End of the World', two of them, carried by two clowns with bulbous head masks like bulldog heads. Also an announcer, announcing the title through a small bullhorn. Music by a quartet, bagpipes, a violin.

---

11. Like all other puppets done quite *crudely*, the bus is of course quite visibly a bus. The red fabric gapes in places so you can see the touring bus's gay cover pictures, a landscape in blue, and grain, flowers and clouds. Thanks to this negligence you can see man's world in flames. Or understand that blood and fire can make this world into a hell.

(In spite of the placement of the signs — which are easily missed — whether the eclectically patriotic Uncle Sam assembly is the tail end of the Death and Evil or the lead of the Simple Folks and Redemption section now coming up and figuring the potential for Good is ambiguous. Schumann probably thought of it as a transition, ambiguous in itself. Most viewers probably without reflection saw it the second way. The ambiguity is dwarfed by the parade as a whole: the pre-emption of the wide street canyon by a river of humanity expressing itself.)

A charming troup of two dozen tiny but bosom-heavy and upholstered washerwomen followed by equally small-seeming middle-aged working men — street cleaners: they are using their brooms and rags and little shovels to actually clean the street — a little. This proletariat of producers of cleanliness and neatness is preceded by a dense troop of fresh faced young carriers of small flags with colored pictures of the washerwomen on them, followed by another holding up small standards with the names of good things printed in color — 'day', 'sun', 'tree', etc. (After so many masks one sees these maskless demonstrators with pleasure, almost with astonishment — or even relief. Their faces are open. Their gay and modest emblems, foolishly small-formated, are similarly refreshing.) A woman carries a sign that is a red heart. At the edge of the procession, she holds it up to us as though a personal declaration.

(The march does not have a continuous flow, but a stop-and-go pattern. Disrupting the succession of the images, but allowing us to dwell on each.)

A small string band playing Blue Grass music.

Twirled flags. (Twirled flags aerate the parade.) Again pictures of washerwomen — working washerwomen, bending over, in blue circles, blue for water.[12]

Three giantesses, washerwoman effigies, abreast, a fourth behind them, their cheery garments country flower gardens — and they carry bouquets. They are pulled on small two-wheeled carriages, girls, sometimes dancing to the country music up ahead or to the kazoos in the mouths of players of carton cutouts of horns that follow them hold up their very big hands: moving them gently. (When the march stops and there happens to be no music, the sound of an airplane may be ominous overhead. On such a stop, one of the young women was looking up at the hand she held and moved it as though in love with it.)

(When early on during the parade I'd seen it up to here for the first time, I no longer felt a story was emerging, but just good will: people seemed to feel flattered that so much trouble had been taken for them. A grateful public.)

---

12. This is the section that during the later part of the parade most people have joined: five, six hundred from the brass band back to the giant washerwomen that follow these flag twirlers.

A group with flags that within solid green circles have black witches waving black flags.

(A female principle of anarchy? But Schumann probably brought along a lot of extra stuff not for sense in his show's statement, but lightening and agreeable filler accomodating perception.)

A yellow, an orange and a purple midnight sun or fantastic planet, enlargements of stars in the spectrum of fire cooled by distance: very tall, narrow stilt-walkers, the flat, flame-bordered puppet head face of each the same color as her tassel costume, the live face agreeably discernible among the strips of felt just below the enigmatic star face. The sound of an accordion embellishes their careful, detached gait.

A flock of yellow grain signs. Large signs of flowers on blue squares.

A herd of inoffensive cows, mauvishly pink, drifting in loose formation in the manner of cows returning from pasture in the evening. The spots on their skins seem to be faces — the faces of Negroes.

On long poles, flowers on white banners so far up the pole-carriers seem jugglers rather than demonstrators.

(The parade fragments into charming detail.)

(Circulating rapidly, I saw the parade several times over. At some point early on, four people abreast carrying large doll corpses followed the flowers. If only by their grimness they were aliens in Schumann's parade. The sign carried by the small congregation of punk individuals in street clothes following them said 'God made the Earth. Men will make it a Sun.' One of them had in large red writing added to the small print of a sign he carried. 'US and USSR Nuclear Freeze', a sign also seen elsewhere outside of Schumann's contingent. 'Go For It, Australia.' The group did not identify itself. When I asked one of them what its name was, she after a moment's hesitation, as though not wanting to identify it, said it had no name. Their grimness benefitted from the gaiety preceding them. The sound attending them, drumming, had the quality of a death rattle. It came from the group surprisingly following *them*, a small group of Buddhist orientals with whom, on their initiation, I exchange bows and smiles. They were chanting OM, and giving body to their voices by beating hand-mirror-shaped, flat-handled circular drums perhaps a quarter of an inch thick: the 'death rattles' I had just heard. Under the group's visual aspect of peaceable courtesy, the deep hollow sound of these instruments carried no reference to death.)

A flute and violins. Elka is playing the small flute, her grey hair in a bun.

A Madonna, alfalfa green, 15 ft. tall, the Child tiny in her far forward strangely turned hands. Imposing herald of an even more grandiose 20 ft. tall bronze Madonna and Child. They advance in a stately manner, each carried by two operators hidden under their dress which is billowed out by a large group of attendants. Their garments are spring-sky blue and the

641

white of clouds, and are hemmed by green, hilly landscapes. Grey veils float from their benign giant faces.[13] On arrests they rotate slowly with the circle of their attendants.

A boat, as long as a Viking ship, its blue hull floating in the air, all *people* under its blue square sail, the fabric band of the hull (held up by the passengers) decorated by a frieze of white figures tumbling, arms uplifted, into swirling white water — as though falling into it from a height rather than caught by rising flood water — and the sail is a painting of a cloud-white tree on which grow white houses, a sail hopeful of a port attainable. The ship is a puppet with a face, blue also, man-high, orange-lipped, shield on the prow. Graffiti on the head — among other words the word 'Children' — proclaim the boat 'The Ark'.

(The parade's displays are very big now. Also white and blue — peaceful. Airy.)

A huge bird, all air of white muslin, a super kite. It has a vast human head, forward-tending of carton: a female face, white also, cut in profile.[14]

(This was the final image. Its last two images end the Bread and Puppet part of the parade on a tremendous upbeat. Their size and airiness and relation to the sky gave them a fading reverberation precluding the disappointment and the dismissive gesture of a more compact and definite final image such as, e.g. that of the Madonnas would have been, whose sustained organ note they resolve into something just short of jubilance. Showmanship!)

(But the Bread and Puppet parade was followed by hundreds of thousands of people. Watching for a while afterward, I saw many marching grimly or simply depressedly, thus reporting on the quality of their lives. And most seemed at only slight remove from their lives: one saw a habitual gesture of abortive protest against a fate. Or perhaps rather, perhaps, a show of consciousness.)

(There were other giant puppets than Schumann's in the parade. E.g. three twenty-foot-tall ones paraded by the 'Heart of the Beast Theatre', Minneapolis. The mark of these other puppets was the lack of artistic intelligence of their makers. Not only could one not from their appearance say what they stood for, but they did not seem to be symbols at all. They were unreal. One could measure Schumann's achievement by these failures. His puppets invariably seem meaningful, denotative of essence. They refer to

---

13. Their faces are tall and shallow: perhaps only 6 inches deep but easily three feet high. They have long necks, at least four feet in length. Each has perhaps twenty attendants, holding the hem of its dress.
14. The head of this Peace Dove/Angel of Peace is held up by a long metal pole. This apparently requires some strength. The visible strain is in contrast to the head's calmness. Its frizzled wings are held out by light-weight wooden poles. Its very long tail, a rectangular piece of fabric, is held down against the air by two strings from its rear corners.

reality. They derive their power from this even when their precise or full denotation escapes you, as mostly perhaps it does. Artistic intelligence having been active in their formation, their appearance guarantees you a meaning.)[15]

The Bread and Puppet marchers other than some hundreds of the adventitious Vermonters, the really Bread and Puppet marchers, did not join the rally at the end of the march route, but turned off east and dismantled in two pleasantly affluent Upper East Side blocks (73rd to both sides of Madison Avenue) in which the rented U-Haul trucks were waiting. The crowd of them in those two blocks around 2 o'clock in the afternoon – after four hours of marching plus an hour or two before 10 a.m. getting into the gear – presented in its elegant and very clean whites almost the aspect of a picnic or afternoon tea party or of a crowd of elegants at some fashionable race meet; clearly an elite, physically, physiognomically, psychologically, their stance predominantly one of non-commital reserve, the expression of pleasure at being among one's likes that would have marked a merely middle class grouping repressed this genuine superior status had already been in evidence in the exterior aspects of the unmasked among the Bread and Puppet marchers during the march, the hundreds of carriers of discreetly indirect or whimsical Bread and Puppet signs, and carriers and twirlers of an astounding and clearly differentiate variety of species of image-bearing Bread and Puppet banners, streamers and flags. They were better looking than the gross of the 100000s of other marchers and more in the possession of their intellects, their faces speaking of the social breathing space that had allowed them a turn to a calm devotion to abstractly universal concerns.) They were, grosso modo, upper class.

The *Fight Against the End of the World* parade suggested a predicament: Schumann had magnificently perfected his instrument of communication but he had nothing more to say. Not that he didn't have opinions. Nor that he didn't feel strongly about them. But there seemed to be, for him, no longer any point in expressing them.

'You know, you turn back to your ancient prophets in the Old Testament and the signs foretelling Armageddon, and I find myself wondering if – if we're the generation that's going to see that coming about. I don't know if you've noted any of those prophecies lately, but believe me, they certainly describe the times we're going through.'

(Ronald Reagen to the executive director of the American-Israeli Public Affairs Committee, *The Jerusalem Post*, October 28, '83.)

---

15. Artistic intelligence: working out of one's center. Not working toward preformulated effect. For this substitutes for the brain's cooperation with the heart the loan of the presumed categories of others.

'Neue Welt,

und es hängt, ein ehrn Gewölbe, der Himmel über uns, es lähmt Fluch die Glider der Menschen, und die erfreuenden Gaben der Erde sind wie Spreu, es spottet unser mit ihren Geschenken die Mutter, und alles ist Schein –

O wann, wann
        schon öffnet sich
        die Flut über die Dürre

Aber wo ist er?
        dass er beschwöre den lebendigen Geist'
                                                (Hölderlin, *Neue Welt . . .*)

'Die Schönheit ist den Kindern eigen,
Ist Gottes Ebenbild vielleicht.
Ihr Eigentum ist Ruh und Schweigen,
Den Engeln auch zum Lob gereicht.'
                                                (Hölderlin, *Die Schönheit.*)

Bibliography and some other references

Selective bibliography and some other references.

1. Some texts of Peter Schumann's.

Bread and Puppet Theater. Pamphlet #1. Apparently a draft, undated, of the program note for *The Puppet Christ*, Easter 1964. Published as first part of Schumann, *Bread and Puppets: A Way of Life*, 1965.

Bread and Puppet Theatre ... at Cate Farm. In: *Goddard Trimester Calendar 1971-1972.* Educational Resources for Spring 1971. Goddard College, Plainfield, Vermont, n.d.

Bread and Puppet White Horse Butcher. The Janus Press, West Burke, Vt., 1977.

Bread and Puppets: A Way of life. In: Motive, February 1965, p28-29. According to Kourilsky, 1971, p247, footn.*, written in 1963.

Bread and Puppets. Program note, Spencer Memorial Church, Brooklyn, Easter 1964, *The Puppet Christ.* Also in: tdr, The Drama Review, vol. 14, no. 3, 1970.

Christmas Story. Charcoal Drawings. Sing Out, December 1968.

(Interview.) tendenzen, Jahrgang 7, No. 41-42, November 1966 – February 1967, Munich.

Problems Concerning Puppetry and Folkmusic in the Light of God and MacNamara. In: Sing Out, February-March 1967. Reprinted in: Puppetry Journal, July-August 1973, and in: Sainer (A.), The Radical Theatre Notebook, 1975.

Puppen und Masken. Das Bread and Puppet Theater. Ein Arbeitsbericht von Peter Schumann. Bilder von Wayne Greene. Fischer Taschenbuch Verlag, Frankfurt, 1973.

St. Francis Preaches to the Birds. Janus Press, West Burke, Vt., 1978.

The Story of the Love and Marriage of the River Winooski and Lake Champlain. Scripts, October 1972.

This is. Janus Press, West Burke, Vt., 1980.

Touring Europe. Silo, Spring of 1972.

An interview with Peter Schumann (by Helen Brown and Jane Seitz). tdr, The Drama Review, vol. 12, no. 2, winter 1968.

2. Articles.

Appleby (Michael) *Revolutionary Change in the urban environment.* In: Long (Priscilla), *The New Left.* Porter Sargent, Boston, 1969.

Argelander (Ron) *Bread and Puppet's Domestic Resurrection. The War is Over.* The Soho Weekly News, August 19, 1976.

Barab (Margarita) *Interview with Peter Schumann.* Country Journal, Plainfield, Vt., July 18, 1974.

Brecht (Stefan) *Peter Schumann's Bread and Puppet Theatre.* tdr, The Drama Review, vol. 14, no. 3, 1970.

Dennison (George) *Fire.* tdr, The Drama Review, vol. 14, no. 3, 1970.

du Vignal (Ph.) *Peter Schumann. Interview exclusive. Des vertus plus simples et plus profondes.* L'Art Vivant, no. 6, December 1969.

Estrin (Marc) *Guerilla Theatre from the American Playground.* tdr, The Drama Review, vol. 13, no. 4, summer 1969.

Goldensohn (Barry) *Peter Schumann's Bread and Puppet Theater.* The Iowa Review, vol. 8, no. 2, spring 1977.

Gustaitis (Rasa) *Bread and Puppet: The Children build a Children's Theatre*. Village Voice, September 1, 1966.

Herms (Dieter) *Mime Troupe, El Teatro, Bread and Puppet – Ansätze zu einem politischen Volkstheater in den USA*. Maske und Kothurn. 1973 (?) 1974 (?)

Hoagland (Edward) *Let them have bread and puppets*. Vanity Fair, July 1983. Cited as Hoagland, *Let 'em*.

Karasek (H.) *Traumatische Genauigkeit*. Theater Heute, February 1972.

Kourilsky (Françoise) *Peter Schumann's Bread and Puppet Theatre. Dada and Circus*. tdr, The Drama Review, vol 18, no. 1, March 1974.

Munk (Erika) *tdr comment*. tdr, The Drama Review, vol. 14, no. 3, 1970.

Nichols (Robert) *Christmas Story, 1962*. tdr, The Drama Review, vol. 14, no. 3, 1970.

Rabin (Jules) *Vietnam: Theory and Theater*. Liberation, March 1966.

Reade (Ben) *The Demonic Protest of the Breat and Puppet Theater*. Renewal, April-May 1967.

Rough (William H.) *The Bread and Puppet Theater. Interview with Peter Schumann*. Dramatics, December 1973.

Schlecht (Monika) *Sie tanzen sich an die Spitze*. Süddeutsche Zeitung, May 9, 1960.

Shank (Theodore) *The Bread and Puppet's Anti-Bicentennial: A Monument to Ishi*. Theatre Quarterly, vol. V, no. 19, 1975.

Sheehy (Gail) *Giving Them Bread and Puppets*. New York Herald Tribune, March 22, 1964.

Sterritt (D.) *Many-Sided Bread and Puppet Man*. Christian Science Monitor, February 9, 1973.

Towsen (John) *The Bread and Puppet Theatre. The Stations of the Cross*. The Drama Review, vol. 16, no. 3, September 1972.

Waldron (Eli) *The new American capital of Bohemia*. Photography by Marvin Lichtner. Saturday Evening Post, May 23, 1964.

Wren (Victoria) *a child's New York*. Village Voice, March 3, 1966.

Zand (Nicole) *'C'est le réveil du monde et nous battons les cymbales', Peter Schumann et l'eclatement du 'Bread and Puppet')*, Le Monde, Paris, November 12, 1970.

3. Books.

Bread and Puppet Masaccio. L'Arte della Fragilita e la Cartepesta. Intervento del Bread and Puppet a Firenze in Toscana 1976/1977. Commune di Fierence, Istituto statale d'arte di Firenze. Centro Studi teatrali di Firenze, 1977.

Dupavillon (Christian), George (Etienne) *Black and White Shows. Bread and Puppet Theatre. Spectacles en noir et blanc*. (Photographie de Etienne George, textes de Chr. Dupavillon.) Les Loges, Paris, 1978.

Fernandez (Benedict) *In Opposition. Images of American Dissent in the '60s*. Da Capo Press, New York City, 1968.

Fine (Ruth E.) *The Janus Press 1975-80. Catalogue raisonné*. Robert Hull Flemming Museum, The University of Vermont, Burlington, Vt., 1982.

Gordon (Larry) (ed.) *The Word of Mouth Early American Songbook*. Published by the Word of Mouth Chorus, Plainfield, Vt., 1975.

Gordon (Larry) (ed.(?)) *The Word of Mouth Roundbook*. The Word of Mouth Chorus, Plainfield, Vt., 1973.

Haskins (James), *The War and the Protest/Viet Nam*, Doubleday, New York City, 1971.

Heilmayer (Jens), Frölich (Pea) *now/Theater der Erfahrung*, Verlag M. Dumont Schauberg, Köln, 1971.

Jotterand (Franck) *Le nouveau théâtre américain*. Eds. du Seuil, Paris, 1970.

Kourilsky (Françoise) *Le Bread and Puppet Théâtre*. La Cité, Lausanne, 1971.

Lesnick (Henry) (ed.) *Guerilla Street Theater*. Avon Books, New York City 1973.

Mueller (John E.) *War, Presidents and Public Opinion*. Wiley, New York City, 1973.

Power (Thomas) *The War at Home. Vietnam and the American People*, 1964-1968. Grossman, New York, 1973.

Radical Theatre Festival. San Francisco State College. September 1968. The San Francisco Mime Troupe, San Francisco, California, 1969.

Roose-Evans (James) *Experimental theatre from Stanislavsky to today*. New revised edition. Universe Books, New York City, 1973.

Sainer (Arthur) *The Radical Theatre Notebook*. Avon Books, New York City, 1975.

Schevill (J.) *Break Out! In Search of New Theatrical Environments*. The Swallow Press, Chicago, 1975.

Schumann (Elka) *The Dream of the Dirty Woman*. Janus Press, West Burke, Vt., 1980.

Taylor (K.) *People's Theatre in America*. Drama Book Specialists, New York City, 1972.

Warhol (Andy), Hackett (Pat), *POPism/The Warhol '60s*, Harper & Row, New York, 1980.

Zaroulis (Nancy), Sullivan (Gerald), *Who Spoke Up? American Protest against the War in Vietnam*. 1963-1975. New York City, 1984.

4. Interviews cited in this book. Unless otherwise mentioned conducted by S. Brecht.

Ashley (George). New York City, v/5/82.

Ashley (George). New York City, ii/4/81.

Bissinger (Karl). New York City, ix/12/79.

Eckhardt (Bruno). Mühlheim, Germany, v/18/83.

Ernstthal (Bob). San Francisco, California, v/79.

Fernandez (Carlene). Plainfield, Vt., iii/4/83.

Konnoff (George). New York City. i/29/83.

Leherrissier (Irene). New York City. vi/79.

Levy (Murray). New York City. viii/21/79.

Lippen (Mary = Mary Benson). New York City, x/5/79.

Oyle (Dr. Irving). Santa Cruz, California, iv/30/79.

Palmer (Helen). Berkley, Californiz, v/1/79.

Schumann (Elka). Glover, Vt., iii/2/83.

Schumann (Peter), Schumann (Elka). Interviewed by Ephraim Schumann, x/79.

Schumann (Peter). New York City, December, 1982. (Schumann, interview, December '82. Photos.)

Schumann (Peter). Glover, Vt., viii/31/82 and ix/1/82. (Schumann, interview, '82.)

Schumann (Peter). New York City, iii/83.

Schumann (Peter). New York City, xii/22/83.

Sherman (Margo Lee). New York City, vi/11/79 and vi/20/79.

Sherman (Margo Lee). New York City, vi/29/82.

Shapli (Professor Omar). New York City, ix/13/79.

Starosky (Dieter). Bad Brückenau, Germany, v/17/83.

5. Films.

A Man Says Goodbye to His Mother. 17½ minutes, Black and white 16 mm. movie with sound, made by Andy Trompetter, at the Old Courthouse, 2nd Ave. and 2nd Street, New York City, November 25, 1967. (According to: '*Bread and Puppet Diary, November 1967-March 1968*'.)

A Man Says Goodbye to His Mother. According to Dupavillon and George, *Black and White Shows*, a black and white videotape of a performance of this play at the Astor Library Building in 1967 was made by Lewis Friedman for P.B.S. National Educational Television.

Birdcatcher in Hell. According to Schumann, interview, '79, 'two Frenchmen' made a movie of a performance in a Harlem parking lot of the 1964/65 first ('blue') version of this play for UNESCO.

Birdcatcher in Hell. According to Schumann, interview, '79, a movie was made of the second ('red') version of this play in January or February 1972 for French television.

The Birdcatcher in Hell. According to Dupavillon and George, *Black and White Shows*, a film of a performance of this play was made by ORTF, Service de la Recherche, in France in 1971. (Most probably this is the film Schumann, interview, 1979, assigns to 1972.)

Bread and Puppets. 'Street theatre during an April 24, 1971 (Washington, D.C.) mass anti-war march.' Ten minute videotape, listed in the Community Video Catalogue, vol. I, no. 1, winter 1971, of the Community Video Center, Federal City College, Division of Community Education, 1411 K. St. NW, Washington, D.C.

Chicken Little. A movie of c. 20 minutes' duration shot by Jules Rabin, of the Bread and Puppet Theatre's work with slum kids in the 'Parks project' of the summer of 1966. It was often shown by the Bread and Puppet Theatre during the later 1960s. According to Mary Lippen, interview, 1979, it includes film of *The Man on the Park Bench* and of *The Hungry Young Man.*

The Christmas Story. According to Oyle, interview, 1979, Dr. I. Oyle made an 8-mm. movie of a 1960s performance, and in 1979 had the film.

Christmas Story. According to a letter of the xi/21/81, from the Rev. Glenesk to George Ashley, a film was made of a 1960s performance at the Spencer Memorial Church, Brooklyn, and is in the archives of the Division of Mass Media of the Presbyterian Church.

Dance of Death. According to a personal communication from Richard O. Tyler in 1979, his wife, Dorothy Baer, made a film of the performance of this piece, September 22, 1962, at Putney School, Putney, Vt., and at that time still had it in her possession.

Dance of Death. According to the archives of R.O. Tyler, a film was made by Ray Wiskowski (Wyzynski (?)) of the performance of this dance May 30, 1962 at the Judson Memorial Church, New York City.

Dead Man Rises. According to Dupavillon and George, *Black and White Shows*, a black and white videotape of a performance of this play at the Astor Library Building in 1967 was made by Lewis Friedman for P.B.S. National Educational Television.

The Grey Lady Cantata #2. According to Dupavillon and George, *Black and White Shows*, a film of a performance of this play was made by ORTF, Service de la Recherche, in France in 1971. Schumann, interview, 1979, remembers it as having been made in 1970, but the Dupavillon and George date is probably the correct one.

King's Story. According to Dupavillon and George, *Black and White Shows*, a black and white videotape of a performance of this play at the Astor Library Building in 1967 was made by Lewis Freidman for P.B.S. National Educational Television.

The Meadows Green. A 16 mm., 25 minute color/sound documentary of the 1974 Domestic Resurrection Circus, Plainfield, Vt., by Deedee Halleck and George Griffin. It in the late 1970s apparently was held by the Gate Hill Coop, Stoney Point, New York.

Other:

the performance of the Bread and Puppet Theatre in the 'peace rally' at Madison Square Garden on December 8, 1966 was, according to Oyle, interview, 1979, filmed for National Educational Television;

a Bread and Puppet Theatre performance at the Radical Theater Festival, San Francisco, California, in September 1968 seems to have been filmed for The American Documentary Film, San Francisco, California;

according to Maurice Blanc, *Clowning with the Life Force*, Village Voice, September 5, 1968, a 'short anti-war play' of the Bread and Puppet Theatre's was filmed in 1968 by Cologne television.

Appendices

Appendices

1. Peter Schumann, program note to the 1964 Spencer Memorial Church Easter show, *The Puppet Christ.*[1]

We sometimes give you a piece of bread along with the puppet show because our bread and theater belong together. For a long time the theater arts have been separated from the stomach. Theater was entertainment. Entertainment was meant for the skin. Bread was meant for the stomach. The old rites of baking, eating, and offering bread were forgotten. The bread decayed and became mush. We would like you to take your shoes off when you come to our puppet show or we would like to bless you with the fiddle bow. The bread shall remind you of the sacrament of eating.

We want you to understand that theater is not yet an established form, not the place of commerce you think it is, where you pay to get something. Theater is different. It is more like bread, more like a necessity. Theater is a form of religion. It is fun. It preaches sermons and it builds up a self-sufficient ritual where the actors try to raise their lives to the purity and ecstasy of the actions in which they participate.

Puppet theater is the theater of all means. Puppets and masks should be played in the street. They are louder than the traffic. They don't teach problems, but they scream and dance and hit each other on the head and display life in its clearest terms. Puppet theater is an extension of sculpture. Imagine a cathedral, not as a decorated religious place, but as a theater with Christ and the saints and gargoyles being set in motion by puppeteers, talking to the worshippers, participating in the ritual of music and words.

Puppet theater is of action rather than dialogue. The action is reduced to the simplest dance-like and specialized gestures. Our ten-foot rod puppets were invented as dancers, each puppet with a different construction for its movement. A puppet may be a hand only, or it may be a complicated body of many heads, hands, rods and fabric. Our puppeteers double as musicians, actors and technicians.

---

2. Peter Schumann, *Bread and Puppets: A Way of Life.*[2] In: Motive, February 1965.

Puppet Theatre is an extension of sculpture

The single puppet as well as the composition of many puppets is sculpture. However good Punch, Kasper and Guignol may have been, they realized only a tiny fraction of the potential puppet theater. Imagine a cathedral not as a decorated religious place, but as a theater with the Madonna and the Child and the saints and the gargoyles being set into motion by hidden puppeteers, talking to the worshippers, praying and participating in the ritual of music and words.

Imagine sculpture as puppet theater. Sculpture was not invented as a decoration or as a concentrated point of interest in an architectural frame. It was more than painting. It affected the eye more directly and immediately, and you could walk around it and touch it as well. And sculpture was painted anyway, color being one of its strongest means of expression. It lacked only a living sound and a movable body to be everything that could be caught in art and could speak out of a piece of art.

For thousands of years, artists have been developing the brain of the arts, sacrificing themselves for the most specialized areas, in order to control art, to know how it works in itself, and how it affects its audience. In the healthiest moments of history it looks as if art is an almost natural by-product of human behavior, an almost useful thing. In the sick periods of history, art[3] is self-sufficient, has loose and superfluous connections to society, is scientific and extremely conscious of its self-imposed limitations. Art is by no means the essentially unchangeable expression of human likeness throughout the centuries that it is believed to be today. Art is longing for its self-fulfillment and its salvation as much as humans are longing for it and actually art is the most dynamic example of the human longing. Its longing for the simple result which puts the countless chaotic streams of feelings and expressions together – and does not leave a single one out – could not be fulfilled if it were not completely one with the human course toward heaven or hell.

What is the end and the salvation of art? Certainly not as a mere object of art in any surroundings. It must be an object or event primarily of *social importance*. It makes little sense to talk about both a development in art or an aim of art if this is not admitted. And still we shall understand art as an inner potency, as a most powerful struggle toward our end, whatever this end is: our death, our belief, or the final good life. Art is a way of life (The Way Of Life), the awareness of the conscience as well as the awareness of the flesh and all the cells of the flesh of the whole world.

Puppet theater is a true consequence of sculpture. And sculpture is an object of the theater in every regard. Even in the museum, sculpture is, in a modest sense, theater (just notice the show that a stillpiece of sculpture is putting on in an art film). In the Bread and Puppet Theater any object, any picture, any sculpture can be an actor, can be pointed at, and even if not moved, will be something more

---

2. Copyright, Peter Schumann, 1965.
3. I am using 'art' in the sense of the German word, *Kunst* which means literature and music as well as painting, etc.

than an object or a piece of sculpture. Naturally, most of our sculptures are puppets and do have a life of movement. Every puppet is constructed with its specific kind of movement. Little hand puppets achieve individuality through a few movements of the puppeteer's hand only. Life size rod puppets are built for one-man operation, using an arm, or two hands, or a head as the main carrier of motion. Much different are the big eight-, ten- and twelve-foot rod puppets. They are conceived in groups either sewn or nailed together, or linked together by the similarity of sculptural appearance, their color and characteristic movements. All this makes these puppets dancers. They are not invented merely as sculpture. Their *movement* is so important that the sculpture derives its main features from it.

Puppet Theater as an extension of dance

The physical limitations of the human body are supposed to be the limitations of dance. The human body is supposed to be the instrument of dance. But the whole world dances; bodies, leaves in the wind, water, light, objects. And dance seems to be a quality of any movement which is separated from its purpose. In the theater, dance is the most powerful means of communication, whether an actor moves, whether a chair is moved, whatever our eyes perceive in the theater belongs to the field of dance and should be treated and made use of *as dance*. The modern theater works with the human being as a unit, as a moving and talking and acting being. But theater becomes powerful only by the strict organization of its primary means. The dance of a scene has to be taken out of its context and has to be studied by itself, as well as the language of a scene which is studied by itself. Puppets educate the theater to the use of dance. They are not alive as actors. They talk with their bodies, and their bodies are constructed for this purpose.

Puppets, being similar to humans, both exaggerate and purify the movements of the human body. The movements of a puppet hand suggest all the positions of hands that we know from Chinese or Romanesque or Baroque painting, the simplification, the elongation, the brutality and tenderness of gesture, which the human hand with its physical limitations can never create. The puppet, playing only the hand, or the puppet, playing only the head, dramatizes hand and head movement to the utmost degree. It is as if the functions of *one* body are distributed among *many* bodies, enlarging every single function and giving it a meaningful life of its own.

3. Peter Schumann, *God Himself/Problems Concerning Puppetry and Folkmusic and Folkart in the Light of God and MacNamara.*[4] In: Sing Out!, March, 1967, Puppetry Journal, July-August 1973, A. Sainer, Radical Theatre Notebook, 1975.

Puppet theater is theater of tiny dolls, theater of huge masks which a dancer operates from inside, theater of men on sticks or men hanging from strings. It ranges from half minute nightclub acts and five minute sidewalk shows to the 365 nights that it takes to perform the 'Legend of Roland' in Sicily. It seems to have been everything from fun-making, slap-stick, social criticism to the terrible reenactment of a hari-kiri on Japan's Bunraku stage. Masks are older than actors, faces of wood and stone are older than mimes. Masked dancers and the effigies they carry are certainly at the origin of theater.

The communion of all, the shape of that communion of all, that which was theater, is no more. Theater is in the present an outlet of spirit, or a check-point of soul of modern society, or, as understood in the USA: show business. In this modern theater puppetry is nothing but an unimportant branch, a low-ranking form of entertainment, which seems to have a comeback right now because some smart people found out how well that little stuff fits the little television screen.

What is left of the great old forms of puppet theater, besides obscure Indian or Persian marionettes and shadow puppets, which very few of us will be lucky enough to see, is the great Bunraku theater of Japan and the Sicilian puppet theater of medieval legends. Both forms are dying out.

I figure the same can be said of the more familiar Western world Punch-, Kasper-, Guignol-, Petrushka-, Pulcinello- theaters. They still happen to be alive someplace, they are sometimes brought back to life with artificial respiration, but their social conditions are no more; you need too many licenses and you are not allowed to play for money in the street, etc., etc. Throwing a baby out of the window is fun, as Punch does even in the days of Batman, but the distinct social and

---

4. Copyright, Peter Schumann, 1967.

Sainer as a preamble to *God Himself* reproduces comments on puppet theater that Peter Schumann made for the 1967 Newport Folk Festival:

STREETS AND PUPPETS The Roman Empire built many roads across Europe. The Vandals and Goths took to those roads and moved and moved until the Roman Empire broke into pieces. Then the tradespeople took to the road, then the missionaries, then the poets and puppeteers.

The poets walked on stilts and the puppeteers beat the drum. They told the news of the world: the size of King Cole, the beauty of the Brooklyn Bridge, and story of the 3 ladies who went swimming in the ocean and how they were saved by a courageous lifeguard.

Modern man believes in the *Daily News* or the *New York Times*. Ancient man believed in Demons mixed with God. That means that the newstelling of poets and puppeteers was a demonic business which scared them and their audience quite a bit. Miss Truth talked to the rosebush. Death sat on the throne of the world. Mr. Nobody shook hands with you.

From the roads puppeteers moved into churches and taverns, were thrown out of churches and taverns, and played on street corners for several hundred years.

Now, in 1967, streets are many and puppeteers are few. Truth is hired by CGS, demons live in NYC, and death still sits on the throne of the world.

The Bread and Puppet Theater bakes bread and makes puppets. Some of our shows are in the street and some are inside. The inside shows are meant for the Insides, the outside shows are meant to be as big and loud as possible. Some of our shows are good and some are bad. But all of our shows are for Good and against Evil.

political criticism that went along with many of these wild shows needs a different street, a different audience and different cops than what we have here.

In 1963 I went to a festival celebrating over 300 American and foreign puppeteers. Thanks to this meeting I became acquainted with the Sicilian puppet theater. Everything else was nice or not nice, sweet or not sweet and by all means little, not so much in size as in content and intent. Everything was plush and latex and Walt-Disney-y and basically about funny- and bunny-rabbits. Maybe I should call that the modest approach of this profession and not complain about it, and I should be glad that there were no Hamlet and Faust productions by foam-rubber specialists. But the Kasper of my childhood had been such a beautifully tough, down-to-earth, real and manly little man that I could not help looking for his like, whatever the shape of that likeness might be. From talking to puppeteers then and later on and from articles in the *N.Y. Times* and other knowledgeable papers I got the impression that in the eyes of the concerned puppetry is on the move, is opening up, is coming back because of foam rubber, because of professional lighting systems, because of television, etc. The saying goes, that when you do in puppet theater what they do in 'solid' theater, then you are on the right track: get a switchboard and dimmers, go three years to the Federal Lighting and Lightening School, get a union garbage collector, a cleaning woman, a director, a playwright, a photographer, a bull-fighter for the bull-fighting scene, etc. And then by harmonizing all these variants it somehow clicks, you get the magic and the audience claps hands when you want it to.

In Bunraku you have to study for years to be allowed to move a hand. In a Kasper show you play twelve voices, seven puppets, thunder, daylight, devil and dragon all at the same time. Liszt locked himself up with his piano for more than ten years. Pan plays the flute without Conservatorium. Both those holy ghosts, the. ghost of Pan and the ghost of the intensely concentrating hermit are altogether missing in modern puppetry, as well as in modern theater.

I don't want to lament about that but I want to ask how are gods brought back to life? The fact is, they are dead, nobody brings them back to life; our life, the life that we lead, buries them.

Safford Cape, the Belgian builder of beautiful, authentic medieval musical instruments plays beautiful, authentic medieval music on the concert stage. Shakespeare is reproduced in Shakespeare-style, Sophocles in Sophocles-style and so on. But the life of people and the language and art which their life brings forth has nothing to do with style. The historian, the thinker and the reflective mind invent style, not the producer. The artist is caught in the current of events and thoughts of his time. If he is concerned with the issues that need his sensitivity and concern, he is necessarily unconscious of style. Sophocles had no choice of style, the decisions that Antigone and Kreon had to make forced a style upon him. Early medieval music had harsh and pure tone and rhythm, was fierce, not cautious, you can hear rust and cracks in the instruments, and babies crying and men shouting in the background. I don't want to hear such music in Lincoln Center, and any garbage can drum solo by any kid in New York is more medieval music to my ears.

I have heard lovely fiddling for dancing in the barn in Nova Scotia last summer. Thank God there are some remnants. Professionalism and its pride, the many spirits and dwarfs that take care of our tiny talents, the salesmen of all those talents, the importance of every little bit of production, all this ridiculous self-concern makes for the kind of show business that we have inherited. I mean that kind that doesn't make any sense. It doesn't make sense because it doesn't even want to make sense. It wants to make something, it's hard to describe what, something tremendously smooth and balanced and fitting the occasion and fitting the enlightened stage or just the upholstered seat. There are puppet plays with 150 solved technical problems but no spirit, and folk singers with a vast repertory of anti-war, pro-grass, anti-washingmachine, pro-river songs and there is just a few times in your life a man singing a truthful song of his own, a song that you might need. And many such potentially good singers are brainwashed by the State Department of Folk-Singing. They start singing outwardly instead of inwardly. All good folk music, like Beethoven or the Nova Scotia barn fiddlers make a lot of mistakes and can afford them and don't care much for mistakes, because 1) God is more important and 2) if you get the big red color of the thing that you want, the holy spirit, you need not care so much for the finesse.

I think a good man is both a man who is able to be good in details and a man who wants to learn at least to fly, or to solve all the problems of the world, or to beat death finally, or to arrange for the second coming. Michelangelo or Rembrandt or all the ever unknown Bavarian, Russian, Mexican painters of the world have been truthfully trying out if our human pains make sense, if we are allowed to happily die, or if we are condemned to unhappily struggle against the fate of all dying and suffering. They have not mixed their colors for the sake of the salesmen, the historians and museums that possess them now.

Still, I was always under the impression that puppeteers and circus people are closest to God and mankind because they don't deal with false gold, because they carry their gifts in their hands, they make fun, they point out some thing and not much more, and I think that God likes that attitude better than the ordinarily pretty messed up human ambitions, the complicated ways of heartbreaking compositions, or the withholding and condensing intellect.

But that kind of holy simpleton and ruffian puppetry is dying out and is not likely to come back, as I have pointed out. At the present it is obviously replaced by the Union of the Professional-Puppet and Gag Institutes and these institutes have money behind them and the simpletons don't have money behind them and so they are going to lose. On the big commercial and *Life*-magazine surface the simpletons will lose. For the recording of time and for the coming revolution the simpletons are the avant-garde. And this is my prophecy: new simpletons are going to grow up all over the world; puppeteers with more puppets than tears and puppeteers with more tears than puppets; – folksingers who don't necessarily have voices or guitars but maybe just clap-hands or some kind of rattles; – painters who don't care so much how their pictures look on the wall; – and theater directors who gives up Broadway and Off-Broadway and Off-Off-Broadway and train cows to balance baseballs on their tails. Nowadays, they find that out in every business, among the shoemakers as well as among the Presbyterian churches: we have neglected the stuff that life is made of so long and the whole cart is on the wrong track so much, that we simply have to get out and start walking.

The masses of audiences are moved in various directions. Certainly in this country the masses of audiences are moved in the directions of the mass media. The mass media are commercial. Their commercialism means that under the cover of free expression of the participating forces gold is being made, and ways of how to make more gold are being explored. Mr. Folksinger and Mrs. Puppeteer hardly realize that with the help of their harmless contribution of good throat and skillful fingers marines are being sent around the world and lipstick is being sold to grandmothers who need exactly the opposite of lipstick. The masses of the audiences, the Pop, the success, are in the moment, for example, very useful to Mr. McNamara and his H-bombs. The biggest. schmalziest, chamber-and-kitchen-orchestra audience is thoroughly taken care of. You can see the most wonderful things in the world on a screen about as big as a behind and you don't even have to pay taxes for it.

The world may not win this time. McNamara or Wall Street or somebody like that may win this time, but that destiny is being weighed on the scales of justice high above the clouds on some unknown star where Greek gods hold residence. If the world loses, then there is little sense to talk about puppetry. But assuming that the good old world succeeds against McNamara and his like, then the simpletons and demons of puppetry are also going to win in their hidden fight against show business. The Stomachache Movement will fight The Big Hunger of the World and The Big Pain of the World; the Heartbeat Movement will set out with lots of music and puppets to beat hearts and to move heartbeats, and we will all be able to work together, puppeteers, folksingers, poets, painters, housewives, everybody, because we are all tired, oh tired of books, like Jack, and long for meadows green and woods where shadowy violets nod their cool leaves between, and we are tired of show and show-off business and we long for better soap and better operas, and we are tired of appetizers and surplus food and we long for nectar and ambrosia, and we are tired of spray guns and machine guns, we want fiddle bows and love instead.

Such is the situation of puppetry today. Thank you.

4. Peter Schumann, *The World Has to be Demonstrated Anew*.[5]
Responses to a questionnaire, 2nd International Student Theater
Festival, University of Wroclaw. In: Poland, March, 1970,
WIN, July, 1970.

Q: What is the purpose of your puppet theater?

The power of bread is obvious. People are hungry. The job of bread baking
involves baking the loaves well for chewing and digestion and making them available to everybody.

Puppeteers and artists never know for sure what they are good for and what
their job does for other people. We want to join the breadbakers, make good
bread and give it out for free.

The world in which we live seems to consist mainly of politics or the organizations of man. War and hunger have to be abolished, water, air and soil have to
be brought back to life. And puppet shows don't feed hungry children.

But war is made by the mind and poverty and hunger exist through our
inefficiencies.

Our mind is hungry, and Jesus says: man does not live from bread alone, but
from puppet shows as well.

Our everyday language is silly and does not tell the truth. Language which
speaks the truth has to be found in a puppet show, hardly any language at all, but
the actions and dealings out of which human dialogue will be born.

What is the purpose of a puppet show? To make the world plain, I guess, to
speak simple language that everybody can understand. To seize the listener, to
persuade him to the new world. To spark the movement of the listener.

We do the listening with drums and bugles and grasshoppers and the quiet
breathing of 500 spectators. We have joined the children's conspiracy against the
boring adult life.

Q: How does your theater relate to the leftist movement?

We are gypsies, and we play puppet shows in all the streets of the world. History
is the history of man oppressing man, or the story of politics succeeding over
people. Revolutions have taken capital from oppressors. Social welfare has been
invented. Bureaucracies have been established. In some places rent is cheap and
coats are expensive, and in other countries coats are cheap and rent is expensive.

The world is meant to be a computer of comfort and solved politics with man
as the primary ingredient, the boss and the vacationeer.

But the minds are dropping out, the peoples' guts are coming alive again, and
we are all marching down 5th Avenue in New York City, demanding the end of
the Pentagon. There is a lot of good marching going on right now. There are
black marches and hungry marches and marches against evil housing. All the
marching together makes for the movement. It's wake-up time in the world and
we beat the cymbals.

Puppet theater is good for sidewalk-story-telling, and it's good for making
things large and visible. The movement has many speeches and theories on the

wrongs of consumer society. A lot of that is lost and does not move anybody. Puppeteers are not theoreticians, they are practical people who play with children and test themselves with children, they have to speak with dolls and beasts with a few necessary words only. They have to learn to speak very slowly, to touch people cautiously in order to move them.

Q: What is important in your opinion?

The movement calls the change that it longs for revolution. But what is revolution? A machine-gun change of government? A class-struggle-masterpiece that the youth of the West is going to apply and to imitate?

The goals of civilization are suspect and peoples' aches and fancies are hardly represented in the program of the future. Our brains create tremendous machines of facilitation, but we die like dogs with only a few aunts and uncles slightly praying for us.

Our wishes are wild and cannot be compared with our comfort. Neither our body nor our soul has arrived at any conclusion of what is worth while. We only know, we want it more and feel it better, and that our hours are holy and that they belong to us.

We want our jobs to be fierce and nice, to be even with our habits, to be as happy as the sleeping with women. We demand a civilization that is human, where the suffering of the individual is embraced by the common care. The world has to be demonstrated anew. Men and women are stuck in the one-way development of our century. Violent changes and speeds have ridded us of old human skills. Our confidence is gone and in our great hurry we invent a lot of stuff that even our famous carniverous stomach cannot digest.

The importance of story-telling and puppetry is little in the face of hunger and mutilation. That little importance is important. The master plan of all the little importances together has a name: liberation, light, the good life.

We will build a circus and with the circus we will travel through small and big towns and in the circus we will demonstrate the whole world.

5. Peter Schumann (amicus poloniae),
Poisons, Worries and Screams,[6]
In: Poland, November 5, 1972.

Old Worries

Worried men, sitting on modern chairs and golden toilet seats diligently read Poland and other magazines to find definitions for their worries. As babies we get these worries like birthday presents, from our parents, bigger and fancier every year. We go to school to study worries and a little bit later we launch our careers as manufacturers, wrappers and salesmen of worries. Growing older with schnapps and sin, the center of the world moves from the forehead, the neck, the chest, the lightningrod towards the outside of my monkeyskin, and now is outside of me, between my toes, in the air in front of me, or even high up in the sky in the middle of the northern lights. But the worries are crawling in. They used to be relationships from distant cities, or talkative aunts and uncles from next door, demanding conversation. And now, while I am here, student of trees, farmer of flower-banners for confrontations in Washington, my worries are growing strong and fight me in my guts.

I would like to be a sunshine man gentle and good, a barefooter if possible, but my worries won't let me. I would like to be a storyteller, dancing and rocking organically while knitting tales, but my worries won't let me. I would like to be a kisser, a mule-driver, a puppet-grandfather, a merry rhyme painter, but my worries won't let me. They won't let me because of poison. The poison is very strong and subtle and it is everywhere, and the daily news are full of descriptions of the sensational effects of it.

I planted 5 children and they grew like the gods of appletrees, hopping and singing joyful, banal little hallelujahs all day long, whenever their mother and I don't yell at them and make them wash dishes. But there are already 5 children too many on this planet, and the fate of mine may be the fate of the 5 too many.

The land where we live is pretty. The sky changes all the time. The hills are wondrously soft and on our way to the school-bus in the morning, the big blue heron rises by the side of the road and bewitches us shortly, that we may not forget our membership in the elderly universe. We walk in it and the composition is done by winds and spirits. Trout from the river should not be eaten! At night we spice our spaghetti with a sprinkling of A&P poisons. Then we read the Odyssee and go to bed. And in our dreams the worries have unfamiliar faces and carry dirt on their backs and put the dirt over our heads. Either that, or steaming white horses in the April snow. When the sun rises, we attempt to be lighthearted, shit on the world, and chant uplifting slogans to ourselves. Then the newspaper arrives with poison and we suffer from heavy words. Muscles and courage and the deliberate routines of an ordinary day bring forth lunch, and a cup of coffee, and supper; it's o.k., we partake humanely, we continue non-stop, like potatoes. After supper the sky changes dangerously. Great blue and grey sky harbors and openly displays demons.

At that point everybody needs a chair to sit in a corner by himself, to manage his thoughts and to be alone. What I am saying is: worries are with us, are friends and enemies, bothering and accompanying us. A few of them go away when approached, loved and bitten; others simply mutate and essentially stay.

2. Poison

The poison is very strong and subtle and it is everywhere and the daily news are full of descriptions of the sensational effects of it. Poison is put into walls to observe us. Poison is put over our heads to fall on us. Poison is sprayed into our words to deprive us of truth. But one poison is a love-potion. That poison was drunk by Tristan and Isolde and they suffered astounding life from it. It is blue like first crocus. It is made in the snow, when the ice breaks, when the wild ducks appear. It is given out carefully in the dark to a single smiling man first. That man will stop acting smart, belching from too much cheese, attending busy time and livelihood-conventions, offices and schools. The poison will be put in his shoes and his feet will go astray. He will walk approximately like a bear. Eventually he will be able to fly. He will be crystal-clear. His purposeful-thinking channels will be flooded by joyous springtime creeks. His eyes will receive immediate training in out-of-sight sightseeing. His ears will specialize in leaves-of-grass chamber music. He is not going to laugh easily for a while. When he perceives of Isolde, he will be utterly unprepared and still serving some crazy, old-fashioned kind. He is silly. He is a good American kid. He has learned sex, he has understood all available mattress-acrobatics. He is a kind of sportsman, not a wild duck, untouched as yet by solitude and big screaming. But the poison works its way from his shoes up through his naked body, until the moon shines. By the light of the moon he will go to her, he will see everything that has ever been seen by a lover: a lot, and the full size of beauty. The light effects are simple, and he will forget what that means, he will be painfully unaware of everything else and stick to his job: to be so poisoned as to see perfectly. What I have described is cold water, not dope. And there isn't much reasonable salvation around, besides the intensity of love-poisoned love.

3. Modern Worries — (tears as big as mountains)

The worries of our times are written into the mutilated faces of sufferers and carry their desperate expressions. Ease and civilization are hiding them. In this here country child-labor, slave-labor, bone-breaking labor harmoniously dissolve into unemployment and automation. The finger-skills that bore home-bake production are gone. The new, electrical skills are boringly specific and need a lot of vacation time in Florida. We are consuming unrestrictedly. Our manners are disposable. Eating, drinking and sleeping are lost in a maze of unenjoyable comfort. Striving, greedy man and his partner, the political bastard, have provided a war- and extinction-machinery that defies all massive virtues achieved. War and cars bring us to our knees. Eat and drink: our decomposition is being discussed in elected offices. Some of us still get sick and still die, but we all suffer from 100,000 protective measures. Our talented private and national egos are organized and exploited by middle-aged champion males, typical little Genghis Khans, with transcendental mass-murdering instincts. Surely our ambitions stink. What are we really longing for? And whose ambitions are running us and are calculated our all-together growth and liberation? When the weather allows, we all long for the same thing: for women and children and anarchy in the dunes and alps of every-

671

where. But now the storm is here, and the clubs and parties that we are entrusted to, are rotting away fast, and we help kicking their arses. Governments are commercial enterprises that fumble with our blood and life, and they deserve to die. Women are older than governments, and they shall win. Now the young people mean quick un-funny revolution through organized mischief. They still believe in trigger dominance and fire and sulphur. They still believe in the same kind of stuff that has already happened in vain. And we: organgrinders, circus directors, poets, lutists, magicians, tightrope-walkers, dramatists, conductors, prophets, hobbyhorse inventors, and all the folks that help produce big eternal nonsense are still trying in vain to persuade our neighbors-in-the-Lord to broader and simpler goals and revolutions. We have come to the end. The planet is almost closing down. Our last hopes and secret devices have been defused by the defence department.

Loving, warm-hearted manure has been remodelled into guerilla warfare weaponry. Sweet singing in the sky, that was always hard to hear, now screams. One hour's worth of screaming shall be installed as a daily practice at the 4 corners of the world! But so much of heaven-above-the-earth is closed off already. Our screaming and participation in heavenly screaming will hardly make a difference. Fighting, screaming, protesting guns and departments, singing sweet and exalting the worried face of our time, horses and monkeys that we are, equipped with our own hearts only, we will roam the fields of the earth for some time more.

Vermont
April, 1971

672

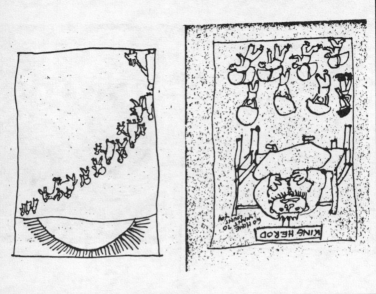

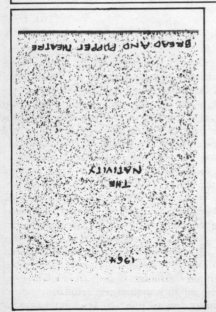

6. Peter Schumann, *The Nativity*, 1964.1

BETHLEHEM

NO ROOMS
NO ROOMS
NO ROOMS
NO ROOMS
NO ROOMS

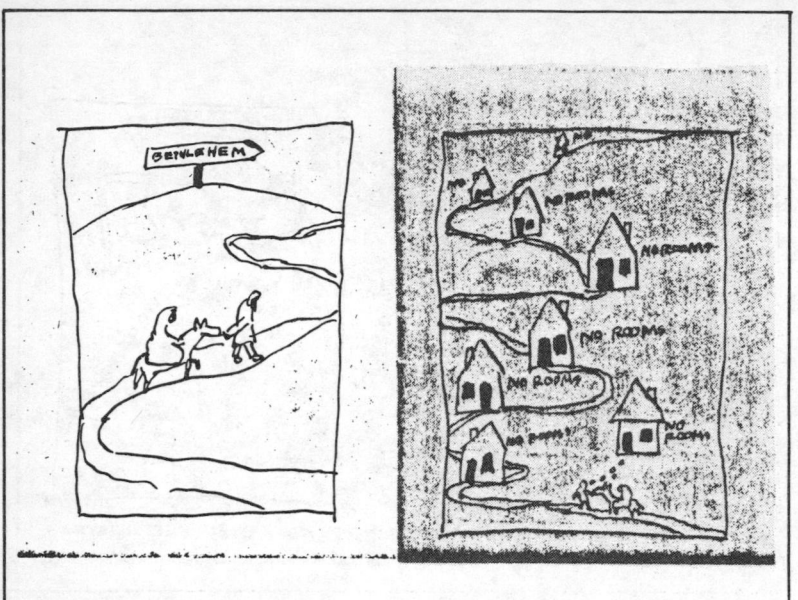

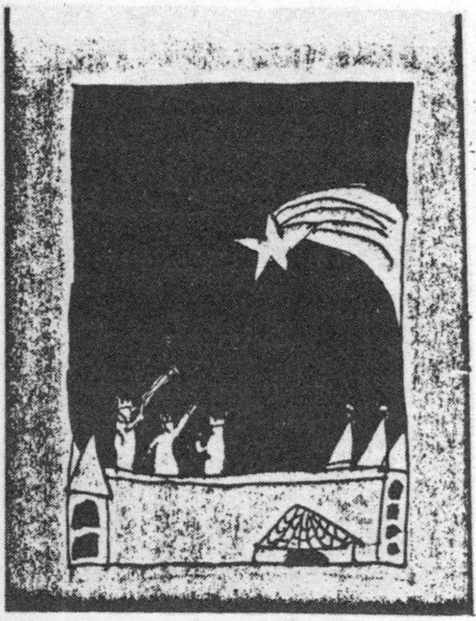

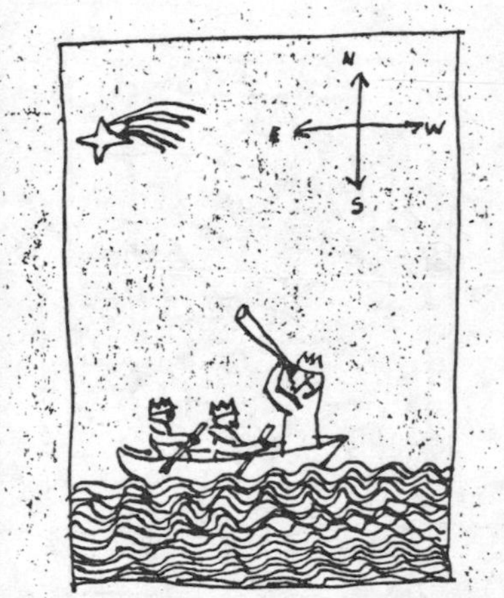
N
E
W
S

ISRAEL
WHERE IS THE NEW KING?
KING HEROD
FIND THE NEW KING!
HA HA
HA HA HA HA

FEAR NOT FOR BEHOLD I BRING YOU GOOD TIDINGS OF GREAT JOY WHICH SHALL BE TO ALL PEOPLE
FOR UNTO YOU IS BORN THIS DAY IN THE CITY OF DAVID A SAVIOUR WHICH IS CHRIST THE LORD AND THIS SHALL BE A SIGN UNTO YOU: YOU SHALL FIND THE BABE WRAPPED IN SWADDLING CLOTHES LYING IN A MANGER.

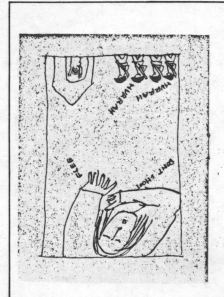

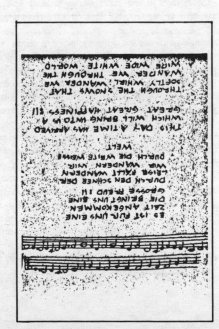

7. Margaret Rigg, *Some Notes on Peter Schumann's Puppet Theater.*[8]
In: Motive, February 1965.

Theater for Peter Schumann is something revolutionary, yet as primary and as old as the kind of drama and ritual that functioned for primitive man out of his tribal necessities.

Rather than being a place for unfolding plot structures, delivering lessons, morals or propaganda, theater for Schumann is the place where all — the participants, players, puppets and audience — are involved in a process of being. There is no secondary goal of edification, intellectualization or even catharsis. Instead he wants to make environment, experience — direct and primary.

This is the new, essential theater. It concerns itself with the essentials of form, color, size (of shapes, puppets, stage, masks), movement, sound. Mr. Schumann has reduced theater to its essence and then given full range to this essence. There is no teacher, no academic tradition for this kind of theater — no preconceptions. Without traditional story line or interpretation or poetry (as with Brecht and Ionesco) Peter Schumann begins from the basis of the theater experience (form, color, size, movement, sound). He allows these elements to function experimentally and imaginatively, playing with forms: letting expressive, round, sculptural forms play against flat mask or hood forms. He uses silence and sound contrapuntally; movement against stillness; color against black or white; small against large.

His puppet theater develops as essentially as theater experience, as folk art does. The old, popular Punch and Judy puppet shows grew out of similar concepts of what a direct dramatic situation could be; of what drama involvement meant for an audience. Puppets understood as sculpture with form, with ability to move, speak, dance, wove an environmental spell over the audience. Punch and Judy had power to delight and attract people of all ages. Yet as folk art the Punch and Judy puppet makers were not conscious sculptors or dramatists. Peter Schumann and his friends believe that their puppet theater should be like that too: rough rather than slick, fun to experience, strong and simple, direct action in place of words, using space and color and sound. Thus the 'story' can be conceived from the sound of it. Like opera, the story is 'carried' with music, Schumann's puppet plays are often 'carried' with their sound structure of movement structure. He draws movement diagrams, like a choreographer, and builds his puppet play around these essential movements. The movement is the meaning.

But, for this kind of theater, the puppeteer has to 'know everything.' He has to know about dance, light, sound, silence, sculpture, space, color. He must experiment with these as meaningful in themselves. He has to find out what happens (what is produced) in their endless variety of relationships. Like a kaleidoscope the range of visual design is endless, always new, yet always basic. But the puppeteer in Peter Schumann's new kind of theater has to keep the sense of wholeness using all the elements. He cannot deal with just one element or the spell, the environment, is broken.

Beyond the vital sense of fun and play that is certainly an important ingredient

---

678

in this kind of theater, there is a deeper joyousness. It is the serious joyousness of an artist dealing with design elements which have laws and integrity in themselves: light as structure, sound as meaning, of puppet as presence.

In the years since coming to the United States Peter Schumann and his wife and friends have delighted many audiences with their new theater. In 1961 the Schumanns came to Vermont from Germany. Peter tried teaching dance, but it was the sort of dance that American audiences found too gloomy for them to endure. As a people we did not want to contemplate the dance of Death. So Mr. Schumann turned to puppets as a more acceptable medium for exploring and celebrating the depths of man's condition. His concept has deepened to present the whole range of human nature as theater-environments where the human drama is played out in a way that frees our emotions and brings them alive again.

Watching his plays I have felt a remarkable communication between myself and this art form. I felt my total being addressed as a participant in a gripping drama which had no slickness of dialogue or neat story line or smoothness of poetry. It is like the ritual of our own existence played before us in colors moving closer yet farther away, in the ponderous forms coming and going, the starkness of the masks and the sober placidity of the larger puppets; the sound meeting our ears and receding into a silence that corresponds to our own silent depths; or the flashing, half-comic form hurtling across the stage space through the maze of lights, intense and nervous, revealing the dimensions of our humanity. But all this is accomplished in relationship; the mystery as well as all the richness and surprise, the fun, sadness, exhaltation, innocence and wisdom . . . all are preserved.

8. Sally Kempton, *Everyman in Scary City: Morality Takes to Streets.*[9] In: Village Voice, July 2, 1964.

At 3:45 on a hot Sunday afternoon a tiny, bright procession winds around Washington Square. It consists of four men, naked to the waist, wearing huge masks painted to represent animals and insects. One man beats a drum, another is blowing a horn, a third carries a pair of cymbals. They hold a sign which advertises 'Everyman, a Street Play presented by the Peace Center,' and by the time they have marched twice around the Square their gay and rackety music has drawn perhaps 50 people away from the folk-singing mob at the fountain. Beating the drum and blowing the horn, the musicians lead their audience to a truck parked on Thompson Street across from Judson Church, where a crowd has already gathered. The audience moves close to the truck, the players step out in their street clothes to be introduced, and the play begins.

It opens, of course, with a drum roll. Then God, wearing a big gold mask with an enormous mouth, comes out and tells the audience what they are about to see. Civilized man, he says, is a bust. With his weapons he has eliminated his own history, and now he must face the consequences of his irresponsibility. God summons Death, who wears a black cloak with a stylized skull around his head, and tells him to fetch Everyman. 'Death, I want you to tell Everyman that I'm sending him on a long journey that will put him in great jeopardy. I'm sending him to SCARY CITY!' There is a hush, and then an immense roll on the drums, and a little blonde girl in the front row bites into her Good Humor and glares menacingly at Death, who glares right back at her.

Responsive Rhythm

'Everyman,' as its title suggests, is a modern morality play; like its medieval predecessor, it is an account of a pilgrimage. That the pilgrimage is hopeless, that Everyman will die in the end, is indicated at the very beginning of the action. So the audience's attention is caught not by the nuances of plot but by the movement of the actors, by the force of a satire very near to burlesque, and by the music, so that on a good day a responsive rhythm is set up between actors and audience which carries the action out of its dramatic context and places it squarely in the street.

The effect of the play depends to an enormous extent on this responsive pattern. Author Grace Paley, who produced 'Everyman' for the Peace Center, has noticed that the caliber of the performances has been greatly influenced by the caliber of the audiences. 'This Sunday the audience got every line,' she says. 'And when that happens the play opens up like a very tight petal. One actor breaks loose and the rest follow.'

'Everyman' was written by landscape architect Robert Nichols, a poet and playwright whose work has been performed at Judson Church and at the Hardware Poets Theatre. Thin, with hair that is startlingly grey above his ruddy face, Nichols looks rather like the leading actor in a medieval version of 'Everyman.' He got the idea of doing a street play after the Living Theater folded; perhaps the streets seemed to him the natural refuge of the avant-garde.

---

9. Copyright, Sally Kempton, 1964.

'Julian Beck was saying that audiences are hopeless, so I wrote this for him. A real audience play.'

Clique and Claque

Nichols has been struck by the fact that there are essentially only two audiences for New York theatre, the 'middle-class suburban Broadway audience' and the tiny clique which supports the avant-garde. There had, he felt to be something in between. 'When the stage is surrounded by your claque of supporters, you can't see over their heads to the real audience. The clique is necessary to avant-garde theatre. But in a street play you don't have the clique, you only have the public. You're fighting against everyone, you're fighting the inertia of all organized New York theatre. The very fact that it's a public play means that you can't do esoteric stuff, or decadent stuff.'

Nichols' material is certainly not esoteric. He has written an anti-war play using characters so universally recognizable as to be archetypes; a newspaper man, a politician, a big businessman, a general, and other bogymen of modern society. But the form of 'Everyman' is dictated avant-garde. The play contains by the street setting, and its technique is almost classically technical borrowings from the Japanese No plays (which, Mr. Nichols points out, were performed in river-beds and are therefore legitimate street theatre), from the commedia, and from the medieval morality plays (the plot of Nichols' 'Everyman' is close to the medieval original). Furthermore, the use of certain expressionist techniques like vaudeville turns, music and direct appeal to the audience, as well as of that essential Brechtian notion that the stage should be used as a soap-box for a political message, come naturally in a street play.

More Radical

Nichols' ideal of street theatre is actually far more radical. He had originally conceived of 'Everyman' as a traveling production, 'rather like a juggling act or a clown show,' in four self contained segments, each performed in a different part of the Village. In this way the dramatic pilgrimage would become a physical pilgrimage, while the street musicians led the audience from place to place, coming to rest finally at the Gansevoort Street Pier. The director, who is used to indoor theater, vetoed this plan, so the play was cut to its present one-act form. Nichols hopes that 'Everyman' will someday be produced the way it was conceived.

'It would be almost like a political meeting, or like a circus. Its very movement would have a political meaning, it would be breaking away from a whole theatrical tradition, because it isn't premised on the holding of an audience in desperate concentration, like indoor theatre.'

Nichols sees street theatre as having both political and artistic effects. The point of a street play, whether one sees it politically or artistically, is to reach as many people as have the power to listen. In order to do this, Nichols feels, it is necessary to work with a plot of whose outcome the audience is certain. Nichols sees plot as a kind of myth in the sense that the commedia plots, concerning stock characters moving in formalized situations, were mythic.

Family as Anagram

'I want to see a theatre of character like Ben Jonson's' he explains. 'Recognizable

681

characters, almost archetypes, acting out a grizzly social satire which is hilariously funny at the same time.' Nichols' particular theme is the family, the family as an anagram for society. But he approaches his theme from what Grace Paley calls 'the anthropoligical rather than the psychological angle.' That is, he puts Mr. and Mrs. Everyman on stage as a myth of the American family, stylized like all allegorical characters. Their story is enacted at one remove from reality, as if it took place in another time or in a country which bears the same resemblance to our own as Lewis Carroll's world bears to Victorian England. 'I think that's what Brecht meant by alienation,' Nichols says. You use realistic characters in a way which suggests that the action took place in a fantasy country. That's why we use masks; masks make myth possible.

Room for Chance

Is the use of myth, then, what defines a theatre of the people? 'Well, it's not the subject matter,' says Nichols, 'so it must have to do with the form. For instance, a lot of people are working on interjecting chance into the theatrical performance. I see "Everyman" as a combination of poetic speeches with vaudevillian scenes which can be improvised. Since each scene goes according to a formula, there's a lot of room for improvisation. But more radical than that are things like some of the dance at Judson, or one of the plays they did at the Living Theatre where the actors drew cards at random and performed according to the instructions on the cards. It's very precious, that stuff, very esoteric and limited, but it may be necessary to liberate these arts. You know, you can have something going on in a loft on Second Avenue, seen only by a tiny audience, which has enormous importance for a theatre of the people.'

'Like a Liturgy'

The point of this liberation, of this interaction of formula and chance, is to arrive at a very basic theatrical form. 'You have to see how close you can get to the edge of the theatrical experience without going over into nothing,' explains Nichols. The object, it seems, is to eliminate the trappings of drama, leaving that confrontation of audience with dramatic experience which was the mainspring of the very earliest theatre. 'By the time the audience is at the edge of the Gansevoort pier watching the fourth act you've cleared out the dead wood, you have the survivors and you have the fabric beneath the conventions,' Nichols says. 'A play should be like a liturgy, so that the audience responds to its rhythms like a drum roll after a dramatic speech.' He smiles. 'After all, poets are starting to write plays again. Which is really going back to the beginning of it all.'

9. Richard Schechner, *Guerrilla Theatre: May 1970.*[10]
In: Tulane Drama Review #47, 1970.

What was most striking (from the New York perspective) about the Maydays of 1970 was that students were organizing themselves to use facilities and resources, not to destroy them. The nihilism so powerfully present in the Columbia uprising of 1968, and always prominent in 'revolutionary' rhetoric within the student movement, was transformed into something more fundamentally revolutionary. 'Burn it down,' 'trash it,' 'shut it down' were not heard so often as 'take it,' 'Use it,' 'open it up,' 'liberate it.' In either case the work is somewhat symbolic – that is, burnt buildings can be and usually are rebuilt and liberated buildings can be and usually are reoccupied. The establishment is not so weak that it will yield everything at once. But it is not so strong that it will last out the decade.

Guerrilla theatre is symbolic action. It is called 'guerrilla' because some of its structures have been adapted from guerrilla warefare – simplicity of tactics, mobility, small bands, pressure at the points of greatest weakness, surprise. The term itself was adapted from war to theatre by Ronnie Davis in his 1966 article 'Guerrilla Theatre' [T32]. Davis says:

The motives, aspirations, and practice of U.S. theatre must be readapted in order to: teach, direct toward change, be an example of change . . . The Guerrilla company must exemplify change as a group. The group formation – its cooperative relationships and corporate identity – must have a morality at its core.

Davis talks about the how-to-do's: get a cheap place to rehearse: 'start with people, not actors'; perform in parks on a portable stage; keep the length of the show 'under an hour'; slowly build a company; don't get sucked into the commercial theatre. Of course, Davis was talking about his Mime Troupe. The guerilla theatre we are now involved in relates back to Davis' ideas – but also, and more strongly, to the things the Provos did in the mid-sixties, both here and abroad. And the things men like Abbie Hoffman [see T44] and, later, Jerry Rubin did. Like dropping dollar bills on the floor of the Stock Exchange; dumping a truck of soot and garbage on the brass of Con Ed; showing up a HUAC hearings dressed as a revolutionary war patriot. To make a swift action or image that gets to the heart of an issue of a feeling – to make people realize where they are living, and under what situation. It is primitive because many Americans still do not know (or believe) what is going down here.

However, the Kent State murders made many people know directly and viscerally. One of the basics of guerrilla theatre is that you use what is at hand. The murders were at hand, and they were used. I found out about Kent State during my seminar on Performance Theory at NYU at 6:00 p.m., May 4. Someone came into the class and handed out a leaflet. It said that six students had been shot down – four at Kent State and two at Penn State. (The Penn State two turned out to be a mistake.) A general meeting was called for 7:30 at the Loeb Student Center. The seminar ended at around 7:45 and several of us went to Loeb.

The meeting was going as usual: lots of speeches to and from about a thousand angry students. Loeb had already been taken. The speech-making lasted about an

---

10. Copyright, Richard Schechner, 1970.

hour and after that committees were formed. I saw Ralph Ortiz in the crowd and went over to him. Joan MacIntosh was with me. We decided to start a guerrilla theatre. I got to the microphone and announced that decision. We took over a corner of the ground floor of Loeb, about fifteen students joined us, and we talked over what we should do. We decided on an action for the next morning. It was a scenario worked out by all of us, based on some ideas from Ortiz.

The Kent State Massacre

Performed in New York City on La Guardia Place in front of the Loeb Student Center and also at the corner of MacDougal and 8th Streets. Groups of students are roped together in subgroups of four. Other students dressed in army uniforms and carrying stage rifles and gallons of animal blood guard the 'prisoners.' The prisoners are abused verbally and physically. Under their clothes they conceal animal organs — brains, hearts, intestines, etc. The soldiers march through the streets calling the student prisoners 'Commy bums,' 'fucking student trash,' 'Red agitators,' and any other insults that come to mind. The students resist but are severely brutalized with kicks and rifle butts by the soldiers. The students are marched through the streets until a large crowd gathers. Anyone in the crowd who laughs at the action is forcibly pulled into it and thrown in with the students. After a brief announcement to the effect that the students are Communists, agitators, bums, and worthless people who care more for politics than for education, they are 'shot' and the blood is thrown over them. The students 'die' slowly, shrieking and pulling out from their clothes the animal guts. The soldiers stand over the dead students, refusing to let anyone come and help them. Persons in the crowd who laugh or argue or resist are thrown on the body pile.

(A variation was done by Ortiz, in Washington on May 9 during the rally. The action was a procession of people holding real animal heads, skinned and bloody, with tongues and eyes.) On 8th Street, outside the student environment of NYU, many people thought the students were actually shot. When it was made clear (through audience word-of-mouth) that this was a street play, people were most responsive to the obvious message: the war was home. The police arrived to break up the performance. The cops were angry that so much blood was spilled on the street and sidewalk. Arguments broke out between the police and some of the onlookers. One of the police finally said, exasperated, 'People who mess up the public streets should be shot.' His remark was not well received.

Later in the week, supported by extensive organizing led by Christina Weppner at the NYU School of the Arts, we began to go out in teams of three or five to instruct people in guerrilla theatre. Our aim was to organize at schools and other places which requested our help and to stimulate extensive guerrilla theatre activity citywide, and later nationwide. Scenarios were duplicated and distributed; a city headquarters was established which could coordinate guerrilla theatre activities; a succinct handbook of guerrilla theatre was issued. Before I discuss these organizing activities in more detail, I would like to report on an action that took place Thursday evening, May 7, at the Broadway theatres showing Plaza Suite, Forty Carats, and Private Lives.

Members of the NYU guerrilla theatre group felt that an action directed toward (or against) Broadway audiences was appropriate. The action was developed during two meetings on May 7 — it involved about thirty people.

684

Tapes were made of a statement by Allison Krause's father. He had appeared on TV the night after Allison's murder and made an eloquent, tearful plea asking whether or not dissent was possible in this country, and calling for a Congressional investigation about why the National Guard was allowed to carry live ammunition. It was a profoundly moving statement by a shocked parent of the middle class. We all felt that it should be heard by other parents of the middle class – and not in the defended situation of their evening TV broadcasts at home. The larger group of thirty was divided into three subgroups. Each had a leader who carried a portable cassette tape recorder loaded with the Krause tape. Each group decided its own strategy.

The Plaza Suite group wished to go into the theatre during intermission, wait until part of the second act had gone by, and then rise, go to the front of the theatre – or onstage if possible – make a brief announcement, and play the tape. But the man carrying the recorder was challenged for his ticket stub as he tried to enter the theatre, and only two of the group got in. They did not know that the leader had not gotten in, so they sat out the whole second act. ('That was a gruesome experience in itself,' one of them told me later.) At the end of the second act, they rose and went to the front of the theatre, said a few words about the Kent State murders, and distributed a leaflet which stated the three national strike goals (End the war in Southeast Asia; Free all political prisoners; Get the war machine off campus); on the reverse side, it had a complete transcript of Mr. Krause's statement.

The Forty Carats group all got into the theatre after intermission. About fifteen minutes into the act (at the start of the second scene), the leader of the group rose and went down the aisle. The other members of the group responded to the cue and soon the bases of both aisles were filled with the eight demonstrators. The leader said, 'Trina, the girl in this play, is seventeen. Allison Krause was just two years older than Trina when she was shot. Her father wants to speak to you.' Then the tape was played. All members of the group wore black mourning veils. All were dressed 'straight,' so as to get into the theatre easily. The tape takes about three minutes to play. The actors onstage – June Allyson and Tom Poston – froze as the demonstration began. They did not attempt to compete with it. Most of the audience was quiet. About halfway through the tape a woman said, 'We didn't pay $8 to hear this kind of thing!' Another woman answered, 'This is more important than this trivial play!' Some of the audience joined in the dispute. Tom Poston said, 'All right, girls, you've made your point.' The stage manager or maybe it was the house manager, came down the aisle and tried to seize the tape recorder. The demonstrators left the theatre peacefully – the last thing on the tape, the last thing heard, was Mr. Krause saying, 'Is it a crime to dissent?' I did not participate in the demonstration, so I stayed in the theatre and listened to the manager apologize to the audience for this 'rude and unauthorized interruption.' He asked for the actors to pick up from where they had left off. They did, but the fizz had gone out of the little comedy.

The Private Lives group waited until the house lights were down as the second act began. Then they got onto the stage and as the lights went up – there they were. The actors did not interfere as they played the tape. Most of the audience listened, but some were very angry that their evening had been thus interrupted. A shouting match broke out in the audience – but the tape was played to the end, and leaflets were distributed to the audience.

Other actions originating at NYU, but not disruptive in nature or intent, occurred during the intermission at several theatres, including the Brooklyn Academy and the City Center. One of these actions centered on a brief dance commemorating the Kent State murders. A plan was made to move the scheduled student performance of Johnny Johnson to the Lincoln Center mall – but nothing came of the proposal. (The week of May 11 some City University students carried their protests into several Broadway theatres. I do not know what they performed.)

The week of May 11 was also the week when we organized guerrilla groups at Lehman College in the Bronx (part of the City system), the New School, the NYU School of Law and School of Education, and City College. I did not participate in all these organizing efforts, and will report extensively only on the three I was present at. However, the team of organizers was 'trained' (if that word has any meaning in such a swift program) under my supervision and we all followed the same plan. It is a very simple plan, and I commend it to everyone who is interested in guerrilla theatre organizing. A team of us go to a group, talk to them, tell them about guerrilla theatre, find out exactly what issues are important to them, organize a scenario, rehearse it with them, and stick around until it has been performed once or twice. Then we leave, and hope that the group will continue on its own – as the Lehman and New School groups have done. If we stay too long, the group will not develop a sense of self-sufficiency; if we leave too soon, it will dissolve.

From the Guerrilla Theatre 'Handbook.'

There are three kinds of guerrilla theatre. (1) That which makes people aware that a problem exists. This kind takes place in 'new' areas – places where social and political awareness is at best rudimentary. The Broadway Theatre Action described before was of this sort. (2) That which shows the workings/results of a problem. This kind is performed in 'middle areas' – places where people know of a problem, are sensitive to it, but have not viscerally experienced it or fully understood it or its consequences. For example, the 'Kent State Massacre' – especially as performed at the corner of MacDougal and 8th Streets – was this kind of theatre. The object was to show people that government oppression exists, is systematic, will attack all who forcibly oppose the government and its policies, and that the government will not hesitate to use maximum force. It exposed the myth that brutality is the result of 'ignorant' people, or of 'maniacs.' It was a direct answer to Nixon's telegram to the murdered victims' families in which the President noted that violent dissent leads to tragedy. We wanted to make it clear who was responsible. (3) That which shows the solution to a problem. This kind of theatre is done in 'sophisticated' areas – where people are already aware of a problem and its dynamics – e.g., certain elements of the 'Kent State Massacare' as performed in front of Loeb. The soldiers shouted to the students – 'We will kill you in small groups until you band together against us!' And the soldiers then seized a person from the audience and threw him/her into the body pile. Soon the NYU students began resisting the soldiers and organized against them. Several students attacked a soldier and grabbed his gun.

686

You must know the differences among friendly, neutral, unfriendly, and hostile places/audiences. And you must expect — that is, be ready to split quickly after an action in an unfriendly place; or, on the other hand, be ready to stick around and rap for a long time in a friendly place. Don't bring the conventions of illusionism from the old theatre into guerrilla theatre. Guerrilla theatre is, in many ways, like wall posters or pamphlets. To people who distrust reading and who are accustomed to less linear means of communicating, guerrilla theatre is a succinct language.

Friendly: At school, in many churches, among friends, before a striking group, etc. Even though everyone will not agree with you at a friendly place, you will be allowed to finish your action and people will be eager to discuss it with you. If there are disagreements, they will come over emphasis and tactics, not goals.

Neutral: Supermarkets, streets in neighborhoods where you are personally known, theatre lobbies, parks. Here there will be arguments, maybe even some heckling. There will probably be city and possibly private police on hand, or nearby. The crowd will be divided between those who want to hear you out and those who do not. Be ready to stop the performance and disband. Or, depending upon the heat of the argument, to defend your right to public dissent.

Unfriendly: Places where people strongly disagree with your politics, but have nothing against you personally — Broadway theatres, hotel lobbies, uptight neighborhoods, etc. In an unfriendly place people will argue with you, heckle, call the police, and threaten violence. If you keep your cool, usually nothing will happen. But if you show fear or extreme hostility an unfriendly place can swiftly transform into a hostile place.

Hostile: Places where violence is likely and therefore where your action has to be swift, cunning, and planned for impact and escape. A KKK meeting is a hostile place, or a rally of construction workers, or the Police Academy. Here people not only hate what you say, they hate you because you represent a way of life they cannot understand and do not accept. If they catch you they will probably beat you up. You are quite literally thought of as 'the enemy.' In these places guerrilla theatre is most like guerrilla warfare. Your goal here is not to convince or change minds — but simply to let people know that you have penetrated a highly defended headquarters. And once you announce your presence you have accomplished your mission and should get out as quickly as possible. More than in any other kind of action, forays into hostile places should be planned in detail. Only the most experienced groups should attempt a raid into hostile territory.

Guerrilla theatre scenarios should be (1) simple and direct, (2) clear and visual, (3) striking and theatrical — that is, even if people can't see or hear everything they should know what it's about, (4) meaningful to you — something you believe in. There is no reason to perform a little piece because of someone else. Where there is a little traditional aesthetic justification for a piece there must be a great deal of political and social conviction. If dialogue is used it should be very direct and simple. Because streets are noisy it is good to have the dialogue shouted and some of it repeated chorically. The use of choruses can be very effective.

A crowd should be leafleted immediately following a piece (not during, because that will distract). The leaflet should not only carry the message, but give precise information about what the onlookers can do. For example, the leaflet accompanying BUSINESS AS USUAL told how blacks and Latins could organize their communities and give the time and place of an organizing meeting. In liberal rather than radical settings the names and addresses of legislators, and a suggested form for writing, should be provided. The leaflet, in other words, is never simply a statement but always a program, however fundamental.

Business as usual

This scenario was developed during the evening of May 13 at the New School in NYC. About fifteen people participated. It was performed that evening along a route that went across 14th Street from Fifth Avenue to University Place, down University Place to 8th Street, along 8th Street to Sixth Avenue, and up Sixth Avenue to 14th Street. About twenty-five performances were given that night. The piece was repeated on May 15. A group of people walk down the street in a disorganized fashion. Four people in the center of the group suddenly scream and drop to the ground. The group immediately forms a circle around the fallen four. A man rushes into the center, as a crowd of bystanders gathers. 'Four people have been shot!' shouts the man. 'My God! They're white!!' The encircling crowd choruses, 'White?! White?! Let's have a national strike!!' The man in the center shouts, 'No, wait a minute! Look! Two of them are niggers! And two of them are spics!' The crowd choruses, 'Niggers?! Spics?! Fuck them! Business as usual!' Then a brief statement is read concerning the different reactions in America elicited by the shooting of white and black or Latin people. The crowd is leafleted, and the performers move on. The piece is done two or three times in every block. On the night of May 13 it was enthusiastically received by people in the street (including blacks and Latins) and by many who watched from apartment house windows. At the intersection of 8th Street and Sixth Avenue a patrol car stopped when a cop thought someone had been hurt. He was very angry when he discovered that he had gotten out of his car to see a street play.

On Friday, May 14, we went to organize a group within the NYU School of Education. These people had extensive theatre experience – they were theatre majors and their professors. They had performed rather complicated pieces at rallies, and these pieces showed sophistication and theatrical abilities. The problems were truly opposite those we faced at Lehman and at the New School. If anything, the NYU students were too theatre oriented. The simplicity of guerrilla theatre disturbed them. Also most of these NYU students were liberals in the classical sense. They were very hung up about the reactions of their parents; they wanted whatever they did to be nonviolent in practice and effort; they tended to be sentimental and guilt-ridden.

We worked with them for about two hours and developed a piece which I call BRINGING THE WAR BACK HOME. It is an adaptation of Hed's *Kill Viet Cong* [T32] which was performed in NYC in 1967. (It is a mark of the anti-war movement, and of the war itself, that a piece more than four years old can still be relevant, perhaps even radical.) Three students were roped together. One wore a sign, NIGGER; another, BUM; another, GOOK. They were marched down the street, shoved and abused by a goose-stepping group of around ten people who were singing *God Bless America*. When the procession got to the crowded corner of University Place and Waverly Place, the procession stopped and a straight-looking man addressed the crowd. He told them that the war was expensive and that everyone deserved to get a piece of the action. He told them

688

that there was no difference between the Vietcong, the black militants, and the white Communist agitators. He said that the government had donated one of each to his patriotic group, and that someone from the audience would have the privilege of shooting the three criminals. A volunteer stepped forward (Rotante in the first few performances). Then the leader said, 'Let's all count him down, just the way they do at Cape Kennedy.' At the end of a ten-point countdown, and using his own arm as rifle, Rotante shot the three tied prisoners. The rest of the group sang *The Star Spangled Banner*, ending on the phrase 'bombs bursting in air,' which was repeated, like a broken record, six times. All gave the Hitler salute. At the end of the National Anthem fragment, the dead got up and the procession resumed.

10. The crisis in U.S. radical theatre in 1970.

Toscan and Ripley in their chronology of the San Francisco Mime Troupe, *Commedia to Collective Creation*, Theatre Quarterly, V, 18, under '1970' report that 'Davis leaves the Troupe, and collective creation becomes the dominant approach'. The troupe (Holden, *Collective Playmaking*, ibid.) in '70 turned to the promotion of specific radical causes of the day (*Los Siete* – the Chicano cause, *The Independent Female* – the feminist cause, *Seize the Time* – the Black Panther cause), doing their plays in consultation with the particular promoters of the causes. Davis responded with the charge that they had 'lost (their) artistic integrity by participating in the radical movement' (Holden, ibid.), and in his *Politics, Art and the San Francisco Mime Troupe* (same issue of Theatre Quarterly) elaborated:

'In 1965 we declared it possible to create theater and some life without elaborate buildings and loads of money. But what was the goal of doing this? In 1965, I stated that our purpose was to teach, to direct toward change, be an example of change. In 1968, I added the thought: We must take power. In 1970, I stopped and asked: Could we do all the above?' (RF. Davis, *1971: Rethinking Guerilla Theater*. Performance, December '71).

According to the F.B.I. Field Office File 100-55612 of the vi/14/71, the Bread and Puppet Theater had some time previously joined the San Francisco Mime Troupe and a number of other groups in 'The New Theater Coalition'. According to the Berkeley Barb of the xii/11-17/70, the coalition had been formed toward the end of 1970.

Valdez, in the summer of '70, asserted his theatre's need for independence from 'pre-established political groups,' going on to make clear he means the union and the strike: he calls for a nationalist theatre for the raza. (Valdez, *Notes on Chicano Theater*, in Lesnick, *Guerilla Street Theater*, '73.) In the fall (*The Actos*, ibid.), while still proclaiming the need for the form he had maintained for his nationalist theatre, that of 'actos', he says they are going into 'myths' (the first of these apparently *The Dark Root of the Scream*, done in September '71 in Los Angeles, cf. Kourilsky, *Approaching Quetzalcoatl*, Performance, Fall '73).

'The acto ... developed its own structure through five years of experimentation. It evolved into a short dramatic form now used primarily by Los Teatros de Aztlán, but utilized to some extent by other non-Chicano guerilla theatre companies throughout the U.S. including the San Francisco Mime Troupe and the Bread and Puppet Theater. (Considerable creative crossfeeding has occurred on other levels, I might add, between the Mime Troupes, the Bread and Puppet, and the Campesino.) Each of the groups may have their own definition of the acto, but the following are some of the guidelines we have established for ourselves over the years:

ACTOS: Inspire the audience to social action. Illuminate specific points about social problems. Satirize the opposition. Show or hint at a solution. Express what people are feeling ... The major emphasis in the acto is the social vision, as opposed to the individual artist's or playwright's vision. Actos are not written, they are created collectively, through improvisation by a group. The reality reflected ... is thus a social reality ... not psychologically deranged self-projections, but rather group archetypes.

690

'Nothing represents the work of El Teatro Campesino (and other teatros Chicanos) better than the *acto*. In a sense, the acto *is* Chicano theater, though we are now moving into a new, more mystical dramatic form we have begun to call the *mito*. The two forms are, in fact, cuates, that complement and balance each other as day goes into night, el sol la sombra, la vidal ma muerte, el pajaro la serpiente. Our rejection of white Western European (gavacho) proscenium theater makes the birth of new Chicano forms necessary – thus, los actos y los mitos: one through the eyes of man; the other, through the eyes of God.' (Valdez, *The Actos*.)

The Pageant Players dissolved in the spring of 1970. Michael Brown, more or less their director, describes the breakup in his *Some Dynamics and Aesthetics in Pageant Players Street Theater* of the summer of 1970 (in Lesnick, *Guerilla Street Theater*, '73.) They were doing workshops of a type apparently somewhat new for them:

'So, all that was a message. For some it was *the* message: Bringing a little human warmth to a street corner; reminding folks at a rally what we're fighting *for*; enlivening the deadliness of academia with a little radical merriment. As years went by and youth culture thinking turned us on, we focused more on this aspect. Life style was embodied in how we appeared doing the plays, as much as in what they said: Change your life! Change your insides *and* the world! Start from your own center! Kill guilt!

At the same time, we had a saying: Bad art doesn't work! Though not polished by any means, the audience could relax and not worry about being embarrassed for us. Our scenarios had many heads contributing, and by performance time most of the serious flaws would be caught by someone. Though we dealt with specific, current issues, the emotions and images we thought in terms of were timeless enough to raise the plays to a higher level. That's why we often used fairy tale or Bible forms. Or feelings of delight, play, exploration, sounds and movement that convey vaguer feelings you can't verbalize, the *bigness* of oppression, the *joy* of rebellion.

It was the heaviest thing we had ever done! Inventing new forms as they needed them to express their own lives, people told the most moving stories I'd ever heard. I learned more about my friends that I ever had, in unforgettable ways. Workshop after workshop broke down and had to be suspended because some number of us were in tears, or were too overcome to go on. Actors broke down crying as they were performing. And it was all exalted, beautiful at the same time . . . Incredible theater – not just psychodrama – pointed, subtle, and true. And political! *The formation of people's character structure is the ultimate politics* – the basis of a society's hold on its members. The cop, judge, and jury in each person's head! This was in the winter of 1970. It would have been our next play in N.Y. – our longest, best, and most profound. But as I said, the ecology issue was strong too. That spring, the group moved to the country – in fact, still lives in Oregon now. They'll be getting back to theater soon. They've performed a little out there, but mostly they're building needed houses, taking care of their farm, and are studying music in a serious way.

Myself, who had been dominant as a leader-type in a leaderless group agreed to leave for a while to figure out a lot of stuff that I had been confronted with. Also, my ex-wife was in the group and that was still heavy. I didn't go back!'

691

(Michael Brown, *Some Dynamics*, from Lesnick, *Guerilla Street Theater*, 1973).

Arthur Sainer in the Village Voice of March 19, '70 reports a 'split, whatever that split actually means,' of the Living Theatre, and that its leaders 'Judith and Julian (are) at last planning to go into the factories, to do a new kind of theatre, in France to begin with.' This split actually then occurred, though Beck and Malina presented it as deliberate, tactical cell-division: their cell, in Paris, was the politically rather than environmentally, spiritually or culturally oriented one: they were trying to get together a film deal as protection for a Brazilian excursion:

'The structure is crumbling. All of the institutions are feeling the tremors. How do you respond to the emergency?

For the sake of mobility The Living Theatre is dividing into four cells. One cell is currently located in Paris and the center of its orientation is chiefly political. Another is located in Berlin and its orientation is environmental. A third is located in London and its orientation is spiritual. If the structure is to be transformed it has to be attacked from many sides. This is what we are seeking to do.

In the world today there are many movements seeking to transform this structure – the Capitalist-Bureaucratic-Military-Authoritarian-Police-Complex – into its opposite: a Non-Violent-Communal-Organism. The structure will fall if it's pushed the right way. Our purpose is to lend our support to all the forces of liberation.

But first we have to get out of the trap. Buildings called theatres are an architectural trap. The man in the street will never enter such a building.

1. Because he can't: The theatre buildings belong to those who can afford to get in; all buildings are property held by the Establishment by force of arms.

2. Because the life he leads at work and out of work exhausts him.

3. Because inside they speak in a code of things which are neither interesting to him nor in his interest.

The Living Theatre doesn't want to perform for the privileged elite anymore because all privilege is violence to the underprivileged.

Therefore The Living Theatre doesn't want to prform in theatre buildings anymore. Get out of the trap; the structure is crumbling.

The Living Theatre doesn't want to be an institution anymore. It is out front clear that all institutions are rigid and support the Establishment. After 20 years the structure of The Living Theatre had become institutionalized. All the institutions are crumbling. The Living Theatre had to crumble or change its form.

How do you get out of the trap?

1. Liberate yourself as much as possible from dependence on the established economic system. It was not easy for The Living Theatre to divide its community, because the community was living and working together in love. Not dissension, but revolutionary needs have divided us. A small group can survive with cunning and daring. It is now for each cell to find means of surviving without becoming a consumer product.

2. Abandon the theatres. Create other circumstances for theatre for the man in the street. Create circumstances that will lead to Action which is the highest form of theatre we know. Create Action.

692

3. Find new forms. Smash the art barrier. Art is confined in the jail of the establishment's mentality. That's how art is made to function to serve the needs of the Upper Classes. If art can't be used to serve the needs of the people, get rid of it. We only need art if it can tell the truth so that it can become clear to everyone what has to be done and how to do it. (Living Theatre, i.e. Beck-Malina, *Living Theater Action Declaration*, January 1970, WIN, July 1970.)

'... am enclosing a copy of the "action declaration" which we made when we changed the form of the company i send you such an official looking document to clarify what has been so badly bungled by the press, twisted to fit their points of view, rather than the truth. the press (and maybe gossip also) would like to think that the living theatre split up because of personal bleep-blops rather than out of ideological recognition of what and where we were . . . it was difficult, the break, a domestic tragedy, as judith puts it, but also, as judith puts it, a break-thru action for the cultural revolution, and for us a real liberation: we are free now: we can't go on doing what we have always been doing always inside the same stream of history, amplifying the same veins of civilization; we are somewhere else, in free space and we are going to dance out the answers.

we feel (tho maybe we aren't) quite youngyoung as this, anyway, this thing we are after.

if plans cohere we shall be leaving for brazil in a few weeks, the general idea is to go there with about 7-10 living theatre actors and to create a company of brazilians and some argentinians a community which will then make a collective creation together, and give the "world premiere" of it in sao paulo (these things are measured to meet the ego of the authorities), and this thing that we are going to create is going to be very flexible so that we can play it at agricultural reform centers, in schools, in factories, in indian villages, in meeting halls, in public ballrooms, in tents, in parks, in gardens, in mines, and hopefully never, but maybe sometimes, in theatre (in a theatre applies to south america, especially to brazil where the situation is highly limited). In fact this program is designed to see how far one can go inside a very limited situation to stimulate the impulses for change. it will be like practicing for the repression we are sure to meet in western europe and usa during the next 10-20 years of the struggle (which say the rabbis is our glory). We would then tour this collective creation to every country in south america and to several central american countries and eventually turn up in california next spring.

at the same time we want to make at least one film, if not two at the same time as we make this "theatrical" tour. we are held up now in europe finalizing the money for making this film. obviously a film produced by a big european/american producing unit will facilitate life for us that part of the world.

the rumors are pretty accurate. after that south american venture we plan to come back to the united states to work, yes maybe in the midwest, for about a year. i really dont want to stay in any one place more than a year if we can help it. that's part of the strategy. we would then probably return to western europe for a year before the next venture wherever that may take us.' (Malina, letter of June 4, '70 to Karl Bissinger, WIN, July 1970.)

11. Ralph J. Gleason, *The Greater Sound*.[11]
In: Tulane Drama Review #44, summer of 1969.

Today, all over the United States, American young people are being spoken to by revolutionists in words they understand, in a style that makes those words acceptable, and through an invisible medium that old professional politicos have not yet picked up on.

This medium is the phonograph record, purveyor of bubble gum music and symbol of Elvis Presley's 'Houn' Dog' and the celebrated 'Get off of my Blue Suede Shoes' (which John Lennon once called a protest song). One of the leading manufacturers, Columbia Records, runs a series of advertisements in the underground press the theme of which is 'The man can't bust our music' and 'Know your friends.' The implication aligns 'us' against 'them,' and the context of the advertising design and illustration is interracial, hippie, pot-smoking youth.

Is Columbia for legalization of marijuana? No. Columbia is for making money. Thus the investment in music aimed at long-haired youth. The music speaks directly to them, it leaps past all barriers and is justified by the sacred principles of the true religion of the United States, making money. Would Columbia invest in an advertising campaign for a product that did not make money? Would it sign a young Texas blues guitarist and singer for a guarantee of $300,000 if there were not millions to be made? (In February 1969 it did so.)

The popular music business – records and personal appearances – is a multi-million dollar proposition, yet the messages it sells to young people imply a distinctly different way of looking at the world than that which is held by their parents – or by the owners of the record companies. The economic momentum of the medium confounds old Marxian analysis. It's possible to say that the expression of youth's disaffiliation through pop music merely siphons off rebellious feelings and makes them assimilable and in the long run harmless – but surely this is offset by the fact that unarticulated protest is made specific, and applied to political subjects like Vietnam, for kids in remote towns who wouldn't otherwise know that they are part of a vast movement or wouldn't connect their discontent to its sources in our social-political setup.

A fallible but useful gauge of the efficacy of a movement may be the degree of reaction which it provokes. Military scientists are fond of looking at 'the other side of the hill,' as Wellington put it, to see how their situation appears to those they are fighting. To Republican Congressman James Tustin of California, the Beatles and the other rock musicians 'use Pavlovian techniques to provoke neurosis in their listeners.' Congressman Tustin also believes that rock 'n roll and sex education (he combines them; a view not far from the mark) are a Communist plot to destroy our nation. *American Opinion* and other organs of the radical right, as well as fundamentalist religious publications, are vehement in their protest against the music of electric guitars. When radical rightists talk about telstars and satellite H-bombs hung in the sky by Russia, when they discuss George C. Marshall as a Communist, they are hallucinating. When they talk of the Beatles as Communists, they are not hallucinating – they are merely mislabeling the contents. They correctly define the Beatles as their enemy.

A new philosophy has been articulated and communicated. And, as Plato warned,

Forms and rhythms in music are never changed without producing changes in the most important political forms and ways ... the new style quietly insinuates itself into manners and customs and from there it issues a greater force ... goes on to attack laws and constitutions, displaying the utmost impudence, until it ends by overthrowing everything, both in public and in private ...

The content of rock lyrics has had the most obvious effect on our 'customs and manners' — and these lyrics are always meant to be heard, although technology trips them up sometimes. But the movement in pop from foxtrot rhythms to black variants of 6/8 time or triplets over a 4/4 beat has brought blues, always an underground communication against the oppressor, overground. There's been a parallel development in dancing, from the rigidity of Arthur-Murray-type box-stepping to a sensuous, individual expression. Dylan's message is in his lines, the Grateful Dead's is in the form of their music, its relation to drug and sexual experiences, its improvising freedom — and in the way that's shown through their collective movements and creation on stage.

The 12-inch long-playing vinylite phonograph record, with its half-hour to 45 minutes of songs, is an intellectual time bomb — even if bought primarily for a hit song heard on thousands of radio stations (and radio means only pop music to all those Americans under 25 who will add up to more than 50% of the population in another year). The album brings to its purchaser other songs as well. They are all heard. Even though Mick Jagger of the Rolling Stones was forced by the Ed Sullivan TV show producers to change 'let's spend the night together' to 'let's spend some time together,' none of the young people who saw the show were fooled. The millions who own the disc, and the millions upon millions who have heard it in the original version on radio stations, know the right words. (Ironically, it was radio's desperate reaction after TV came on the scene which started the stations bringing rhythm and blues — 'nigger music' — to white ears which previously had at best heard Basie and the swing bands.)

The Rolling Stones attack sexual taboos and endorse the directness of today's young people, not an overtly revolutionary act but on which — when coupled with the Beatles singing 'I'd love to turn you on' and 'I get high with a little help from my friends' and Grace Slick in 'White Rabbit' advising listeners to 'feed your head' (after telling them about 'pills which make you large and pills which make you small and the ones that mother gives don't do anything at all') — challenges fundamentals of American behavior. Once you set up a situation in which sacred tenets of the social fabric are treated as obsolete or irrelevant, anything may be questioned. There are also the more directly political songs of Bob Dylan, Country Joe & the Fish, and other groups. Dylan is central. His songs provide phrases to be quoted in political tracts of the underground and college press as well as in conversation. Even American adults have heard of Bob Dylan.

Country Joe & the Fish, with three best-selling albums last year, have a song called 'Fixin' to Die Rag.' Country Joe comes right to the point. 'Put down your books and pick up your gun, we're gonna have a lot of fun,' Country Joe sings. '... One, two, three, what are we fighting for? Don't ask me, I don't give a damn, next stop is Viet Nam!' The song has four verses. The second says, 'Come on Wall Street, don't be slow, why man this is war a-go-go! There's plenty of money to be made by supplying the Army with the tools of its trade.' And in the last one, using a Brechtian image with parallels going back to 'When Johnny Comes Marchin' Home,' the group sings, 'Come on mothers throughout the land, pack your boys off to Viet Nam. Come on father don't hesitate send your son off before it's too late, and you can be the first ones in your block to have your boy come home in a box.' That song has been heard and understood by millions. It is heard by someone every day in all probability. Is there any comparable medium?

In Iowa and Minnesota, in Arizona and Florida and Washington – as well as in the Central Park – Country Joe & the Fish sing that song and lead their audience in the 'Fish Cheer' – 'Gimme an F! Gimme a U! Gimme a C! Gimme a K! All right, F!U!C!K! Fuck!' After they did that in Central park the vice presidents of their booking agency, which handles talent for all the best places and all the best TV shows, staggered unbelievingly back to their plus offices. But they did not stop arranging concerts for the band.

The Democrats in the last election were aware of some of the power of this music. Johnson and Hymphrey tried to reach people through James Brown and the Supremes. Cocoa Cola sells its product via the pop stars. But the James Brown government-sponsored message, 'Don't Be a Drop Out,' had not one-tenth the effect of his ghetto hit, 'Say it Loud, I'm Black and I'm Proud.' The 'sell' is easy to detect in music.

Today there are almost 100 FM stations all around the country constituting what the radio trade calls 'underground' radio – they play adult rock music, not the teeniebopper music of the Monkees and Nancy Sinatra and the plastic contrived rock groups who play the discotheques and dominate the Top 40 radio station play-list. Buffy Sainte-Marie's records get played a good deal on these stations. One of the songs is called 'My Country 'Tis of My People You Are Dying,' a bitter indictment of United States society, which she accuses of lying, of censoring history books, of untrustworthiness ('see what our trust in America brought us'), of genocide, and of ghoulishness ('the graves have been robbed'). Then she applies a fundamental Marxist thesis – 'Can't you see that their poverty is profiting you?'

The Mothers of Invention is a group of electronic music experimenters from Los Angeles who along with creating very serious music, indulge in an all-out satirical commentary on American society rivaled only by that of Lenny Bruce. Their first album for Verve, which made their reputation, sold more than 300,000 copies and is still selling (when a book sells 300,000 copies it is news; a point to be remembered in this discussion). 'Who are the Brain Police?' and 'Trouble Every Day' are on this album and both are sharp, insightful attacks on the structure of the society. Students in schools and universities where the SDS hasn't a slim chance of penetrating hear this message loud and clear. And they believe it as they do not believe the history books in their class and will never again believe their teachers.

Some radical politicos have sensed the importance of this medium, though perhaps not considering it either as revolutionary or as useful as I do. As I see it, the situation is plain: if you want to reach young people in this country (and revolutions are made by the young; the old make counter-revolution) then write a song, don't buy an ad or issue a statement. In the early '50s, Tennessee Ernie Ford made a hit out of 'Sixteen Tons', a song that was a pure economic determinist account of the reality of coal mining life, but nobody took it seriously. At that point in time, American song hits were generally written for someone else to sing and not sung by the man who wrote them. Carl Oglesby of the SDS is writing songs and playing with a rock band. Hubert Humphrey had songs written and played for him. We do not know yet what Oglesby's songs are like, but they are his own. One's imagination may stagger at the sight of Hubert Humphrey arm in arm with the Supremes, but mine at least simply will not accept HHH writing and singing a song.

Dylan, of course, set the mold for all of this. He showed the record companies that there were huge profits to be made with songs that might be labeled controversial and which said things, instead of using innocuous or euphemistic lyrics. And the record companies, discovering he was right, dropped the taboos. It was not only his issue-oriented topical songs which were effective – such as 'Who Killed Davey Moore' (about the death of a boxer; in it, after enumerating those who denied responsibility, he pointed out that boxing was illegal in Cuba) or 'The Lonesome Death of Hattie Carroll' (the story of the brutal murder of a Baltimore house servant by a white employer, in which Dylan named the names). It was the trio of unofficial anthems of the movement: 'Blowin' in the Wind,' 'The Times They Are a Changing,' and 'Chimes of Freedom': sung by Dylan and by others, they became a propaganda campaign that shames the Voice of America. It is no wonder that right-wing congressmen and clergy attacked Baez and Dylan and Pete Seeger and the others who sang the songs. But it was when Dylan abandoned his topical 'folk' songs and devoted himself to composing a series of State-of-the-Union addresses describing the American social and cultural landscape that he made his deepest and most important impression on American youth.

Dylan made a record called 'Subterranean Homesick Blues,' backed by an electric rock 'n roll band. It was an instant hit and he became a pop star. Kids scribbled the words on scraps of paper and duplicated them on high school ditto machines to pass around. In 'chains of flashing images' Dylan described a world in which young people are monotonously advised to 'please her, please him,' urged to be a success, told 'don't steal, don't lift,' and as a reward after 'twenty years of schoolin' . . . they put you on the day shift.' The repeated theme of the song was 'look out kid, it's something you did, God knows when but you're doin' it again.' Dylan hit on the mindless drive to blame the young, the new, and the different, and on the true hypocrisy of the American dream.

'Subterranean Homesick Blues' was a single 45 disc. Dylan's next hit was 'Like a Rolling Stone,' one of the best selling records of 1965. In it he spoke directly to young people, assuming their isolation from the adult world. 'Like a Rolling Stone' was in an album, 'Highway 61 Revisited,' in which there were two other seminal songs, 'Ballad of a Thin Man' and 'Desolation Row.' 'Ballad of a Thin Man' is Dylan's indictment of the liberal intellectual adult. Its refrain, 'something is happening and you don't know what is is, do you, Mr. Jones?' has become a catch phrase to describe the generation gap. Huey P. Newton, the Black Panther leader jailed for the killing of an Oakland policeman, says he could not have written his 'Papers from the Minister of Defense,' the ideological framework of the Panther party, if it had not been for that song. 'Desolation Row' is a poet's prophetic vision of the reality of America. The villains are 'the agents' (after all Dylan lives in a world of show business with concert, recording, and booking agents). At the fatal hour of midnight they appear 'and round up everybody that knows more than they do.' Then the agents bring their victims back to 'the factory' where a 'heart attack machine' is strapped to them and 'kerosene is brought down from the castles' by 'insurance men who go check that nobody is escaping to Desolation Row.'

In that verse, as well as in others in the same song and in other similar songs ('Maggie's Farm' and 'It's Allright Ma' especially), Dylan lays out a view of American society as valueless, its institutions as rotten, and its leaders as immoral and without any motive but greed and power. The body of Dylan's work (and familiarity with it is a prerequisite for political activity in America) adds up to the starkest analysis yet of the poverty of the system, of Orwellian submission to the machine in its anti-human, anti-artist drive, and of the impossibility of change until the entire structure is revised – and until the way in which such change is thought about is revised.

Dylan's poetry is studied today in some university English classes and in many high schools. Sometimes it is part of the established curriculum, but generally it is included either because of a conviction by the teacher of its importance or as a response to the demands of students. In either case, it is being done. The millions who bought the Dylan albums (and a best seller in 1968 was 'The Best of Bob Dylan,' which has 'Rolling Stone,' 'Subterranean,' 'The Times They are a Changing'' and 'Blowin' in the Wind' on it) have heard and absorbed all the lyric content.

In Europe last summer Danny Rifkin, one of the managers of the Grateful Dead, a San Francisco rock group, was hitchhiking through Germany. Everywhere he stopped for the night, in camps, in fields, in hostels where young people gathered, he reports they had miniature tape recorders with cassettes of Dylan music which they played at night, their ears pressed to the tiny speakers. In this country, innumerable people in high school and college (and some older) go to bed nightly, their photographs playing with the automatic turn-off devices set. It is sleep-learning of a kind. As they drift off to sleep the words of the prophet ring in their ears.

Timothy Leary captured the mass media with his 'Turn On, Tune In, Drop Out' slogan, but the Beatles made it stick with their songs of love and pleasure. If Dylan and the Stones represent a relentlessly real (though poetic) description of the world around us, the Beatles speak of hope ('Hey Jude' is almost religious in tone) and of a glorious future ('All we need is love').

The argument over activism in the American Movement has been summed up in music. The Beatles in 'Revolution' said 'if you want money for people with minds that hate, all I can tell you is brother you have to wait' and 'if you go carryin' pictures of Chairman Mao, you ain't gonna make it with anyone anyhow . . .' Nina Simone, the black American singer, sings a response to the Beatles which is currently widely played on radio. 'Sing abut a revolution because I'm talking 'bout a change It's more than just evolution, well you know, you got to clean your brain,' she says, and adds 'the only way that we can stand, in fact, is when you get your foot off my back!'

But beneath the struggle in the Movement today is the central fact that if you accept Dylan you can never again see America as Jackie Gleason or Governor Rockefeller or even, on the good guy scale, as Mayor Lindsay or the text-books

698

see America — nor, especially, as the *New York Review* or the *Nation* see it. Young politicos know Dylan's songs and dig them. Yet the implications of his truths contradict the imperative of their ideology which, despite its radical nature, is imbued with the concept that the engine can be made to work, if only the tracks are changed and the power supply altered. Dylan says flatly it won't work because it is by its nature corrupt and corrupting. The Beatles say it won't work and that we have to walk away from it and change our heads (i.e., change the way we think about all of it, including change itself). 'Lighting a joint is a revolutionary act,' Leary says, and there is deep truth in this, since the act puts the actor outside the law from that time on. But I think that the whole body of rock music, spreading out from the center, with Dylan, the Beatles, and the Stones, involves its audience in an even more fundamental confrontation with the society. It says you are, all of you, wrong.

Rock music has involved young people as no other pop or elite art has ever done. In fact, it has involved young people as nothing else at all, aside from sex, has done in generations. It has made poetry real to them. It has given them the vision that they can literally take over the world, as they see members of their own generation seizing the means of production in one area — concerts, dances, record companies run by under-25's. It has firmly allied youth, bound them together with an invisible chain of sounds and a network of verbal images in defense against the Elders. No amount of public (free) appearances by Jackie Gleason and drummed-up Kids for Decency crusades will diminish the actual popularity of the Doors or Jim Morrison of the Doors unzipping his rig and shaking it out for the audience in Florida to see. But as Lenny Bruce said, if you find something wrong with the product complain to the manufacturer. The rock bands, their life style and their music, say the human body — and hence each human being — is beautiful. American morality to the contrary notwithstanding.

There is as yet no program. But there is intuition that there will be one. In a midwestern university where the few activist students were depressed about the barren cultural landscape and the dim prospect of getting students politicized, they finally decided that the opening wedge would be a series of rock dances and/or concerts. The Living Theatre appeared this winter in Berkeley, where there have been free rock concerts in the park on sunny Sundays for two years and rock dances most weekends. The Living made little impact. 'The rock 'n roll showcase has eliminated all this with swinging music and lots of people,' R.G. Davis of the S.F. Mime Troupe commented. Some weeks earlier a benfit for the Oakland Seven, on trial for leading anti-draft demonstrations against the Oakland Army Base, drew more people than the Living Theatre by presenting a series of rock bands plus speeches by Black Panther Bobby Seale and Kathleen Cleaver.

In the program for the Living Theatre, it is stated that the group is 'in the vanguard of a new phenomenon in theatrical and social history — the spontaneous generation of communal playing troupes sharing voluntary poverty, making experimental collective creations and exploring time, space, minds and bodies in manifold new ways . . .' The rock groups have been doing this since 1965 and reaching an audience infinitely greater. It also might be noted that when asked by *Time* what Aretha Franklin's music (i.e., soul/gospel) was about, Godfrey Cambridge said 'Fucking.' Julian Beck squats morosely on stage and cries 'fuck for peace' like a sentence imposed by a Kafka judge. The rock bands sing 'fuck for joy' in every line, as an invitation to beatification and a command to a state of grace.

The radical movement in the United States has always seen music as an arm of the revolution. Radical sympathy supported the folk music revival, beginning with Leadbelly and Woody Guthrie and coming on down to Peter, Paul and Mary. But radical theoreticians mis-assessed the phenomenon of pop music. Pop music meant mass culture and mass production and was, de facto, anti-art and anti-culture and manipulated by perverted money-makers. Beatle records are smuggled into Russia from East Germany, where they are available principally because the Beatles are slightly associated with Germany, having lived and worked (and first recorded) in Hamburg. Nobody ever smuggled Woody Guthrie records across any curtains, iron or otherwise.

The missed point is not that there is a line from Guthrie to Dylan (of course there is) but that in order to make money, corporate American enterprise will, in a kind of autolysis, allow its own destruction to be preached via a product that is profitable. Marx was not faced with this alternative. None of the radical bards from Guthrie on through the Weavers have had the benefit of the mass audience that Dylan has.

The rock groups reflect something else long alien to American culture. This has been a nation of individualists, of iconoclasts (mythologically, at least) of 'I'm from Missouri, show me' loners, and 'group' meant conspiracy and cooperation and hence distrust. Beginning with the Free Speech Movement at Berkeley and the San Francisco Mime Troupe before that, the concept of activity in which individuals were submerged in the group effort became a part of the political scene and, more importantly at that point (and more quickly, too), part of the music world. Previously music was individually-oriented. Even the most prominent groups (i.e., the big bands of the Thirties) were individual-oriented. They consisted of employees who worked for one leader (star) employer. The labor union for musicians accepted this as such a fundamental that it is built into the union rules and practice. The union actively opposed cooperative groups for years and only now have accepted their reality while still demanding that one man be responsible and sign the contracts. The Casa Loma band in the Thirties and the Modern Jazz Quartet in the Fifties were the only two successful major musical groups operating without using the name of a single leader. The rock bands are cooperative. They are also to a large degree communal. They live together.

The Young Rascals, a real real-version of the West Side Story musical group, have announced that they are not interested in playing the Ed Sullivan show and that they won't appear on a concert bill unless there are also black artists presented. The San Francisco bands inaugurated a novel idea – playing for free. They have been appearing in the parks in San Francisco, Palo Alto, and Berkeley for over two years, a practice that has now spread wondrously as far as London. In concerts organized by rock fans and absolutely free, bands such as the Jefferson Airplane (which regularly turns down offers of up to $15,000 for a single night's engagement) play.

The support which has been given all radical causes by rock groups (particularly in San Francisco) is incalculable. Benefits for everything from Newsreel to the S.F. State College defense fund have been freely held. I mention this not to lavish credit on the bands but to point out that every cause goes to them for help.

700

The reason is the power of the music.

In a culture of noise — not just the jets roaring overhead and the trucks thundering on the streets, but the psychic noise of the crashing of institutions and assumptions and conventions, the whole crescendo of a collapsing civilization — the only peace seems to be in the middle of an even greater sound in which a special kind of one-to-one communication occurs. As for the physical effects of the volume: no rock musician I know has gone deaf, no matter what Ralph Nader says.

Wearing all or part of a costume that identifies them, and using ritualistic pass words ('what's your sign?' is only one), the members of the New International reach out to one another in a gigantic conspiracy of feelings, a network of common understanding. They have seen the empty values of patriotism; they would rather be alive red, white, or blue than dead and there is no cause worth dying for. Dylan has told them 'don't follow leaders' and the only leaders they will hear are those who are determinedly not leaders, a reality which has been appreciated so far only by some of the New Left. They are learning to trust their intuitions and their feelings (two untrustworthy weathervanes by Aristotelian standards), but then again, as Dylan says, you don't need a weather man to know which way the wind blows.

Art is always ahead of culture. The rock musicians have made music out of noise, art out of what began as teenage exploitation and meaningless money-making. In the process, they have begun to rethink the premises of Western society, I believe, and the end product, while not clearly in sight, looms. 'We have to make politics groovy,' Country Joe said in discussing why political rallies were a drag. The poetry of politics is rock music. Once we begin to think of it this way, the power and direction of the music begin to make sense.

12. Dan Friedman, *When the Curtain fell on the Workers' Theatre*. In: The New York Alliance, April 11 '83.[12]

The New Deal of the 1930's was not only a series of innovations initiated from the top to save capitalism, but also a response to the demands and the strengths of mass movements of poor and working people from below. This was true not only in the areas of economic and political reform, but also in relation to the famous cultural programs of the New Deal – the Federal Arts Project and the Federal Theatre Project. Workers in the early '30's were not only organizing unemployed councils, tenants' unions, labor defense funds, and trade unions; they were also organizing themselves culturally, particularly in that most social of art forms – the theatre.

In the early years of the depression workers all across the country began to organize theatre groups in which they acted and directed short plays and skits they had written themselves. They performed these plays for their fellow workers on picket lines, lines, on hunger marches, at protests against evictions, at meetings of unions and social clubs, and at political rallies.

The rapid growth of these independent amateur workers' theatres was remarkable. In 1930, when the first attempt to organize contact among the workers' theatres was made, 21 groups were found. Four years later, in 1934, there were over 400 workers theatres from 28 cities in the United States that had organized themselves into a national organization known as the League of Workers Theatres (L.O.W.T.). The League distributed scripts, held competitions, established a school to teach theatre skills, and carried on a vast network of correspondence. In addition, the League published a monthly magazine called Workers Theatre that grew from a circulation of 200 in April, 1931 to 18,000 by 1935.

Although the theatres were the most extensive, there were also organized in the early 30s a national Workers' Dance League, a national Workers' Photo League, a national graphic artists' club for workers called The Block of Painters (which mostly did fescoes and murals for union and left-wing meeting places), numerous workers' choral societies, and a national club for creative writers called the John Reed Club which included both worker-writers and progressive intellectuals, and whose members often had their writings published in the independent literary journal called New Masses.

Three points should be made about all of these workers' cultural institutions. First, they were independent of the established cultural order. They received no money from the government, no private endowments, and were not connected to any establishment cultural institution. They were created, administrated, financed and patronized by the workers themselves. Second, this cultural upheaval was not spontaneous; it was a response to, and part of, the general economic and political organizing that was going on to combat the effects of the depression. And just as the Communist Party was instrumental in organizing unemployment councils, hunger marches, industrial unions, and raising demands for radical reform, it was also instrumental in encouraging and building an audience for the workers'

12. Copyright, Dan Friedman, 1983. Dan Friedman has a Ph.D. in Theatre History and teaches at York College of C.U.N.Y. and the Princeton Writers' Center. He is also a playwright and a member of Workers' Stage, a theatre that performs for working class audiences throughout the New York City area.

theatres and the other workers' cultural organizations. The leadership it provided demonstrated the vital importance of an independent political party of the working class in establishing and maintaining an independent workers' cultural movement.

These workers' cultural movements did not just ape the form and content of established art, but began to fill their work with reflections of their own lives, their own views, their own politics, leading to a tremendous vitality and experimentation which in turn led to a remarkable enthusiasm from the audience. The early 30s witnessed the growth of a working class audience for theatre, art, dance, etc. that has not been equaled since in the United States.

Thus, the move by the Roosevelt New Dealers to support working class art through the Federal Arts Project and the Federal Theatre Project was not simply an attempt to provide out-of-work artists with jobs and to bring culture to the people. It was a response by the established order to a vast independent workers' cultural movement that had grown up in the early years of the depression. In 1935, the year that the independent workers' theatre movement reached the height of its influence and numbers, the Federal Theatre Project was founded as part of the Works Progress Administration. As with most New Deal projects, its stated purpose was to put people back to work, in this case, the re-employment of unemployed theatre people in federally-financed theatre enterprises offering dramatic entertainment either free or at low cost. It resulted in hundreds of exciting plays for hundreds of thousands of people in every region of the country, and provided us with a glimpse of the possibilities of how wonderful theatre could be when it isn't run for profit but as a right of the people. But four years later, when Congress cut off funds for the Federal Theatre Project, there no longer existed an independent workers' theatre movement – or, for that matter, no dance, art, or photo movement either. What had happened?

Hallie Flannagan, the head of the Federal Theatre Project, was a liberal theatre professor from Vassar who had long followed the development of the workers' theatre movement, and had even been a contributing editor of Workers Theatre for the year before she was made head of the Project. She declared that the Federal Theatre Project had the long-term goal of 'widening theatre to include consciousness of the social scene,' and of bringing great theatre to people who had never seen theatre before. In a general sort of way this was what the workers' theatre had been doing. Many people involved in the workers' theatre movement found the idea of a well-financed institutional theatre that shared some of their concerns very appealing.

What was even more appealing was that for the first time in their lives these political theatre people were offered paying jobs in the theatre. Hanns Bonn, who had been the director of the most popular and influential of the workers' theatre groups, the German language Prolet-Buehne from Yorkville, was appointed to head the entire German-language section of the Federal Theatre Project. There he directed three plays which won tremendous critical acclaim, with critics comparing him with Piscator and Meyerhold as one of the great directors of our century. But when, after three shows, Bonn was forced to resign by right-wing pressures from within his company of German-American professional actors, his former group, the Prolet-Buehne, no longer existed. After an unsuccessful attempt to start a labor theatre in Cleveland, he never did theatre work again.

Another example is what happened to Artef. Artef was the leading Jewish workers' theatre. It had existed since the 20s, and by the mid-30s had obtained semi-professional status with most of its actors earning all or part of their living from Artef. But as Yiddish Theatre historian David Lifton points out in his unpublished 1962 dissertation 'The History of the Yiddish Art Theatre,'

... during the last few years of the 1930s many Artef people obtained steady jobs with the Federal Theatre Project. These actors were not permitted to work for both the government and for Artef. This broke up the ensemble.

The Workers' Laboratory Theatre had been the leading English-language workers' theatre of the period and were recognized, even by their political enemies, as being artistically superb. The Federal Theatre Project took in the entire group, changed its name to The One-Act Experimental Theatre, and after one production split it up. The group's members were distributed to various other theatres within the Federal Theatre Project where they went on to make valuable contributions as directors, stage managers, actors and costume designers. But the independent workers' theatre movement had lost one of its leading lights; the Workers' Laboratory Theatre had ceased to exist.

This happened over and over again. The ranks of the workers' theatre movement were literally devastated. When the Federal Theatre Project was started there were approximately 400 independent workers' theatres in the United States. When it ended four years later, only about five were still in existence. Those groups that did try to survive as independent theatres found their audiences slipping away as the federal government started presenting free or very inexpensive 'socially conscious' theatre more frequently and on a higher technical level than the independent groups were able to provide. Aside from the higher technical level, the major reason the Federal Theatre Project was so successful in taking over the workers' theatre audience was that the Federal Theatre, particularly its Living Newspaper unit, absorbed many of the techniques, dramatic forms, acting styles, and subjects first developed by the workers' theatre and which the American-workers' audience had come to expect and enjoy.

However, while many Federal Theatre productions did speak to the concerns of their worker-audience, they did so from a very different politic. The politic of the independent workers' theatres reflected their consciousness of themselves as a working class with distinct interests in contradiction with the establishment. The politic of the Federal Theatre Project reflected the consciousness of the liberal sector of the establishment for reforming the capitalist system. Unlike the independent workers' theatres, they did not construct conflicts on a clear-cut class basis, but posed a vaguely defined 'Little Man' or 'Consumer' in opposition to specific social issues (unreasonably greedy landlords in One-Third of a Nation, a bad utility company in Power.) Unlike the independent workers' theatres, they did not explore socialist or revolutionary alternatives to the depression, but propagandized instead for isolated reformist partial solutions (public housing projects in One-Third of a Nation, federally funded power projects in Power.)

This is not to say that there wasn't struggle inside the Federal Theatre Project between the government and its workers. Of course there was. But the government almost always won because they had the power to censor or close a show. The first Living Newspaper production, Ethiopia, about the Italian invasion of that country, was never allowed to open because Roosevelt feared it would offend

Mussolini. 'The Cradle Will Rock,' which was a non-radical but pro-union musical, was shut down on opening night. The audience and actors then marched to another theatre and put it on anyway, where it went on to have a successful commercial run. However, that victory for the Federal Theatre workers and their audience was an exception to the rule. Research into the Federal Theatre records in the Library of Congress reveals that many scripts were rejected by Hallie Flannagan for being what she called 'Marxist screams of hate.'

Despite all these attempts at self-censorship, the Federal Theatre Project was considered too radical by conservative forces in Congress who voted it out of existence four years after its birth. All of the federally-funded theatres collapsed, the theatre-artists were once again unemployed, and the independent workers' theatre movement no longer existed for them to go back to. The workers' theatres had been disbanded, the audience lost, and, perhaps most important, the political idea that workers and poor people should have their own independent cultural institutions that reflected their lives, and their politics as a class, was abandoned.

13. Susan Sontag, *A Note on Bunraku.*[13] From the program for the Osaka Bunraku Troupe's performance at the N.Y.C. Japan House, March 12-19, '83.

A NOTE ON BUNRAKU
Susan Sontag

'Art is something which lies in the slender margin between the real and the unreal ... It is unreal, and yet it is not unreal; it is real, and yet it is not real.'

Chikamatsu Monzaemon (1653-1725)

In Bunraku the play is identified, first of all, as physical object: a text. And the text is sacred — that is, generative. Hence, the grave ceremony that opens each performance: the chief reader holds out the text and bows to it, before setting it down on the low lectern and beginning to read. Bunraku is a theatre that transcends the actor, by multiplying and displacing the sources of dramatic pathos.

The play is acted — that is to say, recited — that is, read. The text (declaimed, sung, chanted, wailed) is punctuated or italicized by music produced by a string instrument, the shamisen. It is also, simultaneously, enacted — by piercingly expressive large puppets, half or two-thirds life-size. The enacting of the drama occupies the stage proper, in front of the audience: the wide rectangular space where figures — the puppets and their handlers — move. But the source of the words and the music — the one or more reciters and musicians who sit to the right of the stage on a rostrum — constitutes a parallel performance. The dialogue is not 'off,' as in a certain kind of narrative film, but off-center — displaced, given its own expressive and gestural autonomy.

The drama has a double displacement of emotion, a double scale, a double physical and emotional gait. On the stage proper the leading principle is a kind of anti-hysteria. There is the muteness of the protagonists — who, instead of being living actors, are puppets; there is the impassivity and omnipresence of the humans who make them move. To the joruri reciter, who is not only off-center (from the audience's point of view) but physically immobile, is given the task of maximal expressiveness. Most of the texts, which consists of narrative and commentary as well as dialogue, are floridly emotional, and the narration may modulate into a lengthy crescendo of sobs and gasps. The figure of the reciter, who acts, as it were, by proxy, on behalf of the puppets, is just one of the devices whereby Bunraku isolates — decomposes, illustrates, transcends, intensifies — what acting is.

The puppet is, in prototype, a supple doll operated by a single person. The invention, in 1734, of a puppet to be operated by three persons brought the puppet's emotional and gestural potency to a point never equaled before or since. The Japanese puppet can roll its eyes, raise its eyebrows, smile, clench its fists; it can languish, dress itself, run, convincingly take its own life. No string puppet or hand puppet can perform such complex and detailed actions; and the Bunraku puppets have an ability to move audiences, move them to tears, unmatched in any other puppet tradition.

But apart from widening the emotional range and expressiveness of the puppet (a gain we may or may not choose to identify with 'realism'), the fact of multiplying the operators — and, of necessity, putting them onstage with the puppets —

706

decisively shapes and transforms the emotional register of puppet drama. The puppet is literally outnumbered, beleaguered, surrounded. The presence of three out-sized handlers contributes an unending pathos to the puppet's movements and efforts. The puppets seem helpless, child-like, vulnerable. Yet they also seem sovereign, imperious, in their very smallness and precision and elegance.

Bunraku works on two scales of spatial relations. The often elaborate decor is constructed to the puppets' measurements. The operators are giants, interlopers. Alongside each delicate puppet head are the three large heads of the operators. The operators look at the puppet as they manipulate it. The audience watches the operators observing the puppet, primal spectators to the drama they animate. The three operators sum up the essence of what it is to be a god. To be seen, and impassive. (One has his face bared.) And to be hidden. (The other two wear black hoods.) The puppet gestures. The operators move together, as one giant body, animating the different parts of the puppet body, in a perfected division of labor.

What the audience sees is that to act is to be moved. (And, simultaneously, observed.) What is enacted is the submission to a fate. That one operator's face is bared and two are veiled is another device making Bunraku's characteristic double statement: hyperbole and discretion, presence and absence of the dramatic substance.

This relation between the operators and the puppet is not simply an efficient relation: it is the cruel mystery which is at the center of the Bunraku drama. Handing the puppet a comb, rushing the puppet to its doom – some moments the operators seem like the puppet's servants, at other moments its captors. Sometimes the puppet seems to be reposing solidly on the operators or to be borne placidly aloft by them; other times to be in perpetual, hapless flight. There are constant shifts of scale, to delight the senses and wring the emotions. Sometimes the shadowy manipulators shrink and the puppets swell into a normal scale. Then the operators loom once more and the puppets rebecome fragile, persecuted Lilliputians.

The situation we call art characteristically requires us both to look very attentively and to look 'beyond' (or 'through') what is understood as an impediment, distraction, irrelevance. At an opera performance, we look past or over the orchestra to concentrate on the stage. But in Bunraku we are not supposed to look past the shadowy, black-garbed puppeteers. The presence of the operators is what gives Bunraku its elevated, mythic impersonality and heightened, purified emotionality. In order to make the art of the puppets competitive with the art of living actors, says Chikamatsu, the text must be 'charged with feeling'. But, he adds, 'I take pathos to be entirely a matter of restraint.' Compare Balanchine, which brought the naively emotive classical ballet tradition to its apex by developing the sense in which dancers are co-sharers, with ideal puppets, in the sublimity of the impersonal: 'Silence, placidity, and immobility are perhaps the most powerful forces. They are as impressive, even more so, than rage, delirium, or ecstasy.'

In the most profound Western meditation on puppet theatre (and, by extension, on the dance), Kleist wrote that the very inanimateness of the puppet was the precondition for expressing an ideal state of the spirit. Kleist's speculative fantasy – he was writing, in 1810, about string puppets – is incarnated and fulfilled in Bunraku.

(Program note, performances of the Bunraku Kyokai, Osaka, March 12-19, 1983, Japan House, N.Y.C.)

14. Minutes of Annual Bread and Puppet Meeting, January 9, 1982, Glover Vermont.

Present:

Linda Elbow	Paul Zaloom	Barbara Leber
Helen Rabin	Michael Romanyshyn	Mabel Dennison
Elka Schumann	Mark Dannenhauer	Max Schumann
Ron Kelley	Michael Boylen	Susan Dennison
Poppy Gregory	George Konnoff	Ellen Braithwaite
Peter Schumann	Joanne Schultz	Burt Porter
Jackie Smith	Nancy Tyndall	Erik Porter
Cate Peck	Martin Steingesser	Trudi Cohen
John Bell	John Romanyshyn	

Peter: First, before the financial report, here's a reminder of what we are. We're called a corporation, but we're not. We don't produce a market item responding to the demands of society, but the opposite: first we make something because it's fun, then force it, or tickle it, onto society. Our product doesn't make sense, it's a lunatic fringe product, and therefore our organization is tentative, not fixed. However we work, it can be changed.

List of 1981 productions (see separate sheet)

Finances

1981 Financial report presented by Barbara (see separate sheets)

Trudi reminds us that people who have worked in B & P for 6-7 months a year have access to the Medical Fund (which pays half the cost of medical and dental fees).

Items: — in 1981 per diems went up to $100/wk (from $60/wk);
     — the 3-wk January Nativity tour in France, organized 8-10 months earlier, made $52,000 of which $26,000 was profit;
     — the 6-wk Theater for the New City run in NYC broke even;
     — the 6-wk East Coast Fear tour made $18,000 of which $9,000 was profit;
     — suggested that $10,000 be put into a CD w/checks account for this year's Circus;
     — we bought a (Circus) tent.

Peter: Maurice's estate, first we thought it was for B & P; then in the will we saw that the money was left to Peter Schumann, then in case of his death, to Elka, and in case of her death, to the Schumann children, with the '. . . wish and desire that (it) be used to promote and support the Bread and Puppet Theater . . .' I have decided to split the money half-and-half with B & P and use our half for the Schumann kids' education. (Later, the $32,345.48 was divided into $16,172.74 for B & P, same for Schumanns.)

Peter suggests comparing B & P finances with other theater groups. George briefly describes Two-Penny Theater's finances and organization.

Lots of things we do don't generate income, but cost us money, like parades, exhibits, Cuba. Barbara: 1 week performing in Cuba cost us the travel to Montreal, about $300.

Lunch Break

Circus

Parking problems and alternatives: Michael R. reports about last year's arrangement w/ neighbor Doug Conley, who made a parking-lot and campsite in his field and charged admission. Agreement about the charges was clear and verbal, but Doug ended up raising the prices, which caused a lot of complaints and bad feelings. We decided for next Circus to have a written agreement w/ Doug guaranteeing him a fixed fee; we'd make parking fees voluntary, not compulsory; and Doug would help w/ parking and collecting money.

Food (a surprisingly short and unheated discussion): Peter proposes to cut out all food sales because: the commercial scene is ugly; they make too much money; the cars mess up the field; logistics are complicated and time-consuming. We'll offer bread, water, and aioli, and urge people to bring picnics and free food.

Several people emphasize the importance, starting NOW, of publicizing that the next Circus will have no food sales. On posters, in press releases, and when answering inquiries, tell people to bring picnics. Discussion of various ways to serve food and eat: hang food on trees along edge of field, put up a tent w/ bread and water, serve a giant sit-down meal for thousands, ask people to grow an extra patch of vegetables for the Circus, put up more Bread tents, etc.

Annie: Make it simple, don't emphasize food. (She coordinated the food sales, with Ozzie Henschel, for the last 2 summers.)

Peter: It will be a job for us, but more pleasant than organizing the food sales.

No one was against the no-food-sale policy.

Date: With the Barton Fair on the 3d weekend of August, the choices were the 2nd and 4th weekends.
2nd Weekend means a shorter work period, possible better and warmer weather, and more light.
4th weekend means the possibility of a longer work period, cooler weather, earlier darkness and therefore an earlier Pageant.
It was agreed that the date would not affect the size of the crowd.

Peter wants to start work earlier. Barbara points out that that makes Circus more expensive. (Later, at this meeting, the later date, August 28-29, is voted in; this is confirmed by the Glover puppeteers a week later.)

Other variations of the date are brought up and receive no support: a 4-day Circus, or 3 Sundays, or 2 weekends. Helen: You're asking for burn-out.

Paul again proposes that parts of the Circus be publicly performed, as they get ready, 2-3 weeks before actual event, 'to show each other what we're doing'. Many agree that this is a good idea with solid advantages.

Ellen: Local people who are intimidated by the Circus' size and crowds and difficulty in getting there, would come to smaller shows.

Theme: Peter: No unified theme this year, the theme of the title, Our Domestic Resurrection, is enough.

Scheduling of events: Discussed that: experienced puppeteers work on only 1 sideshow, not switch around among many sideshows, to simplify scheduling during first period; that puppeteers work more with newcomers, not w/ each other; that it's a shame to be limited to only 1 show and that puppeteers enjoy and work well w/ each other; that Peter do his private art projects earlier in order to have more time to work on shows; that there be a big new show again in the afternoon, or that the pageant be expanded to include big new show; that something be done so that participants in pageant can see (more of) it; since more and more frequently people say, 'No thanks, I don't want to be in it this year, I want to watch!'; that shows after the Pageant be eliminated because they are anticlimactic and work against the dynamics of the whole day; that the late shows have been some of the best performances of those pieces and that they honor the die-hard theater-goers who stay; that we weren't always prepared for the big rehearsals when many people came and should prepare better; that the Pageant needs way more people than the Circus, so we should rehearse them on different days; that we make an effort to participate in Hiroshima Day (Aug. 6) events in Vermont.

Children: Ellen: It got difficult with the many little children who come to weekend rehearsals. Parents must know that they can't just leave their kids. Perhaps children should be involved later in the rehearsals, when more of the action is settled and there isn't so much part-changing. The scene with the devils in the bus was scary and dangerous for little kids.

Discussion whether or not to limit or encourage kids' participation? Are there, or are there not, enough adults who can and want to work with children?

Resolved that kids' acts in the Circus get more thought and preparation, more input from experienced puppeteers.

Break

Guest performers and audience participation: Trudi: We need more shows, our sideshows alone cannot accomodate the crowd.

Nancy: What about an action that the audience can participate in, contribute to, like making many, many little figures?

Peter: The bonfire-dance is a kind of contribution; and Trudi and Michael did fairy-tales where people and kids from the audience participated.

Elka: What about a newsletter next year, written by the participants of the Circus, old and new, and dealing with the work, shows, weather, music, parades, people, impressions, etc.?

OTHER BUSINESS

Touring schedule: John B.: We tour to make money for the Circus and we tour a lot. It seems we're away more than ever, and one week off between tours is a problem, psychologically. We were rushed and didn't have time this fall to prepare for winter. Planning future tours requires that someone be here to organize them. This year some tours were made with too short preparation. We need breathing space. We should have time between tours to think about what we do, especially when we travel without Peter.

Barbara: This year we toured for 6 months and worked on the Circus for 2-3 months, not so different from other years. We could take 2 six-week periods aside and arrange tours then to make money.

George: It's as important for someone to be home working on tours as it is to tour, and that role should be rotated.

Peter: We want to show the shows we're working on. And we want to do new shows all the time. Long-range planning for a non-existant show is harder.

Trudi: We want more time to plan and prepare what we do, so that we do it as well as we can. It's in our power to do it better.

Peter: Some radical changes are possible – 2 companies that tour at the same time. There is enough material to occupy 2-3 companies, just look at the projection schedule.

John B.: More companies means more work booking.

Ron: We can set up a tour so it's easier and more profitable. We need better long-range planning.

Michael R.: Obviously we can plan further ahead, but to arrange a whole year and not be open is bad. We need long-range plans for money, and we need to be flexible for last-minute arrangements.

George: It's your decision, so do it. You're complaining about something only you can solve.

Nancy: It sounds as though you, John, want time for another life.

John B.: We don't need more vacation time; the number of tours a year doesn't bother me, but, rather, better preparation time.

Trudi: We should rotate who stays here and arrange tours, and open opportunities for others to participate more on tours. Tours change when Peter isn't on them. A new show needs more and stronger preparation.

Mark: If the company understands a show well enough, it can change it on the road.

Michael R.: It's good to tour older shows, a shame that shows are made and then dropped.

Audience expectations: John B.: When we tour Europe, people don't know what B & P is and come to a show with other expectations than the audience in NYC, where we play more frequently. European audiences see each show as a statement to the world, a definition of what B & P is.

Peter: There's a huge difference between cultivating an audience and just hitting it. If you come often enough, then the audience can compare you to yourself. The real performance isn't Goya or Fear, but the whole cycle which includes the stupid bitso and the big serious shows. A compromise would be to bring street pieces and parades as well as a serious show.

Mark: Match a tour more to the place you go to.

Helen: Either you pay attention to what people expect, or don't, and just do what you want.

George: It's not profitable to go to NYC; in Europe they pay for theater (see financial tour sheet). You can't solve the audiences' problems . . . they get their money's worth.

Peter: In Koln (most recent tour) they expected a lot, and we played Goya, a cold, abstract show, which didn't respond to their desires for communion.

Michael R.: Woyzeck would work better on a traditional stage, and we get open factories. Goya is not a money-making show, it should be played where it feels good.

Barbara: We should feel comfortable with a show; Woyzeck was ready, Goya (new first part) was not.

Annie: You can figure all this out better in a small group.

John R.: What is the problem: too much touring or better planning?

Helen and Michael B.: Tighten operations, improve your efficiency.

Trudi: Peter, you don't have to create another company; people exist who can do it.

Joanne: The Performing Artists for Nuclear Disarmament are working on a big event for Spring '82. Is B & P interested? (Later, actions are being planned for Disarmament events in June '82).

Media: John B.: On this tour Italian TV wanted to video-tape our shows for TV and pay B & P a big fee. There's a big difference between performing live or for TV, where there's no control over the final product. And to do the money right you need a lawyer. We decided not to do it. But other projects were done with film.

Peter: Which are unsatisfactory and disgusting and the best policy is to say NO, and then make exceptions for good reasons. We were loose for home and school videotaping, and now I'm against it. What's all this conserving good for? The best value of theater is that it disappears when it's over.

Martin: When you do shows it's a sharing process, and that's gone with video.

Peter: If we want to make a film, than let's, with those Yale students in NYC.

John B.: We sometimes let TV do shooting for publicity, when we need an audience. A man from Berlin filmed, it didn't bother the show, and it seemed worthwhile to document it.

Mabel: Look what people watch on TV; better for them to see (B & P) like that than not at all.

712

George: Why make movies of live theater? It's no good, it's spoilt.

John B.: In Milan the sponsors were most interested in getting us documented than in getting people in to see the show.

Burt: It's nice that there are some people not dying to get on TV.

Peter: Our policy used to be: no shooting for commercial purposes, and yes to private shooting, and I propose we now say NO, except when we want to make an exception.

Farm projects for this year: In barn: close off West side; make costume area tighter, against snow-drifts; put door between woodshed and museum; lay floor in chicken-coop area; repair big door on South side; work on basement; and maybe put roof over deck.

Fire and Health Insurance: All agree we need more information and need insurance. John Bell volunteers to research Fire, Trudi to research Medical, insurances.

Possible new tours: Maria Rankov to arrange European tour mid-March to mid-April; disarmament events in NYC in early June; Clearwater Festival in June; John B. works on Chicago tour for fall; Venice Biennale invitation for Christmas.

Catalogue of Museum proposed by Elka, possibly with a Vermont Arts Council grant.

Salary raise for puppeteers moved by Michael Boylen, seconded by John Romanyshyn, who recommends that a smaller group decide details. Agreed to by those present.

Trudi: We can't raise our salaries without increasing the per diem.

(Later, a meeting of the Glover members decides to raise their salaries and the per diems by $15 a week, so that Glover puppeteers get $75 (Elka gets $150), and per diems are $115.)

Meeting ends with a feast. Then Mabel shows her slides of Cuba and we view a film, 'Stilt Dancers of Long Bow Village', which the makers, Carma Hinton and Richard Gordon, kindly loaned us, and which Mark and Jackie brought from Boston.

15. Miscellaneous Bread and Puppet Theatre accounts, 1973-81, appended to the Minutes of January 9, 1982.

B+P 1975 PRODUCTIONS

When:	Where:	What:	How many	HOW MUCH Earn'd:	Spent:	Schumann	Puppeteers	B+P survival (lost)
March 2 wk.	Paris	Grey Lady Cantatas	Peter	(\$1050)	\$334	—	—	+\$616
May 2 wks	Davis California	Ishi Pageant	Peter	\$2300	—	\$400		+\$1900
May 3 days	AQJT Quebec	workshop	Peter, Izub	\$800	\$40	300	\$75	\$+385
CIRCUS mid-May - July 10 wks	Glover	short shows, 3 portcimes	many	\$1252	\$3427		(\$220 × extudies)	\$-2175
Aug 10 days Sept 2 wks	Mannheim Martinique	White Horse Butcher, Hallelujah, Kingstory	Peter, Tumor + many -5 + 4	\$8533	\$2350 ca.	\$950	\$400	+\$4833
Sept.- Oct.- Nov.	Local	Circus suits, White Horse Butcher	10-15	\$375	\$175 ca.	—	—	\$+200
Nov.- Dec.	Vermont + New England College Schools	Our B Again Resurrection	8-10	4475	\$1000 ca.	\$360 (12c × 3)	\$1030 (+120 × 3)	+2085

B+P INCOMES BY YEAR

	TOTAL	SHOWS	ORDIV.	DONATIONS	SALES	WORKSHOPS	(from previous year)
1973	\$97,997	\$91,309	\$2,148	\$3,897	\$643	—	\$3,136
1974	30,852	26,859	931	1,372	1,690	—	27,066
1975	14,284	5,363	700	1,249	137	6,835	749
1976	HOME: 36,300 Tout: 80,593 Tatal 116,893	27,290 78,716 106,006	\$906 1000 1906	1,685 114 1799	686 763 1448	5,733 — 5,733	622
1977	HOME: 24,825 Tour 35,898 Total 60,723	12,244 35,898 48,142	1,297	3550	1,810	5,925	4051

B+P EXPENSES' TOTALS BY YEAR

YEAR	TOTAL	FOOD	WORK MATERIALS	TRANSPORTATION	OP.EX.	OR.DIV.	FEES
'73	\$73,601	13,966	\$5,868	15,348	5,876	\$3,040	\$18,337
'74	57,478	15,952	3,099	9,873	4,711	1,300	22,541 (late Faum disbanding bonuses)
'75	14,299	2,983	1,151	3,420	2,244	1,078	3,421
'76	HOME: 30,866 Tour: 67,087 Grand Total 97,953	3,911 5,511 9,422	2,116 749 2,865	3,548 24,726 28,274	4,815 10,769 15,584	3,039 — 3,039	9,076 — 9,076
'77	HOME: 43,683 Tour: 11,710 Grand Total 55,373	4,894 495 5,389	3,064 97 3,161	7,968 6,485 14,453	6,747 224 6,971	2,018 — 2,018	18,754 4,407 23,161

B+P PRODUCTIONS IN 1981

NEW SHOWS	TOURS	OLD SHOWS	WORKSHOPS	LOCAL SHOWS & PARADES	POLITICAL DEMONSTR	HOUSE & FARM	SCULPTURE & PAINTING	EXHIBITS
"Swords & Plowshares"	Nativity in France 12 X	"Nativity"	"Nativity" w/20-30 6 or 8X	6 Summer parades in Vt.	Newlondon Trident demonstration	Red Shed enlarged, new roof, shelves	2 Hiroshima cement- all-ing projects spring & fall	cheap Art Bus
"Goya"		"Venus Rising from the Water"	Swords & Plowshares event at the	Museum Opening	NYC El Salvador parade	garbage shed	cows	3 Vt. tours
"Woyzeck"	"Fear" on East Coast 26 X		"Powerline" workshops	Serious Window		deck to museum entrance	Apocalypse Riders	4 laundromats
"7 Obsessions"		"Halleluja"			NYC Chile		Condemned Bodies	SAMPUL RIVER? +t circus, Johnson NYC, Plainfd
"The Powerline Show"	Circus 12 X	Circus the Cuban Missile Crisis	"Obsessions" workshop	"Fear" in Orleans		stage in bottom-of-barn	Tigers, Apes Giraffes	Puppets masks in Randolph
"The Story of One Who Set Out to Study Fear"	Swords & Plowshares 12 X (4 1/2 only)		"Apocalypse" workshop w/20-25	Vt. Powerline Show, 3-4X			Circus banners, posters, restaurants painted & painted	Apocalypse: Circus Fleming Museum
Swords: The Story of the Plowshare 8; The Epoxy	"Goya" 19 X	"Goya"	Burlington Serious Window w/8 Glover			stage in pine forest		Story- Pictures Circus & Plainf'd
The Trial; Plowshares	Woyzeck 12 X					new Museum floor, new electricity		2 giant puppets in Proving R of A. ex. Plainfd
End of the World Pageant								Masks w/ travelling mask exhibit Cvx
Circus shows: Corpus Christi, Black Water, Fiat Shi Koo The Man Who Slept in his Chair, Exxodo Furioso, This-That-& the Other, Sweet Land of Liberty, Domino Bear Family, MX missile, The Uberght Defeat								New Museum Floor
Apocalypse								Stomach Pictures
"Serious Window"								Earle motion- Mask paintings
"Cave" Prologue								

BREAD & PUPPET THEATER FINANCES for 1981

EXPENSES

TOURS	TOTAL	FOOD	WORK MATERIALS	TRANSPORTATION	PRINTING	OR EX-OFFICE EXPENSES	RENTS & UTILITIES	REPAIRS	6 SALARIES	PER DIEMS	CONTRACT & OTHER SERVICES	MISC.
"Nativity" in France 3 wks.	25,709	3,114	39	11,667	1,152	121	4,572	0	1265	1,774	1,984	16
"Goya", "TNC", TNC/NYC 2 wks.	7,469	1,218	650	363	120	356	212	0	2500	2,050	0	0
"Swords & Plowshares" East Coast 1 wk.	6.26	305	10	294	0	17	0	0	0	0	0	0
"Fear" East Coast 6 wks.	8,813	1,231	396	819	63	336	155	6	1,280	4,470	0	20
"Woyzeck", "Goya" Germany, Italy, 6 wks.	22,860	2,337	269	13,461	0	522	1,989	0	1,412	2,668	48	154
1981 CIRCUS	13,904	4,054	2,505	1,151	499	352	1,383	since 5 friends	not counted	3,192	606	100
1979 CIRCUS	9,098	3,157	2,760	1,107	438	262	430	5 friends	not counted	0	408	19

TOURS	INCOME	PROFIT
Nativity	$52,069	$26,365
TNC	7,723	254
Swords	3,800	3,174
Fear	18,066	9,253
Woyzeck/Goya	34,256	11,396

CIRCUS INCOMES

1981 - $6,144
1979 - 5,180

[Note: any small discrepancies in the figures come from my rounding off figures to nearest dollar. E.S.]

Bread & Puppet Finances for 1981

INCOME	TOTAL	SHOWS	GIFTS	SALES	WORKSHOPS	INTEREST	COMMISSIONS	
1981	147,349	121,218	14,373	9,498	675	1,436	150	
1980	148,142	74,646	10,948	1,574	46,829	710	13,475	1981 Balance in check book: est. $20,000

OTHER ACCOUNTS: Erasmus Prize- $20,034 ; Maurice's Memorial Fund- $8,794 ; Medical- $3,784; House Acct- $802

EXPENSES	TOTAL	FOOD	WORK-MATERIALS	TRANSPORTATION (bus, car, freight)	PRINTING (of articles for sale)	OR EX-office expenses (newspaper)	RENTS & UTILITIES	BUILDING REPAIRS	BUDGET END's (insurance, account.)	6 SALARIES
1981	120,875	13,562	5,756	27,332	3,454	4,726	14,225	1,478	1,140	23,318
1980	140,552	8,899	2,917	25,390	912	3,720	7,920	3,960	2,713	19,775

EXPENSES cont.	FED. TAXES on salaries	PER DIEMS	CONTRACT work	MISC.		
1981	3876	15,558	5,366	1,284	and Medical Fund spent $327.50,	
1980	3016	8,744	6,055	1928 and 45,000+ worth SAVED	House Account spent $12,76.41.	

[Note: any small discrepancies in the figures come from my rounding of figures to nearest dollar, and I have taken the 1981 CIRCUS income of $6,144 and divided it in half, $3072 as gifts and $3072 as sales and then I changed the 1981 GIFT & SALES INCOMES to reflect this. E.S.]

16. Susan Goodman, *New York City rent strikes,* The Village Voice, 1964.[14]

'The words "rent strike" inspire colorful visions of revolutionary tenants manning barricades against the propertied classes. The reality is a far cry from that, judging from the experience to date on the Lower East Side. After months of hard work and complex legal maneuvers, the organizers have barely scratched the surface of the slum-ridden area.

At its height last spring, the participating groups in the Lower East Side Rent Strike Committees had 60 buildings out. About 30 tenements are currently on strike, most of them under the aegis of Downtown CORE. The chill of winter without heat and the expected resurgence of civil rights activities after the election will probably increase this number somewhat.

Over a third of the buildings on the Lower East Side are classified as "substandard." Tenements that used to reek of the overcooked cabbage of East European immigrants now exude the odor of Puerto Rican cuisine. The indestructible cockroaches, the dark hallways, the cracked plaster, and the noise of families quarreling in tiny apartments remain.

Rent strikes, frequent during the Depression, were almost unheard of in recent years until the exploits of Harlem civil rights leader Jesse Gray hit the front pages of the New York Times last winter. The suddenly popular tactic spread to the Lower East Side in January with the help of Mobilization for Youth, an agency supported by funds from the federal government, the City, and the Ford Foundation.

Mobilization, which has come under severe criticism recently for its role, at the time called together representatives of six local groups concerned with housing. They were the Council of Puerto Rican Organizations, Downtown CORE, Integrated Workers (the East Side branch of the far-left Progressive Labor Movement), Negro Action Group, and two local affiliates of the Metropolitan Council on Housing. Some of the groups already had isolated buildings out on strike, but the impetus for concerted action came from Mobilization.

The controversial social agency supplied three full-time organizers, telephones, mimeograph machines, and headquarters space in a housing clinic at 332 East 4th Street. Legal aid, crucial for a successful rent strike, was supplied by a team of volunteer lawyers, whose efforts were also eventually coordinated by a Mobilization staff counsel.

The loose federation fell apart in May. "A power struggle tore the guts out of the 'Lower East Side Rent Strike' committee," according to one member. Tactical difference, political disputes, and distrust of Mobilization's purse strings were among the disintegrating factors. After the federation disbanded, the rent strike lost its zip. Several participants, pointing out that rent strikes are seasonal, ascribed the collapse also to the onset of warm weather.

"Mobilization was useful here," said Alice Jerome, the Progressive Labor Movement's president of Integrated Workers. "They organized buildings from the ground up. But when they got hold of a neighborhood leader and put him on payroll, something very subtle happened to his militancy." She advocates "illegal" rent strikes and tells tenants to pocket the money. Agreeing that they could land out in the street this way, Miss Jerome claimed that the Integrated Workers have been able to stave off evictions by using the tactic of demonstrations.

The other participating groups undertook only "legal" rent strikes. They told tenants first to put their money into escrow and, later, to turn it over to the court. Landlords cannot obtain eviction orders for non-payment of rent if the tenant can prove that City agencies have posted serious violations against the building. Lack of heat or falling plaster usually cause the landlord to lose the dispossess procedings. "One violation for rats is worth 10 for cracked plaster, no paint, or broken windows," according to Nancy LeBlanc, the vivacious Mobilization staff counsel in charge of rent-strike cases.

The tenants never get their rent back. If the landlord repairs the building, he collects the money deposited with the court. Otherwise it goes to the State of New York. The tenants, however, frequently can obtain a rent reduction by applying to the Rent and Rehabilitation Administration, a process that can take up to 10 months. The reduced rent is then paid to the court.

People who work with the Lower East Side tenants feel that the law is property-oriented and that many slips can occur in a "legal" rent strike. Jose Fuentes, one of the Mobilization organizers, noted, "The landlords have an enormous amount of influence in all the City departments and courts."

Fuentes, one of the two remaining organizers in Mobilization's East 4th Street housing clinic, said he had been told to accept rent strike cases if tenants walk in off the street. However, he can no longer go into tenements to try to organize them. His co-worker in the office, LeRoy MacCrae, candidate in 1962 of the Trotskyite Socialist Workers' Party for State Attorney General, has been vociferously attacked by the Daily News.

Even without rent strikes the organizers clearly have enough work to keep them going 12 hours a day until Doomsday.

On a typical day late last month, the tiny clinic, itself in need of paint, was constantly crowded with bewildered people seeking information and help.

A Puerto Rican man, seeking Fuentes' approval of his answers on a rent-control form, was followed by a Ukrainian grandmother, who seemed utterly baffled when told to send a registered letter to her landlord. Someone finally offered to do it for her. Fuentes then went back to a telephone discussion about a heatless building with a Health Department official.

The rapid pace of the clinic continued until 7 p.m. when Fuentes left to look up a near-by tenant who had not come around recently. "I worry if they don't check in after a few days," he explained. "You have to answer all those forms right away. If you don't the case is closed and you have to start all over again."

From the point of view of long-term tenant organization, the energetic Fuentes called the rent strikes a "failure." "However," he added, "many tenants at least learned a few points of law and lost their fear of the landlord. Others haven't learned anything in the past 20 years. So we end up doing a lot of work for them." Almost half the tenants involved in the rent strikes are welfare recipients, a class of people probably least able to cope with municipal bureaucracy.

"I'm encouraged by the whole thing. In many ways it parallels what went on in Mississippi this summer," said Lester Evans, a volunteer rent-strike lawyer and very active member of the Village Independent Democrats. "The tenants were frightened at first. Many of them could not speak English or understand anything going on in the courts." Judges and landlords, who commonly face only bewildered tenants, were "brought up short" by the presence of "well-dressed lawyers wearing clean ties," who appeared for the defense.

The legal effort channeled trhough Mobilization cut down the frequent instances of "rampant perjury," Evans feels. "We've made those landlords down there a little more careful." He gleefully noted that several landlords' attorneys had thanked him privately for the rent strikes. They said their practices have boomed because of the new militancy.' (S. Goodman, *Weather, Power Struggle Blunt Rent Strikes,* Village Voice, November 5 '64.)

17. The Hippies. Allen Ginsberg, *Berkeley Vietnam Days.* [15]
In: Liberation, January, 1966.

1. How To Make a March/Spectacle

If imaginative, pragmatic, fun, gay, happy, *secure* Propaganda is issued to mass media in advance (and pragmatic leaflets handed out days in advance giving marchers instructions)

The parade can be made into an exemplary spectacle on how to handle situations of anxiety and fear/threat (such as Spectre of Hells Angels or Spectre of Communism)

To manifest by concrete example, namely the parade itself, how to change war psychology and surpass, go over, the habit image-reduction of fear/violence.

That is, the parade can embody an example of peaceable health which is the reverse of fighting back blindly.

Announce in advance it is a safe march, bring your grandmother and babies, bring your family and friends. Open declarations, 'We aren't coming out to fight and we simply will not fight.'

We have to use our *imagination*. A spectacle can be made, an unmistakable statement OUTSIDE the war psychology which is leading nowhere. Such statement would be heard around the world with relief.

The following suggestions manifest or embody what I believe to be the conscious psychology of latent understanding of the majority of the youth and many elders who come out to march.

And once clearly enunciated by the leaders of the march will be clearly understood and acted upon by them. Necessity to TRUST the communal sanity of the marchers who already demonstrated that community when they first SAT DOWN.

Needed. An example of health which will paralyze the Angels and also manifest itself thru mass media reportage.

N.B. A negative physcology of becoming scared by threats, adrenalin running in neck, uprush of blood to head, blind resentment, self-righteousness, fear, anger and active return of violence is exactly what the Angels 'power structure' press and fuzz THRIVE ON
> what the young people who come march don't want and are dragged by
> what will decrease the number who come and discourage the great many on
> the fence who wd come to a good scene.

THE FOLLOWING are specific suggestions for organizing march and turning marches on to their roles in the Demonstration.

1. Masses of flowers – a visual spectacle – especially concentrated in the front

---

lines. Can be used to set up barricades, to present to Hells Angels, Police, politicians, and press & spectators whenever needed or at parade's end. Masses of marchers can be asked to bring their own flowers. Front lines shd be organized and provided with flowers in advance.

2. Front lines should be the psychologically less vulnerable groups. The Women for Peace or any other respectable organization, perhaps a line of poets and artists, mothers, families, professors. This shd also be announced (publicized in advance).

3. Marchers should bring CROSSES, to be held up in front in case of violence; like in the movies dealing with Dracula. (This for those who use crosses or Jewish Stars).

4. Marchers who use American Flags should bring those; at least one front row of Marican flags and myriads in the spectacle.

5. Marchers should bring Harmonicas, flutes, recorders, guitars, banjos & violins (Those who don't uses crosses or flags.) Bongoes and tambourines.

6. Marchers should bring certain children's Toys (not fire-crackers or balloons which cause noise hysteria) which can be used for distracting attackers: such as sparklers, toy rubber swords, especially the little whirling carbon wheels which make red-white-blue sparkles. Toy soldiers.

7. In case of heavy anxiety, confusion or struggle in isolated spots marchers could be led in
    Sit Down
    Mass Calisthenics

8. In case of threat of attack marchers could intone en masse the following mantras
    The Lord's Prayer
    Three Blind Mice (sung)
    OM (AUM) long breath in unison
    Star Spangled Banner
    Mary Had a Little Lamb (spoken in unison)

9. More interesting Zen/Spectacle SIGNS
    As in Oakland So in Vietnam
    Everybody's Made of Meat
    Nobody Wants to Get Hurt – Us or Them
    Everybody's Wrong Including U.S.
    Hells Angels   Vietcong   Birch Society
        DON'T FLIP
    We Love You Too

10. Candy bars carried by marchers to offer Hells Angels and Police.

11. Marchers encouraged to carry copies of the Constitution if they have them; or can buy them.

12. Little paper halos to offer angels, police and spectators & patriots.

13. A row of Marchers with white flags, & many white flags in mass.

720

14. Those who have movie cameras bring them & take pictures of spectacle or any action. (To combine for documentary film which could be used in court in case of legal hassels later, and also to circulate for propaganda and profits.) Monitors who can shd have cameras.

OTHER MORE GRANDIOSE POSSIBILITIES.

15. Corps of student newsmen to interview newsmen, propaganzie & soften & charm TV cres etc.

16. Small floats or replicas in front:
>   Christ with sacred heart & cross (invite church groups to prepare)
>   Buddha in Meditation (invite Zen people to come march & meditate on floats)
>   Geo Washington, Lincoln, Whitman etc. (float or living masquerade)
>   Thoreau Behind Bars (float)
>   Hell's Angels Float — With Halos, happy, praying (no ugly provocative caricature)
>   Birch Society Float (Old ladies in tennis sneakers)
>   Dixieland Band Float dressed as Hitler, Stalin, Mussolini, Napoleon & Ceasar (See Universal Soldier song)

17. At first sign of Disturbance, P.A. Systems swing into vast sound *I Wanna Hold Your Hand* and marchers instructed to dance (if not doing calisthenics or Lord's prayer). (These could be schematized as strategy 1, 2, 3, etc. for diverting crowd and angels from Violence.)

18. The Mime Troupe in costume a block down the march, walking doing pantomime.

19. Sound trucks with Bay Area Rock & Roll Bands every two blocks, Jefferson Airplanes, Charlatans, etc. (These bands have their own sound systems.) This scheme to pick up on the universal Youth rockroll protest of Dylan, Eve of Distruction, Universal Soldier, etc. & concertize all that consciousness in the parade.

20. Front (or toward front) — Toy army in costume, Civil War or Rev War or WW I uniforms & signs.

NO MORE
LEAVE ME ALONE

2. To the Hell's Angels

These are the thoughts — anxieties — of anxious marchers
>   That the Angels will attack them
>>   for kicks, or to get publicity, to take the heat off themselves
>>   or to get the goodwill of police & press &/or right wing Money
>   That a conscious deal has been made with Oakland police
>>   or an unconscious rapport, tacit understanding mutual sympathy
>>   that Oakland will lay off persecuting the Angels
>>   if the Angels attack & break up the March & make it a riot

Is any of this true, or is it the paranoia of the less stable-minded marchers?

As long as Angels are ambiguous and don't give open reassurance that they can be
trusted   be tranquil,
The anxious souls, the naturally violent, the insecure, the hysterics among the
marchers have an excuse for policy of
    self-defense thru violence,
    a rationalization for their own inner violence.

That leaves the Marchers with choice of defending themselves thru
    force on account of fear & threat
    unleashing the more irrational minority of rebels
    or at best, defending themselves cooly, under control
        BUT CRITICIZED FOR BEING LAWLESS
    or not defending selves, and possibly abandoned by police
    (for we have no clear assurance from Oakland police that they will sincerely
    try to maintain order and guard our lawful right to march)
    if you attack, & having innocent pacifists, youths & old ladies busted up
        AND CRITICIZED AS IRRESPONSIBLE COWARDS
    By you, by Press, by Public & by Violence loving leftists & rightists.

As it stands the VDC adopted policy of pacifism for marchers, WHO SIMPLY
WILL NOT FIGHT. And will try to make the march a HAPPY
SPECTACLE.

                    *   *   *

Do Angels have any questions for Vietnam Day Committee?
    any suspicions that might be cleared up now?
    What's the main complaint?

What do the Angels plan to do Nov. 20? Do they really have a plan?
    Let's now make a plan that will leave everybody secure.

Because the Fearheads around the VDC public meetings believe the Image
        of Angels as 'They like to bust people up for kicks'
        and naturally you get a bad rep. that way
    especially if you've finally found a group you can beat p
        with some social approval, temporarily,
            & compliance of the cops.

        You don't want to 'change' you want to be yrselves,
            & if that includes sadism, or forced hostility,
            here's a situation where you can get away with it.

BUT NOBODY WANT TO REJECT THE SOULS OF THE HELL'S
ANGELS
or make them change —
                    WE JUST DON'T WANT TO GET BEAT UP
                    *   *   *

The protest march is trying to point out
that the terror in Vietnam is making
same terror here inside our country

722

loosing publicity the same cruel psychology that'll
give approval to busting yellow head gooks in Vietnam
This is infecting peaceful human relations here
allowing for public mass persecution of people who disagree with

the

growth of mass hostility   mass hypocrisy   mass conflict

The mass of marchers are not POLITICAL, they're PSYCHOLOGICAL
HEADS who don't want the country to drift into the habit of blind violence &
unconscious cruelty & egoism   NOT COMMUNICATION – with outside
world or lonely minorities in America
such as yourselves
and ourselves
AND the negroes
AND the teaheads
AND the Communities
AND the Beatnicks
AND the Birchers
AND even the so called Squares

I am afraid that once
the people who hate us peace
Marchers & let you beat us up, – afraid of us Pacifists –
will then, still having this
fear and hate at heart, turn it on you
afraid of you, too
or ask you to turn it on other minorities
the negroes?
Ultimately on you and each other.
(This was the pattern of Brown Shirts in Germany
who were used by hate politicians,
& then creamed in Concentration Camps.
I think.)

*   *   *

I said we were not politicians mostly. And you say you're indifferent to politics.
But you're getting hung on politics and taking Geopolitical positions about
bombing Vietnam.

*   *   *

What ELSE besides this politics, will take the heat off the Hell's Angels?

That heat's on everybody, not just you
To go to war, to be drafted,
to make money on war jobs & economy, to be destroyed
by Bomb, to get busted
for pot –

To take the heat off, you've got
    to take the heat off
        INSIDE YOURSELVES –
Find Peace means stop hating yourself
                stop hating people who hate you
                stop reflecting HEAT
        THERE ARE PEOPLE WHO ARE NOT HEAT
        THE MOST OF PEACE MARCHERS ARE NOT HEAT
They want you to join them to relieve
    the heat on you & on all of us.

Take the heat – Anxiety Paranoia –
    off us, AND off the police, off all the fearful –
REASSURE, and act clearly in such a way
        as to reassure –by being kind not
                    cruel –
                    and it'll be remembered and responded to.

Forcing self, others and police into a corner
            increases heat.

Beating up on Vietnam won't take the heat off –
    even if whole country joined Hell's Angels
    – world will apply heat & world be destroyed –
        (almost happened thru Hitler)

Yes time to take the heat symbolism off the Swastika
        and to give the swastika back to the Indians & Peaceful Mystics
                & Calcutta Ganja Smokers
Can you imagine doing the same for the Hammer and Sickle?
    I've seen Jewish Stars, & there is M 13 & LSD
        & Negro Crescent
                to make HAPPY on yr backs.

I called Beatnick or Vietnick not want a way that is not common for all –
recognizable & acceptable to all – want a way we can't all live
together without heat & rejection.
            My desire to share, not
            MONOPOLIZE the images, because I don't want to be ALONE on
            Earth
        I don't want unnecessary suffering for me, or anybody – you, the police
            the Vietnamese, the entire human universe.

What is the way out of the heat
for you? If stop threat to take over
others, then people let you alone
        Have you stopped threatening the Marcher people
yet?
        If you threat, you must WANT heat
                            We're trying
to take it off you & off us, & off the

724

cops, & off the U.S. & off China & off Vietnam

The heat is human, emotional, not a law
of nature.

How many Angels really dig your political position
            aside from its tactics as heat relief?
            How many hate the marchers, really want to bug them
        Is it you & Tiny's personal goof or really what you all want?

            If you dig POT why don't you, whole generation who don't
dig the heat war also dig pot and consciousness & spontaneity
& they are your natural brothers
            rather than the morality rigid types
            who have fixed warlike
        The great image – which all can buy – is your own ideal image
            WHITMAN's free soul

I asking you be Camarado, friend, kind, lover, because vast majority of peace
marchers
            actually respect & venerate your lonesomeness
            & struggle & would rather be peaceful intimates
                with you than fearful enraged frightened paranoid enemies hitting
                each other.
That probably goes for the police too who have human bodies under uniform.

There are some rigid souls – who believe the universe is evil – frightened of sex &
pot & motorcycles & PEACE even if it was
            all peaceful and tranquil –
            afraid of life, not realizing its harmless emptiness –
These are the people we should be
working on – making love to them –
            blowing our minds and theirs –
softening them, enlarging their consciousness
            and our own too in the process –
not fighting eachother

All separate identities are bankrupt –
Square, beat, Jews, negros, Hell's Angels, Communist & American

Hell's Angels & Tiny's Intervention has probably had good effect –
forced the leaders & marchers to look inside
            themselves to measure
how much their march is blind aggression
            put-on motivated by rage &
            confused desire to find someone to BLAME
                & fight & scream
OR
            How much the march will be a free expression

                of calm people who have controlled
                their own hatreds

725

and are showing the American People
> how to control their own fear & hatred
and once and for all be done with the pressure
> bulding up to annihilate the planet
and take our part ENDING THE HEAT on earth.

Joseph Alsop recently revealed the extent of the government's hypocrisy – and at the same time exposed the plight of that section of the peace movement, which cannot bring itself to break decisively with the Johnson administration, because of the humanitarian rationalizations that are used to cover up American atrocities in Vietnam. In an article entitled 'The Negotiations Nonsense,' Alsop wrote as follows:

The truth is that the President made his original offer of 'unconditional' negotiations, and has since repeated that offer for the main purpose of disarming the domestic and foreign critics of his Vietnamese policy.

The offer's operative word was 'unconditional.' This was and still is intended to express willingness to enter into negotiations about Vietnam without conditions being imposed by either side. While negotiating 'unconditionally,' therefore, the United States would be able to and no doubt would continue its military action in Vietnam, including the bombing of North Vietnam.

More recently . . . recall of the North Vietnamese regulars is described . . . as the minimum quid pro quo for halting our Northern bombing. The negotiations . . . would then be 'conditional.' But the question is obviously academic. . . . (New York Herald Tribune, Nov. 19th)

18. The Diggers

'Normally it wouldn't be tolerated. There are laws against littering the sidewalk if not the air, and, as a guard gruffly explained, the ink stained yellow flowers which sagged like a limp wreath from the ledge above the Con Ed lobby door were "defacing private property." But the guard didn't take them down. When the soot hit the fan he huddled with the others in the lobby, safe from the freaks on the Irving Place sidewalk.

It was Black Flower Day, unexpected, unannounced, and neither the press nor the police were invited. Suddenly there they were, several Diggers, clowns, and friends, gathered around a striking banner which declared "Breathing Is Bad for Your Health." Around 4:30 Wednesday afternoon, they began to pass out flowers on Irving Place. Or, rather, push flowers. It was a pushy demonstration, a novel thing, not a picket line cordoned by cops that a bystander could sneer at, but the kind of thing you admire or avoid. The Diggers offered the blackened mums with a sort of "take this flower and shove it" smirk. Secretaries scurried off.

It began with the flowers and evolved to handfuls of soot which made quick gray clouds in the air. When the soot appeared, the traffic in and out of the 26-story office building came to a halt. The lobby jammed, and when a man in a suit came to the sidewalk to angrily close the doors, he did so in a cloud of black dust. Splotches of soot soiled his white shirt and bald head and the Diggers roared with laughter.

Con Ed was under siege. A clown pranced up and down the sidewalk. A costumed youth sprayed mist out of a vintage Flit can. The Diggers danced over a carpet of stained yellow petals, laughing and throwing soot in the air. Not that they looked dangerous (although several had a Hell's Angels aura) but they were weird. A confrontation promised to be embarrassing. So Con Ed called the cops, and wished the Diggers would leave. Save for a few maverick secretaries, who risked the wrath of the great generators by laughing, Con Ed stayed under cover.

By the time the police arrived, the Diggers had lit several smoke flares downwind from the doors and split. Great clouds of smoke left a film on the face of the building. And only after the police had arrived did many feel it was safe to leave the lobby.

It was classic street theatre, a Digger drama improvised with the idea that a handful of soot down an executive's neck might be more effective than a pile of petitions begging for cleaner air. Even at the sacrifice of good will, the gesture cannot be ignored. It will be remembered long after the deaths during periods of high pollution are passed off as asthma attacks. The medium is the message. Such a versatile phrase.

Street theatre has been copy for the front pages of the San Francisco Chronicle for over a year. The Diggers in San Francisco, many of whom are professional actors in the San Francisco Mime Troupe, are clever masters of media. Clever like bringing flutes to the steps of City Hall for an anti-rat demonstration. They saw the power of the penny-whistle. The simplest prop can unite a crowd for no reason at all. They sought the autonomy to stand on a street corner for an hour or a week. They introduced free food — food so free that you don't even have to eat it. Free to bury in the ground or rub in your face or feed to your dog or fertilize a tree. Free cream pies aren't meant to be eaten. It would be a waste. The Diggers declared war on conditioned responses. They blew minds by breaking subtle mores. They practised public nuisance.

Digger emissaries from the Haight began to appear in Manhattan last spring. They were received in the hippie community like visiting royalty. They rapped to a series of meetings about free stores and fucking leaders and turning on Puerto Ricans, but between their visits the momentum would die and the torch would be snuffed. The organization of the hippie community began at every meeting for months, but it was rarely continued, which may have been a blessing. For all the hopes of Esso and the Jade Companions, the Tribal Council and the block committees, the East Village Defense Committee and the Gallery Gwen, a shower of Digger dollars off the balcony of the New York Stock Exchange seemed the most significant development in months.

Free money is a cinch. It is the surest act in the Digger repertoire. Any scruffy hippie who lights a match to a dollar bill is guaranteed a response. The bystander will inevitably react, thus losing his immunity as a bystander, which is the goal. Furthermore, with a little planning the press will be available to expand the audience, although that audience is secure behind the glass of the evening news, for on television street theatre becomes straight theatre: a rerun at best.

The Press may even expand the act. The recent "expose" of Jim Fouratt in the Daily News could be, from a Digger point of view, a blessing in admirable disguise. It is one thing when some hippie burns or eats or throws away his own money. It's guaranteed to raise a smile. But the News revealed that Fouratt is a ward of the taxpayer. That wasn't his allowance he had stuffed in his mouth, the News reader notes with horror. It was at once a City salary and home relief from the Welfare Department. The freak is complete.

Thus were the Diggers introduced to New York. To drive the point home, last Friday they burned more money on the doorstep of the Daily News. And Saturday several Diggers showed up at the Socialist Scholar's Conference at the Hilton to fire cap pistols at the bewildered politicos. Strange things should be happening on the streets of New York until the media bores. Manhattan is becoming a certified stage.

Of course, it is only the intention that is new. New York, far more than San Francisco, has always been a stage. Even a stray hippie outside his East Side sanctuary is cast in a role. Madison Avenue is a stage for a male hippie in flower. An audience is inevitable. He will react to the audience and the audience will react to him. If both are aware of it, the act is complete. He could hold up a mirror to drive the point home. Finally, as the Diggers say themselves, the street IS theatre. Countless acts on every corner: the panhandler, the prostitute, the poodle, the police. Recognition is the key.

The next rabbit in the Digger hat is a free store, which is set to open soon in a storefront on Avenue A. It will hopefully combine an act with some action. "Once a free store is assumed," explains a digger tract from the Coast, "human wanting and giving, needing and taking become wide open to improvisation. The question of a free store is simply what would you have?"

I have a vision of a glittering marquee on the opening night.' (D. McNeill, *The Hippie in New York. Turning the City into a Theatre.*[16] Village Voice, September 14 '67, Copyright Village Voice 1967.)

---

16. Copyright, Don McNeill, 1967.

728

'Free food, free pads, free grass, free air, free love, free transportation, free money . . .

Free money?

Yes. Free money. If you'd have been on the floor of the New York Stock Exchange Thursday morning, Audust 29th you'd have seen the green stuff come floating down.

This philanthropic act was performed by the East Side Service Organization, who had made arrangements a week before to tour the stock exchange. Their spokesman, a mad bomber and former SNCC worker named George Metesky, explained that these volunteer poverty workers wanted to get into the heart of things, see how the country works.

The exchange complied and at noon about twenty people named George Metesky joined hundreds of tourists on a line leading to the balcony of the exchange. Something exciting must've been going on because there were a lot of press and TV crews milling about.

Finally it was time for the ESSO people to be admitted to the balcony. Some of them had long hair, although one friend of ours, whose commitment to the revolution is total, shaved and cut his hair for the occasion – so the exchange authorities figured that a demonstration was at hand. George Metesky denied it vehemently. "We do not want to protest," he said.

On the balcony, the ESSO people, now augmented by two young men from Illinois and a little old lady from Dubuque, proceeded to pull single dollar bills from their pockets and throw them over the railing. Somewhere between $50 and $1,000 went sailing down, compliments of the Digger money tree (*arborum gratuitous*). It was, some felt, the only decent thing to do for the brokers, to whom wealth is an illusion measured by paper credit, and who, wheeling and dealing down on the floor, never see a genuine green dollar.

The nation's business came to a standstill. A stunned silence, then some cheers when they saw what was being thrown, then some boos when they realized the implications of the whole thing. If money is free, the stock exchange folds. A few people, the non-ideologues in the crowd, bent down to pick up the money. What'll they buy with it?

The press snapped pictures and asked questions. What is the meaning of this? Giggles. Who are you? "George," they said, or "Emmett," or just "Us." How many of you are there? Each stuck up one finger and shouted, "One!" or "None!" or "There's nobody here, can't you see?" Where did you get that money? "Do you ask Cardinal Spellman where he gets his money?" Francis retorted. "Well, I'm Cardinal Spellman." The stock exchange fuzz led them forcefully off the balcony. They retreated to the street, danced in a rhomboid and burned the change.

"I still don't understand the meaning of this," a newsman said to George. "We're trying to show that it's not property or money that counts," replied George, saying his name was Emmett. "It's people. And these people in the stock exchange with their impersonal ticker tape machines forget that it's people whose lives they are dealing with."

George whipped out another bill – a ten-spot this time – and gave it to a pair of imploring shoeshine boys. The effect was instantaneous. "Free shines for everybody!" one shouted, while the other helped "Free beer!" and waved a flip-top can.

The newsmen wrote it all down and walked away. A large black lady walked by, and eyeing the long hair and the cameras, asked what was going on. "Just some people throwing money away," we replied. "Oh. Is that all?" she said and walked on.' (G. Washington (nom de plume of George Metesky), untitled account of Metesky's August 29, '67 *Free Money Stock Exchange demonstration*, WIN, September 15, '67.)

'Irving Place and 14th Street was the scene September 6th of a provocation directed against Consolidated Edison, the utility company responsible for one-half of New York's air pollution. At 4:30, about 25 hippies and concerned anarchists assembled in front of Con Ed's office to greet the well-fed executives leaving the building. The object according to N.Y. Provo, was "to return some soot, ugliness and sulfur dioxide to the executives responsible for the dirt in our air, and to expand consciousness against those who pollute air for profit."

At first the executives paid little attention. Just another demonstration, they muttered, eager to make it home to suburbia. Then the soot and dirt began to fly. Yellow flowers coated with black grease barraged them and soot covered the sidewalk. "How the hell do they get away with it!" they screamed, looking for cover. Lower echelon employees – secretaries and clerks – had punched out, and now they were pushing toward the door so that it was impossible to retreat. At 4:45 the building manager called the police. It was time to split. Under cover of two smoke bombs, the demonstrators vanished.

A N.Y. Provo statement, distributed later in Tompkins Square, stated the case against Con Ed: "Air pollution causes lung failure, emphysema, pneumonia, silicosis, cancer, retardation, debility, asthma, heart trouble, blood poisoning, short breat, tuberculosis, chronic bronchitis and cough, sore eyes, skin irritation and death . . . . Besides provoking national consciousness through mass media, today's provocation reached the executives who run the air pollution, showing them that people will no longer carry resentment silently." ' (D. Herres, untitled account of the Consolidated Edison Black Flower demonstration of September 6, '67, WIN, September 30, '67.)

'Sergeant Pepper's Lonely Hearts Club Hate Parade shambled forward, under lowering skies, for its mind-blowing walk down Fifth Avenue at 12:30 on September 16th, led by Tuli Kupferberg resplendent in khaki shorts, Korean sandals, an Army blouse emblazoned with 11 sets of Brazilian Air Force sergeant's stripes, assorted patriotic buttons of now distant heroic wars (Axe The Axis), and topped with a cracked regulation helmet liner festooned with streamers of unshelled peanuts. All during the intensive leafleting during the preceding week we had promised instead that the parade would be led by 1500 bull dykes wearing front-zip jeans, followed by a contingent of convicted CHILD molesters, rapists, sadists, and leather fetishists, but the closest we came to this was the appearance in Columbus Circle, 15 minutes before we left, of two stalwart and recognizable members of the National Renaissance Party, who shook hands all around, snatched up with great delight signs reading "Disembowel Earl Warren" and announced their intention of staying with us to the end. Both disappeared in five minutes.

Eighty strong, six abreast, we trudged off displaying our hate signs reading "God Is A White Investment Analyst," "Pop Kids' Balloons," "Crush A Crotch for Christ," "We Shall Overkill," "Treat a Nazi to Lunch," "The Soviet Union

Is A Communist Front." I was fond of the one a young man gave me enroute reading "Burn Niggers, Kill Kikes, Whap Wops, Slam Spics, Hang Honkies." Nobody who saw that sign, and some of the others, could feel quite the same again about his most secret, deep-rooted hate. It's all very well to be a liberal, middle-class white and to have this genteel dislike for those small, dirty, jabbering Puerto Ricans who crowd you in the subway, but when "Castrate Puerto Ricans" is flashed at you, in company with hate beamed at every conceivable group extant, the ridiculousness of one's private, personal hatred emerges and must be confronted.

At Times Square, Sgt. Pepper's Hate Parade vociferously urged the well-dressed middle-aged men picketing the Saturday Peace Vigillers with his sign "The Only Good Communist Is A Dead Communist" to join us, but he knew better. Seeing our failure, we released a subdued cheer to the astonished vigillers watching us go by with our "Bomb Peking, Bomb Paris" signs.

Reaching Herald Square, the police, having been so informed in advanced, expected it to end. It felt too good not to take it through Greenwich Village. "You're supposed to end here. Who's in charge?" the police captain asked. "Nobody." "How can that be?" "You'd better let it move on," we said, "otherwise the shoppers will join us thinking it's a re-run of Support Our Boys Parade."

On its zigzag way it went, now led by a lumbering fellow indiscriminately firing a well-primed cap pistol and the helpless police, gaping spectators, bespittled hecklers, and the smiling American people safely ensconced behind shining plate glass windows, buying and consuming as the culture demands. We lost the police completely until they reappeared on lower 5th Avenue, they alone smiling and nodding approval and nudging each other to look at my sign. We had forgotten to include the Irish on it.

Now east across 8th Street we went, intending to have our hate-climax in Tompkins Square Park. This was not to be. No park permit. Sadly we discarded our signs in the nearest trash basket and silently filed into the park. I noticed all the Hate Paraders gathered in the center, milling and pushing slightly. Perhaps we were rallying our forces. I rushed over. All were clustered around the Good Humor wagon.

All over this time. But our Hate Forces are growing and renewing. It is rumored that when the National Mobilization Committee brings hundreds of thousands to Washington on October 21st to confront the Warmakers in the Pentagon, we too will be there, to make our voices heard and to ask the authorities to account to us for our utter failure as the most powerful, white, Christian nation on earth to whip a bunch of brainwashed, drug-crazed little brown Charlies in shorts.

Remember, God was not a Gook.' (M. Shapiro, *GR-R-R!*,[17] WIN, October 16, '67.)

Matesky expounded the theory of this theater:

' "On his first missionary visit to Antioch in Asia Minor, the apostle Paul and those with him found many persons that were unreceptive to the good news that they preached. They were even mobbed out of town by these people, but this unpleasant experience did not cause them to develop the wrong mental attitude to-

17. Copyright, M. Shapiro, 1967.

ward their work and thus cause it to lose its joy." – Acts 13:52 (as interpreted by the Watchtower magazine)

This Digger phenomenon deserves a close examination by the peace movement – not that these jottings will necessarily make things clearer; clarity, alas, is not one of our goals. Confusion is mightier than the sword!

First it is important to distinguish between Hippies and Diggers. Both are myths, that is, there is no definition, there is no organized conspiracy, both are in one sense a huge put-on. Hippies, however, are a myth created by media and as such they are forced to play certain media-oriented roles. They are media-manipulated. Diggers too are myth, but a grass-roots myth created from within. We have learned to manipulate media. Diggers are more politically oriented but at the same time bigger fuckoffs. Diggers are zen-like in that we have totally destroyed words and replaced them with "doing" – action becomes the only reality. Like Lao-tzu: "The way to be is to do." We cry, "No one understands us," while at the same time, winking out the corner of our eye, recognizing that if the straight world understood all this Digger shit, it would render us impotent because understanding is the first step to control and control is the secret to our extinction.

This reluctance to define ourselves gives us glorious freedom in which to fuck with the system. We become communist-racist-acid-head freaks, holding flowers in one hand and bombs in the other. The Old Left says we work for the CIA. Ex-Marines stomp on us as Pinkos. Newport police jail us as smut peddlers. Newark cops arrest us as riot inciters. (These four events were all triggered by passing out free copies of the same poem.) So what the hell are we doing, you ask? We are dynamiting brain cells. We are putting people through changes. The key to the puzzle lies in theatre. We are theatre in the streets: total and committed. We aim to involve people and use (unlike other movements locked in ideology) any weapon (prop) we can find. The aim is not to earn the respect, admiration, and love of everybody – it's to get people to do, to participate, whether positively or negatively. All is relevant, only "the play's the thing."

... Stand on a street corner with 500 leaflets and explode. Give some to a sad-looking female. Tell guys that pass, "Hey, can you help her out? She can't do it by herself and her father's a communist cell leader and will beat her up if she doesn't pass them out." Recruit a person to read the leaflet aloud while all this distribution is going on. Run around tearing the leaflets, selling them, trading them. Rip one in half and give half to one person and half to another and tell them to make love. Do it all fast. Like slapstick movies. Make sure everyone has a good time. People love to laugh – it's a riot. Riot – that's an interesting word-game if you want to play it.

Don't be for or against. Riots – environmental and psychological – are Holy so don't screw around with explanations. Theatre also has some advantages. It is involving for those people that are ready for it while at the same time dismissed as nonthreatening by those that could potentially wreck the stage. It's dynamite. By allowing all: loving, cheating, anger, violence, stealing, trading, you become situation-oriented and as such become more effective. You believe in participatory democracy (especially when talking to a New Left audience) only you call it "everyone doing his thing." You let people decide, no strings attached. During the riots in Newark we smuggled in food, giving it to our underground soul brothers SNCC and NCUP.

732

"We've brought a lot of canned goods, Tom, so the people can eat them or throw them at the cops."

Like many of the people in the riot, we dug the scene. Had a ball passing out food. Seven truckloads in all. And that's another key to the riddle, Dig what you're doing! Make war on paranoia. Don't be afraid. Don't get uptight. There's a war against property going on. I asked an old black woman in Newark "What's going on?" and she tells me they stole her shoes and she's roaring with laughter. Spades and Diggers are one. Diggersareniggers Both stand for the destruction of property. There are many ways to destroy property: to change is to destroy — give it away free. The free thing (another clue) is the most revolutionary thing in America today. Free dances, free food, free theatre (constantly), free stores, free bus rides, free dope, free housing, and most important, free money. Theatre will capture the attention of the country, the destruction of the monetary system will bring it to its knees. Really fuck with money. Burn it, smoke it to get high, trade with it, set up boxes of it in the streets marked "Free Money," pan-handle it, steal it, throw it away.

Scene: Washington Square Park. Actors: one very nicely dressed white liberal, one down and out looking digger. Audience: a large crowd of similar liberals, of various sexes. The title of the play: "Food for Newark Spades."

Dig.: Sir, could you please spare a dollar for some food for Negroes in Newark?

Lib.: Gee, I'm sorry, I don't have much money on me.

Dig.: (still pleading, hat in hand) We're collecting food at Liberty House. Couldn't you buy a dollar's worth and bring it over?

Lib.: If I had a dollar I certainly would.

Dig.: (exploding) I think you're full of shit. Here's ten dollars (pulling out real American money and shoving it in his face) go buy some food and bring it over to Liberty House.

Lib.: (getting a bit annoyed but still wanting to be polite) Oh no, I couldn't take money from you.

Dig.: (throwing the money on the ground) Well, there it is on the ground, do something with it.

The Digger walks away dropping clues to understanding the street drama: Liberty House, Black, Newark, Food, Free, Money.

The rumors begin to fly as rumors always do. Rumors have power. Like myths, people become involved in them, adding, subtracting, multiplying. Get them involved. Let them participate. If it's spelled out to the letter there is no room for participation Nobody participates in ideology. Never lie — diggers never lie. Once committed in a street drama, never turn back. Be prepared to die if it's necessary to gain your point.

Don't rely on words. Words are the absolute in horseshit. Rely on doing—go all the way every time. Move fast. If you spend too long on one play, it becomes boring to you and the audience. When they get bored, they are turned off. They are not receiving information. Get their attention, leave a few clues and vanish. Change your costume, use the props around you. Each morning begin naked. Destroy your name, become unlisted, go underground. Find brothers. Soul brothers. Black people, Puerto Ricans, Dropouts, Bowery Bums. Find out where they're at. Don't fuck with their thing. P.R.s dig manhood, don't play sissy.

Black people dig pot, don't give them acid. Dropouts dig flowers, don't give them I.F. Stone Weeklies. Bowery Bums dig money, don't give them bibles. Become aware of the most effective props. On the Lower East Side pot is an effective prop, it is the least common denominator. It makes us all outlaws, brothers, niggers. Smoke it in public. It really has an effect on P.R.s, really challenges their concept of courage.

"Hey man, you're brave enough to kill someone, and not brave enough to smoke pot in the park!"

That kind of question is a good deal more effective than sermons on the holiness of passive resistance. Use non-verbal props and media. Music is another denominator. Conga-Rock, get together. The Diggers and Pee Wee's gang (largest P.R. gang on New York's lower east side) threw a large dance at the Cheetah, a discotheque, on August 15. Conga-Rock. Something for everybody. Do your thing. Don't give speeches. Don't have meetings. Don't have panel shows. They are all dead. Drama is anything you can get away with. Remember that last peace demonstration? Do you recall the speeches, of the Bread and Puppet Theatre and Stokely yelling "Hell no, we won't go!" That was drama, not explanation. The point is nobody gives a shit anymore about troop strength, escalation, crying over napalm. A peace really speech to me is like reading the National Guardian which is like watching the TV reports on Highway Fatalities which is like praying for riots to end which is like BULLSHIT! Herbert Marcuse says flower children have the answer. He smoked hashish at the big world happening in London in early August. Pray tell, what is a good Marxist to do?

Accept contradictions, that's what life is all about. Have a good time. Scrawled on the wall of the American pavilion at Expo '67 is our slogan in bright dayglo: "It is the duty of all revolutionists to make love." Do weird things. Silly-putty sabotage and monkey warfare. John Roche, who is now intellectual-in-residence-fink at the White House once said that if Hitler had been captured in 1937, brought to Trafalgar Square, and had his pants pulled down, he could never have risen to power. Every time he tried one of those spectacular speeches the people would have just laughed at him because the image of "Mein Fuhrer" with his pants down around his ankles would have been too much.

Think about it.' (G. Metesky, *Diggery is Niggery,*[18] WIN, September 30, '67.)

George Konnoff who joined up with Schumann in '68 came out of the San Francisco Digger movement:

'I was working with a street puppet theatre called Free City Puppets which came out of the San Francisco Mime Troupe which I was in, the Digger Movement which was sort of an anarchistic theater .... (I: You said the Diggers was a theatre movement, you thought they were focused on doing theatre actually?) Yes. I'd have to say they were thrown out of the Mime Troupe because it started there but it was conflicting with Ronnie Davis' idea of having a traditional theatre that's political. The Diggers and the members of the Mime Troupe felt that the streets were a more important place to do theatre in an Artaud sense of the word or to use *Theatre and Its Double* as a springboard for ideas. And the Provos, out of Amsterdam .... (I: In '67 and '68 wasn't the troupe doing things in the park?) Yes. (I: Do you make a distinction between parks and

18. Copyright, G. Metesky.

streets?) Well. See they were a touring company and they had obligations to meet and places to go and rehearsals, and the other mentality was that there might be a riot or event in the movement and it didn't exactly jibe with going off the campus so you could do a show. Plus it was more susceptible to the rest of them, the Mime Troupe had to protect itself as an institution .... Stretching the theatre, a large part of the early Digger theatre events were broadsides, passed out on the street, political tracts that were written in a drug-oriented way, there was a lot of drugs around. The free stores that were opened later were pretty big dispensers of free drugs as free drugs were given out to the Diggers .... We started an event in the park that happened every day at rush hour and the Pan Handle in San Francisco was the main artery out of — to — the Golden Gate Bridge, a lot of people go by there, so every day at 4, there was a free meal which was thought of and created to be more of a happening than anything, than trying to really be a bread line like the Salvation Army. It was there to be sticking out in public there, in the park, and then once the stores were open, about half the events there were theatrical skits, pieces of music, a lot of Ginsberg and poets in there who had time or the inclination to participate. And movies .... (I: What were the performances like?) Well, the first one I recall which resulted in the Haight Ashbury being closed down for several days was a fellow named Robert LaMorticelli (?), he's a sculptor, who made large puppets, not as large as Peter's but definitely very big, and they got a large orange frame and they went around for days before the smaller orange frames looking in the windows and through these frames and doing these raps about reference maybe on the inside and outside world and they finally created a movement where the police were always making them move on Haight Street so they collected people in the four corners so everybody could ... nobody could be accused of refusing to move, but there was somebody to replace them. So at again rush hours ... (I: With those frames?) Yes, everybody had those frames but there was one *huge* frame which eventually, once they closed down the *street*, at the four intersections, was placed in the middle of the street, and there was a Puppet Show that had to do, it was a Vietnam show, I don't remember very clearly but it was Vietnamese ladies and there was a big American Eagle and he had a big erection and raped this other puppet. It looked much like a cross between evil and a bomber. And then of course the police were there. And then — (I: I'm sorry. What did this show have to do with the frames?) Oh it had nothing. The frames had to do with closing down the space, you know, and once the space was closed down which meant there was a lot of police and a lot of people and it was a standoff for a while and then the piece was done, the police charged in and arrested people and there was, you know, a bit of celebrating. (I: Why did the frames have the place closed down?) They didn't. I think it was just a matter of doing a pageant and coming out with a simple idea like a frame and looking at people, just — I think a prop to polarize people you know. A prop. Something to play with. (I: Closed down in what sense though?) It closed down because there was such an attraction of people that traffic was stopped in all directions .... And then of course the police started stopping traffic from coming *in* there — mounting their tactical police lines and — (And who was associated with that particular show?) Oh a fellow who was in the Mime Troupe for a while. A sculptor, Robert LaMorticelli and Emmett Grogan who has written a few books and was in the Mime Troupe for a while and Peter Berg who is a West Coast writer. In fact he collaborated on — he did most of the writing — when they did the

Condemned of Altona and I think they rewrote it to get away from paying the royalties or something . . . . There were a series of probably I don't know what time span but there was a series of street events *like* that, until the street in fact became *secured* or there was so many people there that the Diggers' activities swung into providing food to houses, they dropped the park thing after a bit, they were feeding communes and had their free store and other people took over those things and so they decreased until right about that point they did a last event which was called "*The Death of the Hippies*" or "*Death of the Hippie*" and they buried a casket with a ceremony, the hippie and some money and this and that and basically left Haight Ashbury . . . . Well, there was a lot of political harassment going on and I think that's one of the reasons the Digger stuff broke up. So – I was getting out of town, I had been introduced to Peter and I wanted to see what was happening out here and I knocked on Second Avenue and Second Street and started rehearsing. (I: Were you into drug culture yourself? LSD maybe?) Oh yeah. (I: Was that a big thing in your life then?) No. It was a big thing in the people's lives I was around and that was mainly heroin and not LSD but speed. And that stopped a lot of the work, and I wasn't – One of the reasons I tried to look into Bread and Puppet is that they seemed to be continuing working. The Mime Troupe went through a metamorphosis and cut down that serious thing at that point too. And the people I was around and the Diggers were starting to have real problems.' (Konnoff, interview.)

Warhol, on the West Coast for the L.A. opening of his *Chelsea Girls*, reports on the San Francisco scene of August-September 1967:

'We were sort of in two groups. Ondine, Billy, and a girl they called Orion the Witch of Bleecker Street – an A-head friend of theirs from New York who'd just moved out to San Francisco – formed one group. They went around terrorizing the flower people and saying every minute how they couldn't stand the West Coast another second. I walked into their rooms once when they had all just taken belladonna, and I watched a friend of Ondine's, naked except for polka-dot socks, drop a marble tabletop on his foot and not feel it. Ondine said, "There is no hallucinogen other than belladonna. It is a visual poison." I'd heard that from a few people – that acid was nothing compared to belladonna.

The rest of us just went wandering around the city, getting the feel of the place at the end of the big Love Summer. There were bad vibrations from the San Francisco hippies toward anything that was above a sort of psychedelic poverty level – anything that looked like it cost money was part of the Establishment – and so when we drove around town for a day or two in a Cadillac limousine that the movie theater rented for us, it was like we were waving a red flag; the flower children in the street would turn and glare at us, very contemptuous. That didn't bother us; we thought it was funny, and Paul, of course, was having a ball – he even figured out a way to antagonize the Haight Ashbury types a little more: he'd have our driver pull over beside groups of kids in beads and flowers, then he'd roll down the limousine window and ask them, "Say, where's the nearest Salvation Army? We want to buy ourselves some hippie clothes."

As we drove through the different sections of town, we were all talking about the Black Panthers. (In between "Negro" and "black," the term "Afro-American" had come up, but it had never caught on the way "black" had – it was like trying to make people call Sixth Avenue "Avenue of the Americas.")

The Black Panthers got a lot of attention walking around San Francisco with their guns showing, and nobody could stop them because evidently it wasn't against the law to carry guns openly, just to conceal them. But since nobody much had ever really taken advantage of the technicality before, the sight of those guns was a shocker, especially in the flower-power make-love-not-war city.

It had been a whole year since we were out there at the Fillmore with the Velvets. So many kids were still tripping, but the scene was clearly losing its momentum, and in another month journalists would be writing about what a complete mess Haight Ashbury had become — garbage and scummy soda stains on the sidewalks and the Day-Glo signs that had looked so great when they were new getting all horrible and dirty. October would be the month of the funeral procession through the streets for "Hippie, devoted son of Mass Media," staged by the original hippies who'd been really involved with organizing alternate community living and who now resented all the free-style young kids who'd come in during the summer who they called "irresponsible" hippies. There was a sense that autumn that the whole hippie thing had been ruined the summer before — made too big and commercial.

As we walked around, I realized that in San Francisco the Vietnam war seemed so much more real than it did in New York — if you stood by the bay, you could actually see ships leaving for Southeast Asia.

The girls in California were probably prettier in a standard sense than the New York girls — blonder and in better health, I guess; but I still preferred the way the girls in New York looked — stranger and more neurotic (a girl always looked more beautiful and fragile when she was about to have a nervous breakdown).

Most of the places around the area that had opened as "free" stores or service centers were starting to close down or go into debt. A lot of the hippies were leaving for communes all up and down the California coast and in western Colorado and New Mexico. In New York, the Diggers were only just about to open a free store ("Free Stew and Coffee") on East 10th Street, right near where Paul lived, and Country Joe & the Fish had just played on the same street, in Tompkins Square Park, at a "smoke-in" where Frosty Meyers, the New York artist, had his laser going all around the sky.' (Warhol, *POPism*, 1980.)

19. The Yippies.

Jerry Rubin:
'There is no such thing as an anti-war movement. That's a concept created by the mass media to fuck up our minds. What's happening is energy exploding in thousands of directions and people declaring themselves free:

free from property hangups; free from success fixations;
free from positions, titles, names, hierarchies, responsibilities, schedules, rules, routines, regular habits.

I'm not interested in the so-called anti-war movement – I'm interested in Detroit, Newark, campus disruptions, everyone smoking pot, people learning to speak out and be different.

The capitalist-money-bureaucratic-imperialist – middle class-boring-exploitative-military world structure is crumbling.

The world laughs at America's clumsy, bully attempt to defeat peasant warriors called Vietcong in a never-never land called Vietnam . . .

. . . and in America we are all learning how to become Vietcong.

For the Socialist Workers Party to organize a debate called "What policy next for the anti-war movement?" is an obscenity. It demonstrates once more that ideology is a brain disease. This debate is hinged on the assumption that there is a specific movement that can be directed. It is hinged on the assumption that the movement needs leaders to figure out what's next.

But if there was one lesson learned at the Pentagon and at Whitehall it is that the young people didn't give a hang about the political theories, ideologies, plans, organizations, meetings, or negotiations with the cops.

The activists came to act out of their own sense of what was real.

The only vanguard is the vanguard in action.

All those hundreds of hours of bullshit meetings were just that – bullshit!

Better we had spent the time listening to the Beatles.

We had more reasons why NOT to do things, and we held back the energy of the activists.

An anti-war movement is self-defeating and a waste of time because it is negative. People want to be for, not against. We don't need an "anti-war" movement; we need an American Liberation Movement.

America is trapped within her own contradictions, and it is a joy to watch Huntley-Brinkley and see America squirm. The products of America are not interested in inheriting and protecting a world made for them; we are interested in creating a new world.

The Vietnam war is an old man's war: old men are trying to impose old ideas like property, racism, military force – big countries controlling little countries – upon the New World that is bursting forth in this century.

Ah, that New World!

The people looting in Detroit;

The teenagers who spit at the Pentagon and redecorated it with their urine, and with slogans like "Che Lives";

The guerrillas carrying Che's action throughout Latin America, Asia and Africa.

The thousands of young people in America beginning to ask "why" and finding out that their elders have no answers; they have only power and age.

That's not an anti-war movement — those are movements for liberation, for freedom.

All these movements for liberation add up to a massive energy force which weakens the ability of the United States to carry out the war and all her other decrepit policies . . .

I support everything which puts people into motion, which creates disruption and controversy, which creates chaos and rebirth.

Adlai Stevenson made me a radical in 1952 by picking up my hopes for change. The system crushed those hopes.

Eugene McCarthy is training the future street disrupters of tomorrow in the futility of party politics.

The revolution is taking place everywhere.

The stable middle-class home is falling apart.

The church cannot attract its own children.

The schools are becoming centers of rebellion, and the streets are theater of political action.

I approve of letters to the editor, peace candidates and peace referendums, peaceful marches, symbolic sit-ins, disruptive sit-ins, disruptive street demonstrations, and sabotage.

That is guerrilla war in America: everyone doing his own thing, a sympathy of varied styles, rebellion for every member of the family, each to his own alienation.

The respectable middle class debates LBJ while we try to pull down his pants.

A good question: Can America be changed through "peaceful transition?"

Can the beast be tamed within her own rules and laws? within the electoral system, within law and order, within police permits and regulations, within the boundaries of middle class America?

Can a society which makes distinctions between rich and poor, white and black, employers and employees, landlords and tenants, teachers and students, reform itself? Is it interested in reform, or is it just interested in eliminating nuisance?

What's needed is a new generation of nuisances, a new generation of people who are freaky, crazy, irrational, sexy, angry, irreligious, childish, and mad . . .

> people who burn draft cards
> people who burn dollar bills
> people who burn MA and doctoral degrees
> people who say "To hell with your goals"
> people who lure the youth with music, pot and lsd
> people who proudly carry Vietcong flags
> people who re-define reality, who re-define the norm
> people who wear funny costumes
> people who see property as theft
> people who say "fuck" on television
> people who break with the status-role-consumer game
> people who have nothing material to lose but their bodies

The war in Vietnam will be stopped by the United States when the embarrassment of carrying on the war becomes greater than the embarrassment of defeat.

A lot of things embarrass America, a lot of things embarrass a country so dependent on image:

Youth alienation, campus demonstrations and disruptions, peace candidates, Underground Railroads of draft dodgers to Canada, trips to banned countries, thousands of people giving the middle finger to the Pentagon over national television –

We can end this war – we've got America on the run. We've combined youth, music, sex, drugs, and rebellion with treason – and that's a combination hard to beat. Give LBJ a good grade for effort.

Every so-called democracy, for its own functional wholeness, needs the existence of a Marxist socialist party like the Socialist Workers Party to demonstrate free speech.

Fred Halstead is LBJ's dream presidential opponent.

The overwhelming, overwhelming number of Americans will never hear of Halstead or the SWP which, in this electronic media age, where the world is like a village, is a sad commentary on the SWP.

Even if they did hear him, they would never understand exactly what he is getting at. Too much word-jargon. Fred deals in ideology and in words and slogans, which can be easily ignored, placed into a different context and misinterpreted, or just not understood.

Fred's candidacy confirms belief in the electoral process while threatening no one. His campaign is responsible to no movement or community, but responsible only to a sectarian ideological party.

I like Fred Halstead and I consider him a friend and it was hard for me to work up an anger for tonight because of that. My debate is not so much with him personally as with the party of which he is a disciplined member and candidate.

The dead giveaway of the Trots is at demonstrations. What are the Trots doing? Selling *Militants*! Is that where it's at? They go to demonstrations to sell newspapers! What more need be said, really?

They do all they can to see that the anti-Vietnam war movement does not extend itself even to include Thailand – do you call that socialist education?

They do all they can to see that the anti-war movement not link itself to black power or the fight for liberation in America – is that how they hope to change things?

They gain influence in organizations by working hard in office situations – not by organizing.

They are guilty of the major crime of revolutionary office workers and newspapers salesmen – they put all these pictures of great men – Malcolm and Che – on the wall, and print all these stories about Vietnam and black struggle, yet as individuals or as a group they are careful to take no risks at all. That is inexcusable.

How many Trots were arrested at the Pentagon? Not that arrest is an end in itself, but you didn't do anything if you weren't willing to risk arrest.

The big issues of socialism and capitalism are OK, according to the Trots, for small forums, small newspapers, and for irrelevant situations, but never to be discussed seriously in mass arenas when they might matter. The Trots are uninspiring; they lack music, color, life. Their movement is a pale grey.

They want to be secretaries for somebody else's revolution; they are not revolutionaries themselves; and while waiting for the working class to revolt, they do all they can bureaucratically to see that the movement is contained within the electoral system, within the march and rally "mass demonstration" syndrome, within the style of middle class America, and through the medium of the slogan and the speech and the small circulation newspaper.

What the socialists like the SWP and the Communist Party, with their conversions of Marxism into a natural science, fail to understand is that language does not radicalize people — what changes people is the emotional involvement of action.

What breaks through apathy and complacency are confrontations and action, the creation of new situations which previous mental pictures do not explain, polarizations which define people into rapidly new situations.

The struggle against the war is freeing American youth from authority hang-ups and teaching us democracy through action.

Every draft card burning is a body blow to Mother America because its impact sweeps throughout the elementary schools with the message: baby something's happening, and your teacher don't know what it is, and the draft is not sacred or from heaven, or from Washington and Jefferson, it is up to you.

The movement is a school and its teachers are the Fugs/Dylan/Beatles/Ginsberg/mass media hippies/students fighting cops in Berkeley/blood on draft records/sit-ins/jail.

Repression turns demonstration/protests into wars; actors into heroes; masses of individuals into a community; repression eliminates the bystander, the neutral observer, the theorist; it forces everyone to pick a side.

A movement cannot grow without repression.

The left needs an attack from the center and the right.

Life is theater and we are the guerillas attacking the shrines of authority, from the priest to the holy dollar, to the two-party system, zapping people's minds and putting them through changes in actions in which everyone is emotionally involved.

The street is the stage.

You are the star of the show and everything you were once taught is up for grabs.

The long-haired beast smoking pot, evading the draft, and stopping traffic during demonstrations is a hell of a more of a threat to the system than the so-called "politicos" with their leaflets of support for the Vietcong and the coming working class revolution.

Politics is how you live your life, not whom you vote for or whom you support.

The most important political conflict in the United States today is the generational conflict.

We are all under the influence of a collective historical unconsciousness.

Communism to us means not Stalin, but the heroic romantic fidel che vietcong. Hitler to us represents words on paper.

We are optimistic and idealistic about the future. Our 1984 will be great.

The economy is rich; overproduction is the problem; now everyone can dig life, and we know it. Our 1984 will be great.

We want a communal world where the imagination runs supreme, and where human institutions respond to human needs. Feeling and emotion will be unsuppressed. Everything will be free. People will go to museums to look at dollar bills. There will be no nations, only rich communities and rich cultures.

This generational movement cuts across class and race lines.

The generational revolt in America is not explained by Freud or Marx. It is a war between historical generations, and the future belongs to us because America is defending institutions like ownership and nation – and these institutions no longer respond to needs.

We did not build CBS, the Democratic Party or the Catholic Church and we want no place in them.

Vietnam is a case of the past trying to suppress the future.

The American economy has rendered white middle class youth and black working class youth useless, because we are not needed to make the economy run. Uselessness breeds revolution. The only exciting and meaningful thing to do in America today is to disrupt her institutions and build new ones.

Subvert! that's the task of every young person. Spread ideas that undercut the consistent world of America, and then top it off by burning her symbols – from draft cards to flags to dollar bills.

We must alienate middle class America. We must get middle class America all whipped up emotionally.

America suffers from a great cancer: it's called APATHY.

Moral persuasion may work on the guilt feelings of the American middle classer; it may even win his mind or vote; but how are you going to get him off his ass?

Alienating people is a necessary process in getting them to move.

Mr. America: The War is at Home.

It is not on Huntley-Brinkley; it is right outside your window; wait, now it is inside your living room in your child's head.

Disruption of American society is going to become about as frequent as Yankee planes over Vietnam.

Persuasion will follow the disruption.

Crisis will replace the coffee break.

When we were simply marching, and petitioning, and making moral pleas to the government to end the war, the good hard common sense soul of America knew we were only kids, that we were not serious.

Americans know how hard it is to move City Hall.

"Ah, c'mon off it, you ain't going to end the war that way" was the truck driver's likely response to vigils, marches, peace candidates, and peace literature.

Instinctively, the American knew more about his government than he did the anti-war movement.

He knew that it was way up there, made up of good-for-nothing politicians, hard to reach, and then reachable only through the language of power and violence.

When the movement moved into the streets, and began to act in the dialect of power, when the movement got tough, we broke away all those barriers preventing us from reaching the average guy. America understands Stokely Carmichael and America understands peace demonstrators fighting in the streets, and that's why we are much more dangerous than a hundred Martin Luther Kings.

742

Scenario One

The time: spring 1968   The place: New York City
The city is thrown into a psychological paralysis by the plans of 50,000 peace demonstrators to close down Manhattan by disrupting the 50 most crowded traffic thoroughfares at peak working hours.

Scenario Two

The time: late August 1968   The place: Chicago
Chicago is in panic. The American Youth Festival (Youth International Party) has brought 500,000 young people to Chicago to camp out, smoke pot, dance to wild music, burn draft cards, and roar like wild bands through the streets, forcing the President to bring troops back from Vietnam to keep order in the city while he is nominated under the protection of tear gas and bayonets.

Scenario Three

The time: sometime in the future   The place: America
The government sends more troops to the spreading fires of guerrilla war throughout Laos, Thailand and Vietnam while strikes and the mark of guerrilla action continue to mount in India, Indonesia, the Congo and Brazil.

At home Chicago, Watts, Oakland and Harlem are burning, and the people there have poured into the streets taking the goods they claim are rightfully theirs and broadcasting that all white businesses and buildings now belong to the black community.

Law and order seems to have completely broken down.

100 colleges have been hit by student strikes, and hundreds of thousands of young white people are jamming the downtown areas of many big cities paralyzing traffic.

Some young white and black teen-agers broke into the studios of the major TV networks and are now broadcasting to the nation. They are demanding the withdrawal of all American troops from around the world, the immediate distribution of food and clothing free, the immediate conversion of all areas of the economy to serve people's needs free, and the replacement of the police by a people's militia.

The authority of the government of the United States is in grave danger.'
(Jerry Rubin, *I am the Walrus!* In: WIN, February 15, 1968.)[19]

Abbie Hoffman:
'This sure is fun. You know, the city news bureau here in Chicago, where you can always call and get their version of what's happening, is ST 2-8100. You might want to take care of a cat named Jack Lawrence from CBS who threw me out while I was fuckin' with their teletype machine last night. That was very unfair. I had some good news items. Now, let's see who else is here. The police, there's some good numbers. OK. Now this is a top secret number that like only a few of the top police have. It's the central number for the police station up here in the zoo. They're very fucked up in there. I've been up there, and you think they're organized, well you're full of shit 'cause their walkie-talkies don't work. I mean they're all stoned up there, tripping over each other, you know, they're rapping, all they want to do is fight and they don't care about all the walkie-talkie shit,

19. Copyright, Jerry Rubin, 1968.

they just want to fight, you know. That's their thing. All right, that number is 528-5967. Now — here's the way you use it. There's a Commander Brash of the 18th Precinct who's in charge of the general area of Lincoln Park and there's Deputy Chief Lynsky who's the cop above him. Now, the police have a system of anarchy. See, the Chief might say somethin' is OK, see, then you get some low-level honky cop saying don't do it, you know. The idea is to convince that honky cop on the other end that Chief Lynsky said it was OK, even if you gotta bullshit him a little. You just drop names, like Commander Brash said this was OK, you know, and if Chief Lynsky said this was OK, you know, those cops don't want to lose their jobs. They won't check it out. Cops are like Yippies — you can never find the leaders. So if you're good at guerrilla theatre, you can look a pig right in the eye and say to him, you know, and he'll do it. You know, that's the thing, to get him to do it. You just let 'em know that you're stronger physically than they are. And you are, because you came here for nothin' and they're holdin' on to their fuckin' pig jobs 'cause of that little fuckin' paycheck and workin' themselves up, you know. Up to what? To a fuckin' ulcer. Sergeant. We got them by the balls. The whole thing about guerrilla theatre is gettin' them to believe it. Right.

A guy just said that if you make a call, and just leave your phone off the hook, then that line is tied up. That's groovy. I didn't know about that in Chicago. In New York, that doesn't work. I think we ought to be into jamming up all their lines and everythin' and really fuckin' up their communication thing. 'Cause they broke all our walkie-talkies. They made a definite effort to make sure that we can't communicate with each other so like we ought to start communicatin' with them.

Theatre can be used as defense and as an offensive weapon. I mean, I think like people could survive naked, see. I think you could take all your fuckin' clothes off, a cop won't hit ya. You jump in Lake Michigan, he won't go after you, but people are too chickenshit to do that. It can be used as an offensive and defensive weapon, like blood. We had a demonstration in New York. We had seven gallons of blood in little plastic bags. You know, if you convince 'em you're crazy enough, they won't hurt ya. With the blood thing, cop goes to hit you, right, you have a bag of blood in your hand. He lifts his stick up, you take your bag of blood and go whack over your own head. All this blood pours out, see. Fuckin' cop standin'. Now that says a whole lot more than a picket sign that says end the war in wherever the fuck it is you know. I mean in that demonstration, there was a fuckin' war there. People come down and looked and said holy shit I don't know what it is, blood all over the fuckin' place, smokebombs goin' off, flares, you know, tape recorders with the sounds of machine guns, cops on horses tramplin' Christmas shoppers. It was a fuckin' war. And they say, right, I know what the fuck you're talkin' about. You're talkin' about war. What the fuck has a picket line got to do with war? But people that are into a very literal bag, like that heavy word scene, you know, don't understand the use of communication in this country and the use of media. I mean, if they give a ten-page speech against imperialism, everybody listens and understands and says yeah. But you throw fuckin' money out on the Stock Exchange, and people get that right away. And they say, right, I understand what that's about. And if they don't know what you're doin', fuck 'em. Who cares? Take this, see, you use black space as information. You carry a sign that says END THE. You don't need the next word, you just carry a sign that says END, you know. That's enough. I mean the Yippie symbol is Y. So you say, why, man, why, why? Join the Y, bring your sneakers, bring your helmet, right, bring your thing, whatever you got. Y, you say to the Democrats, baby, Y that's not a V it's a Y. You can do a whole lotta shit. Steal it, steal the V, it's a Y. It's up the revolution like that. Keeping your cool and having good wits is your strongest defense.

If you don't want it on TV, write the word "FUCK" on your head, see, and that won't get on TV, right? But that's where theatre is at, it's TV. I mean our thing's for TV. We don't want to get on Meet the Press. What's that shit? We want Ed Sullivan, Johnny Carson show, we want the shit where people are lookin' at it and diggin' it. They're talking about reachin' the troops in Viet Nam so they write in *The Guardian*! (An independent radical newsweekly published in New York.) That's groovy. I've met a lot of soldiers who read *The Guardian*, you know. But we've had articles in *Jaguar* magazine, *Cavalier*, you know, *National Enquirer* interviews the Queen of the Yippies, somebody nobody ever heard of and she runs a whole riff about the Yippies and Viet Nam or whatever her thing is and the soldiers get it and dig it and smoke a little grass and say yeah I can see where she's at. That's why the long hair. I mean shit, you know, long hair is just another prop. You go on TV and you can say anything you want but the people are lookin' at you and they're lookin' at the cat next to you like David Susskind or some guy like that and they're sayin' hey man there's a choice. I can see it loud and clear. But when they look at a guy from the Mobilization (against the War in Vietnam) and they look at David Susskind, they say well I don't know, they seem to be doing the same thing, can't understand what they're doin'. 'Cause they say we're like exploiting; we're usin' the tools of Madison Ave. But that's because Madison Ave. is effective in what it does. They know what the fuck they're doin'. Meet the Press, Face the Nation, Issues and Answers — all those bullshit shows, you know, where you get a Democrat and a Republican arguin' right back and forth, this and that, this and that, yeah yeah. But at the end of the show nobody changes their fuckin' mind, you see. But they're tryin' to push Brillo, you see, that's good, you ought to use Brillo, see, and 'bout every ten minutes on will come a three-minute thing of Brillo. Brillo is a revolution, man, Brillo is sex, Brillo is fun. Brillo is bl bl bl bl bl bl bl bl. At the end of the show people ain't fuckin' switchin' from Democrat to Republicans or Commies, you know, the right-wingers or any of that shit. They're buying Brillo! And the reason they have those boring shows is because they don't want to get out any information that'll interfere with Brillo. I mean, can you imagine if they had the Beatles going' zing zing zing zing zing zing zing, all that jump and shout, you know, and all of a sudden they put on an ad where the guy comes on very straight: "You ought to buy Brillo because it's rationally the correct decision and it's part of the American political process and it's the right way to do things." You know, fuck, they'll buy the Beatles, they won't buy the Brillo.

We taped a thing for the David Susskind Show. As he said the word hippie, a live duck came out with "HIPPIE" painted on it. The duck flew up in the air and shat on the floor and ran all around the room. The only hippie in the room, there he is. And David went crazy. 'Cause David, see, he's *New York Times* head, he's not *Daily News* freak. And he said the duck is out and blew it. We said, we'll see you David, goodnight. He say, oh no no. We'll leave the duck in. And we watched the show later when it came on, and the fuckin' duck was all gone. He done never existed. And I called up Susskind and went quack quack quack, you motherfucker, that was the best piece of information: that was a hippie. And everything we did, see, non-verbally, he cut out. Like he said, "How do you eat?" and we fed all the people, you know. But he cut that out. He wants to deal with the words. You know, let's play word games, let's analyze it, it's dead, it's over. You read a book and say well now I understand it, and go back to sleep.

The media distorts. But it always works to our advantage. They say there's low numbers, right? 4000, 5000 people here. That's groovy. Think of it, 4000 people causin' all this trouble. If you asked me, I'd say there are four Yippies. I'd say we're bringin' another four on Wednesday. That's good, that freaks 'em out. They're lookin' around. Only four. I mean I saw that trip with the right wing and the Communist conspiracy. You know, you'd have 5000 people out there at the HUAC demonstrations eight years ago in San Francisco and they'd say there are five Communists in the crowd, you know. And they did it all. You say, man that's pretty cool. So you just play on their paranoia like that. Yeah, there're four guys out around there doin' a thing. So distortion's gonna backfire on them, 'cause all of a sudden Wednesday by magic there are gonna be 20,000 fuckin' people marchin' on that amphitheatre. That's how many we're gonna have. And they'll say, "Wow. From 4000 up to 20,000. Those extra four Yippies did a hell of a good job." I dig that, see. I'm not interested in explainin' my way of life to straight people or people that aren't interested. They never gonna understand it anyway and I couldn't explain it anyway. All I know is, in terms of images and how words are used as images to shape your environment, the *New York Times* is death to us. That's the worst fuckin' paper as far as the Yippies are concerned. They say, "Members of the so-called Youth International Party held a demonstration today." That ain't nothin'. What fuckin' people read that? They fall asleep. 'Cause the *New York Times* has all the news that's fit to print, you know, so once they have all the news, what do the people have to do? They just read the *New York Times* and drink their coffee and go back to work, you know. But the *Daily News*, that's a TV set. Look at it, I mean look at the picture right up front and the way they blast those headlines. You know, "Yippies, sex-loving, dope-loving, commie, beatnik, hippie, freako, weirdos." That's groovy man, that's a whole life style, that's a whole thing to be, man. I mean you want to get in on that.

When we stormed the Pentagon, my wife and I we leaped over this fence, see. We were really stoned, I mean I was on acid flying away, which of course is an anti-revolutionary drug you know, you can't do a thing on it. I've been on acid ever since I came to Chicago. It's in the form of honey. We got a lab guy doin' his thing. I think he might have got assassinated, I ain't seen him today. Well, so we jumped this here fence, see, we were sneaking through the woods and people were out to get the Pentagon. We had this flag, it said NOW with a big wing on it, I don't know. The right-wingers said there was definitely evidence of Communist conspiracy 'cause of that flag, I don't know what the fuck it was. So we had Uncle Sam hats on, you know, and we jumped over the fence and we're surrounded by marshals, you know, just closin' us in, about 30 marshals around us. And I plant the fuckin' flag and I said, "I claim this land in the name of free America. We are Mr. and Mrs. America. Mrs. America's pregnant." And we sit down and they're goin' fucking crazy. I mean we got arrested and unarrested

746

like six or seven times. And we finally got arrested, it was under other names. I'm really a digger, I never was a Yippie. Was always a digger. So I said, you know, A. Digger, Abbie Digger, Mr. and Mrs. A. Digger. They say are you a boy or a girl, I say girl. Right. This is where I wanna go. I don't have to prove manliness by beatin' up 14-year-old girls with night-sticks, you know. Fuck 'em. But ideas, you just get stoned, get the ideas in your head and then do 'em. And don't bull-shit. I mean that's the thing about doin' that guerrilla theatre. You be prepared to die to prove your point. You gotta die.

You know, what's life? Life's all that fun shit. Life's doin' what you want to do. *Life*'s an American magazine, and if we hook them right, they're gonna give us 10,000 flowers that are gonna be thrown out of a helicopter tomorrow after-noon. But we'll only allow them to do it if they bring a newsreel person up in the helicopter with 'em. You know, to take the pictures. So we're workin' out that negotiation with *Life* magazine. 'Cause we said, you know, it's called Festival of Life, man, we named it after your magazine. I know that's immoral and I know that's cheatin' and that's stealin'. I wish I was a revolutionist. I wouldn't have those problems. A lot of revolutionists come here, they worry about parking the car. Where we gonna park the car, should we park it in a meter? The meter'll run out, we'll get a ticket. It's a weird revolution. Fuck it. We don't need cars; we travel in wheelbarrows. You see, just worry about your ass. Forget about your clothes, your money, you know, just worry about your ass and all the rest of us's asses. Cars don't mean shit. They grab our walkie-talkies you say yeah, there you go, take it, thank you, it was too heavy to carry.

I think it's a good idea to cut your hair or get a wig or let your hair grow pretty fast or paint your face or change your clothes or get a new hat and a new name. I mean everybody ought to have a new name by Wednesday. And like you know we're all one huge happy family with all new names or no names and no faces. 'Cause when we bust out of this park and go down to Grant Park and then go out to the amphitheatre, there are gonna be some mighty strange theatri-cal events. And you better have your theatre thing down pretty pat.

Well, I've shot my load. I'm for ending the Yippie thing Thursday, killin' it all, 'cause I don't think people are Yippies anymore than they're Mobe or Motherfuckers or whatever they are. They're just people. And I think we oughta burn all our Yippie buttons and laugh at the fuckin' press and say nyah, nyah, we took you for a fuckin' ride. That's what we figured when we started this thing back in December — just a couple of speedfreaks hangin' around the cellar sayin' now how are we gonna do this Chicago trip? We ain't got no fuckin' money, you know, we ain't got no organization, we ain't got no constituency. We went to a New Left meeting, they said where's your constituency, you can't talk here, you know, you ain't against imperialism. I said, man, I don't want any pay toilets in this fuckin' country, I don't want to pay a dime to take a shit. SDS doesn't con-sider that relevant. That's the trouble with the Left you know. Did a trip on a Socialist Scholars Conference, a couple of Hell's Angels guys and I, we went up and had a capgun fight in the Hotel Hilton where the Left has their conferences, it's very interesting. So the heads of the Hilton and the heads of the socialists were gettin' together to decide how to throw us speedfreaks out of the fuckin' place, see. But they didn't, I mean, we stayed to do our thing. The problem with the Left is that there are 10,000 socialist scholars in this country and not one fuckin' socialist. I mean I talk to guys on *The Guardian* and they say yeah, we're working on a serious analysis of the Yippies. I say, that's pretty fuckin' cool, man, that's great. By that time there won't be any Yippies. I mean, what the fuck are you analyzin' for, man, get in and do it.' (Abbie Hoffman, *Media Freaking*. Extracts from a workshop speech, Lincoln Park, Chicago, Ill., August 27, 1968, taped by Charles Harbutt. In: Tulane Drama Review #44, summer of 1969.)[20]

This speech subsequently was part of the evidence against him for his indictment for having conspired to incite riots during the Democratic Convention. Hoffman is a more genuine Hippie than Rubin, who was close to the seriousness of the New Left.

---

20. Copyright, Abbie Hoffman, 1968.

20. Aryeh Neiher, preface to Benedict J. Fernandez, *In Opposition*, 1968.

IN OPPOSITION

Fernandez (Benedict J.), 1968

This is a book about freedom of speech. It is not about freedom of speech as that term might have been understood by the framers of the American constitutional guarantee of the right of free speech. It is about freedom of speech as it is practiced by American dissenters today.

To the framers of the American Constitution, freedom of speech meant the right of anyone to engage in rational discourse. To today's dissenters, freedom of speech means first the right to get attention to one's views, with rational discourse possible only after that attention has been secured.

The protection accorded to free speech by the framers of the Constitution is rooted in the eighteenth-century theory that if ideas are allowed to compete freely in the marketplace, eventually truth and reason will prevail. In the words of Justice Oliver Wendell Holmes:

The best test of truth is the power to get itself accepted in the competition of the market ... That at any rate is the theory of our Constitution.

The Constitution was framed by men who had led a successful revolution. Not only had that revolution secured the independence of the American states, it had given birth to a society in which there were no inherited titles with their concomitant inherited prerogatives of power. With the overthrow of the titled aristocracy, there was every reason for the founding fathers to have faith in the ability of ideas to gain acceptance on the strength of their merits. Each man's ideas would have to stand on their own in this new society, without benefit of the special deference which Europe required to the views of royalty or the nobility.

Of the various dissenters portrayed in this book, perhaps only one fits the model imagined by the eighteenth-century framers of the constitutional provision protecting the right to dissent. Only Norman Thomas, of the dissenters photographed by Benedict Fernandez, has limited his attempts to gain acceptance for his ideas to the modes of rational discourse that the founding fathers had in mind. And since Thomas, who was born in 1884, is much the oldest dissenter portrayed in this book, he can be regarded as the exception that proves the rule that dissent today must function on different lines than in the past if it is to function at all.

Most of the years in which Norman Thomas was a leading dissenter were prior to the advent of television as a major instrument of communication. The last of his six races for the Presidency came in 1948, which was also the first year that television sets became standard household items and long before television became a significant political factor. Although in later years Norman Thomas would frequently appear on television, his dissenting views were largely communicated through such technologically primitive media as writings by and about him and, because of his remarkable oratorical gifts, through speeches by him to 'live' audiences. It is fitting that one of the two photographs of Thomas in this book shows that direct communication with an audience.

That later dissenters have chosen other methods of communicating their views cannot be attributed to any absence of powers of rational discourse or oratory equal to those of Norman Thomas. Certainly, Reverend Martin Luther King, Jr. possessed gifts comparable to those of Thomas. But where Thomas was content, and could be content, to compete in the marketplace of ideas with words alone, King found it necessary to lead marches and sit-ins and pray-ins to get across his message. King was capable of the supreme level of rational discourse embodied in his 'Letter from Birmingham Jail.' But he had to go to jail before anyone would pay attention to what he had to say.

One of the most thoughtful commentators on free speech in the United States, Professor Franklyn S. Haiman of Northwestern University, has used the term 'body rhetoric' to describe the styles of protest favored by King and the other dissenters photographed by Benedict Fernandez. By demonstrating with their bodies, and showing a willingness to endure physical discomfort and risk their own physical safety, these dissenters have made their bid to compete in the marketplace of ideas.

To understand the significance of this 'body rhetoric', it is perhaps necessary to examine the views of some of those who argue that the marketplace concept is no longer relevant and that the tolerance it asks for free trade in ideas has become repressive.

The leading detractor of the marketplace concept is Professor Herbert Marcuse, the philosopher-hero of the 'new left.' Marcuse's essential criticism of the marketplace concept is that like the laissez-faire marketplace economics of the eighteenth century, it has been outmoded by technology. Technological progress rendered a laissez-faire approach to economics repressive because it created great concentrations of economic power which had to be subjected to governmental controls if they were not completely to dominate society. Similarly, Marcuse argues, technological progress has placed in the hands of the few the means for communicating with masses of people. The dissenter who does not have access to, and cannot afford access to, television time, or space in a mass circulation periodical, is not able to secure the attention necessary to communicate effectively with masses of people. Whatever their intrinsic worth, the dissenter's ideas cannot compete effectively with those of the establishment which controls the media of mass communications. If one accepts this thesis, the rationale for the notion that free competition in ideas will enable truth and reason to prevail is detroyed.

Marcuse's reasoning is seductive and his conclusions cannot be dismissed lightly. The point that I suggest Marcuse and his followers overlook is the point that it seems to me is made by these photographs by Benedict Fernandez. They show the marketplace still at work, if only through the ingenuity of the dissenters in our society.

Fernandez's photographs capture the visual drama and excitement that has been generated by dissenters. While you may not previously have seen the particular images that are recorded on these pages, you will surely sense some familiarity with the dissenters shown here. You have seen their faces before, on television, in the newspapers, and in the magazines; you have seen these faces through the very media of communication which the critics of 'bourgeois civil liberties' tell us are barred to dissenters.

The people whose faces appear on these pages are not soap box orators content to preach their messages to themselves, to curiosity seekers, and to the pigeons, at some local equivalent of Hyde Park Corner. They do not seek to express their views solely because of the pleasure they derive from hearing their own voices, though they probably have their fair share of narcissists. When American society permits them to express their views in the manner shown here, it is not using the notion of free speech merely as a safety valve which will allow them to blow off steam without engaging in more disruptive behavior. And when American society prevents the people portrayed in this book from using particular peaceful methods of expressing their views, as when it sends the draft-card burners to federal penitentiaries for long periods of time, the country is seizing upon the style of expression as a means of punishing the substance of an expression that it finds threatening. Whether America gives free range to, or attempts to repress, the dissenters pictured in these pages, unless the repression is total, their extraordinary skill in making the communications media focus on their activities is the major factor in making the marketplace concept still meaningful.

Critics of dissenters are fond of labeling them 'publicity seekers.' Indeed they are. In the contemporary world, the publicity seeking of dissenters represents their attempt to communicate their views.

Most of the photographs in this book are of dissenters from established policy on the two major issues of our times: the war in Viet Nam and race. While it is unlikely that very many of those portrayed in this book will find society as a whole adopting their programs on either the war or the race issue, all of those portrayed in this book have had an impact on the ultimate resolutions of those issues. They have had an impact because even though they have lacked access to the mass media, they have made the media turn to them. Whether or not they have articulated for themselves or others the significance of utilizing the forms of communication shown in these photographs as a means of capturing the attention of the technologically sophisticated media, they seem to have an intuitive grasp of the importance of devising dramatic styles of protest.

Of course, life is not easy for those who choose to communicate through dramatic styles of protest. They run many risks.

Dissenters run the risk of becoming so shrill and so strident in their styles of protest that whatever message they seek to communicate cannot overcome the distaste engendered by their form of protest. Morever, as time goes by, this problem grows ever more serious. What is dramatic the first time is not as dramatic the second or the third time around. If a picket line in front of the draft induction center is tried once, it may be necessary for the protestor to sit down in front of the induction center the next time. If he limits himself to picketing the second time around, he may find that the easily jaded mass media have no further interest in him. He must escalate his style of protest just to keep on being able to get attention to his protest. But the more that style is escalated, the larger the proportion of the potential audience that may be alienated.

Sometimes, of course, the target of the protest plays into the hands of the protestor by providing the escalation. It was not necessary for the Reverend Martin Luther King, Jr., to resort to shrillness or stridency in leading protests when the opposition consisted of the likes of Police Chief Bull Connor of Birmingham or Sheriff Jim Clark of Selma. King could lead a silent and peaceful march, and the drama and excitement would be provided by the water hoses, police dogs, and cattle prods of the police. The pernicious character of segregation in the deep South could readily be demonstrated for the nation as a whole. A Jim Clark or a Bull Connor became a ready-made symbol, for King to use and for all the world to see, of all that was evil in Alabama.

In other parts of the United States, law enforcement authorities have been somewhat more sophisticated than in the deep South. Nevertheless, protest groups intent on confrontation politics have frequently found that the police, or some other group representing the establishment, such as a university administration, will willingly play along. The temptation to respond in a punitive manner which is out of all proportion to the protest which triggered it seems to be a common failing.

A good example of confrontation politics is the Columbia University sit-in of the spring of 1968. The violence of the police in arresting those sitting in inevitably built support for the students. While the outcome of the student demands was in doubt prior to the 'bust,' thereafter it seemed clear that at least the stated goals of the students who sat in would be achieved. The 'Gym Crow' gymnasium that they sought to keep out of Morningside Park would not be built. Columbia University would end or substantially alter its ties with the Institute for Defense Analysis. Both students and faculty would win more power in University affairs. Had the University been able to respond moderately to the sit-in, all might have been different. The violence of the police action changed everything.

Confrontation politics was also the object of Dr. Benjamin Spock, Reverend William Sloane Coffin, and their fellow defendants in bringing about the conspiracy indictments against them in Massachusetts. When the indictments were handed down by a Federal Grand Jury, they announced their pleasure that the government had chosen to prosecute them for their anti-draft activities. Their reasoning was that it would expose what they considered the bankruptcy of the government position.

If the establishment will not rise to the bait of those intent upon confrontation politics, the need to enter the marketplace of ideas may force dissenters to provide the drama themselves. With the departure from the scene of the Jim Clarks and the Bull Connors, no great changes were made in the conditions of black people in the United States. But for Martin Luther King, Jr., and his followers, the drama could no longer be provided by such unwittingly helpful antagonists. It would have to be produced by the protestors themselves.

The last great effort planned by King was the Poor People's Campaign. While that campaign sorely lacked the leadership that King would have given it had he lived, it was, nevertheless, a classic example of creative peaceful protest. The mud of Resurrection City and the mule trains on their way to Resurrection City were powerful images of the lives of the poor. The poor left their homes in the urban slums of the North and the rural slums of the South and parked on an open expanse in the capital city of our government in an area devoted to white marble monuments to the heroes of democracy. The invisible poor became highly visible. People all around the country were told on television that the squalor of life that the cameras recorded in Resurrection City was typical of the squalor of all the years of the lives of poor people in America. Yet those same cameras would never have shown how poor people lived were it not for protests like the Poor People's Campaign.

While there was some scuffling around the edges, the Poor People's Campaign

752

was essentially a fulfillment of the devotion of King and his followers to non-violence. In the late '50's and early '60's, the spirit of non-violence infused the entire civil rights movement. But the failure of the country to make more meaningful changes in the lives of black people inevitably made many persons cynical about non-violence.

A riot is, in some ways, an abandonment of any hope in the power of ideas. Willingness to communicate ideas, whether through rational discourse or otherwise, indicates a certain faith in human rationality. A riot seems an irrational outburst only geared to the production of irrational responses.

One rather doubts that any of the participants in the early riots in Harlem, Philadelphia, Rochester, and Bedford-Stuyvesant in 1964 thought they were communicating viewpoints. Even so, by the time of Watts in 1965, some black militants were referring to the riot as 'our manifesto.' The pity of it is that they were right.

Prior to the 1965 riot in Watts, few persons outside of Los Angeles had ever heard of the area. Even in Los Angeles, many persons were only dimly aware of the existence of Watts. Many of those who had heard of the area knew of it primarily in connection with the fantastic towers constructed by Simon Rodia. Today, Watts, Hough, Bedford-Stuyvesant, and Newark's Central Ward are all imprinted on the consciousness of the nation. The freeways and parkways of our cities are still designed to enable people to commute between suburb and downtown business center by going under, over, or around the black ghettos so as to shield human misery from view. But images from the ghettos find their way into the national consciousness through the media. The fear of the ghettos, stirred by the riots, has been a considerable force in securing the attention of the media to the conditions of the ghettos.

Riots are also the ultimate example of a style of protest so strident that whatever amount of attention they secure to the views of the protestors, the backlash against the rioters may make the form of protest self-defeating. Between the two extremes of backlash-arousing protests such as riots, and wholly ineffectual protest like Hyde Park Corner speeches, the dissenter must steer his course.

An outstanding example of effective protest which does not do violence to others is the Bread and Puppet Theater group, which is portrayed in some of Benedict Fernandez's most striking photographs. The masks used by this group are compelling works of art which force attention to the horrors of war which the group is protesting. The message has a chance of coming across even to the person catching but a fleeting glimpse of the Bread and Puppet Theater in the fifteen or twenty seconds that may be allotted to one of their demonstrations on a television news program.

The ability to construct striking images is not the exclusive property of any particular segment of the political spectrum. An indelible image is created by the photograph of the father and mother of the boy killed in Viet Nam carrying a sign reading 'P.F.C. Ralph Gray Died In Vietnam For You,' as well as by that of the young member of the National Renaissance Party carrying the flag with the lightning bolt symbol.

Sometimes opposite poles of the political spectrum find themselves resorting to identical styles of protest. Dr. Benjamin Spock is photographed by Benedict Fernandez while taking part in an anti-draft protest in front of the draft induction headquarters on Whitehall Street in New York City. To symbolize his opposition to the draft, Spock sat down briefly on the pavement in front of the steps of the building. He did not actually attempt to interfere with the ingress or egress of persons having business in the building. The sit-down was simply an effort to dramatize his protest.

A few years earlier, another dissenter, George Wallace, then Governor of Alabama, vowed to stand in the schoolhouse doorway to block racial integration. Wallace fulfilled his threat but limited himself to a symbolic show of protest by standing aside as soon as he was ordered to do so by Deputy Attorney-General Nicholas Katzenbach. As in the case of Spock, Wallace did not interfere with anyone's entrance or exit but limited his standing in the doorway to an effort to dramatize his protest.

One of the most severe risks faced by those who seek to communicate through unconventional forms of protest is the risk of going to jail. In fact, in some instances, demonstrating a willingness to risk jail or go to jail is the most dramatic way of communicating a point of view short of incinerating oneself in the manner of the Buddhist monks in Viet Nam.

More often, however, being no more masochistic than other people, dissenters would prefer to avoid jail. They are frequently sent to jail because their styles of protest are unconventional and, in the absence of clearly established precedents of court protection for the particular style of protest, the conventional response of law enforcement officials is to jail them. Thereafter, the issue becomes one for the courts, and the publicity attendant upon the litigation of a novel style of protest opens the door to further attention to the views of the dissenter.

If the dissenter has been able to make his chosen form of dissent fit the substance of his message, the public attention to the style of protest may serve his purposes. On the other hand, if his chosen style of protest is irrelevant to the substance of his message, public attention to the style hardly serves his purposes.

The draft-card burners, for example, were successful in focusing attention on discontent with the draft. By contrast, the young people who sat down on the Triborough Bridge to block traffic as a means of protesting the denial of racial equality chose a form of protest too far removed from the substance of their protest. Both draft-card burners and sit-downers eventually went to jail. But the draft-card burners at least had the satisfaction of having provoked discussions of the draft at each step of the way to jail right down to Justice William O. Douglas' dissent from the Supreme Court decision finally affirming their convictions. In his dissent, Justice Douglas called on his brethren on the Supreme Court to take a fresh look at the entire system of peacetime conscription.

There are still other risks faced by today's dissenters, ranging from physical violence at the hands of the police or counter-demonstrators to the ostracism and obloquy that has always been the lot of those with different views. Yet, their willingness to face all manner of hardships is essential if the concept of free competition in ideas as the path to truth is to continue to have relevance. They are, therefore, deserving of the tribute paid to them by this book of photographs by Benedict Fernandez.

As a photographer of dissent, Benedict Fernandez has a point of view. It is not necessarily the viewpoint of any of the subjects of his photographs. Rather, his point of view has been to revel in and glory in the diversity and variety of dissent reflected in his photographs. That is why this is a book about freedom of speech.

21. The authorities and the New York City Nuclear Freeze demonstration of June 12, 1982.[22]

Like two families planning a wedding, the New York City Police and the sponsors of Saturday's disarmament demonstration have been meeting day after day to check — and sometimes tactfully negotiate — the final arrangements.

The police, who expect up to half a million people to converge on the city for the rally, said the planning had taken a month of meetings.

During these sessions, the two sides have negotiated everything from the police plan to have mounted officers patrol the rally to the organizers' request that they issue their own parking permits and that two of the city's trees be cut down.

Although the police denied some requests, they did agree to set aside 100,000 of the best spots at the rally for actual demonstrators, as opposed to music fans out for a day's entertainment.

'It is nothing like the 60's,' said Leslie Cagan, a member of the June 12 Rally Committee, which is organizing the event. 'Then, if there were meetings, we just said, 'We're going to demonstrate.' There was no detailed planning, nothing like this.'

In what both sides have called a 'phenomenal' spirit of cooperation, the police have even presented the organizers with a list of the top-ranking officers who will be managing the rally.

'If there is a problem, one of their officials can ask for the officer in charge in that area by name,' said Patrick J. Murphy, the department's Chief of Operations and the man in charge of policing the event. 'We've never done that before, but some of these people were uneasy about dealing with police, and we wanted to reassure them.'

Indeed, all the events of the day — beginning with 14 'feeder' marches to the United Nations and continuing with larger marches from the United Nations to the big rally at Central Park — have been carefully worked out by organizers and the police.

'There was a lot of give and take,' Chief Murphy said. 'When we wanted to have mounted police at the rally in Central Park, for example, they got very upset. They were afraid of having police on horses. But we finally convinced them that horses are natural to the park environment,' and that the mounted police would only patrol, not charge into the crowd.

When the organizers wanted to build a temporary stage for speakers near the United Nations — the first major rallying point — the police scouted the area and suggested they build it at 42nd Street and First Avenue.

'We told the police that if we put the stage there, they would have to move two trees because the branches would block camera shots of the stage,' said Norma Becker of the June 12 Rally Committee. 'It was a question of the media's line of vision.'

But the police did not want to uproot city trees, Chief Murphy said, so they found another spot, at First Avenue and 47th Street, which was agreeable to both parties.

The police balked again when rally organizers wanted to issue their own press credentials and parking permits.

'We suggested to them that was properly left in our hands,' Chief Murphy said. 'But we assured them we would issue credentials to people they wanted to be there.'

The police also helped rally organizers with an internal problem. The sponsors were fearful that rock superstars, such as Linda Ronstadt, who have agreed to appear in Central Park might attract crowds of music fans who could edge out the demonstrators.

Chief Murphy said the police would close off the two park sections nearest the stage until the marchers arrived.

The police have assigned community affairs officers to accompany neighborhood groups marching in for the event from Brooklyn, Greenwich Village, Chelsea and other points.

The organizers, in turn, have appointed civilian marshals to act as liaisons between the police and the demonstrators.

'If traffic is fouled up or we have to route marchers on alternate streets, the police will pass that information on to the marshals, who will help pass it on to the crowd,' Chief Murphy said.

'Of course,' he added, 'we are not naive anough not to plan for some violent group that might want to try to engage in a confrontation with police.'

The Police Department Intelligence Division has been monitoring fringe groups who have been disruptive in the past, but Chief Murphy would not elaborate.

He said that police helicopters would keep the skies over the rally safe and clear and that more than 5,000 officers, including 1,690 recruits still in the Police Academy, would direct and patrol the marchers and the traffic.

Although the police are reasonably confident they can manage the demonstration, the crowds are expected to be so huge and the traffic and transit facilities so burdened that officials will advise nondemonstrators to stay out of the city.

'Very little but the marchers will be moving in this city that day,' the chief warned.

A second disarmament committee, with some of the same groups from June 12, has planned a blockage of at least five United Nations missions on June 14.

Diane Becker, a spokesman for the Civil Disobedience Campaign, said as many as 1,000 protestors would peacefully block missions in an effort to force their own arrests and dramatize their cause. She said the sponsors had met with police officials, but 'our posture is not to negotiate with the police.' (Basler, *Police and Atom Rally's Sponsors Cooperate*, New York Times, June 9, '82.)

'The march and rally against nuclear arms in Manhattan on June 12 and an incident of civil disobedience two days later cost New York City more than $1.8 million in overtime pay for its workers, according to budget officials.

Most of the money was spent by the Police Department, which received overtime bills of $1.475 million for the two days. Officials said the bulk of that money was for the 5,000 officers assigned to the June 12 march through midtown and a rally in Central Park.

As many as 700,000 people took part in the events, which were peaceful. Because it was a Saturday, most of the officers were on overtime.

Budget officials said that the final cost to the city for the two days would be somewhat more than $1.8 million, but that the figure would be difficult to calculate exactly because there were many minor costs for such items as gasoline to transport city employees and overtime costs for agencies that supplied only a few persons for the events.

"When you get that precise, it becomes a little difficult to calculate," said Bernard Rosen, associate budget director. "I would assume there would be some other minor costs that might be associated with it, but who knows how to calculate that."

When Mayor Koch announced the city's plans for the events in early June, he predicted that the cost to the city might approach $1 million. The final figure is likely to be nearly double that.

The Police Department's bill includes overtime claims for a protest on June 14, when 1,566 persons were arrested for blocking the entrances to the United Nations missions of five countries that possess nuclear arms. Most of those arrested were given summonses for disorderly conduct.

Alice T. McGillion, deputy police commissioner for public information, said the costs to the department were higher than planned primarily because the march and rally on June 12 had attracted more people and lasted longer than expected. The result, she said, was that some officers were kept on duty for more than a full tour.

In addition to the city funds, the Transit Authority reported that it had spent about $100,000 in overtime the day of the rally. Those costs, a spokesman said, paid for longer trains, more token sellers and more security for station platforms.

The agency with the second-largest overtime bill was the Parks Department, which spent $200,000 to prepare Central Park and to clean up afterward. The department had expected to spend as much as $300,000, according to Commissioner Gordon J. Davis.

"It was lower than we thought because the cleanup went extraordinarily well," Mr. Davis said. He added that the huge crowd had been fairly neat.

Other departments that had overtime costs included the Sanitation Department – $112,000, to clean streets and collect garbage – and the Emergency Medical Service – $17,000, to put additional ambulances on the streets and prepare for medical emergencies.' (Goodwin, *Antinuclear Protest to Cost the City $1.8 Million*, New York Times, July 22, 1982.)

22. The U.S. air war against Vietnam[23]

On March 2, 1965, the United States Air Force began to bomb North Vietnam on a round-the-clock basis. By this bombing, the United States hoped to force the Hanoi government to stop helping the National Liberation Front and to negotiate with the United States. It also hoped that the bombings would make the South Vietnamese government troops feel that they could win the war and thus stop deserting. Finally, by bombing the North and escalating the war in other ways, the United States hoped to cut down the number of men killed or wounded in battle. At the time, the United States forces were losing many more men per week than the South Vietnamese forces were.

. . . as the months wore on, it became clear that things were not turning out as planned. After a year of bombing, the United States was dropping two and a half times as many bombs per month over North Vietnam as it had dropped over Korea. Meanwhile, the United States had learned that the Vietcong were receiving supplies from Laos and that their men were being trained there; and the United States was flying almost as many missions over Laos as it was over North Vietnam. Soon the United States was dropping more bombs each week than it had dropped on Germany during the height of World War II. Furthermore, after a year of bombing, the Vietcong controlled more area than it had before the bombing began. Also, as the figures on the number of deserters for 1965 and 1966 . . . show, the desertions by South Vietnamese soldiers were increasing.

But the United States kept on bombing. In the beginning, the bombing raids had been made upon North Vietnamese weapons-supply areas and shipyards. Now larger areas were being bombed. The United States' reason for bombing these larger areas was that the enemy troops seemed to be increasing. Although there was much evidence that these new troops were coming from the South, the United States decided that the reinforcement must be coming down from North Vietnam. United States' planes began to drop bombs on the demilitarized zone as a warning to North Vietnam not to use the zone as a route to the South for its soldiers.

Then the United States also began to treat the countries surrounding Vietnam as enemy territory. It had already begun to bomb Laos, and soon planes were dropping bombs on parts of Thailand where North Vietnam had airfields. United States forces were also given permission to follow retreating enemy troops into Cambodia.

The United States also increased its defoliation missions and the use of gases and other chemicals. As these increased along with the bombing raids, so did the number of civilians accidentally killed by the various kinds of warfare. Just over a year after the bombing pause, statistics given in a report to Congress showed that for every Vietcong killed, two civilians died also. But there was little time to worry about suffering civilians. The war had become a nightmare. Each new step by the United States was matched by the enemy, and the only way out seemed to be more new steps. The number of civilians and soldiers killed only served as a reason to escalate the war further, so that their deaths would not be for nothing . . . .

Meanwhile, the Vietcong were gaining. In January 1968, during the yearly

23. Copyright, James Haskins, 1971. Copyright, Thomas Powers, 1973.

Tet, enemy troops attacked Hue. For twenty-five days they fought United States and South Vietnamese troops in the street and finally made them retreat. This battle, called the Tet Offensive, was one of the bloodiest yet. As usual, the civilians suffered; much of the beautiful religious city was destroyed; five thousand of its citizens died, and another ten thousand were left homeless . . .' (James Haskins, *The War and The Protest*, 1971.)

'In its January, 1967, issue *Ramparts* had published a twenty-four-page story on "The Children of Vietnam" which included sixteen pages of color photographs of war-wounded children. The missing limbs, the scar tissue from napalm burns, the puzzled eyes were eloquent testimony that the war was costing the South Vietnamese more than they could ever hope to gain by victory. On April 7, *Life* published twelve pages of pictures by Lee Lockwood showing the damage caused by the U.S. bombing campaign in North Vietnam. The Defense Department might insist that bombing was directed solely at military targets and conducted with surgical precision; Lockwood's pictures showed ordinary cities smashed flat.

That same month the *New Yorker* devoted most of an issue to Jonathan Schell's long report on the pacification program, "The Village of Ben Suc".

The bland inhumanity of American military technology was captured well by an aviation writer named Frank Harvey. In 1966 he had gone to Vietnam for *Flying* magazine with few doubts about the American right to be there. Gradually he sensed that American military power was largely irrelevant to the political nature of the war and thus amounted to a pointless atrocity. His long report, *Air War – Vietnam*, was expanded into a paperback published by Bantam in July, 1967, and reviewed prominently in the *New York Review of Books*. In a typical passage, Harvey explained that U.S. Navy pilots were introduced to the war from Dixie Station off South Vietnam, where they flew missions over the Mekong Delta before moving up to Yankee Station off North Vietnam:

He learns how it feels to drop bombs on human beings and watch huts go up into a boil of orange flame when his aluminum napalm tanks tumble into them. He gets hardened to pressing the firing button and cutting people down like little cloth dummies, as they sprint frantically under him. He gets his sword bloodied for the rougher things to come.

Harvey wrote about the defoliation program which used C-123 transports built by Fairchild-Hiller to spread eleven-thousand-pound bomb loads of 2,4,5-T, a defoliant later banned after it appeared the substance could cause birth defects. Each mission cost well over $5,000 and would destroy three hundred acres of rice within three to five days, or an equal area of jungle within five to six weeks. The crews flew two missions a day, six days a week, and the motto over their Ready Room door read, "Only you can prevent forests."

Harvey wrote about "Puff, the Magic Dragon," the ancient DC-3s, each outfitted with three electrically operated rapid-fire machine guns which could pour six thousand 7.62-millimeter bullets over the landscape each minute. At night they found their targets with the aid of million-candlepower magnesium flares. (The military once actually toyed with the idea of orbiting a huge reflector around the earth in such a fashion that it would shine perpetual sunlight on Vietnam, thus ending the nightly activities of the Vietcong.)

Among other military gadgets used by the United States in Vietnam were red haze photos taken by RF-4C Phantom jets. Vietcong cooking fires would appear on the film as a white dot with a tail. Processed immediately after return of the plane, the photos were passed on to the artillery which would determine the map position of the fires and zero in with artillery fire. The Vietcong, for example, had been using tunnels since the beginning of the war. The United States would drop napalm on tunnel openings, creating fires that would suck up all the oxygen from the tunnels in seconds, leaving whoever happened to be inside to die of asphyxiation. Other accounts told of the "harassment and interdiction" artillery fire sent into certain areas at random intervals throughout the night, and the "free-fire zones" which the Government of Vietnam had placed off-limits to all its citizens. Anyone in the zone was fair game. In a later *New Yorker* article, "The Military Half," Jonathan Schell brilliantly described the way air force pilots in light planes would roam vast areas of countryside looking for "Vietcong." Whenever one was sighted, plowing a field or planting rice or hovering in the tree line at the edge of a paddy, jets would be called in to finish him off. It did not take correspondents in Vietnam long to discover that the Vietcong insurgency came from the people, that the regime in Siagon felt no hesitation about authorizing attacks on the people, and that the United States complied. It was easy to wonder if any nation, for any reason, could have the right to intrude with such technology into a civil conflict in a backward country halfway around the world.

A television reporter named Desmond Smith told of a military briefing he had attended in an article published in the *Nation* of June 12, 1967. The briefing officer had described the 365 air raids, 300 B-52 raids, millions of artillery shells, and millions of propaganda leaflets used in one operation on the Bong Son Plain. When he was finished, he asked:

"Well, do you correspondents have any question."

"Well, only one. According to your handout, all you captured so far in Operation Pershing is 30 hand grenades, four rounds of larger caliber ammunition, three tons of rice and three tons of salt."

"Sir?"

"It appears that you've levelled virtually every enemy village and hamlet, killed or driven more than 50,000 peasants off the land with your fire power. My question is, how do you intend to go about winning the hearts and minds of these people?"

"I'm afraid you'll have to take that up with the S.5, Sir, but jeeze, it's a real good question."

Winning hearts and minds was a joke referred to by reporters and officers alike as "WHAM." The theory of the military was simple and direct: "Get them by the balls and their hearts and minds will follow." Such a strategy, however, was nothing more than military terror. Inevitably, as the war dragged on, it began to seem a tragic waste which would never solve anything. Young Americans who went to Vietnam were horrified by what they saw, the casual killing and destruction, the unbridgeable gulf between the Vietnamese and the Americans who insisted officially that they were fighting only for the right to go home. What right did the United States have to insist that the government of Vietnam should be this or that sort? On March 27, 1967, the Akron (Ohio) *Beacon-Journal* published a long letter sent to his family by a local boy.

Today a buddy of mine called "la dai" ("Come here") into a hut and an old man came out of the bomb shelter. My buddy told the old man to get away from the hut and since we have to move quickly on a sweep, just threw a hand grenade into the shelter. As he pulled the pin the old man got excited and started jabbering and running toward my buddy and the hut. A GI, not understanding, stopped the old man with a football tackle just as my buddy threw the grenade into the shelter. (There is a four second delay on a hand grenade.) After he threw it, and was running for cover (during this four second delay), we all heard a baby crying from inside the shelter! There was nothing we could do. After the explosion we found the mother, two children (ages about six and 12, boy and girl) and an almost newborn baby. That is what the old man was trying to tell us! The shelter was small and narrow. They were all huddled together. The three of us dragged out the bodies onto the floor of the hut. It was horrible! The children's fragile bodies were torn apart, literally mutilated. We looked at each other and burned the hut. The old man was just whimpering in disbelief outside the burning hut. We walked away and left him there.

Cruelest of all the American weapons used in Vietnam was napalm. The military insisted that nothing else was so effective against an entrenched enemy, and in this the military was probably right, but napalm was also used against villages, and the victims were not only soldiers. In theory only the Vietcong lived in the free-fire zones where napalm was routinely dropped; civilians had all been warned to move away and if they failed to do so, well, they were to blame for the consequences. This bland legalism was too frail to justify the reality of human suffering, the women and children hideously burned, dying in prolonged agony or scarred for life. In the January, 1967, issue of the *Ladies' Home Journal*, a woman's magazine with no history of social activism, Martha Gellhorn wrote that, "It's time to talk of the Vietnam casualties nobody dares talk about: the wounded boys and girls . . . .

In the children's ward of the Qui Nhon province hospital I saw for the first time what napalm does. A child of seven, the size of our four-year-olds, lay in the cot by the door. Napalm had burned his face and back and one hand. The burned skin looked like swollen, raw meat; the fingers of his hand were stretched out, burned rigid. A scrap of cheesecloth covered him, for weight is intolerable, but so is air. His grandfather, an emaciated old man half blind with cataracts was tending the child. A week ago, napalm bombs were dropped on their hamlet. The old man carried his grandson to the nearest town; from there they were flown by helicopter to the hospital. All week, the little boy cried with pain, but now he was better. He has stopped crying. He was only twisting his body, as if trying to dodge his incomprehensible torture . . . .

My interpreter questioned the old man, who said that many had been killed by the fire and many more burned, as well as their houses and orchards and livestock and the few possessions they had worked all their lives to collect. Destitute, homeless, sick with weariness and despair, he watched every move of the small, racked body of his grandson. Vietcong guerrillas had passed through their hamlet in April the old man said, but were long since gone. Late in August, napalm bombs fell from the sky . . . .

A housewife from New Jersey, the mother of six, had adopted three Vietnamese children under the Foster Parents Plan, and visited South Vietnam to learn how Vietnamese children were living. Why? "I am a Christian . . . . These kids don't ask to come into the world – and what a world we give them . . . . Before I went to Saigon, I had heard and read that napalm melts the flesh, and I thought that's nonsense, because I can put a roast in the oven and the fat will melt but the meat stays there. Well, I went and saw these children burned by napalm, and it is absolutely true. The chemical reaction of this napalm does melt the flesh, and the flesh runs right down their faces onto their chests and it sits there and grows there . . . . These children can't turn their heads, they were so thick with flesh . . . . And when gangrene sets in, they cut off their hands or fingers or their feet; the only things they cannot cut off is their head . . . ."

One could quote endlessly from this and similar articles, many of which reached a wide audience. The charter of the International Military Tribunal that conducted the trials of German war criminals at Nuremberg had specified "wanton destruction of cities, towns or villages" and "inhumane acts committed against any civilian population" and "crimes coming within the jurisdiction of the Tribunal for which there shall be individual responsibility." The use of napalm against women and children was certainly "inhumane, and the bombing of villages because they fell within an arbitrary grid on military maps was certainly "wanton." Pictures of napalm-burned children, chins fused to necks, skin flaking off in blackened chunks, legs and arms twisted grotesquely by scar tissue, were reprinted on antiwar leaflets, and the opposition to the war began to focus on napalm as the cruelest, most indiscriminate, and most characteristic example of America's failure to comprehend the nature of a political war.' (Th. Powers, *The War at Home*.)

23. The war in Vietnam, public opinion, and the protest movement. John E. Mueller's *War, Presidents and Public Opinion*, 1973.[24]

Mueller describes changing public opinion in terms of — analyzed and critically regarded — opinion surveys, the Movement under the heading of 'vocal opposition to the war'. The book goes beyond the concerns of my book because it extends to the Korean War and presidential pupularity. But the former extension at least renders his finding regarding the responses to the Vietnamese war more substantial. His chronology for the war in Vietnam is as follows:

Mueller, table 2.3, p.29-32

Table 2.3   Chronology for the War in Vietnam

1954	July 21	Geneva accords end Indochina war between French and Communist-led guerrillas
	September 8	South East Asia Treaty Organization created
	October 23	President Eisenhower offers aid to South Vietnamese government
1955	February 12	United States advisers take over training of South Vietnamese army from French
	October 23	Diem becomes president of South Vietnam
1958		Growth of Viet Cong guerrilla war against government of South Vietnam
1960	November 8	South Vietnamese government charges North Vietnam is infiltrating troops into South Vietnam
	November 10	Revolt of South Vietnamese paratroopers against Diem fails
1961	Fall	Decision by Kennedy Administration to increase military and economic aid to South Vietnam, raise numbers of military advisers from 685 to several thousands.
1962	October 9	Diem says war against Viet Cong now going well
1963	October 2	Defense Secretary McNamara predicts most of the 14,000 United States military personnel in South Vietnam can be withdrawn by the end of 1965
	November 1	After months of internal political and religious turmoil, Diem ousted from office and killed in coup
	November 22	Kennedy assassinated; Johnson becomes president
	December 21	McNamara abandons plans to withdraw by end of 1965, notes gains of Viet Cong after Diem coup

---

24. All texts by Mueller quoted in this appendix: Copyright, John E. Mueller, 1973.

1964	January 30	Another coup in South Vietnam
	March 17	United States pledge of continued assistance to South Vietnam as long as required to control 'Communist aggression'; warnings to North Vietnam repeatedly issued
	August	In response to two firings on American ships in Gulf of Tonkin, North Vietnamese PT boat bases are bombed; Congress passes resolution supporting action and other such measures to protect United States forces and prevent 'further aggression'
	November 3	Johnson reelected president
1965	January 27	Coup in South Vietnam after months of political and religious turmoil
	February 7	North Vietnam bombed by United States planes in retaliation for Viet Cong attack on United States bases in South Vietnam
	February 16	Coup in South Vietnam
	February 24	United States planes bomb Viet Cong targets in South Vietnam for first time
	February 27	State Department White Paper on aggression from the North
	March 8	Marines land in South Vietnam to defend United States base
	March 21	Communist China says it will fight in Vietnam if United States invades the North or if aid is requested by the North Vietnamese
	April 2	United States to increase troops in South Vietnam, increase air strikes
	April 17	15,000 demonstrators in Washington protest bombings; teach-ins follow
	May	Five-day suspension of air raids
	June 21	Ky becomes premier of South Vietnam
	July 28	Johnson announces increased draft calls to allow buildup in Vietnam from current 75,000 to 125,000
	September 23	North Vietnam reaffirms earlier rejections of United States offers to negotiate
	September 30	Attempted coup by Communists in Indonesia fails, leads to massive anti-Communist movement there
	December 24	Month-long bombing halt begins
1966	February	Senate hearings on war in Vietnam
	Spring	Many antiwar demonstrations
	April 12	First B-52 raids over North Vietnam
	May	Rise of Lin Piao in China; beginnings of purges, Red Guard movement, Great Proletarian Cultural Revolution
	June 29	Extension of bombing raids to oil dumps near Hanoi

	September 11	Elections in Vietnam for constituent assembly
	December	Reports from North Vietnam by *New York Times* correspondent on civilian damage caused by United States air strikes
1967	February	Wilson-Kosygin probes for negotiations on war; North Vietnam continues to demand unconditional bombing halt before talks can begin
	April 15	Mass antiwar rally of 100,000 in New York
	September 3	Elections of Thieu and Ky in South Vietnam
	October 21	Antiwar demonstrators storm Pentagon
	November	Bunker-Westmoreland visit to United States, voice optimism on war
1968	January 30	Beginning of major offensive by Communists during Tet cease-fire
	February 28	Military requests 206,000 more men
	March 1	McCarthy gets sizeable vote in challenge to president in New Hampshire primary
	March 22	General Westmoreland removed as commander in Vietnam and promoted
	March 31	Johnson declares partial bombing halt, calls for talks, announces he will not run for reelection
	April 3	North Vietnam agrees to preliminary peace talks
	April 9	Defense Secretary Clifford announces policy of 549,500 troop ceiling and gradual transfer of war responsibility to South Vietnamese
	Spring	Many antiwar demonstrations
	May	Further Communist offensives
	August 8	Nixon nominated by Republicans
	August 29	Humphrey nominated by Democrats at tempestuous convention
	October 31	Full bombing halt agreed to, 'productive discussions' to be begun
	November 6	Nixon elected president
1969	Spring	Communist offensives
	June 8	Nixon announces beginning of troop withdrawals: 25,000 by August.
	September 3	President Ho Chi Minh of North Vietnam dies
	September 16	Nixon announces withdrawals of 35,000 more men as pace of war slackens
	October	Nationwide protests against the war (moratorium)
	November 15	Mass antiwar march in Washington of 250,000 to 300,000
	November 16	Reports of civilian massacre by United States troops in March 1968 at Mylai
	December 15	Nixon announces further withdrawal of 50,000

1970	April 20	Nixon pledges to withdraw 150,000 troops over the next year
	May	Joint United States-South Vietnamese invasion of Cambodia; massive protest in the United States
1971	February	South Vietnamese troops, with United States support, invade Laos
	Spring	Trial and conviction of Lt. Calley for mass murder at Mylai
	June 13	*New York Times* begins its controversial publication of the 'Pentagon Papers'
	October	Reelection of Thieu
	December	Series of bombings raids on North Vietnam
1972	March 23	United States declares indefinite suspension of Paris peace talks
	April	Major Communist offensive; United States resumes massive bombing of North Vietnam
	July	Peace talks resume; one battalion remains as the only American combat unit in South Vietnam

Mueller's table, 2.2 and figure 2.1 quantify the Vietnam war for us:

Table 2.2 United States Troop Strength in South Vietnam

1954 to 1960	(annual average)	650
End of 1960		800
1961		3,200
1962		11,300
1963		16,300
1964		23,300
1965		184,300
1966		389,400
1967		485,600
1968		549,500
1969		474,400
1970		339,200
1971		161,000

Sources.   Congressional Quarterly (1967:1970); *New York Times Index*

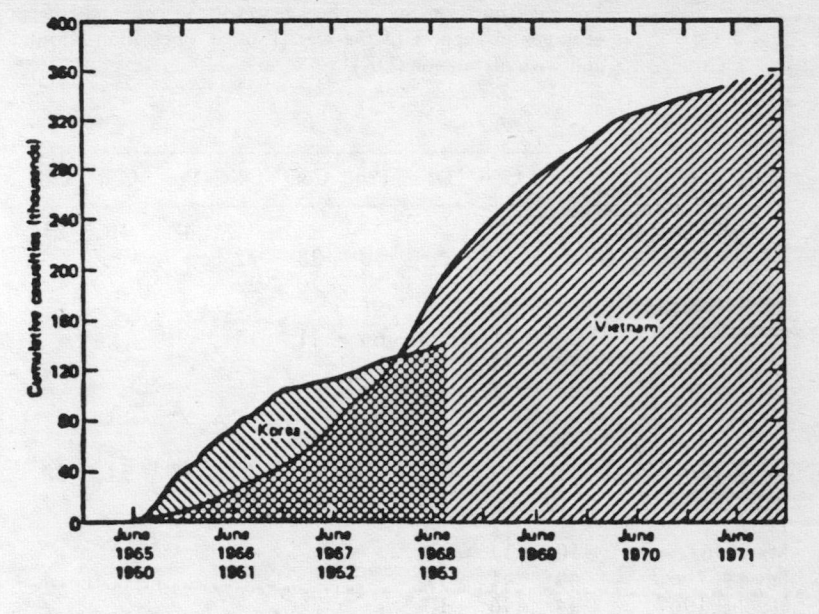

Figure 2.1   Cumulative American casualties for the wars in Korea and Vietnam

13% of the Vietnam casualties in Mueller's figure 2.1 were combat deaths. His table 2.2 makes clear why for Public Opinion the Vietnam war really started in 1965 only.

Support of and opposition to the war vary in the polls somewhat independently of one another:

Table 3.3   Support and Opposition in the Vietnamese War

A: 'In view of the developments since we entered the fighting in Vietnam, do you think the U.S. made a mistake sending troops to fight in Vietnam?' (AIPO)

B: 'Some people think we should not have become involved with our military forces in Southeast Asia, while others think we should have. What is your opinion?' (AIPO)

C: 'Do you think we did the right thing in getting into the fighting in Vietnam or should we have stayed out?'

In 1964 and 1966 asked only of those who said they had been paying attention to what was going on in Vietnam (80 percent of the sample in 1964, 93 percent in 1966). (SRC)

767

For each question the numbers represent, in order, the percentages in support of the war (Pro), in opposition (Con), and with no opinion (DK).

	A			B			C		
	Pro	Con	DK	Pro	Con	DK	Pro	Con	DK
November 1964							47	30	23
January 1965				50	28	22			
May 1965				52	26	22			
August 1965	61	24	15						
November 1965				64	21	15			
March 1966	59	25	16						
May 1966	49	36	15						
Bomb oil dumps									
September 1986	48	35	17						
November 1966	51	31	18				47	31	22
Early February 1967	52	32	16						
May 1967	50	37	13						
July 1967	48	41	11						
October 1967	44	46	10						
Bunker, Westmoreland visit December 1967	46	45	9						
Tet offensive Early February 1968	42	46	12						
March 1968	41	49	10						
April 1968	40	48	12						
GOP Convention August 1968	35	53	12						
Dem. Convention Early October 1968, Nixon elected	37	54	9				30	52	18
February 1969	39	52	9						
September 1969	32	58	10						
January 1970	33	57	10						
March 1970	32	58	10						
April 1970	34	51	15						
Cambodia invaded May 1970	36	56	8						
November 1970	30	49	20						
January 1971	31	59	10						
May 1971	28	61	11						

Sources.   SRC: COI 6,52,56,59,61,69,73.

Mueller's essential finding is that for both the Korean and the Vietnam war, public support varied (declined) as function of cumulative casualties: in proportion to their *logarithm*:

'... the public is sensitive to relatively small losses at the start of the war but only to rather large ones toward its end. Specifically, one does not expect casualties to affect attitudes in a linear manner with a rise from 100 to 1000 being the same as one from 10,000 to 10,900. Rather, a rise from 100 to 1000 is taken as the same as one from 10,000 to 100,000.

When this sort of transformation is applied for Table 3.4 and the result is a set of equations suggesting strikingly similar drops in popular support for the two wars: (the Korean one and the Vietnamese one (SSB)) *in each war, support is projected to have started at much the same level (the intercept figure), and then every time American casualties increased by a factor of 10, support for the war dropped by about 15 percentage points.* Results are not so neat when the dependent variable is the percentage opposing the war, but the patterns remain largely similar: opposition to Vietnam is taken to have begun at a somewhat lower level than in Korea and then to have increased at a somewhat faster rate. Part of this difference is due to the generally lower frequencies of no opinion responses during the Vietnam period.

To summarize, then. When one takes support or opposition for the wars in Korea or Vietnam and correlates either of them (1) with the casualties suffered at the time the poll was conducted or (2) with the duration of the war at the time of the poll, one gets, at least, a reasonably good fit – as would be the case if one correlated support or opposition with any variable that increased (or decreased) continually during the wars. But in all cases, correlating the logarithm of the number of casualties suffered at the time of the poll gives the best fit. Furthermore, and most important, because of the differing patterns under which casualties were suffered in the two wars, the equations relating support or opposition to the logarithm of the casualties are much more similar for the two wars than are the equations generated when the logarithm of the casualties is related to the simple casualty figure or the duration figures.

What this suggests, then, is that Americans, in the aggregate, reacted in similar ways to the two wars. While they did weary of the wars, they generally seem to have become hardened to the wars' costs: they are sensitive to relatively small losses in the early stages, but only to large losses in later stages. Another way of looking at the trends is to see sub-groups of the population dropping off sequentially from the war's support as casualties mount. In the early stages the support of those with considerable misgivings is easily alienated; in later stages the only advocates left are the relatively hardened supporters whose conversion to opposition proves to be more difficult.'

The implication of this is that the vocal opposition to the Vietnam war – there wasn't much to the Korean war – did not much affect public opinion. By 'vocal opposition', Mueller means demonstrations, petitions and organized political campaigns.

'The situation with regard to the data from Korea and Vietnam is rather extraordinary. As observed in Section 2.3.8, the amount of vocal opposition to the war in Vietnam was vastly greater than that for the war in Korea. Yet it has now been found that support for the wars among the general public followed a pattern of decline that was remarkably similar. Although support for the war in Vietnam did finally drop below those levels found during Korea, it did so only after the war had gone on considerably longer and only after American casualties had far surpassed those of the earlier war'.

What does affect public opinion, in fact is its basic determinant, is 'followership'. This is a somewhat general concept. E.g. Mueller in one place extends it to student participation in vocal opposition, once this had become the thing to do for young people, namely '70-'72. But Mueller here means specifically the propensity to follow a president. Presidential policies are endorsed: this is how the public basically arrives at political opinions (though perhaps especially on foreign policy?):

'To deal with this uncertainty and indecision, many in the population grope for cues on which to base their opinion. The perceived issue position of various opinion leaders is very often taken as an important guide. While many public figures and institutions influence public opinion in this way, the most important by far is the president.

Thus there exists, particularly in the area of foreign affairs, an important group of citizens – they can be called 'followers' – who are inclined to rally to the support of the president no matter what he does.

The president's strength in this area seems to derive from the majesty of the office and from his singular position as head of state. Followers seem to identify with the country and with its leadership and tend to be susceptible to social and political influences in this direction. They swim in the mainstream, to apply the jargon of yesteryear. For them, the president is the country for many purposes and, therefore, there is a certain popular loyalty to the man that comes with the office which tends to place him above politics. As will be seen in Chapter 8, whatever his party, the president invariably comes out at or near the top on Gallup's yearly most admired man sweepstakes. In 1968, eight of the ten most admired men were present or past Presidents or were prime contenders for the office.

Followers tend to reject proposals for forceful or accomodating policies in the abstract if they imply an alternation of "our" present course, but once the president has adopted the new policy many in the group will follow his lead. Thus followers cannot be classified in hawk-dove terms: if the administration is using force, followers will respond like hawks; if it is seeking peace, they will respond like doves'; i.e., the public shifted toward more opposition to the support of the war as response to mounting casualties, but within the framework of generally following the president.'

Thus, given

'the ultimate acceptance in mid-1969 by the Nixon Administration of a policy of gradual withdrawal while it also continued and formalized the policy of Vietnamization that had been begun more or less with the Johnson policy changes of the spring of 1968 ... withdrawal of a sort became official presidential policy and administration followers could move to its support. At the same time, of course, leaders of the Democratic opposition became increasingly withdrawal-conscious, and people inclined to follow their lead had a model.'

Followership-determination of 'opinion' is, however, complicated by 'partisanship', by which Mueller means adherence to one or another of the two contending parties, the Republican, the Democratic party. I.e.: presidential patriotic followership is modified – but not really abrogated – by party-followership:

'It is not surprising to learn – but it does seem easy to forget – that much of the public's response to the wars has been influenced by the position taken by the leadership of the political parties. Very simply, many people use their party identification as a shortcut method for arriving at a position on an issue. Rather than sort through the intricacies of argument on the issue, they prefer to take as cues the word of the leadership of their party. It is their method for minimizing information costs ... Party polarization on an issue therefore depends on the degree to which the positions of the leaders of the parties differ and the degree to which the question makes the difference obvious. Where there is little visible difference, little partisan cleavage will be noted in the population. Where the president has a policy and the opposition is unclear in its position, there will be moderate polarization as presidential partisans are attracted disproportionately to support their leader on the issue.

Where leadership divergence is clear, polarization in popular opinion will be quite intense.

As Belknap and Campbell (1951-52) have noted, partisan polarization (measured in their case by voting intention) is likely to be more intense among well-informed people than among poorly informed ones. This seems to be partly because the well-informed are more likely to know what their party's position on an issue happens to be. Thus the well-informed seem to be quite willing to take party cues as a shortcut to policy thinking, and they seem generally to prefer this method of thinking to the application of personal ideological perspectives. It is often easier to predict a well-informed partisan's position on a question of war policy by assuming he will adopt his party's position as his own than it is by assuming he will apply his own predilections toward, say, isolationism or internationalism or toward war or peace.'

The poor ('less educated') were generally less supportive of the war than the others:

'Of the sample subgroups easily separated by polling methods, it is the well-educated segment of the population that most nearly typifies the follower mentality. Thus, contrary to a common belief, it has been the well-educated members of the society who have most consistently supported the prosecution of the wars in Korea and Vietnam ... "Education" in this context, of course, is at least partly a sort of surrogate for social class, since the well educated are generally among the financially better off ... At any rate, as the embodiment of the follower mentality, it is suggested that the better educated tend to possess the characteristics of that view as detailed in Chapter 4: a comparatively close identification with the nation, its leadership, and its destiny; an awareness of and a sympathy for the problems of dealing with other countries in a unified manner; and consequently, a susceptibility to leadership appeals on issues of international policy. In addition, they are likely to know what the present policy is and thus can line themselves up in the appropriate column with a certain efficiency ... As can be seen in the data, the differences among the educational groups are consistently greater for the support scores than they are for the opposition scores. For example, in the 1965 data from Vietnam reported on p. 273, one finds that college-educated respondents are some 20 or 30 percentage points more likely to voice support for the war than those with only a grade-school education. At the same time the poorly educated are only some 5 to 15 percentage points more likely to express opposition to the war. The slack is taken up in the "no opinion" percentage, which is always higher for those with less education. Thus, the difference comes not so much because the poorly educated are willing to assert their opposition to the war as because they are far less willing to assert their support for it.

Higher-status groups tend to reject both plans for withdrawal and plans for extreme escalation. The differences are clearest cut in the educational breakdowns. Those of upper status support the war not because they are necessarily enamored of force as a way of solving problems, but because they see the war as "ours": their country is at war and in such circumstances they are inclined to support their country and its leadership.

Lower status people, from this evidence, seem to adopt a sort of all-or-nothing preference rather than a consistent dove or hawk pose. In part, this point of view may reflect some of the aspects of the "working-class authoritarian" personality as described by S.M. Lipset (1960: 114-15): the desire for "immediate gratification" in life and for "immediate action" in politics ... it is not so much that lower status people favor withdrawal or extreme escalation; rather, they are usually far less likely to oppose them. Again, the active element in the response cadences seems to belong to the higher status people.

Hard Hats. The antipathy of blue collar workers to student antiwar demonstrators during the Vietnam conflict has been often remarked on. It is easy to conclude from such evidence that, since the demonstrators are doves, their antagonists must be hawks. On the other hand, it has sometimes been found that withdrawl sentiment on Vietnam referendums is particularly high in lower class neighborhoods (Hamilton 1968: 442n; Hahn 1970a and 1970b).

The evidence presented here should help to clarify these matters. As seen in the data in Tables 5.2 and 5.3, blue collar workers can be called hawks because they do favor major measures of escalation – or, rather, are relatively less likely to oppose them. However they also are inclined to favor plans for immediate withdrawal – or, rather, are relatively less likely to oppose them. Clearly, viewing such relationships from a follower perspective is sounder than trying to apply the hawk-dove continuum as an explanatory and classificatory tool.'

Young people on the whole were more, not less 'followers' than their elders:

'Most of what has been said for the educational groups can also be said for the age groups – with your people, very much contrary to most of the generation gap discussion, adopting a follower perspective.

But no case can be made for the popular proposition that "youth" was in revolt over the war. This notion was based on the prominence of young people in the antiwar movement, but young people are the most obvious element of almost any political movement presumably because of their physical energy and their lack of occupational and familial obligations – in 1964, it may be recalled, journalistic pundits professed to see an attraction of young people to the Goldwater movement. The poll data argue that, although some young people may have been deeply opposed to the war, "youth" as a whole was generally more supportive of the war than older people.'

Mueller distinguishes information-cost-saving determination of opinion – followership, partisanship – from ideological determination. He finds that the latter counted for relatively little compared to the former in the formation of public opinion: notably as regards the opposition between conservatives and liberal ideology, but also, though for different reasons as regards the third major political ideology, that of the 'intellectual left'. He finds the stands of the intellectual left with fair accuracy recoverable from the polls as the stands of Jews. What made the Jewish and/or intellectually left tend to oppose the war in Vietnam (they didn't particularly oppose the Korean war any more or less than others: perhaps because since at least shortly after WW II they recognized Russia as menace as much as everybody else, and the Korean war was by the public perceived as directly countering that threat) unimportant as contribution to responses to questions asked of the public in the public opinion surveys was the relatively small numbers of Jews and/or intellectually left in the public.

'Jews. Obviously if one had a battery of questions capable of isolating the ideologies from the rest of the population, one could look at the intellectual Left and trace its change of heart. But no sound measure of ideological position has been devised and consistently administered in the polls. The best one can do is to look at the responses of Jews as a sort of imperfect surrogate for the liberal position on most issues. And here one can see a notable shift. As documented in Table 5.5 Jews strongly supported the Korean War but have tended to oppose the war in Vietnam. In fact, Jews seem to be the only subgroup of all those usually sorted out by poll questions whose position on the two wars clearly differs. Since Jews are such a small minority of the population – a few percent – their shift in support, which of course was hardly unanimous anyway, would not appreciably affect the aggregate support for the wars.

For Vietnam, the observation of Rosenberg et al. (1970:74) is sound: "it is clear that Jews have been by some fair quantitative margin more distinctly dovish than any other simply defined group in the electorate." This fact is found "consistent with other data showing that American Jews tend to take a liberal position on the broad range of political issues." Although the Korea data will not allow any casual necessary association of Jews (or liberals) with dovishness, clearly Jews have opposed the Vietnam War as a policy and have been consistently favorable to pleas for withdrawal.

The Jewish shift, then, illustrates the shift of the intellectual Left. But it was the intellectual Left that acted in an ideological manner. Whether Jews as a whole cued on the issue, and thus acted as believers, or took the cue of the Left's opinion leadership, and thus acted as a special breed of followers, cannot be determined from the data. But it does seem that Jews were the only group of those usually sorted out in the polls that joined the intellectual Left in its shift on the wars.'

Vocal opposition to the Vietnam war was carried by the intellectually left. Mueller gives an excellent outline of the shifting focus of this agitationally active group 1950-70:

'As noted in Chapter 2, most of the vocal opposition to the war in Vietnam seems to have come from the intellectual, nonunion Left. For the reasons discussed there, it seems likely that this small group did view the wars differently: Korea seemed an unpleasant, but necessary, episode in the cold war against Stalinist Russia; however, an anti-Communist war in Vietnam, under the substantially altered cold war atmosphere of the mid-1960s, was not found to be worthy of support.

As discussed in Chapter 5, it is difficult in the poll data to measure this shift among intellectual liberals because no questions designed to sort them out from the rest of the population were consistently posed. Looking at the responses of Jews as a surrogate for the liberal position on the issue, however, a notable shift was evident: Jews strongly supported the Korean War but tended to oppose the war in Vietnam. In fact, Jews seem to be about the only subgroup of all those usually sorted by demographic questions in surveys whose position on the two wars differs.

If there were people on the Left in opposition to the Korean War, their expression of dissent may have been smothered by the pall of McCarthyism.[25] In the early 1950s, a war opponent risked the danger of being labeled a Communist. In the 1960s the climate had changed enough so that such labeling was less likely to occur and, more importantly, less likely to be effective if applied.

The years between the Korean and Vietnam wars had seen the gradual emergence of the intellectual Left as a force with political, though not necessarily electoral impact. This seems to have grown out of the opposition to McCarthy and then developed in the late 1950s with movements urging arms-control measures such as atomic test bans, unilateral disarmament initiatives, and alliance readjustments. In the early 1960s it had as a major inspiration the opposition to President Kennedy's fallout shelter program (see Levine 1963).

Around 1963, the intellectual Left moved from a pre-occupation with international cold war issues to an alignment with the fast-emerging civil rights forces. In part, this was a result of the attractive dynamism of the movement and of its aggressive and inspired leadership. And, in part, it was due, after the 1962 Cuban missile crisis, to the notable thaw in the cold war. This seemed to make international threats and issues less pressing. The near evaporation of the arms control movement at this point is quite ironic, since the improved diplomatic atmosphere made it likely that pressure for arms-control measures would finally prove effective.[26]

In its association with the civil rights movement, the intellectual Left picked up and

---

25. It has been suggested that the fear politicians had of McCarthy was somewhat unrealistic. See Polsby (1960).

26. Indicative of the change was the collapse of the *Journal of Arms Control* after two issues in 1963. It proved to be the wrong journal at the wrong time on the wrong subject.

helped develop effective new techniques for political expression: passive disobedience, peaceful mass protest, the use of the media, and obstructionism.

As important legislative and judicial victories were won in the civil rights struggle, as the issue became more technical and cloudy, as blacks showed themselves capable of handling their own movement and, in some quarters, became rather resentful of (even friendly) white interference, and as the movement developed into the destructive, but possibly cathartic and vital, riot stage – as these developments occurred, the civil rights issue became less attractive to the intellectual Left.

Vietnam became at first a competitive cause, then a dominating one, until by 1968 the intellectual Left was almost entirely preoccupied with it. The new techniques of political expression were refashioned and redeveloped to fit the new cause and were put into action. The seeming efficacy of the movement generated a certain attractive inertia, swelling the ranks.

Thus the "new Left" of the late 1960s seems, in this analysis to be the old Left with new methods of expression, a new vocalism. It is not "young people" brought up in the shadow of the bomb or of John Dewey. As stated in Chapter 5, young people are the most obvious element of any political movement presumably because of their physical energy and their lack of occupational and family obligations. In fact, it was found that young people were generally more inclined to support the wars than their elders.

As the Vietnam issue itself faded in 1970 with declining American combat activity and with the continuing withdrawals of United States forces from Vietnam, the intellectual Left – except for a spurt of activity in connection with the Cambodian invasion in the spring of 1970 – for the most part moved on to new areas, most notably the environmental one.

This is not simply to say that the intellectual Left is fickle about its causes. Rather, because it is limited in size and energy, it does not seem able effectively to fight full force on two fronts at the same time and must choose its priorities: the race issue, it was common to hear in the last 1960s, can never be solved until the war in Vietnam is brought to an end.

Thus the difference in vocal opposition between the wars can be traced in part to a shift in attitude by one political group and to the effective use by that group of newly learned techniques of expression. However, none of this is to deny the political impact of the agitation on important elite groups, including those that finance political campaigns (Robison 1970:9). The message here is simply to warn against the assumption that intellectual agitation is the same thing as a mass movement.'[27]

Mueller gives an equally clear picture of who was in the Movement:

'Studies indicate quite clearly that the young people who did oppose the war, as well as their well-educated older colleagues, were very disproportionately associated with the "better" colleges in the country (Converse and Schuman 1970:23-25). In cross-sectional polls, however, their attitudes are overwhelmed by the legions among the young and the educated who enjoy no such association. It is of interest to consider why these associations should correspond with opposition to the war and the president's policy there.

One element in the explanation concerns the relatively liberal and left-liberal atmosphere at the better universities. Since, as noted above, political liberals were inclined to oppose the Vietnam War, it is not surprising to find opposition to the war in Vietnam centered at places where liberals are concentrated: the better universities (see Armor et al. 1967).

But in part this begs the question. What must be discussed is why the better universities are relatively liberal places. It could be that the more intelligent a person is, the more likely he is to adopt the liberal philosophy. However comforting this thought may be to liberals,

---

27. It has been suggested that the fear politicians had of McCarthy was somewhat unrealistic. See Polsby (1960).

it is of questionable validity, since in decades past the better universities were often bastions of conservatism. Or, it may be that pliable student minds are being bent to the Left by a band of liberal professors. But this explanation fits poorly with studies that find student values and attitudes in the aggregate not to be affected in any such gross way, if indeed they are affected at all, by the college experience (Jacob 1957; Goldsen et al. 1960; Feldman and Newcomb 1969). Nor does it fit with those that find faculty members to be particularly ineffective when changes do occur (Feldman and Newcomb 1969:330-31 et passim.). Nor does it fit with those that find college-bound high school seniors already to differ markedly in attitude from their peers (Langton and Jennings 1968:866).

A better explanation might draw on an observation made in Chapter 5 about the liberalism of Jews. Outside of a few sections in a few cities, the only easily identifiable places that Jews are found in strikingly disproportion are the colleges and universities of the land – and very particularly the better ones. Thus the liberalism of those associated with the better universities may not derive from anything endemic in the university situation. Rather, it may stem from the influence of a major subpopulation in the university community inclined toward liberalism and war opposition regardless of its association with the college.[28]

For academicians, an important element of the intellectual Left, economic considerations may have reinforced these pressures, thus discouraging any inclined to oppose the Korean War from loudly voicing their point of view. The academic marketplace of the early 1950s was an extreme buyers' market as the generation born in pre-depression days, embellished by somewhat older people whose graduate education had been postponed by World War II, entered the academic profession to find only the depression generation to teach. Thus job insecurity may have made political protest economically unwise and may have made the academic profession peculiarly susceptible to McCarthyite intimidation.

By the mid-1960s, however, the situation was reversed. The post World War II babies were going to college while depression babies were entering the academic profession which then became a sellers' market. Thus academicians could protest, threaten to resign, and speak freely and impertinently, always aware that jobs were open somewhere. In part, therefore, academic courage may have an economic base.'

The Movement did not move public opinion toward opposition to or away from support of the war. In fact, Mueller thinks it may have had the opposite effect:

'Finally, it should be considered that the protest against the war in Vietnam may have been counterproductive in its impact on public opinion: that is, the war might have been somewhat more unpopular if the protest had not existed.

To assess this proposition, it would be useful to recall a repeated finding from Chapters 4 and 5: many people, in arriving at a position on an issue, do not cue on the elements of the issue itself so much as on the expressed preferences of various opinion leaders. Instead of paying high information costs by sorting through the intracacies of argument of the issue, they prefer to take the word of people and institutions that they have reason to trust. Thus the public does not view an issue in the simple debating-manual sense with arguments pro and con neatly arranged. Rather the issue comes attended by certain public figures who array themselves on various sides and whose visible presence at an issue position may influence public opinon more than any element of the issue itself.

For a war, then, public opinion is going to be influenced by who is for it and who is against it. Now it happens that the opposition to the war in Vietnam came to be associated with rioting, disruption, and bomb throwing, and war protesters, as a group, enjoyed negative popularity ratings to an almost unparalleled degree. This has been shown in a number of studies and is, perhaps, most dramatically evident in the public's reaction to the 1968

---

28. A survey conducted by the President's Commission on Campus Unrest found that campus disturbances occured most often at large, eastern liberal arts colleges with high admissions standards (*New York Times*, November 5, 1970).

Democratic Convention disorders, which was overwhelmingly favorable to the Chicago police (Robinson 1970; Converse et al. 1969:1087-88).

That negative reference groups can harm a cause's impact, a sort of negative follower effect, is quite clear. Cantril reports a poll from 1940, before the United States entered World War II, in which it was found that 57 percent of the American public expressed its agreement with the idea that the country should try to have friendly relations with Germany if she won the war in Europe. However, when the name of Charles Lindbergh, a prominent isolationist leader, was associated with this idea, support for it dropped to 46 percent while opposition climbed 16 percentage points (1947:41).

Thus it seems entirely possible that, because their cause became associated with an extraordinarily unpopular reference group, any gain the opposition to the war in Vietnam may have achieved by forcefully bringing its point of view to public attention was nullified.[29] But, again, it must be observed that the protest may still have been effective in a general political sense if it was successful in altering attitudes among elites and decision-makers.'[30]

---

29. Much of the negative rating may have been inevitable. There seems to have been a rather low tolerance among the public for antiwar protest in general. In 1966 only 35 percent agreed with the right 'to demonstrate against the war' (Lipset 1966:24). The SRC 1968 election study found only 20 percent approving of 'taking part in the protest meetings or marches that are permitted by the local authorities' as a way for 'people to show their disapproval or disagreement with government policies or actions' — (Converse et al. 1969: 1105n).

Opinion on civil liberties, however, seems to be one of the many that are quite sensitive to question wording. Thus, the Harris Poll finds considerably more than 35 percent willing to grant the right to undertake 'peaceful demonstrations' (WP December 18, 1967) and one wonders whether 'approval' in the SRC question was taken to apply to the legitimacy of the demonstrators' actions or their point of view. As noted in Section 1.3, the percentage willing to 'not allow' speeches against democracy was once found to be 16 points higher than the percentage willing to 'forbid' them (Rogg 1941:92). Studies on this subject, perhaps extending those done during the MacCarthy period such as Stouffer (1955), are much needed. There does not appear to be any data in existence to compare the Korean and Vietnam periods in the degree to which dissent was tolerated. The closest thing to extended trend data is given in Table 1.2 (p. 14).

30. One cannot easily conclude, however, that politicians who lead or strongly support stop-the-war movements are forever damaged by such unpopular and 'unpatriotic' associations. In Britain David Lloyd George actively opposed the Boer War and J. Ramsay Macdonald fought against World War I; each later became Prime Minister (see Richardson 1948:151, 159). In the United States Abraham Lincoln opposed the Mexican War of 1848.

24. References to political demonstrations,
Village Voice, January 2, 1964-August 3, 1968,[31]
and pertinent information from Thomas Powers,
*The War At Home/Vietnam and the
American People, 1964-1968.*,[32] 1973.

Date of action	*Village Voice: demonstrations*[33]	Issue of VV
(Feb. 1, 1960)	'Early in 1960 ... the ... civil rights ... movement suddenly expanded to include the young. On February 1 that year, four students at the all-Negro North Carolina Agricultural and Technical College in Greensboro walked into the local Woolworth's, sat down at the segrated lunch counter, and asked to be served. When they returned the following day and the day after that, whites began to respond violently, national attention was captured, students at other black schools in other Southern towns began to follow the Greensboro example, and the sit-in movement was born. The involvement of black students had an immediate effect on white students in the North ... As the movement spread through the Upper South in the spring of 1960, white demonstrators from Northern colleges organized picket lines outside local Woolworth's stores and other chain stores as a gesture of support. The creation of the Student Non-Violent Coordinating Committee by black leaders of the sit-in movement was followed by ...')	Th. Powers, *The War At Home*, p.22

---

31. I looked through the Village Voice microfilm at the New York Public Library, taking note of, I believe, most references — in ads, notices or articles — to demonstrative street actions, i.e. political street agitation. The Village Voice maintained a primary orientation toward the arts and, especially in '64, may have had less concern in the ongoing civil rights, rent control and Puerto Rican independence agitation than it (even then but especially perhaps from '65 on) had in the Vietnam War issue: more a white middle class issue agitating the Village 'community', the arts world, and those putting out and writing for the Voice than those other issues. So the coverage in the Village Voice would not quite correspond to the varying amounts of agitation of different sorts and would not even necessarily quite reflect the growth of the peace agitation (because of the initially especially strong bias towards the arts). And my coverage of the Village Voice coverage is not quite reliable either, chiefly because I had my eye out mostly for stuff more directly pertinent to the Bread and Puppet Theatre. Even so, this record is, I think, pretty good. Remember, though, that in principle I wasn't interested in indoors agitation. Also, the New York Public Library, though splendid, makes one drowsy. I've thrown in some scattered items, 1960-63: but there wasn't much street agitation in New York during those years.
32. Copyright, Thomas Powers, 1964.
33. The dates at the right, except where otherwise indicated, refer to issues of the Village Voice.

(Black impetus for emergence of White New Left; as in music, Black America and young are the praeceptors of White America and young. Qua public protest action, preceded by 5 years by Montgomery, Ala. bus seating infractions of late '55.)

May 3, 1960 Gathering in City Hall Park of individuals refusing to take shelter, or taking shelter only under protest: during the annual nation-wide Civil Defense alert. This rally program reflects **April 27, 1960** the conscientiously cautious and genteel spirit of D. McReynolds and the War Resisters League, and the entire Peace Movement.

January 29, 1962 ff. (Agitation in re atom war danger) Worldwide General Strike for Peace week, in NYC promoted notably by Julian Beck and Judith Malina. Vigil by Bob Nichols, etc. Pete Seeger and Gil Turner sing during march on Jan. 29 (Monday) from the Plaza Hotel to Washington Square ('I Ain't Gonna Study War No **Jan. 25,** More'). **Feb. 1, 1962**

January 30, 1962 Sitdown in front of Atomic Energy Commission. No arrests. **March 8, 1962**

February 1962 ('During the first few years of the 1960s, concern with civil rights issues was paralleled by interest in disarmament and proposals to end nuclear testing. The Committee for a Sane Nuclear Policy (SANE), founded in 1957, began to set up campus chapters and in 1959 the Student peace Union (SPU) was organized by several members of the Socialist Party active in Chicago. In February, 1962, these groups and others joined to organize a demonstration in Washington. Some four thousand students spent the weekend meeting with presidential advisers (one of whom suggested they ought to picket the Pentagon), government officials, and representatives of the Russian embassy. It was the largest peace demonstration in the capital's recent history, but it was also the last on relatively neutral issues like disarmament. By the end of the year the peace groups had been completely overshadowed by civil rights organizations, which demanded moral qualities like courage and self-sacrifice rather than the intellectual discipline involved in the necessarily painstaking study of weapons policy. The most important of the new white groups, the Students for a Democratic Society (SDS), was founded in Port Huron, Michigan, in June, 1962, primarily by students at the University of Michigan active in a campus group called Voice.')

Th. Powers, *The War At Home*, p. 24

March 3, 1962   Demonstration on Times Square protesting Pres. Kennedy's resumption of nuclear testing in the atmosphere. A man faints, others think he is non-violently resisting arrest, sit down with him. Police drag them and verbal protesters off. Julian Beck among latter, his lung punctured by the police. Chaikin among former, arrested. The Living Theatre's Worldwide General Strike for Peace group had planned sit-down, but according to David McReynolds, secretary of the War Resisters League had changed their mind before the demonstration.

March 8, 15, 1961

March 5, 1962   Demonstration at offices of Atomic Energy Commission, Houston and Hudson. Arrests disorderly conduct: sitting down on sidewalk, blocking entrance.

March 8, 1962

November 5-11, 1962   Second General Strike for Peace Week. Sponsored by N.Y. Committee for a General Strike for Peace. P. Schumann's *Totentanz* show and '*Burning Towns*' (?) are part of this. Former planned for Washington Square.

November 1, 8, 1962

November 11, 1962 (Veterans Day)   Veterans' March of Conscientious Objection, as part of GSP Week: down 5th Ave., from 59th St. to Washington Square; following the Veterans' Day Parade; to be followed by a 'draft renouncement' demonstration. Later, at 8 pm, a torchlight parade through midtown Manhattan. Sponsored by Committee for a General Strike for Peace of which Julian Beck is the 'spokesman'.

November 1, 1962

Civil Rights (Black Liberation), not Peace is the Movement issue in 1964.

January 23, 1964   Rent-control Demonstration on Park Row side of City Hall Park by Committee to Save and Strengthen Rent Control. 'The law establishing rent control ends March 31.'

January 23, 1964

Date of action	*Village Voice: demonstrations*	Issue of VV
January 30, 1964	Rent Strike Rally on Stanton St. between Chrystie and Forsythe Streets. Jessie Gray, coordinator of the Harlem rent strikes, will be the major speaker.	January 30, 1964
February 3, 1964 (& ff.?)	(Start of?) school boycott protesting racial segregation in NYC public school system. To focus on Greenwich Village and Upper West Side. Organized by Bayard Rustin who 'achieved national prominence as deputy director of the March on Washington.'	January 30, February 6, 1964
March 6, 1964	Protest tie-up of Triborough Bridge by East River CORE, to 'protest the unsafe and over-crowded schools in East Harlem' – 'designed to make New York commuters stop for a moment to look at Harlem and the people they leave behind.' (CORE leaflet quoted by N. Hentoff).	March 19, 1964
March 29-30, 1964 (March 31: Easter Sunday)	Peace Rally, Washington Square Park. Greenwich Village Peace Center, 224 West 4th Street has an open house – the sponsor?	April 2, 1964
April 3, 1964	Artists' March on City Hall from Lafayette and Howard Sts. to protest evictions from artist's lofts under city's zoning laws (which are not yet in line with state laws legalizing lofts). Sponsored by Artists-Tenants Association. 1000 participate.	April 2, 9, 1964
April 24, 1964	March by artists and sympathizers from Bryant Park to Lincoln Center protesting limitations on the freedom of the arts. (E.g. the persecution of Jonas Mekas' film programs.) Sponsored by Committee for Freedom of the Arts, organized by Julian Beck and Diane de Prima. Carry black coffin labelled 'Will freedom be buried?'	April 30, 1964
May 2, 1964	Anti-Vietnam ('Mass') Rally, 110th St. and Central Park West. 'Get American Boys out of Vietnam ... Stop McNamara's War in Vietnam.' Sponsored by May 2nd Committee of Haverford, Pa. and New York City.	April 30, 1964
May 18, 1964	'A public planning meeting will be held by the Village-Chelsea NAACP ... May 2 at 240 West 4th Street to prepare for a May 18 demonstration at City Hall commemorating the	

Date of action	*Village Voice: demonstrations*	Issue of VV
	10th anniversary of the Supreme Court's outlawing of public school segration.'	April 30, 1964
June 4, 1964	Demonstration for the freeing of South African political prisoners at South African Consulate, 655 Madison Avenue. Walk to UN, rally there. Speakers: Ossie Davis, Ruby Dee, James Forman, etc. Sponsored by 'twelve civil rights groups'.	June 4, 1964
June 13-July 12, 1964	Street performances of R. Nichols' *Everyman*. Sponsored by Judson Poets' Theatre and Greenwich Village Peace Center.	May 7, July 2, 11, 1964
June 15, 1964	Civil Rights March N.Y. to Washington, D.C., i.e. by train from Penn Station, round-trip tickets $8. — from March headquarters at District 65 Building, Astor Place. In 'redemption of a pledge of August 28, 1963 by a group of religious, union and civil rights groups to keep waves of demonstrations coming till passage of the civil rights bill' was secured.	June 11, 1964
(June 29, 1964)	(At a press conference at Second City, it is announced that 100 entertainers will go to Mississippi to aid the civil rights campaign. Speech by James Foreman, executive secretary of Southern Non-Violent Coordinating Committee: he suspects the three disappeared civil rights workers (two white) are dead, points out that since January 1st four Negroes have been killed in Mississippi. The same issue of the VV carries an article on the Mississippi Summer Project. Others in VV, July 16, Aug. 6, Aug. 20, Sept. 17. In December issue, Newfield interview of Robert Moses.)	July 2, 1964
(July 2, 1964)	(Pres. Johnson signs the Civil Rights Act — the broadest since the Civil War — proposed June 19, 1963 by Pres. Kennedy.)	Th. Powers, *The War At Home*, p. 20
July 18-22, 1964	Harlem Rally to protest the murder June 21 of three civil rights workers in Mississippi shifts focus to a white N.Y. cop's killing of a black teenager: the foregathered march to a nearby police station and attack it. Four days of bloody rioting, spreading to Bedford Stuyvesant ghetto, then to other cities in N.Y., N.J. and Penna. July 19th, George Wallace 3rd party racism candidate drops out of race, boost-	

ing Goldwater's chances. Negro leaders, other
than Farmer of CORE and John Lewis of
SNCC meet and agree to call off all demon-   Th. Powers,
trations until after the election in order to   *The War At*
avoid the risk of a white backlash.   *Home*, p. 19

Front-page article and photos on Harlem riots
in July 23 VV, another article, August 6.
Another, August 13, by David McReynolds of
War Resisters League: 'I hesitate, from the
secure comfort of a vacation in southern Cali- July 23, Aug.
fornia, to comment on the tragic violence of   6, Aug. 13,
Harlem.' (Note the commas! (ssb))   1964

Nat Hentoff in his usual intelligent and sensible
manner interviews Bayard Rustin on the July 29
'moratorium' till Nov. 3 on demonstration for   Aug. 27,
civil rights.   1964

(These riots redefine the Civil Rights issue as
issue of a nationwide economic ill done the
black underclass; not just a Southern issue of
political discrimination.)

(August 7,   (Congress adopts Southeast Asia Resolution   Th. Powers,
1964)   ('Tonkin Bay Resolution'), granting Johnson   *The War At*
               who through '64 secretly and cautiously esca- Home, p. 12
               lates the war, but in opposition to Goldwater
               poses as opponent of committing U.S. troops
               authority 'to take all necessary measures to
               repel any armed attack against the forces of the
               United States and to prevent further aggres-
               sion.')

(August 1964) (Johnson orders the first bombardments of
               North Vietnam.)

August 15,   Protest against the war in Vietnam. 47 arrests
1964   Sponsored by May 2nd movement November
               19, 1964.

October 2,   Election rally with Robert Kennedy as speaker
1964   on 'Village Square', 6th Ave. at 8th St., in
               front of the West Side Savings Bank. He
               speaks from the top of a stationwagon to a   October 8,
               crowd of around a thousand.   1964

(November 3,   (Johnson beats Goldwater 77:23 as relatively,
1964)   the peace candidate, but intent on escalation.)

Date of action	*Village Voice: demonstrations*	Issue of VV
November 12-13, 1964	'A dozen pickets from the May 2nd Movement, a radical peace organization, marched outside the Women's House of Detention, 6th Avenue and 10th Street last Thursday and Friday to protest the plight of Carolyn McFedder, 19, of Portland, Oregon . . . one of 47 people arrested during a protest against the war in Vietnam last August 15. Her case hadn't yet come to trial . . .	November 19, 1964
November 14, 1964	'Peace Vigil On. Members of 10 peace groups, including the Village Peace Center, will continue their Vigil Against the War in Vietnam between 1 and 3 pm on Saturday, November 14th at the island in Times Square between 43rd and 44th Streets. Only poster slogans agreed to by the 10 groups will be used. The vigil has been stood for the past six Saturdays.	November 12, 1964
December 9, 1964	Anti-Vietnam War Rally on Thompson St., over 1000 attending. Speaks A. Ph. Randolph, A. J. Muste, Norman Thomas, David McReynolds. Phil Ochs sings his 'Talking Vietnam Blues.' Rally was orginally scheduled for Union Square Park, 'but the city ruled that that site would interfere with Christmas shoppers along 14th Street.' Sponsors not indicated.	December 24, 1964

In 1965, the Peace issue takes over from the Civil Rights issue within the Movement. Also: the Movement goes outdoors, invades the public space.

(February 7-11, 1965)	(U.S. air raids against North Vietnamese military installations: first attacks extending the war beyond South Vietnam. In early March, the U.S. openly adopts a policy of continuous bombing in North Vietnam.	Th. Powers, *The War At Home*, p.42, 46
February 18, 1965	Rally at Community Church, 40 East 35th St. 'End the War in Vietnam. CNVA, SNCC, Student Peace Union (SPU), . . . , Dan Berrigan, Pete Seeger performing, Muste speaks. (Apparently indoors)	February 11, 18, 1965.
February 19, 1965	'An all-day sit-in at UN headquarters will begin at 11 am on February 19. Recruiting centers throughout the city will be picketed at 4 pm. Persons who wish to participate will be instructed on Tuesday February 16th at the Village Peace Center, 224 West 4th St.' (Notice)	February 18, 1964

Date of action	*Village Voice: demonstrations*	Issue of VV
February 20, 1965	'Protest the War against Vietnam! Mass Rally in Union Square, Saturday, February 20 at 2 pm. Hear: Mark Lane, former New York State Assemblyman, ... Mae Mallory, Black Liberation Fighter, ... Joseph Ben-David, President N.Y. Chapter, American Humanist Association, M.S. Arnoni, editor, Minority of One. Auspices Youth Against War and Facism, 1123 Broadway, Room 1214.' (Ad.)	February 18, 1965
February 20, 1965	'A friendly vigil will be held at 11 am, February 20, outside the Hotel Hilton where the 'Pacem in Terris' conference will be coming to a close. Vigilers will walk to the U.S. Mission to the UN at 12:30 for a half-hour vigil.	February 18, 1965
March 6, 1965	Greenwich Village Puppet Parade by the Bread and Puppet Theatre in opposition to the war in Vietnam. Sponsored by Greenwich Village Peace Center.	March 11, 1965
March 26, 1965(?)	Some 'massive march and rally' organized by the 5th Avenue Vietnam Peace Parade Committee.	May 19, 1965
April 10, 1965	'Walk with Dr. Spock for Peace in Vietnam' Columbus Circle to UN. Sponsored by N.Y. Council for a Sane Nuclear Policy, Women Strike for Peace, Student Peace Union, Women's International League for Peace and Freedom.	April 3, 8, 1965
April 17, 1965	'March on Washington to End the War in Vietnam'. Sponsored by Greenwich Village Peace Center, Greenwich Village women Strike for Peace, New York Students for a Democratic Society. (Kourilsky, '71, p. 77-78: B&P.)	April 3, 8, 1965

(Th. Powers seems to view this march as the beginning of the Peace Movement qua Street Action movement as called for after it by Rustin, June 8, 1965. It was first called for by SDS in December 1964; the bombings of North Vietnam February 1965 ff. amplified this call, reiterated March 1965 in a full-page ad in Liberation; the power of the demonstration was due to the SDS's getting the 'long-

established pacifist groups to join in under its
aegis and without excluding Old Left participation.' An ensuing debate between New Left   Th. Powers,
(S. Lynd in Liberation) and Civil Rights (Black   *The War At*
Liberation) (Rustin in Commentary) brings out   *Home*, p.72-
that this SDS oecumenism embodied its rejec-   80
tion of the 'system'. I would say that the
effectiveness, relative to government, of the
Peace Movement, arose from the threat implicit
in this tie-up of the peace-issue with an issue of
social reform profounder than envisaged by the
Civil Rights Movement.)
'The demonstration qua spectacle conjures up
an inspiring image of revolution. This brings
home the profound agitation and its proximity
to rioting: street agitation formally and de facto
approaches insurrection.' (S. Lynd in Liberation)

April 24, 1965   Tenants' Emancipation Rally, City Hall,   April 22,
                  sponsored by Metropolitan Council on   1965
                  Housing.

April 25, 1965   CORE pickets NYC Pavillon to 'dramatize'
                  (note!) its opposition to a 4th term for Mayor
                  R.F. Wagner and his appropriation of $51
                  million to the Fair rather than to Harlem. The
                  Pinkerton Fair guards refuse to protect the   April 29,
                  the pickets against racist harassments, attacks.   1965

May 15, 1965   'Get the GIs out of the Dominican Republic
                and Vietnam!' Sponsored by Youth Against
                War and Facism. Times Square Rally.   May 13, 1965

May 29, 30,   'Digging for the Poverty Program', 'Flower
1965   Mountain' done by B&P Theatre as street-
               plays, off Washington Square Park. Sponsored
               by B&P Theatre and Village Peace Center.   May 27, 1965

June 8, 1965   Emergency Rally on Vietnam, 7 pm, Madison
                Square Garden ('air conditioned') Sen. Wayne
                Morse, Mrs. King, Prof. Hans Morgenthau,
                Dr. Benjamin Spock, Norman Thomas, Bayard
                Rustin. Entertainment: Joan Baez, Irwin
                Corey, Renee Taylor, the Anne Wilson
                Dancers. Chairman: Dr. Harold Taylor. Co-
                chairman: Ossie Davis. Sponsored by SANE –
                National Committee and New York Council
                for a Sane Nuclear Policy. Article by Jack

Newfield, June 17: chants of 'Reds, Reds,
Reds' etc. from right-wing pickets. Full house,
18,000 people. No mention of B&P perfor-   May 27, June
mance.   3, 17, 1965

('A broad strategy for the opposition was proposed on the night of June 8 when 18,000
people attended an antiwar rally held in Madison Square Garden in New York, where they
heard Senator Wayne Morse, Dr. Spock,
Norman Thomas, and Mrs. Martin Luther
King all attack the war. Bayard Rustin, a long-
time pacifist and civil rights activist who had
organized the 1963 March on Washington,
told the crowd that argument must give way to
direct action: 'We know that the Wagner Act
which gave labor the right to organize and
bargain collectively was empty until workers
went into the streets. The civil rights movement has learned this lesson. This is a lesson
that must be applied now to the peace move-   Th. Powers,
ment as well. We must stop meeting indoors   *The War At*
and go to the streets.')   *Home*, p. 71.

June 20, 1965   Rally, Tompkins Park, Brooklyn, to support
the Mississippi Democratic Party's challenge to
seating of illegally elected Mississippi congressmen. Rep. Lindsay, Rep. W.F. Ryan,
James Foreman, etc.

(July 28, 1965) (Johnson announces over nationwide television
that he is sending another fifty thousand troops
to Vietnam immediately. With the exceptions   Th. Powers,
of Hatfield of Oregon and Romney of Michi-   *The War At*
gan, all participants at a National Governors' *Home*, p. 49.
Conference in Minneapolis vote for a revolu-
tion backing him. Hatfield and Romney come
around the next day.)

August 6, 1965   White House Conference on the Declaration
(Hiroshima   of Conscience. Sponsored by Catholic Worker, July 22,
Day)   Committee for Non-Violent Action, Student   August 19,
Peace Union, War Resisters League.   1965

('In the fall of 1964 a group in New York
consciously imitating a public statement by
French intellectuals during the Algerian War,
had circulated a "Declaration of Conscience
Against the War in Vietnam." Eventually

Date of action	*Village Voice: demonstrations*	Issue of VV

signed by 4000 people, the Declaration was delivered to the White House during the Assembly of Unrepresented People'.) — Th. Powers, *The War At Home*, p. 192.

(August 6-9) — (Assembly of Unrepresented People, August 6-9. By coalition of traditional peace organizations. Forced arrests of 350, August 9.) — Th. Powers, *The War At Home*, p. 81-83.

October 14, 1965 — Vietnam Rally, 2:30 pm at West Broadway and 3rd Street. Speakers: Connor Cruise O'Brien, David McReynolds. Sponsored by the NY University Ad Hoc Committee to Protest War in Vietnam. — October 14, 1965

(October 15) — (David J. Miller, as part of the International Days of Protest at the Lower Manhattan Whitehall Induction Center burns his draft card. The gesture is televised nationally.) — Th. Powers, *The War At Home*, p. 85-87.

October 16, 1965 — (First) 5th Avenue (94th to 69th Street) Anti-War Parade: to protest the war in Vietnam. Rally at 68th Street, off 5th Avenue. A.J. Muste, 'noted pacifist' 'featured' speaker. Sponsored by 5th Avenue Vietnam Peace Parade Committee. — October 7, 1965 / October 21, 1965

(This 5th Avenue March was part of International Days of Protest called for by the National Coordinating Committee to End the War in Vietnam, created August 7-8, 1965, and paralleled by Berkeley marches October 15-16. About 20,000 participants in N.Y., not counting about 1,000 hecklers.) — Th. Powers, *The War At Home*, p. 81-85.

B&P participation: Kourilsky, '71, p. 78.

November 6, 1965 — Burning of their draft cards by four pacifists: David McReynolds, 36, Field Secretary of War Resisters League, Thomas Cornell, 31, of the Catholic Peace Fellowship, Roy Lisker, 27 ... Marc Paul Edelman, ... a public parking lot on 17th Street, just east of Broadway. 'A solemn witness against military conscription and war' rendering them liable to a maximum penalty of a $10,000 fine or a 5-year prison sentence or both under a bill passed August 10, 1965, 392 to 1 by the House of Representatives. A.J. Muste and Dorothy Day of the Catholic Worker attend to lend moral support.

Date of action	*Village Voice: demonstrations*	Issue of VV
	Sponsored by the Committee for Non-Violent Action (and the Workshop in Non-Violence ?) (both at 5 Beekman Street in New York) (The action had been planned for October 28, day of D.J. Miller's arraignment, as demonstration of support, but crowd of reporters and hecklers then prevented it. 'Following the draft-card burnings in the fall of 1965, opposition to the draft ... faded into the background' – until April 15, 1967.)	November 4, 11, 1965 Th. Powers, *The War At Home*, p. 87. ibid., p. 186.
(November 9, 1965)	(A week after a 'thirty-two year old Quaker, Norman Morrison ... emptied a gallon jug of gasoline over himself on the steps of the Pentagon ..., struck a match, and was burned alive ..., another pacifist, Roger La Porte ... on November 9 ... burn(s) himself to death at the United Nations.')	Th. Powers, *The War At Home*, p. 87.
November 11, 1965 (Veterans Day)	Union Square Rally to stop the war against Vietnam. Sponsored by Youth Against War and Facism,	November 4, 1965
November 13, 1965	U.S. Get out of Vietnam Rally. 111th Street between Broadway and Riverside Drive. (i.e.: Columbia University area ...) 'Music by (Barbara) Dane and Plastic Arts will dramatize the program.'	November 11, 1965
November 26, 1965	Silent vigil, United Nations Plaza in memory of Norman Morrison, Roger La Porte. Sponsored by Artists and Workers Committee.	November 25, 1965
November 27, 1965	March on Washington. Sponsored by Greenwich Village Peace Center, Village Women Strike for Peace (and ?)	November 11, 1965
March 26, 1966	(Second) 5th Avenue Peace Parade. From 94th Street to Central Park Mall. Sponsored by 5th Avenue Peace Parade Committee. B&P participation.	March 10, 14, 31, 1966
	'Last major demonstration (before the April 15, 1967 Mobilization (SSB) ... probably took place in half a dozen cities. The largest had been in New York where 22,000 people had assembled.'	Th. Powers, *The War At Home*, p. 169.
	B&P participation: Kourilsky, '71, p. 78-79.	
May 1, 1966	Union Square Demonstration: *'The Press*	

Conference' by B&P, with Johnson's State of Union Message of January 12, 1966.

May 7, 1966   'Day Before Mother's Day Women's March to bring our Men home from Vietnam Now'. Beginning at U.S. Armory, Lexington and 33rd Street. Barbara Dane to sing, B&P Theatre to perform. Sponsored by Committee for the Women's Peace March.   May 5, 1966

(May 19, 1966)   (Poets read-in against the War in Vietnam. Sponsored by poets for Peace Now.)   May 19, 1966

May 21, 1966   Picket the Armed Forces Day Parade and Mass Rally to end the War in Vietnam.   May 19, 1966

(May 20, 1966)   (Benefit performances of *Fire* to benefit the New York Workshop in Non-Violence at B&P Museum.)   May 19, 1966

May 30(?), 1966 (Memorial Day)   Memorial Day Peace Parade sponsored by the B&P Theatre and Veterans and Reservists to End the War in Vietnam (an ad of May 26 says the B&P needs women for this parade, asks women to come to a May 20 rehearsal.)   May 26, 1966

June 6, 1966   Lower East Side Mass Rally to End the War in Vietnam and bring the Troops Home Now. Speeches by A.J. Muste, Ted Weiss, Dixie Bayo, chairman of the Movement for Puerto Rican Independence. Entertainment by B&P Theatre, 2nd Ave. and 7th Street. Sponsored by East Side Mobilization for Peace Action (LEMPA), Peace Committee District 65, Teachers Committee to End the War in Vietnam, East Side Emma Lazarus Club, Veterans for Peace in Vietnam, Youth Against War and Fascism, Lower East Side W.E.B. Dubois Club, Movement for Puerto Rican Independance (M.P.I.), Peace Committee East Side Tenants' Council, N.Y. Workshop in Non-violence.   May 26, 1966

August 6, 1966   Hiroshima Day Protest and Mass Rally Against the War in Vietnam. Greenwich Village feeder march designed by Peter Schumann has as its theme 'no more napalm'. Feeder marches merge at times Square. Greenwich Village feeder march from Sheridan Square. Rally at Rockefeller Center. Front page   July 21,

Date of action	*Village Voice: demonstrations*	Issue of VV
	photo of B&P masked women with blackened faces, August 11th issue.	August 4, 11, 18, 1966.
August 6, 1966	('The turn-out was relatively small, but the demonstration further undermined the authority of the National Coordinating Committee to End the War in Vietnam, which had refused to take part for reasons of its own.' The march was organized by the 5th Avenue Peace Parade Committee.)	Th. Powers, *The War At Home*, p. 166.
November 5, 1966	March and Mass Protest Rally to forestall escalation of the war in Vietnam after the November 3 election. Rally just south of Times Square feeder marches from Village (Washington Square Park), Upper West Side, B&P Theatre with, apparently Uncle Fatso, with Lower East Side feeder march. Photos of Muste, Gary Snyder, Allen Ginsberg. Sponsored by 5th Avenue Vietnam Peace Parade Committee. Lower East Side and Village feeder marches sponsored also by New York Workshop in Non-violence and Veterans and Reservists to End the War in Vietnam, and billed as a Walk for Love and Peace and Freedom (with Ginsberg, Snyder, Paul Krassner, the Fugs, USCO, The Yellow Submarine.) (Note hippie overtones in ad, e.g. Love Stops Destruction.)	November 3, 10, 1966
(November 24, 1966 (Thanksgiving Day))	(B&P demonstration outside Radio City Music Hall of this sort dated by Kourilsky as of Thanksgiving Day 1966, – November 24, I guess.)	Kourilsky, 1971, p. 75
Christmas Week 1966	B&P Theatre demonstrations outside Churches to protest U.S. presence in Vietnam, incident at St. Patrick's Cathedral, abduction of Holy Child to Best's Department Store Lost and Found.	January 5, 1967
(January 8, 1967)	(Ad of January 5: 'Rev. Schaef and the B&P Theatre on Vietnam' at the Washington Square Methodist Church.)	January 5, 1967
(January 29-February 5, 1967)	(Week of the Angry Arts Against the War in Vietnam. Sponsored by Painters and Writers Protest Organization and Angry Arts Week.) (B&P participates.)	January 12, 19, 26, February 2, 9, 16, 1967

Date of action	*Village Voice: demonstrations*	Issue of VV
(February 11, 1967)	(A. J. Muste dies.)	February 16, 1967
March 11, 1967	Stop the Bombing March and Rally to protest the 'new escalation'. March from East Broadway and Jefferson Street or LEMPA's Peace Center, Avenue B near 7th Street. Rally at St. Marks Church in the Bouwerie. B&P Theatre leads the march. Sponsored by Lower East Side Mobilization for Peace Action.	March 9, 1967
April 5, 1967	National Mass Mobilization to End the War in Vietnam Now. Sponsored by Spring Mobilization to End the War in Vietnam, founding chairman, A.J. Muste. New York and San Francisco. Speakers include Dr. Martin Luther King and Stokeley Carmichael. Rally Co-chairmen: Dr. B. Spock, Dave Dellinger ... Assembly at Central Park Sheep Meadow. Rally at United Nations. (Preceded by a Peace Fair at Sheep Meadow?) (Ad April 6 calling for many B&P volunteers for Spring Mobilization, rehearsals April 13, 14 at Old Courthouse.)	March 30, April 6, 1967
(April 15, 1967)	(Sponsored by Spring Mobilization to End the War in Vietnam, formed end of November 1966, called in Cleveland by the Inter-University Committee. Non-exclusionary march, i.e. Old Left allowed. 250,000-500,000 (Powers, p. 195) March in New York from east of over 65,000 in San Francisco from west of Mississippi. Important effects of New York demonstration: strengthening the Anti-War Movement: it 'prove(d) that opposition to the war was far broader than public opinion seemed to show, thus encouraging insurgent political campaigns in 1968; ... (it) convince(d) a large segment of the movement that simply *demonstrating* their opposition was not enough.')	Th. Powers, *The War At Home . . .*, origins of march, p. 166-9; political background, p. 170-181; the march, p. 181-3; administration's counter efforts, p. 183-6; effects of march, p. 186.
(April 15, 1967)	(175 draft cards burned at Sheep Meadow – outgrowth of a March 2, 1967 Cornell draft card burning pledge proposal.)	Th. Powers, *The War At Home*, p. 188-91.
(April 24, 1967)	('At the annual luncheon of the Associated Press during the convention of the American	

Newspaper Publishers Association, held in the
Waldorf Astoria on Monday, April 24, while
fifty demonstrators marched in a picket line on
Park Avenue, General Westmoreland said U.S.   Th. Powers,
forces were defeating the North Vietnamese   *The War At*
and Vietcong at every turn.')   *Home*, p. 185.

(April 29,   (Loyalty Day Parade organized by Veterans of
1967)   Foreign Wars to demonstrate, in answer to
Spring Mobilization March, that the majority
support the President and Our Boys. Total of   Th. Powers,
7500 only in two marches in Brooklyn, Man-   *The War At*
hattan.)   *Home*, p. 199.

May 13, 1967   Some kind of violence between authorities and
hippies. (At March to Support Our Boys in
Vietnam sponsored by a coalition of patriotic
organizations. 'A large percentage of the
20,000 people who turned out were union
members, traditionally Democrats and part of   Th. Powers,
the liberal coalition that had dominated Ameri-   *The War At*
can politics since 1932.')   *Home*, p. 199.

May 20, 1967   Flower Power Day hippie demonstration
(Armed Forces   against Armed Forces Parade. Sponsors –
Day)   Committee for Non-violence (WIN) – had
pedaled it down to avoid confrontations.   May 25, 1967

(Week of   (Black street riots – looting, sniping, arson – in
Sunday, July 6   Newark, N.J.: 5 days. 'More than 20 Negroes
to Saturday,   were killed, about 1,200 injured, and some
July 11, 1967)   1,275 sent to jail.' 3,000 National Guardsmen
and 375 state policemen.)   July 20, 1967

August 4-5   Champlain to Montreal Peace Walk (for?) on
1967   Hiroshima Day, B&P participates, performs   August 3,
August 5, on arrival.   1967

August 6,   Protest demonstration visit to a destroyer off
1967   NYC by National Mobilization Committee.
(Hiroshima   Direct Action Project, half of them with black
Day)   hooded blouses and ashen grey death-head masks
on the back of their heads (they are ar-
rested when they put them over their faces).   August 10,
B&P masks (e.g. from *Chairs.*)   1967

(August 19,   (Discussion meeting at Village Theatre on
1967)   topic Vietnam and Black America, Dave
Dellinger, chairman and H. Rap Brown, chairman of the Student Non-violent Coordinating

	Committee (SNCC) to discuss with the Rev. Thomas Lee Hays of the Episcopal Peace Fellowship, with messages from CORE and Women Strike for Peace. Sponsored by National Mobilization Committee to End the War and 5th Avenue Vietnam Peace Parade Committee.) (Brown promotes vilence?)	August 17, September 7, 1967
(August 24, 1967)	(No One Heard the Poet, A Comment on Vietnam program at Village Theatre with major address by James Baldwin, Ossie Davis, the Frank Mitchel Quintet, etc.)	August 17, 1967
October 2, 1967	Rally to support city rent control, sponsored by certain city councilmen. City Hall Plaza.	September 28, 1967
October 16, 1967	Return of draft cards to Federal Court on steps of Foley Square Federal Court by draft-age men identifying themselves. Sponsored by Lower Eastside Mobilization for Peace Action. Marshalls' refusal to accept cards described by Grace Paley in article entitled 'The Anti-War Protest: Resistance Week Begins.' – the peace movement is carried 'from dissent to resistance.'	October 12, 19, 1967

On the demonstrations of October 21-December 8, 1967, cf. Th. Powers, *The War At Home*, ch. 11.[34]

October 21-22	Peace Happening (?) at Pentagon, Washington, D.C. Sponsored by the National Mobilization Committee to End the War in Vietnam. H. Rap Brown among sponsors (for SNCC, I suppose). Also Abbie Hoffman (for Diggers and for hippies generally) (Diggers to levitate Pentagon.)	August 31 September 28, 1967 October 19, 1967
	(Described, Baxandall, *Spectacles*, p. 68-9). Violent government response, tear gas, etc. 700 jailed, several dozen hurt.	October 26, November 7, 1967
November 11 1967 (Veterans Day)	Veteran's Rally against the War, Union Square. Entertainment by Bread & Puppet Theatre, Barbara Dane (?), Joe Frazier, Elaine White. Sponsored by Veterans for Peace in Vietnam, Vietnam Veterans Against the War.	November 2, 9, 1967

34. Powers, *The War At Home*, p. 229, 230, 231, 249, 250, 251A – October 21-22, Washington, D.C., ibid. p. 232-3, 238-42; National Draft Resistance Week, especially in Oakland, October 15-21, p. 233-8; Dean Rusk at the New York Hilton, November 14, p. 243-5; Whitehall Induction Center Blocking, December 4-8, p. 245-9.

Date of action	*Village Voice: demonstrations*	Issue of VV
November 14, 1967	Demonstration against the war at a meeting of the Foreign Policy Association either at the New York Hilton or the Waldorf Astoria Hotel. Sponsored by 5th Avenue Peace Parade Committee. Dozens of bloodied heads at Dean Rusk speech. SDS organizes 'direct actions'.	November 9, 23, 1967
November 25, 1967	Neighborhood Peace Walk with the Bread & Puppet Theatre from the new Gramercy-Stuyvesant Peace Center at the Rutherford Friends Meeting House to the Peace Center Saturday vigil at 20th Street and 1st Avenue.	November 16, 1967
November 25, 1967	Celebration of make-believe end of the war by hippies in Washington Square Park with Phil Ochs, Allen Ginsberg, etc., a 'dramatic group' and a 'mock-general'.	November 30, 1967
December 5-8 1967	Stop the Draft Week with police brutality. Tuesday, December 5 at Induction Center; to Friday, December 8 on Irving Place. Demonstrate 'guerrilla' vs. police empocketing tactics.	December 14, 1967
December 5, 1967	Civil Disobedience against the Draft (called for in an ad): blocking of Whitehall Induction Center at 5:30 am. Sponsored by War Resisters League, Womens Strike for Peace. David McReynolds a 'key organizer'. Dr. Spock tries to get arrested. Group of women led by Grace Paley who gives prior assurance to police that arrests will not be resisted — several in group injured when conflict develops accidentally.	November 23, 30, December 7, 14, 1967
December 9, 1967	Women's Walk of Mourning, wearing black shawls, with distribution of leaflets announcing opening of a Chelsea and a Village draft counseling center. Sponsored by Greenwich Village Peace Center? Walk to St. Peter's Church in Chelsea, on whose steps B&P Theatre will perform.	December 7, 1967
December 9, 1967	Chelsea Village Walk Not our Sons, Not Your Sons, Not Their Sons.	December 7, 1967
December 10, 1967 (Human Rights Day)	March of Mourning for Human Rights, to protest the destruction of democracy in Greece and the loss of human rights. Honorary Chairman: Melina Mercouri. New York Public Library to United Nations Plaza. Sponsored by	

Date of action	*Village Voice: demonstrations*	Issue of VV
	a bunch of Greek organizations and the Village Independent Democrats.	December 7, 1967
(December 17, 1967	(Carnegie Hall meeting 'Vote No on Vietnam in '68'. Senator Vance Hartke, Dem., Ind., Congressional Rep. William F. Ryan, Andrew J. Young, (black) executive director of the Southern Christian Leadership Conference, Sanford Gottlieb, executive director, National SANE. Admission $1.)	December 7, 1967
December 21, 1967	Mass Anti-War Rally in City Hall Park to protest police violence in violation of Bill of Rights, uphold right to oppose the war, demand Mayor Lindsay uphold it. Sponsored by 5th Avenue Vietnam Peace Parade Committee. (The ad calls the week around Tuesday, December 5 to Friday December 8 Stop The Draft Week.)	December 14, 1967
(January 14, 1968)	(Town Hall meeting to demonstrate solidarity with draft resisters and with Dr. Spock and others recently indicted for their support of draft resisters: Mailer, Conor Cruise O'Brien, Chomsky, etc. sign pledges of aid.)	January 18, 1968
January 15, 1968	Demand by Jeannette Rankin Brigade, led by first U.S. Congresswoman, that Congress bring boys back from Vietnam and act on neglected human needs at home. Separate ads 'Susan Sontag says join me in Washington January 15', 'Mrs. Benjamin (sic) says . . .' (Emergence of Feminism!)	January 4, 1968
January 24, 1968	Protest – Festival of the Vultures. Demonstrate Against the Billionaires! 'Diamond Ball' at the Plaza Hotel. Stop the War! Free the Political Prisoners. (No sponsors in ad, two 'coordinators' and their phone numbers.)	January 18, February 1, 1968
February 27	Protest demonstrations in front of the hearings by the Subversive Activities Control Board on the Du Bois clubs sponsored by the 5th Avenue Vietnam Peace Parade Committee	February 15, 1968
March 7, 1968	Rally against the Vietnam War by Jeannette Rankin Rank and File at Community Church. (In this same VV issue, Hentoff reports that Rat: Subterranean News has just succeeded the East Village Other.)	March 7, 1968

Date of action	*Village Voice: demonstrations*	Issue of VV
March 10, 1968	Second Abortion Rally. March from Times Square to Rockefeller Plaza. (Speakers: Paul Krassner, Bill Baird, Ti-Grace Atkinson, Florence Kennedy.) Sponsored by Parent's Aid Society.	March 7, 1968
(March 17, 1968)	(Benefit for David Mitchell. St. Clement's Church. For reservations call Greenwich Village Peace Center. B&P Theatre, Susan Sontag, Eric Bentley, Open Theatre, Cyrelle Forman.)	March 7, 14, 1968
March 22, 1968	Yippie Demonstration at Grand Central Station to promote their coming Festival of Life in Chicago during the Democratic Nominating Convention. Police riot.	March 28, April 4, 1968
March 27, 1968	March for Peace down both sides of Central Park from 100th/95th Streets to Peace Fair and Rally, Sheep Meadow, M.L. King, William Sloane Coffin, Yale Chaplain, Dick Gregory, the comic. Sponsored by 5th Avenue Vietnam Peace Parade Committee.	March 28, 1968
(March 31, 1968 (?))	(Johnson announces (?) rejection of military request for 206,000 additional troops, initiation of a partial bombing halt, request to the North Vietnamese for negotiations, and that he won't run in 1968 presidential race.)	T. Hoopes, *The Limits of Intervention*, p.v.
April 3, 1968	Return of draft cards: 'Young Men of the Resistance will return the draft cards given them by the old men of death and war' in Central Park Band Shell. Sponsored by Resist/ Support-in-Action, Resistance. Weakened by Johnson's announcement he would not run. 85 cards turned in. Joan Baez sings twice.	March 28, 1968 April 11, 1968
April 7, 1968	Martin Luther King Memorial March, Governor Rockefeller arm-in-arm with Harlem Mau-Mau chief Charles 37X Kenyatta. After eulogies at rally, initially disrupted by dissident James Forman of SNCC, all, including Sammy Davis Jr., join in We Shall Overcome. March from 145th Street, down 7th Avenue to Mall. Kenyatta carries a sword sheathed in a bible.	April 11, 1968
April 13, 1968	Reserve Resistance Rally and Parade, Columbus Circle to Union Square. Keith Lampe, speaker. Sponsored by Veterans and Reservists to End the War in Vietnam.	April 11, 1968

Date of action	*Village Voice: demonstrations*	Issue of VV

April 14, 1968   Yip-Out in Sheep Meadow reported on by Sally Kempton — psychedelic rock. Photos of young semi-unclad shaved-head Buddhist males in quasi-Lotus (?) postures.   April 18, 1968

April 20, 1968   Street Rally for Peace sponsored by West 16th Street for Peace. Speakers: Councilmen Edward Koch, Theodore Weiss ... Entertainment by folksinger Marti Rogers, gospel singers Rev. F. Kirkpatrick and Jimmy Collier, and 'Brecht on War' presented by Theatre for Peace under the direction of Viveca Lindfors.   April 18, 1968

April 20, 1968   Lower East Side Peace Rally near Tompkins Square Park, parades there from two assembly points. (East 26th Street, Catherine and Madison). Dr. Spock and others to speak.   April 11, 1968

April 20, 1968   Parade and Rally. The Village Voice on the 18th routinely refers to them as 'mass' parade and rally, and names as their 'theme' 'Peace and Freedom'. Freedom! In honor of Dr. Martin Luther King. Speaker: the Rev. Douglas Kirkpatrick, representative of the Poor People's March on Washington conceived and led by Dr. King, also Dr. Spock and Cleveland Robinson.   April 18, 1968

April 27, 1968   Anti-War Demonstration. Twin March down Central Park West and 5th Avenue, Peace Fair and Rally in Sheep Meadow. 'Prominent' speakers and entertainment. March 28 ad announces that Martin Luther King, William Sloane Coffin, Dick Gregory will be Marching for Peace. In an April 25 notice rebilled as March Protesting the War in Vietnam and the War on Black America. Entertainers: Pete Seeger, Diana Sands, Phil Ochs, Eva Jessye Choir. Full coverage by WBAI-FM, 99.5. Greetings from Major Lindsay and Borough President Percy Sutton (a black) received (accepted). Youth Against War and Fascism and U.S. Committee to Aid the National Liberation Front protest these greetings by an Anti-Imperialist feeder March from Washington Square Park which, having no city permit, is brutally busted by the police.   March 21, 1968   April 25, May 2, 1968

(We might pick this demonstration as marking the virtual end of the Peace Movement.)

Date of action	*Village Voice: demonstrations*	Issue of VV

(May 3, 1968) (First contingent of Poor People's March on Washington, D.C. — sponsored/organized by Southern Christian Leadership Conference — sets out from Memphis, Tenn. March is to reach Washington May 20, is to set up Hope City (Resurrection City) camp there.   May 9, 1968

(May 4, 1968) (Village Independent Democrats collection of food and money for the Poor People's March.)   May 2, 1968

May 11, 1968 Rally in Tompkins Square Park (New York Coordinating Center for the Poor People's Campaign is located there) and march up to Sheep Meadow in support of Poor People's March.   May 9, 1968

May 17, 1968 Rally and picket line, Broadway and 116th Street in support of (striking?) Columbia students against IDA, against The Gym, for amnesty. Columbia Strike Committee, Student Mobilization Committee. Ad by 5th Avenue Vietnam Peace Parade Committee   May 16, 1968

(May 17, 1968) (Father Philip Berrigan, S.J., with his brother, Dan Berrigan, S.J., invades a (N.J.?) Selective Service office, seizes draft records, burns them: he is already under indictment for similar action, pouring animal blood over files in a Baltimore Selective Service office, on May 24, 1968, is sentenced to six years. On June 6, (VV) Dave McReynolds condemns these actions and all other illegal actions, though finding government sentences excessive.)   June 6, 1968

May 18, 1968 Anti-Imperialist Rally (cf. entry for April 27) At Washington Square Park for a permit-less Anti-Imperialist March uptown sponsored by the Coalition for an Anti-Imperialist March (largely those same two organizations). Nearly 1,000 cops there to prevent march (and rally?). Secreted demonstrator unfurls blue and gold faded National Liberation Front over southside of Washington Arch, Washington 'revolutionary' quotation: 'Let us raise a standard to which the wise and honest can repair. The event is in the hands of God' and a blue Youth Against War and Fascism flag over its northside. Cops can't get into the arch, demonstrator negotiates his surrender by walkie-talkie. The

Date of action	*Village Voice: demonstrations*	Issue of VV

6th Street Theatre, a 'group of pantomimists' is performing. March sneaks off in confusion, evades police street barricades.

May 23, 1968

May 19, 1968 — Poor People Rally at Cathedral of St. John the Divine (in or near Harlem, note). Performance of scenes from Martin Duberman's 'In White America' by the Repertory Theatre of Lincoln Center, the Pageant Players, the New York State Choir and guitarists Frederick Kirkpatrick and Jimmy Collier.

May 16, 1968

(May 20, 1968) — (Black Theatre for Black Panthers benefit for Black Panther Defense Fund at Filmore East (formerly Village) Theatre, 2nd Avenue and 6th Street Leroi Jones' Newark Spirit House Players and Movers to do his *Home on the Range*, Ed Bullins' Black Troupe his *How do you do*? Robert Macbeth's Harlem New Lafayette Workshop a *Black Revolutionary Ritual*, Enriquez Vargas' East Harlem Gut Theatre his *A Fair Share*. Also Woodie King's New York Concept East. Speakers: Marlon Brando, Mrs. Eldridge Cleaver, San Francisco Black Panther minister of defense Bobby Seale. Mail orders to Radical Theatre Repertory, c/o The Drama Review's office at 32 Washington Place, a N.Y.U. building.)

May 2, 16, 1968

May 20, 1968 — Rally of support, in front of Federal Courthouse, Foley Square, in support of 5 (Dr. Spock, Rev. Coffin, Mike Ferber, Mitch Goodman, Marcus Raskin) whose trial for conspiracy to counsel draft refusal is beginning in Boston. The Resistance, Resist/Support-in-Action, Workshop in Non-Violence sponsors. Such counseling at rally.

May 16, 1968

(May 23, 1968) — (Rally in N.Y.U School of Education. Auditorium in support of coalition between Peace and Freedom Party and Black Panther Party. Speakers: Eldridge Cleaver, Communications Secretary, Black Panther Party for Self-Defense, Maxwell Geismar, 'noted author and critic', Conrad Lynn. Entertainment: Gut Theatre (street theatre from East Harlem, directed by Enriquez Vargas), The Pageant Players. $1 donation.)

May 23, 1968

799

Date of action	*Village Voice: demonstrations*	Issue of VV
(May 30, 1968 (Memorial Day))	(Washington, D.C. meeting in support of The Poor People's Campaign. Ad solicits attendance or money subsidizing attendance. 5th Avenue Vietnam Peace Parade Committee, New York SANE, Chelsea-Village SANE.)	May 23, 1968
June 5, 1968	'Residents of 12th Street. Bob Simon, a 12th Street neighbor, will refuse induction on Wednesday, June 5, 7 am – Whitehall Street Induction Center. Bob was reclassified 1A after returning his draft card on October 16. To help him say 'no' you are invited to a free breakfast in Battery Park 607 am. Draft Resistance Committee of 12th Street for Peace.'	May 30, 1968
June 14, 1968	Dan Baty, one of April (15?) draft card burners, given sanctuary in Rev. Shaef's Washington Square Methodist Church, finally dragged out by police.	June 20, 1968
(June 19, 1968)	(Rally in Washington, D.C. in support of The Poor People's Campaign, 'making it clear that the poor are not alone in demanding an end to the shameful spectacle of poverty in this land of plenty'. Mobilization in Support of The Poor People's Campaign (National Headquarters: 217 West 125th Street, New York City. Chairman: the Rev. Ralph Abernathy. National Coordinator: Bayard Rustin.))	June 6, 1968
June 20, 1968	Noontime rally, Foley Square in support of the 4 (Spock, Coffin, Goodman, Ferber) convicted of conspiracy the preceding week (in Boston). 'The War is Not Over!' Resist/Support-in-Action. (135 West 4th Street – i.e. the Washington Square Methodist Church)	June 20, 1968
July 20, 1968	Rally: Stand up for Peace and SAY NO to Humphrey and War Politics. Dwight MacDonald, David McReynolds, speakers; entertainment by Theatre for Peace.	July 11, 18, 1968
July 23, 1968	Rally (and/or picket?) at Humphrey's Dinner, Waldorf Astoria Hotel at Park and 50th Street. Protest #2 War Criminal, the Election Fraud. Coalition for an Anti-Imperialist Movement.	July 18, 1968
August 3, 1968	Demonstration to stop the war in Vietnam in Times Square, 'in commemoration of Hiroshima Day.' 5th Avenue Vietnam Peace Parade Committee.	July 25, 1968

800

25. Chronology of Schumann's shows, 1960-1983.[35]

1. *Indoors shows for adults.*
Das Ballett
    Munich, Germany   May 8, '60

Totentanz
    Judson Church   May 15, 30, '62
    Putney School, Putney, Vt.   Sept. 22, '62
    Circle in the Square   Nov. 10, '62
    Woodstock, N.Y.   Aug. 17, '62 (?)

Burning Towns
    Woodstock, N.Y.   Aug. 17, '62
    Judson Church   Aug. 31, '62
                                     Sept. 2, '62
    Living Theatre   Nov. 10, '62

Fire
    Putney School, Putney, Vt.   Fall, '62

A Festival of Puppets
    Living Theatre (perhaps not under this title)   End Dec. '62
    Judson Church   Jan. 2-7, '63

Mr. Miller Stories
    Putney School, Putney, Vt.   Winter '62/'63

2 King Stories (The Great King & the Mosquito,
The Great King makes War)
    Putney School, Putney, Vt.   Winter '62/'63

Ceremony of the Things
    Putney School, Putney, Vt.   Winter '62/'63

Genesis
    Putney School, Putney, Vt.   Winter '62/'63

The Story of the World
    Adams House, Cambridge, Mass.   April 13, '63

---

35. The list is fairly complete. Except for German shows before '61 and perhaps some shows '82/'83 I am reasonably sure it is complete. I have not listed foreign showings of them except when they were the first ones of a given show or the only ones – I mention a few Canadian showings. I have not listed all showings of each show, but am fairly certain I got down most of the earliest ones of each show, and have tried to list N.Y.C. showings rather completely – even when they were not among the earliest showings of a given show. (Place indications lacking indications of city or state refer to New York City showings.) Bread and Puppet Theatre shows – e.g. 'sideshows' at 'circuses' – were listed only if Schumann made some contribution to them more than merely allowing use of his masks or puppets. Even so I may have missed quite a few B & P skits not directed by him that he made some contribution to – e.g. gave the original idea for. Street demonstrations were listed only if they resulted in shows also performed indoors or became part of larger shows not in the nature of street agitation. For a list of overseas tours, cf. II.5.

King Story I
  New England, various places   July-Aug. '63

King Story II
  New England, various places   July-Aug. '63

Apocalypse
  New England, various places   July-Aug. '63

Mr. Miller stories
  New England, various places   July-Aug. '63

Johnnie & Susie
  New England, various places   July-Aug. '63

Elements of World War II
  Delancey St. B & P Museum   Nov. 2-Dec. 7, '63

Apocalypse
  Delancey St.   Winter '63/'64

King Story (I)
  Delancey St.   Feb. 1-April 11, '64
  Delancey St.   Nov. 7-22, '64

Murder Mystery
  Delancey St.   Oct. 3, 10, 17, '64

The Birdcatcher in Hell
  Delancey St.   Oct. 3, 10, 17,
                                              Oct. 24-Dec. 12, '64
                                              Jan. 6, '65
  Spencer Memorial Church   Dec. 20, '64

War Demonstration
  Delancey St.   Sats., Jan. 23-March 27, '65

(The God Pan, King Scheisskopf & His Clown
by Bruno Eckhardt)
  Delancey St.   Sats., Jan. 23-Feb. 6, '65

Harvard College Questionnaire
  Delancey St.   Sats., Feb. 13-March 27, '65

Flower Mountain
  Churchyard, St. Marks in the Bouwerie   May 29, 30, '65
  Metro-North Community Center   June 5, '65
  Delancey St.   June 17-July 10, '65

(Digging for the Poverty Program by
Robert Nichols)[36]
  Churchyard, St. Marks in the Bouwerie   May 29, 30, '65
  Metro-North Community Center   June 5, '65
  Delancey St.   June 17-July 10, '65

36. Schumann may have contributed only masks and costumes to this piece.

Leaf Feeling the Moonlight
 The Bridge Theatre   Nov. 7, 8, 14, 15, 22, '65
 Astor Memorial Library Landmark Building   May 20, 27 (& additional
                                                       Sats.?) '67

Fire
 Delancey St.   Sats., Jan. 29-June 11, '66
 Washington Square Methodist Church   Mondays, Nov. 20, '67-
                                                       April 1, '68

Wounds of Vietnam
 Washington Square Methodist Church   Feb. 4, '67

Bach Cantata #140
 Village Theatre   Feb. 2, 5, '67

Chicken Little, or the Story of the World
 Astor Library Landmark Building   Fris., Sats., Suns., (not nec'y
                                                       every weekend), May 5-
                                                       Oct. 28, '67)

 Newport Folk Festival, Newport, R.I.   July 12, 14, '67
 Gottesman Plaza, West 91st Street (?)   July 31, (?) '67
 Columbus Park, Chinatown   Aug. 20, '67

Speech, Chairs
 Rally to Stop the War Against Vietnam, Union
 Square (Veterans' Day) (?)   Nov. 11, '65
 Mayday rally against the war in Vietnam   May 1, '66
 Astor Library Landmark Building   Sats. (not nec'y all Sats),
                                                       May 20-July 29, Aug.
                                                       19, '67
 Long Wharf Theatre, New Haven   July 19, 20, '67
 Washington Square Memorial Church   March 30, 31, '68

Dead Man Rises
 Astor Memorial Library Landmark Building   May 6-June 3, every 7 days;
                                                       July 21-Aug. 19, weekends;
                                                       Sats., Sept. 16-Nov. 4, '67

A Man Says Goodbye to His Mother
 Rally in protest against Pro-Viet Nam War,
 Veterans' Day, Union Square   Nov. 11, '66
 Astor Landmark Building   Weekends, July 20-
                                                       Aug. 19, '67
 Newport Folk Festival, Newport, R.I.   Bet. July 1- & 16, '67
 Long Wharf Theatre, New Haven   July 19, 20, '67

*Eating & Drinking in the Year of Our Lord
1621-1967*
 Spencer Memorial Church   Nov. 23, 26, '67
 St. Peter's Church   Feb. 23, '68

Eating & Drinking in the Year of Our Lord
1621-1968
    Judson Memorial Church   Thanksgiving '68
    Washington Square Methodist Church   Dec. 4, '68

Eating & Drinking . . . 1970
    Pratt Library, Goddard College,
    Plainfield, Vt.   Nov. 21, '70

When Johnny Comes Marching Home
    St. Peter's Church   Jan. 26, '68
    Washington Square Methodist Church   March 30, 31, '68

Reiteration
    San Francisco State U., San Francisco, Calif.   Sept. '68

The Bible
    Kennebunck, Maine, other Maine
    communities near Strong, Maine   During June-July '68
    Temple Buell College, Denver, Colorado   During July 6-13, '68
    Newport Folk Festival, R. I.   July 26, '68

The Cry of the People for Meat
    The Old Courthouse (open rehearsals)   March '69
    The Ark, Boston, Mass.   April 2 '69
    St. Peter's Church   Dec. 5, 6, 7, '69

Blue Raven Beauty
    The Old Courthouse (Friday Open House
    performances)   Jan. &/or Feb. '69
    La Mama   March &/or April '69

The Difficult Life of Uncle Fatso
    Spencer Memorial Church   March 4-16, '70
    The Old Boston Theatre, Coney Island (?)   During March-June '70 (?)
    Goddard College, Plainfield, Vt.   Mid-April '70
    WBAI Free Music Store   April 24, 25, 26
    Emory U., Atlanta, Ga.   In May '70

Marriage & Revenge of the Statue of Liberty
    The Old Boston Theatre, Coney Island   March-June '70

Tristan & Isolde
    The Old Boston Theatre   March-June '70

Lamentation for Phillip Gibbs and James Green
    The Old Boston Theatre   2nd half of May-June '70

Mississippi
    The Old Boston Theatre   June '70

Bread & Dragon Circus
    The Old Boston Theatre (?)   July '70

Grey Lady Cantata #2
U. of Connecticut, Storrs, Ct. Aug. 21, '70
Cate Farm Barn During Sept. '70,
Feb. 12, '71
Spaulding High School, Barre, Vt. Feb. 19, '71
Shakespeare Festival Building Feb. 24-March 7, '71
Providence, R.I., Cambridge, Mass, Kent
State U., Ohio March-May 4, '71

Domestic Resurrection Circus
Cate Farm meadow (one performance) Sept. '70
Various places, tour Ohio-California Sept.-Oct. or -Nov. '70

Genghis Khan & the Women
Pratt Library, Goddard College, Plainfield, Vt. Jan. 30, '71

Emilia
Cate Farm Barn, Plainfield, Vt. Feb. 6, 7, '71
Shakespeare Festival Theatre Feb. 24-March 7, '71
Cate Farm Barn April 16, '71

The Quest (or Tristan Quest)
Pratt Library, Goddard College, Plainfield, Vt. In Jan. or Feb. '71
Shakespeare Festival Theatre Feb. 24-March 7, '71

Domestic Resurrection Circus
Providence, Rhode Island March '71
Emanuel Church, Cambridge, Mass. April '71
Kent State U., Ohio May 4, '71

The Birdcatcher in Hell
(2nd Version)
Cate Farm meadow June 3, 5, '71
Marlboro College, Plainfield, Brattleboro:
Vermont June 6-19, '71
Sheep Meadow, Central Park June 30, July 1-3, '71
The Old Boston Theatre, Coney Island Etc. July 4, '71

Our Domestic Resurrection Circus
Cate Farm meadow July 30, 31, '71

The Whitewashing of the Dirty Sheets of Attica
Goddard College, Plainfield, Vt. (try-out) Sept. 16, '71
Diverse N.Y. State college campuses Oct. 1-14, '71

Grey Lady Cantata #3
Burlington, Vt. Nov. 7, 14, '71
Cate Farm Barn Nov. 22, '71
Union 32 Highschool, Vt. Nov. '7

Hallelujah
People's Fair, Burlington, Vt. May 13, '72
Washington Square Park (?) Betw. May 22 & 28, '72

The Old Boston Theatre, Coney Island (?)	July-Aug. '72
The Shakespeare Festival Theatre (As part of	
The Coney Island Cycle)	Sept. '72
Cate Farm meadow (as part of circus)	July 27, 28, '74
(And at all (?) subsequent circuses)	

Laos
In front of Statehouse, Montpelier, Vt.	April 15, '72
Amherst College	April 21, '72
Washington Square Park (?)	Between May 22 & 28, '72

*Marriage of the River Winooskie & Lake
Champlain*
| Burklyn Manor, West Burke, Vt. | Spring '72 |

St. George the Dragonkiller
| The Old Boston Theatre, Coney Island | During July-Sept. '72 |

The Story of Harvey McLeod
Goddard College, Plainfield, Vt.	End June or beg. of July '72
The Old Boston Theatre, Coney Island	July-Sept. '72
Shakespeare Festival Theatre (as part of	
Coney Island Cycle)	Sept. '72

Revenge of the Law
The Old Boston Theatre, Coney Island	July-Sept. '72
Shakespeare Festival Theatre (as part of	
The Coney Island Cycle)	Sept. '72

*That Simple Light May Come from Complicated
Darkness*
Cate Farm Barn	Nov. 9, 10, 11, '72
Windham College, Vt. (?)	Dec. 7, 8, 9, '72
St. Clement's Church Theatre	Dec. 12-22, '72
Loeb Drama Center, Cambridge, Mass.	Jan. 13-15, '73
Amherst College	Jan. 20-22, '73

The Tragedy of the Soaring Price Index
Spring Parade, Hardwick, Vt.	Spring '73
(Puppets by Schumann, not directed by him)	
Various parks, New Jersey	Summer '73

He Who is Rich
| Various parks, New Jersey | Summer '73 |
| (Puppets by Schumann, not directed by him) | |

Attica (sometimes billed as: *The Whitewashing
of the Dirty Sheets of Attica*)
Cate Farm Barn or Goddard College (try-out)	Spring or early summer '73
A few New Jersey localities	Summer '73
('Summer in the Parks' program)	

Grey Lady Cantata #4 (The First Garbageman Cantata)

St. Clement's Church	April 24-May 5, '74
Cate Farm meadow	July 27, 28, '74

Our Domestic Resurrection Circus

Cate Farm meadow, Plainfield, Vt.	July 27, 28, '74

Jephtha

Cate Farm meadow	July 27, 28, '74

Grey Lady Cantata #5

Cate Farm barn	End Dec. '74

(Grey Lady Cantata #6

Theatre de l'Aquarium, Paris, France, 1 week)	March '75

A Monument to Ishi

Davis campus of the U. of California, Davis, Calif.	May 23, '75

Our Domestic Resurrection Circus

Dopp Farm, Barton County, Vt.	Aug. 2, 3, '75

Little U.S. Dance of Death

Dopp Farm (puppets, masks, costumes, directorial assistance by Schumann)	Aug. 2, 3, '75

Dirty woman's Dream

Dopp Farm (puppets, masks, costumes, directorial assistance by Schumann)	Aug. 2, 3, '75

Our Domestic Resurrection Circus

Dopp Farm	July 31, Aug. 1, '76

Bach Cantata #40 (Jesu meine Freude)

Dopp Farm	July 31, Aug. 1, '76

The Mountain Man of Chile

Dopp Farm	July 31, Aug. 1, '76

The Garden Show

Dopp Farm (puppets, masks, costumes, directorial assistance, set by Schumann)	July 31, Aug. 1, '76

White Horse Butcher & otherpieces from the Domestic Resurrection Circus

Washington Square Methodist Church	Aug. 20-22, '76

Joan of Arc

John Abbot College, Montreal, Canada	Feb. 27, '77
Montpelier, Vt.	March '77
Southern colleges, perhaps Connecticut colleges	March (-April)? '77
New England college campuses	Oct. '77
Brooklyn Academy of Music	Jan. '79

Our Domestic Resurrection Circus
    Dopp Farm   Aug. 20, 21, '77
    Masaniello (The Ballad of Masaniello)
    Dopp Farm   Aug. 20, 21, '77
    Emmanuel Church, Cambridge, Mass.   Aug. 29-Sept. 3, '77
    Washington Square Methodist Church   Sept. 6-10, '77
    Diversely, New England   Sept. '77

Ave Maris Stella
    Montpelier, Vt.   Dec. 3, 4, '77
    Diverse places, Vermont, Rhode Island   Jan.-Feb. '78
    Brooklyn Academy of Music Etc.   Jan. 25-29, '78
    Dopp Farm   Aug. 19, 20, '78

St. Francis Preaches to the Birds
    Burklyn Manor, West Burke, Vt.   Aug. '78
    Dopp Farm   Aug. 19, 20, '78
    E. 9th St., NYC (8 performances by a B & P
    offshoot)   March-April '79
    Dopp Farm   Aug. 11, 12, '79
    Dopp Farm   Aug. 28, 29, '82

Our Domestic Resurrection Circus
    Dopp Farm   Aug. 19, 20, '78

Wolkenstein
    Dopp Farm   Aug. 19, 20 '78
    Cathedral of St. John the Divine   Weekend of Sept. 15, '78
    Hatford, Ct.   Weekend of Sept. 21, '78

Othello
    Glover Town Hall, Glover, Vt.   Aug. 19, 20, '78
    Theatre for the New City   Jan. 23-Feb. 4, '79

In Danger is Help
    Dopp Farm (puppets, masks, costumes,
    directorial assistance by Schumann)   Aug. 19, 20, '78

Washerwoman Cantata #1 – Ah!
    Alumni Hall, Vermont College, Montpelier, Vt.   Feb. 22, 23, '79
    North Country Union High School,
    Newport, Vt.   Feb. 24, '79
    Trinity College, Burlington, Vt.   Feb. 25, '79
    Dopp Farm   Aug. 11 or 12, '79
    Colleges, Georgia, Pennsylvania, Maryland   Sept. '79
    Brooklyn Academy of Music   Jan. 15-Feb. 3, '80

Our Domestic Resurrection Circus
    Dopp Farm   Aug. 11, 12, '79

Washerwoman Cantata #2 – Nativity
    Dopp Farm   Aug. 11, 12, '79
    Street performances, NYC   Sept. 1-3, '79

Colleges, Georgia, Pennsylvania, Maryland	Sept. '79
Cathedral Church of St. John the Divine	Dec. 9-13, '80
Judson Memorial Church	Dec. 20-23, '82
Judson Memorial Church	Dec. 14-17, '83

King Lear
Dopp Farm — Aug. 11, 12, '79

Cambodia
New York University Experimental Theatre
Wing, loft on Broadway nr. Canal — Feb. 4, '80
Amtec factory, Villeurbanne, nr. Lyons, France — Summer '80

(*Histoire du Pain*
Amtec factory, Villeurbanne, France) — Summer '80

The Cuban Missile Crisis (This Is)
Cathedral of St. John the Divine (not directed
by Schumann) — April 24-27, '80
Amtec factory, Villeurbanne, France — Summer '80
Dopp Farm — Aug. 15, 16, '81

Venus Rising from the Water
Amtec factory, Villeurbanne, France — Summer '80
Theatre for the New City — Feb. 25-March 8, '81

La Necessite
Canada, Vermont (?) — Winter '80/'81

Serious Window
Canada, Vermont (?) (part of *La Necessite* (?)) — Winter '80/'81

Goya
Theatre for the New City — Feb. 25-March 8, '81
Dopp Farm — Aug. 15, 16, '81

Woyzeck
Theatre for the New City — March 18-29, '81

Ploughs & Plowshares
Theatre for the New City — March 28, 29, '81

The Seven Obsession with the End of the World
Theatre for the New City (part of *Ploughs*
etc.) — March 28, 29, '81
Dopp Farm — Aug. 15, 16, '81

Our Domestic Resurrection Circus
Dopp Farm — Aug. 15, 16 '81

The Story of One Who Set Out To Study Fear
Dopp Farm — Aug. 15, 16, '81

The Story of the Plowshare Eight
    Dopp farm (same as or part of *Plows &*
    Ploughshares?)   Aug. 15, 16, '81

Antigone
    Dopp Farm (by the Bread & Puppet Junior
    Drama Club) (Directorial assistance by
    Schumann?)   Aug. 15, 16, '81

The Thunderstorm of the Youngest Child
    Theatre for the New City   Feb. 9-14, '82
    Dopp Farm   Aug. 28, 29, '82

Our Domestic Resurrection Circus
    Dopp Farm   Aug. 28, 29, '82

Ineffective Man – Dream Woman
    Dopp Farm   Aug. 28, 29, '82
Diagonal Man
    Whitcomb High School, Bethel,Vt.   Nov. 19, '82
    Municipal Bldg., Orleans, Vt.   Nov. 21, '82
    Haybarn Theatre, Goddard College, Plainfield.
    Vt.   Nov. 23, '82
    Theatre for the New City   Nov. 30-Dec. 19, '82
Tragedy of Ineffectual Man
    Theatre for the New City   Nov. 30-Dec. 19, '82
    (=*Ineffective Man – Dream Woman?*)   Nov. 30-Dec. 19, '82

Insurrection Symphony #1
    Plainfield Community Center, Plainfield, Vt.   Jan. 27, '83
    Dopp Farm   Aug. 13, 14, '83

The End Falls before the Beginning (Oratorio)
    Dopp Farm   Aug. 14, 15, '83

Our Domestic Resurrection Circus
    Dopp Farm   Aug. 13, 14, '83

2. *Nativity Shows*

The Christmas Story
    Putney School, Putney, Vt.   Bef. Christmas '62
    Living Theatre   End Dec. '62
    Spencer Memorial Church   Dec. 15, 29, '63
    Delancey Street B & P Museum   Dec. 20, Jan. 4, 11, 18, '64
    Spencer Memorial Church   Dec. 20, '64
    Pocket Theatre   Weekends, Dec. 24, '64-
                Jan. 3, '65
    The Bridge Theatre   Dec. 24, 27, 28, '65
    Judson Memorial Church   Dec. 24, '66
    Washington Square Methodist Church   Dec. 30, '66
    Spencer Memorial Church   Dec. 31, '66
    Astor Library Landmark Building   Jan. 7-29, '67

Washington Square Methodist Church	Dec. 9, '67-Jan. 14, '68
Spencer Memorial Church	Dec. 17, '67
P.S. 122, 2nd Ave.	Dec. 20, '67
Brooklyn Academy of Music	Dec. 7, '68
Muse, Bedford Ave. & Lincoln Place, Brooklyn	Dec. 28, '68
Various places in Vermont, in Middlebury, at Spaulding High School, Barre, Waterbury Hospital, St. Johnsbury Academy, c. 20 performances	Dec. 6, '70-Jan. 29, '71
(P.S. directs European presentations only, B & P sub- & splinter groups perform it variously in U.S.)	Dec. '71-Jan. '72
St. Clement's Church	Betw. Dec. 12 & 22, '72
Around Vermont (?)	Dec. '72-Jan. '73
(P.S. directs European presentations only: not many.)	Nov.-Dec. '73

Grey Lady Cantata #5
| Cate Farm Barn | End Dec. '74 |

Ave Maris Stella ·
Montpelier, Vt.	Dec. 3, 4, '77
Diverse places, Vermont, Rhode Island	Jan.-Feb. '78
Brooklyn Academy of Music	Jan. 25-29, '78

Washerwoman Cantata II – Nativity
Dopp farm, Barton County, Vt.	Aug. 11, 12, '79
Street performances, NYC	Sept. 1-3, '79
Colleges, Georgia, Maryland, Pennsylvania	Sept. '79
Cathedral Church of St. John the Divine	Dec. 9-13, '80
Judson Memorial Church	Dec. 20-25, '82
Judson Memorial Church	Dec. 14-17, '82

3. *Easter Shows*

Action Bible Readings
| Delancey Street B & P Museum | Fridays, March '64 |

The Puppet Christ
Spencer Memorial Church	May 23-June 28, '64
(Dance from *The Puppet Christ*) Washington Square Gallery	July 24, 25, '64
Judson Memorial Church	Aug. 31, Sept. 1, 2, '64

The Great Passion
| Spencer Memorial Church | Sundays, March 21 April 18, '65 |

The War Against Jesus
| Emmanuel Presbyterian Church | Fris. & Sats., April 7-May 22, '65 |

811

The Crucifixion
    Spencer Memorial Church   April 10, 17, 24,
                                                   May 24, '66
    Astor Library Landmark Building   Sundays, March
                                                 Easter Sunday '67
    Judson Memorial Church   April 5, 6, 7, 8, '68
    Washington Square Methodist Church   April 12, 13, 14, '68
    American Place Theatre, St. Clement's Church
    Church crucifixion pageant (billed as?)   April 21, '68
    Goddard College campus, Plainfield, Vt.   mid-April '70
    Cornell U., Ithaca, N.Y. crucifixion pageant
    (billed as?)   April 17, '70
    Washington D. C., by Capitol   April 24, '71
Providence, R.I., Cambridge
    Mass., Kent State U. (cf. *Domestic Resurrection*
    Circus)   March-May 4, '71

Stations of the Cross
    Goddard College, Plainfield, Vt.   April '72
    Northfield High gymnasium, Bennington,
    Burlington, Montpelier, all in Vt.   May-June '72
    St. Clement's Church   May 22-28, '72
    (Tour of Southern states, without P.S.)   Spring '74
    Tour, Vt., Canada, Boston, under P.S.   Spring '74
    Washington Square Methodist Church, 3
    performances   Spring '74
    (Cathedral of St. John the Divine, per's directed
    by Larry Gordon)   April 24-27, '80

4. *Children's Shows*

'Puppet show' (Village Voice notice)
    Delancey St. B & P Museum   Sundays, Nov. 15, '63 ff.

King Story (II)
    Delancey St.   Feb. 8-April 11, '64

Fairy Tales
    Delancey St.   Sundays, March 12-
                                     April 30, '64

Punch & Judy, The Rat Movie
    Delancey St.   Sats. Jan. 9, '65 ff.

A Winter Story (Young Man in the Big City)
    The Bridge Theatre   Feb. 24, March 5, 12,
                                       19, '66

The Big City Story
    The Bridge Theatre   June 18, '66

Slapstick Festival
    Shakespeare Festival Building   Sundays, Feb.-Nov. 5, '67

Pied Piper of Harlem
  E. 100th St.(?), Harlem   Summer '65

Chicken Little
  Tompkins Park, Greene, Marcy & Lafayette
  Aves., Bedford-Stuyvesant, Brooklyn (rained
  out);   Aug. 28, '66
  Tompkins Square Park, Lower East side   Aug. 29, '66
  St. Nichols Park, Harlem   Sept. 3, '66
  St. Mary's Park, S. Bronx   Sept. 4, '66

5. *Exhibitions*
Sculptures, drawings
  Hoffman Fuel Co. offices, Danbury, Ct.   Summer or fall '67

Vermont Paper Maché Cathedral
  Cate Farm barn, Plainfield, Vt.   Jan. '71 & ff.
  Pratt Library, Goddard College, Plainfield,
  Vt.   Jan. 30 '71
Attica prisoners, 42 paintings on masonite board
  Shakespeare Festival Building lobby   Sept. '72

Puppets
  Guggenheim Museum, '*Ten Independents*'   Jan. '72

Meadow's Green
  Pratt Library, Goddard College, Plainfield, Vt.   Feb. 14-24, '74
  Hunter Arts Gallery, Hunter College   Sept. '74

The White Horse Butcher (paper maché bas reliefs)
  Lyndon College, Goddard College, both
  Vermont   Feb., March '75
  Dopp Farm, Barton County, Vt.   July 31, Aug. 1, '75
  (under the title *Johnny the Horsebutcher*)

Bread & Puppet Puppet Museum
  Dopp Farm, Barton County, Vt.   June 14, '75 ff.

(Bread & Puppet Masaccio: The Art of Fragility
  Florence, Italy, Rome, Italy, Paris, Nancy,
  Caen, France)   Dec. 16, '76-'78
Untitled (?) show, paintings on masonite (the
apocalypse, the prophet Jeremiah
  Theatre for the New City, lobby   March 18-29, '81

Sumpul River Massacre
  Plainfield, Vt. (Paintings)   June 16-July 14, '81
  N.Y.C.   Sept. 12-Oct. 4, '81

The Chapel of the Condemned
  B & P Puppet Museum, Dopp Farm   (Aug. 15, 16, '81
  (paper maché half-relief & paintings on
  masonite)